Linear Algebra with Applications

Tenth Edition

Steven J. Leon

University of Massachusetts Dartmouth

Lisette G. de Pillis

Harvey Mudd College

 Pearson

Director, Portfolio Management: Deirdre Lynch
Executive Editor: Jeff Weidenaar
Editorial Assistant: Jonathan Krebs
Senior Content Producer: Rachel S. Reeve
Managing Producer: Scott Disanno
Producer: Nicholas Sweeny
Manager, Courseware QA: Mary Durnwald
Product Marketing Manager: Yvonne Vannatta
Product Marketing Assistant: Jon Bryant
Field Marketing Manager: Evan St. Cyr

Senior Author Support/Technology Specialist:
    Joe Vetere
Manager, Rights and Permissions: Gina Cheselka
Text and Cover Design: SPi Global
Full Service Vendor: SPi Global
Manufacturing Buyer: Carol Melville, LSC
    Communications
Cover Image: Dave and Les Jacobs/Blend
    Images/Getty Images

Chapter 5
231 Pearson Education, Inc.
Chapter 6
364 Courtesy of Oak Ridge National Laboratory, U.S. Dept. of Energy.

1 2020

eText Access Card
ISBN 13: 978-0-13-518163-8
ISBN 10: 0-13-518163-1

Rental
ISBN 13: 978-0-13-673163-4
ISBN 10: 0-13-673163-5

Dedication

For their encouragement, patience, and the joy they bring to my life, thank you to my wonderful husband, Jan Lindheim, and my brilliant daughters, Lydia, Sarah, and Alexandra.

For their non-stop enthusiastic support, for teaching me to love learning and to never stop asking why, thank you to my parents.

And for bringing me alongside, and giving me the opportunity to join in the ongoing work of this book, thank you to my co-author Steven Leon.

Lisette de Pillis

To the memory of Judith Russ Leon, my lover and companion for more than 46 years.

Steven J. Leon

Contents

Preface

We are pleased to see the text reach its tenth edition. The continued support and enthusiasm of its many users have been most gratifying. Linear algebra is more exciting now than at almost any time in the past. Its applications continue to spread to more and more fields. Largely due to the computer revolution of the last 75 years, linear algebra has risen to a role of prominence in the mathematical curriculum rivaling that of calculus. Modern software has also made it possible to dramatically improve the way the course is taught.

The first edition of this book was published in 1980. Each of the following editions has seen significant modifications including the addition of comprehensive sets of MATLAB computer exercises, a dramatic increase in the number of applications, and many revisions in the various sections of the book. We have been fortunate to have had outstanding reviewers, and their suggestions have led to many important improvements in the book.

What's New in the Tenth Edition?

You may have noticed something new on the cover of the book. Another author! Yes, after nearly 40 years as a "solo act," Steve Leon has a partner. New co-author Lisette de Pillis is a professor at Harvey Mudd College and brings her passion for teaching and solving real-world problems to this revision.

The focus of this revision was transforming it from a primarily print-based learning tool to a digital learning tool. The eText is therefore filled with content and tools that will help bring the entire course to life for students in new ways and help you improve instruction. Specifically,

- **Interactive figures and utilities.** We have added a number of opportunities for students to interact with content in a dynamic manner in order to build and enhance understanding. Interactive figures allow students to explore concepts geometrically in ways that are not possible without technology. Examples here include:
  - In Chapter 3, Visualizing the span of vectors—Figures 3.2.3, 3.2.4, 3.2.6(a), 3.2.6(b)
  - In Chapter 4, Visualizing linear transformations
    - Simple linear transformations—Figures 4.1.1 through 4.1.4
    - Dilations, reflections, rotations—Figure 4.2.3
    - Yaw, pitch, and roll of an airplane—Figure 4.2.5

- In Chapter 6, Visualization tools for 2×2 matrices
  - Eigenvectors—Figure 6.1.1
  - Singular vectors—Figure 6.5.1
- **Hints.** For selected exercises, we've included hints for students to consider if they get stuck.
- **Notes, Labels, and Highlights.** Notes allow instructors to add their personal teaching style to important topics, call out need-to-know information, or clarify difficult concepts. Students can make their eText their own by creating highlights with meaningful labels and notes, helping them focus on what they need to study. The customizable Notebook allows students to filter, arrange, and group their notes in a way that makes sense to them.
- **Dashboard**. Instructors can create reading assignments and see the time spent in the eText so that they can plan more effective instruction.
- **Portability**. Portable access lets students read their eText whenever they have a moment in their day, on Android and iOS mobile phones and tablets. Even without an Internet connection, offline reading ensures students never miss a chance to learn.
- **Ease-of-Use.** Straightforward setup makes it easy for instructors to get their class up and reading quickly on the first day of class. In addition, Learning Management System (LMS) integration provides institutions, instructors, and students with single sign-on access to the eText via many popular LMSs.

Overview of Text

This book is suitable for either a lower or upper division Linear Algebra course. The student should have some familiarity with the basics of differential and integral calculus. This prerequisite can be met by either one semester or two quarters of elementary calculus.

If the text is used for a lower-level course, the instructor should probably spend more time on the early chapters and omit many of the sections in the later chapters. For more advanced courses, a quick review of the topics in the first two chapters and then a more complete coverage of the later chapters would be appropriate. The explanations in the text are given in sufficient detail so that beginning students should have little trouble reading and understanding the material. To further aid the student, a large number of examples have been worked out completely. Additionally, computer exercises at the end of each chapter give students the opportunity to perform numerical experiments and try to generalize the results. Applications are presented throughout the book. These applications can be used to motivate new material or to illustrate the relevance of material that has already been covered.

The text contains all the topics recommended by the National Science Foundation (NSF) sponsored Linear Algebra Curriculum Study Group (LACSG) and much more. Although there is more material than can be covered in a single course, it is our belief that it is easier for an instructor to leave out or skip material than it is to supplement a book with outside material. Even if many topics are omitted, the book should still provide students with a feeling for the overall scope of the subject matter. Furthermore, students may use the book later as a reference and consequently may end up learning omitted topics on their own.

Suggested Course Outlines

We include here a number of outlines for one-semester courses at either the lower or upper-division levels, and with either a matrix-oriented emphasis or a slightly more theoretical emphasis.

1. One-Semester Lower Division Course

A. Basic Lower Level Course

Chapter 1	Sections 1–6	7 lectures
Chapter 2	Sections 1–2	2 lectures
Chapter 3	Sections 1–6	9 lectures
Chapter 4	Sections 1–3	4 lectures
Chapter 5	Sections 1–6	9 lectures
Chapter 6	Sections 1–3	<u>4 lectures</u>
		Total 35 lectures

B. LACSG Matrix-Oriented Course

The core course recommended by the LACSG involves only the Euclidean vector spaces. Consequently, for this course you should omit Section 1 of Chapter 3 (on general vector spaces) and all references and exercises involving function spaces in Chapters 3 to 6. All the topics in the LACSG core syllabus are included in the text. It is not necessary to introduce any supplementary materials. The LACSG recommended 28 lectures to cover the core material. This is possible if the class is taught in lecture format with an additional recitation section meeting once a week. If the course is taught without recitations, it is our contention that the following schedule of 35 lectures is perhaps more reasonable.

Chapter 1	Sections 1–6	7 lectures
Chapter 2	Sections 1–2	2 lectures
Chapter 3	Sections 2–6	7 lectures
Chapter 4	Sections 1–3	2 lectures
Chapter 5	Sections 1–6	9 lectures
Chapter 6	Sections 1, 3–5	<u>8 lectures</u>
		Total 35 lectures

2. One-Semester Upper-Level Courses

The coverage in an upper-division course is dependent on the background of the students. Following are two possible courses.

Option A: Minimal background in linear algebra

Chapter 1	Sections 1–6	6 lectures
Chapter 2	Sections 1–2	2 lectures
Chapter 3	Sections 1–6	7 lectures
Chapter 5	Sections 1–6	9 lectures
Chapter 6	Sections 1–7, 8*	10 lectures
Chapter 7	Section 4	1 lecture
		Total 35 lectures

* If time allows.

Option B: Some background in linear algebra

Review of Topics in Chapters 1–3		5 lectures
Chapter 4	Sections 1–3	2 lectures
Chapter 5	Sections 1–6	10 lectures
Chapter 6	Sections 1–7, 8*	11 lectures
Chapter 7	Sections 1–3*, 4–7	7 lectures
Chapter 8	Sections 1–2*	2 lectures
		Total 37 lectures

* If time allows.

3. Two-Semester Sequence

Although two semesters of linear algebra have been recommended by the LACSG, it is still not practical at many universities and colleges. At present, there is no universal agreement on a core syllabus for a second course. In a two-semester sequence, it is possible to cover all 43 sections of the book. You might also consider adding a lecture or two in order to demonstrate how to use MATLAB.

Computer Exercises

The text contains a section of computing exercises at the end of each chapter. These exercises are based on the software package MATLAB. The MATLAB Appendix in the book explains the basics of using the software. MATLAB has the advantage that it is a powerful tool for matrix computations, yet it is easy to learn. After reading the Appendix, students should be able to do the computing exercises without having to refer to any other software books or manuals. To help students get started, we recommend a one 50-minute classroom demonstration of the software. The assignments can be done either as ordinary homework assignments or as part of a formally scheduled computer laboratory course.

Although the course can be taught without any reference to a computer, we believe that computer exercises can greatly enhance student learning and provide a new dimension to linear algebra education. One of the recommendations of the LASCG is that technology should be used in a first course in linear algebra. That recommendation has been widely accepted, and it is now common to see mathematical software packages used in linear algebra courses.

Acknowledgments

We would like to express our gratitude to the long list of reviewers who have contributed so much to all previous editions of this book. Thanks also to the many users who have sent in comments and suggestions. Special thanks are also due to the reviewers of the tenth edition:

- Stephen Adams, *Cabrini University*
- Kuzman Adzievski, *South Carolina State University*
- Mike Albanese, *Central Piedmont Community College*
- Alan Alewine, *McKendree University*
- John M. Alongi, *Northwestern University*
- Bonnie Amende, *St. Martin's University*
- Scott Annin, *California State University Fullerton*
- Ioannis K. Argyros, *Cameron University*
- Mark Arnold, *University of Arkansas*
- Victor Barranca, *Swarthmore College*
- Richard Bastian, *Monmouth University*
- Hossein Behforooz, *Utica College*
- Kaddour Boukaabar, *California University of Pennsylvania*
- David Boyd, *Valdosta State University*
- Katherine Brandl, *Centenary College of Louisiana*
- Regina A. Buckley, *Villanova University*
- George Pete Caleodis, *Los Angeles Valley College*
- Gregory L. Cameron, *Brigham Young University, Idaho*
- Jeremy Case, *Taylor University*
- Scott Cook, *Tarleton State University*
- Joyati Debnath, *Winona State University*
- Geoffrey Dietz, *Gannon University*
- Paul Dostert, *Coker College*
- Kevin Farrell, *Lyndon State College*
- Jon Fassett, *Central Washington University*
- Adam C. Fletcher, *Bethany College*
- Lester French, *University of Maine at Augusta*
- Michael Gagliardo, *California Lutheran University*
- Benjamin Gaines, *Iona College*
- Mohammad Ganjizadeh, *Tarrant County College*
- Sanford Geraci, *Broward College*

- Nicholas L. Goins, *St. Clair County Community College*
- Raymond N. Greenwell, *Hofstra University*
- Mark Grinshpon, *Georgia State University*
- Mohammad Hailat, *University of South Carolina, Aiken*
- Maila Brucal Hallare, *Norfolk State University*
- Ryan Andrew Hass, *Oregon State University*
- Mary Juliano, SSJ, *Caldwell University*
- Christiaan Ketelaar, *University of Delaware*
- Yang Kuang, *Arizona State University*
- Shinemin Lin, *Savannah State University*
- Dawn A. Lott, *Delaware State University*
- James E. Martin, *Christopher Newport University*
- Peter McNamara, *Bucknell University*
- Mariana Montiel, *Georgia State University*
- Robert G. Niemeyer, *University of the Incarnate Word*
- Phillip E. Parker, *Wichita State University*
- Katherine A. Porter, *St. Martin's University*
- Pantelimon Stanica, *Naval Postgraduate School*
- J. Varbalow, *Thomas Nelson Community College*
- Haidong Wu, *University of Mississippi*

Thanks to the entire editorial, production, technology, marketing, and sales staff at Pearson for all their efforts.

We would like to acknowledge the contributions of Gene Golub and Jim Wilkinson. Most of the first edition of the book was written in 1977–1978 while Steve was a visiting scholar at Stanford University. During that period, he attended courses and lectures on numerical linear algebra given by Gene Golub and J. H. Wilkinson. Those lectures greatly influenced him in writing this book. Finally, we would like to express gratitude to Germund Dahlquist for his helpful suggestions on earlier editions of the book. Although Gene Golub, Jim Wilkinson, and Germund Dahlquist are no longer with us, they continue to live on in the memories of their friends.

Steven J. Leon
leonste@gmail.com

Lisette de Pillis
depillis@hmc.edu

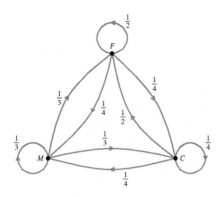

Matrices and Systems of Equations

One of the most important problems in mathematics is that of solving a system of linear equations. Well over 75 percent of all mathematical problems encountered in scientific or industrial applications involve solving a linear system at some stage. By using the methods of modern mathematics, it is often possible to take a sophisticated problem and reduce it to a single system of linear equations. Linear systems arise in applications to such areas as business, economics, sociology, ecology, demography, genetics, electronics, engineering, and physics. Therefore, it seems appropriate to begin this book with a section on linear systems.

1.1 Systems of Linear Equations

A *linear equation in n unknowns* is an equation of the form

$$a_1 x_1 + a_2 x_2 + \cdots + a_n x_n = b$$

where $a_1, a_2, \ldots, a_n$ and b are real numbers and $x_1, x_2, \ldots, x_n$ are variables. A *linear system* of m equations in n unknowns is then a system of the form

$$
\begin{aligned}
a_{11} x_1 + a_{12} x_2 + \cdots + a_{1n} x_n &= b_1 \\
a_{21} x_1 + a_{22} x_2 + \cdots + a_{2n} x_n &= b_2 \\
&\ \vdots \\
a_{m1} x_1 + a_{m2} x_2 + \cdots + a_{mn} x_n &= b_m
\end{aligned}
\tag{1}
$$

where the a_{ij}'s and the b_i's are all real numbers. We will refer to systems of the form (1) as $m \times n$ linear systems. The following are examples of linear systems:

(a)　$x_1 + 2x_2 = 5$
　　　$2x_1 + 3x_2 = 8$

(b)　$x_1 - x_2 + x_3 = 2$
　　　$2x_1 + x_2 - x_3 = 4$

(c)　$x_1 + x_2 = 2$
　　　$x_1 - x_2 = 1$
　　　$x_1 \qquad = 4$

System **(a)** is a 2×2 system, **(b)** is a 2×3 system, and **(c)** is a 3×2 system.

By a solution of an $m \times n$ system, we mean an ordered n-tuple of numbers $(x_1, x_2, \ldots, x_n)$ that satisfies all the equations of the system. For example, the ordered pair $(1, 2)$ is a solution of system **(a)**, since

$$1 \cdot (1) + 2 \cdot (2) = 5$$
$$2 \cdot (1) + 3 \cdot (2) = 8$$

The ordered triple $(2, 0, 0)$ is a solution of system **(b)**, since

$$1 \cdot (2) - 1 \cdot (0) + 1 \cdot (0) = 2$$
$$2 \cdot (2) + 1 \cdot (0) - 1 \cdot (0) = 4$$

Actually, system **(b)** has many solutions. If α is any real number, it is easily seen that the ordered triple $(2, \alpha, \alpha)$ is a solution. However, system **(c)** has no solution. It follows from the third equation that the first coordinate of any solution would have to be 4. Using $x_1 = 4$ in the first two equations, we see that the second coordinate must satisfy

$$4 + x_2 = 2$$
$$4 - x_2 = 1$$

Since there is no real number that satisfies both of these equations, the system has no solution. If a linear system has no solution, we say that the system is *inconsistent*. If the system has at least one solution, we say that it is *consistent*. Thus, system **(c)** is inconsistent, while systems **(a)** and **(b)** are both consistent.

The set of all solutions of a linear system is called the *solution set* of the system. If a system is inconsistent, its solution set is empty. A consistent system will have a nonempty solution set. To solve a consistent system, we must find its solution set.

2×2 Systems

Let us examine geometrically a system of the form

$$a_{11}x_1 + a_{12}x_2 = b_1$$
$$a_{21}x_1 + a_{22}x_2 = b_2$$

Each equation can be represented graphically as a line in the plane. The ordered pair (x_1, x_2) will be a solution of the system if and only if it lies on both lines. For example, consider the three systems

(i) $\quad x_1 + x_2 = 2$ $\qquad$ **(ii)** $\quad x_1 + x_2 = 2$ $\qquad$ **(iii)** $\quad x_1 + x_2 = 2$

$\phantom{\textbf{(i)}\quad} x_1 - x_2 = 2$ $\qquad\phantom{\textbf{(ii)}\quad} x_1 + x_2 = 1$ $\qquad\phantom{\textbf{(iii)}\quad} -x_1 - x_2 = -2$

The two lines in system **(i)** intersect at the point $(2, 0)$. Thus, $\{(2, 0)\}$ is the solution set of **(i)**. In system **(ii)**, the two lines are parallel. Therefore, system **(ii)** is inconsistent and hence its solution set is empty. The two equations in system **(iii)** both represent the same line. Any point on this line will be a solution of the system (see Figure 1.1.1).

In general, there are three possibilities: the lines intersect at a point, they are parallel, or both equations represent the same line. The solution set then contains either one, zero, or infinitely many points.

(i) Unique Solution: Intersecting Lines
Intersecting Point $(2, 0)$

(ii) No Solution: Parallel Lines

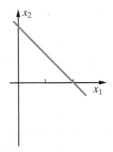

(iii) Infinite Solutions: Same Line

Figure 1.1.1.

The situation is the same for $m \times n$ systems. An $m \times n$ system may or may not be consistent. If it is consistent, it must have either exactly one solution or infinitely many solutions. These are the only possibilities. We will see why this is so in Section 1.2 when we study the row echelon form. Of more immediate concern is the problem of finding all solutions of a given system. To tackle this problem, we introduce the notion of *equivalent systems*.

Equivalent Systems

Consider the two systems

$$
\textbf{(a)} \quad
\begin{aligned}
3x_1 + 2x_2 - x_3 &= -2 \\
x_2 &= 3 \\
2x_3 &= 4
\end{aligned}
\qquad
\textbf{(b)} \quad
\begin{aligned}
3x_1 + 2x_2 - x_3 &= -2 \\
-3x_1 - x_2 + x_3 &= 5 \\
3x_1 + 2x_2 + x_3 &= 2
\end{aligned}
$$

System **(a)** is easy to solve because it is clear from the last two equations that $x_2 = 3$ and $x_3 = 2$. Using these values in the first equation, we get

$$
\begin{aligned}
3x_1 + 2 \cdot 3 - 2 &= -2 \\
x_1 &= -2
\end{aligned}
$$

Thus, the solution of the system is $(-2, 3, 2)$. System **(b)** seems to be more difficult to solve. Actually, system **(b)** has the same solution as system **(a)**. To see this, add the first two equations of the system:

$$
\begin{aligned}
3x_1 + 2x_2 - x_3 &= -2 \\
-3x_1 - x_2 + x_3 &= 5 \\
\hline
x_2 &= 3
\end{aligned}
$$

If (x_1, x_2, x_3) is any solution of **(b)**, it must satisfy all the equations of the system. Thus, it must satisfy any new equation formed by adding two of its equations. Therefore, x_2 must equal 3. Similarly, (x_1, x_2, x_3) must satisfy the new equation formed by subtracting the first equation from the third:

$$
\begin{aligned}
3x_1 + 2x_2 + x_3 &= 2 \\
3x_1 + 2x_2 - x_3 &= -2 \\
\hline
2x_3 &= 4
\end{aligned}
$$

Therefore, any solution of system **(b)** must also be a solution of system **(a)**. By a similar argument, it can be shown that any solution of **(a)** is also a solution of **(b)**. This can be done by subtracting the first equation from the second:

$$
\begin{aligned}
x_2 &= 3 \\
3x_1 + 2x_2 - x_3 &= -2 \\
\hline
-3x_1 - x_2 + x_3 &= 5
\end{aligned}
$$

Then add the first and third equations:

$$
\begin{aligned}
3x_1 + 2x_2 - x_3 &= -2 \\
2x_3 &= 4 \\
\hline
3x_1 + 2x_2 + x_3 &= 2
\end{aligned}
$$

Thus, (x_1, x_2, x_3) is a solution of system **(b)** if and only if it is a solution of system **(a)**. Therefore, both systems have the same solution set, $\{(-2, 3, 2)\}$.

Definition

Two systems of equations involving the same variables are said to be **equivalent** if they have the same solution set.

If we interchange the order in which two equations of a system are written, this will have no effect on the solution set. The reordered system will be equivalent to the original system. For example, the systems

$$
\begin{aligned}
x_1 + 2x_2 &= 4 \\
3x_1 - x_2 &= 2 \quad \text{and} \\
4x_1 + x_2 &= 6
\end{aligned}
\qquad
\begin{aligned}
4x_1 + x_2 &= 6 \\
3x_1 - x_2 &= 2 \\
x_1 + 2x_2 &= 4
\end{aligned}
$$

both involve the same three equations and, consequently, they must have the same solution set.

If one equation of a system is multiplied through by a nonzero real number, this will have no effect on the solution set, and the new system will be equivalent to the original system. For example, the systems

$$\begin{matrix} x_1 + x_2 + x_3 = 3 \\ -2x_1 - x_2 + 4x_3 = 1 \end{matrix} \quad \text{and} \quad \begin{matrix} 2x_1 + 2x_2 + 2x_3 = 6 \\ -2x_1 - x_2 + 4x_3 = 1 \end{matrix}$$

are equivalent.

If a multiple of one equation is added to another equation, the new system will be equivalent to the original system. This follows since the n-tuple $(x_1, \ldots, x_n)$ will satisfy the two equations

$$\begin{aligned} a_{i1}x_1 + \cdots + a_{in}x_n &= b_i \\ a_{j1}x_1 + \cdots + a_{jn}x_n &= b_j \end{aligned}$$

if and only if it satisfies the equations

$$\begin{aligned} a_{i1}x_1 + \cdots + a_{in}x_n &= b_i \\ (a_{j1} + \alpha a_{i1})x_1 + \cdots + (a_{jn} + \alpha a_{in})x_n &= b_j + \alpha b_i \end{aligned}$$

To summarize, there are three operations that can be used on a system to obtain an equivalent system:

I. The order in which any two equations are written may be interchanged.

II. Both sides of an equation may be multiplied by the same nonzero real number.

III. A multiple of one equation may be added to (or subtracted from) another.

Given a system of equations, we may use these operations to obtain an equivalent system that is easier to solve.

$n \times n$ Systems

Let us restrict ourselves to $n \times n$ systems for the remainder of this section. We will show that if an $n \times n$ system has exactly one solution, then operations **I** and **III** can be used to obtain an equivalent "strictly triangular system."

Definition

> A system is said to be in **strict triangular form** if, in the kth equation, the coefficients of the first $k - 1$ variables are all zero and the coefficient of x_k is nonzero $(k = 1, \ldots, n)$.

EXAMPLE I   The system

$$\begin{aligned} 3x_1 + 2x_2 + x_3 &= 1 \\ x_2 - x_3 &= 2 \\ 2x_3 &= 4 \end{aligned}$$

is in strict triangular form, since in the second equation the coefficients are $0, 1, -1$, respectively, and in the third equation the coefficients are $0, 0, 2$, respectively. Because of the strict triangular form, the system is easy to solve. It follows from the third equation that $x_3 = 2$. Using this value in the second equation, we obtain

$$x_2 - 2 = 2 \qquad \text{or} \qquad x_2 = 4$$

Using $x_2 = 4$, $x_3 = 2$ in the first equation, we end up with

$$3x_1 + 2 \cdot 4 + 2 = 1$$
$$x_1 = -3$$

Thus, the solution of the system is $(-3, 4, 2)$.   ■

Any $n \times n$ strictly triangular system can be solved in the same manner as the last example. First, the nth equation is solved for the value of x_n. This value is used in the $(n-1)$st equation to solve for x_{n-1}. The values x_n and x_{n-1} are used in the $(n-2)$nd equation to solve for x_{n-2}, and so on. We will refer to this method of solving a strictly triangular system as *back substitution*.

EXAMPLE 2   Solve the system

$$\begin{aligned} 2x_1 - x_2 + 3x_3 - 2x_4 &= 1 \\ x_2 - 2x_3 + 3x_4 &= 2 \\ 4x_3 + 3x_4 &= 3 \\ 4x_4 &= 4 \end{aligned}$$

Solution

Using back substitution, we obtain

$$\begin{aligned} 4x_4 &= 4 & x_4 &= 1 \\ 4x_3 + 3 \cdot 1 &= 3 & x_3 &= 0 \\ x_2 - 2 \cdot 0 + 3 \cdot 1 &= 2 & x_2 &= -1 \\ 2x_1 - (-1) + 3 \cdot 0 - 2 \cdot 1 &= 1 & x_1 &= 1 \end{aligned}$$

Thus, the solution is $(1, -1, 0, 1)$.   ■

In general, given a system of n linear equations in n unknowns, we will use operations **I** and **III** to try to obtain an equivalent system that is strictly triangular. (We will see in the next section of the book that it is not possible to reduce the system to strictly triangular form in the cases where the system does not have a unique solution.)

EXAMPLE 3   Solve the system

$$\begin{aligned} x_1 + 2x_2 + x_3 &= 3 \\ 3x_1 - x_2 - 3x_3 &= -1 \\ 2x_1 + 3x_2 + x_3 &= 4 \end{aligned}$$

Solution

Subtracting 3 times the first row from the second row yields

$$-7x_2 - 6x_3 = -10$$

Subtracting 2 times the first row from the third row yields

$$-x_2 - x_3 = -2$$

If the second and third equations of our system, respectively, are replaced by these new equations, we obtain the equivalent system

$$
\begin{aligned}
x_1 + \quad 2x_2 + \quad x_3 &= \quad 3 \\
-7x_2 - 6x_3 &= -10 \\
-x_2 - \quad x_3 &= -2
\end{aligned}
$$

If the third equation of this system is replaced by the sum of the third equation and $-\frac{1}{7}$ times the second equation, we end up with the following strictly triangular system:

$$
\begin{aligned}
x_1 + \quad 2x_2 + \quad x_3 &= \quad 3 \\
-7x_2 - \quad 6x_3 &= -10 \\
-\tfrac{1}{7}x_3 &= -\tfrac{4}{7}
\end{aligned}
$$

Using back substitution, we get

$$x_3 = 4, \qquad x_2 = -2, \qquad x_1 = 3$$

Let us look back at the system of equations in the last example. We can associate with that system a 3×3 array of numbers whose entries are the coefficients of the x_i's:

$$
\begin{pmatrix}
1 & 2 & 1 \\
3 & -1 & -3 \\
2 & 3 & 1
\end{pmatrix}
$$

We will refer to this array as the *coefficient matrix* of the system. The term *matrix* means a rectangular array of numbers. A matrix having m rows and n columns is said to be $m \times n$. A matrix is said to be *square* if it has the same number of rows and columns, that is, if $m = n$.

If we attach to the coefficient matrix an additional column whose entries are the numbers on the right-hand side of the system, we obtain the new matrix

$$
\left(
\begin{array}{ccc|c}
1 & 2 & 1 & 3 \\
3 & -1 & -3 & -1 \\
2 & 3 & 1 & 4
\end{array}
\right)
$$

We will refer to this new matrix as the *augmented matrix*. In general, when an $m \times r$ matrix B is attached to an $m \times n$ matrix A in this way, the augmented matrix is denoted by $(A|B)$. Thus, if

$$A = \begin{bmatrix} a_{11} & a_{12} & \cdots & a_{1n} \\ a_{21} & a_{22} & \cdots & a_{2n} \\ \vdots & & & \\ a_{m1} & a_{m2} & \cdots & a_{mn} \end{bmatrix}, \quad B = \begin{bmatrix} b_{11} & b_{12} & \cdots & b_{1r} \\ b_{21} & b_{22} & \cdots & b_{2r} \\ \vdots & & & \\ b_{m1} & b_{m2} & \cdots & b_{mr} \end{bmatrix}$$

then

$$(A|B) = \begin{bmatrix} a_{11} & \cdots & a_{1n} & b_{11} & \cdots & b_{1r} \\ \vdots & & & \vdots & & \\ a_{m1} & \cdots & a_{mn} & b_{m1} & \cdots & b_{mr} \end{bmatrix}$$

With each system of equations, we may associate an augmented matrix of the form

$$\begin{bmatrix} a_{11} & \cdots & a_{1n} & b_1 \\ \vdots & & & \vdots \\ a_{m1} & \cdots & a_{mn} & b_m \end{bmatrix}$$

The system can be solved by performing operations on the augmented matrix. The x_i's are placeholders that can be omitted until the end of the computation. Corresponding to the three operations used to obtain equivalent systems, the following row operations may be applied to the augmented matrix:

Elementary Row Operations

  I. Interchange two rows.
  II. Multiply a row by a nonzero real number.
  III. Replace a row by the sum of that row and a multiple of another row.

Returning to the example, we find that the first row is used to eliminate the elements in the first column of the remaining rows. We refer to the first row as the *pivotal row*. For emphasis, the entries in the pivotal row are all in bold type and the entire row is color shaded. The first nonzero entry in the pivotal row is called the *pivot*.

$$\begin{matrix} \text{(pivot } a_{11} = 1) \\ \text{entries to be eliminated} \\ a_{21} = 3 \text{ and } a_{31} = 2 \end{matrix} \Big\} \rightarrow \begin{bmatrix} \mathbf{1} & \mathbf{2} & \mathbf{1} & \mathbf{3} \\ 3 & -1 & -3 & -1 \\ 2 & 3 & 1 & 4 \end{bmatrix} \leftarrow \text{pivotal row}$$

By using row operation **III**, 3 times the first row is subtracted from the second row and 2 times the first row is subtracted from the third. When this is done, we end up with the matrix

$$\begin{bmatrix} 1 & 2 & 1 & 3 \\ \mathbf{0} & \mathbf{-7} & \mathbf{-6} & \mathbf{-10} \\ 0 & -1 & -1 & -2 \end{bmatrix} \leftarrow \text{pivotal row}$$

At this step, we choose the second row as our new pivotal row and apply row operation **III** to eliminate the last element in the second column. This time the pivot is -7 and the quotient $\frac{-1}{-7} = \frac{1}{7}$ is the multiple of the pivotal row that is subtracted from the third row. We end up with the matrix

$$\begin{pmatrix} 1 & 2 & 1 & 3 \\ 0 & -7 & -6 & -10 \\ 0 & 0 & -\frac{1}{7} & -\frac{4}{7} \end{pmatrix}$$

This is the augmented matrix for the strictly triangular system, which is equivalent to the original system. The solution of the system is easily obtained by back substitution.

EXAMPLE 4   Solve the system

$$\begin{array}{rcrcrcrcr} & & -\ x_2 & - & x_3 & + & x_4 & = & 0 \\ x_1 & + & x_2 & + & x_3 & + & x_4 & = & 6 \\ 2x_1 & + & 4x_2 & + & x_3 & - & 2x_4 & = & -1 \\ 3x_1 & + & x_2 & - & 2x_3 & + & 2x_4 & = & 3 \end{array}$$

Solution

The augmented matrix for this system is

$$\begin{pmatrix} 0 & -1 & -1 & 1 & 0 \\ 1 & 1 & 1 & 1 & 6 \\ 2 & 4 & 1 & -2 & -1 \\ 3 & 1 & -2 & 2 & 3 \end{pmatrix}$$

Since it is not possible to eliminate any entries by using 0 as a pivot element, we will use row operation I to interchange the first two rows of the augmented matrix. The new first row will be the pivotal row and the pivot element will be 1:

$$(\text{pivot } a_{11} = 1) \quad \begin{pmatrix} \mathbf{1} & \mathbf{1} & \mathbf{1} & \mathbf{1} & \mathbf{6} \\ 0 & -1 & -1 & 1 & 0 \\ 2 & 4 & 1 & -2 & -1 \\ 3 & 1 & -2 & 2 & 3 \end{pmatrix} \quad \leftarrow \text{pivotal row}$$

Row operation **III** is then used twice to eliminate the two nonzero entries in the first column:

$$\begin{pmatrix} 1 & 1 & 1 & 1 & 6 \\ \mathbf{0} & \mathbf{-1} & \mathbf{-1} & \mathbf{1} & \mathbf{0} \\ 0 & 2 & -1 & -4 & -13 \\ 0 & -2 & -5 & -1 & -15 \end{pmatrix}$$

Next, the second row is used as the pivotal row to eliminate the entries in the second column below the pivot element -1:

$$\begin{pmatrix} 1 & 1 & 1 & 1 & 6 \\ 0 & -1 & -1 & 1 & 0 \\ \mathbf{0} & \mathbf{0} & \mathbf{-3} & \mathbf{-2} & \mathbf{-13} \\ 0 & 0 & -3 & -3 & -15 \end{pmatrix}$$

Finally, the third row is used as the pivotal row to eliminate the last element in the third column:

$$\begin{pmatrix} 1 & 1 & 1 & 1 & 6 \\ 0 & -1 & -1 & 1 & 0 \\ 0 & 0 & -3 & -2 & -13 \\ 0 & 0 & 0 & -1 & -2 \end{pmatrix}$$

This augmented matrix represents a strictly triangular system. Solving by back substitution, we obtain the solution $(2, -1, 3, 2)$. ∎

In general, if an $n \times n$ linear system can be reduced to strictly triangular form, then it will have a unique solution that can be obtained by performing back substitution on the triangular system. We can think of the reduction process as an algorithm involving $n - 1$ steps. At the first step, a pivot element is chosen from among the nonzero entries in the first column of the matrix. The row containing the pivot element is called the *pivotal row*. We interchange rows (if necessary) so that the pivotal row is the new first row. Multiples of the pivotal row are then subtracted from each of the remaining $n - 1$ rows so as to obtain 0's in the first entries of rows 2 through n. At the second step, a pivot element is chosen from the nonzero entries in column 2, rows 2 through n, of the matrix. The row containing the pivot is then interchanged with the second row of the matrix and is used as the new pivotal row. Multiples of the pivotal row are then subtracted from the remaining $n - 2$ rows so as to eliminate all entries below the pivot in the second column. The same procedure is repeated for columns 3 through $n - 1$. Note that at the second step row 1 and column 1 remain unchanged, at the third step the first two rows and first two columns remain unchanged, and so on. At each step, the overall dimensions of the system are effectively reduced by 1 (see Figure 1.1.2).

If the elimination process can be carried out as described, we will arrive at an equivalent strictly triangular system after $n - 1$ steps. However, the procedure will break down if, at any step, all possible choices for a pivot element are equal to 0. When this happens, the alternative is to reduce the system to certain special echelon, or staircase-shaped, forms. These echelon forms will be studied in the next section. They will also be used for $m \times n$ systems, where $m \neq n$.

Figure 1.1.2.

SECTION 1.1 EXERCISES

1. Use back substitution to solve each of the following systems of equations:

   (a) $x_1 - 3x_2 = 2$
   $2x_2 = 6$

   (b) $x_1 + x_2 + x_3 = 8$
   $2x_2 + x_3 = 5$
   $3x_3 = 9$

   (c) $x_1 + 2x_2 + 2x_3 + x_4 = 5$
   $3x_2 + x_3 - 2x_4 = 1$
   $-x_3 + 2x_4 = -1$
   $4x_4 = 4$

   (d) $x_1 + x_2 + x_3 + x_4 + x_5 = 5$
   $2x_2 + x_3 - 2x_4 + x_5 = 1$
   $4x_3 + x_4 - 2x_5 = 1$
   $x_4 - 3x_5 = 0$
   $2x_5 = 2$

2. Write out the coefficient matrix for each of the systems in Exercise 1.

3. In each of the following systems, interpret each equation as a line in the plane. For each system, graph the lines and determine geometrically the number of solutions.

   (a) $x_1 + x_2 = 4$
   $x_1 - x_2 = 2$

   (b) $x_1 + 2x_2 = 4$
   $-2x_1 - 4x_2 = 4$

   (c) $2x_1 - x_2 = 3$
   $-4x_1 + 2x_2 = -6$

   (d) $x_1 + x_2 = 1$
   $x_1 - x_2 = 1$
   $-x_1 + 3x_2 = 3$

4. Write an augmented matrix for each of the systems in Exercise 3.

5. Write out the system of equations that corresponds to each of the following augmented matrices:

   (a) $\begin{bmatrix} 3 & 2 & | & 8 \\ 1 & 5 & | & 7 \end{bmatrix}$

   (b) $\begin{bmatrix} 5 & -2 & 1 & | & 3 \\ 2 & 3 & -4 & | & 0 \end{bmatrix}$

   (c) $\begin{bmatrix} 2 & 1 & 4 & | & -1 \\ 4 & -2 & 3 & | & 4 \\ 5 & 2 & 6 & | & -1 \end{bmatrix}$

   (d) $\begin{bmatrix} 4 & -3 & 1 & 2 & | & 4 \\ 3 & 1 & -5 & 6 & | & 5 \\ 1 & 1 & 2 & 4 & | & 8 \\ 5 & 1 & 3 & -2 & | & 7 \end{bmatrix}$

6. Solve each of the following systems:

   (a) $x_1 - 2x_2 = 5$
   $3x_1 + x_2 = 1$

   (b) $2x_1 + x_2 = 8$
   $4x_1 - 3x_2 = 6$

   (c) $4x_1 + 3x_2 = 4$
   $\frac{2}{3}x_1 + 4x_2 = 3$

   (d) $x_1 + 2x_2 - x_3 = 1$
   $2x_1 - x_2 + x_3 = 3$
   $-x_1 + 2x_2 + 3x_3 = 7$

   (e) $2x_1 + x_2 + 3x_3 = 1$
   $4x_1 + 3x_2 + 5x_3 = 1$
   $6x_1 + 5x_2 + 5x_3 = -3$

   (f) $3x_1 + 2x_2 + x_3 = 0$
   $-2x_1 + x_2 - x_3 = 2$
   $2x_1 - x_2 + 2x_3 = -1$

   (g) $\frac{1}{3}x_1 + \frac{2}{3}x_2 + 2x_3 = -1$
   $x_1 + 2x_2 + \frac{3}{2}x_3 = \frac{3}{2}$
   $\frac{1}{2}x_1 + 2x_2 + \frac{12}{5}x_3 = \frac{1}{10}$

   (h) $x_2 + x_3 + x_4 = 0$
   $3x_1 + 3x_3 - 4x_4 = 7$
   $x_1 + x_2 + x_3 + 2x_4 = 6$
   $2x_1 + 3x_2 + x_3 + 3x_4 = 6$

7. The two systems

   $2x_1 + x_2 = 3$
   $4x_1 + 3x_2 = 5$

   and

   $2x_1 + x_2 = -1$
   $4x_1 + 3x_2 = 1$

   have the same coefficient matrix but different right-hand sides. Solve both systems simultaneously by eliminating the first entry in the second row of the augmented matrix:

   $$\begin{bmatrix} 2 & 1 & | & 3 & -1 \\ 4 & 3 & | & 5 & 1 \end{bmatrix}$$

   and then performing back substitutions for each of the columns corresponding to the right-hand sides.

8. Solve the two systems

   $x_1 + 2x_2 - 2x_3 = 1$
   $2x_1 + 5x_2 + x_3 = 9$
   $x_1 + 3x_2 + 4x_3 = 9$

   $x_1 + 2x_2 - 2x_3 = 9$
   $2x_1 + 5x_2 + x_3 = 9$
   $x_1 + 3x_2 + 4x_3 = -2$

   by doing elimination on a 3×5 augmented matrix and then performing two back substitutions.

9. Given a system of the form

   $-m_1x_1 + x_2 = b_1$
   $-m_2x_1 + x_2 = b_2$

   where $m_1, m_2, b_1,$ and b_2 are constants:

   (a) Show that the system will have a unique solution if $m_1 \neq m_2$.

(b) Show that if $m_1 = m_2$, then the system will be consistent only if $b_1 = b_2$.

(c) Give a geometric interpretation of parts (a) and (b).

10. Consider a system of the form

$$a_{11}x_1 + a_{12}x_2 = 0$$
$$a_{21}x_1 + a_{22}x_2 = 0$$

where a_{11}, a_{12}, a_{21}, and a_{22} are constants. Explain why a system of this form must be consistent.

11. Give a geometrical interpretation of a linear equation in three unknowns. Give a geometrical description of the possible solution sets for a 3×3 linear system.

1.2 Row Echelon Form

In Section 1.1, we learned a method for reducing an $n \times n$ linear system to strict triangular form. However, this method will fail if, at any stage of the reduction process, all the possible choices for a pivot element in a given column are 0.

EXAMPLE I Consider the system represented by the augmented matrix

$$\left\{ \begin{array}{ccccc|c} \mathbf{1} & \mathbf{1} & \mathbf{1} & \mathbf{1} & \mathbf{1} & \mathbf{1} \\ -1 & -1 & 0 & 0 & 1 & -1 \\ -2 & -2 & 0 & 0 & 3 & 1 \\ 0 & 0 & 1 & 1 & 3 & -1 \\ 1 & 1 & 2 & 2 & 4 & 1 \end{array} \right\} \leftarrow \text{pivotal row}$$

If row operation **III** is used to eliminate the nonzero entries in the last four rows of the first column, the resulting matrix will be

$$\left(\begin{array}{ccccc|c} 1 & 1 & 1 & 1 & 1 & 1 \\ \mathbf{0} & \mathbf{0} & \mathbf{1} & \mathbf{1} & \mathbf{2} & \mathbf{0} \\ 0 & 0 & 2 & 2 & 5 & 3 \\ 0 & 0 & 1 & 1 & 3 & -1 \\ 0 & 0 & 1 & 1 & 3 & 0 \end{array} \right) \leftarrow \text{pivotal row}$$

At this stage, the reduction to strict triangular form breaks down. All four possible choices for the pivot element in the second column are 0. How do we proceed from here? Since our goal is to simplify the system as much as possible, it seems natural to move over to the third column and eliminate the last three entries:

$$\left(\begin{array}{ccccc|c} 1 & 1 & 1 & 1 & 1 & 1 \\ 0 & 0 & 1 & 1 & 2 & 0 \\ \mathbf{0} & \mathbf{0} & \mathbf{0} & \mathbf{0} & \mathbf{1} & \mathbf{3} \\ 0 & 0 & 0 & 0 & 1 & -1 \\ 0 & 0 & 0 & 0 & 1 & 0 \end{array} \right)$$

In the fourth column, all the choices for a pivot element are 0; so again, we move on to the next column. If we use the third row as the pivotal row, the last two entries in the fifth column are eliminated and we end up with the matrix

$$\begin{pmatrix} 1 & 1 & 1 & 1 & 1 & 1 \\ 0 & 0 & 1 & 1 & 2 & 0 \\ 0 & 0 & 0 & 0 & 1 & 3 \\ 0 & 0 & 0 & 0 & 0 & -4 \\ 0 & 0 & 0 & 0 & 0 & -3 \end{pmatrix}$$

The coefficient matrix that we end up with is not in strict triangular form; it is in stair-case, or echelon, form. The horizontal and vertical line segments in the array for the coefficient matrix indicate the structure of the staircase form. Note that the vertical drop is 1 for each step, but the horizontal span for a step can be more than 1.

The equations represented by the last two rows are

$$0x_1 + 0x_2 + 0x_3 + 0x_4 + 0x_5 = -4$$
$$0x_1 + 0x_2 + 0x_3 + 0x_4 + 0x_5 = -3$$

Since there are no 5-tuples that could satisfy these equations, the system is inconsistent.

Suppose now that we change the right-hand side of the system in the last example so as to obtain a consistent system. For example, if we start with

$$\begin{pmatrix} 1 & 1 & 1 & 1 & 1 & 1 \\ -1 & -1 & 0 & 0 & 1 & -1 \\ -2 & -2 & 0 & 0 & 3 & 1 \\ 0 & 0 & 1 & 1 & 3 & 3 \\ 1 & 1 & 2 & 2 & 4 & 4 \end{pmatrix}$$

then the reduction process will yield the echelon-form augmented matrix

$$\begin{pmatrix} 1 & 1 & 1 & 1 & 1 & 1 \\ 0 & 0 & 1 & 1 & 2 & 0 \\ 0 & 0 & 0 & 0 & 1 & 3 \\ 0 & 0 & 0 & 0 & 0 & 0 \\ 0 & 0 & 0 & 0 & 0 & 0 \end{pmatrix}$$

The last two equations of the reduced system will be satisfied for any 5-tuple. Thus, the solution set will be the set of all 5-tuples satisfying the first three equations.

$$\begin{aligned} x_1 + x_2 + x_3 + x_4 + x_5 &= 1 \\ x_3 + x_4 + 2x_5 &= 0 \\ x_5 &= 3 \end{aligned} \tag{1}$$

The variables corresponding to the first nonzero elements in each row of the reduced matrix will be referred to as *lead variables*. Thus, x_1, x_3, and x_5 are the lead variables. The remaining variables corresponding to the columns skipped in the reduction process will be referred to as *free variables*. Hence, x_2 and x_4 are the free variables. If we transfer the free variables over to the right-hand side in (1), we obtain the system

$$
\begin{aligned}
x_1 + x_3 + \ \ x_5 &= 1 - x_2 - x_4 \\
x_3 + 2x_5 &= -x_4 \\
x_5 &= 3
\end{aligned}
\tag{2}
$$

System (2) is strictly triangular in the unknowns x_1, x_3, and x_5. Thus, for each pair of values assigned to x_2 and x_4, there will be a unique solution. For example, if $x_2 = x_4 = 0$, then $x_5 = 3$, $x_3 = -6$, and $x_1 = 4$, and hence $(4, 0, -6, 0, 3)$ is a solution of the system.

Definition

A matrix is said to be in **row echelon form** if

   (i) The first nonzero entry in each nonzero row is 1.
   (ii) If row k does not consist entirely of zeros, the number of leading zero entries in row $k + 1$ is greater than the number of leading zero entries in row k.
   (iii) If there are rows whose entries are all zero, they are below the rows having nonzero entries.

EXAMPLE 2   The following matrices are in row echelon form:

$$
\begin{pmatrix} 1 & 4 & 2 \\ 0 & 1 & 3 \\ 0 & 0 & 1 \end{pmatrix}, \quad
\begin{pmatrix} 1 & 2 & 3 \\ 0 & 0 & 1 \\ 0 & 0 & 0 \end{pmatrix}, \quad
\begin{pmatrix} 1 & 3 & 1 & 0 \\ 0 & 0 & 1 & 3 \\ 0 & 0 & 0 & 0 \end{pmatrix}
\quad ■
$$

EXAMPLE 3   The following matrices are not in row echelon form:

$$
\begin{pmatrix} 2 & 4 & 6 \\ 0 & 3 & 5 \\ 0 & 0 & 4 \end{pmatrix}, \quad
\begin{pmatrix} 0 & 0 & 0 \\ 0 & 1 & 0 \end{pmatrix}, \quad
\begin{pmatrix} 0 & 1 \\ 1 & 0 \end{pmatrix}
$$

The first matrix does not satisfy condition **(i)**. The second matrix fails to satisfy condition **(iii)**, and the third matrix fails to satisfy condition **(ii)**.   ■

Definition

The process of using row operations **I**, **II**, and **III** to transform a linear system into one whose augmented matrix is in row echelon form is called **Gaussian elimination**.

Note that row operation **II** is necessary in order to scale the rows so that the leading coefficients are all 1. If the row echelon form of the augmented matrix contains a row of the form

$$
\begin{pmatrix} 0 & 0 & \cdots & 0 \,|\, 1 \end{pmatrix}
$$

the system is inconsistent. Otherwise, the system will be consistent. If the system is consistent and the nonzero rows of the row echelon form of the matrix form a strictly triangular system, the system will have a unique solution.

Overdetermined Systems

A linear system is said to be *overdetermined* if there are more equations than unknowns. Overdetermined systems are *usually* (but not always) inconsistent.

EXAMPLE 4   Solve each of the following overdetermined systems:

(a)
$$\begin{aligned} x_1 + x_2 &= 1 \\ x_1 - x_2 &= 3 \\ -x_1 + 2x_2 &= -2 \end{aligned}$$

(b)
$$\begin{aligned} x_1 + 2x_2 + x_3 &= 1 \\ 2x_1 - x_2 + x_3 &= 2 \\ 4x_1 + 3x_2 + 3x_3 &= 4 \\ 2x_1 - x_2 + 3x_3 &= 5 \end{aligned}$$

(c)
$$\begin{aligned} x_1 + 2x_2 + x_3 &= 1 \\ 2x_1 - x_2 + x_3 &= 2 \\ 4x_1 + 3x_2 + 3x_3 &= 4 \\ 3x_1 + x_2 + 2x_3 &= 3 \end{aligned}$$

Solution

Gaussian elimination was applied to put these systems into row-echelon form (steps not shown). Thus, we may write

$$\text{System (a):} \quad \left[\begin{array}{rr|r} 1 & 1 & 1 \\ 1 & -1 & 3 \\ -1 & 2 & -2 \end{array} \right] \rightarrow \left[\begin{array}{rr|r} 1 & 1 & 1 \\ 0 & 1 & -1 \\ 0 & 0 & 1 \end{array} \right]$$

The last row of the reduced matrix tells us that $0x_1 + 0x_2 = 1$. Since this is never possible, the system must be inconsistent. The three equations in system (a) represent lines in the plane. The first two lines intersect at the point $(2, -1)$. However, the third line does not pass through this point. Thus, there are no points that lie on all three lines (see Figure 1.2.1).

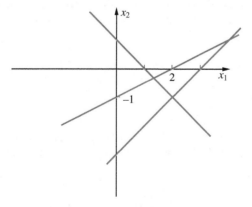

No Solution: Inconsistent System

Figure 1.2.1.

$$\text{System (b):} \quad \begin{bmatrix} 1 & 2 & 1 & 1 \\ 2 & -1 & 1 & 2 \\ 4 & 3 & 3 & 4 \\ 2 & -1 & 3 & 5 \end{bmatrix} \rightarrow \begin{bmatrix} 1 & 2 & 1 & 1 \\ 0 & 1 & \frac{1}{5} & 0 \\ 0 & 0 & 1 & \frac{3}{2} \\ 0 & 0 & 0 & 0 \end{bmatrix}$$

Using back substitution, we see that system (b) has exactly one solution $(0.1, -0.3, 1.5)$. The solution is unique because the nonzero rows of the reduced matrix form a strictly triangular system.

$$\text{System (c):} \quad \begin{bmatrix} 1 & 2 & 1 & 1 \\ 2 & -1 & 1 & 2 \\ 4 & 3 & 3 & 4 \\ 3 & 1 & 2 & 3 \end{bmatrix} \rightarrow \begin{bmatrix} 1 & 2 & 1 & 1 \\ 0 & 1 & \frac{1}{5} & 0 \\ 0 & 0 & 0 & 0 \\ 0 & 0 & 0 & 0 \end{bmatrix}$$

Solving for x_2 and x_1 in terms of x_3, we obtain

$$x_2 = -0.2x_3$$
$$x_1 = 1 - 2x_2 - x_3 = 1 - 0.6x_3$$

It follows that the solution set consists of all ordered triples of the form $(1 - 0.6\alpha, -0.2\alpha, \alpha)$, where α is a real number. This system is consistent and has infinitely many solutions because of the free variable x_3. ∎

Underdetermined Systems

A system of m linear equations in n unknowns is said to be *underdetermined* if there are fewer equations than unknowns ($m < n$). Although it is possible for underdetermined systems to be inconsistent, they are usually consistent with infinitely many solutions. It is not possible for an underdetermined system to have a unique solution. The reason for this is that any row echelon form of the coefficient matrix will involve $r \leq m$ nonzero rows. Thus, there will be r lead variables and $n - r$ free variables, where $n - r \geq n - m > 0$. If the system is consistent, we can assign the free variables arbitrary values and solve for the lead variables. Therefore, a consistent underdetermined system will have infinitely many solutions.

EXAMPLE 5   Solve the following underdetermined systems:

(a) $\begin{aligned} x_1 + 2x_2 + x_3 &= 1 \\ 2x_1 + 4x_2 + 2x_3 &= 3 \end{aligned}$ (b) $\begin{aligned} x_1 + x_2 + x_3 + x_4 + x_5 &= 2 \\ x_1 + x_2 + x_3 + 2x_4 + 2x_5 &= 3 \\ x_1 + x_2 + x_3 + 2x_4 + 3x_5 &= 2 \end{aligned}$

Solution

$$\text{System (a):} \quad \begin{bmatrix} 1 & 2 & 1 & 1 \\ 2 & 4 & 2 & 3 \end{bmatrix} \rightarrow \begin{bmatrix} 1 & 2 & 1 & 1 \\ 0 & 0 & 0 & 1 \end{bmatrix}$$

System (a) is inconsistent. We can think of the two equations in system (a) as representing planes in 3-space. Usually, two planes intersect in a line; however, in this case the planes are parallel.

$$\text{System (b):} \quad \begin{bmatrix} 1 & 1 & 1 & 1 & 1 & | & 2 \\ 1 & 1 & 1 & 2 & 2 & | & 3 \\ 1 & 1 & 1 & 2 & 3 & | & 2 \end{bmatrix} \rightarrow \begin{bmatrix} 1 & 1 & 1 & 1 & 1 & | & 2 \\ 0 & 0 & 0 & 1 & 1 & | & 1 \\ 0 & 0 & 0 & 0 & 1 & | & -1 \end{bmatrix}$$

System (b) is consistent, and since there are two free variables, the system will have infinitely many solutions. In cases such as these, it is convenient to continue the elimination process and simplify the form of the reduced matrix even further. We continue eliminating until all the terms above the leading 1 in each column have been eliminated. Thus, for system (b), we will continue and eliminate the first two entries in the fifth column and then the first element in the fourth column.

$$\begin{bmatrix} 1 & 1 & 1 & 1 & 1 & | & 2 \\ 0 & 0 & 0 & 1 & 1 & | & 1 \\ 0 & 0 & 0 & 0 & 1 & | & -1 \end{bmatrix} \rightarrow \begin{bmatrix} 1 & 1 & 1 & 1 & 0 & | & 3 \\ 0 & 0 & 0 & 1 & 0 & | & 2 \\ 0 & 0 & 0 & 0 & 1 & | & -1 \end{bmatrix}$$
$$\rightarrow \begin{bmatrix} 1 & 1 & 1 & 0 & 0 & | & 1 \\ 0 & 0 & 0 & 1 & 0 & | & 2 \\ 0 & 0 & 0 & 0 & 1 & | & -1 \end{bmatrix}$$

If we put the free variables over on the right-hand side, it follows that

$$x_1 = 1 - x_2 - x_3$$
$$x_4 = 2$$
$$x_5 = -1$$

Thus, for any real numbers α and β, the 5-tuple

$$(1 - \alpha - \beta, \alpha, \beta, 2, -1)$$

is a solution of the system. ■

In the case where the row echelon form of a consistent system has free variables, the standard procedure is to continue the elimination process until all the entries above the leading 1 in each column have been eliminated, as in system (b) of the previous example. The resulting reduced matrix is said to be in *reduced row echelon form*.

Reduced Row Echelon Form

Definition

A matrix is said to be in **reduced row echelon form** if

(i) The matrix is in row echelon form.

(ii) The first nonzero entry in each row is the only nonzero entry in its column.

The following matrices are in reduced row echelon form:

$$\begin{pmatrix} 1 & 0 \\ 0 & 1 \end{pmatrix}, \quad \begin{pmatrix} 1 & 0 & 0 & 3 \\ 0 & 1 & 0 & 2 \\ 0 & 0 & 1 & 1 \end{pmatrix}, \quad \begin{pmatrix} 0 & 1 & 2 & 0 \\ 0 & 0 & 0 & 1 \\ 0 & 0 & 0 & 0 \end{pmatrix}, \quad \begin{pmatrix} 1 & 2 & 0 & 1 \\ 0 & 0 & 1 & 3 \\ 0 & 0 & 0 & 0 \end{pmatrix}$$

The process of using elementary row operations to transform a matrix into reduced row echelon form is called *Gauss–Jordan reduction*.

EXAMPLE 6   Use Gauss–Jordan reduction to solve the system

$$\begin{aligned} -x_1 + x_2 - x_3 + 3x_4 &= 0 \\ 3x_1 + x_2 - x_3 - x_4 &= 0 \\ 2x_1 - x_2 - 2x_3 - x_4 &= 0 \end{aligned}$$

Solution

$$\begin{pmatrix} -1 & 1 & -1 & 3 & | & 0 \\ 3 & 1 & -1 & -1 & | & 0 \\ 2 & -1 & -2 & -1 & | & 0 \end{pmatrix} \rightarrow \begin{pmatrix} -1 & 1 & -1 & 3 & | & 0 \\ 0 & 4 & -4 & 8 & | & 0 \\ 0 & 1 & -4 & 5 & | & 0 \end{pmatrix}$$

$$\rightarrow \begin{pmatrix} -1 & 1 & -1 & 3 & | & 0 \\ 0 & 4 & -4 & 8 & | & 0 \\ 0 & 0 & -3 & 3 & | & 0 \end{pmatrix} \rightarrow \begin{pmatrix} 1 & -1 & 1 & -3 & | & 0 \\ 0 & 1 & -1 & 2 & | & 0 \\ 0 & 0 & 1 & -1 & | & 0 \end{pmatrix} \begin{array}{l} \text{row} \\ \text{echelon} \\ \text{form} \end{array}$$

$$\rightarrow \begin{pmatrix} 1 & -1 & 0 & -2 & | & 0 \\ 0 & 1 & 0 & 1 & | & 0 \\ 0 & 0 & 1 & -1 & | & 0 \end{pmatrix} \rightarrow \begin{pmatrix} 1 & 0 & 0 & -1 & | & 0 \\ 0 & 1 & 0 & 1 & | & 0 \\ 0 & 0 & 1 & -1 & | & 0 \end{pmatrix} \begin{array}{l} \text{reduced} \\ \text{row echelon} \\ \text{form} \end{array}$$

If we set x_4 equal to any real number α, then $x_1 = \alpha$, $x_2 = -\alpha$, and $x_3 = \alpha$. Thus, all ordered 4-tuples of the form $(\alpha, -\alpha, \alpha, \alpha)$ are solutions of the system.   ■

APPLICATION 1   Traffic Flow

In the downtown section of a certain city, two sets of one-way streets intersect as shown in Figure 1.2.2. The average hourly volume of traffic entering and leaving this section during rush hour is given in the diagram. Determine the amount of traffic between each of the four intersections.

Solution

At each intersection, the number of automobiles entering must be the same as the number leaving. For example, at intersection A, the number of automobiles entering is $x_1 + 450$ and the number leaving is $x_2 + 610$. Thus,

$$x_1 + 450 = x_2 + 610 \qquad \text{(intersection } A\text{)}$$

Similarly,

$$x_2 + 520 = x_3 + 480 \qquad \text{(intersection } B\text{)}$$

$$x_3 + 390 = x_4 + 600 \qquad \text{(intersection } C\text{)}$$

$$x_4 + 640 = x_1 + 310 \qquad \text{(intersection } D\text{)}$$

Figure 1.2.2.

The augmented matrix for the system is

$$\left[\begin{array}{cccc|c} 1 & -1 & 0 & 0 & 160 \\ 0 & 1 & -1 & 0 & -40 \\ 0 & 0 & 1 & -1 & 210 \\ -1 & 0 & 0 & 1 & -330 \end{array}\right]$$

The reduced row echelon form for this matrix is

$$\left[\begin{array}{cccc|c} 1 & 0 & 0 & -1 & 330 \\ 0 & 1 & 0 & -1 & 170 \\ 0 & 0 & 1 & -1 & 210 \\ 0 & 0 & 0 & 0 & 0 \end{array}\right]$$

The system is consistent, and since there is a free variable, there are many possible solutions. The traffic flow diagram does not give enough information to determine x_1, x_2, x_3, and x_4 uniquely. If the amount of traffic were known between any pair of intersections, the traffic on the remaining arteries could easily be calculated. For example, if the amount of traffic between intersections C and D averages 200 automobiles per hour, then $x_4 = 200$. Using this value, we can then solve for x_1, x_2, and x_3:

$$x_1 = x_4 + 330 = 530$$
$$x_2 = x_4 + 170 = 370$$
$$x_3 = x_4 + 210 = 410$$

APPLICATION 2   Electrical Networks

In an electrical network, it is possible to determine the amount of current in each branch in terms of the resistances and the voltages. An example of a typical circuit is given in Figure 1.2.3.

Figure 1.2.3.

The symbols in the figure have the following meanings:

———————————— A path along which current may flow

——————|⊢—————— An electrical source

——————∿∿∿———— A resistor

The electrical source is usually a battery with a voltage (measured in volts) that drives a charge and produces a current. The current will flow out from the terminal of the battery that is represented by the longer vertical line. The resistances are measured in ohms. The letters represent nodes and the i's represent the currents between the nodes. The currents are measured in amperes. The arrows show the direction of the currents. If, however, one of the currents, say, i_2, turns out to be negative, this would mean that the current along that branch is in the direction opposite that of the arrow.

To determine the currents, the following rules are used.

Kirchhoff's Laws

1. At every node, the sum of the incoming currents equals the sum of the outgoing currents.
2. Around every closed loop, the algebraic sum of the voltage gains must equal the algebraic sum of the voltage drops.

The voltage drops E for each resistor are given by *Ohm's law*:

$$E = iR$$

where i represents the current in amperes and R the resistance in ohms.

Let us find the currents in the network pictured in Figure 1.2.3. From the first law, we have

$$i_1 - i_2 + i_3 = 0 \qquad \text{(node } A\text{)}$$
$$-i_1 + i_2 - i_3 = 0 \qquad \text{(node } B\text{)}$$

By the second law,

$$4i_1 + 2i_2 = 8 \qquad \text{(top loop)}$$
$$2i_2 + 5i_3 = 9 \qquad \text{(bottom loop)}$$

The network can be represented by the augmented matrix

$$\left(\begin{array}{rrr|r} 1 & -1 & 1 & 0 \\ -1 & 1 & -1 & 0 \\ 4 & 2 & 0 & 8 \\ 0 & 2 & 5 & 9 \end{array}\right)$$

This matrix is easily reduced to the row echelon form

$$\left(\begin{array}{rrr|r} 1 & -1 & 1 & 0 \\ 0 & 1 & -\frac{2}{3} & \frac{4}{3} \\ 0 & 0 & 1 & 1 \\ 0 & 0 & 0 & 0 \end{array}\right)$$

Solving by back substitution, we see that $i_1 = 1$, $i_2 = 2$, and $i_3 = 1$.

Homogeneous Systems

A system of linear equations is said to be *homogeneous* if the constants on the right-hand side are all zero. Homogeneous systems are always consistent. It is straightforward to find a solution; just set all the variables equal to zero. Thus, if an $m \times n$ homogeneous system has a unique solution, it must be the trivial solution $(0, 0, \ldots, 0)$. The homogeneous system in Example 6 consisted of $m = 3$ equations in $n = 4$ unknowns. In the case that $n > m$, there will always be free variables and, consequently, additional nontrivial solutions. This result has essentially been proved in our discussion of underdetermined systems, but, because of its importance, we state it as a theorem.

Theorem 1.2.1   *An $m \times n$ homogeneous system of linear equations has a nontrivial solution if $n > m$.*

Proof   A homogeneous system is always consistent. The row echelon form of the matrix can have at most m nonzero rows. Thus, there are at most m lead variables. Since there are n variables altogether and $n > m$, there must be some free variables. The free variables can be assigned arbitrary values. For each assignment of values to the free variables, there is a solution of the system.   ∎

APPLICATION 3   Chemical Equations

In the process of photosynthesis, plants use radiant energy from sunlight to convert carbon dioxide (CO_2) and water (H_2O) into glucose ($C_6H_{12}O_6$) and oxygen (O_2). The chemical equation of the reaction is of the form

$$x_1 CO_2 + x_2 H_2O \rightarrow x_3 O_2 + x_4 C_6H_{12}O_6$$

To balance the equation, we must choose x_1, x_2, x_3, and x_4 so that the numbers of carbon, hydrogen, and oxygen atoms are the same on each side of the equation. Since carbon dioxide contains one carbon atom and glucose contains six, to balance the carbon atoms we require that

$$x_1 = 6x_4$$

Similarly, to balance the oxygen, we need

$$2x_1 + x_2 = 2x_3 + 6x_4$$

and finally, to balance the hydrogen, we need

$$2x_2 = 12x_4$$

If we move all the unknowns to the left-hand sides of the three equations, we end up with the homogeneous linear system

$$
\begin{aligned}
x_1 \qquad\qquad\quad\ - \ 6x_4 &= 0 \\
2x_1 + \ x_2 - 2x_3 - \ 6x_4 &= 0 \\
2x_2 \qquad\quad - 12x_4 &= 0
\end{aligned}
$$

By Theorem 1.2.1, the system has nontrivial solutions. To balance the equation, we must find solutions (x_1, x_2, x_3, x_4) whose entries are nonnegative integers. If we solve the system in the usual way, we see that x_4 is a free variable and

$$x_1 = x_2 = x_3 = 6x_4$$

In particular, if we take $x_4 = 1$, then $x_1 = x_2 = x_3 = 6$ and the equation takes the form

$$6CO_2 + 6H_2O \rightarrow 6O_2 + C_6H_{12}O_6$$

APPLICATION 4   Economic Models for Exchange of Goods

Suppose that in a primitive society the members of a tribe are engaged in three occupations: farming, manufacturing of tools and utensils, and weaving and sewing of clothing. Assume that initially the tribe has no monetary system and that all goods and services are bartered. Let us denote the three groups by F, M, and C, and suppose that the directed graph in Figure 1.2.4 indicates how the bartering system works in practice.

The figure indicates that the farmers keep half of their produce and give one-fourth of their produce to the manufacturers and one-fourth to the clothing producers. The manufacturers divide the goods evenly among the three groups, one-third going to each group. The group producing clothes gives half of the clothes to the farmers and divides the other half evenly between the manufacturers and themselves. The result is summarized in the following table:

	F	M	C
F	$\frac{1}{2}$	$\frac{1}{3}$	$\frac{1}{2}$
M	$\frac{1}{4}$	$\frac{1}{3}$	$\frac{1}{4}$
C	$\frac{1}{4}$	$\frac{1}{3}$	$\frac{1}{4}$

The first column of the table indicates the distribution of the goods produced by the farmers, the second column indicates the distribution of the manufactured goods, and the third column indicates the distribution of the clothing.

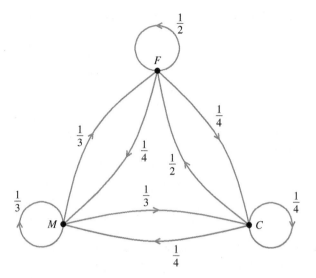

Figure 1.2.4.

As the size of the tribe grows, the system of bartering becomes too cumbersome and, consequently, the tribe decides to institute a monetary system of exchange. For this simple economic system, we assume that there will be no accumulation of capital or debt and that the prices for each of the three types of goods will reflect the values of the existing bartering system. The question is how to assign values to the three types of goods that fairly represent the current bartering system.

The problem can be turned into a linear system of equations using an economic model that was originally developed by the Nobel Prize–winning economist Wassily Leontief. For this model, we will let x_1 be the monetary value of the goods produced by the farmers, x_2 be the value of the manufactured goods, and x_3 be the value of all the clothing produced. According to the first row of the table, the value of the goods received by the farmers amounts to half the value of the farm goods produced, plus one-third the value of the manufactured products, and half the value of the clothing goods. Thus, the total value of goods received by the farmer is $\frac{1}{2}x_1 + \frac{1}{3}x_2 + \frac{1}{2}x_3$. If the system is fair, the total value of goods received by the farmers should equal x_1, the total value of the farm goods produced. Hence, we have the linear equation

$$\frac{1}{2}x_1 + \frac{1}{3}x_2 + \frac{1}{2}x_3 = x_1$$

Using the second row of the table and equating the value of the goods produced and received by the manufacturers, we obtain a second equation:

$$\frac{1}{4}x_1 + \frac{1}{3}x_2 + \frac{1}{4}x_3 = x_2$$

Finally, using the third row of the table, we get

$$\frac{1}{4}x_1 + \frac{1}{3}x_2 + \frac{1}{4}x_3 = x_3$$

These equations can be rewritten as a homogeneous system:

$$-\tfrac{1}{2}x_1 + \tfrac{1}{3}x_2 + \tfrac{1}{2}x_3 = 0$$
$$\tfrac{1}{4}x_1 - \tfrac{2}{3}x_2 + \tfrac{1}{4}x_3 = 0$$
$$\tfrac{1}{4}x_1 + \tfrac{1}{3}x_2 - \tfrac{3}{4}x_3 = 0$$

The reduced row echelon form of the augmented matrix for this system is

$$\left(\begin{array}{ccc|c} 1 & 0 & -\tfrac{5}{3} & 0 \\ 0 & 1 & -1 & 0 \\ 0 & 0 & 0 & 0 \end{array} \right)$$

There is one free variable: x_3. Setting $x_3 = 3$, we obtain the solution $(5, 3, 3)$, and the general solution consists of all multiples of $(5, 3, 3)$. It follows that the variables x_1, x_2, and x_3 should be assigned values in the ratio

$$x_1 : x_2 : x_3 = 5 : 3 : 3$$

This simple system is an example of the closed Leontief input–output model. Leontief's models are fundamental to our understanding of economic systems. Modern applications would involve thousands of industries and lead to very large linear systems. The Leontief models will be studied in greater detail later in Section 6.8 of the book.

SECTION 1.2 EXERCISES

1. Which of the matrices that follow are in row echelon form? Which are in reduced row echelon form?

(a) $\begin{bmatrix} 1 & 2 & 3 & 4 \\ 0 & 0 & 1 & 2 \end{bmatrix}$ (b) $\begin{bmatrix} 1 & 0 & 0 \\ 0 & 0 & 0 \\ 0 & 0 & 1 \end{bmatrix}$

(c) $\begin{bmatrix} 1 & 3 & 0 \\ 0 & 0 & 1 \\ 0 & 0 & 0 \end{bmatrix}$ (d) $\begin{bmatrix} 0 & 1 \\ 0 & 0 \\ 0 & 0 \end{bmatrix}$

(e) $\begin{bmatrix} 1 & 1 & 1 \\ 0 & 1 & 2 \\ 0 & 0 & 3 \end{bmatrix}$ (f) $\begin{bmatrix} 1 & 4 & 6 \\ 0 & 0 & 1 \\ 0 & 1 & 3 \end{bmatrix}$

(g) $\begin{bmatrix} 1 & 0 & 0 & 1 & 2 \\ 0 & 1 & 0 & 2 & 4 \\ 0 & 0 & 1 & 3 & 6 \end{bmatrix}$ (h) $\begin{bmatrix} 0 & 1 & 3 & 4 \\ 0 & 0 & 1 & 3 \\ 0 & 0 & 0 & 0 \end{bmatrix}$

2. The augmented matrices that follow are in row echelon form. For each case, indicate whether the corresponding linear system is consistent. If the system has a unique solution, find it.

(a) $\left[\begin{array}{cc|c} 1 & 2 & 4 \\ 0 & 1 & 3 \\ 0 & 0 & 1 \end{array} \right]$ (b) $\left[\begin{array}{cc|c} 1 & 3 & 1 \\ 0 & 1 & -1 \\ 0 & 0 & 0 \end{array} \right]$

(c) $\left[\begin{array}{ccc|c} 1 & -2 & 4 & 1 \\ 0 & 0 & 1 & 3 \\ 0 & 0 & 0 & 0 \end{array} \right]$

(d) $\left[\begin{array}{ccc|c} 1 & -2 & 2 & -2 \\ 0 & 1 & -1 & 3 \\ 0 & 0 & 1 & 2 \end{array} \right]$

(e) $\left[\begin{array}{ccc|c} 1 & 3 & 2 & -2 \\ 0 & 0 & 1 & 4 \\ 0 & 0 & 0 & 1 \end{array} \right]$

(f) $\left[\begin{array}{ccc|c} 1 & -1 & 3 & 8 \\ 0 & 1 & 2 & 7 \\ 0 & 0 & 1 & 2 \\ 0 & 0 & 0 & 0 \end{array} \right]$

3. The augmented matrices that follow are in reduced row echelon form. In each case, find the solution set to the corresponding linear system.

(a) $\begin{bmatrix} 1 & 0 & 0 & | & -2 \\ 0 & 1 & 0 & | & 5 \\ 0 & 0 & 1 & | & 3 \end{bmatrix}$

(b) $\begin{bmatrix} 1 & 4 & 0 & | & 2 \\ 0 & 0 & 1 & | & 3 \\ 0 & 0 & 0 & | & 1 \end{bmatrix}$

(c) $\begin{bmatrix} 1 & -3 & 0 & | & 2 \\ 0 & 0 & 1 & | & -2 \\ 0 & 0 & 0 & | & 0 \end{bmatrix}$

(d) $\begin{bmatrix} 1 & 2 & 0 & 1 & | & 5 \\ 0 & 0 & 1 & 3 & | & 4 \end{bmatrix}$

(e) $\begin{bmatrix} 1 & 5 & -2 & 0 & | & 3 \\ 0 & 0 & 0 & 1 & | & 6 \\ 0 & 0 & 0 & 0 & | & 0 \\ 0 & 0 & 0 & 0 & | & 0 \end{bmatrix}$

(f) $\begin{bmatrix} 0 & 1 & 0 & | & 2 \\ 0 & 0 & 1 & | & -1 \\ 0 & 0 & 0 & | & 0 \end{bmatrix}$

4. For each of the systems in Exercise 3, make a list of the lead variables and a second list of the free variables.

5. For each of the systems of equations that follow, use Gaussian elimination to obtain an equivalent system whose coefficient matrix is in row echelon form. Indicate whether the system is consistent. If the system is consistent and involves no free variables, use back substitution to find the unique solution. If the system is consistent and there are free variables, transform it to reduced row echelon form and find all solutions.

(a)
$$x_1 - 2x_2 = 3$$
$$2x_1 - x_2 = 9$$

(b)
$$2x_1 - 3x_2 = 5$$
$$-4x_1 + 6x_2 = 8$$

(c)
$$x_1 + x_2 = 0$$
$$2x_1 + 3x_2 = 0$$
$$3x_1 - 2x_2 = 0$$

(d)
$$3x_1 + 2x_2 - x_3 = 4$$
$$x_1 - 2x_2 + 2x_3 = 1$$
$$11x_1 + 2x_2 + x_3 = 14$$

(e)
$$2x_1 + 3x_2 + x_3 = 1$$
$$x_1 + x_2 + x_3 = 3$$
$$3x_1 + 4x_2 + 2x_3 = 4$$

(f)
$$x_1 - x_2 + 2x_3 = 4$$
$$2x_1 + 3x_2 - x_3 = 1$$
$$7x_1 + 3x_2 + 4x_3 = 7$$

(g)
$$x_1 + x_2 + x_3 + x_4 = 0$$
$$2x_1 + 3x_2 - x_3 - x_4 = 2$$
$$3x_1 + 2x_2 + x_3 + x_4 = 5$$
$$3x_1 + 6x_2 - x_3 - x_4 = 4$$

(h)
$$x_1 - 2x_2 = 3$$
$$2x_1 + x_2 = 1$$
$$-5x_1 + 8x_2 = 4$$

(i)
$$-x_1 + 2x_2 - x_3 = 2$$
$$-2x_1 + 2x_2 + x_3 = 4$$
$$3x_1 + 2x_2 + 2x_3 = 5$$
$$-3x_1 + 8x_2 + 5x_3 = 17$$

(j)
$$x_1 + 2x_2 - 3x_3 + x_4 = 1$$
$$-x_1 - x_2 + 4x_3 - x_4 = 6$$
$$-2x_1 - 4x_2 + 7x_3 - x_4 = 1$$

(k)
$$x_1 + 3x_2 + x_3 + x_4 = 3$$
$$2x_1 - 2x_2 + x_3 + 2x_4 = 8$$
$$x_1 - 5x_2 + x_4 = 5$$

(l)
$$x_1 - 3x_2 + x_3 = 1$$
$$2x_1 + x_2 - x_3 = 2$$
$$x_1 + 4x_2 - 2x_3 = 1$$
$$5x_1 - 8x_2 + 2x_3 = 5$$

6. Use Gauss–Jordan reduction to solve each of the following systems:

(a)
$$x_1 + x_2 = -1$$
$$4x_1 - 3x_2 = 3$$

(b)
$$x_1 + 3x_2 + x_3 + x_4 = 3$$
$$2x_1 - 2x_2 + x_3 + 2x_4 = 8$$
$$3x_1 + x_2 + 2x_3 - x_4 = -1$$

(c)
$$x_1 + x_2 + x_3 = 0$$
$$x_1 - x_2 - x_3 = 0$$

(d)
$$x_1 + x_2 + x_3 + x_4 = 0$$
$$2x_1 + x_2 - x_3 + 3x_4 = 0$$
$$x_1 - 2x_2 + x_3 + x_4 = 0$$

7. Give a geometric explanation of why a homogeneous linear system consisting of two equations in three unknowns must have infinitely many solutions. What are the possible numbers of solutions of a nonhomogeneous 2×3 linear system? Give a geometric explanation of your answer.

8. Consider a linear system whose augmented matrix is of the form

$$\begin{bmatrix} 1 & 2 & 1 & | & 1 \\ -1 & 4 & 3 & | & 2 \\ 2 & -2 & a & | & 3 \end{bmatrix}$$

For what values of a will the system have a unique solution?

9. Consider a linear system whose augmented matrix is of the form

$$\begin{bmatrix} 1 & 2 & 1 & | & 0 \\ 2 & 5 & 3 & | & 0 \\ -1 & 1 & \beta & | & 0 \end{bmatrix}$$

(a) Is it possible for the system to be inconsistent? Explain.

(b) For what values of β will the system have infinitely many solutions?

10. Consider a linear system whose augmented matrix is of the form

$$\begin{bmatrix} 1 & 1 & 3 & | & 2 \\ 1 & 2 & 4 & | & 3 \\ 1 & 3 & a & | & b \end{bmatrix}$$

(a) For what values of a and b will the system have infinitely many solutions?

(b) For what values of a and b will the system be inconsistent?

11. Given the linear systems

(i) $x_1 + 2x_2 = 2$ (ii) $x_1 + 2x_2 = 1$

   $3x_1 + 7x_2 = 8$ $3x_1 + 7x_2 = 7$

solve both systems by incorporating the right-hand sides into a 2×2 matrix B and computing the reduced row echelon form of

$$(A|B) = \begin{bmatrix} 1 & 2 & | & 2 & 1 \\ 3 & 7 & | & 8 & 7 \end{bmatrix}$$

12. Given the linear systems

(i) $x_1 + 2x_2 + x_3 = 2$

   $-x_1 - x_2 + 2x_3 = 3$

   $2x_1 + 3x_2 = 0$

(ii) $x_1 + 2x_2 + x_3 = -1$

   $-x_1 - x_2 + 2x_3 = 2$

   $2x_1 + 3x_2 = -2$

solve both systems by computing the row echelon form of an augmented matrix $(A|B)$ and performing back substitution twice.

13. Given a homogeneous system of linear equations, if the system is overdetermined, what are the possibilities as to the number of solutions? Explain.

14. Given a nonhomogeneous system of linear equations, if the system is underdetermined, what are the possibilities as to the number of solutions? Explain.

15. Determine the values of x_1, x_2, x_3, x_4 for the following traffic flow diagram:

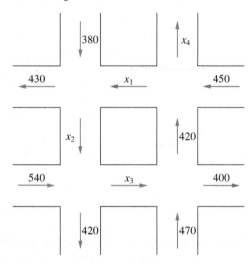

16. Consider the traffic flow diagram that follows, where a_1, a_2, a_3, a_4, b_1, b_2, b_3, b_4 are fixed positive integers. Set up a linear system in the unknowns x_1, x_2, x_3, x_4 and show that the system will be consistent if and only if

$$a_1 + a_2 + a_3 + a_4 = b_1 + b_2 + b_3 + b_4$$

What can you conclude about the number of automobiles entering and leaving the traffic network?

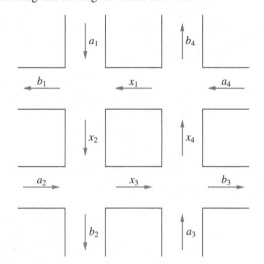

17. Let (c_1, c_2) be a solution of the 2×2 system

$$a_{11}x_1 + a_{12}x_2 = 0$$
$$a_{21}x_1 + a_{22}x_2 = 0$$

Show that for any real number α, the ordered pair $(\alpha c_1, \alpha c_2)$ is also a solution.

18. In Application 3, the solution $(6, 6, 6, 1)$ was obtained by setting the free variable $x_4 = 1$.

    (a) Determine the solution corresponding to $x_4 = 0$. What information, if any, does this solution give about the chemical reaction? Is the term "trivial solution" appropriate in this case?

    (b) Choose some other values of x_4, such as 2, 4, or 5, and determine the corresponding solutions. How are these nontrivial solutions related?

19. Liquid benzene burns in the atmosphere. If a cold object is placed directly over the benzene, water will condense on the object and a deposit of soot (carbon) will also form on the object. The chemical equation for this reaction is of the form

$$x_1 C_6H_6 + x_2 O_2 \rightarrow x_3 C + x_4 H_2O$$

Determine values of x_1, x_2, x_3, and x_4 to balance the equation.

20. Nitric acid is prepared commercially by a series of three chemical reactions. In the first reaction, nitrogen (N_2) is combined with hydrogen (H_2) to form ammonia (NH_3). Next, the ammonia is combined with oxygen (O_2) to form nitrogen dioxide (NO_2) and water. Finally, the NO_2 reacts with some of the water to form nitric acid (HNO_3) and nitric oxide (NO). The amounts of each of the components of these reactions are measured in moles (a standard unit of measurement for chemical reactions). How many moles of nitrogen, hydrogen, and oxygen are necessary to produce eight moles of nitric acid?

21. In Application 4, determine the relative values of x_1, x_2, and x_3 if the distribution of goods is as described in the following table:

	F	M	C
F	$\frac{1}{3}$	$\frac{1}{3}$	$\frac{1}{3}$
M	$\frac{1}{3}$	$\frac{1}{2}$	$\frac{1}{6}$
C	$\frac{1}{3}$	$\frac{1}{6}$	$\frac{1}{2}$

22. Determine the amount of each current for the following networks:

(a)

(b)

(c)

1.3   Matrix Arithmetic

In this section, we introduce the standard notations used for matrices and vectors and define arithmetic operations (addition, subtraction, and multiplication) with matrices. We will also introduce two additional operations: *scalar multiplication* and *transposition*. We will see how to represent linear systems as equations involving matrices and vectors and then derive a theorem characterizing when a linear system is consistent.

The entries of a matrix are called *scalars*. They are usually either real or complex numbers. For the most part, we will be working with matrices whose entries are real numbers. Throughout the first five chapters of the book, the reader may assume that the term *scalar* refers to a real number. However, in Chapter 6 there will be occasions when we will use the set of complex numbers as our scalar field.

Matrix Notation

If we wish to refer to matrices without specifically writing out all their entries, we will use uppercase A, B, C, and so on. In general, a_{ij} will denote the entry of the matrix A that is in the ith row and the jth column. We will refer to this entry as the (i, j) entry of A. Thus, if A is an $m \times n$ matrix, then

$$
A = \begin{bmatrix}
a_{11} & a_{12} & \cdots & a_{1n} \\
a_{21} & a_{22} & \cdots & a_{2n} \\
\vdots & & & \\
a_{m1} & a_{m2} & \cdots & a_{mn}
\end{bmatrix}
$$

We will sometimes shorten this to $A = (a_{ij})$. Similarly, a matrix B may be referred to as (b_{ij}), a matrix C as (c_{ij}), and so on.

Vectors

Matrices that have only one row or one column are of special interest, since they are used to represent solutions of linear systems. A solution of a system of m linear equations in n unknowns is an n-tuple of real numbers. We will refer to an n-tuple of real numbers as a *vector*. If an n-tuple is represented in terms of a $1 \times n$ matrix, then we will refer to it as a *row vector*. Alternatively, if the n-tuple is represented by an $n \times 1$ matrix, then we will refer to it as a *column vector*. For example, the solution of the linear system

$$
\begin{aligned}
x_1 + x_2 &= 3 \\
x_1 - x_2 &= 1
\end{aligned}
$$

can be represented by the row vector $(2, 1)$ or the column vector $\begin{bmatrix} 2 \\ 1 \end{bmatrix}$.

In working with matrix equations, it is generally more convenient to represent the solutions in terms of column vectors ($n \times 1$ matrices). The set of all $n \times 1$ matrices of real numbers is called *Euclidean n-space* and is usually denoted by $\mathbb{R}^n$. Since we will be working almost exclusively with column vectors in the future, we will generally omit the word "column" and refer to the elements of $\mathbb{R}^n$ as simply *vectors*, rather than as column vectors. The standard notation for a column vector is a boldface lowercase letter, as in

$$
\mathbf{x} = \begin{bmatrix} x_1 \\ x_2 \\ \vdots \\ x_n \end{bmatrix}
\tag{1}
$$

For row vectors, there is no universal standard notation. In this book, we will represent both row and column vectors with boldface lowercase letters and to distinguish a row vector from a column vector we will place a horizontal arrow above the letter. Thus, the horizontal arrow indicates an horizontal array (row vector) rather than a vertical array (column vector). For example,

$$\vec{\mathbf{x}} = (x_1, x_2, x_3, x_4) \quad \text{and} \quad \mathbf{y} = \begin{pmatrix} y_1 \\ y_2 \\ y_3 \\ y_4 \end{pmatrix}$$

are row and column vectors, respectively, with four entries each.

Given an $m \times n$ matrix A, it is often necessary to refer to a particular row or column. The standard notation for the jth column vector of A is $\mathbf{a}_j$. There is no universally accepted standard notation for the ith row vector of a matrix A. In this book, since we use horizontal arrows to indicate row vectors, we denote the ith row vector of A by $\vec{\mathbf{a}}_i$.

If A is an $m \times n$ matrix, then the row vectors of A are given by

$$\vec{\mathbf{a}}_i = (a_{i1}, a_{i2}, \ldots, a_{in}) \qquad i = 1, \ldots, m$$

and the column vectors are given by

$$\mathbf{a}_j = \begin{pmatrix} a_{1j} \\ a_{2j} \\ \vdots \\ a_{mj} \end{pmatrix} \qquad j = 1, \ldots, n$$

The matrix A can be represented in terms of either its column vectors or its row vectors:

$$A = (\mathbf{a}_1, \mathbf{a}_2, \ldots, \mathbf{a}_n) \qquad \text{or} \qquad A = \begin{pmatrix} \vec{\mathbf{a}}_1 \\ \vec{\mathbf{a}}_2 \\ \vdots \\ \vec{\mathbf{a}}_m \end{pmatrix}$$

Similarly, if B is an $n \times r$ matrix, then

$$B = (\mathbf{b}_1, \mathbf{b}_2, \ldots, \mathbf{b}_r) = \begin{pmatrix} \vec{\mathbf{b}}_1 \\ \vec{\mathbf{b}}_2 \\ \vdots \\ \vec{\mathbf{b}}_n \end{pmatrix}$$

EXAMPLE I   If

$$A = \begin{bmatrix} 3 & 2 & 5 \\ -1 & 8 & 4 \end{bmatrix}$$

then

$$\mathbf{a}_1 = \begin{bmatrix} 3 \\ -1 \end{bmatrix}, \quad \mathbf{a}_2 = \begin{bmatrix} 2 \\ 8 \end{bmatrix}, \quad \mathbf{a}_3 = \begin{bmatrix} 5 \\ 4 \end{bmatrix}$$

and

$$\vec{\mathbf{a}}_1 = (3, 2, 5), \quad \vec{\mathbf{a}}_2 = (-1, 8, 4) \qquad \blacksquare$$

Equality

For two matrices to be equal, they must have the same dimensions and their corresponding entries must agree.

Definition

> Two $m \times n$ matrices A and B are said to be **equal** if $a_{ij} = b_{ij}$ for each i and j.

Scalar Multiplication

If A is a matrix and α is a scalar, then αA is the matrix formed by multiplying each of the entries of A by α.

Definition

> If A is an $m \times n$ matrix and α is a scalar, then αA is the $m \times n$ matrix whose (i,j) entry is αa_{ij}.

For example, if

$$A = \begin{bmatrix} 4 & 8 & 2 \\ 6 & 8 & 10 \end{bmatrix}$$

then

$$\frac{1}{2}A = \begin{bmatrix} 2 & 4 & 1 \\ 3 & 4 & 5 \end{bmatrix} \quad \text{and} \quad 3A = \begin{bmatrix} 12 & 24 & 6 \\ 18 & 24 & 30 \end{bmatrix}$$

Matrix Addition

Two matrices with the same dimensions can be added by adding their corresponding entries.

Definition

> If $A = (a_{ij})$ and $B = (b_{ij})$ are both $m \times n$ matrices, then the **sum** $A + B$ is the $m \times n$ matrix whose (i,j) entry is $a_{ij} + b_{ij}$ for each ordered pair (i,j).

For example,

$$\begin{bmatrix} 3 & 2 & 1 \\ 4 & 5 & 6 \end{bmatrix} + \begin{bmatrix} 2 & 2 & 2 \\ 1 & 2 & 3 \end{bmatrix} = \begin{bmatrix} 5 & 4 & 3 \\ 5 & 7 & 9 \end{bmatrix}$$

$$\begin{bmatrix} 2 \\ 1 \\ 8 \end{bmatrix} + \begin{bmatrix} -8 \\ 3 \\ 2 \end{bmatrix} = \begin{bmatrix} -6 \\ 4 \\ 10 \end{bmatrix}$$

If we define $A - B$ to be $A + (-1)B$, then it turns out that $A - B$ is formed by subtracting the corresponding entry of B from each entry of A. Thus,

$$
\begin{aligned}
\begin{bmatrix} 2 & 4 \\ 3 & 1 \end{bmatrix} - \begin{bmatrix} 4 & 5 \\ 2 & 3 \end{bmatrix} &= \begin{bmatrix} 2 & 4 \\ 3 & 1 \end{bmatrix} + (-1) \begin{bmatrix} 4 & 5 \\ 2 & 3 \end{bmatrix} \\
&= \begin{bmatrix} 2 & 4 \\ 3 & 1 \end{bmatrix} + \begin{bmatrix} -4 & -5 \\ -2 & -3 \end{bmatrix} \\
&= \begin{bmatrix} 2-4 & 4-5 \\ 3-2 & 1-3 \end{bmatrix} \\
&= \begin{bmatrix} -2 & -1 \\ 1 & -2 \end{bmatrix}
\end{aligned}
$$

If O represents the matrix, with the same dimensions as A, whose entries are all 0, then

$$A + O = O + A = A$$

We will refer to O as the *zero matrix*. It acts as an additive identity on the set of all $m \times n$ matrices. Furthermore, each $m \times n$ matrix A has an additive inverse. Indeed,

$$A + (-1)A = O = (-1)A + A$$

It is customary to denote the additive inverse by $-A$. Thus,

$$-A = (-1)A$$

Matrix Multiplication and Linear Systems

We have yet to define the most important operation: the multiplication of two matrices. Much of the motivation behind the definition comes from the applications to linear systems of equations. If we have a system of one linear equation in one unknown, it can be written in the form

$$ax = b \tag{2}$$

We generally think of a, x, and b as being scalars; however, they could also be treated as 1×1 matrices. Our goal now is to generalize equation (2) so that we can represent an $m \times n$ linear system by a single matrix equation of the form

$$A\mathbf{x} = \mathbf{b}$$

where A is an $m \times n$ matrix, $\mathbf{x}$ is an unknown vector in $\mathbb{R}^n$, and $\mathbf{b}$ is in $\mathbb{R}^m$. We consider first the case of one equation in several unknowns.

Case 1. One Equation in Several Unknowns
Let us begin by examining the case of one equation in several variables. Consider, for example, the equation

$$3x_1 + 2x_2 + 5x_3 = 4$$

If we set

$$A = \begin{bmatrix} 3 & 2 & 5 \end{bmatrix} \quad \text{and} \quad \mathbf{x} = \begin{bmatrix} x_1 \\ x_2 \\ x_3 \end{bmatrix}$$

and define the product $A\mathbf{x}$ by

$$A\mathbf{x} = \begin{bmatrix} 3 & 2 & 5 \end{bmatrix} \begin{bmatrix} x_1 \\ x_2 \\ x_3 \end{bmatrix} = 3x_1 + 2x_2 + 5x_3$$

then the equation $3x_1 + 2x_2 + 5x_3 = 4$ can be written as the matrix equation

$$A\mathbf{x} = 4$$

For a linear equation with n unknowns of the form

$$a_1x_1 + a_2x_2 + \cdots + a_nx_n = b$$

if we let

$$A = \begin{bmatrix} a_1 & a_2 & \cdots & a_n \end{bmatrix} \quad \text{and} \quad \mathbf{x} = \begin{bmatrix} x_1 \\ x_2 \\ \vdots \\ x_n \end{bmatrix}$$

and define the product $A\mathbf{x}$ by

$$A\mathbf{x} = a_1x_1 + a_2x_2 + \cdots + a_nx_n$$

then the system can be written in the form $A\mathbf{x} = \mathbf{b}$.

For example, if

$$A = \begin{bmatrix} 2 & 1 & -3 & 4 \end{bmatrix} \quad \text{and} \quad \mathbf{x} = \begin{bmatrix} 3 \\ 2 \\ 1 \\ -2 \end{bmatrix}$$

then

$$A\mathbf{x} = 2 \cdot 3 + 1 \cdot 2 + (-3) \cdot 1 + 4 \cdot (-2) = -3$$

Note that the result of multiplying a row vector on the left by a column vector on the right is a scalar. Consequently, this type of multiplication is often referred to as a *scalar product*.

Case 2. *M* Equations in *N* Unknowns

Consider now an $m \times n$ linear system

$$
\begin{aligned}
a_{11}x_1 + a_{12}x_2 + \cdots + a_{1n}x_n &= b_1 \\
a_{21}x_1 + a_{22}x_2 + \cdots + a_{2n}x_n &= b_2 \\
&\ \vdots \\
a_{m1}x_1 + a_{m2}x_2 + \cdots + a_{mn}x_n &= b_m
\end{aligned}
\tag{3}
$$

It is desirable to write the system (3) in a form similar to (2), that is, as a matrix equation

$$A\mathbf{x} = \mathbf{b} \tag{4}$$

where $A = (a_{ij})$ is known, $\mathbf{x}$ is an $n \times 1$ matrix of unknowns, and $\mathbf{b}$ is an $m \times 1$ matrix representing the right-hand side of the system. Thus, if we set

$$A = \begin{bmatrix} a_{11} & a_{12} & \cdots & a_{1n} \\ a_{21} & a_{22} & \cdots & a_{2n} \\ \vdots & & & \\ a_{m1} & a_{m2} & \cdots & a_{mn} \end{bmatrix}, \quad \mathbf{x} = \begin{bmatrix} x_1 \\ x_2 \\ \vdots \\ x_n \end{bmatrix}, \quad \mathbf{b} = \begin{bmatrix} b_1 \\ b_2 \\ \vdots \\ b_m \end{bmatrix}$$

and define the product $A\mathbf{x}$ by

$$A\mathbf{x} = \begin{bmatrix} a_{11}x_1 + a_{12}x_2 + \cdots + a_{1n}x_n \\ a_{21}x_1 + a_{22}x_2 + \cdots + a_{2n}x_n \\ \vdots \\ a_{m1}x_1 + a_{m2}x_2 + \cdots + a_{mn}x_n \end{bmatrix} \tag{5}$$

then the linear system of equations (3) is equivalent to the matrix equation (4).

Given an $m \times n$ matrix A and a vector $\mathbf{x}$ in $\mathbb{R}^n$, it is possible to compute a product $A\mathbf{x}$ by (5). The product $A\mathbf{x}$ will be an $m \times 1$ matrix, that is, a vector in $\mathbb{R}^m$. The rule for determining the ith entry of $A\mathbf{x}$ is

$$a_{i1}x_1 + a_{i2}x_2 + \cdots + a_{in}x_n$$

which is equal to $\vec{\mathbf{a}}_i\mathbf{x}$, the scalar product of the ith row vector of A and the column vector $\mathbf{x}$. Thus,

$$A\mathbf{x} = \begin{bmatrix} \vec{\mathbf{a}}_1\mathbf{x} \\ \vec{\mathbf{a}}_2\mathbf{x} \\ \vdots \\ \vec{\mathbf{a}}_n\mathbf{x} \end{bmatrix}$$

EXAMPLE 2

$$A = \begin{bmatrix} 4 & 2 & 1 \\ 5 & 3 & 7 \end{bmatrix}, \quad \mathbf{x} = \begin{bmatrix} x_1 \\ x_2 \\ x_3 \end{bmatrix}$$

$$A\mathbf{x} = \begin{bmatrix} 4x_1 + 2x_2 + x_3 \\ 5x_1 + 3x_2 + 7x_3 \end{bmatrix}$$

EXAMPLE 3

$$A = \begin{bmatrix} -3 & 1 \\ 2 & 5 \\ 4 & 2 \end{bmatrix}, \quad \mathbf{x} = \begin{bmatrix} 2 \\ 4 \end{bmatrix}$$

$$A\mathbf{x} = \begin{bmatrix} -3 \cdot 2 + 1 \cdot 4 \\ 2 \cdot 2 + 5 \cdot 4 \\ 4 \cdot 2 + 2 \cdot 4 \end{bmatrix} = \begin{bmatrix} -2 \\ 24 \\ 16 \end{bmatrix}$$

EXAMPLE 4 Write the following system of equations as a matrix equation of the form $A\mathbf{x} = \mathbf{b}$:

$$\begin{aligned} 3x_1 + 2x_2 + x_3 &= 5 \\ x_1 - 2x_2 + 5x_3 &= -2 \\ 2x_1 + x_2 - 3x_3 &= 1 \end{aligned}$$

Solution

$$\begin{pmatrix} 3 & 2 & 1 \\ 1 & -2 & 5 \\ 2 & 1 & -3 \end{pmatrix} \begin{pmatrix} x_1 \\ x_2 \\ x_3 \end{pmatrix} = \begin{pmatrix} 5 \\ -2 \\ 1 \end{pmatrix}$$

∎

An alternative way to represent the linear system (3) as a matrix equation is to express the product $A\mathbf{x}$ as a sum of column vectors:

$$A\mathbf{x} = \begin{pmatrix} a_{11}x_1 + a_{12}x_2 + \cdots + a_{1n}x_n \\ a_{21}x_1 + a_{22}x_2 + \cdots + a_{2n}x_n \\ \vdots \\ a_{m1}x_1 + a_{m2}x_2 + \cdots + a_{mn}x_n \end{pmatrix}$$

$$= x_1 \begin{pmatrix} a_{11} \\ a_{21} \\ \vdots \\ a_{m1} \end{pmatrix} + x_2 \begin{pmatrix} a_{12} \\ a_{22} \\ \vdots \\ a_{m2} \end{pmatrix} + \cdots + x_n \begin{pmatrix} a_{1n} \\ a_{2n} \\ \vdots \\ a_{mn} \end{pmatrix}$$

Thus, we have

$$A\mathbf{x} = x_1\mathbf{a}_1 + x_2\mathbf{a}_2 + \cdots + x_n\mathbf{a}_n \tag{6}$$

Using this formula, we can represent the system of equations (3) as a matrix equation of the form

$$x_1\mathbf{a}_1 + x_2\mathbf{a}_2 + \cdots + x_n\mathbf{a}_n = \mathbf{b} \tag{7}$$

EXAMPLE 5   The linear system

$$2x_1 + 3x_2 - 2x_3 = 5$$
$$5x_1 - 4x_2 + 2x_3 = 6$$

can be written as a matrix equation

$$x_1 \begin{pmatrix} 2 \\ 5 \end{pmatrix} + x_2 \begin{pmatrix} 3 \\ -4 \end{pmatrix} + x_3 \begin{pmatrix} -2 \\ 2 \end{pmatrix} = \begin{pmatrix} 5 \\ 6 \end{pmatrix}$$

∎

Definition   If $\mathbf{a}_1, \mathbf{a}_2, \ldots, \mathbf{a}_n$ are vectors in $\mathbb{R}^m$ and $c_1, c_2, \ldots, c_n$ are scalars, then a sum of the form

$$c_1\mathbf{a}_1 + c_2\mathbf{a}_2 + \cdots + c_n\mathbf{a}_n$$

is said to be a **linear combination** of the vectors $\mathbf{a}_1, \mathbf{a}_2, \ldots, \mathbf{a}_n$.

It follows from equation (6) that the product $A\mathbf{x}$ is a linear combination of the column vectors of A. Some books even use this linear combination representation as the definition of matrix vector multiplication.

> If A is an $m \times n$ matrix and $\mathbf{x}$ is a vector in $\mathbb{R}^n$, then
>
> $$A\mathbf{x} = x_1\mathbf{a}_1 + x_2\mathbf{a}_2 + \cdots + x_n\mathbf{a}_n$$

EXAMPLE 6   If we choose $x_1 = 2$, $x_2 = 3$, and $x_3 = 4$ in Example 5, then

$$\begin{Bmatrix} 5 \\ 6 \end{Bmatrix} = 2 \begin{Bmatrix} 2 \\ 5 \end{Bmatrix} + 3 \begin{Bmatrix} 3 \\ -4 \end{Bmatrix} + 4 \begin{Bmatrix} -2 \\ 2 \end{Bmatrix}$$

Thus, the vector $\begin{pmatrix} 5 \\ 6 \end{pmatrix}$ is a linear combination of the three column vectors of the coefficient matrix. It follows that the linear system in Example 5 is consistent and

$$\mathbf{x} = \begin{Bmatrix} 2 \\ 3 \\ 4 \end{Bmatrix}$$

is a solution of the system.   ▪

The matrix equation (7) provides a nice way of characterizing whether a linear system of equations is consistent. Indeed, the following theorem is a direct consequence of (7).

Theorem 1.3.1   Consistency Theorem for Linear Systems

A linear system $A\mathbf{x} = \mathbf{b}$ is consistent if and only if $\mathbf{b}$ can be written as a linear combination of the column vectors of A.

EXAMPLE 7   The linear system

$$\begin{aligned} x_1 + 2x_2 &= 1 \\ 2x_1 + 4x_2 &= 1 \end{aligned}$$

is inconsistent since the vector $\begin{bmatrix} 1 \\ 1 \end{bmatrix}$ cannot be written as a linear combination of the column vectors $\begin{bmatrix} 1 \\ 2 \end{bmatrix}$ and $\begin{bmatrix} 2 \\ 4 \end{bmatrix}$. Note that any linear combination of these vectors would be of the form

$$x_1 \begin{bmatrix} 1 \\ 2 \end{bmatrix} + x_2 \begin{bmatrix} 2 \\ 4 \end{bmatrix} = \begin{bmatrix} x_1 + 2x_2 \\ 2x_1 + 4x_2 \end{bmatrix}$$

and hence the second entry of the vector must be double the first entry.   ▪

Matrix Multiplication

More generally, it is possible to multiply a matrix A times a matrix B if the number of columns of A equals the number of rows of B. The first column of the product is determined by the first column of B; that is, the first column of AB is $A\mathbf{b}_1$, the second column of AB is $A\mathbf{b}_2$, and so on. Thus, the product AB is the matrix whose columns are $A\mathbf{b}_1, A\mathbf{b}_2, \dots, A\mathbf{b}_n$.

$$AB = (A\mathbf{b}_1, A\mathbf{b}_2, \dots, A\mathbf{b}_n)$$

The (i, j) entry of AB is the ith entry of the column vector $A\mathbf{b}_j$. It is determined by multiplying the ith row vector of A times the jth column vector of B.

Definition

> If $A = (a_{ij})$ is an $m \times n$ matrix and $B = (b_{ij})$ is an $n \times r$ matrix, then the product $AB = C = (c_{ij})$ is the $m \times r$ matrix whose entries are defined by
> $$c_{ij} = \vec{\mathbf{a}}_i \mathbf{b}_j = \sum_{k=1}^{n} a_{ik} b_{kj}$$

EXAMPLE 8 If

$$A = \begin{bmatrix} 3 & -2 \\ 2 & 4 \\ 1 & -3 \end{bmatrix} \qquad \text{and} \qquad B = \begin{bmatrix} -2 & 1 & 3 \\ 4 & 1 & 6 \end{bmatrix}$$

then

$$AB = \begin{bmatrix} 3 & -2 \\ 2 & 4 \\ 1 & -3 \end{bmatrix} \begin{bmatrix} -2 & 1 & 3 \\ 4 & 1 & 6 \end{bmatrix}$$

$$= \begin{bmatrix} 3 \cdot (-2) - 2 \cdot 4 & 3 \cdot 1 - 2 \cdot 1 & 3 \cdot 3 - 2 \cdot 6 \\ 2 \cdot (-2) + 4 \cdot 4 & 2 \cdot 1 + 4 \cdot 1 & 2 \cdot 3 + 4 \cdot 6 \\ 1 \cdot (-2) - 3 \cdot 4 & 1 \cdot 1 - 3 \cdot 1 & 1 \cdot 3 - 3 \cdot 6 \end{bmatrix}$$

$$= \begin{bmatrix} -14 & 1 & -3 \\ 12 & 6 & 30 \\ -14 & -2 & -15 \end{bmatrix}$$

The shading indicates how the $(2, 3)$ entry of the product AB is computed as a scalar product of the second row vector of A and the third column vector of B. It is also possible to multiply B times A; however, the resulting matrix BA is not equal to AB. In fact, AB and BA do not even have the same dimensions.

$$BA = \begin{bmatrix} -2 \cdot 3 + 1 \cdot 2 + 3 \cdot 1 & -2 \cdot (-2) + 1 \cdot 4 + 3 \cdot (-3) \\ 4 \cdot 3 + 1 \cdot 2 + 6 \cdot 1 & 4 \cdot (-2) + 1 \cdot 4 + 6 \cdot (-3) \end{bmatrix}$$

$$= \begin{bmatrix} -1 & -1 \\ 20 & -22 \end{bmatrix}$$

`EXAMPLE 9   If

$$A = \begin{pmatrix} 3 & 4 \\ 1 & 2 \end{pmatrix} \qquad \text{and} \qquad B = \begin{bmatrix} 1 & 2 \\ 4 & 5 \\ 3 & 6 \end{bmatrix}$$

then it is impossible to multiply A times B, since the number of columns of A does not equal the number of rows of B. However, it is possible to multiply B times A.

$$BA = \begin{bmatrix} 1 & 2 \\ 4 & 5 \\ 3 & 6 \end{bmatrix} \begin{pmatrix} 3 & 4 \\ 1 & 2 \end{pmatrix} = \begin{bmatrix} 5 & 8 \\ 17 & 26 \\ 15 & 24 \end{bmatrix}$$

If A and B are both $n \times n$ matrices, then AB and BA will also be $n \times n$ matrices, but, in general, they will not be equal. *Multiplication of matrices is not commutative.*

EXAMPLE 10   If

$$A = \begin{pmatrix} 1 & 1 \\ 0 & 0 \end{pmatrix} \qquad \text{and} \qquad B = \begin{pmatrix} 1 & 1 \\ 2 & 2 \end{pmatrix}$$

then

$$AB = \begin{pmatrix} 1 & 1 \\ 0 & 0 \end{pmatrix} \begin{pmatrix} 1 & 1 \\ 2 & 2 \end{pmatrix} = \begin{pmatrix} 3 & 3 \\ 0 & 0 \end{pmatrix}$$

and

$$BA = \begin{pmatrix} 1 & 1 \\ 2 & 2 \end{pmatrix} \begin{pmatrix} 1 & 1 \\ 0 & 0 \end{pmatrix} = \begin{pmatrix} 1 & 1 \\ 2 & 2 \end{pmatrix}$$

Hence, $AB \neq BA$.

APPLICATION 1   Production Costs

A company manufactures three products. Its production expenses are divided into three categories. In each category, an estimate is given for the cost of producing a single item of each product. An estimate is also made of the amount of each product to be produced per quarter. These estimates are given in Tables 1.3.1 and 1.3.2. At its stockholders' meeting the company would like to present a single table showing the total costs for each quarter in each of the three categories: raw materials, labor, and overhead.

Table 1.3.1   Production Costs per Item (dollars)

	Product		
Expenses	**A**	**B**	**C**
Raw materials	0.10	0.30	0.15
Labor	0.30	0.40	0.25
Overhead and miscellaneous	0.10	0.20	0.15

Table 1.3.2 Amount Produced per Quarter

Product	Summer	Fall	Winter	Spring
		Season		
A	4000	4500	4500	4000
B	2000	2600	2400	2200
C	5800	6200	6000	6000

Solution

Let us consider the problem in terms of matrices. Each of the two tables can be represented by a matrix, namely,

$$M = \begin{bmatrix} 0.10 & 0.30 & 0.15 \\ 0.30 & 0.40 & 0.25 \\ 0.10 & 0.20 & 0.15 \end{bmatrix}$$

and

$$P = \begin{bmatrix} 4000 & 4500 & 4500 & 4000 \\ 2000 & 2600 & 2400 & 2200 \\ 5800 & 6200 & 6000 & 6000 \end{bmatrix}$$

If we form the product MP, the first column of MP will represent the costs for the summer quarter:

Raw materials: $(0.10)(4000) + (0.30)(2000) + (0.15)(5800) = 1870$
Labor: $(0.30)(4000) + (0.40)(2000) + (0.25)(5800) = 3450$
Overhead and
miscellaneous: $(0.10)(4000) + (0.20)(2000) + (0.15)(5800) = 1670$

The costs for the fall quarter are given in the second column of MP:

Raw materials: $(0.10)(4500) + (0.30)(2600) + (0.15)(6200) = 2160$
Labor: $(0.30)(4500) + (0.40)(2600) + (0.25)(6200) = 3940$
Overhead and
miscellaneous: $(0.10)(4500) + (0.20)(2600) + (0.15)(6200) = 1900$

Columns 3 and 4 of MP represent the costs for the winter and spring quarters.

$$MP = \begin{bmatrix} 1870 & 2160 & 2070 & 1960 \\ 3450 & 3940 & 3810 & 3580 \\ 1670 & 1900 & 1830 & 1740 \end{bmatrix}$$

The entries in row 1 of MP represent the total cost of raw materials for each of the four quarters. The entries in rows 2 and 3 represent the total cost for labor and overhead, respectively, for each of the four quarters. The yearly expenses in each category may be obtained by adding the entries in each row. The numbers in each of the columns may be added to obtain the total production costs for each quarter. Table 1.3.3 summarizes the total production costs. ∎

Table 1.3.3

	Season				
	Summer	**Fall**	**Winter**	**Spring**	**Year**
Raw materials	1870	2160	2070	1960	8060
Labor	3450	3940	3810	3580	14,780
Overhead and miscellaneous	1670	1900	1830	1740	7140
Total production costs	6990	8000	7710	7280	29,980

APPLICATION 2   Management Science—Analytic Hierarchy Process

The analytic hierarchy process (AHP) is a common technique that is used for analyzing complex decisions. The technique was developed by T. L. Saaty during the 1970s. AHP is used in a wide variety of areas including business, industry, government, education, and health care. The technique is applied to problems with a specific goal and a fixed number of alternatives for achieving the goal. The decision as to which alternative to pick is based on a list of evaluation criteria. In the case of more complex decisions, each evaluation criterion could have a list of subcritera and these, in turn, could also have subcriteria, and so on. Thus for complex decisions, one could have a multilayered hierarchy of decision criteria.

To illustrate how AHP actually works, we consider a simple example. A search and screen committee in the Mathematics Department of a state university is conducting a screening process to fill a full professor position in the department. The committee does a preliminary round of screening and narrows the pool down to three candidates: Dr. Gauss, Dr. O'Leary, and Dr. Taussky. After interviewing the finalists, the committee must pick the candidate best qualified for the position. To do this, they must evaluate each of the candidates in terms of the following criteria: Research, Teaching Ability, and Professional Activities. The hierarchal structural of the decision-making process is illustrated in Figure 1.3.1.

The first step of the AHP process is to determine the relative importance of the three areas of evaluation. This can be done using pairwise comparisons. Suppose, for example, that the committee decides that Research and Teaching should be given equal

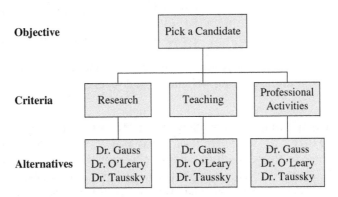

Figure 1.3.1.   Analytic Hierarchy Process

importance and that both of these categories are twice as important as the category of Professional Activities. These relative ratings can be expressed mathematically by assigning the weights 0.40, 0.40, and 0.20 to the respective categories of evaluation. Note that the weights of the first two evaluation criteria are equal and have double the weight of the third. Note also that the weights are chosen so that they all add up to 1. The weight vector

$$\mathbf{w} = \begin{pmatrix} 0.40 \\ 0.40 \\ 0.20 \end{pmatrix}$$

provides a numerical representation of the relative importance of the search criteria.

The next step in the process is to assign relative ratings or weights to the three candidates for each of the criteria in our list. Methods for assigning these weights may be either quantitative or qualitative. For example, one could do a quantitative evaluation of research using weights based on the total number of pages published by the candidates in research journals. Thus if Gauss has published 500 pages, O'Leary 250 pages, and Taussky 250 pages, then one could obtain weights by dividing each of these page counts by 1000 (the combined page count for all three individuals). Thus, the quantitative weights produced in this manner would be 0.50, 0.25, and 0.25. The quantitative method does not factor in differences in the quality of the publications. Determining qualitative weights involves making some judgments, but the process need not be entirely subjective. Later in the text (in Chapters 5 and 6), we will revisit this example and discuss how to determine qualitative weights. The methods we will consider involve making pairwise comparisons and then using advanced matrix techniques to assign weights based on those comparisons.

Another way the committee could refine the search process would be to break up the research criteria into two subclasses, quantitative research and qualitative research. In this case, one would add a subcriteria row to Figure 1.3.1 directly below the row for criteria. We will incorporate this refinement later when we revisit the AHP application in Section 3 of Chapter 5.

For now, let us assume that the search committee has determined the relative weights for each of the three criteria and that those weights are specified in Figure 1.3.2. The relative ratings for the candidates for research, teaching, and professional activities are given by the vectors

$$\mathbf{a}_1 = \begin{pmatrix} 0.50 \\ 0.25 \\ 0.25 \end{pmatrix}, \quad \mathbf{a}_2 = \begin{pmatrix} 0.20 \\ 0.50 \\ 0.30 \end{pmatrix}, \quad \mathbf{a}_3 = \begin{pmatrix} 0.25 \\ 0.50 \\ 0.25 \end{pmatrix}$$

To determine the overall ranking for the candidates, we multiply each of these vectors by the corresponding weights w_1, w_2, w_3 and add.

$$\mathbf{r} = w_1\mathbf{a}_1 + w_2\mathbf{a}_2 + w_3\mathbf{a}_3 = 0.40 \begin{pmatrix} 0.50 \\ 0.25 \\ 0.25 \end{pmatrix} + 0.40 \begin{pmatrix} 0.20 \\ 0.50 \\ 0.30 \end{pmatrix} + 0.20 \begin{pmatrix} 0.25 \\ 0.50 \\ 0.25 \end{pmatrix} = \begin{pmatrix} 0.33 \\ 0.40 \\ 0.27 \end{pmatrix}$$

Note that if we set $A = \begin{pmatrix} \mathbf{a}_1 & \mathbf{a}_2 & \mathbf{a}_3 \end{pmatrix}$, then the vector $\mathbf{r}$ of relative ratings is determined by multiplying the matrix A times the vector $\mathbf{w}$.

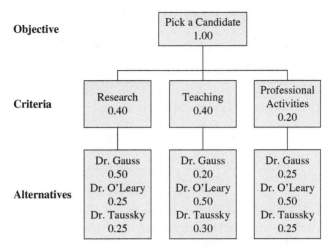

Figure 1.3.2. AHP Diagram with Weights

$$\mathbf{r} = A\mathbf{w} = \begin{bmatrix} 0.50 & 0.20 & 0.25 \\ 0.25 & 0.50 & 0.50 \\ 0.25 & 0.30 & 0.25 \end{bmatrix} \begin{bmatrix} 0.40 \\ 0.40 \\ 0.20 \end{bmatrix} = \begin{bmatrix} 0.33 \\ 0.40 \\ 0.27 \end{bmatrix}$$

In this example, the second candidate has the highest relative rating, so the committee eliminates Gauss and Taussky and offers the position to O'Leary. If O'Leary refuses the offer, then next in line is Gauss, the candidate with the second highest rating.

Reference

1. Saaty, T. L., *The Analytic Hierarchy Process*, McGraw-Hill, 1980

Notational Rules

Just as in ordinary algebra, if an expression involves both multiplication and addition and there are no parentheses to indicate the order of the operations, multiplications are carried out before additions. This is true for both scalar and matrix multiplications. For example, if

$$A = \begin{bmatrix} 3 & 4 \\ 1 & 2 \end{bmatrix}, \qquad B = \begin{bmatrix} 1 & 3 \\ 2 & 1 \end{bmatrix}, \qquad C = \begin{bmatrix} -2 & 1 \\ 3 & 2 \end{bmatrix}$$

then

$$A + BC = \begin{bmatrix} 3 & 4 \\ 1 & 2 \end{bmatrix} + \begin{bmatrix} 7 & 7 \\ -1 & 4 \end{bmatrix} = \begin{bmatrix} 10 & 11 \\ 0 & 6 \end{bmatrix}$$

and

$$3A + B = \begin{bmatrix} 9 & 12 \\ 3 & 6 \end{bmatrix} + \begin{bmatrix} 1 & 3 \\ 2 & 1 \end{bmatrix} = \begin{bmatrix} 10 & 15 \\ 5 & 7 \end{bmatrix}$$

The Transpose of a Matrix

Given an $m \times n$ matrix A, it is often useful to form a new $n \times m$ matrix whose columns are the rows of A.

Definition

The **transpose** of an $m \times n$ matrix A is the $n \times m$ matrix B defined by

$$b_{ji} = a_{ij} \tag{8}$$

for $j = 1, \ldots, n$ and $i = 1, \ldots, m$. The transpose of A is denoted by A^T.

It follows from (8) that the jth row of A^T has the same entries, respectively, as the jth column of A, and the ith column of A^T has the same entries, respectively, as the ith row of A.

EXAMPLE 11

(a) If $A = \begin{bmatrix} 1 & 2 & 3 \\ 4 & 5 & 6 \end{bmatrix}$, then $A^T = \begin{bmatrix} 1 & 4 \\ 2 & 5 \\ 3 & 6 \end{bmatrix}$.

(b) If $B = \begin{bmatrix} -3 & 2 & 1 \\ 4 & 3 & 2 \\ 1 & 2 & 5 \end{bmatrix}$, then $B^T = \begin{bmatrix} -3 & 4 & 1 \\ 2 & 3 & 2 \\ 1 & 2 & 5 \end{bmatrix}$.

(c) If $C = \begin{bmatrix} 1 & 2 \\ 2 & 3 \end{bmatrix}$, then $C^T = \begin{bmatrix} 1 & 2 \\ 2 & 3 \end{bmatrix}$.   ■

The matrix C in Example 11 is its own transpose. This frequently happens with matrices that arise in applications.

Definition

An $n \times n$ matrix A is said to be **symmetric** if $A^T = A$.

The following are some examples of symmetric matrices:

$$\begin{bmatrix} 1 & 0 \\ 0 & -4 \end{bmatrix} \qquad \begin{bmatrix} 2 & 3 & 4 \\ 3 & 1 & 5 \\ 4 & 5 & 3 \end{bmatrix} \qquad \begin{bmatrix} 0 & 1 & 2 \\ 1 & 1 & -2 \\ 2 & -2 & -3 \end{bmatrix}$$

APPLICATION 3   Information Retrieval

The growth of digital libraries on the Internet has led to dramatic improvements in the storage and retrieval of information. Modern retrieval methods are based on matrix theory and linear algebra.

In a typical situation, a database consists of a collection of documents and we wish to search the collection and find the documents that best match some particular search conditions. Depending on the type of database, we could search for such items as research articles in journals, Web pages on the Internet, books in a library, or movies in a film collection.

To see how the searches are done, let us assume that our database consists of m documents and that there are n dictionary words that can be used as keywords for searches. Not all words are allowable since it would not be practical to search for common words such as articles or prepositions. If the key dictionary words are ordered alphabetically, then we can represent the database by an $m \times n$ matrix A. Each document is represented by a column of the matrix. The first entry in the jth column of A would be a number representing the relative frequency of the first key dictionary word in the jth document. The entry a_{2j} represents the relative frequency of the second word in the jth document, and so on. The list of keywords to be used in the search is represented by a vector $\mathbf{x}$ in $\mathbb{R}^m$. The ith entry of $\mathbf{x}$ is taken to be 1 if the ith word in the list of keywords is on our search list; otherwise, we set $x_i = 0$. To carry out the search, we simply multiply A^T times $\mathbf{x}$.

Simple Matching Searches

The simplest type of search determines how many of the key search words are in each document; it does not take into account the relative frequencies of the words. Suppose, for example, that our database consists of these book titles:

B1. *Applied Linear Algebra*
B2. *Elementary Linear Algebra*
B3. *Elementary Linear Algebra with Applications*
B4. *Linear Algebra and Its Applications*
B5. *Linear Algebra with Applications*
B6. *Matrix Algebra with Applications*
B7. *Matrix Theory*

The collection of keywords is given by the following alphabetical list:

algebra, application, elementary, linear, matrix, theory

For a simple matching search, we just use 0's and 1's, rather than relative frequencies, for the entries of the database matrix. Thus, the (i,j) entry of the matrix will be 1 if the ith word appears in the title of the jth book and 0 if it does not. We will assume that our search engine is sophisticated enough to equate various forms of a word. So, for example, in our list of titles the words *applied* and *applications* are both counted as forms of the word *application*. The database matrix for our list of books is the array defined by Table 1.3.4.

If the words we are searching for are *applied, linear*, and *algebra*, then the database matrix and search vector are, respectively, given by

$$
A = \begin{bmatrix}
1 & 1 & 1 & 1 & 1 & 1 & 0 \\
1 & 0 & 1 & 1 & 1 & 1 & 0 \\
0 & 1 & 1 & 0 & 0 & 0 & 0 \\
1 & 1 & 1 & 1 & 1 & 0 & 0 \\
0 & 0 & 0 & 0 & 0 & 1 & 1 \\
0 & 0 & 0 & 0 & 0 & 0 & 1
\end{bmatrix}, \qquad
\mathbf{x} = \begin{bmatrix}
1 \\
1 \\
0 \\
1 \\
0 \\
0
\end{bmatrix}
$$

Table 1.3.4   Array Representation for Database of Linear Algebra Books

Keywords	Books						
	B1	B2	B3	B4	B5	B6	B7
algebra	1	1	1	1	1	1	0
application	1	0	1	1	1	1	0
elementary	0	1	1	0	0	0	0
linear	1	1	1	1	1	0	0
matrix	0	0	0	0	0	1	1
theory	0	0	0	0	0	0	1

If we set $\mathbf{y} = A^T\mathbf{x}$, then

$$
\mathbf{y} = \begin{bmatrix} 1 & 1 & 0 & 1 & 0 & 0 \\ 1 & 0 & 1 & 1 & 0 & 0 \\ 1 & 1 & 1 & 1 & 0 & 0 \\ 1 & 1 & 0 & 1 & 0 & 0 \\ 1 & 1 & 0 & 1 & 0 & 0 \\ 1 & 1 & 0 & 0 & 1 & 0 \\ 0 & 0 & 0 & 0 & 1 & 1 \end{bmatrix} \begin{bmatrix} 1 \\ 1 \\ 1 \\ 0 \\ 1 \\ 0 \\ 0 \end{bmatrix} = \begin{bmatrix} 3 \\ 2 \\ 3 \\ 3 \\ 3 \\ 2 \\ 0 \end{bmatrix}
$$

The value of y_1 is the number of search word matches in the title of the first book, the value of y_2 is the number of matches in the second book title, and so on. Since $y_1 = y_3 = y_4 = y_5 = 3$, the titles of books B1, B3, B4, and B5 must contain all three search words. If the search is set up to find titles matching all search words, then the search engine will report the titles of the first, third, fourth, and fifth books.

Relative Frequency Searches

Searches of noncommercial databases generally find all documents containing the key search words and then order the documents based on the relative frequency. In this case, the entries of the database matrix should represent the relative frequencies of the keywords in the documents. For example, suppose that in the dictionary of all keywords of the database, the sixth word is *algebra* and the eighth word is *applied*, where all words are listed alphabetically. If, say, document 9 in the database contains a total of 200 occurrences of keywords from the dictionary, and if the word *algebra* occurred 10 times in the document and the word *applied* occurred 6 times, then the relative frequencies for these words would be $\frac{10}{200}$ and $\frac{6}{200}$, and the corresponding entries in the database matrix would be

$$a_{69} = 0.05 \quad \text{and} \quad a_{89} = 0.03$$

To search for these two words, we take our search vector $\mathbf{x}$ to be the vector whose entries x_6 and x_8 are both equal to 1 and whose remaining entries are all 0. We then compute

$$\mathbf{y} = A^T\mathbf{x}$$

The entry of **y** corresponding to document 9 is

$$y_9 = a_{69} \cdot 1 + a_{89} \cdot 1 = 0.08$$

Note that 16 of the 200 words (8 percent of the words) in document 9 match the key search words. If y_j is the largest entry of **y**, this would indicate that the jth document in the database is the one that contains the keywords with the greatest relative frequencies.

Advanced Search Methods

A search for the keywords *linear* and *algebra* could easily turn up hundreds of documents, some of which may not even be about linear algebra. If we were to increase the number of search words and require that all search words be matched, then we would run the risk of excluding some crucial linear algebra documents. Rather than match all words of the expanded search list, our database search should give priority to those documents which match most of the keywords with high relative frequencies. To accomplish this, we need to find the columns of the database matrix A that are "closest" to the search vector **x**. One way to measure how close two vectors are is to define *the angle between the vectors*. We will do this later in Section 5.1 of the book.

The information retrieval application will also be revisited after we have learned about the *singular value decomposition* (Section 6.5) This decomposition can be used to find a simpler approximation to the database matrix, which will speed up the searches dramatically. Often it has the added advantage of filtering out *noise*; that is, using the approximate version of the database matrix may automatically have the effect of eliminating documents that use keywords in unwanted contexts. For example, a dental student and a mathematics student could both use *calculus* as one of their search words. Since the list of mathematics search words does not contain any other dental terms, a mathematics search using an approximate database matrix is likely to eliminate all documents relating to dentistry. Similarly, the mathematics documents would be filtered out in the dental student's search.

Web Searches and Page Ranking

Modern Web searches could easily involve billions of documents with hundreds of thousands of keywords. Indeed, as of July 2008, there were more than 1 trillion Web pages on the Internet, and it is not uncommon for search engines to acquire or update as many as 10 million Web pages in a single day. Although the database matrix for pages on the Internet is extremely large, searches can be simplified dramatically, since the matrices and search vectors are *sparse*; that is, most of the entries in any column are 0's.

For Internet searches, the better search engines will do simple matching searches to find all pages matching the keywords, but they will not order them on the basis of the relative frequencies of the keywords. Because of the commercial nature of the Internet, people who want to sell products may deliberately make repeated use of keywords to ensure that their Web site is highly ranked in any relative-frequency search. In fact, it is easy to surreptitiously list a keyword hundreds of times. If the font color of the word matches the background color of the page, then the viewer will not be aware that the word is listed repeatedly.

For Web searches, a more sophisticated algorithm is necessary for ranking the pages that contain all of the key search words. In Chapter 6, we will study a special type of matrix model for assigning probabilities in certain random processes. This type of model is referred to as a *Markov process* or a *Markov chain*. In Section 6.3, we will see how to use Markov chains to model Web surfing and obtain rankings of webpages.

References

1. Berry, Michael W., and Murray Browne, *Understanding Search Engines: Mathematical Modeling and Text Retrieval*, SIAM, Philadelphia, 1999.

2. Langville, Amy N., and Carl D. Meyer, *Google's PageRank and Beyond: The Science of Search Engine Rankings*, Princeton University Press, 2012.

SECTION 1.3 EXERCISES

1. If

$$A = \begin{bmatrix} 3 & 1 & 4 \\ -2 & 0 & 1 \\ 1 & 2 & 2 \end{bmatrix} \quad \text{and } B = \begin{bmatrix} 1 & 0 & 2 \\ -3 & 1 & 1 \\ 2 & -4 & 1 \end{bmatrix}$$

compute

(a) $2A$

(b) $A + B$

(c) $2A - 3B$

(d) $(2A)^T - (3B)^T$

(e) AB

(f) BA

(g) $A^T B^T$

(h) $(BA)^T$

2. For each of the pairs of matrices that follow, determine whether it is possible to multiply the first matrix times the second. If it is possible, perform the multiplication.

(a) $\begin{bmatrix} 3 & 5 & 1 \\ -2 & 0 & 2 \end{bmatrix} \begin{bmatrix} 2 & 1 \\ 1 & 3 \\ 4 & 1 \end{bmatrix}$

(b) $\begin{bmatrix} 4 & -2 \\ 6 & -4 \\ 8 & -6 \end{bmatrix} \begin{bmatrix} 1 & 2 & 3 \end{bmatrix}$

(c) $\begin{bmatrix} 1 & 4 & 3 \\ 0 & 1 & 4 \\ 0 & 0 & 2 \end{bmatrix} \begin{bmatrix} 3 & 2 \\ 1 & 1 \\ 4 & 5 \end{bmatrix}$

(d) $\begin{bmatrix} 4 & 6 \\ 2 & 1 \end{bmatrix} \begin{bmatrix} 3 & 1 & 5 \\ 4 & 1 & 6 \end{bmatrix}$

(e) $\begin{bmatrix} 4 & 6 & 1 \\ 2 & 1 & 1 \end{bmatrix} \begin{bmatrix} 3 & 1 & 5 \\ 4 & 1 & 6 \end{bmatrix}$

(f) $\begin{bmatrix} 2 \\ -1 \\ 3 \end{bmatrix} \begin{bmatrix} 3 & 2 & 4 & 5 \end{bmatrix}$

3. For which of the pairs in Exercise 2 is it possible to multiply the second matrix times the first, and what would the dimension of the product matrix be?

4. Write each of the following systems of equations as a matrix equation:

(a) $3x_1 + 2x_2 = 1$
$\quad 2x_1 - 3x_2 = 5$

(b) $x_1 + x_2 = 5$
$\quad 2x_1 + x_2 - x_3 = 6$
$\quad 3x_1 - 2x_2 + 2x_3 = 7$

(c) $2x_1 + x_2 + x_3 = 4$
$\quad x_1 - x_2 + 2x_3 = 2$
$\quad 3x_1 - 2x_2 - x_3 = 0$

5. If

$$A = \begin{bmatrix} 3 & 4 \\ 1 & 1 \\ 2 & 7 \end{bmatrix}$$

verify that

(a) $5A = 3A + 2A$

(b) $6A = 3(2A)$

(c) $(A^T)^T = A$

6. If

$$A = \begin{bmatrix} 4 & 1 & 6 \\ 2 & 3 & 5 \end{bmatrix} \quad \text{and } B = \begin{bmatrix} 1 & 3 & 0 \\ -2 & 2 & -4 \end{bmatrix}$$

verify that

(a) $A + B = B + A$

(b) $3(A + B) = 3A + 3B$

(c) $(A + B)^T = A^T + B^T$

7. If

$$A = \begin{bmatrix} 2 & 1 \\ 6 & 3 \\ -2 & 4 \end{bmatrix} \quad \text{and} \quad B = \begin{bmatrix} 2 & 4 \\ 1 & 6 \end{bmatrix}$$

verify that

(a) $3(AB) = (3A)B = A(3B)$,

(b) $(AB)^T = B^T A^T$

8. If

$$A = \begin{bmatrix} 2 & 4 \\ 1 & 3 \end{bmatrix}, \quad B = \begin{bmatrix} -2 & 1 \\ 0 & 4 \end{bmatrix}, \quad C = \begin{bmatrix} 3 & 1 \\ 2 & 1 \end{bmatrix}$$

verify that

(a) $(A + B) + C = A + (B + C)$

(b) $(AB)C = A(BC)$

(c) $A(B + C) = AB + AC$

(d) $(A + B)C = AC + BC$

9. Let

$$A = \begin{bmatrix} 1 & 2 \\ 1 & -2 \end{bmatrix}, \quad \mathbf{b} = \begin{bmatrix} 4 \\ 0 \end{bmatrix}, \quad \mathbf{c} = \begin{bmatrix} -3 \\ -2 \end{bmatrix}$$

(a) Write $\mathbf{b}$ as a linear combination of the column vectors $\mathbf{a}_1$ and $\mathbf{a}_2$.

(b) Use the result from part (a) to determine a solution of the linear system $A\mathbf{x} = \mathbf{b}$. Does the system have any other solutions? Explain.

(c) Write $\mathbf{c}$ as a linear combination of the column vectors $\mathbf{a}_1$ and $\mathbf{a}_2$.

10. For each of the choices of A and $\mathbf{b}$ that follow, determine whether the system $A\mathbf{x} = \mathbf{b}$ is consistent by examining how $\mathbf{b}$ relates to the column vectors of A. Explain your answers in each case.

(a) $A = \begin{bmatrix} 2 & 1 \\ -2 & -1 \end{bmatrix}, \quad \mathbf{b} = \begin{bmatrix} 3 \\ 1 \end{bmatrix}$

(b) $A = \begin{bmatrix} 1 & 4 \\ 2 & 3 \end{bmatrix}, \quad \mathbf{b} = \begin{bmatrix} 5 \\ 5 \end{bmatrix}$

(c) $A = \begin{bmatrix} 3 & 2 & 1 \\ 3 & 2 & 1 \\ 3 & 2 & 1 \end{bmatrix}, \quad \mathbf{b} = \begin{bmatrix} 1 \\ 0 \\ -1 \end{bmatrix}$

11. Let A be a 5×3 matrix. If

$$\mathbf{b} = \mathbf{a}_1 + \mathbf{a}_2 = \mathbf{a}_2 + \mathbf{a}_3$$

then what can you conclude about the number of solutions of the linear system $A\mathbf{x} = \mathbf{b}$? Explain.

12. Let A be a 3×4 matrix. If

$$\mathbf{b} = \mathbf{a}_1 + \mathbf{a}_2 + \mathbf{a}_3 + \mathbf{a}_4$$

then what can you conclude about the number of solutions to the linear system $A\mathbf{x} = \mathbf{b}$? Explain.

13. Let $A\mathbf{x} = \mathbf{b}$ be a linear system whose augmented matrix $(A|\mathbf{b})$ has reduced row echelon form

$$\begin{bmatrix} 1 & 2 & 0 & 3 & 1 & | & -2 \\ 0 & 0 & 1 & 2 & 4 & | & 5 \\ 0 & 0 & 0 & 0 & 0 & | & 0 \\ 0 & 0 & 0 & 0 & 0 & | & 0 \end{bmatrix}$$

(a) Find all solutions to the system.

(b) If

$$\mathbf{a}_1 = \begin{bmatrix} 1 \\ 1 \\ 3 \\ 4 \end{bmatrix} \quad \text{and} \quad \mathbf{a}_3 = \begin{bmatrix} 2 \\ -1 \\ 1 \\ 3 \end{bmatrix}$$

determine $\mathbf{b}$.

14. Suppose in the search and screen example in Application 2 the committee decides that research is actually 1.5 times as important as teaching and 3 times as important as professional activities. The committee still rates teaching twice as important as professional activities. Determine a new weight vector $\mathbf{w}$ that reflects these revised priorities. Determine also a new rating vector $\mathbf{r}$. Will the new weights have any effect on the overall rankings of the candidates?

15. Let A be an $m \times n$ matrix. Explain why the matrix multiplications $A^T A$ and AA^T are possible.

16. A matrix A is said to be *skew symmetric* if $A^T = -A$. Show that if a matrix is skew symmetric, then its diagonal entries must all be 0.

17. In Application 3, suppose that we are searching the database of seven linear algebra books for the search words *elementary, matrix, algebra*. Form a search vector $\mathbf{x}$, and then compute a vector $\mathbf{y}$ that represents the results of the search. Explain the significance of the entries of the vector $\mathbf{y}$.

18. Let A be a 2×2 matrix with $a_{11} \neq 0$ and let $\alpha = a_{21}/a_{11}$. Show that A can be factored into a product of the form

$$\begin{bmatrix} 1 & 0 \\ \alpha & 1 \end{bmatrix} \begin{bmatrix} a_{11} & a_{12} \\ 0 & b \end{bmatrix}$$

What is the value of b?

1.4   Matrix Algebra

The algebraic rules used for real numbers may or may not work when matrices are used. For example, if a and b are real numbers, then

$$a + b = b + a \quad \text{and} \quad ab = ba$$

For real numbers, the operations of addition and multiplication are both commutative. The first of these algebraic rules works when we replace a and b by square matrices A and B, that is,

$$A + B = B + A$$

However, we have already seen that matrix multiplication is not commutative. This fact deserves special emphasis.

Warning: In general, $AB \neq BA$. Matrix multiplication is *not* commutative.

In this section, we examine which algebraic rules work for matrices and which do not.

Algebraic Rules

The following theorem provides some useful rules for doing matrix algebra.

Theorem 1.4.1   *Each of the following statements is valid for any scalars α and β and for any matrices A, B, and C for which the indicated operations are defined.*

1. $A + B = B + A$
2. $(A + B) + C = A + (B + C)$
3. $(AB)C = A(BC)$
4. $A(B + C) = AB + AC$
5. $(A + B)C = AC + BC$
6. $(\alpha\beta)A = \alpha(\beta A)$
7. $\alpha(AB) = (\alpha A)B = A(\alpha B)$
8. $(\alpha + \beta)A = \alpha A + \beta A$
9. $\alpha(A + B) = \alpha A + \alpha B$

We will prove two of the rules and leave the rest for the reader to verify.

Proof of Rule 4   Assume that $A = (a_{ij})$ is an $m \times n$ matrix and $B = (b_{ij})$ and $C = (c_{ij})$ are both $n \times r$ matrices. Let $D = A(B + C)$ and $E = AB + AC$. It follows that

$$d_{ij} = \sum_{k=1}^{n} a_{ik}(b_{kj} + c_{kj})$$

and

$$e_{ij} = \sum_{k=1}^{n} a_{ik}b_{kj} + \sum_{k=1}^{n} a_{ik}c_{kj}$$

But

$$\sum_{k=1}^{n} a_{ik}(b_{kj} + c_{kj}) = \sum_{k=1}^{n} a_{ik}b_{kj} + \sum_{k=1}^{n} a_{ik}c_{kj}$$

so that $d_{ij} = e_{ij}$ and hence $A(B + C) = AB + AC$. ∎

Proof of   Let A be an $m \times n$ matrix, B an $n \times r$ matrix, and C an $r \times s$ matrix. Let $D = AB$ and
Rule 3 $E = BC$. We must show that $DC = AE$. By the definition of matrix multiplication,

$$d_{il} = \sum_{k=1}^{n} a_{ik}b_{kl} \quad \text{and} \quad e_{kj} = \sum_{l=1}^{r} b_{kl}c_{lj}$$

The ijth term of DC is

$$\sum_{l=1}^{r} d_{il}c_{lj} = \sum_{l=1}^{r} \left(\sum_{k=1}^{n} a_{ik}b_{kl} \right) c_{lj}$$

and the (i,j) entry of AE is

$$\sum_{k=1}^{n} a_{ik}e_{kj} = \sum_{k=1}^{n} a_{ik} \left(\sum_{l=1}^{r} b_{kl}c_{lj} \right)$$

Since

$$\sum_{l=1}^{r} \left(\sum_{k=1}^{n} a_{ik}b_{kl} \right) c_{lj} = \sum_{l=1}^{r} \left(\sum_{k=1}^{n} a_{ik}b_{kl}c_{lj} \right) = \sum_{k=1}^{n} a_{ik} \left(\sum_{l=1}^{r} b_{kl}c_{lj} \right)$$

it follows that

$$(AB)C = DC = AE = A(BC) \qquad \blacksquare$$

The algebraic rules given in Theorem 1.4.1 seem quite natural, since they are similar to the rules that we use with real numbers. However, there are important differences between the rules for matrix algebra and the algebraic rules for real numbers. Some of these differences are illustrated in Exercises 1 through 5 at the end of this section.

EXAMPLE 1   If

$$A = \begin{bmatrix} 1 & 2 \\ 3 & 4 \end{bmatrix}, \quad B = \begin{bmatrix} 2 & 1 \\ -3 & 2 \end{bmatrix}, \quad \text{and} \quad C = \begin{bmatrix} 1 & 0 \\ 2 & 1 \end{bmatrix}$$

verify that $A(BC) = (AB)C$ and $A(B + C) = AB + AC$.

Solution

$$A(BC) = \begin{bmatrix} 1 & 2 \\ 3 & 4 \end{bmatrix} \begin{bmatrix} 4 & 1 \\ 1 & 2 \end{bmatrix} = \begin{bmatrix} 6 & 5 \\ 16 & 11 \end{bmatrix}$$

$$(AB)C = \begin{bmatrix} -4 & 5 \\ -6 & 11 \end{bmatrix} \begin{bmatrix} 1 & 0 \\ 2 & 1 \end{bmatrix} = \begin{bmatrix} 6 & 5 \\ 16 & 11 \end{bmatrix}$$

Thus,

$$A(BC) = \begin{bmatrix} 6 & 5 \\ 16 & 11 \end{bmatrix} = (AB)C$$

$$A(B + C) = \begin{bmatrix} 1 & 2 \\ 3 & 4 \end{bmatrix} \begin{bmatrix} 3 & 1 \\ -1 & 3 \end{bmatrix} = \begin{bmatrix} 1 & 7 \\ 5 & 15 \end{bmatrix}$$

$$AB + AC = \begin{bmatrix} -4 & 5 \\ -6 & 11 \end{bmatrix} + \begin{bmatrix} 5 & 2 \\ 11 & 4 \end{bmatrix} = \begin{bmatrix} 1 & 7 \\ 5 & 15 \end{bmatrix}$$

Therefore,

$$A(B + C) = AB + AC$$

∎

Notation

Since $(AB)C = A(BC)$, we may simply omit the parentheses and write ABC. The same is true for a product of four or more matrices. In the case where an $n \times n$ matrix is multiplied by itself a number of times, it is convenient to use exponential notation. Thus, if k is a positive integer, then

$$A^k = \underbrace{AA \cdots A}_{k \text{ times}}$$

EXAMPLE 2   If

$$A = \begin{bmatrix} 1 & 1 \\ 1 & 1 \end{bmatrix}$$

then

$$A^2 = \begin{bmatrix} 1 & 1 \\ 1 & 1 \end{bmatrix} \begin{bmatrix} 1 & 1 \\ 1 & 1 \end{bmatrix} = \begin{bmatrix} 2 & 2 \\ 2 & 2 \end{bmatrix}$$

$$A^3 = AAA = AA^2 = \begin{bmatrix} 1 & 1 \\ 1 & 1 \end{bmatrix} \begin{bmatrix} 2 & 2 \\ 2 & 2 \end{bmatrix} = \begin{bmatrix} 4 & 4 \\ 4 & 4 \end{bmatrix}$$

and, in general,

$$A^n = \begin{bmatrix} 2^{n-1} & 2^{n-1} \\ 2^{n-1} & 2^{n-1} \end{bmatrix}$$

∎

APPLICATION 1   A Simple Model for Marital Status Computations

In a certain town, 30 percent of the married women get divorced each year and 20 percent of the single women get married each year. There are 8000 married women and 2000 single women. Assuming that the total population of women remains constant, how many married women and how many single women will there be after one year? After two years?

Solution

Form a matrix A as follows: The entries in the first row of A will be the percentages of married and single women, respectively, who are married after one year. The entries in the second row will be the percentages of women who are single after one year. Thus,

$$A = \begin{pmatrix} 0.70 & 0.20 \\ 0.30 & 0.80 \end{pmatrix}$$

If we let $\mathbf{x} = \begin{pmatrix} 8000 \\ 2000 \end{pmatrix}$, the number of married and single women after one year can be computed by multiplying A times $\mathbf{x}$.

$$A\mathbf{x} = \begin{pmatrix} 0.70 & 0.20 \\ 0.30 & 0.80 \end{pmatrix} \begin{pmatrix} 8000 \\ 2000 \end{pmatrix} = \begin{pmatrix} 6000 \\ 4000 \end{pmatrix}$$

After one year, there will be 6000 married women and 4000 single women. To find the number of married and single women after two years, compute

$$A^2\mathbf{x} = A(A\mathbf{x}) = \begin{pmatrix} 0.70 & 0.20 \\ 0.30 & 0.80 \end{pmatrix} \begin{pmatrix} 6000 \\ 4000 \end{pmatrix} = \begin{pmatrix} 5000 \\ 5000 \end{pmatrix}$$

After two years, half of the women will be married and half will be single. In general, the number of married and single women after n years can be determined by computing $A^n\mathbf{x}$. ∎

APPLICATION 2   Ecology: Demographics of the Loggerhead Sea Turtle

The management and preservation of many wildlife species depend on our ability to model population dynamics. A standard modeling technique is to divide the life cycle of a species into a number of stages. The models assume that the population sizes for each stage depend only on the female population and that the probability of survival of an individual female from one year to the next depends only on the stage of the life cycle and not on the actual age of an individual. For example, let us consider a four-stage model for analyzing the population dynamics of the loggerhead sea turtle (see Figure 1.4.1).

At each stage, we estimate the probability of survival over a one-year period. We also estimate the ability to reproduce in terms of the expected number of eggs laid in a

Figure 1.4.1. Loggerhead Sea Turtle

Table 1.4.1   Four-Stage Model for Loggerhead Sea Turtle Demographics

Stage Number	Description (age in years)	Annual Survivorship	Eggs Laid per Year
1	Eggs, hatchlings (<1)	0.67	0
2	Juveniles and subadults (1–21)	0.74	0
3	Novice breeders (22)	0.81	127
4	Mature breeders (23–54)	0.81	79

given year. The results are summarized in Table 1.4.1. The approximate ages for each stage are listed in parentheses next to the stage description.

If d_i represents the duration of the ith stage and s_i is the annual survivorship rate for that stage, then it can be shown that the proportion remaining in stage i the following year will be

$$p_i = \left(\frac{1 - s_i^{d_i-1}}{1 - s_i^{d_i}} \right) s_i \tag{1}$$

and the proportion of the population that will survive and move into stage $i + 1$ the following year will be

$$q_i = \frac{s_i^{d_i}(1 - s_i)}{1 - s_i^{d_i}} \tag{2}$$

If we let e_i denote the average number of eggs laid by a member of stage i ($i = 2, 3, 4$) in one year and form the matrix

$$L = \begin{bmatrix} p_1 & e_2 & e_3 & e_4 \\ q_1 & p_2 & 0 & 0 \\ 0 & q_2 & p_3 & 0 \\ 0 & 0 & q_3 & p_4 \end{bmatrix} \tag{3}$$

then L can be used to predict the turtle populations at each stage in future years. A matrix of the form (3) is called a *Leslie matrix*, and the corresponding population model is sometimes referred to as a *Leslie population model*. Using the figures from Table 1.4.1, the Leslie matrix for our model is

$$L = \begin{bmatrix} 0 & 0 & 127 & 79 \\ 0.67 & 0.7394 & 0 & 0 \\ 0 & 0.0006 & 0 & 0 \\ 0 & 0 & 0.81 & 0.8097 \end{bmatrix}$$

Suppose that the initial populations at each stage were 200,000, 300,000, 500, and 1500, respectively. If we represent these initial populations by a vector $\mathbf{x}_0$, the populations at each stage after one year are determined by computing

$$\mathbf{x}_1 = L\mathbf{x}_0 = \begin{bmatrix} 0 & 0 & 127 & 79 \\ 0.67 & 0.7394 & 0 & 0 \\ 0 & 0.0006 & 0 & 0 \\ 0 & 0 & 0.81 & 0.8097 \end{bmatrix} \begin{bmatrix} 200{,}000 \\ 300{,}000 \\ 500 \\ 1500 \end{bmatrix} = \begin{bmatrix} 182{,}000 \\ 355{,}820 \\ 180 \\ 1620 \end{bmatrix}$$

Table 1.4.2   Loggerhead Sea Turtle Population Projections

Stage Number	Initial Population	10 Years	25 Years	50 Years	100 Years
1	200,000	115,403	75,768	37,623	9276
2	300,000	331,274	217,858	108,178	26,673
3	500	215	142	70	17
4	1500	1074	705	350	86

(The computations have been rounded to the nearest integer.) To determine the population vector after two years, we multiply again by the matrix L.

$$\mathbf{x}_2 = L\mathbf{x}_1 = L^2\mathbf{x}_0$$

In general, the population after k years is determined by computing $\mathbf{x}_k = L^k\mathbf{x}_0$. To see longer-range trends, we compute $\mathbf{x}_{10}$, $\mathbf{x}_{25}$, $\mathbf{x}_{50}$, and $\mathbf{x}_{100}$. The results are summarized in Table 1.4.2. The model predicts that the total number of breeding-age turtles will decrease by approximately 95 percent over a 100-year period.

A seven-stage model describing the population dynamics is presented in reference [1] that follows. We will use the seven-stage model in the computer exercises at the end of this chapter. Reference [2] is the original paper by Leslie.

References

1. Crouse, Deborah T., Larry B. Crowder, and Hal Caswell, "A Stage-Based Population Model for Loggerhead Sea Turtles and Implications for Conservation," *Ecology*, 68(5), 1987.
2. Leslie, P. H., "On the Use of Matrices in Certain Population Mathematics," *Biometrika*, 33, 1945.

The Identity Matrix

Just as the number 1 acts as an identity for the multiplication of real numbers, there is a special matrix I that acts as an identity for matrix multiplication; that is,

$$IA = AI = A \tag{4}$$

for any $n \times n$ matrix A. It is easy to verify that, if we define I to be an $n \times n$ matrix with 1's on the main diagonal and 0's elsewhere, then I satisfies equation (4) for any $n \times n$ matrix A. More formally, we have the following definition.

Definition

The $n \times n$ **identity matrix** is the matrix $I = (\delta_{ij})$, where

$$\delta_{ij} = \begin{cases} 1 & \text{if } i = j \\ 0 & \text{if } i \neq j \end{cases}$$

As an example, let us verify equation (4) in the case $n = 3$:

$$\begin{pmatrix} 1 & 0 & 0 \\ 0 & 1 & 0 \\ 0 & 0 & 1 \end{pmatrix} \begin{pmatrix} 3 & 4 & 1 \\ 2 & 6 & 3 \\ 0 & 1 & 8 \end{pmatrix} = \begin{pmatrix} 3 & 4 & 1 \\ 2 & 6 & 3 \\ 0 & 1 & 8 \end{pmatrix}$$

and

$$\begin{pmatrix} 3 & 4 & 1 \\ 2 & 6 & 3 \\ 0 & 1 & 8 \end{pmatrix} \begin{pmatrix} 1 & 0 & 0 \\ 0 & 1 & 0 \\ 0 & 0 & 1 \end{pmatrix} = \begin{pmatrix} 3 & 4 & 1 \\ 2 & 6 & 3 \\ 0 & 1 & 8 \end{pmatrix}$$

In general, if B is any $m \times n$ matrix and C is any $n \times r$ matrix, then

$$BI = B \quad \text{and} \quad IC = C$$

The column vectors of the $n \times n$ identity matrix I are the standard vectors used to define a coordinate system in Euclidean n-space. The standard notation for the jth column vector of I is $\mathbf{e}_j$, rather than the usual $\mathbf{i}_j$. Thus, the $n \times n$ identity matrix can be written

$$I = (\mathbf{e}_1, \mathbf{e}_2, \ldots, \mathbf{e}_n)$$

Matrix Inversion

A real number a is said to have a multiplicative inverse if there exists a number b such that $ab = 1$. Any nonzero number a has a multiplicative inverse $b = \frac{1}{a}$. We generalize the concept of multiplicative inverses to matrices with the following definition.

Definition

> An $n \times n$ matrix A is said to be **nonsingular** or **invertible** if there exists a matrix B such that $AB = BA = I$. The matrix B is said to be a **multiplicative inverse** of A.

If B and C are both multiplicative inverses of A, then

$$B = BI = B(AC) = (BA)C = IC = C$$

Thus, a matrix can have at most one multiplicative inverse. We will refer to the multiplicative inverse of a nonsingular matrix A as simply the *inverse* of A and denote it by A^{-1}.

EXAMPLE 3   The matrices

$$\begin{pmatrix} 2 & 4 \\ 3 & 1 \end{pmatrix} \quad \text{and} \quad \begin{pmatrix} -\frac{1}{10} & \frac{2}{5} \\ \frac{3}{10} & -\frac{1}{5} \end{pmatrix}$$

are inverses of each other, since

$$\begin{pmatrix} 2 & 4 \\ 3 & 1 \end{pmatrix} \begin{pmatrix} -\frac{1}{10} & \frac{2}{5} \\ \frac{3}{10} & -\frac{1}{5} \end{pmatrix} = \begin{pmatrix} 1 & 0 \\ 0 & 1 \end{pmatrix}$$

and

$$\begin{bmatrix} -\frac{1}{10} & \frac{2}{5} \\ \frac{3}{10} & -\frac{1}{5} \end{bmatrix} \begin{bmatrix} 2 & 4 \\ 3 & 1 \end{bmatrix} = \begin{bmatrix} 1 & 0 \\ 0 & 1 \end{bmatrix}$$ ∎

EXAMPLE 4   The 3×3 matrices

$$\begin{bmatrix} 1 & 2 & 3 \\ 0 & 1 & 4 \\ 0 & 0 & 1 \end{bmatrix} \quad \text{and} \quad \begin{bmatrix} 1 & -2 & 5 \\ 0 & 1 & -4 \\ 0 & 0 & 1 \end{bmatrix}$$

are inverses, since

$$\begin{bmatrix} 1 & 2 & 3 \\ 0 & 1 & 4 \\ 0 & 0 & 1 \end{bmatrix} \begin{bmatrix} 1 & -2 & 5 \\ 0 & 1 & -4 \\ 0 & 0 & 1 \end{bmatrix} = \begin{bmatrix} 1 & 0 & 0 \\ 0 & 1 & 0 \\ 0 & 0 & 1 \end{bmatrix}$$

and

$$\begin{bmatrix} 1 & -2 & 5 \\ 0 & 1 & -4 \\ 0 & 0 & 1 \end{bmatrix} \begin{bmatrix} 1 & 2 & 3 \\ 0 & 1 & 4 \\ 0 & 0 & 1 \end{bmatrix} = \begin{bmatrix} 1 & 0 & 0 \\ 0 & 1 & 0 \\ 0 & 0 & 1 \end{bmatrix}$$ ∎

EXAMPLE 5   The matrix

$$A = \begin{bmatrix} 1 & 0 \\ 0 & 0 \end{bmatrix}$$

has no inverse. Indeed, if B is any 2×2 matrix, then

$$BA = \begin{bmatrix} b_{11} & b_{12} \\ b_{21} & b_{22} \end{bmatrix} \begin{bmatrix} 1 & 0 \\ 0 & 0 \end{bmatrix} = \begin{bmatrix} b_{11} & 0 \\ b_{21} & 0 \end{bmatrix}$$

Thus, BA cannot equal I.   ∎

Definition

An $n \times n$ matrix is said to be **singular** if it does not have a multiplicative inverse.

Note

Only square matrices have multiplicative inverses. One should not use the terms *singular* and *nonsingular* when referring to nonsquare matrices.

Often we will be working with products of nonsingular matrices. It turns out that any product of nonsingular matrices is nonsingular. The following theorem characterizes how the inverse of the product of a pair of nonsingular matrices A and B is related to the inverses of A and B:

Theorem 1.4.2   *If A and B are nonsingular $n \times n$ matrices, then AB is also nonsingular and $(AB)^{-1} = B^{-1}A^{-1}$.*

Proof
$$(B^{-1}A^{-1})AB = B^{-1}(A^{-1}A)B = B^{-1}B = I$$
$$(AB)(B^{-1}A^{-1}) = A(BB^{-1})A^{-1} = AA^{-1} = I \qquad \blacksquare$$

It follows by induction that, if $A_1, \ldots, A_k$ are all nonsingular $n \times n$ matrices, then the product $A_1 A_2 \cdots A_k$ is nonsingular and

$$(A_1 A_2 \cdots A_k)^{-1} = A_k^{-1} \cdots A_2^{-1} A_1^{-1}$$

In the next section, we will learn how to determine whether a matrix has a multiplicative inverse. We will also learn a method for computing the inverse of a nonsingular matrix.

Algebraic Rules for Transposes

There are four basic algebraic rules involving transposes.

Algebraic Rules for Transposes

1. $(A^T)^T = A$
2. $(\alpha A)^T = \alpha A^T$
3. $(A + B)^T = A^T + B^T$
4. $(AB)^T = B^T A^T$

The first three rules are straightforward. We leave it to the reader to verify that they are valid. To prove the fourth rule, we need only show that the (i, j) entries of $(AB)^T$ and $B^T A^T$ are equal. If A is an $m \times n$ matrix, then, for the multiplications to be possible, B must have n rows. The (i, j) entry of $(AB)^T$ is the (j, i) entry of AB. It is computed by multiplying the jth row vector of A times the ith column vector of B:

$$\vec{\mathbf{a}}_j \mathbf{b}_i = (a_{j1}, a_{j2}, \ldots, a_{jn}) \begin{bmatrix} b_{1i} \\ b_{2i} \\ \vdots \\ b_{ni} \end{bmatrix} = a_{j1} b_{1i} + a_{j2} b_{2i} + \cdots + a_{jn} b_{ni} \qquad (5)$$

The (i, j) entry of $B^T A^T$ is computed by multiplying the ith row of B^T times the jth column of A^T. Since the ith row of B^T is the transpose of the ith column of B and the jth column of A^T is the transpose of the jth row of A, it follows that the (i, j) entry of $B^T A^T$ is given by

$$\mathbf{b}_i^T \vec{\mathbf{a}}_j^T = (b_{1i}, b_{2i}, \ldots, b_{ni}) \begin{bmatrix} a_{j1} \\ a_{j2} \\ \vdots \\ a_{jn} \end{bmatrix} = b_{1i} a_{j1} + b_{2i} a_{j2} + \cdots + b_{ni} a_{jn} \qquad (6)$$

It follows from (5) and (6) that the (i, j) entries of $(AB)^T$ and $B^T A^T$ are equal.

The next example illustrates the idea behind the last proof.

EXAMPLE 6   Let

$$A = \begin{bmatrix} 1 & 2 & 1 \\ 3 & 3 & 5 \\ 2 & 4 & 1 \end{bmatrix}, \qquad B = \begin{bmatrix} 1 & 0 & 2 \\ 2 & 1 & 1 \\ 5 & 4 & 1 \end{bmatrix}$$

Note that, on the one hand, the $(3, 2)$ entry of AB is computed taking the scalar product of the third row of A and the second column of B.

$$AB = \begin{bmatrix} 1 & 2 & 1 \\ 3 & 3 & 5 \\ \mathbf{2} & \mathbf{4} & \mathbf{1} \end{bmatrix} \begin{bmatrix} 1 & \mathbf{0} & 2 \\ 2 & \mathbf{1} & 1 \\ 5 & \mathbf{4} & 1 \end{bmatrix} = \begin{bmatrix} 10 & 6 & 5 \\ 34 & 23 & 14 \\ 15 & \mathbf{8} & 9 \end{bmatrix}$$

When the product is transposed, the $(3, 2)$ entry of AB becomes the $(2, 3)$ entry of $(AB)^T$.

$$(AB)^T = \begin{bmatrix} 10 & 34 & 15 \\ 6 & 23 & \mathbf{8} \\ 5 & 14 & 9 \end{bmatrix}$$

On the other hand, the $(2, 3)$ entry of $B^T A^T$ is computed taking the scalar product of the second row of B^T and the third column of A^T.

$$B^T A^T = \begin{bmatrix} 1 & 2 & 5 \\ \mathbf{0} & \mathbf{1} & \mathbf{4} \\ 2 & 1 & 1 \end{bmatrix} \begin{bmatrix} 1 & 3 & \mathbf{2} \\ 2 & 3 & \mathbf{4} \\ 1 & 5 & \mathbf{1} \end{bmatrix} = \begin{bmatrix} 10 & 34 & 15 \\ 6 & 23 & \mathbf{8} \\ 5 & 14 & 9 \end{bmatrix}$$

In both cases, the arithmetic for computing the $(2, 3)$ entry is the same.   ■

Symmetric Matrices and Networks

Recall that a matrix A is symmetric if $A^T = A$. One type of application that leads to symmetric matrices is problems involving networks. These problems are often solved using the techniques of an area of mathematics called *graph theory*.

APPLICATION 3   Networks and Graphs

Graph theory is an important area of applied mathematics. It is used to model problems in virtually all the applied sciences. Graph theory is particularly useful in applications involving communications networks.

A *graph* is defined to be a set of points called *vertices*, together with a set of unordered pairs of vertices, which are referred to as *edges*. Figure 1.4.2 gives a geometrical representation of a graph. We can think of the vertices V_1, V_2, V_3, V_4, and V_5 as corresponding to the nodes in a communications network.

The line segments joining the vertices correspond to the edges:

$$\{V_1, V_2\}, \ \{V_2, V_5\}, \ \{V_3, V_4\}, \ \{V_3, V_5\}, \ \{V_4, V_5\}$$

Each edge represents a direct communications link between two nodes of the network.

An actual communications network could involve a large number of vertices and edges. Indeed, if there are millions of vertices, a graphical picture of the network would

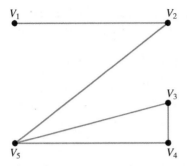

Figure 1.4.2.

be quite confusing. An alternative is to use a matrix representation for the network. If the graph contains a total of n vertices, we can define an $n \times n$ matrix A by

$$
a_{ij} = \begin{cases} 1 & \text{if } \{V_i, V_j\} \text{ is an edge of the graph} \\ 0 & \text{if there is no edge joining } V_i \text{ and } V_j \end{cases}
$$

The matrix A is called the *adjacency matrix* of the graph. The adjacency matrix for the graph in Figure 1.4.2 is given by

$$
A = \begin{bmatrix} 0 & 1 & 0 & 0 & 0 \\ 1 & 0 & 0 & 0 & 1 \\ 0 & 0 & 0 & 1 & 1 \\ 0 & 0 & 1 & 0 & 1 \\ 0 & 1 & 1 & 1 & 0 \end{bmatrix}
$$

Note that the matrix A is symmetric. Indeed, any adjacency matrix must be symmetric, for if $\{V_i, V_j\}$ is an edge of the graph, then $a_{ij} = a_{ji} = 1$ and $a_{ij} = a_{ji} = 0$ if there is no edge joining V_i and V_j. In either case, $a_{ij} = a_{ji}$.

We can think of a *walk* in a graph as a sequence of edges linking one vertex to another. For example, in Figure 1.4.2 the edges $\{V_1, V_2\}$, $\{V_2, V_5\}$ represent a walk from vertex V_1 to vertex V_5. The length of the walk is said to be 2 since it consists of two edges. A simple way to describe the walk is to indicate the movement between vertices by arrows. Thus, $V_1 \rightarrow V_2 \rightarrow V_5$ denotes a walk of length 2 from V_1 to V_5. Similarly, $V_4 \rightarrow V_5 \rightarrow V_2 \rightarrow V_1$ represents a walk of length 3 from V_4 to V_1. It is possible to traverse the same edges more than once in a walk. For example, $V_5 \rightarrow V_3 \rightarrow V_5 \rightarrow V_3$ is a walk of length 3 from V_5 to V_3. In general, by taking powers of the adjacency matrix, we can determine the number of walks of any specified length between two vertices.

Theorem 1.4.3   *If A is an $n \times n$ adjacency matrix of a graph and $a_{ij}^{(k)}$ represents the (i, j) entry of A^k, then $a_{ij}^{(k)}$ is equal to the number of walks of length k from V_i to V_j.*

Proof   The proof is by mathematical induction. In the case $k = 1$, it follows from the definition of the adjacency matrix that a_{ij} represents the number of walks of length 1 from V_i to V_j. Assume for some m that each entry of A^m is equal to the number of walks of length m between the corresponding vertices. Thus, $a_{il}^{(m)}$ is the number of walks of length m

from V_i to V_l. Now on the one hand, if there is an edge $\{V_l, V_j\}$, then $a_{il}^{(m)} a_{lj} = a_{il}^{(m)}$ is the number of walks of length $m + 1$ from V_i to V_j of the form

$$V_i \rightarrow \cdots \rightarrow V_l \rightarrow V_j$$

On the other hand, if $\{V_l, V_j\}$ is not an edge, then there are no walks of length $m + 1$ of this form from V_i to V_j and

$$a_{il}^{(m)} a_{lj} = a_{il}^{(m)} \cdot 0 = 0$$

It follows that the total number of walks of length $m + 1$ from V_i to V_j is given by

$$a_{i1}^{(m)} a_{1j} + a_{i2}^{(m)} a_{2j} + \cdots + a_{in}^{(m)} a_{nj}$$

But this is just the (i, j) entry of A^{m+1}.   ■

EXAMPLE 7   To determine the number of walks of length 3 between any two vertices of the graph in Figure 1.4.2, we need only compute

$$A^3 = \begin{bmatrix} 0 & 2 & 1 & 1 & 0 \\ 2 & 0 & 1 & 1 & 4 \\ 1 & 1 & 2 & 3 & 4 \\ 1 & 1 & 3 & 2 & 4 \\ 0 & 4 & 4 & 4 & 2 \end{bmatrix}$$

Thus, the number of walks of length 3 from V_3 to V_5 is $a_{35}^{(3)} = 4$. Note that the matrix A^3 is symmetric. This reflects the fact that there are the same number of walks of length 3 from V_i to V_j as there are from V_j to V_i.   ■

SECTION 1.4 EXERCISES

1. Explain why each of the following algebraic rules will not work, in general, when the real numbers a and b are replaced by $n \times n$ matrices A and B:

(a) $(a + b)^2 = a^2 + 2ab + b^2$

(b) $(a + b)(a - b) = a^2 - b^2$

2. Will the rules in Exercise 1 work if a is replaced by an $n \times n$ matrix A and b is replaced by the $n \times n$ identity matrix I?

3. Find nonzero 2×2 matrices A and B such that $AB = O$.

4. Find nonzero matrices A, B, and C such that

$$AC = BC \quad \text{and} \quad A \neq B$$

5. The matrix

$$A = \begin{bmatrix} 1 & -1 \\ 1 & -1 \end{bmatrix}$$

has the property that $A^2 = O$. Is it possible for a nonzero symmetric 2×2 matrix to have this property? Prove your answer.

6. Prove the associative law of multiplication for 2×2 matrices; that is, let

$$A = \begin{bmatrix} a_{11} & a_{12} \\ a_{21} & a_{22} \end{bmatrix}, \quad B = \begin{bmatrix} b_{11} & b_{12} \\ b_{21} & b_{22} \end{bmatrix},$$

$$C = \begin{bmatrix} c_{11} & c_{12} \\ c_{21} & c_{22} \end{bmatrix}$$

and show that

$$(AB)C = A(BC)$$

7. Let

$$A = \begin{bmatrix} \frac{1}{2} & -\frac{1}{2} \\ -\frac{1}{2} & \frac{1}{2} \end{bmatrix}$$

Compute A^2 and A^3. What will A^n turn out to be?

8. Let

$$A = \begin{bmatrix} \frac{1}{2} & -\frac{1}{2} & -\frac{1}{2} & -\frac{1}{2} \\ -\frac{1}{2} & \frac{1}{2} & -\frac{1}{2} & -\frac{1}{2} \\ -\frac{1}{2} & -\frac{1}{2} & \frac{1}{2} & -\frac{1}{2} \\ -\frac{1}{2} & -\frac{1}{2} & -\frac{1}{2} & \frac{1}{2} \end{bmatrix}$$

Compute A^2 and A^3. What will A^{2n} and A^{2n+1} turn out to be?

9. Let

$$A = \begin{bmatrix} 0 & 1 & 0 & 0 \\ 0 & 0 & 1 & 0 \\ 0 & 0 & 0 & 1 \\ 0 & 0 & 0 & 0 \end{bmatrix}$$

Show that $A^n = O$ for $n \geq 4$.

10. Let A and B be symmetric $n \times n$ matrices. For each of the following, determine whether the given matrix must be symmetric or could be nonsymmetric:

(a) $C = A + B$ (b) $D = A^2$
(c) $E = AB$ (d) $F = ABA$
(e) $G = AB + BA$ (f) $H = AB - BA$

11. Let C be a nonsymmetric $n \times n$ matrix. For each of the following, determine whether the given matrix must necessarily be symmetric or could possibly be nonsymmetric:

(a) $A = C + C^T$ (b) $B = C - C^T$
(c) $D = C^T C$ (d) $E = C^T C - CC^T$
(e) $F = (I + C)(I + C^T)$
(f) $G = (I + C)(I - C^T)$

12. Let

$$A = \begin{bmatrix} a_{11} & a_{12} \\ a_{21} & a_{22} \end{bmatrix}$$

Show that if $d = a_{11}a_{22} - a_{21}a_{12} \neq 0$, then

$$A^{-1} = \frac{1}{d} \begin{bmatrix} a_{22} & -a_{12} \\ -a_{21} & a_{11} \end{bmatrix}$$

13. Use the result from Exercise 12 to find the inverse of each of the following matrices:

(a) $\begin{bmatrix} 7 & 2 \\ 3 & 1 \end{bmatrix}$ (b) $\begin{bmatrix} 3 & 5 \\ 2 & 3 \end{bmatrix}$ (c) $\begin{bmatrix} 4 & 3 \\ 2 & 2 \end{bmatrix}$

14. Let A and B be $n \times n$ matrices. Show that if

$$AB = A \quad \text{and} \quad B \neq I$$

then A must be singular.

15. Let A be a nonsingular matrix. Show that A^{-1} is also nonsingular and $(A^{-1})^{-1} = A$.

16. Prove that if A is nonsingular, then A^T is nonsingular and

$$(A^T)^{-1} = (A^{-1})^T$$

Hint: $(AB)^T = B^T A^T$.

17. Let A be an $n \times n$ matrix and let $\mathbf{x}$ and $\mathbf{y}$ be vectors in $\mathbb{R}^n$. Show that if $A\mathbf{x} = A\mathbf{y}$ and $\mathbf{x} \neq \mathbf{y}$, then the matrix A must be singular.

18. Let A be a nonsingular $n \times n$ matrix. Use mathematical induction to prove that A^m is nonsingular and

$$(A^m)^{-1} = (A^{-1})^m$$

for $m = 1, 2, 3, \ldots$.

19. Let A be an $n \times n$ matrix. Show that if $A^2 = O$, then $I - A$ is nonsingular and $(I - A)^{-1} = I + A$.

20. Let A be an $n \times n$ matrix. Show that if $A^{k+1} = O$, then $I - A$ is nonsingular and

$$(I - A)^{-1} = I + A + A^2 + \cdots + A^k$$

21. Given

$$R = \begin{bmatrix} \cos\theta & -\sin\theta \\ \sin\theta & \cos\theta \end{bmatrix}$$

show that R is nonsingular and $R^{-1} = R^T$.

22. An $n \times n$ matrix A is said to be an *involution* if $A^2 = I$. Show that if G is any matrix of the form

$$G = \begin{bmatrix} \cos\theta & \sin\theta \\ \sin\theta & -\cos\theta \end{bmatrix}$$

then G is an involution.

23. Let $\mathbf{u}$ be a unit vector in $\mathbb{R}^n$ (i.e., $\mathbf{u}^T\mathbf{u} = 1$) and let $H = I - 2\mathbf{u}\mathbf{u}^T$. Show that H is an involution.

24. A matrix A is said to be *idempotent* if $A^2 = A$. Show that each of the following matrices are idempotent:

(a) $\begin{bmatrix} 1 & 0 \\ 1 & 0 \end{bmatrix}$ (b) $\begin{bmatrix} \frac{2}{3} & \frac{1}{3} \\ \frac{2}{3} & \frac{1}{3} \end{bmatrix}$

(c) $\begin{bmatrix} \frac{1}{4} & \frac{1}{4} & \frac{1}{4} \\ \frac{1}{4} & \frac{1}{4} & \frac{1}{4} \\ \frac{1}{2} & \frac{1}{2} & \frac{1}{2} \end{bmatrix}$

25. Let A be an idempotent matrix.

(a) Show that $I - A$ is also idempotent.

(b) Show that $I + A$ is nonsingular and

$$(I + A)^{-1} = I - \frac{1}{2}A.$$

26. Let D be an $n \times n$ diagonal matrix whose diagonal entries are either 0 or 1.

(a) Show that D is idempotent.

(b) Show that if X is a nonsingular matrix and $A = XDX^{-1}$, then A is idempotent.

27. Let A be an involution matrix and let

$$B = \frac{1}{2}(I + A) \quad \text{and} \quad C = \frac{1}{2}(I - A)$$

Show that B and C are both idempotent and $BC = O$.

28. Let A be an $m \times n$ matrix. Show that $A^T A$ and $A A^T$ are both symmetric.

29. Let A and B be symmetric $n \times n$ matrices. Prove that $AB = BA$ if and only if AB is also symmetric.

30. Let A be an $n \times n$ matrix and let

$$B = A + A^T \quad \text{and} \quad C = A - A^T$$

(a) Show that B is symmetric and C is skew symmetric.

(b) Show that every $n \times n$ matrix can be represented as a sum of a symmetric matrix and a skew-symmetric matrix.

31. In Application 1, how many married women and how many single women will there be after 3 years?

32. Consider the matrix

$$A = \begin{bmatrix} 0 & 1 & 0 & 1 & 1 \\ 1 & 0 & 1 & 1 & 0 \\ 0 & 1 & 0 & 0 & 1 \\ 1 & 1 & 0 & 0 & 1 \\ 1 & 0 & 1 & 1 & 0 \end{bmatrix}$$

(a) Draw a graph that has A as its adjacency matrix. Be sure to label the vertices of the graph.

(b) By inspecting the graph, determine the number of walks of length 2 from V_2 to V_3 and from V_2 to V_5.

(c) Compute the second row of A^3 and use it to determine the number of walks of length 3 from V_2 to V_3 and from V_2 to V_5.

33. Consider the graph

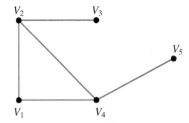

(a) Determine the adjacency matrix A of the graph.

(b) Compute A^2. What do the entries in the first row of A^2 tell you about walks of length 2 that start from V_1?

(c) Compute A^3. How many walks of length 3 are there from V_2 to V_4? How many walks of length less than or equal to 3 are there from V_2 to V_4?

For each of the conditional statements that follow, answer true *if the statement is always true and answer* false *otherwise. In the case of a true statement, explain or prove your answer. In the case of a false statement, give an example to show that the statement is not always true.*

34. If $A\mathbf{x} = B\mathbf{x}$ for some nonzero vector $\mathbf{x}$, then the matrices A and B must be equal.

35. If A and B are singular $n \times n$ matrices, then $A + B$ is also singular.

36. If A and B are nonsingular matrices, then $(AB)^T$ is nonsingular and

$$((AB)^T)^{-1} = (A^{-1})^T (B^{-1})^T$$

1.5 Elementary Matrices

In this section, we view the process of solving a linear system in terms of matrix multiplications rather than row operations. Given a linear system $A\mathbf{x} = \mathbf{b}$, we can multiply both sides by a sequence of special matrices to obtain an equivalent system in row echelon form. The special matrices we will use are called *elementary matrices*. We will use them to see how to compute the inverse of a nonsingular matrix and also to obtain an important matrix factorization. We begin by considering the effects of multiplying both sides of a linear system by a nonsingular matrix.

Equivalent Systems

Given an $m \times n$ linear system $A\mathbf{x} = \mathbf{b}$, we can obtain an equivalent system by multiplying both sides of the equation by a nonsingular $m \times m$ matrix M:

$$A\mathbf{x} = \mathbf{b} \qquad (1)$$
$$MA\mathbf{x} = M\mathbf{b} \qquad (2)$$

Clearly, any solution of (1) will also be a solution of (2). However, if $\hat{\mathbf{x}}$ is a solution of (2), then

$$M^{-1}(MA\hat{\mathbf{x}}) = M^{-1}(M\mathbf{b})$$
$$A\hat{\mathbf{x}} = \mathbf{b}$$

and it follows that the two systems are equivalent.

To obtain an equivalent system that is easier to solve, we can apply a sequence of nonsingular matrices $E_1, \dots, E_k$ to both sides of the equation $A\mathbf{x} = \mathbf{b}$ to obtain a simpler system of the form

$$U\mathbf{x} = \mathbf{c}$$

where $U = E_k \cdots E_1 A$ and $\mathbf{c} = E_k \cdots E_2 E_1 \mathbf{b}$. The new system will be equivalent to the original, provided that $M = E_k \cdots E_1$ is nonsingular. However, M is nonsingular since it is a product of nonsingular matrices.

We will show next that any of the three elementary row operations can be accomplished by multiplying A on the left by a nonsingular matrix.

Elementary Matrices

If we start with the identity matrix I and then perform exactly one elementary row operation, the resulting matrix is called an *elementary* matrix.

There are three types of elementary matrices corresponding to the three types of elementary row operations.

Type I   An elementary matrix of type I is a matrix obtained by interchanging two rows of I.

EXAMPLE I   The matrix

$$E_1 = \begin{bmatrix} 0 & 1 & 0 \\ 1 & 0 & 0 \\ 0 & 0 & 1 \end{bmatrix}$$

is an elementary matrix of type I since it was obtained by interchanging the first two rows of I. If A is a 3×3 matrix, then

$$E_1 A = \begin{bmatrix} 0 & 1 & 0 \\ 1 & 0 & 0 \\ 0 & 0 & 1 \end{bmatrix} \begin{bmatrix} a_{11} & a_{12} & a_{13} \\ a_{21} & a_{22} & a_{23} \\ a_{31} & a_{32} & a_{33} \end{bmatrix} = \begin{bmatrix} a_{21} & a_{22} & a_{23} \\ a_{11} & a_{12} & a_{13} \\ a_{31} & a_{32} & a_{33} \end{bmatrix}$$

$$A E_1 = \begin{bmatrix} a_{11} & a_{12} & a_{13} \\ a_{21} & a_{22} & a_{23} \\ a_{31} & a_{32} & a_{33} \end{bmatrix} \begin{bmatrix} 0 & 1 & 0 \\ 1 & 0 & 0 \\ 0 & 0 & 1 \end{bmatrix} = \begin{bmatrix} a_{12} & a_{11} & a_{13} \\ a_{22} & a_{21} & a_{23} \\ a_{32} & a_{31} & a_{33} \end{bmatrix}$$

Multiplying A on the left by E_1 interchanges the first and second rows of A. Right multiplication of A by E_1 is equivalent to the elementary column operation of interchanging the first and second columns.   ■

Type II   An elementary matrix of type II is a matrix obtained by multiplying a row of I by a nonzero constant.

EXAMPLE 2

$$E_2 = \begin{bmatrix} 1 & 0 & 0 \\ 0 & 1 & 0 \\ 0 & 0 & 3 \end{bmatrix}$$

is an elementary matrix of type II. If A is a 3×3 matrix, then

$$E_2 A = \begin{bmatrix} 1 & 0 & 0 \\ 0 & 1 & 0 \\ 0 & 0 & 3 \end{bmatrix} \begin{bmatrix} a_{11} & a_{12} & a_{13} \\ a_{21} & a_{22} & a_{23} \\ a_{31} & a_{32} & a_{33} \end{bmatrix} = \begin{bmatrix} a_{11} & a_{12} & a_{13} \\ a_{21} & a_{22} & a_{23} \\ 3a_{31} & 3a_{32} & 3a_{33} \end{bmatrix}$$

$$A E_2 = \begin{bmatrix} a_{11} & a_{12} & a_{13} \\ a_{21} & a_{22} & a_{23} \\ a_{31} & a_{32} & a_{33} \end{bmatrix} \begin{bmatrix} 1 & 0 & 0 \\ 0 & 1 & 0 \\ 0 & 0 & 3 \end{bmatrix} = \begin{bmatrix} a_{11} & a_{12} & 3a_{13} \\ a_{21} & a_{22} & 3a_{23} \\ a_{31} & a_{32} & 3a_{33} \end{bmatrix}$$

Multiplication on the left by E_2 performs the elementary row operation of multiplying the third row by 3, while multiplication on the right by E_2 performs the elementary column operation of multiplying the third column by 3.   ■

Type III   An elementary matrix of type III is a matrix obtained from I by adding a multiple of one row to another row.

EXAMPLE 3

$$E_3 = \begin{bmatrix} 1 & 0 & 3 \\ 0 & 1 & 0 \\ 0 & 0 & 1 \end{bmatrix}$$

is an elementary matrix of type III. If A is a 3×3 matrix, then

$$E_3 A = \begin{bmatrix} a_{11} + 3a_{31} & a_{12} + 3a_{32} & a_{13} + 3a_{33} \\ a_{21} & a_{22} & a_{23} \\ a_{31} & a_{32} & a_{33} \end{bmatrix}$$

$$A E_3 = \begin{bmatrix} a_{11} & a_{12} & 3a_{11} + a_{13} \\ a_{21} & a_{22} & 3a_{21} + a_{23} \\ a_{31} & a_{32} & 3a_{31} + a_{33} \end{bmatrix}$$

Multiplication on the left by E_3 adds 3 times the third row to the first row. Multiplication on the right adds 3 times the first column to the third column.   ■

In general, suppose that E is an $n \times n$ elementary matrix. We can think of E as being obtained from I by either a row operation or a column operation. If A is an $n \times r$

matrix, *premultiplying A by E has the effect of performing that same row operation on A. If B is an $m \times n$ matrix, postmultiplying B by E is equivalent to performing that same column operation on B.*

Theorem 1.5.1   *If E is an elementary matrix, then E is nonsingular and E^{-1} is an elementary matrix of the same type.*

Proof   If E is the elementary matrix of type I formed from I by interchanging the ith and jth rows, then E can be transformed back into I by interchanging these same rows again. Therefore, $EE = I$ and hence E is its own inverse. If E is the elementary matrix of type II formed by multiplying the ith row of I by a nonzero scalar α, then E can be transformed into the identity matrix by multiplying either its ith row or its ith column by $1/\alpha$. Thus,

$$
E^{-1} = \begin{bmatrix}
1 & & & & & & \\
& \ddots & & & & O & \\
& & 1 & & & & \\
& & & 1/\alpha & & & \\
& & & & 1 & & \\
& O & & & & \ddots & \\
& & & & & & 1
\end{bmatrix} \quad i\text{th row}
$$

Finally, if E is the elementary matrix of type III formed from I by adding m times the ith row to the jth row, that is,

$$
E = \begin{bmatrix}
1 & & & & & & \\
\vdots & \ddots & & & O & & \\
0 & \cdots & 1 & & & & \\
\vdots & & & \ddots & & & \\
0 & \cdots & m & \cdots & 1 & & \\
\vdots & & & & & \ddots & \\
0 & \cdots & 0 & \cdots & 0 & \cdots & 1
\end{bmatrix} \quad \begin{array}{l} i\text{th row} \\ \\ \\ j\text{th row} \end{array}
$$

then E can be transformed back into I either by subtracting m times the ith row from the jth row or by subtracting m times the jth column from the ith column. Thus,

$$
E^{-1} = \begin{bmatrix}
1 & & & & & & \\
\vdots & \ddots & & & O & & \\
0 & \cdots & 1 & & & & \\
\vdots & & & \ddots & & & \\
0 & \cdots & -m & \cdots & 1 & & \\
\vdots & & & & & \ddots & \\
0 & \cdots & 0 & \cdots & 0 & \cdots & 1
\end{bmatrix}
$$

Definition

A matrix B is **row equivalent** to a matrix A if there exists a finite sequence $E_1, E_2, \ldots, E_k$ of elementary matrices such that

$$B = E_k E_{k-1} \cdots E_1 A$$

In other words, B is row equivalent to A if B can be obtained from A by a finite number of row operations. In particular, if two augmented matrices $(A \mid \mathbf{b})$ and $(B \mid \mathbf{c})$ are row equivalent, then $A\mathbf{x} = \mathbf{b}$ and $B\mathbf{x} = \mathbf{c}$ are equivalent systems.

The following properties of row equivalent matrices are easily established:

I. If A is row equivalent to B, then B is row equivalent to A.

II. If A is row equivalent to B, and B is row equivalent to C, then A is row equivalent to C.

Property **(I)** can be proved using Theorem 1.5.1. The details of the proofs of **(I)** and **(II)** are left as an exercise for the reader.

Theorem 1.5.2   Equivalent Conditions for Nonsingularity

Let A be an $n \times n$ matrix. The following are equivalent:

(a) *A is nonsingular.*

(b) *$A\mathbf{x} = \mathbf{0}$ has only the trivial solution $\mathbf{0}$.*

(c) *A is row equivalent to I.*

Proof   We prove first that statement **(a)** implies statement **(b)**. If A is nonsingular and $\hat{\mathbf{x}}$ is a solution of $A\mathbf{x} = \mathbf{0}$, then

$$\hat{\mathbf{x}} = I\hat{\mathbf{x}} = (A^{-1}A)\hat{\mathbf{x}} = A^{-1}(A\hat{\mathbf{x}}) = A^{-1}\mathbf{0} = \mathbf{0}$$

Thus, $A\mathbf{x} = \mathbf{0}$ has only the trivial solution. Next, we show that statement **(b)** implies statement **(c)**. If we use elementary row operations, the system can be transformed into the form $U\mathbf{x} = \mathbf{0}$, where U is in row echelon form. If one of the diagonal elements of U were 0, the last row of U would consist entirely of 0's. But then $A\mathbf{x} = \mathbf{0}$ would be equivalent to a system with more unknowns than equations and hence, by Theorem 1.2.1, would have a nontrivial solution. Thus, U must be a strictly triangular matrix with diagonal elements all equal to 1. It then follows that I is the reduced row echelon form of A and hence A is row equivalent to I.

Finally, we will show that statement **(c)** implies statement **(a)**. If A is row equivalent to I, there exist elementary matrices $E_1, E_2, \ldots, E_k$ such that

$$A = E_k E_{k-1} \cdots E_1 I = E_k E_{k-1} \cdots E_1$$

But since E_i is invertible, $i = 1, \ldots, k$, the product $E_k E_{k-1} \cdots E_1$ is also invertible. Hence, A is nonsingular and

$$A^{-1} = (E_k E_{k-1} \cdots E_1)^{-1} = E_1^{-1} E_2^{-1} \cdots E_k^{-1}$$ ∎

Corollary 1.5.3 *The system $A\mathbf{x} = \mathbf{b}$ of n linear equations in n unknowns has a unique solution if and only if A is nonsingular.*

Proof If A is nonsingular, and $\hat{\mathbf{x}}$ is any solution of $A\mathbf{x} = \mathbf{b}$, then

$$A\hat{\mathbf{x}} = \mathbf{b}$$

Multiplying both sides of this equation by A^{-1}, we see that $\hat{\mathbf{x}}$ must be equal to $A^{-1}\mathbf{b}$.

Conversely, if $A\mathbf{x} = \mathbf{b}$ has a unique solution $\hat{\mathbf{x}}$, then we claim that A cannot be singular. Indeed, if A were singular, then the equation $A\mathbf{x} = \mathbf{0}$ would have a solution $\mathbf{z} \neq \mathbf{0}$. But this would imply that $\mathbf{y} = \hat{\mathbf{x}} + \mathbf{z}$ is a second solution of $A\mathbf{x} = \mathbf{b}$, since

$$A\mathbf{y} = A(\hat{\mathbf{x}} + \mathbf{z}) = A\hat{\mathbf{x}} + A\mathbf{z} = \mathbf{b} + \mathbf{0} = \mathbf{b}$$

Therefore, if $A\mathbf{x} = \mathbf{b}$ has a unique solution, then A must be nonsingular. ∎

If A is nonsingular, then A is row equivalent to I and hence there exist elementary matrices $E_1, \ldots, E_k$ such that

$$E_k E_{k-1} \cdots E_1 A = I$$

Multiplying both sides of this equation on the right by A^{-1}, we obtain

$$E_k E_{k-1} \cdots E_1 I = A^{-1}$$

Thus, the same series of elementary row operations that transforms a nonsingular matrix A into I will transform I into A^{-1}. This gives us a method for computing A^{-1}. If we augment A by I and perform the elementary row operations that transform A into I on the augmented matrix, then I will be transformed into A^{-1}. That is, the reduced row echelon form of the augmented matrix $(A|I)$ will be $(I|A^{-1})$.

EXAMPLE 4 Compute A^{-1} if

$$A = \begin{pmatrix} 1 & 4 & 3 \\ -1 & -2 & 0 \\ 2 & 2 & 3 \end{pmatrix}$$

Solution

$$\left[\begin{array}{ccc|ccc} 1 & 4 & 3 & 1 & 0 & 0 \\ -1 & -2 & 0 & 0 & 1 & 0 \\ 2 & 2 & 3 & 0 & 0 & 1 \end{array}\right] \rightarrow \left[\begin{array}{ccc|ccc} 1 & 4 & 3 & 1 & 0 & 0 \\ 0 & 2 & 3 & 1 & 1 & 0 \\ 0 & -6 & -3 & -2 & 0 & 1 \end{array}\right]$$

$$\rightarrow \left[\begin{array}{ccc|ccc} 1 & 4 & 3 & 1 & 0 & 0 \\ 0 & 2 & 3 & 1 & 1 & 0 \\ 0 & 0 & 6 & 1 & 3 & 1 \end{array}\right] \rightarrow \left[\begin{array}{ccc|ccc} 1 & 4 & 0 & \frac{1}{2} & -\frac{3}{2} & -\frac{1}{2} \\ 0 & 2 & 0 & \frac{1}{2} & -\frac{1}{2} & -\frac{1}{2} \\ 0 & 0 & 6 & 1 & 3 & 1 \end{array}\right]$$

$$\rightarrow \left[\begin{array}{ccc|ccc} 1 & 0 & 0 & -\frac{1}{2} & -\frac{1}{2} & \frac{1}{2} \\ 0 & 2 & 0 & \frac{1}{2} & -\frac{1}{2} & -\frac{1}{2} \\ 0 & 0 & 6 & 1 & 3 & 1 \end{array}\right] \rightarrow \left[\begin{array}{ccc|ccc} 1 & 0 & 0 & -\frac{1}{2} & -\frac{1}{2} & \frac{1}{2} \\ 0 & 1 & 0 & \frac{1}{4} & -\frac{1}{4} & -\frac{1}{4} \\ 0 & 0 & 1 & \frac{1}{6} & \frac{1}{2} & \frac{1}{6} \end{array}\right]$$

Thus,

$$
A^{-1} = \begin{bmatrix} -\frac{1}{2} & -\frac{1}{2} & \frac{1}{2} \\ \frac{1}{4} & -\frac{1}{4} & -\frac{1}{4} \\ \frac{1}{6} & \frac{1}{2} & \frac{1}{6} \end{bmatrix}
$$

■

EXAMPLE 5 Solve the system

$$
\begin{array}{rcl}
x_1 + 4x_2 + 3x_3 &=& 12 \\
-x_1 - 2x_2 &=& -12 \\
2x_1 + 2x_2 + 3x_3 &=& 8
\end{array}
$$

Solution

The coefficient matrix of this system is the matrix A of the last example. The solution of the system is then

$$
\mathbf{x} = A^{-1}\mathbf{b} = \begin{bmatrix} -\frac{1}{2} & -\frac{1}{2} & \frac{1}{2} \\ \frac{1}{4} & -\frac{1}{4} & -\frac{1}{4} \\ \frac{1}{6} & \frac{1}{2} & \frac{1}{6} \end{bmatrix} \begin{bmatrix} 12 \\ -12 \\ 8 \end{bmatrix} = \begin{bmatrix} 4 \\ 4 \\ -\frac{8}{3} \end{bmatrix}
$$

■

Diagonal and Triangular Matrices

An $n \times n$ matrix A is said to be *upper triangular* if $a_{ij} = 0$ for $i > j$ and *lower triangular* if $a_{ij} = 0$ for $i < j$. Also, A is said to be *triangular* if it is either upper triangular or lower triangular. For example, the 3×3 matrices

$$
\begin{bmatrix} 3 & 2 & 1 \\ 0 & 2 & 1 \\ 0 & 0 & 5 \end{bmatrix} \qquad \text{and} \qquad \begin{bmatrix} 1 & 0 & 0 \\ 6 & 0 & 0 \\ 1 & 4 & 3 \end{bmatrix}
$$

are both triangular. The first is upper triangular and the second is lower triangular.

A triangular matrix may have 0's on the diagonal. However, for a linear system $A\mathbf{x} = \mathbf{b}$ to be in strict triangular form, the coefficient matrix A must be upper triangular with nonzero diagonal entries.

An $n \times n$ matrix A is *diagonal* if $a_{ij} = 0$ whenever $i \neq j$. The matrices

$$
\begin{bmatrix} 1 & 0 \\ 0 & 2 \end{bmatrix}, \qquad \begin{bmatrix} 1 & 0 & 0 \\ 0 & 3 & 0 \\ 0 & 0 & 1 \end{bmatrix}, \qquad \begin{bmatrix} 0 & 0 & 0 \\ 0 & 2 & 0 \\ 0 & 0 & 0 \end{bmatrix}
$$

are all diagonal. A diagonal matrix is both upper triangular and lower triangular.

Triangular Factorization

If an $n \times n$ matrix A can be reduced to strict upper triangular form using only row operation **III**, then it is possible to represent the reduction process in terms of a matrix factorization. We illustrate how this is done in the next example.

EXAMPLE 6 Let

$$A = \begin{pmatrix} 2 & 4 & 2 \\ 1 & 5 & 2 \\ 4 & -1 & 9 \end{pmatrix}$$

and let us use only row operation **III** to carry out the reduction process. At the first step, we subtract $\frac{1}{2}$ times the first row from the second and then we subtract twice the first row from the third.

$$\begin{pmatrix} 2 & 4 & 2 \\ 1 & 5 & 2 \\ 4 & -1 & 9 \end{pmatrix} \rightarrow \begin{pmatrix} 2 & 4 & 2 \\ 0 & 3 & 1 \\ 0 & -9 & 5 \end{pmatrix}$$

To keep track of the multiples of the first row that were subtracted, we set $l_{21} = \frac{1}{2}$ and $l_{31} = 2$. We complete the elimination process by eliminating the -9 in the (3,2) position.

$$\begin{pmatrix} 2 & 4 & 2 \\ 0 & 3 & 1 \\ 0 & -9 & 5 \end{pmatrix} \rightarrow \begin{pmatrix} 2 & 4 & 2 \\ 0 & 3 & 1 \\ 0 & 0 & 8 \end{pmatrix}$$

Let $l_{32} = -3$, the multiple of the second row subtracted from the third row. If we call the resulting matrix U and set

$$L = \begin{pmatrix} 1 & 0 & 0 \\ l_{21} & 1 & 0 \\ l_{31} & l_{32} & 1 \end{pmatrix} = \begin{pmatrix} 1 & 0 & 0 \\ \frac{1}{2} & 1 & 0 \\ 2 & -3 & 1 \end{pmatrix}$$

then it is easily verified that

$$LU = \begin{pmatrix} 1 & 0 & 0 \\ \frac{1}{2} & 1 & 0 \\ 2 & -3 & 1 \end{pmatrix} \begin{pmatrix} 2 & 4 & 2 \\ 0 & 3 & 1 \\ 0 & 0 & 8 \end{pmatrix} = \begin{pmatrix} 2 & 4 & 2 \\ 1 & 5 & 2 \\ 4 & -1 & 9 \end{pmatrix} = A \qquad \blacksquare$$

The matrix L in the previous example is lower triangular with 1's on the diagonal. We say that L is *unit lower triangular*. The factorization of the matrix A into a product of a unit lower triangular matrix L times a strictly upper triangular matrix U is often referred to as an *LU factorization*.

To see why the factorization in Example 6 works, let us view the reduction process in terms of elementary matrices. The three row operations that were applied to the matrix A can be represented in terms of multiplications by elementary matrices

$$E_3 E_2 E_1 A = U \qquad (3)$$

where

$$E_1 = \begin{bmatrix} 1 & 0 & 0 \\ -\frac{1}{2} & 1 & 0 \\ 0 & 0 & 1 \end{bmatrix}, \quad E_2 = \begin{bmatrix} 1 & 0 & 0 \\ 0 & 1 & 0 \\ -2 & 0 & 1 \end{bmatrix}, \quad E_3 = \begin{bmatrix} 1 & 0 & 0 \\ 0 & 1 & 0 \\ 0 & 3 & 1 \end{bmatrix}$$

correspond to the row operations in the reduction process. Since each of the elementary matrices is nonsingular, we can multiply equation (3) by their inverses.

$$A = E_1^{-1} E_2^{-1} E_3^{-1} U$$

[We multiply in reverse order because $(E_3 E_2 E_1)^{-1} = E_1^{-1} E_2^{-1} E_3^{-1}$.] However, when the inverses are multiplied in this order, the multipliers l_{21}, l_{31}, l_{32} fill in below the diagonal in the product:

$$E_1^{-1} E_2^{-1} E_3^{-1} = \begin{bmatrix} 1 & 0 & 0 \\ \frac{1}{2} & 1 & 0 \\ 0 & 0 & 1 \end{bmatrix} \begin{bmatrix} 1 & 0 & 0 \\ 0 & 1 & 0 \\ 2 & 0 & 1 \end{bmatrix} \begin{bmatrix} 1 & 0 & 0 \\ 0 & 1 & 0 \\ 0 & -3 & 1 \end{bmatrix} = L$$

In general, if an $n \times n$ matrix A can be reduced to strict upper triangular form using only row operation **III**, then A has an LU factorization. The matrix L is unit lower triangular, and if $i > j$, then l_{ij} is the multiple of the jth row subtracted from the ith row during the reduction process.

The LU factorization is a very useful way of viewing the elimination process. We will find it particularly useful in Chapter 7 when we study computer methods for solving linear systems. Many of the major topics in linear algebra can be viewed in terms of matrix factorizations. We will study other interesting and important factorizations in Chapters 5 through 7.

SECTION 1.5 EXERCISES

1. Which of the matrices that follow are elementary matrices? Classify each elementary matrix by type.

(a) $\begin{bmatrix} 0 & 1 \\ 1 & 0 \end{bmatrix}$

(b) $\begin{bmatrix} 2 & 0 \\ 0 & 3 \end{bmatrix}$

(c) $\begin{bmatrix} 1 & 0 & 0 \\ 0 & 1 & 0 \\ 5 & 0 & 1 \end{bmatrix}$

(d) $\begin{bmatrix} 1 & 0 & 0 \\ 0 & 5 & 0 \\ 0 & 0 & 1 \end{bmatrix}$

2. Find the inverse of each matrix in Exercise 1. For each elementary matrix, verify that its inverse is an elementary matrix of the same type.

3. For each of the following pairs of matrices, find an elementary matrix E such that $EA = B$:

(a) $A = \begin{bmatrix} 2 & -1 \\ 5 & 3 \end{bmatrix}$, $B = \begin{bmatrix} -4 & 2 \\ 5 & 3 \end{bmatrix}$

(b) $A = \begin{bmatrix} 2 & 1 & 3 \\ -2 & 4 & 5 \\ 3 & 1 & 4 \end{bmatrix}$, $B = \begin{bmatrix} 2 & 1 & 3 \\ 3 & 1 & 4 \\ -2 & 4 & 5 \end{bmatrix}$

(c) $A = \begin{bmatrix} 4 & -2 & 3 \\ 1 & 0 & 2 \\ -2 & 3 & 1 \end{bmatrix}$, $B = \begin{bmatrix} 4 & -2 & 3 \\ 1 & 0 & 2 \\ 0 & 3 & 5 \end{bmatrix}$

4. For each of the following pairs of matrices, find an elementary matrix E such that $AE = B$:

(a) $A = \begin{bmatrix} 4 & 1 & 3 \\ 2 & 1 & 4 \\ 1 & 3 & 2 \end{bmatrix}$, $B = \begin{bmatrix} 3 & 1 & 4 \\ 4 & 1 & 2 \\ 2 & 3 & 1 \end{bmatrix}$

(b) $A = \begin{bmatrix} 2 & 4 \\ 1 & 6 \end{bmatrix}$, $B = \begin{bmatrix} 2 & -2 \\ 1 & 3 \end{bmatrix}$

(c) $A = \begin{bmatrix} 4 & -2 & 3 \\ -2 & 4 & 2 \\ 6 & 1 & -2 \end{bmatrix}$,

$\quad\quad B = \begin{bmatrix} 2 & -2 & 3 \\ -1 & 4 & 2 \\ 3 & 1 & -2 \end{bmatrix}$

5. Let

$$A = \begin{bmatrix} 1 & 2 & 4 \\ 2 & 1 & 3 \\ 1 & 0 & 2 \end{bmatrix}, \quad B = \begin{bmatrix} 1 & 2 & 4 \\ 2 & 1 & 3 \\ 2 & 2 & 6 \end{bmatrix},$$

$$C = \begin{bmatrix} 1 & 2 & 4 \\ 0 & -1 & -3 \\ 2 & 2 & 6 \end{bmatrix}.$$

(a) Find an elementary matrix E such that $EA = B$.

(b) Find an elementary matrix F such that $FB = C$.

(c) Is C row equivalent to A? Explain.

6. Let

$$A = \begin{bmatrix} 2 & 1 & 1 \\ 6 & 4 & 5 \\ 4 & 1 & 3 \end{bmatrix}$$

(a) Find elementary matrices E_1, E_2, E_3 such that

$$E_3 E_2 E_1 A = U$$

where U is an upper triangular matrix.

(b) Determine the inverses of E_1, E_2, E_3 and set $L = E_1^{-1} E_2^{-1} E_3^{-1}$. What type of matrix is L? Verify that $A = LU$.

7. Let

$$A = \begin{bmatrix} 2 & 1 \\ 6 & 4 \end{bmatrix}$$

(a) Express A^{-1} as a product of elementary matrices.

(b) Express A as a product of elementary matrices.

8. Compute the LU factorization of each of the following matrices:

(a) $\begin{bmatrix} 3 & 1 \\ 9 & 5 \end{bmatrix}$ **(b)** $\begin{bmatrix} 2 & 4 \\ -2 & 1 \end{bmatrix}$

(c) $\begin{bmatrix} 1 & 1 & 1 \\ 3 & 5 & 6 \\ -2 & 2 & 7 \end{bmatrix}$ **(d)** $\begin{bmatrix} -2 & 1 & 2 \\ 4 & 1 & -2 \\ -6 & -3 & 4 \end{bmatrix}$

9. Let

$$A = \begin{bmatrix} 1 & 0 & 1 \\ 3 & 3 & 4 \\ 2 & 2 & 3 \end{bmatrix}$$

(a) Verify that

$$A^{-1} = \begin{bmatrix} 1 & 2 & -3 \\ -1 & 1 & -1 \\ 0 & -2 & 3 \end{bmatrix}$$

(b) Use A^{-1} to solve $Ax = b$ for the following choices of b:

(i) $b = (1, 1, 1)^T$ (ii) $b = (1, 2, 3)^T$

(iii) $b = (-2, 1, 0)^T$

10. Find the inverse of each of the following matrices:

(a) $\begin{bmatrix} -1 & 1 \\ 1 & 0 \end{bmatrix}$ **(b)** $\begin{bmatrix} 2 & 5 \\ 1 & 3 \end{bmatrix}$

(c) $\begin{bmatrix} 2 & 6 \\ 3 & 8 \end{bmatrix}$ **(d)** $\begin{bmatrix} 3 & 0 \\ 9 & 3 \end{bmatrix}$

(e) $\begin{bmatrix} 1 & 1 & 1 \\ 0 & 1 & 1 \\ 0 & 0 & 1 \end{bmatrix}$ **(f)** $\begin{bmatrix} 2 & 0 & 5 \\ 0 & 3 & 0 \\ 1 & 0 & 3 \end{bmatrix}$

(g) $\begin{bmatrix} -1 & -3 & -3 \\ 2 & 6 & 1 \\ 3 & 8 & 3 \end{bmatrix}$ **(h)** $\begin{bmatrix} 1 & 0 & 1 \\ -1 & 1 & 1 \\ -1 & -2 & -3 \end{bmatrix}$

11. Given

$$A = \begin{bmatrix} 3 & 1 \\ 5 & 2 \end{bmatrix} \text{ and } B = \begin{bmatrix} 1 & 2 \\ 3 & 4 \end{bmatrix}$$

compute A^{-1} and use it to:

(a) find a 2×2 matrix X such that $AX = B$.

(b) find a 2×2 matrix Y such that $YA = B$.

12. Let

$$A = \begin{bmatrix} 5 & 3 \\ 3 & 2 \end{bmatrix}, B = \begin{bmatrix} 6 & 2 \\ 2 & 4 \end{bmatrix}, C = \begin{bmatrix} 4 & -2 \\ -6 & 3 \end{bmatrix}$$

Solve each of the following matrix equations:

(a) $AX + B = C$ **(b)** $XA + B = C$

(c) $AX + B = X$ **(d)** $XA + C = X$

13. Is the transpose of an elementary matrix an elementary matrix of the same type? Is the product of two elementary matrices an elementary matrix?

14. Let U and R be $n \times n$ upper triangular matrices and set $T = UR$. Show that T is also upper triangular and that $t_{jj} = u_{jj} r_{jj}$ for $j = 1, \ldots, n$.

15. Let A be a 3×3 matrix and suppose that

$$2a_1 + a_2 - 4a_3 = 0$$

How many solutions will the system $Ax = 0$ have? Explain. Is A nonsingular? Explain.

16. Let A be a 3×3 matrix and suppose that

$$a_1 = 3a_2 - 2a_3$$

Will the system $Ax = 0$ have a nontrivial solution? Is A nonsingular? Explain your answers.

17. Let A and B be $n \times n$ matrices and let $C = A - B$. Show that if $A\mathbf{x}_0 = B\mathbf{x}_0$ and $\mathbf{x}_0 \neq \mathbf{0}$, then C must be singular.

18. Let A and B be $n \times n$ matrices and let $C = AB$. Prove that if B is singular, then C must be singular. *Hint*: Use Theorem 1.5.2.

19. Let U be an $n \times n$ upper triangular matrix with nonzero diagonal entries.
    (a) Explain why U must be nonsingular.
    (b) Explain why U^{-1} must be upper triangular.

20. Let A be a nonsingular $n \times n$ matrix and let B be an $n \times r$ matrix. Show that the reduced row echelon form of $(A|B)$ is $(I|C)$, where $C = A^{-1}B$.

21. In general, matrix multiplication is not commutative (i.e., $AB \neq BA$). However, in certain special cases the commutative property does hold. Show that
    (a) if D_1 and D_2 are $n \times n$ diagonal matrices, then $D_1D_2 = D_2D_1$.
    (b) if A is an $n \times n$ matrix and
    $$B = a_0I + a_1A + a_2A^2 + \cdots + a_kA^k$$
    where $a_0, a_1, \ldots, a_k$ are scalars, then $AB = BA$.

22. Show that if A is a symmetric nonsingular matrix, then A^{-1} is also symmetric.

23. Prove that if A is row equivalent to B, then B is row equivalent to A.

24. (a) Prove that if A is row equivalent to B and B is row equivalent to C, then A is row equivalent to C.
    (b) Prove that any two nonsingular $n \times n$ matrices are row equivalent.

25. Let A and B be an $m \times n$ matrix. Prove that if B is row equivalent to A and U is any row echelon form of A, then B is row equivalent to U.

26. Prove that B is row equivalent to A if and only if there exists a nonsingular matrix M such that $B = MA$.

27. Is it possible for a singular matrix B to be row equivalent to a nonsingular matrix A? Explain.

28. Given a vector $\mathbf{x} \in \mathbb{R}^{n+1}$, the $(n+1) \times (n+1)$ matrix V defined by
    $$v_{ij} = \begin{cases} 1 & \text{if } j = 1 \\ x_i^{j-1} & \text{for } j = 2, \ldots, n+1 \end{cases}$$
    is called the Vandermonde matrix.
    (a) Show that if
    $$V\mathbf{c} = \mathbf{y}$$
    and
    $$p(x) = c_1 + c_2x + \cdots + c_{n+1}x^n$$
    then
    $$p(x_i) = y_i, \qquad i = 1, 2, \ldots, n+1$$
    (b) Suppose that $x_1, x_2, \ldots, x_{n+1}$ are all distinct. Show that if $\mathbf{c}$ is a solution of $V\mathbf{x} = \mathbf{0}$, then the coefficients $c_1, c_2, \ldots, c_n$ must all be zero, and hence V must be nonsingular.

For each of following, answer true *if the statement is always true and answer* false *otherwise. In the case of a true statement, explain or prove your answer. In the case of a false statement, give an example to show that the statement is not always true.*

29. If A is row equivalent to I and $AB = AC$, then B must equal C.

30. If E and F are elementary matrices and $G = EF$, then G is nonsingular.

31. If A is a 4×4 matrix and $\mathbf{a}_1 + \mathbf{a}_2 = \mathbf{a}_3 + 2\mathbf{a}_4$, then A must be singular.

32. If A is row equivalent to both B and C, then A is row equivalent to $B + C$.

1.6 Partitioned Matrices

Often it is useful to think of a matrix as being composed of a number of submatrices. A matrix C can be partitioned into smaller matrices by drawing horizontal lines between the rows and vertical lines between the columns. The smaller matrices are often referred to as *blocks*. For example, let

$$C = \begin{bmatrix} 1 & -2 & 4 & 1 & 3 \\ 2 & 1 & 1 & 1 & 1 \\ 3 & 3 & 2 & -1 & 2 \\ 4 & 6 & 2 & 2 & 4 \end{bmatrix}$$

If lines are drawn between the second and third rows and between the third and fourth columns, then C will be divided into four submatrices, C_{11}, C_{12}, C_{21}, and C_{22}.

$$\begin{pmatrix} C_{11} & C_{12} \\ C_{21} & C_{22} \end{pmatrix} = \left[\begin{array}{ccc|cc} 1 & -2 & 4 & 1 & 3 \\ 2 & 1 & 1 & 1 & 1 \\ \hline 3 & 3 & 2 & -1 & 2 \\ 4 & 6 & 2 & 2 & 4 \end{array} \right]$$

One useful way of partitioning a matrix is to partition it into columns. For example, if

$$B = \begin{pmatrix} -1 & 2 & 1 \\ 2 & 3 & 1 \\ 1 & 4 & 1 \end{pmatrix}$$

we can partition B into three column submatrices:

$$B = (\mathbf{b}_1 \ \mathbf{b}_2 \ \mathbf{b}_3) = \left[\begin{array}{c|c|c} -1 & 2 & 1 \\ 2 & 3 & 1 \\ 1 & 4 & 1 \end{array} \right]$$

Suppose that we are given a matrix A with three columns; then the product AB can be viewed as a block multiplication. Each block of B is multiplied by A and the result is a matrix with three blocks: $A\mathbf{b}_1$, $A\mathbf{b}_2$, and $A\mathbf{b}_3$; that is,

$$AB = A(\mathbf{b}_1 \ \mathbf{b}_2 \ \mathbf{b}_3) = \left[\begin{array}{ccc} A\mathbf{b}_1 & A\mathbf{b}_2 & A\mathbf{b}_3 \end{array} \right]$$

For example, if

$$A = \begin{pmatrix} 1 & 3 & 1 \\ 2 & 1 & -2 \end{pmatrix}$$

then

$$A\mathbf{b}_1 = \begin{pmatrix} 6 \\ -2 \end{pmatrix}, \quad A\mathbf{b}_2 = \begin{pmatrix} 15 \\ -1 \end{pmatrix}, \quad A\mathbf{b}_3 = \begin{pmatrix} 5 \\ 1 \end{pmatrix}$$

and hence

$$A(\mathbf{b}_1 \ \mathbf{b}_2 \ \mathbf{b}_3) = \left[\begin{array}{c|c|c} 6 & 15 & 5 \\ -2 & -1 & 1 \end{array} \right]$$

In general, if A is an $m \times n$ matrix and B is an $n \times r$ matrix that has been partitioned into columns $\left[\begin{array}{ccc} \mathbf{b}_1 & \cdots & \mathbf{b}_r \end{array} \right]$, then the block multiplication of A times B is given by

$$AB = (A\mathbf{b}_1 \ A\mathbf{b}_2 \ \cdots \ A\mathbf{b}_r)$$

In particular,

$$(\mathbf{a}_1 \ \cdots \ \mathbf{a}_n) = A = AI = (A\mathbf{e}_1 \ \cdots \ A\mathbf{e}_n)$$

Let A be an $m \times n$ matrix. If we partition A into rows, then

$$A = \begin{pmatrix} \vec{\mathbf{a}}_1 \\ \vec{\mathbf{a}}_2 \\ \vdots \\ \vec{\mathbf{a}}_m \end{pmatrix}$$

If B is an $n \times r$ matrix, the ith row of the product AB is determined by multiplying the ith row of A times B. Thus, the ith row of AB is $\vec{\mathbf{a}}_i B$. In general, the product AB can be partitioned into rows as follows:

$$AB = \begin{pmatrix} \vec{\mathbf{a}}_1 B \\ \vec{\mathbf{a}}_2 B \\ \vdots \\ \vec{\mathbf{a}}_m B \end{pmatrix}$$

To illustrate this result, let us look at an example. If

$$A = \begin{bmatrix} 2 & 5 \\ 3 & 4 \\ 1 & 7 \end{bmatrix} \quad \text{and} \quad B = \begin{pmatrix} 3 & 2 & -3 \\ -1 & 1 & 1 \end{pmatrix}$$

then

$$\vec{\mathbf{a}}_1 B = \begin{bmatrix} 1 & 9 & -1 \end{bmatrix}$$

$$\vec{\mathbf{a}}_2 B = \begin{bmatrix} 5 & 10 & -5 \end{bmatrix}$$

$$\vec{\mathbf{a}}_3 B = \begin{bmatrix} -4 & 9 & 4 \end{bmatrix}$$

These are the row vectors of the product AB:

$$AB = \begin{bmatrix} \vec{\mathbf{a}}_1 B \\ \vec{\mathbf{a}}_2 B \\ \vec{\mathbf{a}}_3 B \end{bmatrix} = \begin{bmatrix} 1 & 9 & -1 \\ \hline 5 & 10 & -5 \\ \hline -4 & 9 & 4 \end{bmatrix}$$

Next, we consider how to compute the product AB in terms of more general partitions of A and B.

Block Multiplication

Let A be an $m \times n$ matrix and B an $n \times r$ matrix. It is often useful to partition A and B and express the product in terms of the submatrices of A and B. Consider the following four cases.

Case 1. If $B = \begin{bmatrix} B_1 & B_2 \end{bmatrix}$, where B_1 is an $n \times t$ matrix and B_2 is an $n \times (r-t)$ matrix, then

$$
\begin{aligned}
AB &= A(\mathbf{b}_1, \ldots, \mathbf{b}_t, \mathbf{b}_{t+1} \ldots \mathbf{b}_r) \\
&= (A\mathbf{b}_1, \ldots, A\mathbf{b}_t, A\mathbf{b}_{t+1}, \ldots, A\mathbf{b}_r) \\
&= (A(\mathbf{b}_1 \ldots \mathbf{b}_t), A(\mathbf{b}_{t+1} \cdots \mathbf{b}_r)) \\
&= \begin{bmatrix} AB_1 & AB_2 \end{bmatrix}
\end{aligned}
$$

Thus,

$$
A \begin{bmatrix} B_1 & B_2 \end{bmatrix} = \begin{bmatrix} AB_1 & AB_2 \end{bmatrix}
$$

Case 2. If $A = \begin{bmatrix} A_1 \\ A_2 \end{bmatrix}$, where A_1 is a $k \times n$ matrix and A_2 is an $(m-k) \times n$ matrix, then

$$
\begin{bmatrix} A_1 \\ A_2 \end{bmatrix} B = \begin{bmatrix} \vec{\mathbf{a}}_1 \\ \vdots \\ \vec{\mathbf{a}}_k \\ \hline \vec{\mathbf{a}}_{k+1} \\ \vdots \\ \vec{\mathbf{a}}_m \end{bmatrix} B = \begin{bmatrix} \vec{\mathbf{a}}_1 B \\ \vdots \\ \vec{\mathbf{a}}_k B \\ \hline \vec{\mathbf{a}}_{k+1} B \\ \vdots \\ \vec{\mathbf{a}}_m B \end{bmatrix}
$$

$$
= \begin{bmatrix} \begin{bmatrix} \vec{\mathbf{a}}_1 \\ \vdots \\ \vec{\mathbf{a}}_k \end{bmatrix} B \\ \begin{bmatrix} \vec{\mathbf{a}}_{k+1} \\ \vdots \\ \vec{\mathbf{a}}_m \end{bmatrix} B \end{bmatrix} = \begin{bmatrix} A_1 B \\ A_2 B \end{bmatrix}
$$

Thus,

$$
\begin{bmatrix} A_1 \\ A_2 \end{bmatrix} B = \begin{bmatrix} A_1 B \\ A_2 B \end{bmatrix}
$$

Case 3. Let $A = \begin{bmatrix} A_1 & A_2 \end{bmatrix}$ and $B = \begin{bmatrix} B_1 \\ B_2 \end{bmatrix}$, where A_1 is an $m \times s$ matrix, A_2 is an $m \times (n-s)$ matrix, B_1 is an $s \times r$ matrix, and B_2 is an $(n-s) \times r$ matrix. If $C = AB$, then

$$
c_{ij} = \sum_{l=1}^{n} a_{il} b_{lj} = \sum_{l=1}^{s} a_{il} b_{lj} + \sum_{l=s+1}^{n} a_{il} b_{lj}
$$

Thus, c_{ij} is the sum of the (i,j) entry of A_1B_1 and the (i,j) entry of A_2B_2. Therefore,

$$AB = C = A_1B_1 + A_2B_2$$

and it follows that

$$\begin{bmatrix} A_1 & A_2 \end{bmatrix} \begin{bmatrix} B_1 \\ B_2 \end{bmatrix} = A_1B_1 + A_2B_2$$

Case 4. Let A and B both be partitioned as follows:

$$A = \begin{bmatrix} A_{11} & A_{12} \\ \hline A_{21} & A_{22} \end{bmatrix} \begin{matrix} k \\ m-k \end{matrix} , \qquad B = \begin{bmatrix} B_{11} & B_{12} \\ \hline B_{21} & B_{22} \end{bmatrix} \begin{matrix} s \\ n-s \end{matrix}$$
$$\quad\;\; s \quad\; n-s \qquad\qquad\qquad t \quad\;\; r-t$$

Let

$$A_1 = \begin{bmatrix} A_{11} \\ A_{21} \end{bmatrix}, \qquad A_2 = \begin{bmatrix} A_{12} \\ A_{22} \end{bmatrix},$$

$$B_1 = \begin{bmatrix} B_{11} & B_{12} \end{bmatrix}, \qquad B_2 = \begin{bmatrix} B_{21} & B_{22} \end{bmatrix}$$

It follows from case 3 that

$$AB = \begin{bmatrix} A_1 & A_2 \end{bmatrix} \begin{bmatrix} B_1 \\ B_2 \end{bmatrix} = A_1B_1 + A_2B_2$$

It follows from cases 1 and 2 that

$$A_1B_1 = \begin{bmatrix} A_{11} \\ A_{21} \end{bmatrix} B_1 = \begin{bmatrix} A_{11}B_1 \\ A_{21}B_1 \end{bmatrix} = \begin{bmatrix} A_{11}B_{11} & A_{11}B_{12} \\ A_{21}B_{11} & A_{21}B_{12} \end{bmatrix}$$

$$A_2B_2 = \begin{bmatrix} A_{12} \\ A_{22} \end{bmatrix} B_2 = \begin{bmatrix} A_{12}B_2 \\ A_{22}B_2 \end{bmatrix} = \begin{bmatrix} A_{12}B_{21} & A_{12}B_{22} \\ A_{22}B_{21} & A_{22}B_{22} \end{bmatrix}$$

Therefore,

$$\begin{bmatrix} A_{11} & A_{12} \\ A_{21} & A_{22} \end{bmatrix} \begin{bmatrix} B_{11} & B_{12} \\ B_{21} & B_{22} \end{bmatrix} = \begin{bmatrix} A_{11}B_{11} + A_{12}B_{21} & A_{11}B_{12} + A_{12}B_{22} \\ A_{21}B_{11} + A_{22}B_{21} & A_{21}B_{12} + A_{22}B_{22} \end{bmatrix}$$

In general, if the blocks have the proper dimensions, the block multiplication can be carried out in the same manner as ordinary matrix multiplication, that is, if

$$A = \begin{bmatrix} A_{11} & \cdots & A_{1t} \\ \vdots & & \\ A_{s1} & \cdots & A_{st} \end{bmatrix} \qquad \text{and} \qquad B = \begin{bmatrix} B_{11} & \cdots & B_{1r} \\ \vdots & & \\ B_{t1} & \cdots & B_{tr} \end{bmatrix}$$

then

$$AB = \begin{pmatrix} C_{11} & \cdots & C_{1r} \\ \vdots & & \\ C_{s1} & \cdots & C_{sr} \end{pmatrix}$$

where

$$C_{ij} = \sum_{k=1}^{t} A_{ik} B_{kj}$$

The multiplication can be carried out in this manner only if the number of columns of A_{ik} equals the number of rows of B_{kj} for each k.

EXAMPLE 1   Let

$$A = \begin{pmatrix} 1 & 1 & 1 & 1 \\ 2 & 2 & 1 & 1 \\ 3 & 3 & 2 & 2 \end{pmatrix}$$

and

$$B = \begin{pmatrix} B_{11} & B_{12} \\ B_{21} & B_{22} \end{pmatrix} = \left(\begin{array}{cc|cc} 1 & 1 & 1 & 1 \\ 1 & 2 & 1 & 1 \\ \hline 3 & 1 & 1 & 1 \\ 3 & 2 & 1 & 2 \end{array} \right)$$

Partition A into four blocks and perform the block multiplication.

Solution

Since each B_{kj} has two rows, the A_{ik}'s must each have two columns. Thus, we have one of two possibilities:

(i)
$$\begin{pmatrix} A_{11} & A_{12} \\ A_{21} & A_{22} \end{pmatrix} = \left(\begin{array}{cc|cc} 1 & 1 & 1 & 1 \\ 2 & 2 & 1 & 1 \\ \hline 3 & 3 & 2 & 2 \end{array} \right)$$

in which case

$$\left(\begin{array}{cc|cc} 1 & 1 & 1 & 1 \\ 2 & 2 & 1 & 1 \\ \hline 3 & 3 & 2 & 2 \end{array} \right) \left(\begin{array}{cc|cc} 1 & 1 & 1 & 1 \\ 1 & 2 & 1 & 1 \\ \hline 3 & 1 & 1 & 1 \\ 3 & 2 & 1 & 2 \end{array} \right) = \left(\begin{array}{cc|cc} 8 & 6 & 4 & 5 \\ 10 & 9 & 6 & 7 \\ \hline 18 & 15 & 10 & 12 \end{array} \right)$$

or

(ii)
$$\begin{pmatrix} A_{11} & A_{12} \\ A_{21} & A_{22} \end{pmatrix} = \left(\begin{array}{cc|cc} 1 & 1 & 1 & 1 \\ 2 & 2 & 1 & 1 \\ \hline 3 & 3 & 2 & 2 \end{array} \right)$$

in which case

$$\begin{bmatrix} 1 & 1 & 1 & 1 \\ 2 & 2 & 1 & 1 \\ \hline 3 & 3 & 2 & 2 \end{bmatrix} \begin{bmatrix} 1 & 1 & 1 & 1 \\ 1 & 2 & 1 & 1 \\ \hline 3 & 1 & 1 & 1 \\ 3 & 2 & 1 & 2 \end{bmatrix} = \begin{bmatrix} 8 & 6 & 4 & 5 \\ 10 & 9 & 6 & 7 \\ \hline 18 & 15 & 10 & 12 \end{bmatrix}$$ ∎

EXAMPLE 2   Let A be an $n \times n$ matrix of the form

$$\begin{bmatrix} A_{11} & O \\ O & A_{22} \end{bmatrix}$$

where A_{11} is a $k \times k$ matrix $(k < n)$. Show that A is nonsingular if and only if A_{11} and A_{22} are nonsingular.

Solution

If A_{11} and A_{22} are nonsingular, then

$$\begin{bmatrix} A_{11}^{-1} & O \\ O & A_{22}^{-1} \end{bmatrix} \begin{bmatrix} A_{11} & O \\ O & A_{22} \end{bmatrix} = \begin{bmatrix} I_k & O \\ O & I_{n-k} \end{bmatrix} = I$$

and

$$\begin{bmatrix} A_{11} & O \\ O & A_{22} \end{bmatrix} \begin{bmatrix} A_{11}^{-1} & O \\ O & A_{22}^{-1} \end{bmatrix} = \begin{bmatrix} I_k & O \\ O & I_{n-k} \end{bmatrix} = I$$

so A is nonsingular and

$$A^{-1} = \begin{bmatrix} A_{11}^{-1} & O \\ O & A_{22}^{-1} \end{bmatrix}$$

Conversely, if A is nonsingular, then let $B = A^{-1}$ and partition B in the same manner as A. Since

$$BA = I = AB$$

it follows that

$$\begin{bmatrix} B_{11} & B_{12} \\ B_{21} & B_{22} \end{bmatrix} \begin{bmatrix} A_{11} & O \\ O & A_{22} \end{bmatrix} = \begin{bmatrix} I_k & O \\ O & I_{n-k} \end{bmatrix} = \begin{bmatrix} A_{11} & O \\ O & A_{22} \end{bmatrix} \begin{bmatrix} B_{11} & B_{12} \\ B_{21} & B_{22} \end{bmatrix}$$

$$\begin{bmatrix} B_{11}A_{11} & B_{12}A_{22} \\ B_{21}A_{11} & B_{22}A_{22} \end{bmatrix} = \begin{bmatrix} I_k & O \\ O & I_{n-k} \end{bmatrix} = \begin{bmatrix} A_{11}B_{11} & A_{11}B_{12} \\ A_{22}B_{21} & A_{22}B_{22} \end{bmatrix}$$

Thus,

$$B_{11}A_{11} = I_k = A_{11}B_{11}$$
$$B_{22}A_{22} = I_{n-k} = A_{22}B_{22}$$

Hence, A_{11} and A_{22} are both nonsingular with inverses B_{11} and B_{22}, respectively.   ∎

Outer Product Expansions

Given two vectors $\mathbf{x}$ and $\mathbf{y}$ in $\mathbb{R}^n$, it is possible to perform a matrix multiplication of the vectors if we transpose one of the vectors first. The matrix product $\mathbf{x}^T\mathbf{y}$ is the product of a row vector (a $1 \times n$ matrix) and a column vector (an $n \times 1$ matrix). The result will be a 1×1 matrix, or simply a scalar:

$$\mathbf{x}^T\mathbf{y} = \begin{pmatrix} x_1 & x_2 & \cdots & x_n \end{pmatrix} \begin{pmatrix} y_1 \\ y_2 \\ \vdots \\ y_n \end{pmatrix} = x_1 y_1 + x_2 y_2 + \cdots + x_n y_n$$

This type of product is referred to as a *scalar product* or an *inner product*. The scalar product is one of the most commonly performed operations. For example, when we multiply two matrices, each entry of the product is computed as a scalar product (a row vector times a column vector).

It is also useful to multiply a column vector times a row vector. The matrix product $\mathbf{x}\mathbf{y}^T$ is the product of an $n \times 1$ matrix times a $1 \times n$ matrix. The result is a full $n \times n$ matrix.

$$\mathbf{x}\mathbf{y}^T = \begin{pmatrix} x_1 \\ x_2 \\ \vdots \\ x_n \end{pmatrix} \begin{pmatrix} y_1 & y_2 & \cdots & y_n \end{pmatrix} = \begin{pmatrix} x_1 y_1 & x_1 y_2 & \cdots & x_1 y_n \\ x_2 y_1 & x_2 y_2 & \cdots & x_2 y_n \\ \vdots & & & \\ x_n y_1 & x_n y_2 & \cdots & x_n y_n \end{pmatrix}$$

The product $\mathbf{x}\mathbf{y}^T$ is referred to as the *outer product* of $\mathbf{x}$ and $\mathbf{y}$. The outer product matrix has special structure in that each of its rows is a multiple of $\mathbf{y}^T$ and each of its column vectors is a multiple of $\mathbf{x}$. For example, if

$$\mathbf{x} = \begin{pmatrix} 4 \\ 1 \\ 3 \end{pmatrix} \quad \text{and} \quad \mathbf{y} = \begin{pmatrix} 3 \\ 5 \\ 2 \end{pmatrix}$$

then

$$\mathbf{x}\mathbf{y}^T = \begin{pmatrix} 4 \\ 1 \\ 3 \end{pmatrix} \begin{pmatrix} 3 & 5 & 2 \end{pmatrix} = \begin{pmatrix} 12 & 20 & 8 \\ 3 & 5 & 2 \\ 9 & 15 & 6 \end{pmatrix}$$

Note that each row is a multiple of $(3, 5, 2)$ and each column is a multiple of $\mathbf{x}$.

We are now ready to generalize the idea of an outer product from vectors to matrices. Suppose that we start with an $m \times n$ matrix X and a $k \times n$ matrix Y. We can then form a matrix product XY^T. If we partition X into columns and Y^T into rows and perform the block multiplication, we see that XY^T can be represented as a sum of outer products of vectors:

$$XY^T = \begin{pmatrix} \mathbf{x}_1 & \mathbf{x}_2 & \cdots & \mathbf{x}_n \end{pmatrix} \begin{pmatrix} \mathbf{y}_1^T \\ \mathbf{y}_2^T \\ \vdots \\ \mathbf{y}_n^T \end{pmatrix} = \mathbf{x}_1 \mathbf{y}_1^T + \mathbf{x}_2 \mathbf{y}_2^T + \cdots + \mathbf{x}_n \mathbf{y}_n^T$$

This representation is referred to as an *outer product expansion*. These types of expansions play an important role in many applications. In Section 6.5, we will see how outer product expansions are used in digital imaging and in information retrieval applications.

EXAMPLE 3   Given

$$X = \begin{bmatrix} 3 & 1 \\ 2 & 4 \\ 1 & 2 \end{bmatrix} \quad \text{and} \quad Y = \begin{bmatrix} 1 & 2 \\ 2 & 4 \\ 3 & 1 \end{bmatrix}$$

compute the outer product expansion of XY^T.

Solution

$$XY^T = \begin{bmatrix} 3 & 1 \\ 2 & 4 \\ 1 & 2 \end{bmatrix} \begin{pmatrix} 1 & 2 & 3 \\ 2 & 4 & 1 \end{pmatrix}$$

$$= \begin{bmatrix} 3 \\ 2 \\ 1 \end{bmatrix} \begin{pmatrix} 1 & 2 & 3 \end{pmatrix} + \begin{bmatrix} 1 \\ 4 \\ 2 \end{bmatrix} \begin{pmatrix} 2 & 4 & 1 \end{pmatrix}$$

$$= \begin{bmatrix} 3 & 6 & 9 \\ 2 & 4 & 6 \\ 1 & 2 & 3 \end{bmatrix} + \begin{bmatrix} 2 & 4 & 1 \\ 8 & 16 & 4 \\ 4 & 8 & 2 \end{bmatrix}$$

SECTION 1.6 EXERCISES

1. Let A be a nonsingular $n \times n$ matrix. Perform the following multiplications:

(a) $A^{-1} \begin{bmatrix} A & I \end{bmatrix}$

(b) $\begin{bmatrix} A \\ I \end{bmatrix} A^{-1}$

(c) $\begin{bmatrix} A & I \end{bmatrix}^T \begin{bmatrix} A & I \end{bmatrix}$

(d) $\begin{bmatrix} A & I \end{bmatrix} \begin{bmatrix} A & I \end{bmatrix}^T$

(e) $\begin{bmatrix} A^{-1} \\ I \end{bmatrix} \begin{bmatrix} A & I \end{bmatrix}$

2. Let $B = A^T A$. Show that $b_{ij} = \mathbf{a}_i^T \mathbf{a}_j$.

3. Let

$$A = \begin{bmatrix} 1 & 1 \\ 2 & -1 \end{bmatrix} \quad \text{and} \quad B = \begin{bmatrix} 2 & 1 \\ 1 & 3 \end{bmatrix}$$

(a) Calculate $A\mathbf{b}_1$ and $A\mathbf{b}_2$.

(b) Calculate $\vec{\mathbf{a}}_1 B$ and $\vec{\mathbf{a}}_2 B$.

(c) Multiply AB and verify that its column vectors are the vectors in part (a) and its row vectors are the vectors in part (b).

4. Let

$$I = \begin{bmatrix} 1 & 0 \\ 0 & 1 \end{bmatrix}, \quad E = \begin{bmatrix} 0 & 1 \\ 1 & 0 \end{bmatrix}, \quad O = \begin{bmatrix} 0 & 0 \\ 0 & 0 \end{bmatrix}$$

$$C = \begin{bmatrix} 1 & 0 \\ -1 & 1 \end{bmatrix}, \quad D = \begin{bmatrix} 2 & 0 \\ 0 & 2 \end{bmatrix}$$

and

$$B = \begin{bmatrix} B_{11} & B_{12} \\ B_{21} & B_{22} \end{bmatrix} = \begin{bmatrix} 1 & 1 & 1 & 1 \\ 1 & 2 & 1 & 1 \\ 3 & 1 & 1 & 1 \\ 3 & 2 & 1 & 2 \end{bmatrix}$$

Perform each of the following block multiplications:

(a) $\begin{bmatrix} O & I \\ I & O \end{bmatrix} \begin{bmatrix} B_{11} & B_{12} \\ B_{21} & B_{22} \end{bmatrix}$

(b) $\begin{bmatrix} C & O \\ O & C \end{bmatrix} \begin{bmatrix} B_{11} & B_{12} \\ B_{21} & B_{22} \end{bmatrix}$

(c) $\begin{bmatrix} D & O \\ O & I \end{bmatrix} \begin{bmatrix} B_{11} & B_{12} \\ B_{21} & B_{22} \end{bmatrix}$

(d) $\begin{bmatrix} E & O \\ O & E \end{bmatrix} \begin{bmatrix} B_{11} & B_{12} \\ B_{21} & B_{22} \end{bmatrix}$

5. Perform each of the following block multiplications:

(a) $\begin{bmatrix} 1 & 1 & 1 & -1 \\ 2 & 1 & 2 & -1 \end{bmatrix} \begin{bmatrix} 4 & -2 & 1 \\ 2 & 3 & 1 \\ 1 & 1 & 2 \\ 1 & 2 & 3 \end{bmatrix}$

(b) $\begin{bmatrix} 4 & -2 \\ 2 & 3 \\ 1 & 1 \\ 1 & 2 \end{bmatrix} \begin{bmatrix} 1 & 1 & 1 & -1 \\ 2 & 1 & 2 & -1 \end{bmatrix}$

(c) $\begin{bmatrix} \frac{3}{5} & -\frac{4}{5} & 0 & 0 \\ \frac{4}{5} & \frac{3}{5} & 0 & 0 \\ 0 & 0 & 1 & 0 \end{bmatrix} \begin{bmatrix} \frac{3}{5} & \frac{4}{5} & 0 \\ -\frac{4}{5} & \frac{3}{5} & 0 \\ 0 & 0 & 1 \\ 0 & 0 & 0 \end{bmatrix}$

(d) $\begin{bmatrix} 0 & 0 & 1 & 0 & 0 \\ 0 & 1 & 0 & 0 & 0 \\ 1 & 0 & 0 & 0 & 0 \\ 0 & 0 & 0 & 0 & 1 \\ 0 & 0 & 0 & 1 & 0 \end{bmatrix} \begin{bmatrix} 1 & -1 \\ 2 & -2 \\ 3 & -3 \\ 4 & -4 \\ 5 & -5 \end{bmatrix}$

6. Given

$$X = \begin{bmatrix} 2 & 1 & 5 \\ 4 & 2 & 3 \end{bmatrix}, \qquad Y = \begin{bmatrix} 1 & 2 & 4 \\ 2 & 3 & 1 \end{bmatrix}$$

(a) Compute the outer product expansion of XY^T.

(b) Compute the outer product expansion of YX^T. How is the outer product expansion of YX^T related to the outer product expansion of XY^T?

7. Let

$$A = \begin{bmatrix} A_{11} & A_{12} \\ A_{21} & A_{22} \end{bmatrix} \quad \text{and} \quad A^T = \begin{bmatrix} A_{11}^T & A_{21}^T \\ A_{12}^T & A_{22}^T \end{bmatrix}$$

Is it possible to perform the block multiplications of AA^T and A^TA? Explain.

8. Let A be an $m \times n$ matrix, X an $n \times r$ matrix, and B an $m \times r$ matrix. Show that

$$AX = B$$

if and only if

$$A\mathbf{x}_j = \mathbf{b}_j, \quad j = 1, \ldots, r$$

9. Let A be an $n \times n$ matrix and let D be an $n \times n$ diagonal matrix.

(a) Show that $D = (d_{11}\mathbf{e}_1, d_{22}\mathbf{e}_2, \ldots, d_{nn}\mathbf{e}_n)$.

(b) Show that $AD = (d_{11}\mathbf{a}_1, d_{22}\mathbf{a}_2, \ldots, d_{nn}\mathbf{a}_n)$.

10. Let U be an $m \times m$ matrix, let V be an $n \times n$ matrix, and let

$$\Sigma = \begin{bmatrix} \Sigma_1 \\ O \end{bmatrix}$$

where Σ_1 is an $n \times n$ diagonal matrix with diagonal entries $\sigma_1, \sigma_2, \ldots, \sigma_n$ and O is the $(m-n) \times n$ zero matrix.

(a) Show that if $U = (U_1, U_2)$, where U_1 has n columns, then

$$U\Sigma = U_1\Sigma_1$$

(b) Show that if $A = U\Sigma V^T$, then A can be expressed as an outer product expansion of the form

$$A = \sigma_1 \mathbf{u}_1 \mathbf{v}_1^T + \sigma_2 \mathbf{u}_2 \mathbf{v}_2^T + \cdots + \sigma_n \mathbf{u}_n \mathbf{v}_n^T$$

11. Let

$$A = \begin{bmatrix} A_{11} & A_{12} \\ O & A_{22} \end{bmatrix}$$

where all four blocks are $n \times n$ matrices.

(a) If A_{11} and A_{22} are nonsingular, show that A must also be nonsingular and that A^{-1} must be of the form

$$\begin{bmatrix} A_{11}^{-1} & C \\ \hline O & A_{22}^{-1} \end{bmatrix}$$

(b) Determine C.

12. Let A and B be $n \times n$ matrices and let M be a block matrix of the form

$$M = \begin{bmatrix} A & O \\ O & B \end{bmatrix}$$

Use condition (b) of Theorem 1.5.2 to show that if either A or B is singular, then M must be singular.

13. Let

$$A = \begin{bmatrix} O & I \\ B & O \end{bmatrix}$$

where all four submatrices are $k \times k$. Determine A^2 and A^4.

14. Let I denote the $n \times n$ identity matrix. Find a block form for the inverse of each of the following $2n \times 2n$ matrices:

(a) $\begin{bmatrix} O & I \\ I & O \end{bmatrix}$

(b) $\begin{bmatrix} I & O \\ B & I \end{bmatrix}$

15. Let O be the $k \times k$ matrix whose entries are all 0, I be the $k \times k$ identity matrix, and B be a $k \times k$ matrix with the property that $B^2 = O$. If

$$A = \begin{pmatrix} O & I \\ I & B \end{pmatrix}$$

determine the block form of $A^{-1} + A^2 + A^3$.

16. Let A and B be $n \times n$ matrices and define $2n \times 2n$ matrices S and M by

$$S = \begin{pmatrix} I & A \\ O & I \end{pmatrix}, \qquad M = \begin{pmatrix} AB & O \\ B & O \end{pmatrix}$$

Determine the block form of S^{-1} and use it to compute the block form of the product $S^{-1}MS$.

17. Let

$$A = \begin{pmatrix} A_{11} & A_{12} \\ A_{21} & A_{22} \end{pmatrix}$$

where A_{11} is a $k \times k$ nonsingular matrix. Show that A can be factored into a product

$$\begin{pmatrix} I & O \\ B & I \end{pmatrix} \begin{pmatrix} A_{11} & A_{12} \\ O & C \end{pmatrix}$$

where

$$B = A_{21}A_{11}^{-1} \qquad \text{and} \qquad C = A_{22} - A_{21}A_{11}^{-1}A_{12}$$

(Note that this problem gives a block matrix version of the factorization in Exercise 18 of Section 1.3.)

18. Let A, B, L, M, S, and T be $n \times n$ matrices with A, B, and M nonsingular and L, S, and T singular. Determine whether it is possible to find matrices X and Y such that

$$\begin{pmatrix} O & I & O & O & O & O \\ O & O & I & O & O & O \\ O & O & O & I & O & O \\ O & O & O & O & I & O \\ O & O & O & O & O & X \\ Y & O & O & O & O & O \end{pmatrix} \begin{pmatrix} M \\ A \\ T \\ L \\ A \\ B \end{pmatrix} = \begin{pmatrix} A \\ T \\ L \\ A \\ S \\ T \end{pmatrix}$$

If so, show how; if not, explain why.

19. Let A be an $n \times n$ matrix and $\mathbf{x} \in \mathbb{R}^n$.

(a) A scalar c can also be considered as a 1×1 matrix $C = (c)$, and a vector $\mathbf{b} \in \mathbb{R}^n$ can be considered as an $n \times 1$ matrix B. Although the matrix multiplication CB is not defined, show that the matrix product BC is equal to $c\mathbf{b}$, the scalar multiplication of c times $\mathbf{b}$.

(b) Partition A into columns and $\mathbf{x}$ into rows and perform the block multiplication of A times $\mathbf{x}$.

(c) Show that

$$A\mathbf{x} = x_1\mathbf{a}_1 + x_2\mathbf{a}_2 + \cdots + x_n\mathbf{a}_n$$

20. If A is an $n \times n$ matrix with the property that $A\mathbf{x} = \mathbf{0}$ for all $\mathbf{x} \in \mathbb{R}^n$, show that $A = O$. *Hint:* Let $\mathbf{x} = \mathbf{e}_j$ for $j = 1, \ldots, n$.

21. Let B and C be $n \times n$ matrices with the property that $B\mathbf{x} = C\mathbf{x}$ for all $\mathbf{x} \in \mathbb{R}^n$. Show that $B = C$.

22. Consider a system of the form

$$\begin{pmatrix} A & \mathbf{a} \\ \mathbf{c}^T & \beta \end{pmatrix} \begin{pmatrix} \mathbf{x} \\ x_{n+1} \end{pmatrix} = \begin{pmatrix} \mathbf{b} \\ b_{n+1} \end{pmatrix}$$

where A is a nonsingular $n \times n$ matrix and $\mathbf{a}$, $\mathbf{b}$, and $\mathbf{c}$ are vectors in $\mathbb{R}^n$.

(a) Multiply both sides of the system by

$$\begin{pmatrix} A^{-1} & \mathbf{0} \\ -\mathbf{c}^T A^{-1} & 1 \end{pmatrix}$$

to obtain an equivalent triangular system.

(b) Set $\mathbf{y} = A^{-1}\mathbf{a}$ and $\mathbf{z} = A^{-1}\mathbf{b}$. Show that if $\beta - \mathbf{c}^T\mathbf{y} \neq 0$, then the solution of the system can be determined by letting

$$x_{n+1} = \frac{b_{n+1} - \mathbf{c}^T\mathbf{z}}{\beta - \mathbf{c}^T\mathbf{y}}$$

and then setting

$$\mathbf{x} = \mathbf{z} - x_{n+1}\mathbf{y}$$

Chapter I Exercises

MATLAB EXERCISES

The exercises that follow are to be solved computationally with the software package MATLAB, which is described in the appendix of this book. The exercises also contain questions that are related to the underlying mathematical principles illustrated in the computations. Save a record of your session in a file. After editing and printing out the file, you can fill in the answers to the questions directly on the printout.

MATLAB has a help facility that explains all its operations and commands. For example, to obtain information on the MATLAB command **rand**, *you need only type* `help rand` *The commands used in the MATLAB exercises for this chapter are* **inv, floor, rand, tic, toc, rref, abs, max, round, sum, eye, triu, ones, zeros,** *and* **magic**. *The operations introduced are* $+, -, *, ',$ *and* \. *The* $+$ *and* $-$ *represent the usual addition and subtraction operations for both scalars and matrices. The* $*$ *corresponds to multiplication of either scalars or matrices. For matrices whose entries are all real numbers, the* $'$ *operation corresponds to the transpose operation. If A is a nonsingular* $n \times n$ *matrix and B is any* $n \times r$ *matrix, the operation* $A \backslash B$ *is equivalent to computing* $A^{-1}B$.

1. Use MATLAB to generate random 4×4 matrices A and B. For each of the following, compute $A1$, $A2$, $A3$, and $A4$ as indicated and determine which of the matrices are equal (you can use MATLAB to test whether two matrices are equal by computing their difference).

   (a) $A1 = A * B$, $A2 = B * A$, $A3 = (A' * B')'$, $A4 = (B' * A')'$

   (b) $A1 = A' * B'$, $A2 = (A * B)'$, $A3 = B' * A'$, $A4 = (B * A)'$

   (c) $A1 = \text{inv}(A * B)$, $A2 = \text{inv}(A) * \text{inv}(B)$, $A3 = \text{inv}(B * A)$, $A4 = \text{inv}(B) * \text{inv}(A)$

   (d) $A1 = \text{inv}((A * B)')$, $A2 = \text{inv}(A' * B')$, $A3 = \text{inv}(A') * \text{inv}(B')$, $A4 = (\text{inv}(A) * \text{inv}(B))'$

2. Set $n = 200$ and generate an $n \times n$ matrix and two vectors in $\mathbb{R}^n$, both having integer entries, by setting

   $$A = \text{floor}(10 * \text{rand}(n));$$
   $$\mathbf{b} = \text{sum}(A')';$$
   $$\mathbf{z} = \text{ones}(n, 1);$$

   (Since the matrix and vectors are large, we use semicolons to suppress the printout.)

   (a) The exact solution of the system $A\mathbf{x} = \mathbf{b}$ should be the vector $\mathbf{z}$. Why? Explain. One could compute the solution in MATLAB using the "\" operation or by computing A^{-1} and then multiplying A^{-1} times $\mathbf{b}$. Let us compare these two computational methods for both speed and accuracy. One can use MATLAB's **tic** and **toc** commands to measure the elapsed time for each computation. To do this, use the commands

   $$\text{tic, } \mathbf{x} = A \backslash \mathbf{b}; \text{ toc}$$
   $$\text{tic, } \mathbf{y} = \text{inv}(A) * \mathbf{b}; \text{ toc}$$

   Which method is faster?

To compare the accuracy of the two methods, we can measure how close the computed solutions $\mathbf{x}$ and $\mathbf{y}$ are to the exact solution $\mathbf{z}$. Do this with the commands

$$\text{max(abs}(\mathbf{x} - \mathbf{z}))$$
$$\text{max(abs}(\mathbf{y} - \mathbf{z}))$$

Which method produces the most accurate solution?

   (b) Repeat part (a), using $n = 500$ and $n = 1000$.

3. Set $A = \text{floor}(10 * \text{rand}(6))$. By construction, the matrix A will have integer entries. Let us change the sixth column of A so as to make the matrix singular. Set

   $$B = A', \qquad A(:, 6) = -\text{sum}(B(1:5, :))'$$

   (a) Set $\mathbf{x} = \text{ones}(6, 1)$ and use MATLAB to compute $A\mathbf{x}$. Why do we know that A must be singular? Explain. Check that A is singular by computing its reduced row echelon form.

   (b) Set

   $$B = \mathbf{x} * [1:6]$$

   The product AB should equal the zero matrix. Why? Explain. Verify that this is so by computing AB with the MATLAB operation $*$.

   (c) Set
   $$C = \text{floor}(10 * \text{rand}(6))$$

   and

   $$D = B + C$$

   Although $C \neq D$, the products AC and AD should be equal. Why? Explain. Compute $A * C$ and $A * D$, and verify that they are indeed equal.

4. Construct a matrix as follows: Set

   $$B = \text{eye}(10) - \text{triu}(\text{ones}(10), 1)$$

   Why do we know that B must be nonsingular? Set

   $$C = \text{inv}(B) \qquad \text{and} \qquad \mathbf{x} = C(:, 10)$$

   Now change B slightly by setting $B(10, 1) = -1/256$. Use MATLAB to compute the product $B\mathbf{x}$. From the result of this computation, what can you conclude about the new matrix B? Is it still nonsingular? Explain. Use MATLAB to compute its reduced row echelon form.

5. Generate a matrix A by setting

$$A = \texttt{floor}(10 * \texttt{rand}(6))$$

and generate a vector **b** by setting

$$\mathbf{b} = \texttt{floor}(20 * \texttt{rand}(6,1)) - 10$$

(a) Since A was generated randomly, we would expect it to be nonsingular. The system $A\mathbf{x} = \mathbf{b}$ should have a unique solution. Find the solution using the "\" operation. Use MATLAB to compute the reduced row echelon form U of $[A\ \mathbf{b}]$. How does the last column of U compare with the solution $\mathbf{x}$? In exact arithmetic, they should be the same. Why? Explain. To compare the two, compute the difference $U(:, 7) - \mathbf{x}$ or examine both using **format long**.

(b) Let us now change A so as to make it singular. Set

$$A(:,3) = A(:,1:2) * [4\ 3]'$$

Use MATLAB to compute $\texttt{rref}([A\ \mathbf{b}])$. How many solutions will the system $A\mathbf{x} = \mathbf{b}$ have? Explain.

(c) Set

$$\mathbf{y} = \texttt{floor}(20 * \texttt{rand}(6,1)) - 10$$

and

$$\mathbf{c} = A * \mathbf{y}$$

Why do we know that the system $A\mathbf{x} = \mathbf{c}$ must be consistent? Explain. Compute the reduced row echelon form U of $[A\ \mathbf{c}]$. How many solutions does the system $A\mathbf{x} = \mathbf{c}$ have? Explain.

(d) The free variable determined by the echelon form should be x_3. By examining the system corresponding to the matrix U, you should be able to determine the solution corresponding to $x_3 = 0$. Enter this solution into MATLAB as a column vector **w**. To check that $A\mathbf{w} = \mathbf{c}$, compute the residual vector $\mathbf{c} - A\mathbf{w}$.

(e) Set $U(:, 7) = \texttt{zeros}(6, 1)$. The matrix U should now correspond to the reduced row echelon form of $(A\ |\ \mathbf{0})$. Use U to determine the solution of the homogeneous system when the free variable $x_3 = 1$ (do this by hand) and enter your result as a vector **z**. Check your answer by computing $A * \mathbf{z}$.

(f) Set $\mathbf{v} = \mathbf{w} + 3 * \mathbf{z}$. The vector **v** should be a solution of the system $A\mathbf{x} = \mathbf{c}$. Why? Explain. Verify that **v** is a solution by using MATLAB to compute the residual vector $\mathbf{c} - A\mathbf{v}$. What is the value of the free variable x_3 for this solution? How could we determine all possible solutions of the system in terms of the vectors **w** and **z**? Explain.

6. Consider the graph

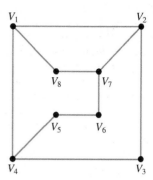

(a) Determine the adjacency matrix A for the graph and enter it in MATLAB.

(b) Compute A^2 and determine the number of walks of length 2 from (i) V_1 to V_7, (ii) V_4 to V_8, (iii) V_5 to V_6, and (iv) V_8 to V_3.

(c) Compute A^4, A^6, and A^8 and answer the questions in part (b) for walks of lengths 4, 6, and 8. Make a conjecture as to when there will be no walks of even length from vertex V_i to vertex V_j.

(d) Compute A^3, A^5, and A^7 and answer the questions from part (b) for walks of lengths 3, 5, and 7. Does your conjecture from part (c) hold for walks of odd length? Explain. Make a conjecture as to whether there are any walks of length k from V_i to V_j based on whether $i + j + k$ is odd or even.

(e) If we add the edges $\{V_3, V_6\}$, $\{V_5, V_8\}$ to the graph, the adjacency matrix B for the new graph can be generated by setting $B = A$ and then setting

$$B(3,6) = 1, \qquad B(6,3) = 1,$$
$$B(5,8) = 1, \qquad B(8,5) = 1$$

Compute B^k for $k = 2, 3, 4, 5$. Is your conjecture from part (d) still valid for the new graph?

(f) Add the edge $\{V_6, V_8\}$ to the figure and construct the adjacency matrix C for the resulting graph. Compute powers of C to determine whether your conjecture from part (d) will still hold for this new graph.

7. In Application 1 of Section 1.4, the numbers of married and single women after 1 and 2 years were determined by computing the products AX and A^2X for the given matrices A and X. Use **format long** and enter these matrices in MATLAB. Compute A^k and A^kX for $k = 5, 10, 15, 20$. What is happening to A^k as k gets large? What is the long-run distribution of married and single women in the town?

8. The following table describes a seven-stage model for the life cycle of the loggerhead sea turtle:

Seven-Stage Model for Loggerhead Sea Turtle Demographics

Stage Number	Description (age in years)	Annual Survivorship	Eggs Laid per Year
1	Eggs, hatchlings (<1)	0.6747	0
2	Small juveniles (1–7)	0.7857	0
3	Large juveniles (8–15)	0.6758	0
4	Subadults (16–21)	0.7425	0
5	Novice breeders (22)	0.8091	127
6	First-year remigrants (23)	0.8091	4
7	Mature breeders (24–54)	0.8091	80

The corresponding Leslie matrix is

$$L = \begin{bmatrix} 0 & 0 & 0 & 0 & 127 & 4 & 80 \\ 0.6747 & 0.7370 & 0 & 0 & 0 & 0 & 0 \\ 0 & 0.0486 & 0.6610 & 0 & 0 & 0 & 0 \\ 0 & 0 & 0.0147 & 0.6907 & 0 & 0 & 0 \\ 0 & 0 & 0 & 0.0518 & 0 & 0 & 0 \\ 0 & 0 & 0 & 0 & 0.8091 & 0 & 0 \\ 0 & 0 & 0 & 0 & 0 & 0.8091 & 0.8089 \end{bmatrix}$$

Suppose that the number of turtles in each stage of the initial turtle population is described by the vector

$$\mathbf{x}_0 = (200,000 \quad 130,000 \quad 100,000 \quad 70,000 \quad 500 \quad 400 \quad 1100)^T$$

(a) Enter L into MATLAB and then set

x0 = [200000, 130000, 100000, 70000, 500, 400, 1100]′

Use the command

$$x50 = \text{round}(L\hat{\,}50 * x0)$$

to compute $\mathbf{x}_{50}$. Compute also the values of $\mathbf{x}_{100}$, $\mathbf{x}_{150}$, $\mathbf{x}_{200}$, $\mathbf{x}_{250}$, and $\mathbf{x}_{300}$.

(b) Loggerhead sea turtles lay their eggs on land. Suppose that conservationists take special measures to protect these eggs and, as a result, the survival rate for eggs and hatchlings increases to 77 percent. To incorporate this change into our model, we need only change the (2,1) entry of L to 0.77. Make this modification to the matrix L and repeat part (a). Has the survival potential of the loggerhead sea turtle improved significantly?

(c) Suppose that, instead of improving the survival rate for eggs and hatchlings, we could devise a means of protecting the small juveniles so that their survival rate increases to 88 percent. Use equations (1) and

(2) from Application 2 of Section 1.4 to determine the proportion of small juveniles that survive and remain in the same stage and the proportion that survive and grow to the next stage. Modify your original matrix L accordingly and repeat part (a), using the new matrix. Has the survival potential of the loggerhead sea turtle improved significantly?

9. Set $A = \textbf{magic}(8)$ and then compute its reduced row echelon form. The leading 1's should correspond to the first three variables x_1, x_2, and x_3, and the remaining five variables are all free.

(a) Set $\mathbf{c} = [1 : 8]′$ and determine whether the system $A\mathbf{x} = \mathbf{c}$ is consistent by computing the reduced row echelon form of $[A \ \mathbf{c}]$. Does the system turn out to be consistent? Explain.

(b) Set

$$\mathbf{b} = [8 \ -8 \ -8 \ 8 \ 8 \ -8 \ -8 \ 8]′;$$

and consider the system $A\mathbf{x} = \mathbf{b}$. This system should be consistent. Verify that it is by computing $U = \textbf{rref}([A \ \mathbf{b}])$. We should be able to find a solution for any choice of the five free variables. Indeed, set $\mathbf{x2} = \mathbf{floor}(10 * \mathbf{rand}(5, 1))$. If $\mathbf{x2}$ represents the last five coordinates of a solution of the system, then we should be able to determine $\mathbf{x1} = (x_1, x_2, x_3)^T$ in terms of $\mathbf{x2}$. To do this, set $U = \mathbf{rref}([A \quad \mathbf{b}])$. The nonzero rows of U correspond to a linear system with block form

$$\begin{bmatrix} I & V \end{bmatrix} \begin{bmatrix} \mathbf{x1} \\ \mathbf{x2} \end{bmatrix} = \mathbf{c} \qquad (1)$$

To solve equation (1), set

$$V = U(1:3, 4:8), \quad \mathbf{c} = U(1:3, 9)$$

and use MATLAB to compute $\mathbf{x1}$ in terms of $\mathbf{x2}$, $\mathbf{c}$, and V. Set $\mathbf{x} = [\mathbf{x1}; \quad \mathbf{x2}]$ and verify that $\mathbf{x}$ is a solution of the system.

10. Set

$$B = [-1, -1; \ 1, 1]$$

and

$$A = [\mathbf{zeros}(2), \mathbf{eye}(2); \ \mathbf{eye}(2), B]$$

and verify that $B^2 = O$.

(a) Use MATLAB to compute A^2, A^4, A^6, and A^8. Make a conjecture as to what the block form of A^{2k} will be in terms of the submatrices I, O, and B. Use mathematical induction to prove that your conjecture is true for any positive integer k.

(b) Use MATLAB to compute A^3, A^5, A^7, and A^9. Make a conjecture as to what the block form of A^{2k-1} will

be in terms of the submatrices I, O, and B. Prove your conjecture.

11. (a) The MATLAB commands

$$A = \mathbf{floor}(10 * \mathbf{rand}(6)), \quad B = A' * A$$

will result in a symmetric matrix with integer entries. Why? Explain. Compute B in this way and verify these claims. Next, partition B into four 3×3 submatrices. To determine the submatrices in MATLAB, set

$$B11 = B(1:3, 1:3), \quad B12 = B(1:3, 4:6)$$

and define $B21$ and $B22$ in a similar manner using rows 4 through 6 of B.

(b) Set $C = \mathbf{inv}(B11)$. It should be the case that $C^T = C$ and $B21^T = B12$. Why? Explain. Use the MATLAB operation $'$ to compute the transposes and verify these claims. Next, set

$$E = B21 * C \quad \text{and} \quad F = B22 - B21 * C * B21'$$

and use the MATLAB functions $\mathbf{eye}$ and $\mathbf{zeros}$ to construct

$$L = \begin{bmatrix} I & O \\ E & I \end{bmatrix}, \quad D = \begin{bmatrix} B11 & O \\ O & F \end{bmatrix}$$

Compute $H = L * D * L'$ and compare H with B by computing $H - B$. Prove that if all computations had been done in exact arithmetic, LDL^T would equal B exactly.

CHAPTER TEST A   True or False

This chapter test consists of true or false questions. In each case, answer *true* if the statement is always true and *false* otherwise. In the case of a true statement, explain or prove your answer. In the case of a false statement, give an example to show that the statement is not always true. For example, consider the following statements about $n \times n$ matrices A and B:

(i) $A + B = B + A$

(ii) $AB = BA$

Statement **(i)** is always *true*. Explanation: The (i, j) entry of $A + B$ is $a_{ij} + b_{ij}$ and the (i, j) entry of $B + A$ is $b_{ij} + a_{ij}$. Since $a_{ij} + b_{ij} = b_{ij} + a_{ij}$ for each i and j, it follows that $A + B = B + A$.

The answer to statement **(ii)** is *false*. Although the statement may be true in some cases, it is not always true. To show this, we need only exhibit one instance in which equality fails to hold. For example, if

$$A = \begin{bmatrix} 1 & 2 \\ 3 & 1 \end{bmatrix} \quad \text{and} \quad B = \begin{bmatrix} 2 & 3 \\ 1 & 1 \end{bmatrix}$$

then

$$AB = \begin{bmatrix} 4 & 5 \\ 7 & 10 \end{bmatrix} \quad \text{and} \quad BA = \begin{bmatrix} 11 & 7 \\ 4 & 3 \end{bmatrix}$$

This proves that statement **(ii)** is false.

1. If the row reduced echelon form of A involves free variables, then the system $A\mathbf{x} = \mathbf{b}$ will have infinitely many solutions.

2. Every homogeneous linear system is consistent.

3. An $n \times n$ matrix A is nonsingular if and only if the reduced row echelon form of A is I (the identity matrix).

4. If A is nonsingular, then A can be factored into a product of elementary matrices.

5. If A and B are nonsingular $n \times n$ matrices, then $A + B$ is also nonsingular and $(A + B)^{-1} = A^{-1} + B^{-1}$.

6. If $A = A^{-1}$, then A must be equal to either I or $-I$.

7. If A and B are $n \times n$ matrices, then $(A - B)^2 = A^2 - 2AB + B^2$.

8. If $AB = AC$ and $A \neq O$ (the zero matrix), then $B = C$.

9. If $AB = O$, then $BA = O$.

10. If A is a 3×3 matrix and $\mathbf{a}_1 + 2\mathbf{a}_2 - \mathbf{a}_3 = \mathbf{0}$, then A must be singular.

11. If A is a 4×3 matrix and $\mathbf{b} = \mathbf{a}_1 + \mathbf{a}_3$, then the system $A\mathbf{x} = \mathbf{b}$ must be consistent.

12. Let A be a 4×3 matrix with $\mathbf{a}_2 = \mathbf{a}_3$. If $\mathbf{b} = \mathbf{a}_1 + \mathbf{a}_2 + \mathbf{a}_3$, then the system $A\mathbf{x} = \mathbf{b}$ will have infinitely many solutions.

13. If E is an elementary matrix, then E^T is also an elementary matrix.

14. The product of two elementary matrices is an elementary matrix.

15. If $\mathbf{x}$ and $\mathbf{y}$ are nonzero vectors in $\mathbb{R}^n$ and $A = \mathbf{x}\mathbf{y}^T$, then the row echelon form of A will have exactly one nonzero row.

CHAPTER TEST B

1. Find all solutions of the linear system

$$
\begin{aligned}
x_1 - x_2 + 3x_3 + 2x_4 &= 1 \\
-x_1 + x_2 - 2x_3 + x_4 &= -2 \\
2x_1 - 2x_2 + 7x_3 + 7x_4 &= 1
\end{aligned}
$$

2.(a) A linear equation in two unknowns corresponds to a line in the plane. Give a similar geometric interpretation of a linear equation in three unknowns.

(b) Given a linear system consisting of two equations in three unknowns, what is the possible number of solutions? Give a geometric explanation of your answer.

(c) Given a homogeneous linear system consisting of two equations in three unknowns, how many solutions will it have? Explain.

3. Let $A\mathbf{x} = \mathbf{b}$ be a system of n linear equations in n unknowns and suppose that $\mathbf{x}_1$ and $\mathbf{x}_2$ are both solutions and $\mathbf{x}_1 \neq \mathbf{x}_2$.

(a) How many solutions will the system have? Explain.

(b) Is the matrix A nonsingular? Explain.

4. Let A be a matrix of the form

$$
A = \begin{bmatrix} \alpha & \beta \\ 2\alpha & 2\beta \end{bmatrix}
$$

where α and β are fixed scalars not both equal to 0.

(a) Explain why the system

$$
A\mathbf{x} = \begin{bmatrix} 3 \\ 1 \end{bmatrix}
$$

must be inconsistent.

(b) How can one choose a nonzero vector $\mathbf{b}$ so that the system $A\mathbf{x} = \mathbf{b}$ will be consistent? Explain.

5. Let

$$
A = \begin{bmatrix} 2 & 1 & 3 \\ 4 & 2 & 7 \\ 1 & 3 & 5 \end{bmatrix}, \quad
B = \begin{bmatrix} 2 & 1 & 3 \\ 1 & 3 & 5 \\ 4 & 2 & 7 \end{bmatrix},
$$

$$
C = \begin{bmatrix} 0 & 1 & 3 \\ 0 & 2 & 7 \\ -5 & 3 & 5 \end{bmatrix}
$$

(a) Find an elementary matrix E such that $EA = B$.

(b) Find an elementary matrix F such that $AF = C$.

6. Let A be a 3×3 matrix and let

$$
\mathbf{b} = 3\mathbf{a}_1 + \mathbf{a}_2 + 4\mathbf{a}_3
$$

Will the system $A\mathbf{x} = \mathbf{b}$ be consistent? Explain.

7. Let A be a 3×3 matrix and suppose that

$$
\mathbf{a}_1 - 3\mathbf{a}_2 + 2\mathbf{a}_3 = \mathbf{0} \text{ (the zero vector)}
$$

Is A nonsingular? Explain.

8. Given the vector

$$
\mathbf{x}_0 = \begin{bmatrix} 1 \\ 1 \end{bmatrix}
$$

is it possible to find 2×2 matrices A and B so that $A \neq B$ and $A\mathbf{x}_0 = B\mathbf{x}_0$? Explain.

9. Let A and B be symmetric $n \times n$ matrices and let $C = AB$. Is C symmetric? Explain.

10. Let E and F be $n \times n$ elementary matrices and let $C = EF$. Is C nonsingular? Explain.

11. Given

$$
A = \begin{bmatrix} I & O & O \\ O & I & O \\ O & B & I \end{bmatrix}
$$

where all of the submatrices are $n \times n$, determine the block form of A^{-1}.

12. Let A and B be 10×10 matrices that are partitioned into submatrices as follows:

$$
A = \begin{bmatrix} A_{11} & A_{12} \\ A_{21} & A_{22} \end{bmatrix}, \quad
B = \begin{bmatrix} B_{11} & B_{12} \\ B_{21} & B_{22} \end{bmatrix}
$$

(a) If A_{11} is a 6×5 matrix, and B_{11} is a $k \times r$ matrix, what conditions, if any, must k and r satisfy in order to make the block multiplication of A times B possible?

(b) Assuming that the block multiplication is possible, how would the $(2, 2)$ block of the product be determined?

CHAPTER

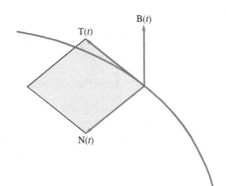

2

Determinants

With each square matrix, it is possible to associate a real number called the determinant of the matrix. The value of this number will tell us whether the matrix is singular.

In Section 2.1, the definition of the determinant of a matrix is given. In Section 2.2, we study properties of determinants and derive an elimination method for evaluating determinants. The elimination method is generally the simplest method to use for evaluating the determinant of an $n \times n$ matrix when $n > 3$. In Section 2.3, we see how determinants can be applied to solving $n \times n$ linear systems and how they can be used to calculate the inverse of a matrix. Two applications of determinants are presented in Section 2.3. Additional applications will also be presented later in Chapters 3 and 6.

2.1 The Determinant of a Matrix

With each $n \times n$ matrix A, it is possible to associate a scalar, $\det(A)$, whose value will tell us whether the matrix is nonsingular. Before proceeding to the general definition, let us consider the following cases.

Case 1. 1 × 1 Matrices If $A = (a)$ is a 1×1 matrix, then A will have a multiplicative inverse if and only if $a \neq 0$. Thus, if we define

$$\det(A) = a$$

then A will be nonsingular if and only if $\det(A) \neq 0$.

Case 2. 2 × 2 Matrices Let

$$A = \begin{bmatrix} a_{11} & a_{12} \\ a_{21} & a_{22} \end{bmatrix}$$

By Theorem 1.5.2, A will be nonsingular if and only if it is row equivalent to I. Then, if $a_{11} \neq 0$, we can test whether A is row equivalent to I by performing the following operations:

1. Multiply the second row of A by a_{11}:

$$\begin{pmatrix} a_{11} & a_{12} \\ a_{11}a_{21} & a_{11}a_{22} \end{pmatrix}$$

2. Subtract a_{21} times the first row from the new second row:

$$\begin{pmatrix} a_{11} & a_{12} \\ 0 & a_{11}a_{22} - a_{21}a_{12} \end{pmatrix}$$

Since $a_{11} \neq 0$, the resulting matrix will be row equivalent to I if and only if

$$a_{11}a_{22} - a_{21}a_{12} \neq 0 \tag{1}$$

If $a_{11} = 0$, we can switch the two rows of A. The resulting matrix

$$\begin{pmatrix} a_{21} & a_{22} \\ 0 & a_{12} \end{pmatrix}$$

will be row equivalent to I if and only if $a_{21}a_{12} \neq 0$. This requirement is equivalent to condition (1) when $a_{11} = 0$. Thus, if A is any 2×2 matrix and we define

$$\det(A) = a_{11}a_{22} - a_{12}a_{21}$$

then A is nonsingular if and only if $\det(A) \neq 0$.

Notation

We can refer to the determinant of a specific matrix by enclosing the array between vertical lines. For example, if

$$A = \begin{pmatrix} 3 & 4 \\ 2 & 1 \end{pmatrix}$$

then

$$\begin{vmatrix} 3 & 4 \\ 2 & 1 \end{vmatrix}$$

represents the determinant of A.

Case 3. 3 × 3 Matrices We can test whether a 3×3 matrix is nonsingular by performing row operations to see if the matrix is row equivalent to the identity matrix I. To carry out the elimination in the first column of an arbitrary 3×3 matrix A, let us first assume that $a_{11} \neq 0$. The elimination can then be performed by subtracting a_{21}/a_{11} times the first row from the second and a_{31}/a_{11} times the first row from the third:

$$\begin{pmatrix} a_{11} & a_{12} & a_{13} \\ a_{21} & a_{22} & a_{23} \\ a_{31} & a_{32} & a_{33} \end{pmatrix} \rightarrow \begin{pmatrix} a_{11} & a_{12} & a_{13} \\ 0 & \dfrac{a_{11}a_{22} - a_{21}a_{12}}{a_{11}} & \dfrac{a_{11}a_{23} - a_{21}a_{13}}{a_{11}} \\ 0 & \dfrac{a_{11}a_{32} - a_{31}a_{12}}{a_{11}} & \dfrac{a_{11}a_{33} - a_{31}a_{13}}{a_{11}} \end{pmatrix}$$

The matrix on the right will be row equivalent to I if and only if

$$a_{11} \begin{vmatrix} \dfrac{a_{11}a_{22} - a_{21}a_{12}}{a_{11}} & \dfrac{a_{11}a_{23} - a_{21}a_{13}}{a_{11}} \\ \dfrac{a_{11}a_{32} - a_{31}a_{12}}{a_{11}} & \dfrac{a_{11}a_{33} - a_{31}a_{13}}{a_{11}} \end{vmatrix} \neq 0$$

Although the algebra is somewhat messy, this condition can be simplified to

$$a_{11}a_{22}a_{33} \ - \ a_{11}a_{32}a_{23} - a_{12}a_{21}a_{33} + a_{12}a_{31}a_{23} \qquad (2)$$
$$+ \ a_{13}a_{21}a_{32} - a_{13}a_{31}a_{22} \neq 0$$

Thus, if we define

$$\det(A) \ = \ a_{11}a_{22}a_{33} - a_{11}a_{32}a_{23} - a_{12}a_{21}a_{33} \qquad (3)$$
$$+ \ a_{12}a_{31}a_{23} + a_{13}a_{21}a_{32} - a_{13}a_{31}a_{22}$$

then, for the case $a_{11} \neq 0$, the matrix will be nonsingular if and only if $\det(A) \neq 0$.

What if $a_{11} = 0$? Consider the following possibilities:

(i) $a_{11} = 0, a_{21} \neq 0$

(ii) $a_{11} = a_{21} = 0, a_{31} \neq 0$

(iii) $a_{11} = a_{21} = a_{31} = 0$

In case **(i)**, one can show that A is row equivalent to I if and only if

$$-a_{12}a_{21}a_{33} + a_{12}a_{31}a_{23} + a_{13}a_{21}a_{32} - a_{13}a_{31}a_{22} \neq 0$$

But this condition is the same as condition (2) with $a_{11} = 0$. The details of case **(i)** are left as an exercise for the reader (see Exercise 7 at the end of the section).

In case **(ii)**, it follows that

$$A = \begin{bmatrix} 0 & a_{12} & a_{13} \\ 0 & a_{22} & a_{23} \\ a_{31} & a_{32} & a_{33} \end{bmatrix}$$

is row equivalent to I if and only if

$$a_{31}(a_{12}a_{23} - a_{22}a_{13}) \neq 0$$

Again, this is a special case of condition (2) with $a_{11} = a_{21} = 0$.

Clearly, in case **(iii)** the matrix A cannot be row equivalent to I and hence must be singular. In this case, if we set a_{11}, a_{21}, and a_{31} equal to 0 in formula (3), the result will be $\det(A) = 0$.

In general, then, formula (2) gives a necessary and sufficient condition for a 3×3 matrix A to be nonsingular (regardless of the value of a_{11}).

We would now like to define the determinant of an $n \times n$ matrix. To see how to do this, note that the determinant of a 2×2 matrix

$$A = \begin{bmatrix} a_{11} & a_{12} \\ a_{21} & a_{22} \end{bmatrix}$$

can be defined in terms of the two 1×1 matrices

$$M_{11} = (a_{22}) \qquad \text{and} \qquad M_{12} = (a_{21})$$

The matrix M_{11} is formed from A by deleting its first row and first column, and M_{12} is formed from A by deleting its first row and second column.

The determinant of A can be expressed in the form

$$\det(A) = a_{11}a_{22} - a_{12}a_{21} = a_{11}\det(M_{11}) - a_{12}\det(M_{12}) \qquad (4)$$

For a 3×3 matrix A, we can rewrite equation (3) in the form

$$\det(A) = a_{11}(a_{22}a_{33} - a_{32}a_{23}) - a_{12}(a_{21}a_{33} - a_{31}a_{23}) + a_{13}(a_{21}a_{32} - a_{31}a_{22})$$

For $j = 1, 2, 3$, let M_{1j} denote the 2×2 matrix formed from A by deleting its first row and jth column. The determinant of A can then be represented in the form

$$\det(A) = a_{11}\det(M_{11}) - a_{12}\det(M_{12}) + a_{13}\det(M_{13}) \qquad (5)$$

where

$$M_{11} = \begin{bmatrix} a_{22} & a_{23} \\ a_{32} & a_{33} \end{bmatrix}, \qquad M_{12} = \begin{bmatrix} a_{21} & a_{23} \\ a_{31} & a_{33} \end{bmatrix}, \qquad M_{13} = \begin{bmatrix} a_{21} & a_{22} \\ a_{31} & a_{32} \end{bmatrix}$$

To see how to generalize (4) and (5) to the case $n > 3$, we introduce the following definition.

Definition

Let $A = (a_{ij})$ be an $n \times n$ matrix and let M_{ij} denote the $(n-1) \times (n-1)$ matrix obtained from A by deleting the row and column containing a_{ij}. The determinant of M_{ij} is called the **minor** of a_{ij}. We define the **cofactor** A_{ij} of a_{ij} by

$$A_{ij} = (-1)^{i+j}\det(M_{ij})$$

In view of this definition, for a 2×2 matrix A, we may rewrite equation (4) in the form

$$\det(A) = a_{11}A_{11} + a_{12}A_{12} \qquad (n = 2) \qquad (6)$$

Equation (6) is called the *cofactor expansion* of $\det(A)$ along the first row of A. Note that we could also write

$$\det(A) = a_{21}(-a_{12}) + a_{22}a_{11} = a_{21}A_{21} + a_{22}A_{22} \qquad (7)$$

Equation (7) expresses $\det(A)$ in terms of the entries of the second row of A and their cofactors. Actually, there is no reason that we must expand along a row of the matrix; the determinant could just as well be represented by the cofactor expansion along one of the columns:

$$\begin{aligned} \det(A) &= a_{11}a_{22} + a_{21}(-a_{12}) \\ &= a_{11}A_{11} + a_{21}A_{21} && \text{(first column)} \\ \det(A) &= a_{12}(-a_{21}) + a_{22}a_{11} \\ &= a_{12}A_{12} + a_{22}A_{22} && \text{(second column)} \end{aligned}$$

For a 3×3 matrix A, we have

$$\det(A) = a_{11}A_{11} + a_{12}A_{12} + a_{13}A_{13} \qquad (8)$$

Thus, the determinant of a 3×3 matrix can be defined in terms of the elements in the first row of the matrix and their corresponding cofactors.

EXAMPLE I   If

$$A = \begin{bmatrix} 2 & 5 & 4 \\ 3 & 1 & 2 \\ 5 & 4 & 6 \end{bmatrix}$$

then

$$
\begin{aligned}
\det(A) &= a_{11}A_{11} + a_{12}A_{12} + a_{13}A_{13} \\
&= (-1)^2 a_{11} \det(M_{11}) + (-1)^3 a_{12} \det(M_{12}) + (-1)^4 a_{13} \det(M_{13}) \\
&= 2\begin{vmatrix} 1 & 2 \\ 4 & 6 \end{vmatrix} - 5\begin{vmatrix} 3 & 2 \\ 5 & 6 \end{vmatrix} + 4\begin{vmatrix} 3 & 1 \\ 5 & 4 \end{vmatrix} \\
&= 2(6 - 8) - 5(18 - 10) + 4(12 - 5) \\
&= -16
\end{aligned}
$$

As in the case of 2×2 matrices, the determinant of a 3×3 matrix can be represented as a cofactor expansion using any row or column. For example, equation (3) can be rewritten in the form

$$
\begin{aligned}
\det(A) &= a_{12}a_{31}a_{23} - a_{13}a_{31}a_{22} - a_{11}a_{32}a_{23} + a_{13}a_{21}a_{32} + a_{11}a_{22}a_{33} - a_{12}a_{21}a_{33} \\
&= a_{31}(a_{12}a_{23} - a_{13}a_{22}) - a_{32}(a_{11}a_{23} - a_{13}a_{21}) + a_{33}(a_{11}a_{22} - a_{12}a_{21}) \\
&= a_{31}A_{31} + a_{32}A_{32} + a_{33}A_{33}
\end{aligned}
$$

This is the cofactor expansion along the third row of A.

EXAMPLE 2   Let A be the matrix in Example 1. The cofactor expansion of $\det(A)$ along the second column is given by

$$
\begin{aligned}
\det(A) &= -5\begin{vmatrix} 3 & 2 \\ 5 & 6 \end{vmatrix} + 1\begin{vmatrix} 2 & 4 \\ 5 & 6 \end{vmatrix} - 4\begin{vmatrix} 2 & 4 \\ 3 & 2 \end{vmatrix} \\
&= -5(18 - 10) + 1(12 - 20) - 4(4 - 12) = -16
\end{aligned}
$$

The determinant of a 4×4 matrix can be defined in terms of a cofactor expansion along any row or column. To compute the value of the 4×4 determinant, we would have to evaluate four 3×3 determinants.

Definition

> The **determinant** of an $n \times n$ matrix A, denoted $\det(A)$, is a scalar associated with the matrix A that is defined inductively as
>
> $$\det(A) = \begin{cases} a_{11} & \text{if } n = 1 \\ a_{11}A_{11} + a_{12}A_{12} + \cdots + a_{1n}A_{1n} & \text{if } n > 1 \end{cases}$$
>
> where
>
> $$A_{1j} = (-1)^{1+j} \det(M_{1j}) \qquad j = 1, \ldots, n$$
>
> are the cofactors associated with the entries in the first row of A.

As we have seen, it is not necessary to limit ourselves to using the first row for the cofactor expansion. We state the following theorem without proof:

Theorem 2.1.1 *If A is an $n \times n$ matrix with $n \geq 2$, then $\det(A)$ can be expressed as a cofactor expansion using any row or column of A:*

$$\det(A) = a_{i1}A_{i1} + a_{i2}A_{i2} + \cdots + a_{in}A_{in}$$
$$= a_{1j}A_{1j} + a_{2j}A_{2j} + \cdots + a_{nj}A_{nj}$$

for $i = 1, \ldots, n$ and $j = 1, \ldots, n$.

The cofactor expansion of a 4×4 determinant will involve four 3×3 determinants. We can often save work by expanding along the row or column that contains the most zeros. For example, to evaluate

$$\begin{vmatrix} 0 & 2 & 3 & 0 \\ 0 & 4 & 5 & 0 \\ 0 & 1 & 0 & 3 \\ 2 & 0 & 1 & 3 \end{vmatrix}$$

we would expand down the first column. The first three terms will drop out, leaving

$$-2 \begin{vmatrix} 2 & 3 & 0 \\ 4 & 5 & 0 \\ 1 & 0 & 3 \end{vmatrix} = -2 \cdot 3 \cdot \begin{vmatrix} 2 & 3 \\ 4 & 5 \end{vmatrix} = 12$$

For $n \leq 3$, we have seen that an $n \times n$ matrix A is nonsingular if and only if $\det(A) \neq 0$. In the next section, we will show that this result holds for all values of n. In that section, we also look at the effect of row operations on the value of the determinant, and we will make use of row operations to derive a more efficient method for computing the value of a determinant.

We close this section with three theorems that are consequences of the cofactor expansion definition. The proofs of the last two theorems are left for the reader (see Exercises 8, 9, and 10 at the end of this section).

Theorem 2.1.2 *If A is an $n \times n$ matrix, then $\det(A^T) = \det(A)$.*

Proof   The proof is by induction on n. Clearly, the result holds if $n = 1$, since a 1×1 matrix is necessarily symmetric. Assume that the result holds for all $k \times k$ matrices and that A is a $(k+1) \times (k+1)$ matrix. Expanding $\det(A)$ along the first row of A, we get

$$\det(A) = a_{11} \det(M_{11}) - a_{12} \det(M_{12}) + - \cdots \pm a_{1,k+1} \det(M_{1,k+1})$$

Since the M_{ij}'s are all $k \times k$ matrices, it follows from the induction hypothesis that

$$\det(A) = a_{11} \det(M_{11}^T) - a_{12} \det(M_{12}^T) + - \cdots \pm a_{1,k+1} \det(M_{1,k+1}^T) \qquad (9)$$

The right-hand side of (9) is just the expansion by minors of $\det(A^T)$ using the first column of A^T. Therefore,

$$\det(A^T) = \det(A)$$

  ■

Theorem 2.1.3   *If A is an $n \times n$ triangular matrix, then the determinant of A equals the product of the diagonal elements of A.*

Proof   In view of Theorem 2.1.2, it suffices to prove the theorem for lower triangular matrices. The result follows easily using the cofactor expansion and induction on n. The details are left for the reader (see Exercise 8 at the end of the section).   ■

Theorem 2.1.4   *Let A be an $n \times n$ matrix.*

    (i) If A has a row or column consisting entirely of zeros, then $\det(A) = 0$.

    (ii) If A has two identical rows or two identical columns, then $\det(A) = 0$.

Both of these results can be easily proved with the use of the cofactor expansion. The proofs are left for the reader (see Exercises 9 and 10).   ■

In the next section, we look at the effect of row operations on the value of the determinant. This will allow us to make use of Theorem 2.1.3 to derive a more efficient method for computing the value of a determinant.

SECTION 2.1 EXERCISES

1. Let

$$A = \begin{bmatrix} 3 & 2 & 4 \\ 1 & -2 & 3 \\ 2 & 3 & 2 \end{bmatrix}$$

(a) Find the values of $\det(M_{21})$, $\det(M_{22})$, and $\det(M_{23})$.

(b) Find the values of A_{21}, A_{22}, and A_{23}.

(c) Use your answers from part (b) to compute $\det(A)$.

2. Use determinants to determine whether the following 2×2 matrices are nonsingular:

(a) $\begin{bmatrix} 3 & 5 \\ 2 & 4 \end{bmatrix}$ **(b)** $\begin{bmatrix} 3 & 6 \\ 2 & 4 \end{bmatrix}$

(c) $\begin{bmatrix} 3 & -6 \\ 2 & 4 \end{bmatrix}$

3. Evaluate the following determinants:

(a) $\begin{vmatrix} 3 & 5 \\ -2 & -3 \end{vmatrix}$ **(b)** $\begin{vmatrix} 5 & -2 \\ -8 & 4 \end{vmatrix}$

(c) $\begin{vmatrix} 3 & 1 & 2 \\ 2 & 4 & 5 \\ 2 & 4 & 5 \end{vmatrix}$ **(d)** $\begin{vmatrix} 4 & 3 & 0 \\ 3 & 1 & 2 \\ 5 & -1 & -4 \end{vmatrix}$

(e) $\begin{vmatrix} 1 & 3 & 2 \\ 4 & 1 & -2 \\ 2 & 1 & 3 \end{vmatrix}$ (f) $\begin{vmatrix} 2 & -1 & 2 \\ 1 & 3 & 2 \\ 5 & 1 & 6 \end{vmatrix}$

(g) $\begin{vmatrix} 2 & 0 & 0 & 1 \\ 0 & 1 & 0 & 0 \\ 1 & 6 & 2 & 0 \\ 1 & 1 & -2 & 3 \end{vmatrix}$

(h) $\begin{vmatrix} 2 & 1 & 2 & 1 \\ 3 & 0 & 1 & 1 \\ -1 & 2 & -2 & 1 \\ -3 & 2 & 3 & 1 \end{vmatrix}$

4. Evaluate the following determinants by inspection:

(a) $\begin{vmatrix} 3 & 5 \\ 2 & 4 \end{vmatrix}$ (b) $\begin{vmatrix} 2 & 0 & 0 \\ 4 & 1 & 0 \\ 7 & 3 & -2 \end{vmatrix}$

(c) $\begin{vmatrix} 3 & 0 & 0 \\ 2 & 1 & 1 \\ 1 & 2 & 2 \end{vmatrix}$ (d) $\begin{vmatrix} 4 & 0 & 2 & 1 \\ 5 & 0 & 4 & 2 \\ 2 & 0 & 3 & 4 \\ 1 & 0 & 2 & 3 \end{vmatrix}$

5. Evaluate the following determinant. Write your answer as a polynomial in x:

$$\begin{vmatrix} a-x & b & c \\ 1 & -x & 0 \\ 0 & 1 & -x \end{vmatrix}$$

6. Find all values of λ for which the following determinant will equal 0:

$$\begin{vmatrix} 2-\lambda & 4 \\ 3 & 3-\lambda \end{vmatrix}$$

7. Let A be a 3×3 matrix with $a_{11} = 0$ and $a_{21} \neq 0$. Show that A is row equivalent to I if and only if

$$-a_{12}a_{21}a_{33} + a_{12}a_{31}a_{23}$$
$$+ a_{13}a_{21}a_{32} - a_{13}a_{31}a_{22} \neq 0$$

8. Write out the details of the proof of Theorem 2.1.3.

9. Prove that if a row or a column of an $n \times n$ matrix A consists entirely of zeros, then $\det(A) = 0$.

10. Use mathematical induction to prove that if A is an $(n+1) \times (n+1)$ matrix with two identical rows, then $\det(A) = 0$.

11. Let A and B be 2×2 matrices.
   (a) Does $\det(A+B) = \det(A) + \det(B)$?
   (b) Does $\det(AB) = \det(A)\det(B)$?
   (c) Does $\det(AB) = \det(BA)$?
   Justify your answers.

12. Let A and B be 2×2 matrices and let

$$C = \begin{bmatrix} a_{11} & a_{12} \\ b_{21} & b_{22} \end{bmatrix}, \quad D = \begin{bmatrix} b_{11} & b_{12} \\ a_{21} & a_{22} \end{bmatrix},$$

$$E = \begin{bmatrix} 0 & \alpha \\ \beta & 0 \end{bmatrix}$$

   (a) Show that $\det(A+B) = \det(A) + \det(B) + \det(C) + \det(D)$.
   (b) Show that if $B = EA$, then $\det(A+B) = \det(A) + \det(B)$.

13. Let A be a symmetric tridiagonal matrix (i.e., A is symmetric and $a_{ij} = 0$ whenever $|i - j| > 1$). Let B be the matrix formed from A by deleting the first two rows and columns. Show that

$$\det(A) = a_{11}\det(M_{11}) - a_{12}^2\det(B)$$

2.2   Properties of Determinants

In this section, we consider the effects of row operations on the determinant of a matrix. Once these effects have been established, we will prove that a matrix A is singular if and only if its determinant is zero, and we will develop a method for evaluating determinants by using row operations. Also, we will establish an important theorem about the determinant of the product of two matrices. We begin with the following lemma:

Lemma 2.2.1   *Let A be an $n \times n$ matrix. If A_{jk} denotes the cofactor of a_{jk} for $k = 1, \ldots, n$, then*

$$a_{i1}A_{j1} + a_{i2}A_{j2} + \cdots + a_{in}A_{jn} = \begin{cases} \det(A) & \text{if } i = j \\ 0 & \text{if } i \neq j \end{cases} \tag{1}$$

Proof   If $i = j$, (1) is just the cofactor expansion of $\det(A)$ along the ith row of A. To prove (1) in the case $i \neq j$, let A^* be the matrix obtained by replacing the jth row of A by the ith row of A:

$$A^* = \begin{bmatrix} a_{11} & a_{12} & \cdots & a_{1n} \\ & \vdots & & \\ a_{i1} & a_{i2} & \cdots & a_{in} \\ & \vdots & & \\ a_{i1} & a_{i2} & \cdots & a_{in} \\ & \vdots & & \\ a_{n1} & a_{n2} & \cdots & a_{nn} \end{bmatrix} \quad j\text{th row}$$

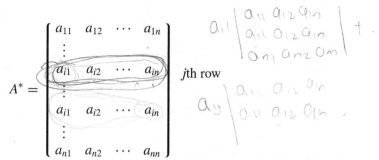

Since two rows of A^* are the same, its determinant must be zero. It follows from the cofactor expansion of $\det(A^*)$ along the jth row that

$$0 = \det(A^*) = a_{i1}A^*_{j1} + a_{i2}A^*_{j2} + \cdots + a_{in}A^*_{jn}$$
$$= a_{i1}A_{j1} + a_{i2}A_{j2} + \cdots + a_{in}A_{jn}$$

Let us now consider the effects of each of the three row operations on the value of the determinant.

Row Operation I

Two rows of A are interchanged.

If A is a 2×2 matrix and

$$E = \begin{bmatrix} 0 & 1 \\ 1 & 0 \end{bmatrix}$$

then

$$\det(EA) = \begin{vmatrix} a_{21} & a_{22} \\ a_{11} & a_{12} \end{vmatrix} = a_{21}a_{12} - a_{22}a_{11} = -\det(A)$$

For $n > 2$, let E_{ij} be the elementary matrix that switches rows i and j of A. An induction proof can show that $\det(E_{ij}A) = -\det(A)$. We illustrate the idea behind the proof for the case $n = 3$. Suppose that the first and third rows of a 3×3 matrix A have been interchanged. Expanding $\det(E_{13}A)$ along the second row and making use of the result for 2×2 matrices, we see that

$$\det(E_{13}A) = \begin{vmatrix} a_{31} & a_{32} & a_{33} \\ a_{21} & a_{22} & a_{23} \\ a_{11} & a_{12} & a_{13} \end{vmatrix}$$

$$= -a_{21}\begin{vmatrix} a_{32} & a_{33} \\ a_{12} & a_{13} \end{vmatrix} + a_{22}\begin{vmatrix} a_{31} & a_{33} \\ a_{11} & a_{13} \end{vmatrix} - a_{23}\begin{vmatrix} a_{31} & a_{32} \\ a_{11} & a_{12} \end{vmatrix}$$

$$= a_{21}\begin{vmatrix} a_{12} & a_{13} \\ a_{32} & a_{33} \end{vmatrix} - a_{22}\begin{vmatrix} a_{11} & a_{13} \\ a_{31} & a_{33} \end{vmatrix} + a_{23}\begin{vmatrix} a_{11} & a_{12} \\ a_{31} & a_{32} \end{vmatrix}$$

$$= -\det(A)$$

In general, if A is an $n \times n$ matrix and E_{ij} is the $n \times n$ elementary matrix formed by interchanging the ith and jth rows of I, then

$$\det(E_{ij}A) = -\det(A)$$

In particular,

$$\det(E_{ij}) = \det(E_{ij}I) = -\det(I) = -1$$

Thus, for any elementary matrix E of type I,

$$\det(EA) = -\det(A) = \det(E)\det(A)$$

Row Operation II

A row of A is multiplied by a nonzero scalar.

Let E denote the elementary matrix of type II formed from I by multiplying the ith row by the nonzero scalar α. If $\det(EA)$ is expanded by cofactors along the ith row, then

$$\begin{aligned}
\det(EA) &= \alpha a_{i1}A_{i1} + \alpha a_{i2}A_{i2} + \cdots + \alpha a_{in}A_{in} \\
&= \alpha(a_{i1}A_{i1} + a_{i2}A_{i2} + \cdots + a_{in}A_{in}) \\
&= \alpha \det(A)
\end{aligned}$$

In particular,

$$\det(E) = \det(EI) = \alpha \det(I) = \alpha$$

and hence,

$$\det(EA) = \alpha \det(A) = \det(E)\det(A)$$

Row Operation III

A multiple of one row is added to another row.

Let E be the elementary matrix of type III formed from I by adding c times the ith row to the jth row. Since E is triangular and its diagonal elements are all 1, it follows that $\det(E) = 1$. We will show that

$$\det(EA) = \det(A) = \det(E)\det(A)$$

If $\det(EA)$ is expanded by cofactors along the jth row, it follows from Lemma 2.2.1 that

$$\begin{aligned}
\det(EA) &= (a_{j1} + ca_{i1})A_{j1} + (a_{j2} + ca_{i2})A_{j2} + \cdots + (a_{jn} + ca_{in})A_{jn} \\
&= (a_{j1}A_{j1} + \cdots + a_{jn}A_{jn}) + c(a_{i1}A_{j1} + \cdots + a_{in}A_{jn}) \\
&= \det(A)
\end{aligned}$$

Thus,

$$\det(EA) = \det(A) = \det(E)\det(A)$$

SUMMARY

In summation, if E is an elementary matrix, then

$$\det(EA) = \det(E)\det(A)$$

where

$$\det(E) = \begin{cases} -1 & \text{if } E \text{ is of type I} \\ \alpha \neq 0 & \text{if } E \text{ is of type II} \\ 1 & \text{if } E \text{ is of type III} \end{cases} \qquad (2)$$

Similar results hold for column operations. Indeed, if E is an elementary matrix, then E^T is also an elementary matrix (see Exercise 8 at the end of the section) and

$$\det(AE) = \det\left((AE)^T\right) = \det\left(E^T A^T\right)$$
$$= \det\left(E^T\right)\det\left(A^T\right) = \det(E)\det(A)$$

Thus, the effects that row or column operations have on the value of the determinant can be summarized as follows:

   I. Interchanging two rows (or columns) of a matrix changes the sign of the determinant.

  II. Multiplying a single row or column of a matrix by a scalar has the effect of multiplying the value of the determinant by that scalar.

 III. Adding a multiple of one row (or column) to another does not change the value of the determinant.

Note

As a consequence of **III**, if one row (or column) of a matrix is a multiple of another, the determinant of the matrix must equal zero.

Main Results

We can now make use of the effects of row operations on determinants to prove two major theorems and to establish a simpler method of computing determinants. It follows from (2) that all elementary matrices have nonzero determinants. This observation can be used to prove the following theorem.

Theorem 2.2.2   *An $n \times n$ matrix A is singular if and only if*

$$\det(A) = 0$$

Proof   The matrix A can be reduced to row echelon form with a finite number of row operations. Thus,

$$U = E_k E_{k-1} \cdots E_1 A$$

where U is in row echelon form and the E_i's are all elementary matrices. It follows that

$$\det(U) = \det(E_k E_{k-1} \cdots E_1 A)$$
$$= \det(E_k) \det(E_{k-1}) \cdots \det(E_1) \det(A)$$

Since the determinants of the E_i's are all nonzero, it follows that $\det(A) = 0$ if and only if $\det(U) = 0$. If A is singular, then U has a row consisting entirely of zeros, and hence $\det(U) = 0$. If A is nonsingular, then U is triangular with 1's along the diagonal and hence $\det(U) = 1$.   ∎

From the proof of Theorem 2.2.2, we can obtain a method for computing $\det(A)$. We reduce A to row echelon form.

$$U = E_k E_{k-1} \cdots E_1 A$$

If the last row of U consists entirely of zeros, A is singular and $\det(A) = 0$. Otherwise, A is nonsingular and

$$\det(A) = [\det(E_k) \det(E_{k-1}) \cdots \det(E_1)]^{-1}$$

Actually, if A is nonsingular, it is simpler to reduce A to triangular form. This can be done using only row operations **I** and **III**. Thus,

$$T = E_m E_{m-1} \cdots E_1 A$$

and hence,

$$\det(A) = \pm \det(T) = \pm t_{11} t_{22} \cdots t_{nn}$$

where the t_{ii}'s are the diagonal entries of T. The sign will be positive if row operation I has been used an even number of times and negative otherwise.

EXAMPLE I   Evaluate

$$\begin{vmatrix} 2 & 1 & 3 \\ 4 & 2 & 1 \\ 6 & -3 & 4 \end{vmatrix}$$

Solution

$$\begin{vmatrix} 2 & 1 & 3 \\ 4 & 2 & 1 \\ 6 & -3 & 4 \end{vmatrix} = \begin{vmatrix} 2 & 1 & 3 \\ 0 & 0 & -5 \\ 0 & -6 & -5 \end{vmatrix} = (-1) \begin{vmatrix} 2 & 1 & 3 \\ 0 & -6 & -5 \\ 0 & 0 & -5 \end{vmatrix}$$
$$= (-1)(2)(-6)(-5)$$
$$= -60$$ ∎

We now have two methods for evaluating the determinant of an $n \times n$ matrix A. If $n > 3$ and A has nonzero entries, elimination is the most efficient method, in the sense that it involves fewer arithmetic operations. In Table 2.2.1, the number of arithmetic operations involved in each method is given for $n = 2, 3, 4, 5, 10$. It is not difficult

Table 2.2.1   Operation Counts

	Cofactors		Elimination	
n	Additions	Multiplications	Additions	Multiplications and Divisions
2	1	2	1	3
3	5	9	5	10
4	23	40	14	23
5	119	205	30	44
10	3,628,799	6,235,300	285	339

to derive general formulas for the number of operations in each of the methods (see Exercises 20 and 21 at the end of the section).

We have seen that, for any elementary matrix E,

$$\det(EA) = \det(E)\det(A) = \det(AE)$$

This is a special case of the following theorem.

Theorem 2.2.3   *If A and B are $n \times n$ matrices, then*

$$\det(AB) = \det(A)\det(B)$$

Proof   If B is singular, it follows from Theorem 1.5.2 that AB is also singular (see Exercise 14 of Section 1.5), and therefore,

$$\det(AB) = 0 = \det(A)\det(B)$$

If B is nonsingular, B can be written as a product of elementary matrices. We have already seen that the result holds for elementary matrices. Thus,

$$\begin{aligned}
\det(AB) &= \det(AE_k E_{k-1} \cdots E_1) \\
&= \det(A)\det(E_k)\det(E_{k-1}) \cdots \det(E_1) \\
&= \det(A)\det(E_k E_{k-1} \cdots E_1) \\
&= \det(A)\det(B)
\end{aligned}$$

$\blacksquare$

If A is singular, the computed value of $\det(A)$ using exact arithmetic must be 0. However, this result is unlikely if the computations are done by computer. Since computers use a finite number system, roundoff errors are usually unavoidable. Consequently, it is more likely that the computed value of $\det(A)$ will only be near 0. Because of roundoff errors, it is virtually impossible to determine computationally whether a matrix is exactly singular. In computer applications, it is often more meaningful to ask whether a matrix is "close" to being singular. In general, the value of $\det(A)$ is not a good indicator of nearness to singularity. In Section 6.5, we will discuss how to determine whether a matrix is close to being singular.

SECTION 2.2 EXERCISES

1. Evaluate each of the following determinants by inspection:

(a) $\begin{vmatrix} 0 & 0 & 3 \\ 0 & 4 & 1 \\ 2 & 3 & 1 \end{vmatrix}$

(b) $\begin{vmatrix} 1 & 1 & 1 & 3 \\ 0 & 3 & 1 & 1 \\ 0 & 0 & 2 & 2 \\ -1 & -1 & -1 & 2 \end{vmatrix}$

(c) $\begin{vmatrix} 0 & 0 & 0 & 1 \\ 1 & 0 & 0 & 0 \\ 0 & 1 & 0 & 0 \\ 0 & 0 & 1 & 0 \end{vmatrix}$

2. Let

$$A = \begin{bmatrix} 0 & 1 & 2 & 3 \\ 1 & 1 & 1 & 1 \\ -2 & -2 & 3 & 3 \\ 1 & 2 & -2 & -3 \end{bmatrix}$$

(a) Use the elimination method to evaluate $\det(A)$.

(b) Use the value of $\det(A)$ to evaluate

$$\begin{vmatrix} 0 & 1 & 2 & 3 \\ -2 & -2 & 3 & 3 \\ 1 & 2 & -2 & -3 \\ 1 & 1 & 1 & 1 \end{vmatrix} + \begin{vmatrix} 0 & 1 & 2 & 3 \\ 1 & 1 & 1 & 1 \\ -1 & -1 & 4 & 4 \\ 2 & 3 & -1 & -2 \end{vmatrix}$$

3. For each of the following, compute the determinant and state whether the matrix is singular or nonsingular:

(a) $\begin{bmatrix} 3 & 1 \\ 6 & 2 \end{bmatrix}$

(b) $\begin{bmatrix} 3 & 1 \\ 4 & 2 \end{bmatrix}$

(c) $\begin{bmatrix} 3 & 3 & 1 \\ 0 & 1 & 2 \\ 0 & 2 & 3 \end{bmatrix}$

(d) $\begin{bmatrix} 2 & 1 & 1 \\ 4 & 3 & 5 \\ 2 & 1 & 2 \end{bmatrix}$

(e) $\begin{bmatrix} 2 & -1 & 3 \\ -1 & 2 & -2 \\ 1 & 4 & 0 \end{bmatrix}$

(f) $\begin{bmatrix} 1 & 1 & 1 & 1 \\ 2 & -1 & 3 & 2 \\ 0 & 1 & 2 & 1 \\ 0 & 0 & 7 & 3 \end{bmatrix}$

4. Find all possible choices of c that would make the following matrix singular:

$$\begin{bmatrix} 1 & 1 & 1 \\ 1 & 9 & c \\ 1 & c & 3 \end{bmatrix}$$

5. Let A be an $n \times n$ matrix and α a scalar. Show that

$$\det(\alpha A) = \alpha^n \det(A)$$

6. Let A be a nonsingular matrix. Show that

$$\det(A^{-1}) = \frac{1}{\det(A)}$$

7. Let A and B be 3×3 matrices with $\det(A) = 4$ and $\det(B) = 5$. Find the value of

(a) $\det(AB)$ (b) $\det(3A)$

(c) $\det(2AB)$ (d) $\det(A^{-1}B)$

8. Show that if E is an elementary matrix, then E^T is an elementary matrix of the same type as E.

9. Let E_1, E_2, and E_3 be 3×3 elementary matrices of types **I**, **II**, and **III**, respectively, and let A be a 3×3 matrix with $\det(A) = 6$. Assume, additionally, that E_2 was formed from I by multiplying its second row by 3. Find the values of each of the following:

(a) $\det(E_1 A)$ (b) $\det(E_2 A)$

(c) $\det(E_3 A)$ (d) $\det(A E_1)$

(e) $\det(E_1^2)$ (f) $\det(E_1 E_2 E_3)$

10. Let A and B be row equivalent matrices, and suppose that B can be obtained from A by using only row operations **I** and **III**. How do the values of $\det(A)$ and $\det(B)$ compare? How will the values compare if B can be obtained from A using only row operation **III**? Explain your answers.

11. Let A be an $n \times n$ matrix. Is it possible for $A^2 + I = O$ in the case where n is odd? Answer the same question in the case where n is even.

12. Consider the 3×3 Vandermonde matrix

$$V = \begin{bmatrix} 1 & x_1 & x_1^2 \\ 1 & x_2 & x_2^2 \\ 1 & x_3 & x_3^2 \end{bmatrix}$$

(a) Show that $\det(V) = (x_2 - x_1)(x_3 - x_1)(x_3 - x_2)$. *Hint*: Make use of row operation **III**.

(b) What conditions must the scalars x_1, x_2, and x_3 satisfy in order for V to be nonsingular?

13. Suppose that a 3×3 matrix A factors into a product:

$$\begin{bmatrix} 1 & 0 & 0 \\ l_{21} & 1 & 0 \\ l_{31} & l_{32} & 1 \end{bmatrix} \begin{bmatrix} u_{11} & u_{12} & u_{13} \\ 0 & u_{22} & u_{23} \\ 0 & 0 & u_{33} \end{bmatrix}$$

Determine the value of $\det(A)$.

14. Let A and B be $n \times n$ matrices. Prove that the product AB is nonsingular if and only if A and B are both nonsingular.

15. Let A and B be $n \times n$ matrices. Prove that if $AB = I$, then $BA = I$. What is the significance of this result in terms of the definition of a nonsingular matrix?

16. A matrix A is said to be *skew symmetric* if $A^T = -A$. For example,

$$A = \begin{bmatrix} 0 & 1 \\ -1 & 0 \end{bmatrix}$$

is skew symmetric, since

$$A^T = \begin{bmatrix} 0 & -1 \\ 1 & 0 \end{bmatrix} = -A$$

If A is an $n \times n$ skew-symmetric matrix and n is odd, show that A must be singular.

17. Let A be a nonsingular $n \times n$ matrix with a nonzero cofactor A_{nn}, and set

$$c = \frac{\det(A)}{A_{nn}}$$

Show that if we subtract c from a_{nn}, then the resulting matrix will be singular.

18. Let A be a $k \times k$ matrix and let B be an $(n - k) \times (n - k)$ matrix. Let

$$E = \begin{bmatrix} I_k & O \\ O & B \end{bmatrix}, \quad F = \begin{bmatrix} A & O \\ O & I_{n-k} \end{bmatrix},$$

$$C = \begin{bmatrix} A & O \\ O & B \end{bmatrix}$$

where I_k and I_{n-k} are the $k \times k$ and $(n - k) \times (n - k)$ identity matrices.

(a) Show that $\det(E) = \det(B)$.

(b) Show that $\det(F) = \det(A)$.

(c) Show that $\det(C) = \det(A) \det(B)$.

19. Let A and B be $k \times k$ matrices and let

$$M = \begin{bmatrix} O & B \\ A & O \end{bmatrix}$$

Show that $\det(M) = (-1)^k \det(A) \det(B)$.

20. Show that evaluating the determinant of an $n \times n$ matrix by cofactors involves $(n! - 1)$ additions and $\displaystyle\sum_{k=1}^{n-1} n!/k!$ multiplications.

21. Show that the elimination method of computing the value of the determinant of an $n \times n$ matrix involves $[n(n-1)(2n-1)]/6$ additions and $[(n-1)(n^2+n+3)]/3$ multiplications and divisions. *Hint:* At the ith step of the reduction process, it takes $n-i$ divisions to calculate the multiples of the ith row that are to be subtracted from the remaining rows below the pivot. We must then calculate new values for the $(n - i)^2$ entries in rows $i + 1$ through n and columns $i + 1$ through n.

2.3 Additional Topics and Applications

In this section, we learn a method for computing the inverse of a nonsingular matrix A using determinants and we learn a method for solving linear systems using determinants. Both methods depend on Lemma 2.2.1. We also show how to use determinants to define the cross product of two vectors. The cross product is useful in physics applications involving the motion of a particle in 3-space.

The Adjoint of a Matrix

Let A be an $n \times n$ matrix. We define a new matrix called the *adjoint* of A by

$$\text{adj } A = \begin{bmatrix} A_{11} & A_{21} & \cdots & A_{n1} \\ A_{12} & A_{22} & \cdots & A_{n2} \\ \vdots & & & \\ A_{1n} & A_{2n} & \cdots & A_{nn} \end{bmatrix}$$

Thus, to form the adjoint, we must replace each term by its cofactor and then transpose the resulting matrix. By Lemma 2.2.1,

$$a_{i1}A_{j1} + a_{i2}A_{j2} + \cdots + a_{in}A_{jn} = \begin{cases} \det(A) & \text{if } i = j \\ 0 & \text{if } i \neq j \end{cases}$$

and it follows that

$$A(\operatorname{adj} A) = \det(A)I$$

If A is nonsingular, $\det(A)$ is a nonzero scalar, and we may write

$$A\left(\frac{1}{\det(A)} \operatorname{adj} A\right) = I$$

Thus,

$$A^{-1} = \frac{1}{\det(A)} \operatorname{adj} A \quad \text{when } \det(A) \neq 0$$

EXAMPLE I For a 2×2 matrix,

$$\operatorname{adj} A = \begin{bmatrix} a_{22} & -a_{12} \\ -a_{21} & a_{11} \end{bmatrix}$$

If A is nonsingular, then

$$A^{-1} = \frac{1}{a_{11}a_{22} - a_{12}a_{21}} \begin{bmatrix} a_{22} & -a_{12} \\ -a_{21} & a_{11} \end{bmatrix}$$

EXAMPLE 2 Let

$$A = \begin{bmatrix} 2 & 1 & 2 \\ 3 & 2 & 2 \\ 1 & 2 & 3 \end{bmatrix}$$

Compute $\operatorname{adj} A$ and A^{-1}.

Solution

$$\operatorname{adj} A = \begin{bmatrix} \begin{vmatrix} 2 & 2 \\ 2 & 3 \end{vmatrix} & -\begin{vmatrix} 3 & 2 \\ 1 & 3 \end{vmatrix} & \begin{vmatrix} 3 & 2 \\ 1 & 2 \end{vmatrix} \\[2ex] -\begin{vmatrix} 1 & 2 \\ 2 & 3 \end{vmatrix} & \begin{vmatrix} 2 & 2 \\ 1 & 3 \end{vmatrix} & -\begin{vmatrix} 2 & 1 \\ 1 & 2 \end{vmatrix} \\[2ex] \begin{vmatrix} 1 & 2 \\ 2 & 2 \end{vmatrix} & -\begin{vmatrix} 2 & 2 \\ 3 & 2 \end{vmatrix} & \begin{vmatrix} 2 & 1 \\ 3 & 2 \end{vmatrix} \end{bmatrix}^T = \begin{bmatrix} 2 & 1 & -2 \\ -7 & 4 & 2 \\ 4 & -3 & 1 \end{bmatrix}$$

$$A^{-1} = \frac{1}{\det(A)} \operatorname{adj} A = \frac{1}{5} \begin{bmatrix} 2 & 1 & -2 \\ -7 & 4 & 2 \\ 4 & -3 & 1 \end{bmatrix}$$ ∎

Using the formula

$$A^{-1} = \frac{1}{\det(A)} \operatorname{adj} A$$

we can derive a rule for representing the solution to the system $A\mathbf{x} = \mathbf{b}$ in terms of determinants.

Cramer's Rule

Theorem 2.3.1   Cramer's Rule

Let A be a nonsingular $n \times n$ matrix, and let $\mathbf{b} \in \mathbb{R}^n$. Let A_i be the matrix obtained by replacing the ith column of A by $\mathbf{b}$. If $\mathbf{x}$ is the unique solution of $A\mathbf{x} = \mathbf{b}$, then

$$x_i = \frac{\det(A_i)}{\det(A)} \quad \text{for} \quad i = 1, 2, \ldots, n$$

Proof   Since

$$\mathbf{x} = A^{-1}\mathbf{b} = \frac{1}{\det(A)}(\operatorname{adj} A)\mathbf{b}$$

it follows that

$$x_i = \frac{b_1 A_{1i} + b_2 A_{2i} + \cdots + b_n A_{ni}}{\det(A)}$$
$$= \frac{\det(A_i)}{\det(A)}$$ ∎

EXAMPLE 3   Use Cramer's rule to solve

$$\begin{aligned} x_1 + 2x_2 + \ x_3 &= 5 \\ 2x_1 + 2x_2 + \ x_3 &= 6 \\ x_1 + 2x_2 + 3x_3 &= 9 \end{aligned}$$

Solution

$$\det(A) = \begin{vmatrix} 1 & 2 & 1 \\ 2 & 2 & 1 \\ 1 & 2 & 3 \end{vmatrix} = -4 \qquad \det(A_1) = \begin{vmatrix} 5 & 2 & 1 \\ 6 & 2 & 1 \\ 9 & 2 & 3 \end{vmatrix} = -4$$

$$\det(A_2) = \begin{vmatrix} 1 & 5 & 1 \\ 2 & 6 & 1 \\ 1 & 9 & 3 \end{vmatrix} = -4 \qquad \det(A_3) = \begin{vmatrix} 1 & 2 & 5 \\ 2 & 2 & 6 \\ 1 & 2 & 9 \end{vmatrix} = -8$$

Therefore,

$$x_1 = \frac{-4}{-4} = 1, \qquad x_2 = \frac{-4}{-4} = 1, \qquad x_3 = \frac{-8}{-4} = 2 \qquad \blacksquare$$

Cramer's rule gives us a convenient method for writing the solution of an $n \times n$ system of linear equations in terms of determinants. To compute the solution, however, we must evaluate $n+1$ determinants of order n. Evaluating even two of these determinants generally involves more computation than solving the system by Gaussian elimination.

APPLICATION I   Coded Messages

A common way of sending a coded message is to assign an integer value to each letter of the alphabet and to send the message as a string of integers. For example, the message

SEND MONEY

might be coded as

5, 8, 10, 21, 7, 2, 10, 8, 3

Here, the S is represented by a 5, the E by an 8, and so on. Unfortunately, this type of code is generally easy to break. In a longer message, we might be able to guess which letter is represented by a number on the basis of the relative frequency of occurrence of that number. For example, if 8 is the most frequently occurring number in the coded message, then it is likely that it represents the letter E, the letter that occurs most frequently in the English language.

We can disguise the message further by using matrix multiplications. If A is a matrix whose entries are all integers and whose determinant is ± 1, then, since $A^{-1} = \pm \operatorname{adj} A$, the entries of A^{-1} will be integers. We can use such a matrix to transform the message. The transformed message will be more difficult to decipher. To illustrate the technique, let

$$A = \begin{bmatrix} 1 & 2 & 1 \\ 2 & 5 & 3 \\ 2 & 3 & 2 \end{bmatrix}$$

The coded message is put into the columns of a matrix B having three rows:

$$B = \begin{bmatrix} 5 & 21 & 10 \\ 8 & 7 & 8 \\ 10 & 2 & 3 \end{bmatrix}$$

The product

$$AB = \begin{bmatrix} 1 & 2 & 1 \\ 2 & 5 & 3 \\ 2 & 3 & 2 \end{bmatrix} \begin{bmatrix} 5 & 21 & 10 \\ 8 & 7 & 8 \\ 10 & 2 & 3 \end{bmatrix} = \begin{bmatrix} 31 & 37 & 29 \\ 80 & 83 & 69 \\ 54 & 67 & 50 \end{bmatrix}$$

gives the coded message to be sent:

31, 80, 54, 37, 83, 67, 29, 69, 50

The person receiving the message can decode it by multiplying by A^{-1}:

$$\begin{bmatrix} 1 & -1 & 1 \\ 2 & 0 & -1 \\ -4 & 1 & 1 \end{bmatrix} \begin{bmatrix} 31 & 37 & 29 \\ 80 & 83 & 69 \\ 54 & 67 & 50 \end{bmatrix} = \begin{bmatrix} 5 & 21 & 10 \\ 8 & 7 & 8 \\ 10 & 2 & 3 \end{bmatrix}$$

To construct a coding matrix A, we can begin with the identity I and successively apply row operation **III**, being careful to add integer multiples of one row to another. Row operation **I** can also be used. The resulting matrix A will have integer entries, and since

$$\det(A) = \pm \det(I) = \pm 1$$

A^{-1} will also have integer entries.

Reference

1. Hansen, Robert, "Integer Matrices Whose Inverses Contain Only Integers," *Two-Year College Mathematics Journal*, 13(1), 1982.

The Cross Product

Given two vectors $\mathbf{x}$ and $\mathbf{y}$ in $\mathbb{R}^3$, one can define a third vector, the *cross product*, denoted $\mathbf{x} \times \mathbf{y}$, by

$$\mathbf{x} \times \mathbf{y} = \begin{bmatrix} x_2 y_3 - y_2 x_3 \\ y_1 x_3 - x_1 y_3 \\ x_1 y_2 - y_1 x_2 \end{bmatrix} \tag{1}$$

If C is any matrix of the form

$$C = \begin{bmatrix} w_1 & w_2 & w_3 \\ x_1 & x_2 & x_3 \\ y_1 & y_2 & y_3 \end{bmatrix}$$

then

$$\mathbf{x} \times \mathbf{y} = C_{11}\mathbf{e}_1 + C_{12}\mathbf{e}_2 + C_{13}\mathbf{e}_3 = \begin{bmatrix} C_{11} \\ C_{12} \\ C_{13} \end{bmatrix}$$

Expanding $\det(C)$ by cofactors along the first row, we see that

$$\det(C) = w_1 C_{11} + w_2 C_{12} + w_3 C_{13} = \mathbf{w}^T(\mathbf{x} \times \mathbf{y})$$

In particular, if we choose $\mathbf{w} = \mathbf{x}$ or $\mathbf{w} = \mathbf{y}$, then the matrix C will have two identical rows, and hence its determinant will be 0. We then have

$$\mathbf{x}^T(\mathbf{x} \times \mathbf{y}) = \mathbf{y}^T(\mathbf{x} \times \mathbf{y}) = 0 \tag{2}$$

In calculus books, it is standard to use row vectors

$$\mathbf{x} = (x_1, x_2, x_3) \qquad \text{and} \qquad \mathbf{y} = (y_1, y_2, y_3)$$

and to define the cross product to be the row vector:

$$\mathbf{x} \times \mathbf{y} = (x_2 y_3 - y_2 x_3)\mathbf{i} - (x_1 y_3 - y_1 x_3)\mathbf{j} + (x_1 y_2 - y_1 x_2)\mathbf{k}$$

where $\mathbf{i}$, $\mathbf{j}$, and $\mathbf{k}$ are the row vectors of the 3×3 identity matrix. If one uses $\mathbf{i}$, $\mathbf{j}$, and $\mathbf{k}$ in place of w_1, w_2, and w_3, respectively, in the first row of the matrix M, then the cross product can be written as a determinant.

$$\mathbf{x} \times \mathbf{y} = \begin{vmatrix} \mathbf{i} & \mathbf{j} & \mathbf{k} \\ x_1 & x_2 & x_3 \\ y_1 & y_2 & y_3 \end{vmatrix}$$

In linear algebra courses, it is generally more standard to view $\mathbf{x}$, $\mathbf{y}$ and $\mathbf{x} \times \mathbf{y}$ as column vectors. In this case, we can represent the cross product in terms of the determinant of a matrix whose entries in the first row are $\mathbf{e}_1$, $\mathbf{e}_2$, $\mathbf{e}_3$, the column vectors of the 3×3 identity matrix:

$$\mathbf{x} \times \mathbf{y} = \begin{vmatrix} \mathbf{e}_1 & \mathbf{e}_2 & \mathbf{e}_3 \\ x_1 & x_2 & x_3 \\ y_1 & y_2 & y_3 \end{vmatrix}$$

The relation given in equation (2) has applications in Newtonian mechanics. In particular, the cross product can be used to define a *binormal* direction, which Newton used to derive the laws of motion for a particle in 3-space.

APPLICATION 2   Newtonian Mechanics

If $\mathbf{x}$ is a vector in either $\mathbb{R}^2$ or $\mathbb{R}^3$ then, we can define the *length* of $\mathbf{x}$, denoted $\|\mathbf{x}\|$, by

$$\|\mathbf{x}\| = (\mathbf{x}^T \mathbf{x})^{\frac{1}{2}}$$

A vector $\mathbf{x}$ is said to be a *unit* vector if $\|\mathbf{x}\| = 1$. Unit vectors were used by Newton to derive the laws of motion for a particle in either the plane or 3-space. If $\mathbf{x}$ and $\mathbf{y}$ are nonzero vectors in $\mathbb{R}^2$, then the angle θ between the vectors is the smallest angle of rotation necessary to rotate one of the two vectors clockwise so that it ends up in the same direction as the other vector (see Figure 2.3.1).

A particle moving in a plane traces out a curve in the plane. The position of the particle at any time t can be represented by a vector $(x_1(t), x_2(t))$. In describing the motion of a particle, Newton found it convenient to represent the position of vectors at time t as linear combinations of the vectors $\mathbf{T}(t)$ and $\mathbf{N}(t)$, where $\mathbf{T}(t)$ is a unit vector in the direction of the tangent line to curve at the point $(x_1(t), x_2(t))$ and $\mathbf{N}(t)$ is a unit vector in the direction of a normal line (a line perpendicular to the tangent line) to the curve at the given point (see Figure 2.3.2).

In Chapter 5, we will show that if $\mathbf{x}$ and $\mathbf{y}$ are nonzero vectors and θ is the angle between the vectors, then

$$\mathbf{x}^T \mathbf{y} = \|\mathbf{x}\| \|\mathbf{y}\| \cos \theta \tag{3}$$

This equation can also be used to define the angle between nonzero vectors in $\mathbb{R}^3$. It follows from (3) that the angle between the vectors is a right angle if and only if $\mathbf{x}^T \mathbf{y} = 0$.

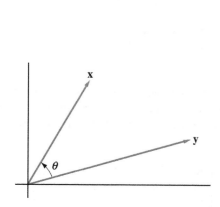

Figure 2.3.1. Figure 2.3.2.

In this case, we say that the vectors $\mathbf{x}$ and $\mathbf{y}$ are *orthogonal*. In particular, since $\mathbf{T}(t)$ and $\mathbf{N}(t)$ are unit orthogonal vectors in $\mathbb{R}^2$, we have $\|\mathbf{T}(t)\| = \|\mathbf{N}(t)\| = 1$ and the angle between the vectors is $\frac{\pi}{2}$. It follows from (3) that

$$\mathbf{T}(t)^T \mathbf{N}(t) = 0$$

In Chapter 5, we will also show that if $\mathbf{x}$ and $\mathbf{y}$ are vectors in $\mathbb{R}^3$ and θ is the angle between the vectors, then

$$\|\mathbf{x} \times \mathbf{y}\| = \|\mathbf{x}\|\|\mathbf{y}\| \sin \theta \tag{4}$$

A particle moving in three dimensions will trace out a curve in 3-space. In this case, at time t the tangent and normal lines to the curve at the point $(x_1(t), x_2(t))$ determine a plane in 3-space. However, in 3-space the motion is not restricted to a plane. To derive laws describing the motion, Newton needed to use a third vector, a vector in a direction normal to the plane determined by $\mathbf{T}(t)$ and $\mathbf{N}(t)$. If $\mathbf{z}$ is any nonzero vector in the direction of the normal line to this plane, then the angle between the vectors $\mathbf{z}$ and $\mathbf{T}(t)$ and the angle between $\mathbf{z}$ and $\mathbf{N}(t)$ should both be right angles. If we set

$$\mathbf{B}(t) = \mathbf{T}(t) \times \mathbf{N}(t) \tag{5}$$

then it follows from (2) that $\mathbf{B}(t)$ is orthogonal to both $\mathbf{T}(t)$ and $\mathbf{N}(t)$ and hence is in the direction of the normal line. Furthermore, $\mathbf{B}(t)$ is a unit vector since it follows from (4) that

$$\|\mathbf{B}(t)\| = \|\mathbf{T}(t) \times \mathbf{N}(t)\| = \|\mathbf{T}(t)\|\|\mathbf{N}(t)\| \sin \frac{\pi}{2} = 1$$

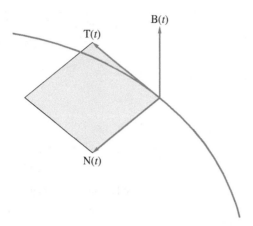

Figure 2.3.3.

The vector $\mathbf{B}(t)$ defined by (5) is called the *binormal* vector (see Figure 2.3.3).

SECTION 2.3 EXERCISES

1. For each of the following, compute (i) det(A), (ii) adj A, and (iii) A^{-1}:

(a) $A = \begin{bmatrix} 1 & 2 \\ 3 & -1 \end{bmatrix}$ **(b)** $A = \begin{bmatrix} 3 & 1 \\ 2 & 4 \end{bmatrix}$

(c) $A = \begin{bmatrix} 1 & 3 & 1 \\ 2 & 1 & 1 \\ -2 & 2 & -1 \end{bmatrix}$

(d) $A = \begin{bmatrix} 1 & 1 & 1 \\ 0 & 1 & 1 \\ 0 & 0 & 1 \end{bmatrix}$

2. Use Cramer's rule to solve each of the following systems:

(a) $\begin{aligned} x_1 + 2x_2 &= 3 \\ 3x_1 - x_2 &= 1 \end{aligned}$ **(b)** $\begin{aligned} 2x_1 + 3x_2 &= 2 \\ 3x_1 + 2x_2 &= 5 \end{aligned}$

(c) $\begin{aligned} 2x_1 + x_2 - 3x_3 &= 0 \\ 4x_1 + 5x_2 + x_3 &= 8 \\ -2x_1 - x_2 + 4x_3 &= 2 \end{aligned}$

(d) $\begin{aligned} x_1 + 3x_2 + x_3 &= 1 \\ 2x_1 + x_2 + x_3 &= 5 \\ -2x_1 + 2x_2 - x_3 &= -8 \end{aligned}$

(e) $\begin{aligned} x_1 + x_2 \qquad\qquad &= 0 \\ x_2 + x_3 - 2x_4 &= 1 \\ x_1 \qquad + 2x_3 + x_4 &= 0 \\ x_1 + x_2 \qquad\quad + x_4 &= 0 \end{aligned}$

3. Given

$$A = \begin{bmatrix} 1 & 2 & 1 \\ 0 & 4 & 3 \\ 1 & 2 & 2 \end{bmatrix}$$

determine the $(2, 3)$ entry of A^{-1} by computing a quotient of two determinants.

4. Let A be the matrix in Exercise 3. Compute the third column of A^{-1} by using Cramer's rule to solve $A\mathbf{x} = \mathbf{e}_3$.

5. Let

$$A = \begin{bmatrix} 1 & 2 & 3 \\ 2 & 3 & 4 \\ 3 & 4 & 5 \end{bmatrix}$$

(a) Compute the determinant of A. Is A nonsingular?

(b) Compute adj A and the product A adj A.

6. If A is singular, what can you say about the product A adj A?

7. Let B_j denote the matrix obtained by replacing the jth column of the identity matrix with a vector $\mathbf{b} = (b_1,\ldots,b_n)^T$. Use Cramer's rule to show that

$$b_j = \det(B_j) \qquad \text{for} \quad j = 1,\ldots,n$$

8. Let A be a nonsingular $n \times n$ matrix with $n > 1$. Show that

$$\det(\operatorname{adj} A) = (\det(A))^{n-1}$$

9. Let A be a 4×4 matrix. If

$$\operatorname{adj} A = \begin{pmatrix} 2 & 0 & 0 & 0 \\ 0 & 2 & 1 & 0 \\ 0 & 4 & 3 & 2 \\ 0 & -2 & -1 & 2 \end{pmatrix}$$

(a) calculate the value of $\det(\operatorname{adj} A)$. What should the value of $\det(A)$ be? *Hint:* Use the result from Exercise 8.

(b) find A.

10. Show that if A is nonsingular, then $\operatorname{adj} A$ is nonsingular and

$$(\operatorname{adj} A)^{-1} = \det(A^{-1})A = \operatorname{adj} A^{-1}$$

11. Show that if A is singular, then $\operatorname{adj} A$ is also singular.

12. Show that if $\det(A) = 1$, then

$$\operatorname{adj}(\operatorname{adj} A) = A$$

13. Suppose that Q is a matrix with the property $Q^{-1} = Q^T$. Show that

$$q_{ij} = \frac{Q_{ij}}{\det(Q)}$$

14. In coding a message, a blank space was represented by 0, an A by 1, a B by 2, a C by 3, and so on. The message was transformed using the matrix

$$A = \begin{pmatrix} -1 & -1 & 2 & 0 \\ 1 & 1 & -1 & 0 \\ 0 & 0 & -1 & 1 \\ 1 & 0 & 0 & -1 \end{pmatrix}$$

and sent as

$$-19, 19, 25, -21, 0, 18, -18, 15, 3, 10,$$
$$-8, 3, -2, 20, -7, 12$$

What was the message?

15. Let $\mathbf{x}$, $\mathbf{y}$, and $\mathbf{z}$ be vectors in $\mathbb{R}^3$. Show each of the following:

(a) $\mathbf{x} \times \mathbf{x} = \mathbf{0}$ (b) $\mathbf{y} \times \mathbf{x} = -(\mathbf{x} \times \mathbf{y})$

(c) $\mathbf{x} \times (\mathbf{y} + \mathbf{z}) = (\mathbf{x} \times \mathbf{y}) + (\mathbf{x} \times \mathbf{z})$

(d) $\mathbf{z}^T(\mathbf{x} \times \mathbf{y}) = \begin{vmatrix} x_1 & x_2 & x_3 \\ y_1 & y_2 & y_3 \\ z_1 & z_2 & z_3 \end{vmatrix}$

16. Let $\mathbf{x}$ and $\mathbf{y}$ be vectors in $\mathbb{R}^3$ and define the skew-symmetric matrix A_x by

$$A_x = \begin{pmatrix} 0 & -x_3 & x_2 \\ x_3 & 0 & -x_1 \\ -x_2 & x_1 & 0 \end{pmatrix}$$

(a) Show that $\mathbf{x} \times \mathbf{y} = A_x\mathbf{y}$.

(b) Show that $\mathbf{y} \times \mathbf{x} = A_x^T\mathbf{y}$.

Chapter 2 Exercises

MATLAB EXERCISES

The first four exercises that follow involve integer matrices and illustrate some of the properties of determinants that were covered in this chapter. The last two exercises illustrate some of the differences that may arise when we work with determinants in floating-point arithmetic.

In theory, the value of the determinant should tell us whether the matrix is nonsingular. However, if the matrix is singular and its determinant is computed using finite-precision arithmetic, then, because of round-off errors, the computed value of the determinant may not equal zero. A computed value near zero does not *necessarily mean that the matrix is singular or even close to being singular. Furthermore, a matrix may be nearly singular and have a determinant that is not even close to zero (see Exercise 6).*

1. Generate random 5×5 matrices with integer entries by setting

$$A = \mathbf{round}(10 * \mathbf{rand}(5))$$

and

$$B = \mathbf{round}(20 * \mathbf{rand}(5)) - 10$$

Use MATLAB to compute each of the pairs of numbers that follow. In each case, check whether the first number is equal to the second.

(a) $\det(A)$ $\det(A^T)$

(b) $\det(A + B)$ $\det(A) + \det(B)$

(c) $\det(AB)$ $\det(A)\det(B)$

(d) $\det(A^T B^T)$ $\det(A^T)\det(B^T)$

(e) $\det(A^{-1})$ $1/\det(A)$

(f) $\det(AB^{-1})$ $\det(A)/\det(B)$

2. Are $n \times n$ magic squares nonsingular? Use the MATLAB command **det(magic**(n)) to compute the determinants of the magic squares matrices in the cases $n = 3, 4, \ldots, 10$. What seems to be happening? Check the cases $n = 24$ and 25 to see if the pattern still holds.

3. Set $A = $ **round**($10 *$ **rand**(6)). In each of the following, use MATLAB to compute a second matrix as indicated. State how the second matrix is related to A and compute the determinants of both matrices. How are the determinants related?

(a) $B = A$; $B(2,:) = A(1,:)$; $B(1,:) = A(2,:)$

(b) $C = A$; $C(3,:) = 4 * A(3,:)$

(c) $D = A$; $D(5,:) = A(5,:) + 2 * A(4,:)$

4. We can generate a random 6×6 matrix A whose entries consist entirely of 0's and 1's by setting

$$A = \textbf{round}(\textbf{rand}(6))$$

(a) What percentage of these random 0–1 matrices are singular? You can estimate the percentage in MATLAB by setting

$$y = \textbf{zeros}(1, 100);$$

and then generating 100 test matrices and setting $y(j) = 1$ if the jth matrix is singular and 0 otherwise. The easy way to do this in MATLAB is to use a *for loop*. Generate the loop as follows:

```
for   j = 1 : 100
      A = round(rand(6));
      y(j) = (det(A) == 0);
end
```

(*Note*: A semicolon at the end of a line suppresses printout. It is recommended that you include one at the end of each line of calculation that occurs inside a for loop.) To determine how many singular matrices were generated, use the MATLAB command **sum(y)**. What percentage of the matrices generated were singular?

(b) For any positive integer n, we can generate a random 6×6 matrix A whose entries are integers from 0 to n by setting

$$A = \textbf{round}(n * \textbf{rand}(6))$$

What percentage of random integer matrices generated in this manner will be singular if $n = 3$? If $n = 6$? If $n = 10$? We can estimate the answers to these questions by using MATLAB. In each case, generate 100 test matrices and determine how many of the matrices are singular.

5. If a matrix is sensitive to roundoff errors, the computed value of its determinant may differ drastically from the exact value. For an example of this, set

$$U = \textbf{round}(100 * \textbf{rand}(10));$$
$$U = \textbf{triu}(U, 1) + 0.1 * \textbf{eye}(10)$$

In theory,

$$\det(U) = \det(U^T) = 10^{-10}$$

and

$$\det(UU^T) = \det(U)\det(U^T) = 10^{-20}$$

Compute $\det(U)$, $\det(U')$, and $\det(U * U')$ with MATLAB. Do the computed values match the theoretical values?

6. Use MATLAB to construct a matrix A by setting

$$A = \textbf{vander}(1 : 6);   \quad A = A - \textbf{diag}(\textbf{sum}(A'))$$

(a) By construction, the entries in each row of A should all add up to zero. To check this, set $\mathbf{x} = \textbf{ones}(6, 1)$ and use MATLAB to compute the product $A\mathbf{x}$. The matrix A should be singular. Why? Explain. Use the MATLAB functions **det** and **inv** to compute the values of $\det(A)$ and A^{-1}. Which MATLAB function is a more reliable indicator of singularity?

(b) Use MATLAB to compute $\det(A^T)$. Are the computed values of $\det(A)$ and $\det(A^T)$ equal? Another way to check if a matrix is singular is to compute its reduced row echelon form. Use MATLAB to compute the reduced row echelon forms of A and A^T.

(c) To see what is going wrong, it helps to know how MATLAB computes determinants. The MATLAB routine for determinants first computes a form of the LU factorization of the matrix. The determinant of the matrix L is ± 1, depending on whether an even or odd number of row interchanges were used in the computation. The computed value of the determinant of A is the product of the diagonal entries of U and $\det(L) = \pm 1$. To see what is happening with our original matrix, use the following commands to compute and display the factor U:

$$\textbf{format short e}$$
$$[\,L, U\,] = \textbf{lu}(A); \ U$$

In exact arithmetic, U should be singular. Is the computed matrix U singular? If not, what goes wrong? Use the following commands to see the rest of the computation of $d = \det(A)$:

$$\textbf{format short}$$
$$d = \textbf{prod}(\textbf{diag}(U))$$

CHAPTER TEST A True or False

For each statement that follows, answer *true* if the statement is always true and *false* otherwise. In the case of a true statement, explain or prove your answer. In the case of a false statement, give an example to show that the statement is not always true. Assume that all the given matrices are $n \times n$.

1. $\det(AB) = \det(BA)$
2. $\det(A + B) = \det(A) + \det(B)$
3. $\det(cA) = c \det(A)$
4. $\det((AB)^T) = \det(A)\det(B)$
5. $\det(A) = \det(B)$ implies $A = B$.
6. $\det(A^k) = \det(A)^k$
7. A triangular matrix is nonsingular if and only if its diagonal entries are all nonzero.
8. If $\mathbf{x}$ is a nonzero vector in $\mathbb{R}^n$ and $A\mathbf{x} = \mathbf{0}$, then $\det(A) = 0$.
9. If A and B are row equivalent matrices, then their determinants are equal.
10. If $A \neq O$, but $A^k = O$ (where O denotes the zero matrix) for some positive integer k, then A must be singular.

CHAPTER TEST B

1. Let A and B be 3×3 matrices with $\det(A) = 4$ and $\det(B) = 6$, and let E be an elementary matrix of type I. Determine the value of each of the following:
   (a) $\det(\frac{1}{2}A)$ **(b)** $\det(B^{-1}A^T)$ **(c)** $\det(EA^2)$

2. Let
$$A = \begin{bmatrix} x & 1 & 1 \\ 1 & x & -1 \\ -1 & -1 & x \end{bmatrix}$$

   (a) Compute the value of $\det(A)$ (Your answer should be a function of x.)
   (b) For what values of x will the matrix be singular? Explain.

3. Let
$$A = \begin{bmatrix} 1 & 1 & 1 & 1 \\ 1 & 2 & 3 & 4 \\ 1 & 3 & 6 & 10 \\ 1 & 4 & 10 & 20 \end{bmatrix}$$

   (a) Compute the LU factorization of A.
   (b) Use the LU factorization to determine the value of $\det(A)$.

4. If A is a nonsingular $n \times n$ matrix, show that $A^T A$ is nonsingular and $\det(A^T A) > 0$.

5. Let A be an $n \times n$ matrix. Show that if $B = S^{-1}AS$ for some nonsingular matrix S, then $\det(B) = \det(A)$.

6. Let A and B be $n \times n$ matrices and let $C = AB$. Use determinants to show that if either A or B is singular, then C must be singular.

7. Let A be an $n \times n$ matrix and let λ be a scalar. Show that
$$\det(A - \lambda I) = 0$$
   if and only if
$$A\mathbf{x} = \lambda\mathbf{x} \text{ for some } \mathbf{x} \neq \mathbf{0}$$

8. Let $\mathbf{x}$ and $\mathbf{y}$ be vectors in $\mathbb{R}^n$, $n > 1$. Show that if $A = \mathbf{x}\mathbf{y}^T$, then $\det(A) = 0$.

9. Let $\mathbf{x}$ and $\mathbf{y}$ be distinct vectors in $\mathbb{R}^n$ (i.e., $\mathbf{x} \neq \mathbf{y}$), and let A be an $n \times n$ matrix with the property that $A\mathbf{x} = A\mathbf{y}$. Show that $\det(A) = 0$.

10. Let A be a matrix with integer entries. If $|\det(A)| = 1$, then what can you conclude about the nature of the entries of A^{-1}? Explain.

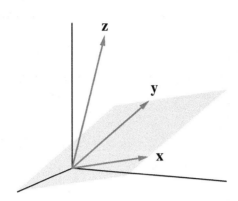

3

Vector Spaces

The operations of addition and scalar multiplication are used in many diverse contexts in mathematics. Regardless of the context, however, these operations usually obey the same set of algebraic rules. Thus, a general theory of mathematical systems involving addition and scalar multiplication will be applicable to many areas in mathematics. Mathematical systems of this form are called vector spaces or linear spaces. In this chapter, the definition of a vector space is given and some of the general theory of vector spaces is developed.

3.1 Definition and Examples

In this section, we present the formal definition of a vector space. Before doing this, however, it is instructive to look at a number of examples. We begin with the Euclidean vector spaces $\mathbb{R}^n$.

Euclidean Vector Spaces

Perhaps the most elementary vector spaces are the Euclidean vector spaces $\mathbb{R}^n$, $n = 1, 2, \ldots$. For simplicity, let us consider first $\mathbb{R}^2$. Nonzero vectors in $\mathbb{R}^2$ can be represented geometrically by directed line segments. This geometric representation will help us to visualize how the operations of scalar multiplication and addition work in $\mathbb{R}^2$.

Given a nonzero vector $\mathbf{x} = \begin{bmatrix} x_1 \\ x_2 \end{bmatrix}$, we can associate it with the directed line segment in the plane from $(0,0)$ to (x_1, x_2) (see Figure 3.1.1). If we equate line segments that have the same length and direction (Figure 3.1.2), $\mathbf{x}$ can be represented by any line segment from (a, b) to $(a + x_1, b + x_2)$.

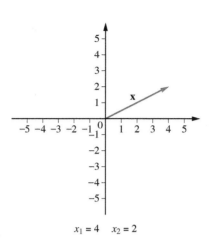

$x_1 = 4 \quad x_2 = 2$

Figure 3.1.1.

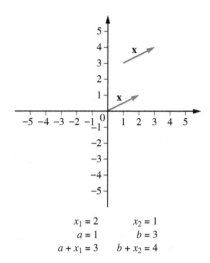

$x_1 = 2 \qquad x_2 = 1$
$a = 1 \qquad b = 3$
$a + x_1 = 3 \qquad b + x_2 = 4$

Figure 3.1.2.

For example, the vector $\mathbf{x} = \begin{bmatrix} 2 \\ 1 \end{bmatrix}$ in $\mathbb{R}^2$ could just as well be represented by the directed line segment from $(2, 2)$ to $(4, 3)$ or from $(-1, -1)$ to $(1, 0)$, as shown in Figure 3.1.3.

Figure 3.1.3.

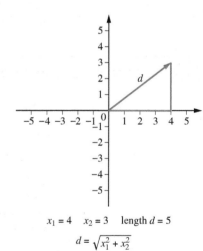

$x_1 = 4 \quad x_2 = 3 \quad \text{length } d = 5$

$$d = \sqrt{x_1^2 + x_2^2}$$

Figure 3.1.4.

We can think of the Euclidean length of a vector $\mathbf{x} = \begin{bmatrix} x_1 \\ x_2 \end{bmatrix}$ as the length of any directed line segment representing $\mathbf{x}$. The length of the line segment from $(0, 0)$ to (x_1, x_2) is $\sqrt{x_1^2 + x_2^2}$ (see Figure 3.1.4). For each vector $\mathbf{x} = \begin{bmatrix} x_1 \\ x_2 \end{bmatrix}$ and each scalar α, the product $\alpha\mathbf{x}$ is defined by

$$\alpha \begin{bmatrix} x_1 \\ x_2 \end{bmatrix} = \begin{bmatrix} \alpha x_1 \\ \alpha x_2 \end{bmatrix}$$

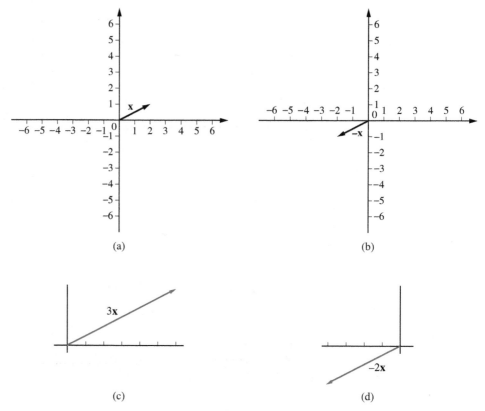

Figure 3.1.5.

For example, as shown in Figure 3.1.5, if $\mathbf{x} = \begin{bmatrix} 2 \\ 1 \end{bmatrix}$, then

$$-\mathbf{x} = \begin{bmatrix} -2 \\ -1 \end{bmatrix}, \qquad 3\mathbf{x} = \begin{bmatrix} 6 \\ 3 \end{bmatrix}, \qquad -2\mathbf{x} = \begin{bmatrix} -4 \\ -2 \end{bmatrix}$$

The vector $3\mathbf{x}$ is in the same direction as $\mathbf{x}$, but its length is three times that of $\mathbf{x}$. The vector $-\mathbf{x}$ has the same length as $\mathbf{x}$, but it points in the opposite direction. The vector $-2\mathbf{x}$ is twice as long as $\mathbf{x}$ and it points in the same direction as $-\mathbf{x}$. The sum of two vectors

$$\mathbf{u} = \begin{bmatrix} u_1 \\ u_2 \end{bmatrix} \qquad \text{and} \qquad \mathbf{v} = \begin{bmatrix} v_1 \\ v_2 \end{bmatrix}$$

is defined by

$$\mathbf{u} + \mathbf{v} = \begin{bmatrix} u_1 + v_1 \\ u_2 + v_2 \end{bmatrix}$$

Note that if $\mathbf{v}$ is placed at the terminal point of $\mathbf{u}$, then $\mathbf{u}+\mathbf{v}$ is represented by the directed line segment from the initial point of $\mathbf{u}$ to the terminal point of $\mathbf{v}$ (Figure 3.1.6). If both $\mathbf{u}$ and $\mathbf{v}$ are placed at the origin and a parallelogram is formed as in Figure 3.1.7, the diagonals of the parallelogram will represent the sum $\mathbf{u}+\mathbf{v}$ and the difference $\mathbf{v}-\mathbf{u}$. In

Figure 3.1.6.   Figure 3.1.7.

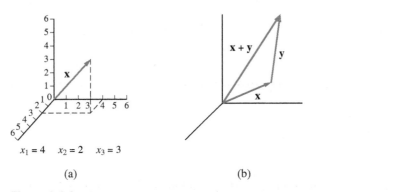

(a)   (b)

Figure 3.1.8.

a similar manner, vectors in $\mathbb{R}^3$ can be represented by directed line segments in 3-space (see Figure 3.1.8).

In general, scalar multiplication and addition in $\mathbb{R}^n$ are, respectively, defined by

$$
\alpha \mathbf{x} = \begin{bmatrix} \alpha x_1 \\ \alpha x_2 \\ \vdots \\ \alpha x_n \end{bmatrix} \quad \text{and} \quad \mathbf{x} + \mathbf{y} = \begin{bmatrix} x_1 + y_1 \\ x_2 + y_2 \\ \vdots \\ x_n + y_n \end{bmatrix}
$$

for any $\mathbf{x}, \mathbf{y} \in \mathbb{R}^n$ and any scalar α.

The Vector Space $\mathbb{R}^{m \times n}$

We can also view $\mathbb{R}^n$ as the set of all $n \times 1$ matrices with real entries. The addition and scalar multiplication of vectors in $\mathbb{R}^n$ are just the usual addition and scalar multiplication of matrices. More generally, let $\mathbb{R}^{m \times n}$ denote the set of all $m \times n$ matrices with real entries. If $A = (a_{ij})$ and $B = (b_{ij})$, then the sum $A + B$ is defined to be the $m \times n$ matrix $C = (c_{ij})$, where $c_{ij} = a_{ij} + b_{ij}$. Given a scalar α, we can define αA to be the $m \times n$ matrix whose (i, j) entry is αa_{ij}. Thus, by defining operations on the set $\mathbb{R}^{m \times n}$, we have created a mathematical system. The operations of addition and scalar multiplication of $\mathbb{R}^{m \times n}$ obey certain algebraic rules. These rules form the axioms that are used to define the concept of a vector space.

Vector Space Axioms

Definition

> Let V be a set on which the operations of addition and scalar multiplication are defined. By this we mean that, with each pair of elements $\mathbf{x}$ and $\mathbf{y}$ in V, we can associate a unique element $\mathbf{x} + \mathbf{y}$ that is also in V, and with each element $\mathbf{x}$ in V and each scalar α, we can associate a unique element $\alpha \mathbf{x}$ in V. The set V together with the operations of addition and scalar multiplication is said to form a **vector space** if the following axioms are satisfied:
>
> **A1.** $\mathbf{x} + \mathbf{y} = \mathbf{y} + \mathbf{x}$ for any $\mathbf{x}$ and $\mathbf{y}$ in V.
> **A2.** $(\mathbf{x} + \mathbf{y}) + \mathbf{z} = \mathbf{x} + (\mathbf{y} + \mathbf{z})$ for any $\mathbf{x}, \mathbf{y}$, and $\mathbf{z}$ in V.
> **A3.** There exists an element $\mathbf{0}$ in V such that $\mathbf{x} + \mathbf{0} = \mathbf{x}$ for each $\mathbf{x} \in V$.
> **A4.** For each $\mathbf{x} \in V$, there exists an element $-\mathbf{x}$ in V such that $\mathbf{x} + (-\mathbf{x}) = \mathbf{0}$.
> **A5.** $\alpha(\mathbf{x} + \mathbf{y}) = \alpha \mathbf{x} + \alpha \mathbf{y}$ for each scalar α and any $\mathbf{x}$ and $\mathbf{y}$ in V.
> **A6.** $(\alpha + \beta)\mathbf{x} = \alpha \mathbf{x} + \beta \mathbf{x}$ for any scalars α and β and any $\mathbf{x} \in V$.
> **A7.** $(\alpha\beta)\mathbf{x} = \alpha(\beta \mathbf{x})$ for any scalars α and β and any $\mathbf{x} \in V$.
> **A8.** $1\mathbf{x} = \mathbf{x}$ for all $\mathbf{x} \in V$.

We will refer to the set V as the universal set for the vector space. Its elements are called **vectors** and are usually denoted by boldface letters such as $\mathbf{u}, \mathbf{v}, \mathbf{w}, \mathbf{x}, \mathbf{y}$, and $\mathbf{z}$. The term *scalar* will generally refer to a real number, although in some cases it will be used to refer to complex numbers. Scalars will generally be represented by lowercase italic letters such as a, b, and c or lowercase Greek letters such as α, β, and γ. In the first five chapters of this book, the term *scalars* will always refer to real numbers. Often the term *real vector space* is used to indicate that the set of scalars is the set of real numbers. The boldface symbol $\mathbf{0}$ was used in Axiom 3 in order to distinguish the zero vector from the scalar 0.

An important component of the definition is the closure properties of the two operations. These properties can be summarized as follows:

C1. If $\mathbf{x} \in V$ and α is a scalar, then $\alpha \mathbf{x} \in V$.
C2. If $\mathbf{x}, \mathbf{y} \in V$, then $\mathbf{x} + \mathbf{y} \in V$.

To illustrate the necessity of the closure properties, consider the following example. Let

$$W = \{(a, 1) \mid a \text{ real}\}$$

with addition and scalar multiplication defined in the usual way. The elements $(3, 1)$ and $(5, 1)$ are in W, but the sum

$$(3, 1) + (5, 1) = (8, 2)$$

is not an element of W. The operation $+$ is not really an operation on the set W because property **C2** fails to hold. Similarly, scalar multiplication is not defined on W, because property **C1** fails to hold. The set W, together with the operations of addition and scalar multiplication, is *not* a vector space.

If, however, we are given a set U on which the operations of addition and scalar multiplication have been defined and satisfy properties **C1** and **C2**, then we must check to see if the eight axioms are valid in order to determine whether U is a vector space. We leave it to the reader to verify that $\mathbb{R}^n$ and $\mathbb{R}^{m \times n}$, with the usual addition and scalar multiplication of matrices, are both vector spaces. There are a number of other important examples of vector spaces.

The Vector Space $C[a, b]$

Let $C[a, b]$ denote the set of all real-valued functions that are defined and continuous on the closed interval $[a, b]$. In this case, our universal set is a set of functions. Thus, our vectors are the functions in $C[a, b]$. The sum $f + g$ of two functions in $C[a, b]$ is defined by

$$(f + g)(x) = f(x) + g(x)$$

for all x in $[a, b]$. The new function $f + g$ is an element of $C[a, b]$ since the sum of two continuous functions is continuous. If f is a function in $C[a, b]$ and α is a real number, define αf by

$$(\alpha f)(x) = \alpha f(x)$$

for all x in $[a, b]$. Clearly, αf is in $C[a, b]$ since a constant times a continuous function is always continuous. Thus, we have defined the operations of addition and scalar multiplication on $C[a, b]$. To show that the first axiom, $f + g = g + f$, is satisfied, we must show that

$$(f + g)(x) = (g + f)(x) \qquad \text{for every } x \text{ in } [a, b]$$

This follows because

$$(f + g)(x) = f(x) + g(x) = g(x) + f(x) = (g + f)(x)$$

for every x in $[a, b]$. Axiom 3 is satisfied, since the function

$$z(x) = 0 \quad \text{for all } x \text{ in } [a, b]$$

acts as the zero vector; that is,

$$f + z = f \quad \text{for all } f \text{ in } C[a, b]$$

We leave it to the reader to verify that the remaining vector space axioms are all satisfied.

The Vector Space P_n

Let P_n denote the set of all polynomials of degree less than n. Define $p + q$ and αp, respectively, by

$$(p + q)(x) = p(x) + q(x)$$

and

$$(\alpha p)(x) = \alpha p(x)$$

for all real numbers x. In this case, the zero vector is the zero polynomial:

$$z(x) = 0x^{n-1} + 0x^{n-2} + \cdots + 0x + 0$$

It is easily verified that all the vector space axioms hold. Thus, P_n, with the standard addition and scalar multiplication of functions, is a vector space.

Additional Properties of Vector Spaces

We close this section with a theorem that states three more fundamental properties of vector spaces. Other important properties are given in Exercises 7, 8, and 9 at the end of the section.

Theorem 3.1.1   *If V is a vector space and* $\mathbf{x}$ *is any element of V, then*

(i) $0\mathbf{x} = \mathbf{0}$.

(ii) $\mathbf{x} + \mathbf{y} = \mathbf{0}$ *implies that* $\mathbf{y} = -\mathbf{x}$ *(i.e., the additive inverse of* $\mathbf{x}$ *is unique).*

(iii) $(-1)\mathbf{x} = -\mathbf{x}$.

Proof   It follows from axioms A6 and A8 that

$$\mathbf{x} = 1\mathbf{x} = (1 + 0)\mathbf{x} = 1\mathbf{x} + 0\mathbf{x} = \mathbf{x} + 0\mathbf{x}$$

Thus,

$$-\mathbf{x} + \mathbf{x} = -\mathbf{x} + (\mathbf{x} + 0\mathbf{x}) = (-\mathbf{x} + \mathbf{x}) + 0\mathbf{x} \qquad \textbf{(A2)}$$
$$\mathbf{0} = \mathbf{0} + 0\mathbf{x} = 0\mathbf{x} \qquad \textbf{(A1, A3, and A4)}$$

To prove **(ii)**, suppose that $\mathbf{x} + \mathbf{y} = \mathbf{0}$. Then

$$-\mathbf{x} = -\mathbf{x} + \mathbf{0} = -\mathbf{x} + (\mathbf{x} + \mathbf{y})$$

Therefore,

$$-\mathbf{x} = (-\mathbf{x} + \mathbf{x}) + \mathbf{y} = \mathbf{0} + \mathbf{y} = \mathbf{y} \qquad \textbf{(A1, A2, A3, and A4)}$$

Finally, to prove **(iii)**, note that

$$\mathbf{0} = 0\mathbf{x} = (1 + (-1))\mathbf{x} = 1\mathbf{x} + (-1)\mathbf{x} \qquad \textbf{[(i) and A6]}$$

Thus,

$$\mathbf{x} + (-1)\mathbf{x} = \mathbf{0} \qquad \textbf{(A8)}$$

and it follows from part **(ii)** that

$$(-1)\mathbf{x} = -\mathbf{x} \qquad \blacksquare$$

SECTION 3.1 EXERCISES

1. Consider the vectors $\mathbf{x}_1 = (8, \ 6)^T$ and $\mathbf{x}_2 = (4, \ -1)^T$ in $\mathbb{R}^2$.

    (a) Determine the length of each vector.

    (b) Let $\mathbf{x}_3 = \mathbf{x}_1 + \mathbf{x}_2$. Determine the length of $\mathbf{x}_3$. How does its length compare with the sum of the lengths of $\mathbf{x}_1$ and $\mathbf{x}_2$?

    (c) Draw a graph illustrating how $\mathbf{x}_3$ can be constructed geometrically using $\mathbf{x}_1$ and $\mathbf{x}_2$. Use this graph to give a geometrical interpretation of your answer to the question in part (b).

2. Repeat Exercise 1 for the vectors $\mathbf{x}_1 = (2, \ 1)^T$ and $\mathbf{x}_2 = (6, \ 3)^T$.

3. Let C be the set of complex numbers. Define addition on C by

    $$(a + bi) + (c + di) = (a + c) + (b + d)i$$

    and define scalar multiplication by

    $$\alpha(a + bi) = \alpha a + \alpha bi$$

    for all real numbers α. Show that C is a vector space with these operations.

4. Show that $\mathbb{R}^{m \times n}$, together with the usual addition and scalar multiplication of matrices, satisfies the eight axioms of a vector space.

5. Show that $C[a, b]$, together with the usual scalar multiplication and addition of functions, satisfies the eight axioms of a vector space.

6. Let P be the set of all polynomials. Show that P, together with the usual addition and scalar multiplication of functions, forms a vector space.

7. Show that the element $\mathbf{0}$ in a vector space is unique.

8. Let $\mathbf{x}$, $\mathbf{y}$, and $\mathbf{z}$ be vectors in a vector space V. Prove that if

    $$\mathbf{x} + \mathbf{y} = \mathbf{x} + \mathbf{z}$$

    then $\mathbf{y} = \mathbf{z}$.

9. Let V be a vector space and let $\mathbf{x} \in V$. Show that
    (a) $\beta \mathbf{0} = \mathbf{0}$ for each scalar β.

    (b) if $\alpha \mathbf{x} = \mathbf{0}$, then either $\alpha = 0$ or $\mathbf{x} = \mathbf{0}$.

10. Let S be the set of all ordered pairs of real numbers. Define scalar multiplication and addition on S by

    $$\alpha(x_1, x_2) = (\alpha x_1, \alpha x_2)$$

    $$(x_1, x_2) \oplus (y_1, y_2) = (x_1 + y_1, 0)$$

We use the symbol $\oplus$ to denote the addition operation for this system in order to avoid confusion with the usual addition $\mathbf{x} + \mathbf{y}$ of row vectors. Show that S, together with the ordinary scalar multiplication and the addition operation $\oplus$, is not a vector space. Which of the eight axioms fail to hold?

11. Let V be the set of all ordered pairs of real numbers with addition defined by

    $$(x_1, x_2) + (y_1, y_2) = (x_1 + y_1, x_2 + y_2)$$

    and scalar multiplication defined by

    $$\alpha \circ (x_1, x_2) = (\alpha x_1, x_2)$$

    Scalar multiplication for this system is defined in an unusual way, and consequently, we use the symbol $\circ$ to avoid confusion with the ordinary scalar multiplication of row vectors. Is V a vector space with these operations? Justify your answer.

12. Let R^+ denote the set of positive real numbers. Define the operation of scalar multiplication, denoted $\circ$, by

    $$\alpha \circ x = x^\alpha$$

    for each $x \in R^+$ and for any real number α. Define the operation of addition, denoted $\oplus$, by

    $$x \oplus y = x \cdot y \qquad \text{for all} \qquad x, y \in R^+$$

    Thus, for this system, the scalar product of -3 times $\frac{1}{2}$ is given by

    $$-3 \circ \frac{1}{2} = \left(\frac{1}{2}\right)^{-3} = 8$$

    and the sum of 2 and 5 is given by

    $$2 \oplus 5 = 2 \cdot 5 = 10$$

    Is R^+ a vector space with these operations? Prove your answer.

13. Let R denote the set of real numbers. Define scalar multiplication by

    $$\alpha x = \alpha \cdot x \qquad \text{(the usual multiplication of real numbers)}$$

    and define addition, denoted $\oplus$, by

    $$x \oplus y = \max(x, y) \qquad \text{(the maximum of the two numbers)}$$

    Is R a vector space with these operations? Prove your answer.

14. Let Z denote the set of all integers with addition defined in the usual way and define scalar multiplication, denoted $\circ$, by

    $$\alpha \circ k = [[\alpha]] \cdot k \qquad \text{for all} \qquad k \in Z$$

where $[[\alpha]]$ denotes the greatest integer less than or equal to α. For example,

$$2.25 \circ 4 = [[2.25]] \cdot 4 = 2 \cdot 4 = 8$$

Show that Z, together with these operations, is not a vector space. Which axioms fail to hold?

15. Let S denote the set of all infinite sequences of real numbers with scalar multiplication and addition defined by

$$\alpha\{a_n\} = \{\alpha a_n\}$$
$$\{a_n\} + \{b_n\} = \{a_n + b_n\}$$

Show that S is a vector space.

16. We can define a one-to-one correspondence between the elements of P_n and $\mathbb{R}^n$ by

$$p(x) = a_1 + a_2 x + \cdots + a_n x^{n-1}$$
$$\leftrightarrow (a_1, \ldots, a_n)^T = \mathbf{a}$$

Show that if $p \leftrightarrow \mathbf{a}$ and $q \leftrightarrow \mathbf{b}$, then

(a) $\alpha p \leftrightarrow \alpha\mathbf{a}$ for any scalar α.

(b) $p + q \leftrightarrow \mathbf{a} + \mathbf{b}$.

[In general, two vector spaces are said to be *isomorphic* if their elements can be put into a one-to-one correspondence that is preserved under scalar multiplication and addition as in (a) and (b).]

3.2   Subspaces

Given a vector space V, it is often possible to form another vector space by taking a subset S of V and using the operations of V. Since V is a vector space, the operations of addition and scalar multiplication always produce another vector in V. For a new system using a subset S of V as its universal set to be a vector space, the set S must be closed under the operations of addition and scalar multiplication. That is, the sum of two elements of S must always be an element of S, and the product of a scalar and an element of S must always be an element of S.

EXAMPLE I   Let

$$S = \left\{ \left. \begin{bmatrix} x_1 \\ x_2 \end{bmatrix} \right| \; x_2 = 2x_1 \right\}$$

S is a subset of $\mathbb{R}^2$. If

$$\mathbf{x} = \begin{bmatrix} c \\ 2c \end{bmatrix}$$

is any element of S and α is any scalar, then

$$\alpha\mathbf{x} = \alpha \begin{bmatrix} c \\ 2c \end{bmatrix} = \begin{bmatrix} \alpha c \\ 2\alpha c \end{bmatrix}$$

is also an element of S. If

$$\begin{bmatrix} a \\ 2a \end{bmatrix} \quad \text{and} \quad \begin{bmatrix} b \\ 2b \end{bmatrix}$$

are any two elements of S, then their sum

$$\begin{bmatrix} a + b \\ 2a + 2b \end{bmatrix} = \begin{bmatrix} a + b \\ 2(a + b) \end{bmatrix}$$

is also an element of S. It is easily seen that the mathematical system consisting of the set S (instead of $\mathbb{R}^2$), together with the operations from $\mathbb{R}^2$, is itself a vector space. ∎

Definition

If S is a nonempty subset of a vector space V, and S satisfies the conditions

    (i) $\alpha \mathbf{x} \in S$ whenever $\mathbf{x} \in S$ for any scalar α

    (ii) $\mathbf{x} + \mathbf{y} \in S$ whenever $\mathbf{x} \in S$ and $\mathbf{y} \in S$

then S is said to be a **subspace** of V.

Condition **(i)** says that S is closed under scalar multiplication. That is, whenever an element of S is multiplied by a scalar, the result is an element of S. Condition **(ii)** says that S is closed under addition. That is, the sum of two elements of S is always an element of S. Thus, if we use the operations from V and the elements of S, to do arithmetic, then we will always end up with elements of S. A subspace of V, then, is a subset S that is closed under the operations of V.

Let S be a subspace of a vector space V. Using the operations of addition and scalar multiplication as defined on V, we can form a new mathematical system with S as the universal set. It is easily seen that all eight axioms will remain valid for this new system. Axioms A3 and A4 follow from Theorem 3.1.1 and condition **(i)** of the definition of a subspace. The remaining six axioms are valid for any elements of V, so, in particular, they are valid for the elements of S. Thus, the mathematical system with universal set S and the two operations inherited from the vector space V satisfies all the conditions in the definition of a vector space. *Every subspace of a vector space is a vector space in its own right.*

Remarks

1. In a vector space V, it can be readily verified that $\{\mathbf{0}\}$ and V are subspaces of V. All other subspaces are referred to as *proper subspaces*. We refer to $\{\mathbf{0}\}$ as the *zero subspace*.

2. To show that a subset S of a vector space forms a subspace, we must show that S is nonempty and that the closure properties **(i)** and **(ii)** in the definition are satisfied. Since every subspace must contain the zero vector, we can verify that S is nonempty by showing that $\mathbf{0} \in S$.

EXAMPLE 2 Let $S = \{(x_1, x_2, x_3)^T \mid x_1 = x_2\}$. The set S is nonempty since $\mathbf{0} = (0, 0, 0)^T \in S$. To show that S is a subspace of $\mathbb{R}^3$, we need to verify that the two closure properties hold:

    (i) If $\mathbf{x} = (a, a, b)^T$ is any vector in S, then

$$\alpha \mathbf{x} = (\alpha a, \alpha a, \alpha b)^T \in S$$

    (ii) If $(a, a, b)^T$ and $(c, c, d)^T$ are arbitrary elements of S, then

$$(a, a, b)^T + (c, c, d)^T = (a + c, a + c, b + d)^T \in S$$

Since S is nonempty and satisfies the two closure conditions, it follows that S is a subspace of $\mathbb{R}^3$. ∎

EXAMPLE 3 Let

$$S = \left\{ \begin{bmatrix} x \\ 1 \end{bmatrix} \,\middle|\, x \text{ is a real number} \right\}$$

If either of the two conditions in the definition fails to hold, then S will not be a subspace. In this case, the first condition fails since

$$\alpha \begin{bmatrix} x \\ 1 \end{bmatrix} = \begin{bmatrix} \alpha x \\ \alpha \end{bmatrix} \notin S \quad \text{when } \alpha \neq 1$$

Therefore, S is not a subspace. Actually, both conditions fail to hold. S is not closed under addition, since

$$\begin{bmatrix} x \\ 1 \end{bmatrix} + \begin{bmatrix} y \\ 1 \end{bmatrix} = \begin{bmatrix} x+y \\ 2 \end{bmatrix} \notin S$$

■

EXAMPLE 4   Let $S = \{A \in \mathbb{R}^{2 \times 2} \mid a_{12} = -a_{21}\}$. The set S is nonempty, since O (the zero matrix) is in S. To show that S is a subspace, we verify that the closure properties are satisfied:

(i) If $A \in S$, then A must be of the form

$$A = \begin{bmatrix} a & b \\ -b & c \end{bmatrix}$$

and hence,

$$\alpha A = \begin{bmatrix} \alpha a & \alpha b \\ -\alpha b & \alpha c \end{bmatrix}$$

Since the $(2, 1)$ entry of αA is the negative of the $(1, 2)$ entry, $\alpha A \in S$.

(ii) If $A, B \in S$, then they must be of the form

$$A = \begin{bmatrix} a & b \\ -b & c \end{bmatrix} \quad \text{and} \quad B = \begin{bmatrix} d & e \\ -e & f \end{bmatrix}$$

It follows that

$$A + B = \begin{bmatrix} a+d & b+e \\ -(b+e) & c+f \end{bmatrix}$$

Hence, $A + B \in S$.

■

EXAMPLE 5   Let S be the set of all polynomials of degree less than n with the property that $p(0) = 0$. The set S is nonempty since it contains the zero polynomial. We claim that S is a subspace of P_n. This follows, because

(i) if $p(x) \in S$ and α is a scalar, then

$$\alpha p(0) = \alpha \cdot 0 = 0$$

and hence $\alpha p \in S$; and

(ii) if $p(x)$ and $q(x)$ are elements of S, then

$$(p + q)(0) = p(0) + q(0) = 0 + 0 = 0$$

and hence $p + q \in S$.

■

EXAMPLE 6   Let $C^n[a, b]$ be the set of all functions f that have a continuous nth derivative on $[a, b]$. We leave it to the reader to verify that $C^n[a, b]$ is a subspace of $C[a, b]$.

■

EXAMPLE 7   The function $f(x) = |x|$ is in $C[-1, 1]$, but it is not differentiable at $x = 0$ and hence it is not in $C^1[-1, 1]$. This shows that $C^1[-1, 1]$ is a proper subspace of $C[-1, 1]$. The function $g(x) = x|x|$ is in $C^1[-1, 1]$ since it is differentiable at every point in $[-1, 1]$ and $g'(x) = 2|x|$ is continuous on $[-1, 1]$. However, $g \notin C^2[-1, 1]$ since $g''(x)$ is not defined when $x = 0$. Thus, the vector space $C^2[-1, 1]$ is a proper subspace of both $C[-1, 1]$ and $C^1[-1, 1]$.   ■

EXAMPLE 8   Let S be the set of all f in $C^2[a, b]$ such that

$$f''(x) + f(x) = 0$$

for all x in $[a, b]$. The set S is nonempty since the zero function is in S. If $f \in S$ and α is any scalar, then for any x in $[a, b]$

$$(\alpha f)''(x) + (\alpha f)(x) = \alpha f''(x) + \alpha f(x)$$
$$= \alpha(f''(x) + f(x)) = \alpha \cdot 0 = 0$$

Thus, $\alpha f \in S$. If f and g are both in S, then

$$(f + g)''(x) + (f + g)(x) = f''(x) + g''(x) + f(x) + g(x)$$
$$= [f''(x) + f(x)] + [g''(x) + g(x)]$$
$$= 0 + 0 = 0$$

Thus, the set of all solutions on $[a, b]$ to the differential equation $y'' + y = 0$ forms a subspace of $C^2[a, b]$. If we note that $f(x) = \sin x$ and $g(x) = \cos x$ are both in S, it follows that any function of the form $c_1 \sin x + c_2 \cos x$ must also be in S. We can easily verify that functions of this form are solutions to $y'' + y = 0$.   ■

The Null Space of a Matrix

Let A be an $m \times n$ matrix. Let $N(A)$ denote the set of all solutions to the homogeneous system $A\mathbf{x} = \mathbf{0}$. Thus,

$$N(A) = \{\mathbf{x} \in \mathbb{R}^n \mid A\mathbf{x} = \mathbf{0}\}$$

We claim that $N(A)$ is a subspace of $\mathbb{R}^n$. Clearly, $\mathbf{0} \in N(A)$, so $N(A)$ is nonempty. If $\mathbf{x} \in N(A)$ and α is a scalar, then

$$A(\alpha \mathbf{x}) = \alpha A\mathbf{x} = \alpha\mathbf{0} = \mathbf{0}$$

and hence $\alpha\mathbf{x} \in N(A)$. If $\mathbf{x}$ and $\mathbf{y}$ are elements of $N(A)$, then

$$A(\mathbf{x} + \mathbf{y}) = A\mathbf{x} + A\mathbf{y} = \mathbf{0} + \mathbf{0} = \mathbf{0}$$

Therefore, $\mathbf{x} + \mathbf{y} \in N(A)$. It then follows that $N(A)$ is a subspace of $\mathbb{R}^n$. The set of all solutions of the homogeneous system $A\mathbf{x} = \mathbf{0}$ forms a subspace of $\mathbb{R}^n$. The subspace $N(A)$ is called the *null space* of A.

EXAMPLE 9   Determine $N(A)$ if

$$A = \begin{pmatrix} 1 & 1 & 1 & 0 \\ 2 & 1 & 0 & 1 \end{pmatrix}$$

Solution

Using Gauss–Jordan reduction to solve $A\mathbf{x} = \mathbf{0}$, we obtain

$$\left[\begin{array}{cccc|c} 1 & 1 & 1 & 0 & 0 \\ 2 & 1 & 0 & 1 & 0 \end{array}\right] \rightarrow \left[\begin{array}{cccc|c} 1 & 1 & 1 & 0 & 0 \\ 0 & -1 & -2 & 1 & 0 \end{array}\right]$$

$$\rightarrow \left[\begin{array}{cccc|c} 1 & 0 & -1 & 1 & 0 \\ 0 & -1 & -2 & 1 & 0 \end{array}\right] \rightarrow \left[\begin{array}{cccc|c} 1 & 0 & -1 & 1 & 0 \\ 0 & 1 & 2 & -1 & 0 \end{array}\right]$$

The reduced row echelon form involves two free variables, x_3 and x_4.

$$x_1 = x_3 - x_4$$
$$x_2 = -2x_3 + x_4$$

Thus, if we set $x_3 = \alpha$ and $x_4 = \beta$, then

$$\mathbf{x} = \left[\begin{array}{c} \alpha - \beta \\ -2\alpha + \beta \\ \alpha \\ \beta \end{array}\right] = \alpha \left[\begin{array}{c} 1 \\ -2 \\ 1 \\ 0 \end{array}\right] + \beta \left[\begin{array}{c} -1 \\ 1 \\ 0 \\ 1 \end{array}\right]$$

is a solution of $A\mathbf{x} = \mathbf{0}$. The vector space $N(A)$ consists of all vectors of the form

$$\alpha \left[\begin{array}{c} 1 \\ -2 \\ 1 \\ 0 \end{array}\right] + \beta \left[\begin{array}{c} -1 \\ 1 \\ 0 \\ 1 \end{array}\right]$$

where α and β are scalars.   ∎

The Span of a Set of Vectors

Definition

> Let $\mathbf{v}_1, \mathbf{v}_2, \ldots, \mathbf{v}_n$ be vectors in a vector space V. A sum of the form $\alpha_1\mathbf{v}_1 + \alpha_2\mathbf{v}_2 + \cdots + \alpha_n\mathbf{v}_n$, where $\alpha_1, \ldots, \alpha_n$ are scalars, is called a **linear combination** of $\mathbf{v}_1, \mathbf{v}_2, \ldots, \mathbf{v}_n$. The set of all linear combinations of $\mathbf{v}_1, \mathbf{v}_2, \ldots, \mathbf{v}_n$ is called the **span** of $\mathbf{v}_1, \ldots, \mathbf{v}_n$. The span of $\mathbf{v}_1, \ldots, \mathbf{v}_n$ will be denoted by $\mathrm{Span}(\mathbf{v}_1, \ldots, \mathbf{v}_n)$.

In Example 9, we saw that the null space of A was the span of the vectors $(1, -2, 1, 0)^T$ and $(-1, 1, 0, 1)^T$.

EXAMPLE 10   In $\mathbb{R}^3$, the span of $\mathbf{e}_1$ and $\mathbf{e}_2$ is the set of all vectors of the form

$$\alpha\mathbf{e}_1 + \beta\mathbf{e}_2 = \left[\begin{array}{c} \alpha \\ \beta \\ 0 \end{array}\right]$$

The reader may verify that $\mathrm{Span}(\mathbf{e}_1, \mathbf{e}_2)$ is a subspace of $\mathbb{R}^3$. The subspace can be interpreted geometrically as the set of all vectors in 3-space that lie in the x_1x_2-plane (see Figure 3.2.1). The span of $\mathbf{e}_1, \mathbf{e}_2, \mathbf{e}_3$ is the set of all vectors of the form

$$\alpha_1\mathbf{e}_1 + \alpha_2\mathbf{e}_2 + \alpha_3\mathbf{e}_3 = \begin{bmatrix} \alpha_1 \\ \alpha_2 \\ \alpha_3 \end{bmatrix}$$

Thus, $\mathrm{Span}(\mathbf{e}_1, \mathbf{e}_2, \mathbf{e}_3) = \mathbb{R}^3$. ■

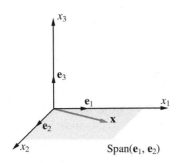

Figure 3.2.1.

Theorem 3.2.1 *If $\mathbf{v}_1, \mathbf{v}_2, \ldots, \mathbf{v}_n$ are elements of a vector space V, then $\mathrm{Span}(\mathbf{v}_1, \mathbf{v}_2, \ldots, \mathbf{v}_n)$ is a subspace of V.*

Proof Let β be a scalar and let $\mathbf{v} = \alpha_1\mathbf{v}_1 + \alpha_2\mathbf{v}_2 + \cdots + \alpha_n\mathbf{v}_n$ be an arbitrary element of $\mathrm{Span}(\mathbf{v}_1, \mathbf{v}_2, \ldots, \mathbf{v}_n)$. Since

$$\beta\mathbf{v} = (\beta\alpha_1)\mathbf{v}_1 + (\beta\alpha_2)\mathbf{v}_2 + \cdots + (\beta\alpha_n)\mathbf{v}_n$$

it follows that $\beta\mathbf{v} \in \mathrm{Span}(\mathbf{v}_1, \ldots, \mathbf{v}_n)$. Next, we must show that any sum of elements of $\mathrm{Span}(\mathbf{v}_1, \ldots, \mathbf{v}_n)$ is in $\mathrm{Span}(\mathbf{v}_1, \ldots, \mathbf{v}_n)$. Let $\mathbf{v} = \alpha_1\mathbf{v}_1 + \cdots + \alpha_n\mathbf{v}_n$ and $\mathbf{w} = \beta_1\mathbf{v}_1 + \cdots + \beta_n\mathbf{v}_n$.

$$\mathbf{v} + \mathbf{w} = (\alpha_1 + \beta_1)\mathbf{v}_1 + \cdots + (\alpha_n + \beta_n)\mathbf{v}_n \in \mathrm{Span}(\mathbf{v}_1, \ldots, \mathbf{v}_n)$$

Therefore, $\mathrm{Span}(\mathbf{v}_1, \ldots, \mathbf{v}_n)$ is a subspace of V. ■

A vector $\mathbf{x}$ in $\mathbb{R}^3$ is in $\mathrm{Span}(\mathbf{e}_1, \mathbf{e}_2)$ if and only if it lies in the x_1x_2-plane in 3-space. Thus, we can think of the x_1x_2-plane as the geometrical representation of the subspace $\mathrm{Span}(\mathbf{e}_1, \mathbf{e}_2)$ (see Figure 3.2.1). Similarly, given two vectors $\mathbf{x}$ and $\mathbf{y}$, if $(0, 0, 0)$, (x_1, x_2, x_3), and (y_1, y_2, y_3) are not collinear, these points determine a plane. If $\mathbf{z} = c_1\mathbf{x} + c_2\mathbf{y}$, then $\mathbf{z}$ is a sum of vectors parallel to $\mathbf{x}$ and $\mathbf{y}$ and hence must lie on the plane determined by the two vectors (see Figure 3.2.2). In general, if two vectors $\mathbf{x}$ and $\mathbf{y}$ can be used to determine a plane in 3-space, that plane is the geometrical representation of $\mathrm{Span}(\mathbf{x}, \mathbf{y})$.

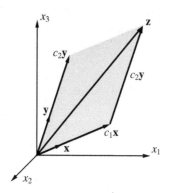

Figure 3.2.2.

Spanning Set for a Vector Space

Let $\mathbf{v}_1, \mathbf{v}_2, \ldots, \mathbf{v}_n$ be vectors in a vector space V. We will refer to $\mathrm{Span}(\mathbf{v}_1, \ldots, \mathbf{v}_n)$ as the subspace of V *spanned* by $\mathbf{v}_1, \mathbf{v}_2, \ldots, \mathbf{v}_n$. It may happen that $\mathrm{Span}(\mathbf{v}_1, \ldots, \mathbf{v}_n) = V$, in which case we say that the vectors $\mathbf{v}_1, \ldots, \mathbf{v}_n$ span V, or that $\{\mathbf{v}_1, \ldots, \mathbf{v}_n\}$ is a *spanning set* for V. Thus, we have the following definition.

Definition

> The set $\{\mathbf{v}_1, \ldots, \mathbf{v}_n\}$ is a **spanning set** for V if and only if every vector in V can be written as a linear combination of $\mathbf{v}_1, \mathbf{v}_2, \ldots, \mathbf{v}_n$.

We can easily visualize the span of a set of vectors in $\mathbb{R}^2$. If $\mathbf{v}_1$ is a single nonzero vector in $\mathbb{R}^2$, then $\mathrm{Span}(\mathbf{v}_1)$ consists of all vectors of the form $c_1\mathbf{v}_1$. Since c_1 can be positive, negative, or zero, we see that the subspace corresponds geometrically to a line in the plane that passes through the origin. For any point not on that line, the corresponding vector will not be in $\mathrm{Span}(\mathbf{v}_1)$. A single nonzero vector $\mathbf{v}_1$ will span a proper subspace of $\mathbb{R}^2$, but it cannot span the entire space. You need at least two vectors in order to form a spanning set for $\mathbb{R}^2$.

The simplest choice of a spanning set for $\mathbb{R}^2$ is to use the vectors $\mathbf{e}_1$ and $\mathbf{e}_2$. Figure 3.2.3 shows the vectors $\mathbf{e}_1$ and $\mathbf{e}_2$ and a small circle representing a target point in the plane. We can start at the origin and get to the target point by moving 2 units in the direction of $\mathbf{e}_1$ and then moving 3 units in the direction of $\mathbf{e}_2$. The resulting vector $\mathbf{v} = (2, 3)^T$ is shown in Figure 3.2.4. If we change the target point to some other coordinates (a, b), then the corresponding vector will be

$$\mathbf{x} = a\mathbf{e}_1 + b\mathbf{e}_2 = \begin{bmatrix} a \\ b \end{bmatrix}$$

Thus, any vector $\mathbf{x}$ in $\mathbb{R}^2$ can be represented as a linear combination of $\mathbf{e}_1$ and $\mathbf{e}_2$ and hence $\{\mathbf{e}_1, \mathbf{e}_2\}$ is a spanning set for $\mathbb{R}^2$.

In Figure 3.2.5, the vectors $\mathbf{e}_1$ and $\mathbf{e}_2$ have been rotated and scaled to form the vectors $\mathbf{v}_1$ and $\mathbf{v}_2$ and the target point has been moved to a new position. If we can start at the origin and reach the target point moving only in the directions of $\mathbf{v}_1$, $-\mathbf{v}_1$, $\mathbf{v}_2$, and $-\mathbf{v}_2$, then we can express the target vector as a linear combination of the given

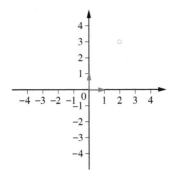

Terminal point of first vector $(1, 0)$
Terminal point of second vector $(0, 1)$
Target point $(2, 3)$

Figure 3.2.3.

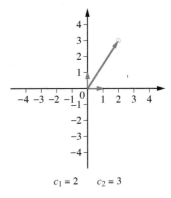

$c_1 = 2$ $c_2 = 3$

Figure 3.2.4.

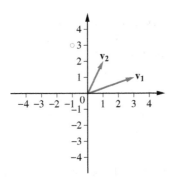

Figure 3.2.5.

vectors. Reasoning this way, one can often come up with good approximations to the correct values of the scalars c_1 and c_2. However, it is much more difficult to approximate the scalars using this type of geometric reasoning when the angle between the vectors is small. Actually, if the values of the given vectors and the target vector are known, it is not necessary to approximate. You can solve for the scalars directly. For example, if the vectors in Figure 3.2.5 are given as

$$\mathbf{v}_1 = \begin{bmatrix} 3 \\ 1 \end{bmatrix}, \qquad \mathbf{v}_2 = \begin{bmatrix} 1 \\ 2 \end{bmatrix}, \qquad \mathbf{x} = \begin{bmatrix} -1 \\ 3 \end{bmatrix}$$

then we can determine scalars by solving the equation

$$c_1\mathbf{v}_1 + c_2\mathbf{v}_2 = \begin{bmatrix} -1 \\ 3 \end{bmatrix}$$

for c_1 and c_2. The vectors $\mathbf{v}_1$ and $\mathbf{v}_2$ will span $\mathbb{R}^2$ if we can use these vectors to reach any point (a, b) in the plane. This will be possible if the systems

$$c_1\mathbf{v}_1 + c_2\mathbf{v}_2 = \begin{bmatrix} a \\ b \end{bmatrix}$$

are consistent for all choices of a and b.

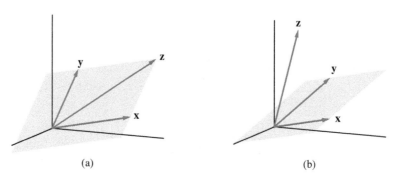

Figure 3.2.6.

Let us now consider the problem of finding a spanning set for $\mathbb{R}^3$. As was the case for $\mathbb{R}^2$, we see that a single nonzero vector $\mathbf{x}$ cannot span. In this case, Span($\mathbf{x}$) can be represented geometrically by a line through the origin in 3-space. What about the span of two nonzero vectors $\mathbf{x}$ and $\mathbf{y}$ in $\mathbb{R}^3$? If $\mathbf{y}$ is not a multiple of $\mathbf{x}$, then we can represent the sum $\mathbf{z} = \mathbf{x} + \mathbf{y}$ geometrically as a vector corresponding to the diagonal of a parallelogram in 3-space. The parallelogram, which has one corner at the origin, can be extended to form a plane passing through the origin [see Figure 3.2.6(a)]. Any linear combination $c_1\mathbf{x} + c_2\mathbf{y}$ will correspond to a point in the plane. We can reach that point by starting at the origin and moving in the directions of $\mathbf{x}$ and $\mathbf{y}$ or, if the scalars are negative, the directions of $-\mathbf{x}$ and $-\mathbf{y}$. Indeed, if $\mathbf{x}$ and $\mathbf{y}$ are nonzero vectors and one of the vectors is not a scalar multiple of the other, then Span($\mathbf{x}, \mathbf{y}$) corresponds to a plane through the origin. If (z_1, z_2, z_3) is a point that does not lie on the plane, then the vector $\mathbf{z} = (z_1, z_2, z_3)^T$ is not in Span($\mathbf{x}, \mathbf{y}$) [see Figure 3.2.6(b)]. In general, one cannot span $\mathbb{R}^3$ using only one or two vectors. To span $\mathbb{R}^3$, you need at least three vectors, and if the span of the first two vectors is represented by a plane through the origin, then the third vector must correspond to a point that does not lie in that plane [see Figure 3.2.6(b)].

While the the vectors $\mathbf{x}, \mathbf{y}$, and $\mathbf{z}$ in Figure 3.2.6(a) do not form a spanning set, the three vectors in Figure 3.2.6(b) do span $\mathbb{R}^3$. To see this geometrically, let (a, b, c) be any point in 3-space. If the point is not on the plane corresponding to the span of $\mathbf{x}$ and $\mathbf{y}$, draw a line through the point in a direction parallel to the vector $\mathbf{z}$ and then draw a vector $\mathbf{v}$ from the origin to the point where this line intersects the plane (see Figure 3.2.7). From the tip of the vector $\mathbf{v}$, we can get to the point (a, b, c) by moving an appropriate distance in the direction of $\mathbf{z}$ or $-\mathbf{z}$. Thus, if $\mathbf{b} = (a, b, c)^T$, then $\mathbf{b} = \mathbf{v} + c_3\mathbf{z}$ for some scalar c_3. Since $\mathbf{v} \in$ Span($\mathbf{x}, \mathbf{y}$), we can find scalars c_1 and c_2 such that $\mathbf{v} = c_1\mathbf{x} + c_2\mathbf{y}$. Since the vector $\mathbf{b}$ was arbitrary and

$$\mathbf{b} = \mathbf{v} + c_3\mathbf{z} = c_1\mathbf{x} + c_2\mathbf{y} + c_3\mathbf{z}$$

it follows that $\mathbf{x}, \mathbf{y}$, and $\mathbf{z}$ span $\mathbb{R}^3$.

EXAMPLE 11   Which of the following are spanning sets for $\mathbb{R}^3$?

(a) $\{\mathbf{e}_1, \mathbf{e}_2, \mathbf{e}_3, (1, 2, 3)^T\}$

(b) $\{(1, 1, 1)^T, (1, 1, 0)^T, (1, 0, 0)^T\}$

(c) $\{(1, 0, 1)^T, (0, 1, 0)^T\}$

(d) $\{(1, 2, 4)^T, (2, 1, 3)^T, (4, -1, 1)^T\}$

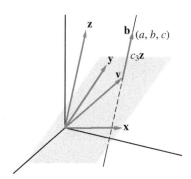

Figure 3.2.7.

Solution

To determine whether a set spans $\mathbb{R}^3$, we must determine whether an arbitrary vector $(a, b, c)^T$ in $\mathbb{R}^3$ can be written as a linear combination of the vectors in the set. In part (a), it is easily seen that $(a, b, c)^T$ can be written as

$$(a, b, c)^T = a\mathbf{e}_1 + b\mathbf{e}_2 + c\mathbf{e}_3 + 0(1, 2, 3)^T$$

For part (b), we must determine whether it is possible to find constants α_1, α_2, and α_3 such that

$$\begin{bmatrix} a \\ b \\ c \end{bmatrix} = \alpha_1 \begin{bmatrix} 1 \\ 1 \\ 1 \end{bmatrix} + \alpha_2 \begin{bmatrix} 1 \\ 1 \\ 0 \end{bmatrix} + \alpha_3 \begin{bmatrix} 1 \\ 0 \\ 0 \end{bmatrix}$$

This leads to the system of equations

$$\begin{aligned} \alpha_1 + \alpha_2 + \alpha_3 &= a \\ \alpha_1 + \alpha_2 \phantom{{} + \alpha_3} &= b \\ \alpha_1 \phantom{{} + \alpha_2 + \alpha_3} &= c \end{aligned}$$

Since the coefficient matrix of the system is nonsingular, the system has a unique solution. In fact, we find that

$$\begin{bmatrix} \alpha_1 \\ \alpha_2 \\ \alpha_3 \end{bmatrix} = \begin{bmatrix} c \\ b - c \\ a - b \end{bmatrix}$$

Thus,

$$\begin{bmatrix} a \\ b \\ c \end{bmatrix} = c \begin{bmatrix} 1 \\ 1 \\ 1 \end{bmatrix} + (b - c) \begin{bmatrix} 1 \\ 1 \\ 0 \end{bmatrix} + (a - b) \begin{bmatrix} 1 \\ 0 \\ 0 \end{bmatrix}$$

so the three vectors span $\mathbb{R}^3$.

For part (c), we should note that linear combinations of $(1, 0, 1)^T$ and $(0, 1, 0)^T$ produce vectors of the form $(\alpha, \beta, \alpha)^T$. Thus, any vector $(a, b, c)^T$ in $\mathbb{R}^3$, where $a \neq c$, would not be in the span of these two vectors.

Part (d) can be done in the same manner as part (b). If

$$\begin{bmatrix} a \\ b \\ c \end{bmatrix} = \alpha_1 \begin{bmatrix} 1 \\ 2 \\ 4 \end{bmatrix} + \alpha_2 \begin{bmatrix} 2 \\ 1 \\ 3 \end{bmatrix} + \alpha_3 \begin{bmatrix} 4 \\ -1 \\ 1 \end{bmatrix}$$

then

$$\alpha_1 + 2\alpha_2 + 4\alpha_3 = a$$
$$2\alpha_1 + \alpha_2 - \alpha_3 = b$$
$$4\alpha_1 + 3\alpha_2 + \alpha_3 = c$$

In this case, however, the coefficient matrix is singular. Gaussian elimination will yield a system of the form

$$\alpha_1 + 2\alpha_2 + 4\alpha_3 = a$$
$$\alpha_2 + 3\alpha_3 = \frac{2a - b}{3}$$
$$0 = 2a - 3c + 5b$$

If

$$2a - 3c + 5b \neq 0$$

then the system is inconsistent. Hence, for most choices of a, b, and c, it is impossible to express $(a, b, c)^T$ as a linear combination of $(1, 2, 4)^T$, $(2, 1, 3)^T$, and $(4, -1, 1)^T$. The vectors do not span $\mathbb{R}^3$. ∎

EXAMPLE 12 The vectors $1 - x^2$, $x + 2$, and x^2 span P_3. Thus, if $ax^2 + bx + c$ is any polynomial in P_3, it is possible to find scalars α_1, α_2, and α_3 such that

$$ax^2 + bx + c = \alpha_1(1 - x^2) + \alpha_2(x + 2) + \alpha_3 x^2$$

Indeed,

$$\alpha_1(1 - x^2) + \alpha_2(x + 2) + \alpha_3 x^2 = (\alpha_3 - \alpha_1)x^2 + \alpha_2 x + (\alpha_1 + 2\alpha_2)$$

Setting

$$\alpha_3 - \alpha_1 = a$$
$$\alpha_2 = b$$
$$\alpha_1 + 2\alpha_2 = c$$

and solving, we see that $\alpha_1 = c - 2b$, $\alpha_2 = b$, and $\alpha_3 = a + c - 2b$. ∎

In Example 11(a), we saw that the vectors $\mathbf{e}_1, \mathbf{e}_2, \mathbf{e}_3, (1, 2, 3)^T$ span $\mathbb{R}^3$. Clearly, $\mathbb{R}^3$ could be spanned with only the vectors $\mathbf{e}_1, \mathbf{e}_2, \mathbf{e}_3$. The vector $(1, 2, 3)^T$ is really not necessary. In the next section, we consider the problem of finding minimal spanning sets for a vector space V (i.e., spanning sets that contain the smallest possible number of vectors).

Linear Systems Revisited

Let S be the solution set to a consistent $m \times n$ linear system $A\mathbf{x} = \mathbf{b}$. In the case that $\mathbf{b} = \mathbf{0}$, we have $S = N(A)$, and consequently, the solution set forms a subspace of $\mathbb{R}^n$. If $\mathbf{b} \neq \mathbf{0}$, then S does not form a subspace of $\mathbb{R}^n$; however, if one can find a particular solution $\mathbf{x}_0$, then it is possible to represent any solution vector in terms of $\mathbf{x}_0$ and a vector $\mathbf{z}$ from the null space of A.

Let $A\mathbf{x} = \mathbf{b}$ be a consistent linear system and let $\mathbf{x}_0$ be a particular solution to the system. If there is another solution $\mathbf{x}_1$ to the system, then the difference vector $\mathbf{z} = \mathbf{x}_1 - \mathbf{x}_0$ must be in $N(A)$ since

$$A\mathbf{z} = A\mathbf{x}_1 - A\mathbf{x}_0 = \mathbf{b} - \mathbf{b} = \mathbf{0}$$

Thus, if there is a second solution, it must be of the form $\mathbf{x}_1 = \mathbf{x}_0 + \mathbf{z}$, where $\mathbf{z} \in N(A)$.

In general, if $\mathbf{x}_0$ is a particular solution to $A\mathbf{x} = \mathbf{b}$ and $\mathbf{z}$ is any vector in $N(A)$, then setting $\mathbf{y} = \mathbf{x}_0 + \mathbf{z}$, we have

$$A\mathbf{y} = A\mathbf{x}_0 + A\mathbf{z} = \mathbf{b} + \mathbf{0} = \mathbf{b}$$

So $\mathbf{y} = \mathbf{x}_0 + \mathbf{z}$ must also be a solution to the system $A\mathbf{x} = \mathbf{b}$.

These observations are summarized in the following theorem.

Theorem 3.2.2   *If the linear system $A\mathbf{x} = \mathbf{b}$ is consistent and $\mathbf{x}_0$ is a particular solution, then a vector $\mathbf{y}$ will also be a solution if and only if $\mathbf{y} = \mathbf{x}_0 + \mathbf{z}$, where $\mathbf{z} \in N(A)$.*

To help understand the meaning of Theorem 3.2.2, let us consider the case of an $m \times 3$ matrix whose null space is spanned by two nonzero vectors $\mathbf{z}_1$ and $\mathbf{z}_2$. If $\mathbf{z}_1$ is not a multiple of $\mathbf{z}_2$, then the set of all linear combinations of $\mathbf{z}_1$ and $\mathbf{z}_2$ corresponds to a plane through the origin in 3-space (see Figure 3.2.8). If $\mathbf{x}_0$ is a vector in $\mathbb{R}^3$ and $\mathbf{b} = A\mathbf{x}_0$ is a nonzero vector, then $\mathbf{x}_0$ is a particular solution to the nonhomogeneous system $A\mathbf{x} = \mathbf{b}$. It follows from Theorem 3.2.2 that the solution set S consists of all vectors of the form

$$\mathbf{y} = \mathbf{x}_0 + c_1\mathbf{z}_1 + c_2\mathbf{z}_2$$

where c_1 and c_2 are arbitrary scalars. The solution set S corresponds to a plane in 3-space that does not pass through the origin. See Figure 3.2.8.

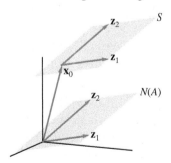

Figure 3.2.8.

SECTION 3.2 EXERCISES

1. Determine whether the following sets form subspaces of $\mathbb{R}^2$:

(a) $\{(x_1, x_2)^T \mid x_1 + x_2 = 0\}$

(b) $\{(x_1, x_2)^T \mid x_1 x_2 = 0\}$

(c) $\{(x_1, x_2)^T \mid x_1 = 3x_2\}$

(d) $\{(x_1, x_2)^T \mid |x_1| = |x_2|\}$

(e) $\{(x_1, x_2)^T \mid x_1^2 = x_2^2\}$

2. Determine whether the following sets form subspaces of $\mathbb{R}^3$:

(a) $\{(x_1, x_2, x_3)^T \mid x_1 + x_3 = 1\}$

(b) $\{(x_1, x_2, x_3)^T \mid x_1 = x_2 = x_3\}$

(c) $\{(x_1, x_2, x_3)^T \mid x_3 = x_1 + x_2\}$

(d) $\{(x_1, x_2, x_3)^T \mid x_3 = x_1 \text{ or } x_3 = x_2\}$

3. Determine whether the following are subspaces of $\mathbb{R}^{2 \times 2}$:

(a) The set of all 2×2 diagonal matrices

(b) The set of all 2×2 triangular matrices

(c) The set of all 2×2 lower triangular matrices

(d) The set of all 2×2 matrices A such that $a_{12} = 1$

(e) The set of all 2×2 matrices B such that $b_{11} = 0$

(f) The set of all symmetric 2×2 matrices

(g) The set of all singular 2×2 matrices

4. Determine the null space of each of the following matrices:

(a) $\begin{pmatrix} 2 & 1 \\ 3 & 2 \end{pmatrix}$

(b) $\begin{pmatrix} 1 & 2 & -3 & -1 \\ -2 & -4 & 6 & 3 \end{pmatrix}$

(c) $\begin{pmatrix} 1 & 3 & -4 \\ 2 & -1 & -1 \\ -1 & -3 & 4 \end{pmatrix}$

(d) $\begin{pmatrix} 1 & 1 & -1 & 2 \\ 2 & 2 & -3 & 1 \\ -1 & -1 & 0 & -5 \end{pmatrix}$

5. Determine whether the following are subspaces of P_4 (be careful!):

(a) The set of polynomials in P_4 of even degree

(b) The set of all polynomials of degree 3

(c) The set of all polynomials $p(x)$ in P_4 such that $p(0) = 0$

(d) The set of all polynomials in P_4 having at least one real root

6. Determine whether the following are subspaces of $C[-1, 1]$:

(a) The set of functions f in $C[-1, 1]$ such that $f(-1) = f(1)$

(b) The set of odd functions in $C[-1, 1]$

(c) The set of continuous nondecreasing functions on $[-1, 1]$

(d) The set of functions f in $C[-1, 1]$ such that $f(-1) = 0$ and $f(1) = 0$

(e) The set of functions f in $C[-1, 1]$ such that $f(-1) = 0$ or $f(1) = 0$

7. Show that $C^n[a, b]$ is a subspace of $C[a, b]$.

8. Let A be a fixed vector in $\mathbb{R}^{n \times n}$ and let S be the set of all matrices that commute with A, that is,

$$S = \{B \mid AB = BA\}$$

Show that S is a subspace of $\mathbb{R}^{n \times n}$.

9. In each of the following, determine the subspace of $\mathbb{R}^{2 \times 2}$ consisting of all matrices that commute with the given matrix:

(a) $\begin{pmatrix} 1 & 0 \\ 0 & -1 \end{pmatrix}$

(b) $\begin{pmatrix} 0 & 0 \\ 1 & 0 \end{pmatrix}$

(c) $\begin{pmatrix} 1 & 1 \\ 0 & 1 \end{pmatrix}$

(d) $\begin{pmatrix} 1 & 1 \\ 1 & 1 \end{pmatrix}$

10. Let A be a particular vector in $\mathbb{R}^{2 \times 2}$. Determine whether the following are subspaces of $\mathbb{R}^{2 \times 2}$:

(a) $S_1 = \{B \in \mathbb{R}^{2 \times 2} \mid BA = O\}$

(b) $S_2 = \{B \in \mathbb{R}^{2 \times 2} \mid AB \neq BA\}$

(c) $S_3 = \{B \in \mathbb{R}^{2 \times 2} \mid AB + B = O\}$

11. Determine whether the following are spanning sets for $\mathbb{R}^2$:

(a) $\left\{ \begin{bmatrix} 2 \\ 1 \end{bmatrix}, \begin{bmatrix} 3 \\ 2 \end{bmatrix} \right\}$ (b) $\left\{ \begin{bmatrix} 2 \\ 3 \end{bmatrix}, \begin{bmatrix} 4 \\ 6 \end{bmatrix} \right\}$

(c) $\left\{ \begin{bmatrix} -2 \\ 1 \end{bmatrix}, \begin{bmatrix} 1 \\ 3 \end{bmatrix}, \begin{bmatrix} 2 \\ 4 \end{bmatrix} \right\}$

(d) $\left\{ \begin{bmatrix} -1 \\ 2 \end{bmatrix}, \begin{bmatrix} 1 \\ -2 \end{bmatrix}, \begin{bmatrix} 2 \\ -4 \end{bmatrix} \right\}$

(e) $\left\{ \begin{bmatrix} 1 \\ 2 \end{bmatrix}, \begin{bmatrix} -1 \\ 1 \end{bmatrix} \right\}$

12. Which of the sets that follow are spanning sets for $\mathbb{R}^3$? Justify your answers.

(a) $\{(1, 0, 0)^T, (0, 1, 1)^T, (1, 0, 1)^T\}$

(b) $\{(1, 0, 0)^T, (0, 1, 1)^T, (1, 0, 1)^T, (1, 2, 3)^T\}$

(c) $\{(2, 1, -2)^T, (3, 2, -2)^T, (2, 2, 0)^T\}$

(d) $\{(2, 1, -2)^T, (-2, -1, 2)^T, (4, 2, -4)^T\}$

(e) $\{(1, 1, 3)^T, (0, 2, 1)^T\}$

13. Given

$$\mathbf{x}_1 = \begin{bmatrix} -1 \\ 2 \\ 3 \end{bmatrix}, \quad \mathbf{x}_2 = \begin{bmatrix} 3 \\ 4 \\ 2 \end{bmatrix},$$

$$\mathbf{x} = \begin{bmatrix} 2 \\ 6 \\ 6 \end{bmatrix}, \quad \mathbf{y} = \begin{bmatrix} -9 \\ -2 \\ 5 \end{bmatrix}$$

(a) Is $\mathbf{x} \in \text{Span}(\mathbf{x}_1, \mathbf{x}_2)$?

(b) Is $\mathbf{y} \in \text{Span}(\mathbf{x}_1, \mathbf{x}_2)$?

Prove your answers.

14. Let A be a 4×3 matrix and let $\mathbf{b} \in \mathbb{R}^4$. How many possible solutions could the system $A\mathbf{x} = \mathbf{b}$ have if $N(A) = \{\mathbf{0}\}$? Answer the same question in the case $N(A) \neq \{\mathbf{0}\}$. Explain your answers.

15. Let A be a 4×3 matrix and let

$$\mathbf{c} = 2\mathbf{a}_1 + \mathbf{a}_2 + \mathbf{a}_3$$

(a) If $N(A) = \{\mathbf{0}\}$, what can you conclude about the solutions to the linear system $A\mathbf{x} = \mathbf{c}$?

(b) If $N(A) \neq \{\mathbf{0}\}$, how many solutions will the system $A\mathbf{x} = \mathbf{c}$ have? Explain.

16. Let $\mathbf{x}_1$ be a particular solution to a system $A\mathbf{x} = \mathbf{b}$ and let $\{\mathbf{z}_1, \mathbf{z}_2, \mathbf{z}_3\}$ be a spanning set for $N(A)$. If

$$Z = \begin{bmatrix} \mathbf{z}_1 & \mathbf{z}_2 & \mathbf{z}_3 \end{bmatrix},$$

show that $\mathbf{y}$ will be a solution to $A\mathbf{x} = \mathbf{b}$ if and only if $\mathbf{y} = \mathbf{x}_1 + Z\mathbf{c}$ for some $\mathbf{c} \in \mathbb{R}^3$.

17. Figure 3.2.6 gives a geometric illustration of the solution set S to a system $A\mathbf{x} = \mathbf{b}$, where A is an $m \times 3$ matrix, $N(A) = \text{Span}(\mathbf{z}_1, \mathbf{z}_2)$, and $\mathbf{b} = A\mathbf{x}_0$, for some $\mathbf{x}_0 \notin N(A)$. Suppose we change $\mathbf{b}$ by setting it equal to $A\mathbf{x}_1$, where $\mathbf{x}_1$ is a different vector that is also not in $N(A)$. Explain the effect that this change will have on the original figure. Geometrically, how will the new solution set S_1 compare to the original solution set S and to $N(A)$?

18. Let $\{\mathbf{x}_1, \mathbf{x}_2, \dots, \mathbf{x}_k\}$ be a spanning set for a vector space V.

(a) If we add another vector, $\mathbf{x}_{k+1}$, to the set, will we still have a spanning set? Explain.

(b) If we delete one of the vectors, say, $\mathbf{x}_k$, from the set, will we still have a spanning set? Explain.

19. In $\mathbb{R}^{2\times2}$, let

$$E_{11} = \begin{bmatrix} 1 & 0 \\ 0 & 0 \end{bmatrix}, \quad E_{12} = \begin{bmatrix} 0 & 1 \\ 0 & 0 \end{bmatrix}$$

$$E_{21} = \begin{bmatrix} 0 & 0 \\ 1 & 0 \end{bmatrix}, \quad E_{22} = \begin{bmatrix} 0 & 0 \\ 0 & 1 \end{bmatrix}$$

Show that $E_{11}, E_{12}, E_{21}, E_{22}$ span $\mathbb{R}^{2\times2}$.

20. Which of the sets that follow are spanning sets for P_3? Justify your answers.

(a) $\{1, x^2, x^2 - 2\}$ ____ (b) $\{2, x^2, x, 2x + 3\}$

(c) $\{x + 2, x + 1, x^2 - 1\}$ ____ (d) $\{x + 2, x^2 - 1\}$

21. Let S be the vector space of infinite sequences defined in Exercise 15 of Section 3.1. Let S_0 be the set of $\{a_n\}$ with the property that $a_n \to 0$ as $n \to \infty$. Show that S_0 is a subspace of S.

22. Prove that if S is a subspace of $\mathbb{R}^1$, then either $S = \{\mathbf{0}\}$ or $S = \mathbb{R}^1$.

23. Let A be an $n \times n$ matrix. Prove that the following statements are equivalent:

(a) $N(A) = \{\mathbf{0}\}$. ____ (b) A is nonsingular.

(c) For each $\mathbf{b} \in \mathbb{R}^n$, the system $A\mathbf{x} = \mathbf{b}$ has a unique solution.

24. Let U and V be subspaces of a vector space W. Prove that their intersection $U \cap V$ is also a subspace of W.

25. Let S be the subspace of $\mathbb{R}^2$ spanned by $\mathbf{e}_1$ and let T be the subspace of $\mathbb{R}^2$ spanned by $\mathbf{e}_2$. Is $S \cup T$ a subspace of $\mathbb{R}^2$? Explain.

26. Let U and V be subspaces of a vector space W. Define

$$U + V = \{\mathbf{z} \mid \mathbf{z} = \mathbf{u} + \mathbf{v}, \text{ where } \mathbf{u} \in U \text{ and } \mathbf{v} \in V\}.$$

Show that $U + V$ is a subspace of W.

27. Let S, T, and U be subspaces of a vector space V. We can form new subspaces using the operations of $\cap$ and $+$ defined in Exercises 24 and 26. When we do arithmetic with numbers, we know that the operation of multiplication distributes over the operation of addition in the sense that

$$a(b + c) = ab + ac$$

It is natural to ask whether similar distributive laws hold for the two operations with subspaces.

(a) Does the intersection operation for subspaces distribute over the addition operation? That is, does

$$S \cap (T + U) = (S \cap T) + (S \cap U)?$$

(b) Does the addition operation for subspaces distribute over the intersection operation? That is, does

$$S + (T \cap U) = (S + T) \cap (S + U)?$$

3.3 Linear Independence

In this section, we look more closely at the structure of vector spaces. To begin with, we restrict ourselves to vector spaces that can be generated from a finite set of elements. Each vector in the vector space can be built up from the elements in this generating set using only the operations of addition and scalar multiplication. The generating set is usually referred to as a spanning set. In particular, it is desirable to find a *minimal* spanning set. By "minimal," we mean a spanning set with no unnecessary elements (i.e., all the elements in the set are needed in order to span the vector space). To see how to find a minimal spanning set, it is necessary to consider how the vectors in the collection *depend* on each other. Consequently, we introduce the concepts of *linear dependence* and *linear independence*. These concepts provide the keys to understanding the structure of vector spaces.

Consider the following vectors in $\mathbb{R}^3$:

$$\mathbf{x}_1 = \begin{bmatrix} 1 \\ -1 \\ 2 \end{bmatrix}, \qquad \mathbf{x}_2 = \begin{bmatrix} -2 \\ 3 \\ 1 \end{bmatrix}, \qquad \mathbf{x}_3 = \begin{bmatrix} -1 \\ 3 \\ 8 \end{bmatrix}$$

Let S be the subspace of $\mathbb{R}^3$ spanned by $\mathbf{x}_1, \mathbf{x}_2, \mathbf{x}_3$. Actually, S can be represented in terms of the two vectors $\mathbf{x}_1$ and $\mathbf{x}_2$, since the vector $\mathbf{x}_3$ is already in the span of $\mathbf{x}_1$ and $\mathbf{x}_2$; that is,

$$\mathbf{x}_3 = 3\mathbf{x}_1 + 2\mathbf{x}_2 \tag{1}$$

Any linear combination of $\mathbf{x}_1, \mathbf{x}_2$, and $\mathbf{x}_3$ can be reduced to a linear combination of $\mathbf{x}_1$ and $\mathbf{x}_2$:

$$\begin{aligned} \alpha_1\mathbf{x}_1 + \alpha_2\mathbf{x}_2 + \alpha_3\mathbf{x}_3 &= \alpha_1\mathbf{x}_1 + \alpha_2\mathbf{x}_2 + \alpha_3(3\mathbf{x}_1 + 2\mathbf{x}_2) \\ &= (\alpha_1 + 3\alpha_3)\mathbf{x}_1 + (\alpha_2 + 2\alpha_3)\mathbf{x}_2 \end{aligned}$$

Thus,

$$S = \text{Span}(\mathbf{x}_1, \mathbf{x}_2, \mathbf{x}_3) = \text{Span}(\mathbf{x}_1, \mathbf{x}_2)$$

Equation (1) can be rewritten in the form

$$3\mathbf{x}_1 + 2\mathbf{x}_2 - 1\mathbf{x}_3 = \mathbf{0} \tag{2}$$

Since the three coefficients in (2) are nonzero, we could solve for any vector in terms of the other two:

$$\mathbf{x}_1 = -\frac{2}{3}\mathbf{x}_2 + \frac{1}{3}\mathbf{x}_3, \qquad \mathbf{x}_2 = -\frac{3}{2}\mathbf{x}_1 + \frac{1}{2}\mathbf{x}_3, \qquad \mathbf{x}_3 = 3\mathbf{x}_1 + 2\mathbf{x}_2$$

It follows that

$$\text{Span}(\mathbf{x}_1, \mathbf{x}_2, \mathbf{x}_3) = \text{Span}(\mathbf{x}_2, \mathbf{x}_3) = \text{Span}(\mathbf{x}_1, \mathbf{x}_3) = \text{Span}(\mathbf{x}_1, \mathbf{x}_2)$$

Because of the dependency relation (2), the subspace S can be represented as the span of any two of the given vectors.

In contrast, no such dependency relationship exists between $\mathbf{x}_1$ and $\mathbf{x}_2$. Indeed, if there were scalars c_1 and c_2, not both 0, such that

$$c_1\mathbf{x}_1 + c_2\mathbf{x}_2 = \mathbf{0} \tag{3}$$

then we could solve for one of the vectors in terms of the other:

$$\mathbf{x}_1 = -\frac{c_2}{c_1}\mathbf{x}_2 \quad (c_1 \neq 0) \qquad \text{or} \qquad \mathbf{x}_2 = -\frac{c_1}{c_2}\mathbf{x}_1 \quad (c_2 \neq 0)$$

However, neither of the two vectors in question is a multiple of the other. Therefore, $\text{Span}(\mathbf{x}_1)$ and $\text{Span}(\mathbf{x}_2)$ are both proper subspaces of $\text{Span}(\mathbf{x}_1, \mathbf{x}_2)$, and the only way that (3) can hold is if $c_1 = c_2 = 0$.

We can generalize this example by making the following observations:

(I) If $\mathbf{v}_1, \mathbf{v}_2, \ldots, \mathbf{v}_n$ span a vector space V and one of these vectors can be written as a linear combination of the other $n - 1$ vectors, then those $n - 1$ vectors span V.

(II) Given n vectors $\mathbf{v}_1, \ldots, \mathbf{v}_n$, it is possible to write one of the vectors as a linear combination of the other $n - 1$ vectors if and only if there exist scalars $c_1, \ldots, c_n$, not all zero, such that

$$c_1\mathbf{v}_1 + c_2\mathbf{v}_2 + \cdots + c_n\mathbf{v}_n = \mathbf{0}$$

Proof of (I) Suppose that $\mathbf{v}_n$ can be written as a linear combination of the vectors $\mathbf{v}_1, \mathbf{v}_2, \ldots, \mathbf{v}_{n-1}$; that is,

$$\mathbf{v}_n = \beta_1\mathbf{v}_1 + \beta_2\mathbf{v}_2 + \cdots + \beta_{n-1}\mathbf{v}_{n-1}$$

Let $\mathbf{v}$ be any element of V. Since $\mathbf{v}_1, \ldots, \mathbf{v}_n$ span V, we can write

$$\begin{aligned}
\mathbf{v} &= \alpha_1\mathbf{v}_1 + \alpha_2\mathbf{v}_2 + \cdots + \alpha_{n-1}\mathbf{v}_{n-1} + \alpha_n\mathbf{v}_n \\
&= \alpha_1\mathbf{v}_1 + \alpha_2\mathbf{v}_2 + \cdots + \alpha_{n-1}\mathbf{v}_{n-1} + \alpha_n(\beta_1\mathbf{v}_1 + \cdots + \beta_{n-1}\mathbf{v}_{n-1}) \\
&= (\alpha_1 + \alpha_n\beta_1)\mathbf{v}_1 + (\alpha_2 + \alpha_n\beta_2)\mathbf{v}_2 + \cdots + (\alpha_{n-1} + \alpha_n\beta_{n-1})\mathbf{v}_{n-1}
\end{aligned}$$

Thus, any vector $\mathbf{v}$ in V can be written as a linear combination of $\mathbf{v}_1, \mathbf{v}_2, \ldots, \mathbf{v}_{n-1}$, and hence these vectors span V. ∎

Proof of (II) Suppose that one of the vectors $\mathbf{v}_1, \mathbf{v}_2, \ldots, \mathbf{v}_n$, say, $\mathbf{v}_n$, can be written as a linear combination of the others.

$$\mathbf{v}_n = \alpha_1\mathbf{v}_1 + \alpha_2\mathbf{v}_2 + \cdots + \alpha_{n-1}\mathbf{v}_{n-1}$$

Subtracting $\mathbf{v}_n$ from both sides of this equation, we get

$$\alpha_1\mathbf{v}_1 + \alpha_2\mathbf{v}_2 + \cdots + \alpha_{n-1}\mathbf{v}_{n-1} - \mathbf{v}_n = \mathbf{0}$$

If we set $c_i = \alpha_i$ for $i = 1, \ldots, n - 1$, and set $c_n = -1$, then it follows that

$$c_1\mathbf{v}_1 + c_2\mathbf{v}_2 + \cdots + c_n\mathbf{v}_n = \mathbf{0}$$

Conversely, if

$$c_1\mathbf{v}_1 + c_2\mathbf{v}_2 + \cdots + c_n\mathbf{v}_n = \mathbf{0}$$

and at least one of the c_i's, say, c_n, is nonzero, then

$$\mathbf{v}_n = \frac{-c_1}{c_n}\mathbf{v}_1 + \frac{-c_2}{c_n}\mathbf{v}_2 + \cdots + \frac{-c_{n-1}}{c_n}\mathbf{v}_{n-1} \qquad \blacksquare$$

Definition

> The vectors $\mathbf{v}_1, \mathbf{v}_2, \ldots, \mathbf{v}_n$ in a vector space V are said to be **linearly independent** if
>
> $$c_1\mathbf{v}_1 + c_2\mathbf{v}_2 + \cdots + c_n\mathbf{v}_n = \mathbf{0}$$
>
> implies that all the scalars $c_1, \ldots, c_n$ must equal 0.

It follows from **(I)** and **(II)** that, if $\{\mathbf{v}_1, \mathbf{v}_2, \ldots, \mathbf{v}_n\}$ is a minimal spanning set, then $\mathbf{v}_1, \mathbf{v}_2, \ldots, \mathbf{v}_n$ are linearly independent. Conversely, if $\mathbf{v}_1, \ldots, \mathbf{v}_n$ are linearly independent and span V, then $\{\mathbf{v}_1, \ldots, \mathbf{v}_n\}$ is a minimal spanning set for V (see Exercise 20 at the end of this section). A minimal spanning set is called a *basis*. The concept of a basis will be studied in more detail in the next section.

EXAMPLE I   The vectors $\begin{bmatrix} 1 \\ 1 \end{bmatrix}$ and $\begin{bmatrix} 1 \\ 2 \end{bmatrix}$ are linearly independent, since if

$$c_1 \begin{bmatrix} 1 \\ 1 \end{bmatrix} + c_2 \begin{bmatrix} 1 \\ 2 \end{bmatrix} = \begin{bmatrix} 0 \\ 0 \end{bmatrix}$$

then

$$\begin{aligned} c_1 + c_2 &= 0 \\ c_1 + 2c_2 &= 0 \end{aligned}$$

and the only solution to this system is $c_1 = 0, c_2 = 0$. $\qquad \blacksquare$

Definition

> The vectors $\mathbf{v}_1, \mathbf{v}_2, \ldots, \mathbf{v}_n$ in a vector space V are said to be **linearly dependent** if there exist scalars $c_1, c_2, \ldots, c_n$, not all zero, such that
>
> $$c_1\mathbf{v}_1 + c_2\mathbf{v}_2 + \cdots + c_n\mathbf{v}_n = \mathbf{0}$$

EXAMPLE 2   Let $\mathbf{x} = (1, 2, 3)^T$. The vectors $\mathbf{e}_1, \mathbf{e}_2, \mathbf{e}_3$, and $\mathbf{x}$ are linearly dependent, since

$$\mathbf{e}_1 + 2\mathbf{e}_2 + 3\mathbf{e}_3 - \mathbf{x} = \mathbf{0}$$

(In this case, $c_1 = 1, c_2 = 2, c_3 = 3, c_4 = -1$.) $\qquad \blacksquare$

Given a set of vectors $\{\mathbf{v}_1, \mathbf{v}_2, \ldots, \mathbf{v}_n\}$ in a vector space V, we can find scalars $c_1, c_2, \ldots, c_n$ such that

$$c_1\mathbf{v}_1 + c_2\mathbf{v}_2 + \cdots + c_n\mathbf{v}_n = \mathbf{0}$$

Just take

$$c_1 = c_2 = \cdots = c_n = 0$$

If there are nontrivial choices of scalars for which the linear combination $c_1\mathbf{v}_1 + \cdots + c_n\mathbf{v}_n$ equals the zero vector, then $\mathbf{v}_1, \ldots, \mathbf{v}_n$ are linearly dependent. If the *only* way the linear combination $c_1\mathbf{v}_1 + \cdots + c_n\mathbf{v}_n$ can equal the zero vector is for all the scalars $c_1, \ldots, c_n$ to be 0, then $\mathbf{v}_1, \ldots, \mathbf{v}_n$ are linearly independent.

Geometric Interpretation

If $\mathbf{x}$ and $\mathbf{y}$ are linearly dependent in $\mathbb{R}^2$, then

$$c_1\mathbf{x} + c_2\mathbf{y} = \mathbf{0}$$

where c_1 and c_2 are not both 0. If, say, $c_1 \neq 0$, we can write

$$\mathbf{x} = -\frac{c_2}{c_1}\mathbf{y}$$

If two vectors in $\mathbb{R}^2$ are linearly dependent, one of the vectors can be written as a scalar multiple of the other. Thus, if both vectors are nonzero and they are placed at the origin, then they will lie along the same line (see Figure 3.3.1).

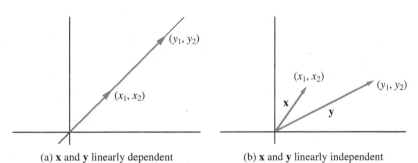

(a) $\mathbf{x}$ and $\mathbf{y}$ linearly dependent   (b) $\mathbf{x}$ and $\mathbf{y}$ linearly independent

Figure 3.3.1.

If

$$\mathbf{x} = \begin{bmatrix} x_1 \\ x_2 \\ x_3 \end{bmatrix} \quad \text{and} \quad \mathbf{y} = \begin{bmatrix} y_1 \\ y_2 \\ y_3 \end{bmatrix}$$

are linearly independent in $\mathbb{R}^3$, then the two points (x_1, x_2, x_3) and (y_1, y_2, y_3) will not lie on the same line through the origin in 3-space. Since $(0, 0, 0)$, (x_1, x_2, x_3), and (y_1, y_2, y_3) are not collinear, they determine a plane. If (z_1, z_2, z_3) lies on this plane, the vector $\mathbf{z} = (z_1, z_2, z_3)^T$ can be written as a linear combination of $\mathbf{x}$ and $\mathbf{y}$, and hence $\mathbf{x}$, $\mathbf{y}$, and $\mathbf{z}$ are linearly dependent. If (z_1, z_2, z_3) does not lie on the plane, the three vectors will be linearly independent (see Figure 3.3.2).

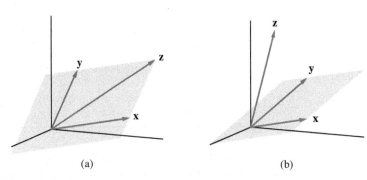

(a)   (b)

Figure 3.3.2.

Theorems and Examples

EXAMPLE 3   Which of the following collections of vectors are linearly independent in $\mathbb{R}^3$?

     (a) $(1, 1, 1)^T, (1, 1, 0)^T, (1, 0, 0)^T$
     (b) $(1, 0, 1)^T, (0, 1, 0)^T$
     (c) $(1, 2, 4)^T, (2, 1, 3)^T, (4, -1, 1)^T$

Solution

(a) These three vectors are linearly independent. To verify this, we must show that the only way for

$$c_1(1, 1, 1)^T + c_2(1, 1, 0)^T + c_3(1, 0, 0)^T = (0, 0, 0)^T \qquad (4)$$

is if the scalars c_1, c_2, c_3 are all zero. Equation (4) can be written as a linear system with unknowns c_1, c_2, c_3:

$$
\begin{aligned}
c_1 + c_2 + c_3 &= 0 \\
c_1 + c_2 \phantom{{}+ c_3} &= 0 \\
c_1 \phantom{{}+ c_2 + c_3} &= 0
\end{aligned}
$$

The only solution of this system is $c_1 = 0$, $c_2 = 0$, $c_3 = 0$.

(b) If

$$c_1(1, 0, 1)^T + c_2(0, 1, 0)^T = (0, 0, 0)^T$$

then

$$(c_1, c_2, c_1)^T = (0, 0, 0)^T$$

so $c_1 = c_2 = 0$. Therefore, the two vectors are linearly independent.

(c) If

$$c_1(1, 2, 4)^T + c_2(2, 1, 3)^T + c_3(4, -1, 1)^T = (0, 0, 0)^T$$

then

$$c_1 + 2c_2 + 4c_3 = 0$$
$$2c_1 + c_2 - c_3 = 0$$
$$4c_1 + 3c_2 + c_3 = 0$$

The coefficient matrix of the system is singular and hence the system has nontrivial solutions. Therefore, the vectors are linearly dependent. ■

Notice in Example 3, parts (a) and (c), that it was necessary to solve a 3×3 system to determine whether the three vectors were linearly independent. In part (a), where the coefficient matrix was nonsingular, the vectors were linearly independent, while in part (c), where the coefficient matrix was singular, the vectors were linearly dependent. This illustrates a special case of the following theorem.

Theorem 3.3.1 *Let $\mathbf{x}_1, \mathbf{x}_2, \ldots, \mathbf{x}_n$ be n vectors in $\mathbb{R}^n$ and let $X = (\mathbf{x}_1, \ldots, \mathbf{x}_n)$. The vectors $\mathbf{x}_1, \mathbf{x}_2, \ldots, \mathbf{x}_n$ will be linearly dependent if and only if X is singular.*

Proof The equation

$$c_1\mathbf{x}_1 + c_2\mathbf{x}_2 + \cdots + c_n\mathbf{x}_n = \mathbf{0}$$

can be rewritten as a matrix equation:

$$X\mathbf{c} = \mathbf{0}$$

This equation will have a nontrivial solution if and only if X is singular. Thus, $\mathbf{x}_1, \ldots, \mathbf{x}_n$ will be linearly dependent if and only if X is singular. ■

EXAMPLE 4 The following vectors are pictured in Figure 3.3.3.

$$\mathbf{x}_1 = \begin{Bmatrix} 2 \\ 3 \\ 1 \end{Bmatrix}, \qquad \mathbf{x}_2 = \begin{Bmatrix} 3 \\ 2 \\ 1 \end{Bmatrix}, \qquad \mathbf{x}_3 = \begin{Bmatrix} 5 \\ 5 \\ 2 \end{Bmatrix}, \qquad \mathbf{x}_4 = \begin{Bmatrix} 2 \\ 2 \\ 4 \end{Bmatrix}$$

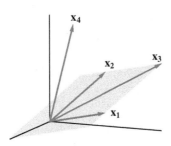

Figure 3.3.3.

We can see a dependency relation among the first three of the vectors since

$$\mathbf{x}_3 = \mathbf{x}_1 + \mathbf{x}_2$$

In this case, the vector $\mathbf{x}_3$ lies in the plane spanned by $\mathbf{x}_1$ and $\mathbf{x}_2$. It follows then that

$$\mathbf{x}_1 + \mathbf{x}_2 - \mathbf{x}_3 + 0\mathbf{x}_4 = 0$$

The collection of four vectors must be linearly dependent since the scalars $c_1 = 1$, $c_2 = 1, c_3 = -1, c_4 = 0$ are not all 0. ∎

In the next section of the book, we will show that any collection of three linearly independent vectors in $\mathbb{R}^3$ will form a spanning set. If we then add a fourth vector to the collection, the new vector can be expressed as a linear combination of the three spanning vectors. Hence, the collection of four vectors must be linearly dependent.

We can use Theorem 3.3.1 to test whether n vectors are linearly independent, in $\mathbb{R}^n$. Simply form a matrix X whose columns are the vectors being tested. To determine whether X is singular, calculate the value of $\det(X)$. If $\det(X) = 0$, the vectors are linearly dependent. If $\det(X) \neq 0$, the vectors are linearly independent.

EXAMPLE 5   Determine whether the vectors $(4, 2, 3)^T$, $(2, 3, 1)^T$, and $(2, -5, 3)^T$ are linearly dependent.

Solution

Since

$$\begin{vmatrix} 4 & 2 & 2 \\ 2 & 3 & -5 \\ 3 & 1 & 3 \end{vmatrix} = 0$$

the vectors are linearly dependent. ∎

To determine whether k vectors $\mathbf{x}_1, \mathbf{x}_2, \ldots \mathbf{x}_k$ in $\mathbb{R}^n$ are linearly independent, we can rewrite the equation

$$c_1\mathbf{x}_1 + c_2\mathbf{x}_2 + \cdots + c_k\mathbf{x}_k = 0$$

as a linear system $X\mathbf{c} = 0$, where $X = (\mathbf{x}_1, \mathbf{x}_2, \ldots, \mathbf{x}_k)$. If $k \neq n$, then the matrix X is not square, so we cannot use determinants to decide whether the vectors are linearly independent. The system is homogeneous, so it has the trivial solution $\mathbf{c} = 0$. It will have nontrivial solutions if and only if the row echelon forms of X involve free variables. If there are nontrivial solutions, then the vectors are linearly dependent. If there are no free variables, then $\mathbf{c} = 0$ is the only solution, and hence the vectors must be linearly independent.

EXAMPLE 6   Given

$$\mathbf{x}_1 = \begin{pmatrix} 1 \\ -1 \\ 2 \\ 3 \end{pmatrix}, \quad \mathbf{x}_2 = \begin{pmatrix} -2 \\ 3 \\ 1 \\ -2 \end{pmatrix}, \quad \mathbf{x}_3 = \begin{pmatrix} 1 \\ 0 \\ 7 \\ 7 \end{pmatrix}$$

To determine whether the vectors are linearly independent, we reduce the system $X\mathbf{c} = \mathbf{0}$ to row echelon form:

$$\left[\begin{array}{rrr|r} 1 & -2 & 1 & 0 \\ -1 & 3 & 0 & 0 \\ 2 & 1 & 7 & 0 \\ 3 & -2 & 7 & 0 \end{array}\right] \rightarrow \left[\begin{array}{rrr|r} 1 & -2 & 1 & 0 \\ 0 & 1 & 1 & 0 \\ 0 & 0 & 0 & 0 \\ 0 & 0 & 0 & 0 \end{array}\right]$$

Since the echelon form involves a free variable c_3, there are nontrivial solutions and hence the vectors must be linearly dependent. ∎

Next, we consider a very important property of linearly independent vectors: Linear combinations of linearly independent vectors are unique. More precisely, we have the following theorem.

Theorem 3.3.2   *Let $\mathbf{v}_1, \ldots, \mathbf{v}_n$ be vectors in a vector space V. A vector $\mathbf{v} \in \text{Span}(\mathbf{v}_1, \ldots, \mathbf{v}_n)$ can be written uniquely as a linear combination of $\mathbf{v}_1, \ldots, \mathbf{v}_n$ if and only if $\mathbf{v}_1, \ldots, \mathbf{v}_n$ are linearly independent.*

Proof   If $\mathbf{v} \in \text{Span}(\mathbf{v}_1, \ldots, \mathbf{v}_n)$, then $\mathbf{v}$ can be written as a linear combination:

$$\mathbf{v} = \alpha_1 \mathbf{v}_1 + \alpha_2 \mathbf{v}_2 + \cdots + \alpha_n \mathbf{v}_n \tag{5}$$

Suppose that $\mathbf{v}$ can also be expressed as a linear combination:

$$\mathbf{v} = \beta_1 \mathbf{v}_1 + \beta_2 \mathbf{v}_2 + \cdots + \beta_n \mathbf{v}_n \tag{6}$$

We will show that, if $\mathbf{v}_1, \ldots, \mathbf{v}_n$ are linearly independent, then $\beta_i = \alpha_i$, $i = 1, \ldots, n$, and if $\mathbf{v}_1, \ldots, \mathbf{v}_n$ are linearly dependent, then it is possible to choose the β_i's different from the α_i's.

If $\mathbf{v}_1, \ldots, \mathbf{v}_n$ are linearly independent, then subtracting (6) from (5) yields

$$(\alpha_1 - \beta_1)\mathbf{v}_1 + (\alpha_2 - \beta_2)\mathbf{v}_2 + \cdots + (\alpha_n - \beta_n)\mathbf{v}_n = \mathbf{0} \tag{7}$$

By the linear independence of $\mathbf{v}_1, \ldots, \mathbf{v}_n$, the coefficients of (7) must all be 0. Hence,

$$\alpha_1 = \beta_1, \ \alpha_2 = \beta_2, \ \ldots, \ \alpha_n = \beta_n$$

Thus, the representation (5) is unique when $\mathbf{v}_1, \ldots, \mathbf{v}_n$ are linearly independent.

On the other hand, if $\mathbf{v}_1, \ldots, \mathbf{v}_n$ are linearly dependent, then there exist $c_1, \ldots, c_n$, not all 0, such that

$$\mathbf{0} = c_1 \mathbf{v}_1 + c_2 \mathbf{v}_2 + \cdots + c_n \mathbf{v}_n \tag{8}$$

Now if we set

$$\beta_1 = \alpha_1 + c_1, \ \beta_2 = \alpha_2 + c_2, \ \ldots, \ \beta_n = \alpha_n + c_n$$

then, adding (5) and (8), we get

$$\begin{aligned} \mathbf{v} &= (\alpha_1 + c_1)\mathbf{v}_1 + (\alpha_2 + c_2)\mathbf{v}_2 + \cdots + (\alpha_n + c_n)\mathbf{v}_n \\ &= \beta_1 \mathbf{v}_1 + \beta_2 \mathbf{v}_2 + \cdots + \beta_n \mathbf{v}_n \end{aligned}$$

Since the c_i's are not all 0, $\beta_i \neq \alpha_i$ for at least one value of i. Thus, if $\mathbf{v}_1, \ldots, \mathbf{v}_n$ are linearly dependent, the representation of a vector as a linear combination of $\mathbf{v}_1, \ldots, \mathbf{v}_n$ is not unique. ∎

Vector Spaces of Functions

To determine whether a set of vectors is linearly independent in $\mathbb{R}^n$, we must solve a homogeneous linear system of equations. A similar situation holds for the vector space P_n.

The Vector Space P_n

To test whether the following polynomials $p_1, p_2, \ldots, p_k$ are linearly independent in P_n, we set

$$c_1 p_1 + c_2 p_2 + \cdots + c_k p_k = z \tag{9}$$

where z represents the zero polynomial; that is,

$$z(x) = 0x^{n-1} + 0x^{n-2} + \cdots + 0x + 0$$

If the polynomial on the left-hand side of equation (9) is rewritten in the form $a_1 x^{n-1} + a_2 x^{n-2} + \cdots + a_{n-1} x + a_n$, then, since two polynomials are equal if and only if their coefficients are equal, it follows that the coefficients a_i must all be 0. But each of the a_i's is a linear combination of the c_j's. This leads to a homogeneous linear system with unknowns $c_1, c_2, \ldots, c_k$. If the system has only the trivial solution, the polynomials are linearly independent; otherwise, they are linearly dependent.

EXAMPLE 7   To test whether the vectors

$$p_1(x) = x^2 - 2x + 3, \quad p_2(x) = 2x^2 + x + 8, \quad p_3(x) = x^2 + 8x + 7$$

are linearly independent, set

$$c_1 p_1(x) + c_2 p_2(x) + c_3 p_3(x) = 0x^2 + 0x + 0$$

Grouping terms by powers of x, we get

$$(c_1 + 2c_2 + c_3)x^2 + (-2c_1 + c_2 + 8c_3)x + (3c_1 + 8c_2 + 7c_3) = 0x^2 + 0x + 0$$

Equating coefficients leads to the system

$$\begin{aligned}
c_1 + 2c_2 + c_3 &= 0 \\
-2c_1 + c_2 + 8c_3 &= 0 \\
3c_1 + 8c_2 + 7c_3 &= 0
\end{aligned}$$

The coefficient matrix for this system is singular and hence there are nontrivial solutions. Therefore, p_1, p_2, and p_3 are linearly dependent. ∎

The Vector Space $C^{(n-1)}[a, b]$

In Example 5, a determinant was used to test whether three vectors were linearly independent in $\mathbb{R}^3$. Determinants can also be used to help to decide whether a set of n vectors is linearly independent in $C^{(n-1)}[a, b]$. Indeed, let $f_1, f_2, \ldots, f_n$ be elements of $C^{(n-1)}[a, b]$. If these vectors are linearly dependent, then there exist scalars $c_1, c_2, \ldots, c_n$, not all zero, such that

$$c_1 f_1(x) + c_2 f_2(x) + \cdots + c_n f_n(x) = 0 \qquad (10)$$

for each x in $[a, b]$. Taking the derivative with respect to x of both sides of (10) yields

$$c_1 f_1'(x) + c_2 f_2'(x) + \cdots + c_n f_n'(x) = 0$$

If we continue taking derivatives of both sides, we end up with the system

$$
\begin{aligned}
c_1 f_1(x) &+ c_2 f_2(x) &+ \cdots + &c_n f_n(x) &= 0 \\
c_1 f_1'(x) &+ c_2 f_2'(x) &+ \cdots + &c_n f_n'(x) &= 0 \\
&\vdots & & & \\
c_1 f_1^{(n-1)}(x) &+ c_2 f_2^{(n-1)}(x) &+ \cdots + &c_n f_n^{(n-1)}(x) &= 0
\end{aligned}
$$

For each fixed x in $[a, b]$, the matrix equation

$$
\begin{bmatrix}
f_1(x) & f_2(x) & \cdots & f_n(x) \\
f_1'(x) & f_2'(x) & \cdots & f_n'(x) \\
\vdots & & & \\
f_1^{(n-1)}(x) & f_2^{(n-1)}(x) & \cdots & f_n^{(n-1)}(x)
\end{bmatrix}
\begin{bmatrix}
\alpha_1 \\ \alpha_2 \\ \vdots \\ \alpha_n
\end{bmatrix}
=
\begin{bmatrix}
0 \\ 0 \\ \vdots \\ 0
\end{bmatrix}
\qquad (11)
$$

will have the same nontrivial solution $(c_1, c_2, \ldots, c_n)^T$. Thus, if $f_1, \ldots, f_n$ are linearly dependent in $C^{(n-1)}[a, b]$, then, for each fixed x in $[a, b]$, the coefficient matrix of system (11) is singular. If the matrix is singular, its determinant is zero.

Definition

> Let $f_1, f_2, \ldots, f_n$ be functions in $C^{(n-1)}[a, b]$, and define the function $W[f_1, f_2, \ldots, f_n](x)$ on $[a, b]$ by
>
> $$
> W[f_1, f_2, \ldots, f_n](x) =
> \begin{vmatrix}
> f_1(x) & f_2(x) & \cdots & f_n(x) \\
> f_1'(x) & f_2'(x) & \cdots & f_n'(x) \\
> \vdots & & & \\
> f_1^{(n-1)}(x) & f_2^{(n-1)}(x) & \cdots & f_n^{(n-1)}(x)
> \end{vmatrix}
> $$
>
> The function $W[f_1, f_2, \ldots, f_n]$ is called the **Wronskian** of $f_1, f_2, \ldots, f_n$.

Theorem 3.3.3   *Let $f_1, f_2, \ldots, f_n$ be elements of $C^{(n-1)}[a, b]$. If there exists a point x_0 in $[a, b]$ such that $W[f_1, f_2, \ldots, f_n](x_0) \neq 0$, then $f_1, f_2, \ldots, f_n$ are linearly independent.*

Proof If $f_1, f_2, \ldots, f_n$ were linearly dependent, then by the preceding discussion, the coefficient matrix in (11) would be singular for each x in $[a, b]$ and hence $W[f_1, f_2, \ldots, f_n](x)$ would be identically zero on $[a, b]$. ∎

If $f_1, f_2, \ldots, f_n$ are linearly independent in $C^{(n-1)}[a, b]$, they will also be linearly independent in $C[a, b]$.

EXAMPLE 8 Show that e^x and e^{-x} are linearly independent in $C(-\infty, \infty)$.

Solution

$$W[e^x, e^{-x}] = \begin{vmatrix} e^x & e^{-x} \\ e^x & -e^{-x} \end{vmatrix} = -2$$

Since $W[e^x, e^{-x}]$ is not identically zero, e^x and e^{-x} are linearly independent. ∎

EXAMPLE 9 Consider the functions x^2 and $x|x|$ in $C[-1, 1]$. Both functions are in the subspace $C^1[-1, 1]$ (see Example 7 of Section 3.2), so we can compute the Wronskian:

$$W[x^2, x|x|] = \begin{vmatrix} x^2 & x|x| \\ 2x & 2|x| \end{vmatrix} \equiv 0$$

Since the Wronskian is identically zero, it gives no information as to whether the functions are linearly independent. To answer the question, suppose that

$$c_1 x^2 + c_2 x|x| = 0$$

for all x in $[-1, 1]$. Then, in particular for $x = 1$ and $x = -1$, we have

$$c_1 + c_2 = 0$$
$$c_1 - c_2 = 0$$

and the only solution of this system is $c_1 = c_2 = 0$. Thus, the functions x^2 and $x|x|$ are linearly independent in $C[-1, 1]$ even though $W[x^2, x|x|] \equiv 0$.

This example shows that the converse of Theorem 3.3.3 is not valid. ∎

EXAMPLE 10 Show that the vectors $1, x, x^2$, and x^3 are linearly independent in $C((-\infty, \infty))$.

Solution

$$W[1, x, x^2, x^3] = \begin{vmatrix} 1 & x & x^2 & x^3 \\ 0 & 1 & 2x & 3x^2 \\ 0 & 0 & 2 & 6x \\ 0 & 0 & 0 & 6 \end{vmatrix} = 12$$

Since $W[1, x, x^2, x^3] \neq 0$, the vectors are linearly independent. ∎

SECTION 3.3 EXERCISES

1. Determine whether the following vectors are linearly independent in $\mathbb{R}^2$:

    (a) $\begin{bmatrix} 2 \\ 1 \end{bmatrix}, \begin{bmatrix} 3 \\ 2 \end{bmatrix}$ (b) $\begin{bmatrix} 2 \\ 3 \end{bmatrix}, \begin{bmatrix} 4 \\ 6 \end{bmatrix}$

    (c) $\begin{bmatrix} -2 \\ 1 \end{bmatrix}, \begin{bmatrix} 1 \\ 3 \end{bmatrix}, \begin{bmatrix} 2 \\ 4 \end{bmatrix}$

    (d) $\begin{bmatrix} -1 \\ 2 \end{bmatrix}, \begin{bmatrix} 1 \\ -2 \end{bmatrix}, \begin{bmatrix} 2 \\ -4 \end{bmatrix}$

    (e) $\begin{bmatrix} 1 \\ 2 \end{bmatrix}, \begin{bmatrix} -1 \\ 1 \end{bmatrix}$

2. Determine whether the following vectors are linearly independent in $\mathbb{R}^3$:

    (a) $\begin{bmatrix} 1 \\ 0 \\ 0 \end{bmatrix}, \begin{bmatrix} 0 \\ 1 \\ 1 \end{bmatrix}, \begin{bmatrix} 1 \\ 0 \\ 1 \end{bmatrix}$

    (b) $\begin{bmatrix} 1 \\ 0 \\ 0 \end{bmatrix}, \begin{bmatrix} 0 \\ 1 \\ 1 \end{bmatrix}, \begin{bmatrix} 1 \\ 0 \\ 1 \end{bmatrix}, \begin{bmatrix} 1 \\ 2 \\ 3 \end{bmatrix}$

    (c) $\begin{bmatrix} 2 \\ 1 \\ -2 \end{bmatrix}, \begin{bmatrix} 3 \\ 2 \\ -2 \end{bmatrix}, \begin{bmatrix} 2 \\ 2 \\ 0 \end{bmatrix}$

    (d) $\begin{bmatrix} 2 \\ 1 \\ -2 \end{bmatrix}, \begin{bmatrix} -2 \\ -1 \\ 2 \end{bmatrix}, \begin{bmatrix} 4 \\ 2 \\ -4 \end{bmatrix}$

    (e) $\begin{bmatrix} 1 \\ 1 \\ 3 \end{bmatrix}, \begin{bmatrix} 0 \\ 2 \\ 1 \end{bmatrix}$

3. For each of the sets of vectors in Exercise 2, describe geometrically the span of the given vectors.

4. Determine whether the following vectors are linearly independent in $\mathbb{R}^{2 \times 2}$:

    (a) $\begin{bmatrix} 1 & 0 \\ 1 & 1 \end{bmatrix}, \begin{bmatrix} 0 & 1 \\ 0 & 0 \end{bmatrix}$

    (b) $\begin{bmatrix} 1 & 0 \\ 0 & 1 \end{bmatrix}, \begin{bmatrix} 0 & 1 \\ 0 & 0 \end{bmatrix}, \begin{bmatrix} 0 & 0 \\ 1 & 0 \end{bmatrix}$

    (c) $\begin{bmatrix} 1 & 0 \\ 0 & 1 \end{bmatrix}, \begin{bmatrix} 0 & 1 \\ 0 & 0 \end{bmatrix}, \begin{bmatrix} 2 & 3 \\ 0 & 2 \end{bmatrix}$

5. Let $\mathbf{x}_1, \mathbf{x}_2, \ldots, \mathbf{x}_k$ be linearly independent vectors in a vector space V.

    (a) If we add a vector $\mathbf{x}_{k+1}$ to the collection, will we still have a linearly independent collection of vectors? Explain.

    (b) If we delete a vector, say, $\mathbf{x}_k$, from the collection, will we still have a linearly independent collection of vectors? Explain.

6. Let $\mathbf{x}_1$, $\mathbf{x}_2$, and $\mathbf{x}_3$ be linearly independent vectors in $\mathbb{R}^n$ and let

    $$\mathbf{y}_1 = \mathbf{x}_1 + \mathbf{x}_2, \quad \mathbf{y}_2 = \mathbf{x}_2 + \mathbf{x}_3, \quad \mathbf{y}_3 = \mathbf{x}_3 + \mathbf{x}_1$$

    Are $\mathbf{y}_1$, $\mathbf{y}_2$, and $\mathbf{y}_3$ linearly independent? Prove your answer.

7. Let $\mathbf{x}_1$, $\mathbf{x}_2$, and $\mathbf{x}_3$ be linearly independent vectors in $\mathbb{R}^n$ and let

    $$\mathbf{y}_1 = \mathbf{x}_2 - \mathbf{x}_1, \quad \mathbf{y}_2 = \mathbf{x}_3 - \mathbf{x}_2, \quad \mathbf{y}_3 = \mathbf{x}_3 - \mathbf{x}_1$$

    Are $\mathbf{y}_1$, $\mathbf{y}_2$, and $\mathbf{y}_3$ linearly independent? Prove your answer.

8. Determine whether the following vectors are linearly independent in P_3:

    (a) $1, x^2, x^2 - 2$ (b) $2, x^2, x, 2x + 3$

    (c) $x + 2, x + 1, x^2 - 1$ (d) $x + 2, x^2 - 1$

9. For each of the following, show that the given vectors are linearly independent in $C[0, 1]$:

    (a) $\cos \pi x, \sin \pi x$ (b) $x^{3/2}, x^{5/2}$

    (c) $1, e^x + e^{-x}, e^x - e^{-x}$ (d) e^x, e^{-x}, e^{2x}

10. Determine whether the vectors $\cos x$, 1, and $\sin^2(x/2)$ are linearly independent in $C[-\pi, \pi]$.

11. Consider the vectors $\cos(x + \alpha)$ and $\sin x$ in $C[-\pi, \pi]$. For what values of α will the two vectors be linearly dependent? Give a graphical interpretation of your answer.

12. Given the functions $2x$ and $|x|$, show that

    (a) these two vectors are linearly independent in $C[-1, 1]$.

    (b) the vectors are linearly dependent in $C[0, 1]$.

13. Prove that any finite set of vectors that contains the zero vector must be linearly dependent.

14. Let $\mathbf{v}_1$, and $\mathbf{v}_2$ be two vectors in a vector space V. Show that $\mathbf{v}_1$ and $\mathbf{v}_2$ are linearly dependent if and only if one of the vectors is a scalar multiple of the other.

15. Prove that any nonempty subset of a linearly independent set of vectors $\{\mathbf{v}_1, \ldots, \mathbf{v}_n\}$ is also linearly independent.

16. Let A be an $m \times n$ matrix. Show that if A has linearly independent column vectors, then $N(A) = \{\mathbf{0}\}$.

[*Hint*: For any $\mathbf{x} \in \mathbb{R}^n$,
$A\mathbf{x} = x_1\mathbf{a}_1 + x_2\mathbf{a}_2 + \cdots + x_n\mathbf{a}_n$.]

17. Let $\mathbf{x}_1, \ldots, \mathbf{x}_k$ be linearly independent vectors in $\mathbb{R}^n$, and let A be a nonsingular $n \times n$ matrix. Define $\mathbf{y}_i = A\mathbf{x}_i$ for $i = 1, \ldots, k$. Show that $\mathbf{y}_1, \ldots, \mathbf{y}_k$ are linearly independent.

18. Let A be a 3×3 matrix and let $\mathbf{x}_1, \mathbf{x}_2, \mathbf{x}_3$ be vectors in $\mathbb{R}^3$. Show that if the vectors

$$\mathbf{y}_1 = A\mathbf{x}_1, \quad \mathbf{y}_2 = A\mathbf{x}_2, \quad \mathbf{y}_3 = A\mathbf{x}_3$$

are linearly independent, then the matrix A must be nonsingular and the vectors $\mathbf{x}_1$, $\mathbf{x}_2$, and $\mathbf{x}_3$ must be linearly independent.

19. Let $\{\mathbf{v}_1, \ldots, \mathbf{v}_n\}$ be a spanning set for the vector space V, and let $\mathbf{v}$ be any other vector in V. Show that $\mathbf{v}, \mathbf{v}_1, \ldots, \mathbf{v}_n$ are linearly dependent.

20. Let $\mathbf{v}_1, \mathbf{v}_2, \ldots, \mathbf{v}_n$ be linearly independent vectors in a vector space V. Show that $\mathbf{v}_2, \ldots, \mathbf{v}_n$ cannot span V.

3.4   Basis and Dimension

In Section 3.3, we showed that a spanning set for a vector space is minimal if its elements are linearly independent. The elements of a minimal spanning set form the basic building blocks for the whole vector space, and consequently, we say that they form a *basis* for the vector space.

Definition

> The vectors $\mathbf{v}_1, \mathbf{v}_2, \ldots, \mathbf{v}_n$ form a **basis** for a vector space V if and only if
>
> **(i)** $\mathbf{v}_1, \ldots, \mathbf{v}_n$ are linearly independent.
> **(ii)** $\mathbf{v}_1, \ldots, \mathbf{v}_n$ span V.

EXAMPLE 1   The *standard basis* for $\mathbb{R}^3$ is $\{\mathbf{e}_1, \mathbf{e}_2, \mathbf{e}_3\}$; however, there are many bases that we could choose for $\mathbb{R}^3$. For example,

$$\left\{ \begin{bmatrix} 1 \\ 1 \\ 1 \end{bmatrix}, \begin{bmatrix} 0 \\ 1 \\ 1 \end{bmatrix}, \begin{bmatrix} 2 \\ 0 \\ 1 \end{bmatrix} \right\} \quad \text{and} \quad \left\{ \begin{bmatrix} 1 \\ 1 \\ 1 \end{bmatrix}, \begin{bmatrix} 1 \\ 1 \\ 0 \end{bmatrix}, \begin{bmatrix} 1 \\ 0 \\ 1 \end{bmatrix} \right\}$$

are both bases for $\mathbb{R}^3$. We will see shortly that any basis for $\mathbb{R}^3$ must have exactly three elements. ∎

EXAMPLE 2   In $\mathbb{R}^{2 \times 2}$, consider the set $\{E_{11}, E_{12}, E_{21}, E_{22}\}$, where

$$E_{11} = \begin{bmatrix} 1 & 0 \\ 0 & 0 \end{bmatrix}, \qquad E_{12} = \begin{bmatrix} 0 & 1 \\ 0 & 0 \end{bmatrix},$$

$$E_{21} = \begin{bmatrix} 0 & 0 \\ 1 & 0 \end{bmatrix}, \qquad E_{22} = \begin{bmatrix} 0 & 0 \\ 0 & 1 \end{bmatrix}$$

If

$$c_1 E_{11} + c_2 E_{12} + c_3 E_{21} + c_4 E_{22} = O$$

then

$$\begin{bmatrix} c_1 & c_2 \\ c_3 & c_4 \end{bmatrix} = \begin{bmatrix} 0 & 0 \\ 0 & 0 \end{bmatrix}$$

so $c_1 = c_2 = c_3 = c_4 = 0$. Therefore, E_{11}, E_{12}, E_{21}, and E_{22} are linearly independent. If A is in $\mathbb{R}^{2 \times 2}$, then

$$A = a_{11} E_{11} + a_{12} E_{12} + a_{21} E_{21} + a_{22} E_{22}$$

Thus, $E_{11}, E_{12}, E_{21}, E_{22}$ span $\mathbb{R}^{2 \times 2}$ and hence form a basis for $\mathbb{R}^{2 \times 2}$. ∎

In many applications, it is necessary to find a particular subspace of a vector space V. This can be done by finding a set of basis elements of the subspace. For example, to find all solutions of the system

$$\begin{array}{rrrr} x_1 + x_2 + x_3 & = 0 \\ 2x_1 + x_2 \quad\quad + x_4 & = 0 \end{array}$$

we must find the null space of the matrix

$$A = \begin{bmatrix} 1 & 1 & 1 & 0 \\ 2 & 1 & 0 & 1 \end{bmatrix}$$

In Example 9 of Section 3.2, we saw that $N(A)$ is the subspace of $\mathbb{R}^4$ spanned by the vectors

$$\begin{bmatrix} 1 \\ -2 \\ 1 \\ 0 \end{bmatrix} \quad \text{and} \quad \begin{bmatrix} -1 \\ 1 \\ 0 \\ 1 \end{bmatrix}$$

Since these two vectors are linearly independent, they form a basis for $N(A)$.

Theorem 3.4.1   *If $\{v_1, v_2, \ldots, v_n\}$ is a spanning set for a vector space V, then any collection of m vectors in V, where $m > n$, is linearly dependent.*

Proof   Let $u_1, u_2, \ldots, u_m$ be m vectors in V where $m > n$. Then, since $v_1, v_2, \ldots, v_n$ span V, we have

$$u_i = a_{i1} v_1 + a_{i2} v_2 + \cdots + a_{in} v_n \qquad \text{for} \qquad i = 1, 2, \ldots, m$$

A linear combination $c_1 u_1 + c_2 u_2 + \cdots + c_m u_m$ can be written in the form

$$c_1 \sum_{j=1}^{n} a_{1j} v_j + c_2 \sum_{j=1}^{n} a_{2j} v_j + \cdots + c_m \sum_{j=1}^{n} a_{mj} v_j$$

Rearranging the terms, we see that

$$c_1 u_1 + c_2 u_2 + \cdots + c_m u_m = \sum_{i=1}^{m} \left[c_i \left(\sum_{j=1}^{n} a_{ij} v_j \right) \right] = \sum_{j=1}^{n} \left(\sum_{i=1}^{m} a_{ij} c_i \right) v_j$$

Now consider the system of equations

$$\sum_{i=1}^{m} a_{ij}c_i = 0 \qquad j = 1, 2, \ldots, n$$

This is a homogeneous system with more unknowns than equations. Therefore, by Theorem 1.2.1, the system must have a nontrivial solution $(\hat{c}_1, \hat{c}_2, \ldots, \hat{c}_m)^T$. But then

$$\hat{c}_1\mathbf{u}_1 + \hat{c}_2\mathbf{u}_2 + \cdots + \hat{c}_m\mathbf{u}_m = \sum_{j=1}^{n} 0\mathbf{v}_j = \mathbf{0}$$

Hence, $\mathbf{u}_1, \mathbf{u}_2, \ldots, \mathbf{u}_m$ are linearly dependent.   ∎

Corollary 3.4.2   *If both* $\{\mathbf{v}_1, \ldots, \mathbf{v}_n\}$ *and* $\{\mathbf{u}_1, \ldots, \mathbf{u}_m\}$ *are bases for a vector space* V, *then* $n = m$.

Proof   Let $\mathbf{v}_1, \mathbf{v}_2, \ldots, \mathbf{v}_n$ and $\mathbf{u}_1, \mathbf{u}_2, \ldots, \mathbf{u}_m$ both be bases for V. Since $\mathbf{v}_1, \mathbf{v}_2, \ldots, \mathbf{v}_n$ span V and $\mathbf{u}_1, \mathbf{u}_2, \ldots, \mathbf{u}_m$ are linearly independent, it follows from Theorem 3.4.1 that $m \leq n$. By the same reasoning, $\mathbf{u}_1, \mathbf{u}_2, \ldots, \mathbf{u}_m$ span V, and $\mathbf{v}_1, \mathbf{v}_2, \ldots, \mathbf{v}_n$ are linearly independent, so $n \leq m$.   ∎

In view of Corollary 3.4.2, we can now refer to the number of elements in any basis for a given vector space. This leads to the following definition.

Definition   Let V be a vector space. If V has a basis consisting of n vectors, we say that V has **dimension** n. The subspace $\{\mathbf{0}\}$ of V is said to have dimension 0. V is said to be **finite dimensional** if there is a finite set of vectors that spans V; otherwise, we say that V is **infinite dimensional**.

If $\mathbf{x}$ is a nonzero vector in $\mathbb{R}^3$, then $\mathbf{x}$ spans a one-dimensional subspace $\text{Span}(\mathbf{x}) = \{\alpha\mathbf{x} \mid \alpha \text{ is a scalar}\}$. A vector $(a, b, c)^T$ will be in $\text{Span}(\mathbf{x})$ if and only if the point (a, b, c) is on the line determined by $(0, 0, 0)$ and (x_1, x_2, x_3). Thus, a one-dimensional subspace of $\mathbb{R}^3$ can be represented geometrically by a line through the origin.

If $\mathbf{x}$ and $\mathbf{y}$ are linearly independent in $\mathbb{R}^3$, then

$$\text{Span}(\mathbf{x}, \mathbf{y}) = \{\alpha\mathbf{x} + \beta\mathbf{y} \mid \alpha \text{ and } \beta \text{ are scalars}\}$$

is a two-dimensional subspace of $\mathbb{R}^3$. A vector $(a, b, c)^T$ will be in $\text{Span}(\mathbf{x}, \mathbf{y})$ if and only if (a, b, c) lies on the plane determined by $(0, 0, 0)$, (x_1, x_2, x_3), and (y_1, y_2, y_3). Thus, we can think of a two-dimensional subspace of $\mathbb{R}^3$ as a plane through the origin. If $\mathbf{x}$, $\mathbf{y}$, and $\mathbf{z}$ are linearly independent in $\mathbb{R}^3$, they form a basis for $\mathbb{R}^3$ and $\text{Span}(\mathbf{x}, \mathbf{y}, \mathbf{z}) = \mathbb{R}^3$. Hence, any fourth point $(a, b, c)^T$ must lie in $\text{Span}(\mathbf{x}, \mathbf{y}, \mathbf{z})$ (see Figure 3.4.1).

EXAMPLE 3   Let P be the vector space of all polynomials. We claim that P is infinite dimensional. If P were finite dimensional, say, of dimension n, any set of $n + 1$ vectors would be linearly dependent. However, $1, x, x^2, \ldots, x^n$ are linearly independent, since $W[1, x, x^2, \ldots, x^n] > 0$. Therefore, P cannot be of dimension n. Since n was arbitrary,

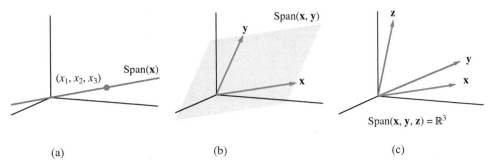

Figure 3.4.1.

P must be infinite dimensional. The same argument shows that $C[a, b]$ is infinite dimensional.   ∎

Theorem 3.4.3   *If V is a vector space of dimension n > 0, then*

(**I**) *any set of n linearly independent vectors spans V.*

(**II**) *any n vectors that span V are linearly independent.*

Proof   To prove (**I**), suppose that $\mathbf{v}_1, \ldots, \mathbf{v}_n$ are linearly independent and $\mathbf{v}$ is any other vector in V. Since V has dimension n, it has a basis consisting of n vectors and these vectors span V. It follows from Theorem 3.4.1 that $\mathbf{v}_1, \mathbf{v}_2, \ldots, \mathbf{v}_n$, and $\mathbf{v}$ must be linearly dependent. Thus, there exist scalars $c_1, c_2, \ldots, c_n, c_{n+1}$, not all zero, such that

$$c_1\mathbf{v}_1 + c_2\mathbf{v}_2 + \cdots + c_n\mathbf{v}_n + c_{n+1}\mathbf{v} = \mathbf{0} \tag{1}$$

The scalar c_{n+1} cannot be zero, for then (1) would imply that $\mathbf{v}_1, \ldots, \mathbf{v}_n$ are linearly dependent. Hence, (1) can be solved for $\mathbf{v}$.

$$\mathbf{v} = \alpha_1\mathbf{v}_1 + \alpha_2\mathbf{v}_2 + \cdots + \alpha_n\mathbf{v}_n$$

Here, $\alpha_i = -c_i/c_{n+1}$ for $i = 1, 2, \ldots, n$. Since $\mathbf{v}$ was an arbitrary vector in V, it follows that $\mathbf{v}_1, \mathbf{v}_2, \ldots, \mathbf{v}_n$ span V.

To prove (**II**), suppose that $\mathbf{v}_1, \ldots, \mathbf{v}_n$ span V. If $\mathbf{v}_1, \ldots, \mathbf{v}_n$ are linearly dependent, then one of the $\mathbf{v}_i$'s, say, $\mathbf{v}_n$, can be written as a linear combination of the others. It follows that $\mathbf{v}_1, \ldots, \mathbf{v}_{n-1}$ will still span V. If $\mathbf{v}_1, \ldots, \mathbf{v}_{n-1}$ are linearly dependent, we can eliminate another vector and still have a spanning set. We can continue eliminating vectors in this way until we arrive at a linearly independent spanning set with $k < n$ elements. But this contradicts $\dim V = n$. Therefore, $\mathbf{v}_1, \ldots, \mathbf{v}_n$ must be linearly independent.   ∎

EXAMPLE 4   Show that $\left\{ \begin{bmatrix} 1 \\ 2 \\ 3 \end{bmatrix}, \begin{bmatrix} -2 \\ 1 \\ 0 \end{bmatrix}, \begin{bmatrix} 1 \\ 0 \\ 1 \end{bmatrix} \right\}$ is a basis for $\mathbb{R}^3$.

Solution

Since $\dim \mathbb{R}^3 = 3$, we need only show that these three vectors are linearly independent. This follows, since

$$\begin{vmatrix} 1 & -2 & 1 \\ 2 & 1 & 0 \\ 3 & 0 & 1 \end{vmatrix} = 2$$

■

Theorem 3.4.4   *If V is a vector space of dimension n > 0, then*

(i) *no set of fewer than n vectors can span V.*

(ii) *any subset of fewer than n linearly independent vectors can be extended to form a basis for V.*

(iii) *any spanning set containing more than n vectors can be pared down to form a basis for V.*

Proof   Statement **(i)** follows by the same reasoning that was used to prove part (I) of Theorem 3.4.3. To prove **(ii)**, suppose that $\mathbf{v}_1, \ldots, \mathbf{v}_k$ are linearly independent and $k < n$. It follows from **(i)** that $\mathrm{Span}(\mathbf{v}_1, \ldots, \mathbf{v}_k)$ is a proper subspace of V and hence there exists a vector $\mathbf{v}_{k+1}$ that is in V but not in $\mathrm{Span}(\mathbf{v}_1, \ldots, \mathbf{v}_k)$. It then follows that $\mathbf{v}_1, \mathbf{v}_2, \ldots, \mathbf{v}_k, \mathbf{v}_{k+1}$ must be linearly independent. If $k + 1 < n$, then, in the same manner, $\{\mathbf{v}_1, \ldots, \mathbf{v}_k, \mathbf{v}_{k+1}\}$ can be extended to a set of $k + 2$ linearly independent vectors. This extension process may be continued until a set $\{\mathbf{v}_1, \mathbf{v}_2, \ldots, \mathbf{v}_k, \mathbf{v}_{k+1}, \ldots, \mathbf{v}_n\}$ of n linearly independent vectors is obtained.

To prove **(iii)**, suppose that $\mathbf{v}_1, \ldots, \mathbf{v}_m$ span V and $m > n$. Then, by Theorem 3.4.1, $\mathbf{v}_1, \ldots, \mathbf{v}_m$ must be linearly dependent. It follows that one of the vectors, say, $\mathbf{v}_m$, can be written as a linear combination of the others. Hence, if $\mathbf{v}_m$ is eliminated from the set, the remaining $m - 1$ vectors will still span V. If $m - 1 > n$, we can continue to eliminate vectors in this manner until we arrive at a spanning set containing n vectors.

■

Standard Bases

In Example 1, we referred to the set $\{\mathbf{e}_1, \mathbf{e}_2, \mathbf{e}_3\}$ as the *standard basis* for $\mathbb{R}^3$. We refer to this basis as the standard basis because it is the most natural one to use for representing vectors in $\mathbb{R}^3$. More generally, the standard basis for $\mathbb{R}^n$ is the set $\{\mathbf{e}_1, \mathbf{e}_2, \ldots, \mathbf{e}_n\}$.

The most natural way to represent matrices in $\mathbb{R}^{2 \times 2}$ is in terms of the basis $\{E_{11}, E_{12}, E_{21}, E_{22}\}$ given in Example 2. This, then, is the standard basis for $\mathbb{R}^{2 \times 2}$.

The standard way to represent a polynomial in P_n is in terms of the functions $1, x, x^2, \ldots, x^{n-1}$, and consequently, the standard basis for P_n is $\{1, x, x^2, \ldots, x^{n-1}\}$.

Although these standard bases appear to be the simplest and most natural to use, they are not the most appropriate bases for many applied problems. (See, for example, the least squares problems in Chapter 5 or the eigenvalue applications in Chapter 6.) Indeed, the key to solving many applied problems is to switch from one of the standard bases to a basis that is in some sense natural for the particular application. Once the application is solved in terms of the new basis, it is a simple matter to switch back and represent the solution in terms of the standard basis. In the next section, we will learn how to switch from one basis to another.

SECTION 3.4 EXERCISES

1. In Exercise 1 of Section 3.3, indicate whether the given vectors form a basis for $\mathbb{R}^2$.

2. In Exercise 2 of Section 3.3, indicate whether the given vectors form a basis for $\mathbb{R}^3$.

3. Consider the vectors
$$\mathbf{x}_1 = \begin{bmatrix} 2 \\ 1 \end{bmatrix}, \qquad \mathbf{x}_2 = \begin{bmatrix} 4 \\ 3 \end{bmatrix}, \qquad \mathbf{x}_3 = \begin{bmatrix} 7 \\ -3 \end{bmatrix}$$

(a) Show that $\mathbf{x}_1$ and $\mathbf{x}_2$ form a basis for $\mathbb{R}^2$.

(b) Why must $\mathbf{x}_1, \mathbf{x}_2, \mathbf{x}_3$ be linearly dependent?

(c) What is the dimension of $\text{Span}(\mathbf{x}_1, \mathbf{x}_2, \mathbf{x}_3)$?

4. Given the vectors
$$\mathbf{x}_1 = \begin{bmatrix} 3 \\ -2 \\ 4 \end{bmatrix}, \qquad \mathbf{x}_2 = \begin{bmatrix} -3 \\ 2 \\ -4 \end{bmatrix}, \qquad \mathbf{x}_3 = \begin{bmatrix} -6 \\ 4 \\ -8 \end{bmatrix}$$

what is the dimension of $\text{Span}(\mathbf{x}_1, \mathbf{x}_2, \mathbf{x}_3)$?

5. Let
$$\mathbf{x}_1 = \begin{bmatrix} 2 \\ 1 \\ 3 \end{bmatrix}, \qquad \mathbf{x}_2 = \begin{bmatrix} 3 \\ -1 \\ 4 \end{bmatrix}, \qquad \mathbf{x}_3 = \begin{bmatrix} 2 \\ 6 \\ 4 \end{bmatrix}$$

(a) Show that $\mathbf{x}_1, \mathbf{x}_2$, and $\mathbf{x}_3$ are linearly dependent.

(b) Show that $\mathbf{x}_1$ and $\mathbf{x}_2$ are linearly independent.

(c) What is the dimension of $\text{Span}(\mathbf{x}_1, \mathbf{x}_2, \mathbf{x}_3)$?

(d) Give a geometric description of $\text{Span}(\mathbf{x}_1, \mathbf{x}_2, \mathbf{x}_3)$.

6. In Exercise 2 of Section 3.2, some of the sets formed subspaces of $\mathbb{R}^3$. In each of these cases, find a basis for the subspace and determine its dimension.

7. Find a basis for the subspace S of $\mathbb{R}^4$ consisting of all vectors of the form $(a + b, a - b + 2c, b, c)^T$, where a, b, and c are all real numbers. What is the dimension of S?

8. Given $\mathbf{x}_1 = (1, \ 1, \ 1)^T$ and $\mathbf{x}_2 = (3, \ -1, \ 4)^T$:

(a) Do $\mathbf{x}_1$ and $\mathbf{x}_2$ span $\mathbb{R}^3$? Explain.

(b) Let $\mathbf{x}_3$ be a third vector in $\mathbb{R}^3$ and set $X = (\ \mathbf{x}_1 \ \mathbf{x}_2 \ \mathbf{x}_3 \ )$. What condition(s) would X have to satisfy in order for $\mathbf{x}_1, \mathbf{x}_2$, and $\mathbf{x}_3$ to form a basis for $\mathbb{R}^3$?

(c) Find a third vector $\mathbf{x}_3$ that will extend the set $\{\mathbf{x}_1, \mathbf{x}_2\}$ to a basis for $\mathbb{R}^3$.

9. Let $\mathbf{a}_1$ and $\mathbf{a}_2$ be linearly independent vectors in $\mathbb{R}^3$, and let $\mathbf{x}$ be a vector in $\mathbb{R}^2$.

(a) Describe geometrically $\text{Span}(\mathbf{a}_1, \mathbf{a}_2)$.

(b) If $A = (\mathbf{a}_1, \mathbf{a}_2)$ and $\mathbf{b} = A\mathbf{x}$, then what is the dimension of $\text{Span}(\mathbf{a}_1, \mathbf{a}_2, \mathbf{b})$? Explain.

10. The vectors
$$\mathbf{x}_1 = \begin{bmatrix} 1 \\ 2 \\ 2 \end{bmatrix}, \qquad \mathbf{x}_2 = \begin{bmatrix} 2 \\ 5 \\ 4 \end{bmatrix},$$
$$\mathbf{x}_3 = \begin{bmatrix} 1 \\ 3 \\ 2 \end{bmatrix}, \qquad \mathbf{x}_4 = \begin{bmatrix} 2 \\ 7 \\ 4 \end{bmatrix}, \qquad \mathbf{x}_5 = \begin{bmatrix} 1 \\ 1 \\ 0 \end{bmatrix}$$

span $\mathbb{R}^3$. Pare down the set $\{\mathbf{x}_1, \mathbf{x}_2, \mathbf{x}_3, \mathbf{x}_4, \mathbf{x}_5\}$ to form a basis for $\mathbb{R}^3$.

11. Let S be the subspace of P_3 consisting of all polynomials of the form $ax^2 + bx + 2a + 3b$. Find a basis for S.

12. In Exercise 3 of Section 3.2, some of the sets formed subspaces of $\mathbb{R}^{2 \times 2}$. In each of these cases, find a basis for the subspace and determine its dimension.

13. In $C[-\pi, \pi]$, find the dimension of the subspace spanned by 1, $\cos 2x$, $\cos^2 x$.

14. In each of the following, find the dimension of the subspace of P_3 spanned by the given vectors:

(a) $x, x - 1, x^2 + 1$

(b) $x, x - 1, x^2 + 1, x^2 - 1$

(c) $x^2, x^2 - x - 1, x + 1$ (d) $2x, x - 2$

15. Let S be the subspace of P_3 consisting of all polynomials $p(x)$ such that $p(0) = 0$, and let T be the subspace of all polynomials $q(x)$ such that $q(1) = 0$. Find bases for

(a) S (b) T (c) $S \cap T$

16. In $\mathbb{R}^4$, let U be the subspace of all vectors of the form $(u_1, u_2, 0, 0)^T$, and let V be the subspace of all vectors of the form $(0, v_2, v_3, 0)^T$. What are the dimensions of U, V, $U \cap V$, $U + V$? Find a basis for each of these four subspaces. (See Exercises 24 and 26 of Section 3.2.)

17. Is it possible to find a pair of two-dimensional subspaces U and V of $\mathbb{R}^3$ whose intersection is $\{\mathbf{0}\}$? Prove your answer. Give a geometrical interpretation of your conclusion. [*Hint:* Let $\{\mathbf{u}_1, \mathbf{u}_2\}$ and $\{\mathbf{v}_1, \mathbf{v}_2\}$ be bases for U and V, respectively. Show that $\mathbf{u}_1, \mathbf{u}_2, \mathbf{v}_1, \mathbf{v}_2$ are linearly dependent.]

18. Show that if U and V are subspaces of $\mathbb{R}^n$ and $U \cap V = \{\mathbf{0}\}$, then
$$\dim (U + V) = \dim \ U + \dim V$$

3.5   Change of Basis

Many applied problems can be simplified by changing from one coordinate system to another. Changing coordinate systems in a vector space is essentially the same as changing from one basis to another. For example, in describing the motion of a particle in the plane at a particular time, it is often convenient to use a basis for $\mathbb{R}^2$ consisting of a unit tangent vector $\mathbf{t}$ and a unit normal vector $\mathbf{n}$ instead of the standard basis $\{\mathbf{e}_1, \mathbf{e}_2\}$.

In this section, we discuss the problem of switching from one coordinate system to another. We will show that this can be accomplished by multiplying a given coordinate vector $\mathbf{x}$ by a nonsingular matrix S. The product $\mathbf{y} = S\mathbf{x}$ will be the coordinate vector for the new coordinate system.

Changing Coordinates in $\mathbb{R}^2$

The standard basis for $\mathbb{R}^2$ is $\{\mathbf{e}_1, \mathbf{e}_2\}$. Any vector $\mathbf{x}$ in $\mathbb{R}^2$ can be expressed as a linear combination:

$$\mathbf{x} = x_1 \mathbf{e}_1 + x_2 \mathbf{e}_2$$

The scalars x_1 and x_2 can be thought of as the *coordinates* of $\mathbf{x}$ with respect to the standard basis. Actually, for any basis $\{\mathbf{y}, \mathbf{z}\}$ for $\mathbb{R}^2$, it follows from Theorem 3.3.2 that a given vector $\mathbf{x}$ can be represented uniquely as a linear combination:

$$\mathbf{x} = \alpha \mathbf{y} + \beta \mathbf{z}$$

The scalars α and β are the coordinates of $\mathbf{x}$ with respect to the basis $\{\mathbf{y}, \mathbf{z}\}$. Let us order the basis elements so that $\mathbf{y}$ is considered the first basis vector and $\mathbf{z}$ is considered the second, and denote the ordered basis by $[\mathbf{y}, \mathbf{z}]$. We can then refer to the vector $(\alpha, \beta)^T$ as the *coordinate vector* of $\mathbf{x}$ with respect to $[\mathbf{y}, \mathbf{z}]$. Note that, if we reverse the order of the basis vectors and take $[\mathbf{z}, \mathbf{y}]$, then we must also reorder the coordinate vector. The coordinate vector of $\mathbf{x}$ with respect to $[\mathbf{z}, \mathbf{y}]$ will be $(\beta, \alpha)^T$. When we refer to a basis using subscripts, such as $\{\mathbf{u}_1, \mathbf{u}_2\}$, the subscripts assign an ordering to the basis vectors.

EXAMPLE I   Let $\mathbf{y} = (2, 1)^T$ and $\mathbf{z} = (1, 4)^T$. The vectors $\mathbf{y}$ and $\mathbf{z}$ are linearly independent and hence form a basis for $\mathbb{R}^2$. The vector $\mathbf{x} = (7, 7)^T$ can be written as a linear combination:

$$\mathbf{x} = 3\mathbf{y} + \mathbf{z}$$

Thus, the coordinate vector of $\mathbf{x}$ with respect to $[\mathbf{y}, \mathbf{z}]$ is $(3, 1)^T$. Geometrically, the coordinate vector specifies how to get from the origin to the point $(7, 7)$ by moving first in the direction of $\mathbf{y}$ and then in the direction of $\mathbf{z}$. If, instead, we treat $\mathbf{z}$ as our first basis vector and $\mathbf{y}$ as the second basis vector, then

$$\mathbf{x} = \mathbf{z} + 3\mathbf{y}$$

The coordinate vector of $\mathbf{x}$ with respect to the ordered basis $[\mathbf{z}, \mathbf{y}]$ is $(1, 3)^T$. Geometrically, this vector tells us how to get from the origin to $(7, 7)$ by moving first in the direction of $\mathbf{z}$ and then in the direction of $\mathbf{y}$ (see Figure 3.5.1). ∎

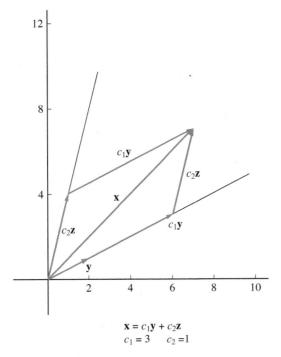

$$\mathbf{x} = c_1\mathbf{y} + c_2\mathbf{z}$$
$$c_1 = 3 \qquad c_2 = 1$$

Figure 3.5.1.

As an example of a problem for which it is helpful to change coordinates, consider the following application.

APPLICATION I   Population Migration

Suppose that the total population of a large metropolitan area remains relatively fixed; however, each year 6 percent of the people living in the city move to the suburbs and 2 percent of the people living in the suburbs move to the city. If, initially, 30 percent of the population lives in the city and 70 percent lives in the suburbs, what will these percentages be in 10 years? 30 years? 50 years? What are the long-term implications?

The changes in population can be determined by matrix multiplications. If we set

$$A = \begin{bmatrix} 0.94 & 0.02 \\ 0.06 & 0.98 \end{bmatrix} \qquad \text{and} \qquad \mathbf{x}_0 = \begin{bmatrix} 0.30 \\ 0.70 \end{bmatrix}$$

then the percentages of people living in the city and suburbs after one year can be calculated by setting $\mathbf{x}_1 = A\mathbf{x}_0$. The percentages after two years can be calculated by setting $\mathbf{x}_2 = A\mathbf{x}_1 = A^2\mathbf{x}_0$. In general, the percentages after n years will be given by $\mathbf{x}_n = A^n\mathbf{x}_0$. If we calculate these percentages for $n = 10$, 30, and 50 years and round to the nearest percent, we get

$$\mathbf{x}_{10} = \begin{bmatrix} 0.27 \\ 0.73 \end{bmatrix} \qquad \mathbf{x}_{30} = \begin{bmatrix} 0.25 \\ 0.75 \end{bmatrix} \qquad \mathbf{x}_{50} = \begin{bmatrix} 0.25 \\ 0.75 \end{bmatrix}$$

In fact, as n increases, the sequence of vectors $\mathbf{x}_n = A^n\mathbf{x}_0$ converges to a limit $\mathbf{x} = (0.25, 0.75)^T$. The limit vector $\mathbf{x}$ is called a *steady-state vector* for the process.

To understand why the process approaches a steady state, it is helpful to switch to a different coordinate system. For the new coordinate system, we will pick vectors $\mathbf{u}_1$ and $\mathbf{u}_2$, for which it is easy to see the effect of multiplication by the matrix A. In particular, if we pick $\mathbf{u}_1$ to be any multiple of the steady-state vector $\mathbf{x}$, then $A\mathbf{u}_1$ will equal $\mathbf{u}_1$. Let us choose $\mathbf{u}_1 = (1 \ \ 3)^T$ and $\mathbf{u}_2 = (-1 \ \ 1)^T$. The second vector was chosen because the effect of multiplying by A is just to scale the vector by a factor of 0.92. Thus, our new basis vectors satisfy

$$A\mathbf{u}_1 = \begin{pmatrix} 0.94 & 0.02 \\ 0.06 & 0.98 \end{pmatrix} \begin{bmatrix} 1 \\ 3 \end{bmatrix} = \begin{bmatrix} 1 \\ 3 \end{bmatrix} = \mathbf{u}_1$$

$$A\mathbf{u}_2 = \begin{pmatrix} 0.94 & 0.02 \\ 0.06 & 0.98 \end{pmatrix} \begin{bmatrix} -1 \\ 1 \end{bmatrix} = \begin{bmatrix} -0.92 \\ 0.92 \end{bmatrix} = 0.92\mathbf{u}_2$$

The initial vector $\mathbf{x}_0$ can be written as a linear combination of the new basis vectors:

$$\mathbf{x}_0 = \begin{bmatrix} 0.30 \\ 0.70 \end{bmatrix} = 0.25 \begin{bmatrix} 1 \\ 3 \end{bmatrix} - 0.05 \begin{bmatrix} -1 \\ 1 \end{bmatrix} = 0.25\mathbf{u}_1 - 0.05\mathbf{u}_2$$

It follows that

$$\mathbf{x}_n = A^n\mathbf{x}_0 = 0.25\mathbf{u}_1 - 0.05(0.92)^n\mathbf{u}_2$$

The entries of the second component approach 0 as n gets large. In fact, for $n > 27$, the entries will be small enough so that the rounded values of $\mathbf{x}_n$ are all equal to

$$0.25\mathbf{u}_1 = \begin{bmatrix} 0.25 \\ 0.75 \end{bmatrix}$$

This application is an example of a type of mathematical model called a *Markov process*. The sequence of vectors $\mathbf{x}_1, \mathbf{x}_2, \dots$ is called a *Markov chain*. The matrix A has a special structure in that its entries are nonnegative and its columns all add up to 1. Such matrices are called *stochastic matrices*. More precise definitions will be given later when we study these types of applications in Chapter 6. What we want to stress here is that the key to understanding such processes is to switch to a basis for which the effect of the matrix is quite simple. In particular, if A is $n \times n$, then we will want to choose basis vectors so that the effect of the matrix A on each basis vector $\mathbf{u}_j$ is simply to scale it by some factor λ_j, that is,

$$A\mathbf{u}_j = \lambda_j\mathbf{u}_j \quad j = 1, 2, \dots, n \tag{1}$$

In many applied problems involving an $n \times n$ matrix A, the key to solving the problem often is to find basis vectors $\mathbf{u}_1, \dots, \mathbf{u}_n$ and scalars $\lambda_1, \dots, \lambda_n$ such that (1) is satisfied. The new basis vectors can be thought of as a natural coordinate system to use with the matrix A, and the scalars can be thought of as natural frequencies for the basis vectors. We will study these types of applications in more detail in Chapter 6.

Changing Coordinates

Once we have decided to work with a new basis, we have the problem of finding the coordinates with respect to that basis. Suppose, for example, that instead of using the standard basis $\{\mathbf{e}_1, \mathbf{e}_2\}$ for $\mathbb{R}^2$, we wish to use a different basis, say,

$$\mathbf{u}_1 = \begin{pmatrix} 3 \\ 2 \end{pmatrix}, \qquad \mathbf{u}_2 = \begin{pmatrix} 1 \\ 1 \end{pmatrix}$$

Indeed, we may want to switch back and forth between the two coordinate systems. Let us consider the following two problems:

    I. Given a vector $\mathbf{x} = (x_1, x_2)^T$, find its coordinates with respect to $\mathbf{u}_1$ and $\mathbf{u}_2$.

    II. Given a vector $c_1\mathbf{u}_1 + c_2\mathbf{u}_2$, find its coordinates with respect to $\mathbf{e}_1$ and $\mathbf{e}_2$.

We will solve **II** first, since it turns out to be the easier problem. To switch bases from $\{\mathbf{u}_1, \mathbf{u}_2\}$ to $\{\mathbf{e}_1, \mathbf{e}_2\}$, we must express the old basis elements $\mathbf{u}_1$ and $\mathbf{u}_2$ in terms of the new basis elements $\mathbf{e}_1$ and $\mathbf{e}_2$.

$$\mathbf{u}_1 = 3\mathbf{e}_1 + 2\mathbf{e}_2$$
$$\mathbf{u}_2 = \mathbf{e}_1 + \mathbf{e}_2$$

It follows then that

$$c_1\mathbf{u}_1 + c_2\mathbf{u}_2 = (3c_1\mathbf{e}_1 + 2c_1\mathbf{e}_2) + (c_2\mathbf{e}_1 + c_2\mathbf{e}_2)$$
$$= (3c_1 + c_2)\mathbf{e}_1 + (2c_1 + c_2)\mathbf{e}_2$$

Thus, the coordinate vector of $c_1\mathbf{u}_1 + c_2\mathbf{u}_2$ with respect to $\{\mathbf{e}_1, \mathbf{e}_2\}$ is

$$\mathbf{x} = \begin{pmatrix} 3c_1 + c_2 \\ 2c_1 + c_2 \end{pmatrix} = \begin{pmatrix} 3 & 1 \\ 2 & 1 \end{pmatrix} \begin{pmatrix} c_1 \\ c_2 \end{pmatrix}$$

If we set

$$U = (\mathbf{u}_1, \mathbf{u}_2) = \begin{pmatrix} 3 & 1 \\ 2 & 1 \end{pmatrix}$$

then, given any coordinate vector $\mathbf{c}$ with respect to $\{\mathbf{u}_1, \mathbf{u}_2\}$, to find the corresponding coordinate vector $\mathbf{x}$ with respect to $\{\mathbf{e}_1, \mathbf{e}_2\}$, we simply multiply U times $\mathbf{c}$:

$$\mathbf{x} = U\mathbf{c} \qquad\qquad (2)$$

The matrix U is called the *transition matrix* from the ordered basis $\{\mathbf{u}_1, \mathbf{u}_2\}$ to the standard basis $\{\mathbf{e}_1, \mathbf{e}_2\}$.

    To solve problem **I**, we must find the transition matrix from $\{\mathbf{e}_1, \mathbf{e}_2\}$ to $\{\mathbf{u}_1, \mathbf{u}_2\}$. The matrix U in (2) is nonsingular, since its column vectors, $\mathbf{u}_1$ and $\mathbf{u}_2$, are linearly independent. It follows from (2) that

$$\mathbf{c} = U^{-1}\mathbf{x}$$

Thus, given a vector

$$\mathbf{x} = (x_1, x_2)^T = x_1\mathbf{e}_1 + x_2\mathbf{e}_2$$

we need only multiply by U^{-1} to find its coordinate vector with respect to $\{\mathbf{u}_1, \mathbf{u}_2\}$. U^{-1} is the transition matrix from $\{\mathbf{e}_1, \mathbf{e}_2\}$ to $\{\mathbf{u}_1, \mathbf{u}_2\}$.

EXAMPLE 2   Let $\mathbf{u}_1 = (3, 2)^T$, $\mathbf{u}_2 = (1, 1)^T$, and $\mathbf{x} = (7, 4)^T$. Find the coordinates of $\mathbf{x}$ with respect to $\mathbf{u}_1$ and $\mathbf{u}_2$.

Solution

By the preceding discussion, the transition matrix from $\{\mathbf{e}_1, \mathbf{e}_2\}$ to $\{\mathbf{u}_1, \mathbf{u}_2\}$ is the inverse of

$$U = (\mathbf{u}_1, \mathbf{u}_2) = \begin{bmatrix} 3 & 1 \\ 2 & 1 \end{bmatrix}$$

Thus,

$$\mathbf{c} = U^{-1}\mathbf{x} = \begin{bmatrix} 1 & -1 \\ -2 & 3 \end{bmatrix} \begin{bmatrix} 7 \\ 4 \end{bmatrix} = \begin{bmatrix} 3 \\ -2 \end{bmatrix}$$

is the desired coordinate vector and

$$\mathbf{x} = 3\mathbf{u}_1 - 2\mathbf{u}_2 \qquad \blacksquare$$

EXAMPLE 3   Let $\mathbf{b}_1 = (1, -1)^T$ and $\mathbf{b}_2 = (-2, 3)^T$. Find the transition matrix from $\{\mathbf{e}_1, \mathbf{e}_2\}$ to $\{\mathbf{b}_1, \mathbf{b}_2\}$ and determine the coordinates of $\mathbf{x} = (1, 2)^T$ with respect to $\{\mathbf{b}_1, \mathbf{b}_2\}$.

Solution

The transition matrix from $\{\mathbf{b}_1, \mathbf{b}_2\}$ to $\{\mathbf{e}_1, \mathbf{e}_2\}$ is

$$B = (\mathbf{b}_1, \mathbf{b}_2) = \begin{bmatrix} 1 & -2 \\ -1 & 3 \end{bmatrix}$$

and hence the transition matrix from $\{\mathbf{e}_1, \mathbf{e}_2\}$ to $\{\mathbf{b}_1, \mathbf{b}_2\}$ is

$$B^{-1} = \begin{bmatrix} 3 & 2 \\ 1 & 1 \end{bmatrix}$$

The coordinate vector of $\mathbf{x}$ with respect to $\{\mathbf{b}_1, \mathbf{b}_2\}$ is

$$\mathbf{c} = B^{-1}\mathbf{x} = \begin{bmatrix} 3 & 2 \\ 1 & 1 \end{bmatrix} \begin{bmatrix} 1 \\ 2 \end{bmatrix} = \begin{bmatrix} 7 \\ 3 \end{bmatrix}$$

and hence

$$\mathbf{x} = 7\mathbf{b}_1 + 3\mathbf{b}_2 \qquad \blacksquare$$

Now let us consider the general problem of changing from one ordered basis $\{\mathbf{v}_1, \mathbf{v}_2\}$ of $\mathbb{R}^2$ to another ordered basis $\{\mathbf{u}_1, \mathbf{u}_2\}$. In this case, we assume that, for a given vector $\mathbf{x}$, its coordinates with respect to $\{\mathbf{v}_1, \mathbf{v}_2\}$ are known:

$$\mathbf{x} = c_1\mathbf{v}_1 + c_2\mathbf{v}_2$$

Now we wish to represent $\mathbf{x}$ as a sum $d_1\mathbf{u}_1 + d_2\mathbf{u}_2$. Thus, we must find scalars d_1 and d_2 so that

$$c_1\mathbf{v}_1 + c_2\mathbf{v}_2 = d_1\mathbf{u}_1 + d_2\mathbf{u}_2 \qquad (3)$$

If we set $V = (\mathbf{v}_1, \mathbf{v}_2)$ and $U = (\mathbf{u}_1, \mathbf{u}_2)$, then equation (3) can be written in matrix form:

$$V\mathbf{c} = U\mathbf{d}$$

It follows that

$$\mathbf{d} = U^{-1}V\mathbf{c}$$

Thus, given a vector $\mathbf{x}$ in $\mathbb{R}^2$ and its coordinate vector $\mathbf{c}$ with respect to the ordered basis $\{\mathbf{v}_1, \mathbf{v}_2\}$, to find the coordinate vector of $\mathbf{x}$ with respect to the new basis $\{\mathbf{u}_1, \mathbf{u}_2\}$, we simply multiply $\mathbf{c}$ by the transition matrix $S = U^{-1}V$.

EXAMPLE 4 Find the transition matrix corresponding to the change of basis from $\{\mathbf{v}_1, \mathbf{v}_2\}$ to $\{\mathbf{u}_1, \mathbf{u}_2\}$, where

$$\mathbf{v}_1 = \begin{bmatrix} 5 \\ 2 \end{bmatrix}, \quad \mathbf{v}_2 = \begin{bmatrix} 7 \\ 3 \end{bmatrix} \quad \text{and} \quad \mathbf{u}_1 = \begin{bmatrix} 3 \\ 2 \end{bmatrix}, \quad \mathbf{u}_2 = \begin{bmatrix} 1 \\ 1 \end{bmatrix}$$

Solution

The transition matrix from $\{\mathbf{v}_1, \mathbf{v}_2\}$ to $\{\mathbf{u}_1, \mathbf{u}_2\}$ is given by

$$S = U^{-1}V = \begin{bmatrix} 1 & -1 \\ -2 & 3 \end{bmatrix} \begin{bmatrix} 5 & 7 \\ 2 & 3 \end{bmatrix} = \begin{bmatrix} 3 & 4 \\ -4 & -5 \end{bmatrix} \qquad \blacksquare$$

The change of basis from $\{\mathbf{v}_1, \mathbf{v}_2\}$ to $\{\mathbf{u}_1, \mathbf{u}_2\}$ can also be viewed as a two-step process. First we change from $\{\mathbf{v}_1, \mathbf{v}_2\}$ to the standard basis, $\{\mathbf{e}_1, \mathbf{e}_2\}$, and then we change from the standard basis to $\{\mathbf{u}_1, \mathbf{u}_2\}$. Given a vector $\mathbf{x}$ in $\mathbb{R}^2$, if $\mathbf{c}$ is the coordinate vector of $\mathbf{x}$ with respect to $\{\mathbf{v}_1, \mathbf{v}_2\}$ and $\mathbf{d}$ is the coordinate vector of $\mathbf{x}$ with respect to $\{\mathbf{u}_1, \mathbf{u}_2\}$, then

$$c_1\mathbf{v}_1 + c_2\mathbf{v}_2 = x_1\mathbf{e}_1 + x_2\mathbf{e}_2 = d_1\mathbf{u}_1 + d_2\mathbf{u}_2$$

Since V is the transition matrix from $\{\mathbf{v}_1, \mathbf{v}_2\}$ to $\{\mathbf{e}_1, \mathbf{e}_2\}$ and U^{-1} is the transition matrix from $\{\mathbf{e}_1, \mathbf{e}_2\}$ to $\{\mathbf{u}_1, \mathbf{u}_2\}$, it follows that

$$V\mathbf{c} = \mathbf{x} \quad \text{and} \quad U^{-1}\mathbf{x} = \mathbf{d}$$

and hence

$$U^{-1}V\mathbf{c} = U^{-1}\mathbf{x} = \mathbf{d}$$

As before, we see that the transition matrix from $\{\mathbf{v}_1, \mathbf{v}_2\}$ to $\{\mathbf{u}_1, \mathbf{u}_2\}$ is $U^{-1}V$ (see Figure 3.5.2).

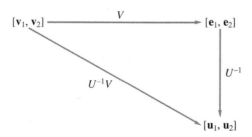

Figure 3.5.2.

Change of Basis for a General Vector Space

Everything we have done so far can easily be generalized to apply to any finite-dimensional vector space. We begin by defining coordinate vectors for an n-dimensional vector space.

Definition

Let V be a vector space and let $E = \{\mathbf{v}_1, \mathbf{v}_2, \ldots, \mathbf{v}_n\}$ be an ordered basis for V. If $\mathbf{v}$ is any element of V, then $\mathbf{v}$ can be written in the form

$$\mathbf{v} = c_1 \mathbf{v}_1 + c_2 \mathbf{v}_2 + \cdots + c_n \mathbf{v}_n$$

where $c_1, c_2, \ldots, c_n$ are scalars. Thus, we can associate with each vector $\mathbf{v}$ a unique vector $\mathbf{c} = (c_1, c_2, \ldots, c_n)^T$ in $\mathbb{R}^n$. The vector $\mathbf{c}$ defined in this way is called the **coordinate vector** of $\mathbf{v}$ with respect to the ordered basis E and is denoted $[\mathbf{v}]_E$. The c_i's are called the **coordinates** of $\mathbf{v}$ relative to E.

The examples considered so far have all dealt with changing coordinates in $\mathbb{R}^2$. Similar techniques could be used for $\mathbb{R}^n$. In the case of $\mathbb{R}^n$, the transition matrices will be $n \times n$.

EXAMPLE 5 If

$$\mathbf{v}_1 = \begin{bmatrix} 1 \\ 1 \\ 1 \end{bmatrix}, \quad \mathbf{v}_2 = \begin{bmatrix} 2 \\ 3 \\ 2 \end{bmatrix}, \quad \mathbf{v}_3 = \begin{bmatrix} 1 \\ 5 \\ 4 \end{bmatrix}$$

and

$$\mathbf{u}_1 = \begin{bmatrix} 1 \\ 1 \\ 0 \end{bmatrix}, \quad \mathbf{u}_2 = \begin{bmatrix} 1 \\ 2 \\ 0 \end{bmatrix}, \quad \mathbf{u}_3 = \begin{bmatrix} 1 \\ 2 \\ 1 \end{bmatrix}$$

then $E = \{\mathbf{v}_1, \mathbf{v}_2, \mathbf{v}_3\}$ and $F = \{\mathbf{u}_1, \mathbf{u}_2, \mathbf{u}_3\}$ are ordered bases for $\mathbb{R}^3$. Let

$$\mathbf{x} = 3\mathbf{v}_1 + 2\mathbf{v}_2 - \mathbf{v}_3 \qquad \text{and} \qquad \mathbf{y} = \mathbf{v}_1 - 3\mathbf{v}_2 + 2\mathbf{v}_3$$

Find the transition matrix from E to F and use it to find the coordinates of $\mathbf{x}$ and $\mathbf{y}$ with respect to the ordered basis F.

Solution

As in Example 4, the transition matrix is given by

$$U^{-1}V = \begin{bmatrix} 2 & -1 & 0 \\ -1 & 1 & -1 \\ 0 & 0 & 1 \end{bmatrix} \begin{bmatrix} 1 & 2 & 1 \\ 1 & 3 & 5 \\ 1 & 2 & 4 \end{bmatrix} = \begin{bmatrix} 1 & 1 & -3 \\ -1 & -1 & 0 \\ 1 & 2 & 4 \end{bmatrix}$$

The coordinate vectors of $\mathbf{x}$ and $\mathbf{y}$ with respect to the ordered basis F are given by

$$[\mathbf{x}]_F = \begin{bmatrix} 1 & 1 & -3 \\ -1 & -1 & 0 \\ 1 & 2 & 4 \end{bmatrix} \begin{bmatrix} 3 \\ 2 \\ -1 \end{bmatrix} = \begin{bmatrix} 8 \\ -5 \\ 3 \end{bmatrix}$$

and

$$[\mathbf{y}]_F = \begin{bmatrix} 1 & 1 & -3 \\ -1 & -1 & 0 \\ 1 & 2 & 4 \end{bmatrix} \begin{bmatrix} 1 \\ -3 \\ 2 \end{bmatrix} = \begin{bmatrix} -8 \\ 2 \\ 3 \end{bmatrix}$$

The reader may verify that

$$8\mathbf{u}_1 - 5\mathbf{u}_2 + 3\mathbf{u}_3 = 3\mathbf{v}_1 + 2\mathbf{v}_2 - \mathbf{v}_3$$
$$-8\mathbf{u}_1 + 2\mathbf{u}_2 + 3\mathbf{u}_3 = \mathbf{v}_1 - 3\mathbf{v}_2 + 2\mathbf{v}_3$$ ■

If V is any n-dimensional vector space, it is possible to change from one basis to another by means of an $n \times n$ transition matrix. We will show that such a transition matrix is necessarily nonsingular. To see how this is done, let $E = \{\mathbf{w}_1, \ldots, \mathbf{w}_n\}$ and $F = \{\mathbf{v}_1, \ldots, \mathbf{v}_n\}$ be two ordered bases for V. The key step is to express each basis vector $\mathbf{w}_j$ as a linear combination of the $\mathbf{v}_i$'s.

$$\begin{aligned} \mathbf{w}_1 &= s_{11}\mathbf{v}_1 + s_{21}\mathbf{v}_2 + \cdots + s_{n1}\mathbf{v}_n \\ \mathbf{w}_2 &= s_{12}\mathbf{v}_1 + s_{22}\mathbf{v}_2 + \cdots + s_{n2}\mathbf{v}_n \\ &\vdots \\ \mathbf{w}_n &= s_{1n}\mathbf{v}_1 + s_{2n}\mathbf{v}_2 + \cdots + s_{nn}\mathbf{v}_n \end{aligned} \tag{4}$$

Let $\mathbf{v} \in V$. If $\mathbf{x} = [\mathbf{v}]_E$, it follows from (4) that

$$\mathbf{v} = x_1\mathbf{w}_1 + x_2\mathbf{w}_2 + \cdots + x_n\mathbf{w}_n$$
$$= \left(\sum_{j=1}^n s_{1j}x_j\right)\mathbf{v}_1 + \left(\sum_{j=1}^n s_{2j}x_j\right)\mathbf{v}_2 + \cdots + \left(\sum_{j=1}^n s_{nj}x_j\right)\mathbf{v}_n$$

Thus, if $\mathbf{y} = [\mathbf{v}]_F$, then

$$y_i = \sum_{j=1}^n s_{ij}x_j \qquad i = 1, \ldots, n$$

and hence,

$$\mathbf{y} = S\mathbf{x}$$

The matrix S defined by (4) is referred to as the *transition matrix*. Once S has been determined, it is a simple matter to change coordinate systems. To find the coordinates of $\mathbf{v} = x_1\mathbf{w}_1 + \cdots + x_n\mathbf{w}_n$ with respect to $\{\mathbf{v}_1, \ldots, \mathbf{v}_n\}$, we need only calculate $\mathbf{y} = S\mathbf{x}$.

The transition matrix S corresponding to the change of basis from $\{\mathbf{w}_1, \ldots, \mathbf{w}_n\}$ to $\{\mathbf{v}_1, \ldots, \mathbf{v}_n\}$ can be characterized by the condition

$$S\mathbf{x} = \mathbf{y} \quad \text{if and only if} \quad x_1\mathbf{w}_1 + \cdots + x_n\mathbf{w}_n = y_1\mathbf{v}_1 + \cdots + y_n\mathbf{v}_n \tag{5}$$

Taking $\mathbf{y} = \mathbf{0}$ in (5), we see that $S\mathbf{x} = \mathbf{0}$ implies that

$$x_1\mathbf{w}_1 + \cdots + x_n\mathbf{w}_n = \mathbf{0}$$

Since the $\mathbf{w}_i$'s are linearly independent, it follows that $\mathbf{x} = \mathbf{0}$. Thus, the equation $S\mathbf{x} = \mathbf{0}$ has only the trivial solution and hence the matrix S is nonsingular. The inverse matrix is characterized by the condition

$$S^{-1}\mathbf{y} = \mathbf{x} \qquad \text{if and only if} \qquad y_1\mathbf{v}_1 + \cdots + y_n\mathbf{v}_n = x_1\mathbf{w}_1 + \cdots + x_n\mathbf{w}_n$$

Thus, S^{-1} is the transition matrix used to change basis from $\{\mathbf{v}_1, \ldots, \mathbf{v}_n\}$ to $\{\mathbf{w}_1, \ldots, \mathbf{w}_n\}$.

EXAMPLE 6   Suppose that in P_3 we want to change from the ordered basis $[1, x, x^2]$ to the ordered basis $[1, 2x, 4x^2 - 2]$. Because $[1, x, x^2]$ is the standard basis for P_3, it is easier to find the transition matrix from $[1, 2x, 4x^2 - 2]$ to $[1, x, x^2]$. Since

$$
\begin{aligned}
1 &= 1 \cdot 1 + 0x + 0x^2 \\
2x &= 0 \cdot 1 + 2x + 0x^2 \\
4x^2 - 2 &= -2 \cdot 1 + 0x + 4x^2
\end{aligned}
$$

the transition matrix is

$$
S = \begin{pmatrix} 1 & 0 & -2 \\ 0 & 2 & 0 \\ 0 & 0 & 4 \end{pmatrix}
$$

The inverse of S will be the transition matrix from $[1, x, x^2]$ to $[1, 2x, 4x^2 - 2]$:

$$
S^{-1} = \begin{pmatrix} 1 & 0 & \frac{1}{2} \\ 0 & \frac{1}{2} & 0 \\ 0 & 0 & \frac{1}{4} \end{pmatrix}
$$

Given any $p(x) = a + bx + cx^2$ in P_3, to find the coordinates of $p(x)$ with respect to $[1, 2x, 4x^2 - 2]$, we multiply

$$
\begin{pmatrix} 1 & 0 & \frac{1}{2} \\ 0 & \frac{1}{2} & 0 \\ 0 & 0 & \frac{1}{4} \end{pmatrix} \begin{pmatrix} a \\ b \\ c \end{pmatrix} = \begin{pmatrix} a + \frac{1}{2}c \\ \frac{1}{2}b \\ \frac{1}{4}c \end{pmatrix}
$$

Thus,

$$
p(x) = (a + \tfrac{1}{2}c) \cdot 1 + (\tfrac{1}{2}b) \cdot 2x + \tfrac{1}{4}c \cdot (4x^2 - 2) \qquad \blacksquare
$$

We have seen that each transition matrix is nonsingular. Actually, any nonsingular matrix can be thought of as a transition matrix. If S is an $n \times n$ nonsingular matrix and $\{\mathbf{v}_1, \ldots, \mathbf{v}_n\}$ is an ordered basis for V, then define $\{\mathbf{w}_1, \mathbf{w}_2, \ldots, \mathbf{w}_n\}$ by (4). To see that the $\mathbf{w}_j$'s are linearly independent, suppose that

$$\sum_{j=1}^{n} x_j \mathbf{w}_j = \mathbf{0}$$

It follows from (4) that

$$\sum_{i=1}^{n} \left(\sum_{j=1}^{n} s_{ij} x_j \right) \mathbf{v}_j = \mathbf{0}$$

By the linear independence of the $\mathbf{v}_i$'s, it follows that

$$\sum_{j=1}^{n} s_{ij} x_j = 0 \qquad i = 1, \ldots, n$$

or, equivalently,

$$S\mathbf{x} = \mathbf{0}$$

Since S is nonsingular, $\mathbf{x}$ must equal $\mathbf{0}$. Therefore, $\mathbf{w}_1, \ldots, \mathbf{w}_n$ are linearly independent and hence they form a basis for V. The matrix S is the transition matrix corresponding to the change from the ordered basis $\{\mathbf{w}_1, \ldots, \mathbf{w}_n\}$ to $\{\mathbf{v}_1, \ldots, \mathbf{v}_n\}$.

In many applied problems, it is important to use the right type of basis for the particular application. In Chapter 5, we will see that the key to solving least squares problems is to switch to a special type of basis called an *orthonormal* basis. In Chapter 6, we will consider a number of applications involving the *eigenvalues* and *eigenvectors* associated with an $n \times n$ matrix A. The key to solving these types of problems is to switch to a basis for $\mathbb{R}^n$ consisting of eigenvectors of A.

SECTION 3.5 EXERCISES

1. For each of the following, find the transition matrix corresponding to the change of basis from $\{\mathbf{u}_1, \mathbf{u}_2\}$ to $\{\mathbf{e}_1, \mathbf{e}_2\}$:
   (a) $\mathbf{u}_1 = (1, 1)^T$, $\quad \mathbf{u}_2 = (-1, 1)^T$
   (b) $\mathbf{u}_1 = (1, 2)^T$, $\quad \mathbf{u}_2 = (2, 5)^T$
   (c) $\mathbf{u}_1 = (0, 1)^T$, $\quad \mathbf{u}_2 = (1, 0)^T$

2. For each of the ordered bases $\{\mathbf{u}_1, \mathbf{u}_2\}$ in Exercise 1, find the transition matrix corresponding to the change of basis from $\{\mathbf{e}_1, \mathbf{e}_2\}$ to $\{\mathbf{u}_1, \mathbf{u}_2\}$.

3. Let $\mathbf{v}_1 = (3, 2)^T$ and $\mathbf{v}_2 = (4, 3)^T$. For each ordered basis $\{\mathbf{u}_1, \mathbf{u}_2\}$ given in Exercise 1, find the transition matrix from $\{\mathbf{v}_1, \mathbf{v}_2\}$ to $\{\mathbf{u}_1, \mathbf{u}_2\}$.

4. Let $E = [(5, 3)^T, (3, 2)^T]$ and let $\mathbf{x} = (1, 1)^T$, $\mathbf{y} = (1, -1)^T$, and $\mathbf{z} = (10, 7)^T$. Determine the values of $[\mathbf{x}]_E$, $[\mathbf{y}]_E$, and $[\mathbf{z}]_E$.

5. Let $\mathbf{u}_1 = (1, 1, 1)^T$, $\mathbf{u}_2 = (1, 2, 2)^T$, and $\mathbf{u}_3 = (2, 3, 4)^T$.
   (a) Find the transition matrix corresponding to the change of basis from $\{\mathbf{e}_1, \mathbf{e}_2, \mathbf{e}_3\}$ to $\{\mathbf{u}_1, \mathbf{u}_2, \mathbf{u}_3\}$.

   (b) Find the coordinates of each of the following vectors with respect to the ordered basis $\{\mathbf{u}_1, \mathbf{u}_2, \mathbf{u}_3\}$:
   (i) $(3, 2, 5)^T$ (ii) $(1, 1, 2)^T$ (iii) $(2, 3, 2)^T$

6. Let $\mathbf{v}_1 = (4, 6, 7)^T$, $\mathbf{v}_2 = (0, 1, 1)^T$, and $\mathbf{v}_3 = (0, 1, 2)^T$, and let $\mathbf{u}_1, \mathbf{u}_2,$ and $\mathbf{u}_3$ be the vectors given in Exercise 5.
   (a) Find the transition matrix from $\{\mathbf{v}_1, \mathbf{v}_2, \mathbf{v}_3\}$ to $\{\mathbf{u}_1, \mathbf{u}_2, \mathbf{u}_3\}$.
   (b) If $\mathbf{x} = 2\mathbf{v}_1 + 3\mathbf{v}_2 - 4\mathbf{v}_3$, determine the coordinates of $\mathbf{x}$ with respect to $\{\mathbf{u}_1, \mathbf{u}_2, \mathbf{u}_3\}$.

7. Given
   $$\mathbf{v}_1 = \begin{bmatrix} 1 \\ 2 \end{bmatrix}, \quad \mathbf{v}_2 = \begin{bmatrix} 2 \\ 3 \end{bmatrix}, \quad S = \begin{bmatrix} 3 & 5 \\ 1 & -2 \end{bmatrix}$$
   find vectors $\mathbf{w}_1$ and $\mathbf{w}_2$ so that S will be the transition matrix from $\{\mathbf{w}_1, \mathbf{w}_2\}$ to $\{\mathbf{v}_1, \mathbf{v}_2\}$.

8. Given
   $$\mathbf{v}_1 = \begin{bmatrix} 2 \\ 6 \end{bmatrix}, \quad \mathbf{v}_2 = \begin{bmatrix} 1 \\ 4 \end{bmatrix}, \quad S = \begin{bmatrix} 4 & 1 \\ 2 & 1 \end{bmatrix}$$

find vectors $\mathbf{u}_1$ and $\mathbf{u}_2$ so that S will be the transition matrix from $\{\mathbf{v}_1, \mathbf{v}_2\}$ to $\{\mathbf{u}_1, \mathbf{u}_2\}$.

9. Let $[x, 1]$ and $[2x - 1, 2x + 1]$ be ordered bases for P_2.

   (a) Find the transition matrix representing the change in coordinates from $[2x - 1, 2x + 1]$ to $[x, 1]$.

   (b) Find the transition matrix representing the change in coordinates from $[x, 1]$ to $[2x - 1, 2x + 1]$.

10. Find the transition matrix representing the change of coordinates on P_3 from the ordered basis $[1, x, x^2]$ to the ordered basis

$$[1, 1 + x, 1 + x + x^2]$$

11. Let $E = \{\mathbf{u}_1, \ldots, \mathbf{u}_n\}$ and $F = \{\mathbf{v}_1, \ldots, \mathbf{v}_n\}$ be two ordered bases for $\mathbb{R}^n$, and set

$$U = (\mathbf{u}_1, \ldots, \mathbf{u}_n), \qquad V = (\mathbf{v}_1, \ldots, \mathbf{v}_n)$$

Show that the transition matrix from E to F can be determined by calculating the reduced row echelon form of $(V|U)$.

3.6   Row Space and Column Space

If A is an $m \times n$ matrix, each row of A is an n-tuple of real numbers and hence can be considered as a vector in $\mathbb{R}^{1 \times n}$. The m vectors corresponding to the rows of A will be referred to as the *row vectors* of A. Similarly, each column of A can be considered as a vector in $\mathbb{R}^m$, and we can associate n *column vectors* with the matrix A.

Definition

If A is an $m \times n$ matrix, the subspace of $\mathbb{R}^{1 \times n}$ spanned by the row vectors of A is called the **row space** of A. The subspace of $\mathbb{R}^m$ spanned by the column vectors of A is called the **column space** of A.

EXAMPLE I   Let

$$A = \begin{bmatrix} 1 & 0 & 0 \\ 0 & 1 & 0 \end{bmatrix}$$

The row space of A is the set of all 3-tuples of the form

$$\alpha(1, 0, 0) + \beta(0, 1, 0) = (\alpha, \beta, 0)$$

The column space of A is the set of all vectors of the form

$$\alpha \begin{bmatrix} 1 \\ 0 \end{bmatrix} + \beta \begin{bmatrix} 0 \\ 1 \end{bmatrix} + \gamma \begin{bmatrix} 0 \\ 0 \end{bmatrix} = \begin{bmatrix} \alpha \\ \beta \end{bmatrix}$$

Thus, the row space of A is a two-dimensional subspace of $\mathbb{R}^{1 \times 3}$, and the column space of A is $\mathbb{R}^2$.   ∎

Theorem 3.6.1   *Two row equivalent matrices have the same row space.*

Proof   If B is row equivalent to A, then B can be formed from A by a finite sequence of row operations. Thus, the row vectors of B must be linear combinations of the row vectors of A. Consequently, the row space of B must be a subspace of the row space of A. Since A is row equivalent to B, by the same reasoning, the row space of A is a subspace of the row space of B. ∎

Definition

> The **rank** of a matrix A, denoted rank(A), is the dimension of the row space of A.

To determine the rank of a matrix, we can reduce the matrix to row echelon form. The nonzero rows of the row echelon matrix will form a basis for the row space.

EXAMPLE 2 Let

$$A = \begin{pmatrix} 1 & -2 & 3 \\ 2 & -5 & 1 \\ 1 & -4 & -7 \end{pmatrix}$$

Reducing A to row echelon form, we obtain the matrix

$$U = \begin{pmatrix} 1 & -2 & 3 \\ 0 & 1 & 5 \\ 0 & 0 & 0 \end{pmatrix}$$

Clearly, $(1, -2, 3)$ and $(0, 1, 5)$ form a basis for the row space of U. Since U and A are row equivalent, they have the same row space, and hence the rank of A is 2. ∎

Linear Systems

The concepts of row space and column space are useful in the study of linear systems. A system $A\mathbf{x} = \mathbf{b}$ can be written in the form

$$x_1 \begin{pmatrix} a_{11} \\ a_{21} \\ \vdots \\ a_{m1} \end{pmatrix} + x_2 \begin{pmatrix} a_{12} \\ a_{22} \\ \vdots \\ a_{m2} \end{pmatrix} + \cdots + x_n \begin{pmatrix} a_{1n} \\ a_{2n} \\ \vdots \\ a_{mn} \end{pmatrix} = \begin{pmatrix} b_1 \\ b_2 \\ \vdots \\ b_m \end{pmatrix} \tag{1}$$

In Chapter 1 we used this representation to characterize when a linear system will be consistent. The result, Theorem 1.3.1, can now be restated in terms of the column space of the matrix.

Theorem 3.6.2 Consistency Theorem for Linear Systems

A linear system $A\mathbf{x} = \mathbf{b}$ is consistent if and only if $\mathbf{b}$ is in the column space of A.

If $\mathbf{b}$ is replaced by the zero vector, then (1) becomes

$$x_1\mathbf{a}_1 + x_2\mathbf{a}_2 \cdots + x_n\mathbf{a}_n = \mathbf{0} \tag{2}$$

It follows from (2) that the system $A\mathbf{x} = \mathbf{0}$ will have only the trivial solution $\mathbf{x} = \mathbf{0}$ if and only if the column vectors of A are linearly independent.

Theorem 3.6.3   *Let A be an $m \times n$ matrix. The linear system $A\mathbf{x} = \mathbf{b}$ is consistent for every $\mathbf{b} \in \mathbb{R}^m$ if and only if the column vectors of A span $\mathbb{R}^m$. The system $A\mathbf{x} = \mathbf{b}$ has at most one solution for every $\mathbf{b} \in \mathbb{R}^m$ if and only if the column vectors of A are linearly independent.*

Proof   We have seen that the system $A\mathbf{x} = \mathbf{b}$ is consistent if and only if $\mathbf{b}$ is in the column space of A. It follows that $A\mathbf{x} = \mathbf{b}$ will be consistent for every $\mathbf{b} \in \mathbb{R}^m$ if and only if the column vectors of A span $\mathbb{R}^m$. To prove the second statement, note that, if $A\mathbf{x} = \mathbf{b}$ has at most one solution for every $\mathbf{b}$, then in particular the system $A\mathbf{x} = \mathbf{0}$ can have only the trivial solution, and hence the column vectors of A must be linearly independent. Conversely, if the column vectors of A are linearly independent, $A\mathbf{x} = \mathbf{0}$ has only the trivial solution. Now, if $\mathbf{x}_1$ and $\mathbf{x}_2$ were both solutions of $A\mathbf{x} = \mathbf{b}$, then $\mathbf{x}_1 - \mathbf{x}_2$ would be a solution of $A\mathbf{x} = \mathbf{0}$:

$$A(\mathbf{x}_1 - \mathbf{x}_2) = A\mathbf{x}_1 - A\mathbf{x}_2 = \mathbf{b} - \mathbf{b} = \mathbf{0}$$

It follows that $\mathbf{x}_1 - \mathbf{x}_2 = \mathbf{0}$, and hence $\mathbf{x}_1$ must equal $\mathbf{x}_2$.   ∎

Let A be an $m \times n$ matrix. If the column vectors of A span $\mathbb{R}^m$, then n must be greater than or equal to m, since no set of fewer than m vectors could span $\mathbb{R}^m$. If the columns of A are linearly independent, then n must be less than or equal to m, since every set of more than m vectors in $\mathbb{R}^m$ is linearly dependent. Thus, if the column vectors of A form a basis for $\mathbb{R}^m$, then n must equal m.

Corollary 3.6.4   *An $n \times n$ matrix A is nonsingular if and only if the column vectors of A form a basis for $\mathbb{R}^n$.*

In general, the rank and the dimension of the null space always add up to the number of columns of the matrix. The dimension of the null space of a matrix is called the *nullity* of the matrix.

Theorem 3.6.5   The Rank–Nullity Theorem

If A is an $m \times n$ matrix, then the rank of A plus the nullity of A equals n.

Proof   Let U be the reduced row echelon form of A. The system $A\mathbf{x} = \mathbf{0}$ is equivalent to the system $U\mathbf{x} = \mathbf{0}$. If A has rank r, then U will have r nonzero rows, and consequently, the system $U\mathbf{x} = \mathbf{0}$ will involve r lead variables and $n - r$ free variables. The dimension of $N(A)$ will equal the number of free variables.   ∎

EXAMPLE 3   Let

$$A = \begin{bmatrix} 1 & 2 & -1 & 1 \\ 2 & 4 & -3 & 0 \\ 1 & 2 & 1 & 5 \end{bmatrix}$$

Find a basis for the row space of A and a basis for $N(A)$. Verify that $\dim N(A) = n - r$.

Solution

The reduced row echelon form of A is given by

$$U = \begin{bmatrix} 1 & 2 & 0 & 3 \\ 0 & 0 & 1 & 2 \\ 0 & 0 & 0 & 0 \end{bmatrix}$$

Thus, $\{(1, 2, 0, 3), (0, 0, 1, 2)\}$ is a basis for the row space of A, and A has rank 2. Since the systems $A\mathbf{x} = \mathbf{0}$ and $U\mathbf{x} = \mathbf{0}$ are equivalent, it follows that $\mathbf{x}$ is in $N(A)$ if and only if

$$x_1 + 2x_2 + \quad 3x_4 = 0$$
$$x_3 + 2x_4 = 0$$

The lead variables x_1 and x_3 can be solved for in terms of the free variables x_2 and x_4:

$$x_1 = -2x_2 - 3x_4$$
$$x_3 = -2x_4$$

Let $x_2 = \alpha$ and $x_4 = \beta$. It follows that $N(A)$ consists of all vectors of the form

$$\begin{bmatrix} x_1 \\ x_2 \\ x_3 \\ x_4 \end{bmatrix} = \begin{bmatrix} -2\alpha - 3\beta \\ \alpha \\ -2\beta \\ \beta \end{bmatrix} = \alpha \begin{bmatrix} -2 \\ 1 \\ 0 \\ 0 \end{bmatrix} + \beta \begin{bmatrix} -3 \\ 0 \\ -2 \\ 1 \end{bmatrix}$$

The vectors $(-2, 1, 0, 0)^T$ and $(-3, 0, -2, 1)^T$ form a basis for $N(A)$. Note that

$$n - r = 4 - 2 = 2 = \dim N(A)$$

The Column Space

The matrices A and U in Example 3 have different column spaces; however, their column vectors satisfy the same dependency relations. For the matrix U, the column vectors $\mathbf{u}_1$ and $\mathbf{u}_3$ are linearly independent, while

$$\mathbf{u}_2 = 2\mathbf{u}_1$$
$$\mathbf{u}_4 = 3\mathbf{u}_1 + 2\mathbf{u}_3$$

The same relations hold for the columns of A: The vectors $\mathbf{a}_1$ and $\mathbf{a}_3$ are linearly independent, while

$$\mathbf{a}_2 = 2\mathbf{a}_1$$
$$\mathbf{a}_4 = 3\mathbf{a}_1 + 2\mathbf{a}_3$$

In general, if A is an $m \times n$ matrix and U is the row echelon form of A, then, since $A\mathbf{x} = \mathbf{0}$ if and only if $U\mathbf{x} = \mathbf{0}$, their column vectors satisfy the same dependency relations. We will use this property to prove that the dimension of the column space of A is equal to the dimension of the row space of A.

Theorem 3.6.6 *If A is an m × n matrix, the dimension of the row space of A equals the dimension of the column space of A.*

Proof If A is an $m \times n$ matrix of rank r, the row echelon form U of A will have r leading 1's. The columns of U corresponding to the leading 1's will be linearly independent. They do not, however, form a basis for the column space of A, since, in general, A and U will have different column spaces. Let U_L denote the matrix obtained from U by deleting all the columns corresponding to the free variables. Delete the same columns from A and denote the new matrix by A_L. The matrices A_L and U_L are row equivalent. Thus, if $\mathbf{x}$ is a solution of $A_L\mathbf{x} = \mathbf{0}$, then $\mathbf{x}$ must also be a solution of $U_L\mathbf{x} = \mathbf{0}$. Since the columns of U_L are linearly independent, $\mathbf{x}$ must equal $\mathbf{0}$. It follows from the remarks preceding Theorem 3.6.3 that the columns of A_L are linearly independent. Since A_L has r columns, the dimension of the column space of A is at least r.

We have proved that, for any matrix, the dimension of the column space is greater than or equal to the dimension of the row space. Applying this result to the matrix A^T, we see that

$$
\begin{aligned}
\dim(\text{row space of } A) &= \dim(\text{column space of } A^T) \\
&\geq \dim(\text{row space of } A^T) \\
&= \dim(\text{column space of } A)
\end{aligned}
$$

Thus, for any matrix A, the dimension of the row space must equal the dimension of the column space. ∎

We can use the row echelon form U of A to find a basis for the column space of A. We need only determine the columns of U that correspond to the leading 1's. These same columns of A will be linearly independent and form a basis for the column space of A.

Note

The row echelon form U tells us only which columns of A to use to form a basis. We cannot use the column vectors from U, since, in general, U and A have different column spaces.

EXAMPLE 4 Let

$$
A = \begin{pmatrix} 1 & -2 & 1 & 1 & 2 \\ -1 & 3 & 0 & 2 & -2 \\ 0 & 1 & 1 & 3 & 4 \\ 1 & 2 & 5 & 13 & 5 \end{pmatrix}
$$

The row echelon form of A is given by

$$
U = \begin{pmatrix} 1 & -2 & 1 & 1 & 2 \\ 0 & 1 & 1 & 3 & 0 \\ 0 & 0 & 0 & 0 & 1 \\ 0 & 0 & 0 & 0 & 0 \end{pmatrix}
$$

The leading 1's occur in the first, second, and fifth columns. Thus,

$$\mathbf{a}_1 = \begin{pmatrix} 1 \\ -1 \\ 0 \\ 1 \end{pmatrix}, \qquad \mathbf{a}_2 = \begin{pmatrix} -2 \\ 3 \\ 1 \\ 2 \end{pmatrix}, \qquad \mathbf{a}_5 = \begin{pmatrix} 2 \\ -2 \\ 4 \\ 5 \end{pmatrix}$$

form a basis for the column space of A.

EXAMPLE 5   Find the dimension of the subspace of $\mathbb{R}^4$ spanned by

$$\mathbf{x}_1 = \begin{pmatrix} 1 \\ 2 \\ -1 \\ 0 \end{pmatrix}, \quad \mathbf{x}_2 = \begin{pmatrix} 2 \\ 5 \\ -3 \\ 2 \end{pmatrix}, \quad \mathbf{x}_3 = \begin{pmatrix} 2 \\ 4 \\ -2 \\ 0 \end{pmatrix}, \quad \mathbf{x}_4 = \begin{pmatrix} 3 \\ 8 \\ -5 \\ 4 \end{pmatrix}$$

Solution

The subspace Span($\mathbf{x}_1, \mathbf{x}_2, \mathbf{x}_3, \mathbf{x}_4$) is the same as the column space of the matrix

$$X = \begin{pmatrix} 1 & 2 & 2 & 3 \\ 2 & 5 & 4 & 8 \\ -1 & -3 & -2 & -5 \\ 0 & 2 & 0 & 4 \end{pmatrix}$$

The row echelon form of X is

$$\begin{pmatrix} 1 & 2 & 2 & 3 \\ 0 & 1 & 0 & 2 \\ 0 & 0 & 0 & 0 \\ 0 & 0 & 0 & 0 \end{pmatrix}.$$

The first two columns $\mathbf{x}_1, \mathbf{x}_2$ of X will form a basis for the column space of X. Thus, dim Span($\mathbf{x}_1, \mathbf{x}_2, \mathbf{x}_3, \mathbf{x}_4$) = 2.

SECTION 3.6 EXERCISES

1. For each of the following matrices, find a basis for the row space, a basis for the column space, and a basis for the null space:

(a) $\begin{bmatrix} 1 & 3 & 2 \\ 2 & 1 & 4 \\ 4 & 7 & 8 \end{bmatrix}$

(b) $\begin{bmatrix} -3 & 1 & 3 & 4 \\ 1 & 2 & -1 & -2 \\ -3 & 8 & 4 & 2 \end{bmatrix}$

(c) $\begin{bmatrix} 1 & 3 & -2 & 1 \\ 2 & 1 & 3 & 2 \\ 3 & 4 & 5 & 6 \end{bmatrix}$

2. In each of the following, determine the dimension of the subspace of $\mathbb{R}^3$ spanned by the given vectors:

(a) $\begin{bmatrix} 1 \\ -2 \\ 2 \end{bmatrix}, \begin{bmatrix} 2 \\ -2 \\ 4 \end{bmatrix}, \begin{bmatrix} -3 \\ 3 \\ 6 \end{bmatrix}$

(b) $\begin{bmatrix} 1 \\ 1 \\ 1 \end{bmatrix}, \begin{bmatrix} 1 \\ 2 \\ 3 \end{bmatrix}, \begin{bmatrix} 2 \\ 3 \\ 1 \end{bmatrix}$

(c) $\begin{bmatrix} 1 \\ -1 \\ 2 \end{bmatrix}, \begin{bmatrix} -2 \\ 2 \\ -4 \end{bmatrix}, \begin{bmatrix} 3 \\ -2 \\ 5 \end{bmatrix}, \begin{bmatrix} 2 \\ -1 \\ 3 \end{bmatrix}$

3. Let

$$A = \begin{bmatrix} 1 & 2 & 2 & 3 & 1 & 4 \\ 2 & 4 & 5 & 5 & 4 & 9 \\ 3 & 6 & 7 & 8 & 5 & 9 \end{bmatrix}$$

(a) Compute the reduced row echelon form U of A. Which column vectors of U correspond to the free variables? Write each of these vectors as a linear combination of the column vectors corresponding to the lead variables.

(b) Which column vectors of A correspond to the lead variables of U? These column vectors form a basis for the column space of A. Write each of the remaining column vectors of A as a linear combination of these basis vectors.

4. For each of the following choices of A and $\mathbf{b}$, determine whether $\mathbf{b}$ is in the column space of A and state whether the system $A\mathbf{x} = \mathbf{b}$ is consistent:

(a) $A = \begin{bmatrix} 1 & 2 \\ 2 & 4 \end{bmatrix}$, $\mathbf{b} = \begin{bmatrix} 4 \\ 8 \end{bmatrix}$

(b) $A = \begin{bmatrix} 3 & 6 \\ 1 & 2 \end{bmatrix}$, $\mathbf{b} = \begin{bmatrix} 1 \\ 1 \end{bmatrix}$

(c) $A = \begin{bmatrix} 2 & 1 \\ 3 & 4 \end{bmatrix}$, $\mathbf{b} = \begin{bmatrix} 4 \\ 6 \end{bmatrix}$

(d) $A = \begin{bmatrix} 1 & 1 & 2 \\ 1 & 1 & 2 \\ 1 & 1 & 2 \end{bmatrix}$, $\mathbf{b} = \begin{bmatrix} 1 \\ 2 \\ 3 \end{bmatrix}$

(e) $A = \begin{bmatrix} 0 & 1 \\ 1 & 0 \\ 0 & 1 \end{bmatrix}$, $\mathbf{b} = \begin{bmatrix} 2 \\ 5 \\ 2 \end{bmatrix}$

(f) $A = \begin{bmatrix} 1 & 2 \\ 2 & 4 \\ 1 & 2 \end{bmatrix}$, $\mathbf{b} = \begin{bmatrix} 5 \\ 10 \\ 5 \end{bmatrix}$

5. For each consistent system in Exercise 4, determine whether there will be one or infinitely many solutions by examining the column vectors of the coefficient matrix A.

6. How many solutions will the linear system $A\mathbf{x} = \mathbf{b}$ have if $\mathbf{b}$ is in the column space of A and the column vectors of A are linearly dependent? Explain.

7. Let A be a $6 \times n$ matrix of rank r and let $\mathbf{b}$ be a vector in $\mathbb{R}^6$. For each choice of r and n that follows, indicate the possibilities as to the number of solutions one could have for the linear system $A\mathbf{x} = \mathbf{b}$. Explain your answers.

(a) $n = 7, r = 5$ (b) $n = 7, r = 6$

(c) $n = 5, r = 5$ (d) $n = 5, r = 4$

8. Let A be an $m \times n$ matrix with $m > n$. Let $\mathbf{b} \in \mathbb{R}^m$ and suppose that $N(A) = \{\mathbf{0}\}$.

(a) What can you conclude about the column vectors of A? Are they linearly independent? Do they span $\mathbb{R}^m$? Explain.

(b) How many solutions will the system $A\mathbf{x} = \mathbf{b}$ have if $\mathbf{b}$ is not in the column space of A? How many solutions will there be if $\mathbf{b}$ is in the column space of A? Explain.

9. Let A and B be 6×5 matrices. If $\dim N(A) = 2$, what is the rank of A? If the rank of B is 4, what is the dimension of $N(B)$?

10. Let A be an $m \times n$ matrix whose rank is equal to n. If $A\mathbf{c} = A\mathbf{d}$, does this imply that $\mathbf{c}$ must be equal to $\mathbf{d}$? What if the rank of A is less than n? Explain your answers.

11. Let A be an $m \times n$ matrix. Prove that

$$\text{rank}(A) \leq \min(m, n)$$

12. Let A and B be row equivalent matrices.

(a) Show that the dimension of the column space of A equals the dimension of the column space of B.

(b) Are the column spaces of the two matrices necessarily the same? Justify your answer.

13. Let A be a 4×3 matrix and suppose that the vectors

$$\mathbf{z}_1 = \begin{bmatrix} 1 \\ 1 \\ 2 \end{bmatrix}, \quad \mathbf{z}_2 = \begin{bmatrix} 1 \\ 0 \\ -1 \end{bmatrix}$$

form a basis for $N(A)$. If $\mathbf{b} = \mathbf{a}_1 + 2\mathbf{a}_2 + \mathbf{a}_3$, find all solutions of the system $A\mathbf{x} = \mathbf{b}$.

14. Let A be a 4×4 matrix with reduced row echelon form given by

$$U = \begin{bmatrix} 1 & 0 & 2 & 1 \\ 0 & 1 & 1 & 4 \\ 0 & 0 & 0 & 0 \\ 0 & 0 & 0 & 0 \end{bmatrix}$$

If

$$\mathbf{a}_1 = \begin{bmatrix} -3 \\ 5 \\ 2 \\ 1 \end{bmatrix} \quad \text{and} \quad \mathbf{a}_2 = \begin{bmatrix} 4 \\ -3 \\ 7 \\ -1 \end{bmatrix}$$

find $\mathbf{a}_3$ and $\mathbf{a}_4$.

15. Let A be a 4×5 matrix and let U be the reduced row echelon form of A. If

$$\mathbf{a}_1 = \begin{bmatrix} 2 \\ 1 \\ -3 \\ -2 \end{bmatrix}, \quad \mathbf{a}_2 = \begin{bmatrix} -1 \\ 2 \\ 3 \\ 1 \end{bmatrix},$$

$$U = \begin{bmatrix} 1 & 0 & 2 & 0 & -1 \\ 0 & 1 & 3 & 0 & -2 \\ 0 & 0 & 0 & 1 & 5 \\ 0 & 0 & 0 & 0 & 0 \end{bmatrix}$$

(a) find a basis for $N(A)$.

(b) given that $\mathbf{x}_0$ is a solution to $A\mathbf{x} = \mathbf{b}$, where

$$\mathbf{b} = \begin{bmatrix} 0 \\ 5 \\ 3 \\ 4 \end{bmatrix} \quad \text{and} \quad \mathbf{x}_0 = \begin{bmatrix} 3 \\ 2 \\ 0 \\ 2 \\ 0 \end{bmatrix}$$

   (i) find all solutions to the system.
   (ii) determine the remaining column vectors of A.

16. Let A be a 5×8 matrix with rank equal to 5 and let $\mathbf{b}$ be any vector in $\mathbb{R}^5$. Explain why the system $A\mathbf{x} = \mathbf{b}$ must have infinitely many solutions.

17. Let A be a 4×5 matrix. If $\mathbf{a}_1$, $\mathbf{a}_2$, and $\mathbf{a}_4$ are linearly independent and

$$\mathbf{a}_3 = \mathbf{a}_1 + 2\mathbf{a}_2, \quad \mathbf{a}_5 = 2\mathbf{a}_1 - \mathbf{a}_2 + 3\mathbf{a}_4$$

   determine the reduced row echelon form of A.

18. Let A be a 5×3 matrix of rank 3 and let $\{\mathbf{x}_1, \mathbf{x}_2, \mathbf{x}_3\}$ be a basis for $\mathbb{R}^3$.
   (a) Show that $N(A) = \{\mathbf{0}\}$.
   (b) Show that if $\mathbf{y}_1 = A\mathbf{x}_1$, $\mathbf{y}_2 = A\mathbf{x}_2$, and $\mathbf{y}_3 = A\mathbf{x}_3$, then $\mathbf{y}_1, \mathbf{y}_2$, and $\mathbf{y}_3$ are linearly independent.
   (c) Do the vectors $\mathbf{y}_1, \mathbf{y}_2, \mathbf{y}_3$ from part (b) form a basis for $\mathbb{R}^5$? Explain.

19. Let A be an $m \times n$ matrix with rank equal to n. Show that if $\mathbf{x} \neq \mathbf{0}$ and $\mathbf{y} = A\mathbf{x}$, then $\mathbf{y} \neq \mathbf{0}$.

20. Prove that a linear system $A\mathbf{x} = \mathbf{b}$ is consistent if and only if the rank of $(A \mid \mathbf{b})$ equals the rank of A.

21. Let A and B be $m \times n$ matrices. Show that

$$\text{rank}(A + B) \leq \text{rank}(A) + \text{rank}(B)$$

22. Let A be an $m \times n$ matrix.
   (a) Show that if B is a nonsingular $m \times m$ matrix, then BA and A have the same null space and hence the same rank.
   (b) Show that if C is a nonsingular $n \times n$ matrix, then AC and A have the same rank.

23. Prove Corollary 3.6.4.

24. Show that if A and B are $n \times n$ matrices and $N(A - B) = \mathbb{R}^n$, then $A = B$.

25. Let A and B be $n \times n$ matrices.
   (a) Show that $AB = O$ if and only if the column space of B is a subspace of the null space of A.
   (b) Show that if $AB = O$, then the sum of the ranks of A and B cannot exceed n.

26. Let $A \in \mathbb{R}^{m \times n}$ and $\mathbf{b} \in \mathbb{R}^m$, and let $\mathbf{x}_0$ be a particular solution of the system $A\mathbf{x} = \mathbf{b}$. Prove that if $N(A) = \{\mathbf{0}\}$, then the solution $\mathbf{x}_0$ must be unique.

27. Let $\mathbf{x}$ and $\mathbf{y}$ be nonzero vectors in $\mathbb{R}^m$ and $\mathbb{R}^n$, respectively, and let $A = \mathbf{x}\mathbf{y}^T$.
   (a) Show that $\{\mathbf{x}\}$ is a basis for the column space of A and that $\{\mathbf{y}^T\}$ is a basis for the row space of A.
   (b) What is the dimension of $N(A)$?

28. Let $A \in \mathbb{R}^{m \times n}$, $B \in \mathbb{R}^{n \times r}$, and $C = AB$. Show that
   (a) the column space of C is a subspace of the column space of A.
   (b) the row space of C is a subspace of the row space of B.
   (c) $\text{rank}(C) \leq \min\{\text{rank}(A), \text{rank}(B)\}$.

29. Let $A \in \mathbb{R}^{m \times n}$, $B \in \mathbb{R}^{n \times r}$, and $C = AB$. Show that
   (a) if A and B both have linearly independent column vectors, then the column vectors of C will also be linearly independent.
   (b) if A and B both have linearly independent row vectors, then the row vectors of C will also be linearly independent.
   [Hint: Apply part (a) to C^T.]

30. Let $A \in \mathbb{R}^{m \times n}$, $B \in \mathbb{R}^{n \times r}$, and $C = AB$. Show that
   (a) if the column vectors of B are linearly dependent, then the column vectors of C must be linearly dependent.
   (b) if the row vectors of A are linearly dependent, then the row vectors of C are linearly dependent.
   [Hint: Apply part (a) to C^T.]

31. An $m \times n$ matrix A is said to have a *right inverse* if there exists an $n \times m$ matrix C such that $AC = I_m$. The matrix A is said to have a *left inverse* if there exists an $n \times m$ matrix D such that $DA = I_n$.
   (a) Show that if A has a right inverse, then the column vectors of A span $\mathbb{R}^m$.
   (b) Is it possible for an $m \times n$ matrix to have a right inverse if $n < m$? $n \geq m$? Explain.

32. Prove: If A is an $m \times n$ matrix and the column vectors of A span $\mathbb{R}^m$, then A has a right inverse. [Hint: Let $\mathbf{e}_j$ denote the jth column of I_m and solve $A\mathbf{x} = \mathbf{e}_j$ $j = 1, \ldots, m$.]

33. Show that a matrix B has a left inverse if and only if B^T has a right inverse.

34. Let B be an $n \times m$ matrix whose columns are linearly independent. Show that B has a left inverse.

35. Prove that if a matrix B has a left inverse, then the columns of B are linearly independent.

36. Show that if a matrix U is in row echelon form, then the nonzero row vectors of U form a basis for the row space of U.

Chapter 3 Exercises

MATLAB EXERCISES

1. (Change of Basis) Set

$$U = \mathbf{round}(20 * \mathbf{rand}(4)) - 10,$$
$$V = \mathbf{round}(10 * \mathbf{rand}(4))$$

and set $\mathbf{b} = \mathbf{ones}(4, 1)$.

(a) We can use the MATLAB function **rank** to determine whether the column vectors of a matrix are linearly independent. What should the rank be if the column vectors of U are linearly independent? Compute the rank of U, and verify that its column vectors are linearly independent and hence form a basis for $\mathbb{R}^4$. Compute the rank of V, and verify that its column vectors also form a basis for $\mathbb{R}^4$.

(b) Use MATLAB to compute the transition matrix from the standard basis for $\mathbb{R}^4$ to the ordered basis $E = \{\mathbf{u}_1, \mathbf{u}_2, \mathbf{u}_3, \mathbf{u}_4\}$. [Note that in MATLAB, the notation for the jth column vector $\mathbf{u}_j$ is $U(:, j)$.] Use this transition matrix to compute the coordinate vector $\mathbf{c}$ of $\mathbf{b}$ with respect to E. Verify that

$$\mathbf{b} = c_1 \mathbf{u}_1 + c_2 \mathbf{u}_2 + c_3 \mathbf{u}_3 + c_4 \mathbf{u}_4 = U\mathbf{c}$$

(c) Use MATLAB to compute the transition matrix from the standard basis to the ordered basis $F = \{\mathbf{v}_1, \mathbf{v}_2, \mathbf{v}_3, \mathbf{v}_4\}$, and use this transition matrix to find the coordinate vector $\mathbf{d}$ of $\mathbf{b}$ with respect to F. Verify that

$$\mathbf{b} = d_1 \mathbf{v}_1 + d_2 \mathbf{v}_2 + d_3 \mathbf{v}_3 + d_4 \mathbf{v}_4 = V\mathbf{d}$$

(d) Use MATLAB to compute the transition matrix S from E to F and the transition matrix T from F to E. How are S and T related? Verify that $S\mathbf{c} = \mathbf{d}$ and $T\mathbf{d} = \mathbf{c}$.

2. (Rank-Deficient Matrices) In this exercise, we consider how to use MATLAB to generate matrices with specified ranks.

(a) In general, if A is an $m \times n$ matrix with rank r, then $r \leq \min(m, n)$. Why? Explain. If the entries of A are random numbers, we would expect that $r = \min(m, n)$. Why? Explain. Check this out by generating random 6×6, 8×6, and 5×8 matrices and using the MATLAB command **rank** to compute their ranks. Whenever

the rank of an $m \times n$ matrix equals $\min(m, n)$, we say that the matrix has *full rank*. Otherwise, we say that the matrix is *rank deficient*.

(b) MATLAB's **rand** and **round** commands can be used to generate random $m \times n$ matrices with integer entries in a given range $[a, b]$. This can be done with a command of the form

$$A = \mathbf{round}((b - a) * \mathbf{rand}(m, n)) + a$$

For example, the command

$$A = \mathbf{round}(4 * \mathbf{rand}(6, 8)) + 3$$

will generate a 6×8 matrix whose entries are random integers in the range from 3 to 7. Using the range $[1, 10]$, create random integer 10×7, 8×12, and 10×15 matrices and in each case check the rank of the matrix. Do these integer matrices all have full rank?

(c) Suppose that we want to use MATLAB to generate matrices with less than full rank. It is easy to generate matrices of rank 1. If $\mathbf{x}$ and $\mathbf{y}$ are nonzero vectors in $\mathbb{R}^m$ and $\mathbb{R}^n$, respectively, then $A = \mathbf{x}\mathbf{y}^T$ will be an $m \times n$ matrix with rank 1. Why? Explain. Verify this in MATLAB by setting

$$\mathbf{x} = \mathbf{round}(9 * \mathbf{rand}(8, 1)) + 1,$$
$$\mathbf{y} = \mathbf{round}(9 * \mathbf{rand}(6, 1)) + 1$$

and using these vectors to construct an 8×6 matrix A. Check the rank of A with the MATLAB command **rank**.

(d) In general,

$$\mathrm{rank}(AB) \leq \min(\mathrm{rank}(A), \mathrm{rank}(B)) \qquad (1)$$

(See Exercise 28 in Section 3.6.) If A and B are non-integer random matrices, the relation (1) should be an equality. Generate an 8×6 matrix A by setting

$$X = \mathbf{rand}(8, 2), \quad Y = \mathbf{rand}(6, 2),$$
$$A = X * Y'$$

What would you expect the rank of A to be? Explain. Test the rank of A with MATLAB.

(e) Use MATLAB to generate matrices A, B, and C such that

    (i) A is 8×8 with rank 3.

    (ii) B is 6×9 with rank 4.

    (iii) C is 10×7 with rank 5.

3. (Column Space and Reduced Row Echelon Form) Set

$$B = \mathbf{round}(10 * \mathbf{rand}(8, 4))$$
$$X = \mathbf{round}(10 * \mathbf{rand}(4, 3))$$
$$C = B * X$$
$$A = [B \quad C]$$

(a) How are the column spaces of B and C related? (See Exercise 28 in Section 3.6.) What would you expect the rank of A to be? Explain. Use MATLAB to check your answer.

(b) Which column vectors of A should form a basis for its column space? Explain. If U is the reduced row echelon form of A, what would you expect its first four columns to be? Explain. What would you expect its last four rows to be? Explain. Use MATLAB to verify your answers by computing U.

(c) Use MATLAB to construct another matrix $D = (E \quad EY)$, where E is a random 6×4 matrix and Y is a random 4×2 matrix. What would you expect the reduced row echelon form of D to be? Compute it with MATLAB. Show that, in general, if B is an $m \times n$ matrix of rank n and X is an $n \times k$ matrix, the reduced row echelon form of $(B \quad BX)$ will have block structure

$$(I \quad X) \text{ if } m = n \quad \text{or} \quad \begin{bmatrix} I & X \\ O & O \end{bmatrix} \text{ if } m > n$$

4. (Rank-1 Updates of Linear Systems)
(a) Set

$$A = \mathbf{round}(10 * \mathbf{rand}(8))$$
$$b = \mathbf{round}(10 * \mathbf{rand}(8, 1))$$
$$M = \mathbf{inv}(A)$$

Use the matrix M to solve the system $A\mathbf{y} = \mathbf{b}$ for $\mathbf{y}$.

(b) Consider now a new system $C\mathbf{x} = \mathbf{b}$, where C is constructed as follows:

$$\mathbf{u} = \mathbf{round}(10 * \mathbf{rand}(8, 1))$$
$$\mathbf{v} = \mathbf{round}(10 * \mathbf{rand}(8, 1))$$
$$E = \mathbf{u} * \mathbf{v}'$$
$$C = A + E$$

The matrices C and A differ by the rank-1 matrix E. Use MATLAB to verify that the rank of E is 1. Use MATLAB's "\" operator to solve the system $C\mathbf{x} = \mathbf{b}$ and then compute the residual vector $\mathbf{r} = \mathbf{b} - C\mathbf{x}$.

(c) Let us now solve $C\mathbf{x} = \mathbf{b}$ by a new method that takes advantage of the fact that A and C differ by a rank-1 matrix. This new procedure is called a *rank-1 update* method. Set

$$\mathbf{z} = M * \mathbf{u}, \quad c = \mathbf{v}' * \mathbf{y},$$
$$d = \mathbf{v}' * \mathbf{z}, \quad e = c/(1 + d)$$

and then compute the solution $\mathbf{x}$ by

$$\mathbf{x} = \mathbf{y} - e * \mathbf{z}$$

Compute the residual vector $\mathbf{b} - C\mathbf{x}$ and compare it with the residual vector in part (b). This new method may seem more complicated, but it actually is much more computationally efficient.

(d) To see why the rank-1 update method works, use MATLAB to compute and compare

$$C\mathbf{y} \quad \text{and} \quad \mathbf{b} + c\mathbf{u}$$

Prove that if all computations had been carried out in exact arithmetic, these two vectors would be equal. Also, compute

$$C\mathbf{z} \quad \text{and} \quad (1 + d)\mathbf{u}$$

Prove that if all computations had been carried out in exact arithmetic, these two vectors would be equal. Use these identities to prove that $C\mathbf{x} = \mathbf{b}$. Assuming that A is nonsingular, will the rank-1 update method always work? Under what conditions could it fail? Explain.

CHAPTER TEST A   True or False

Indicate whether each of the following statements is true *or* false. *In each case, explain or prove your answer.*

1. If S is a subspace of a vector space V, then S is a vector space.

2. $\mathbb{R}^2$ is a subspace of $\mathbb{R}^3$.

3. It is possible to find a pair of two-dimensional subspaces S and T of $\mathbb{R}^3$ such that $S \cap T = \{\mathbf{0}\}$.

4. If S and T are subspaces of a vector space V, then $S \cup T$ is a subspace of V.

5. If S and T are subspaces of a vector space V, then $S \cap T$ is a subspace of V.

6. If $\mathbf{x}_1, \mathbf{x}_2, \ldots, \mathbf{x}_n$ span $\mathbb{R}^n$, then they are linearly independent.

7. If $\mathbf{x}_1, \mathbf{x}_2, \ldots, \mathbf{x}_n$ span a vector space V, then they are linearly independent.

8. If $\mathbf{x}_1, \mathbf{x}_2, \ldots, \mathbf{x}_k$ are vectors in a vector space V and

$$\text{Span}(\mathbf{x}_1, \mathbf{x}_2, \ldots, \mathbf{x}_k) = \text{Span}(\mathbf{x}_1, \mathbf{x}_2, \ldots, \mathbf{x}_{k-1})$$

then $\mathbf{x}_1, \mathbf{x}_2, \ldots, \mathbf{x}_k$ are linearly dependent.

9. If A is an $m \times n$ matrix, then A and A^T have the same rank.

10. If A is an $m \times n$ matrix, then A and A^T have the same nullity.

11. If U is the reduced row echelon form of A, then A and U have the same row space.

12. If U is the reduced row echelon form of A, then A and U have the same column space.

13. Let x_1, x_2,..., x_k be linearly independent vectors in $\mathbb{R}^n$. If $k < n$ and x_{k+1} is a vector that is not in Span($x_1, x_2, \ldots, x_k$), then the vectors $x_1, x_2, \ldots, x_k, x_{k+1}$ are linearly independent.

14. Let $\{u_1, u_2\}$, $\{v_1, v_2\}$, and $\{w_1, w_2\}$ be bases for $\mathbb{R}^2$. If X is the transition matrix corresponding to a change of basis from $\{u_1, u_2\}$ to $\{v_1, v_2\}$ and Y is the transition matrix corresponding to a change of basis from $\{v_1, v_2\}$ to $\{w_1, w_2\}$, then $Z = XY$ is the transition matrix corresponding to the change of basis from $\{u_1, u_2\}$ to $\{w_1, w_2\}$.

15. If A and B are $n \times n$ matrices that have the same rank, then the rank of A^2 must equal the rank of B^2.

CHAPTER TEST B

1. In $\mathbb{R}^3$, let x_1 and x_2 be linearly independent vectors and let $x_3 = 0$ (the zero vector). Are x_1, x_2, and x_3 linearly independent? Prove your answer.

2. For each set that follows determine whether it is a subspace of $\mathbb{R}^2$. Prove your answers.

(a) $S_1 = \left\{ x = \begin{bmatrix} x_1 \\ x_2 \end{bmatrix} \,\middle|\, x_1 + x_2 = 0 \right\}$

(b) $S_2 = \left\{ x = \begin{bmatrix} x_1 \\ x_2 \end{bmatrix} \,\middle|\, x_1 x_2 = 0 \right\}$

3. Let

$$A = \begin{bmatrix} 1 & 3 & 1 & 3 & 4 \\ 0 & 0 & 1 & 1 & 1 \\ 0 & 0 & 2 & 2 & 2 \\ 0 & 0 & 3 & 3 & 3 \end{bmatrix}$$

(a) Find a basis for $N(A)$ (the null space of A). What is the dimension of $N(A)$?

(b) Find a basis for the column space of A. What is the rank of A?

4. How do the dimensions of the null space and column space of a matrix relate to the number of lead and free variables in the reduced row echelon form of the matrix? Explain.

5. Answer the following questions and, in each case, give geometric explanations of your answers:

(a) Is it possible to have a pair of one-dimensional subspaces U_1 and U_2 of $\mathbb{R}^3$ such that $U_1 \cap U_2 = \{0\}$?

(b) Is it possible to have a pair of two-dimensional subspaces V_1 and V_2 of $\mathbb{R}^3$ such that $V_1 \cap V_2 = \{0\}$?

6. Let S be the set of all symmetric 2×2 matrices with real entries.

(a) Show that S is a subspace of $\mathbb{R}^{2 \times 2}$.

(b) Find a basis for S.

7. Let A be a 6×4 matrix of rank 4.

(a) What is the dimension of $N(A)$? What is the dimension of the column space of A?

(b) Do the column vectors of A span $\mathbb{R}^6$? Are the column vectors of A linearly independent? Explain your answers.

(c) How many solutions will the linear system $Ax = b$ have if b is in the column space of A? Explain.

8. Given the vectors

$$x_1 = \begin{bmatrix} 1 \\ 2 \\ 2 \end{bmatrix}, \quad x_2 = \begin{bmatrix} 1 \\ 3 \\ 3 \end{bmatrix},$$

$$x_3 = \begin{bmatrix} 1 \\ 5 \\ 5 \end{bmatrix}, \quad x_4 = \begin{bmatrix} 1 \\ 2 \\ 3 \end{bmatrix}$$

(a) Are x_1, x_2, x_3, and x_4 linearly independent in $\mathbb{R}^3$? Explain.

(b) Do x_1, x_2 span $\mathbb{R}^3$? Explain.

(c) Do x_1, x_2, x_3 span $\mathbb{R}^3$? Are they linearly independent? Do they form a basis for $\mathbb{R}^3$? Explain.

(d) Do x_1, x_2, x_4 span $\mathbb{R}^3$? Are they linearly independent? Do they form a basis for $\mathbb{R}^3$? Explain or prove your answers.

9. Let x_1, x_2, and x_3 be linearly independent vectors in $\mathbb{R}^4$ and let A be a nonsingular 4×4 matrix. Prove that if

$$y_1 = Ax_1, \quad y_2 = Ax_2, \quad y_3 = Ax_3$$

then y_1, y_2, and y_3 are linearly independent.

10. Let A be a 6×5 matrix with linearly independent column vectors a_1, a_2, a_3 and whose remaining column vectors satisfy

$$a_4 = a_1 + 3a_2 + a_3, \quad a_5 = 2a_1 - a_3$$

(a) What is the dimension of $N(A)$? Explain.

(b) Determine the reduced row echelon form of A.

11. Let $\{\mathbf{u}_1, \mathbf{u}_2\}$ and $\{\mathbf{v}_1, \mathbf{v}_2\}$ be ordered bases for $\mathbb{R}^2$, where

$$\mathbf{u}_1 = \begin{bmatrix} 1 \\ 3 \end{bmatrix}, \ \mathbf{u}_2 = \begin{bmatrix} 2 \\ 7 \end{bmatrix}$$

and

$$\mathbf{v}_1 = \begin{bmatrix} 5 \\ 2 \end{bmatrix}, \ \mathbf{v}_2 = \begin{bmatrix} 4 \\ 9 \end{bmatrix}$$

(a) Determine the transition matrix corresponding to a change of basis from the standard basis $\{\mathbf{e}_1, \mathbf{e}_2\}$ to the ordered basis $\{\mathbf{u}_1, \mathbf{u}_2\}$. Use this transition matrix to find the coordinates of $\mathbf{x} = (1, \ 1)^T$ with respect to $\{\mathbf{u}_1, \mathbf{u}_2\}$.

(b) Determine the transition matrix corresponding to a change of basis from the ordered basis $\{\mathbf{v}_1, \mathbf{v}_2\}$ to the ordered basis $\{\mathbf{u}_1, \mathbf{u}_2\}$. Use this transition matrix to find the coordinates of $\mathbf{z} = 2\mathbf{v}_1 + 3\mathbf{v}_2$ with respect to $\{\mathbf{u}_1, \mathbf{u}_2\}$.

CHAPTER

4

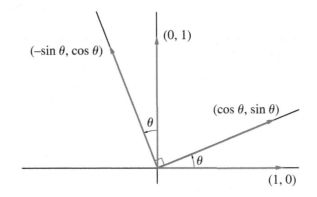

Linear Transformations

Linear mappings from one vector space to another play an important role in mathematics. This chapter provides an introduction to the theory of such mappings. In Section 4.1, the definition of a linear transformation is given and a number of examples are presented. In Section 4.2, it is shown that each linear transformation L mapping an n-dimensional vector space V into an m-dimensional vector space W can be represented by an $m \times n$ matrix A. Thus, we can work with the matrix A in place of the mapping L. In the case that the linear transformation L maps V into itself, the matrix representing L will depend on the ordered basis chosen for V. Hence, L may be represented by a matrix A with respect to one ordered basis and by another matrix B with respect to another ordered basis. In Section 4.3, we consider the relationship between different matrices that represent the same linear transformation. In many applications, it is desirable to choose the basis for V so that the matrix representing the linear transformation is either diagonal or in some other simple form.

4.1 Definition and Examples

In the study of vector spaces, the most important types of mappings are linear transformations.

Definition

A mapping L from a vector space V into a vector space W is said to be a **linear transformation** if

$$L(\alpha \mathbf{v}_1 + \beta \mathbf{v}_2) = \alpha L(\mathbf{v}_1) + \beta L(\mathbf{v}_2) \tag{1}$$

for all $\mathbf{v}_1, \mathbf{v}_2 \in V$ and for all scalars α and β.

If L is a linear transformation mapping a vector space V into a vector space W, then it follows from (1) that

$$L(\mathbf{v}_1 + \mathbf{v}_2) = L(\mathbf{v}_1) + L(\mathbf{v}_2) \qquad (\alpha = \beta = 1) \tag{2}$$

and

$$L(\alpha \mathbf{v}) = \alpha L(\mathbf{v}) \qquad (\mathbf{v} = \mathbf{v}_1, \beta = 0) \tag{3}$$

Conversely, if L satisfies (2) and (3), then

$$
\begin{aligned}
L(\alpha \mathbf{v}_1 + \beta \mathbf{v}_2) &= L(\alpha \mathbf{v}_1) + L(\beta \mathbf{v}_2) \\
&= \alpha L(\mathbf{v}_1) + \beta L(\mathbf{v}_2)
\end{aligned}
$$

Thus, L is a linear transformation if and only if L satisfies (2) and (3).

Notation

A mapping L from a vector space V into a vector space W will be denoted

$$L: V \rightarrow W$$

When the arrow notation is used, it will be assumed that V and W represent vector spaces.

In the case that the vector spaces V and W are the same, we will refer to a linear transformation $L: V \rightarrow V$ as a *linear operator* on V. Thus, a linear operator is a linear transformation that maps a vector space V into itself.

Let us now consider some examples of linear transformations. We begin with linear operators on $\mathbb{R}^2$. In this case, it is easier to see the geometric effect of the operator.

Linear Operators on $\mathbb{R}^2$

EXAMPLE 1 Let L be the operator defined by

$$L(\mathbf{x}) = 3\mathbf{x}$$

for each $\mathbf{x} \in \mathbb{R}^2$. Since

$$L(\alpha \mathbf{x}) = 3(\alpha \mathbf{x}) = \alpha(3\mathbf{x}) = \alpha L(\mathbf{x})$$

and

$$L(\mathbf{x} + \mathbf{y}) = 3(\mathbf{x} + \mathbf{y}) = 3\mathbf{x} + 3\mathbf{y} = L(\mathbf{x}) + L(\mathbf{y})$$

it follows that L is a linear operator. We can think of L as a stretching by a factor of 3 (see Figure 4.1.1). In general, if α is a positive scalar, the linear operator $F(\mathbf{x}) = \alpha \mathbf{x}$ can be thought of as a stretching or shrinking by a factor of α. ∎

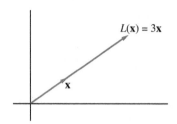

Figure 4.1.1.

EXAMPLE 2 Consider the mapping L defined by

$$L(\mathbf{x}) = x_1 \mathbf{e}_1$$

for each $\mathbf{x} \in \mathbb{R}^2$. Thus, if $\mathbf{x} = (x_1, x_2)^T$, then $L(\mathbf{x}) = (x_1, 0)^T$. If $\mathbf{y} = (y_1, y_2)^T$, then

$$\alpha \mathbf{x} + \beta \mathbf{y} = \begin{bmatrix} \alpha x_1 + \beta y_1 \\ \alpha x_2 + \beta y_2 \end{bmatrix}$$

and it follows that

$$L(\alpha \mathbf{x} + \beta \mathbf{y}) = (\alpha x_1 + \beta y_1)\mathbf{e}_1 = \alpha(x_1 \mathbf{e}_1) + \beta(y_1 \mathbf{e}_1) = \alpha L(\mathbf{x}) + \beta L(\mathbf{y})$$

Hence, L is a linear operator. We can think of L as a projection onto the x_1-axis (see Figure 4.1.2). ∎

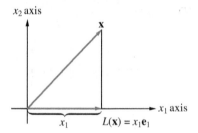

Figure 4.1.2.

EXAMPLE 3 Let L be the operator defined by

$$L(\mathbf{x}) = (x_1, -x_2)^T$$

for each $\mathbf{x} = (x_1, x_2)^T$ in $\mathbb{R}^2$. Since

$$L(\alpha \mathbf{x} + \beta \mathbf{y}) = \begin{bmatrix} \alpha x_1 + \beta y_1 \\ -(\alpha x_2 + \beta y_2) \end{bmatrix}$$

$$= \alpha \begin{bmatrix} x_1 \\ -x_2 \end{bmatrix} + \beta \begin{bmatrix} y_1 \\ -y_2 \end{bmatrix}$$

$$= \alpha L(\mathbf{x}) + \beta L(\mathbf{y})$$

it follows that L is a linear operator. The operator L has the effect of reflecting vectors about the x_1-axis (see Figure 4.1.3). ∎

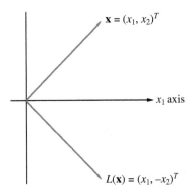

Figure 4.1.3.

EXAMPLE 4 The operator L defined by

$$L(\mathbf{x}) = (-x_2, x_1)^T$$

is linear, since

$$L(\alpha\mathbf{x} + \beta\mathbf{y}) = \begin{bmatrix} -(\alpha x_2 + \beta y_2) \\ \alpha x_1 + \beta y_1 \end{bmatrix}$$

$$= \alpha \begin{bmatrix} -x_2 \\ x_1 \end{bmatrix} + \beta \begin{bmatrix} -y_2 \\ y_1 \end{bmatrix}$$

$$= \alpha L(\mathbf{x}) + \beta L(\mathbf{y})$$

The operator L has the effect of rotating each vector in $\mathbb{R}^2$ by $90°$ in the counterclockwise direction (see Figure 4.1.4). ∎

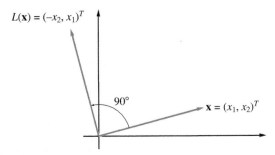

Figure 4.1.4.

Linear Transformations from $\mathbb{R}^n$ to $\mathbb{R}^m$

EXAMPLE 5   The mapping $L: \mathbb{R}^2 \to \mathbb{R}^1$ defined by

$$L(\mathbf{x}) = x_1 + x_2$$

is a linear transformation, since

$$
\begin{aligned}
L(\alpha\mathbf{x} + \beta\mathbf{y}) &= (\alpha x_1 + \beta y_1) + (\alpha x_2 + \beta y_2) \\
&= \alpha(x_1 + x_2) + \beta(y_1 + y_2) \\
&= \alpha L(\mathbf{x}) + \beta L(\mathbf{y})
\end{aligned}
$$

$\blacksquare$

EXAMPLE 6   Consider the mapping M defined by

$$M(\mathbf{x}) = (x_1^2 + x_2^2)^{1/2}$$

Since

$$M(\alpha\mathbf{x}) = (\alpha^2 x_1^2 + \alpha^2 x_2^2)^{1/2} = |\alpha|M(\mathbf{x})$$

it follows that

$$\alpha M(\mathbf{x}) \neq M(\alpha\mathbf{x})$$

whenever $\alpha < 0$ and $\mathbf{x} \neq \mathbf{0}$. Therefore, M is not a linear operator.

$\blacksquare$

EXAMPLE 7   The mapping L from $\mathbb{R}^2$ to $\mathbb{R}^3$ defined by

$$L(\mathbf{x}) = (x_2, x_1, x_1 + x_2)^T$$

is linear, since

$$L(\alpha\mathbf{x}) = (\alpha x_2, \alpha x_1, \alpha x_1 + \alpha x_2)^T = \alpha L(\mathbf{x})$$

and

$$
\begin{aligned}
L(\mathbf{x} + \mathbf{y}) &= (x_2 + y_2, x_1 + y_1, x_1 + y_1 + x_2 + y_2)^T \\
&= (x_2, x_1, x_1 + x_2)^T + (y_2, y_1, y_1 + y_2)^T \\
&= L(\mathbf{x}) + L(\mathbf{y})
\end{aligned}
$$

Note that if we define the matrix A by

$$
A = \begin{bmatrix} 0 & 1 \\ 1 & 0 \\ 1 & 1 \end{bmatrix}
$$

then

$$
L(\mathbf{x}) = \begin{bmatrix} x_2 \\ x_1 \\ x_1 + x_2 \end{bmatrix} = A\mathbf{x}
$$

for each $\mathbf{x} \in \mathbb{R}^2$.

$\blacksquare$

In general, if A is any $m \times n$ matrix, we can define a linear transformation L_A from $\mathbb{R}^n$ to $\mathbb{R}^m$ by

$$L_A(\mathbf{x}) = A\mathbf{x}$$

for each $\mathbf{x} \in \mathbb{R}^n$. The transformation L_A is linear, since

$$
\begin{aligned}
L_A(\alpha\mathbf{x} + \beta\mathbf{y}) &= A(\alpha\mathbf{x} + \beta\mathbf{y}) \\
&= \alpha A\mathbf{x} + \beta A\mathbf{y} \\
&= \alpha L_A(\mathbf{x}) + \beta L_A(\mathbf{y})
\end{aligned}
$$

Thus, we can think of each $m \times n$ matrix A as defining a linear transformation from $\mathbb{R}^n$ to $\mathbb{R}^m$.

In Example 7, we saw that the linear transformation L could have been defined in terms of a matrix A. In the next section, we will see that this is true for all linear transformations from $\mathbb{R}^n$ to $\mathbb{R}^m$.

Linear Transformations from V to W

If L is a linear transformation mapping a vector space V into a vector space W, then

(i) $L(\mathbf{0}_V) = \mathbf{0}_W$ (where $\mathbf{0}_V$ and $\mathbf{0}_W$ are the zero vectors in V and W, respectively).

(ii) if $\mathbf{v}_1, \ldots, \mathbf{v}_n$ are elements of V and $\alpha_1, \ldots, \alpha_n$ are scalars, then

$$L(\alpha_1\mathbf{v}_1 + \alpha_2\mathbf{v}_2 + \cdots + \alpha_n\mathbf{v}_n) = \alpha_1 L(\mathbf{v}_1) + \alpha_2 L(\mathbf{v}_2) + \cdots + \alpha_n L(\mathbf{v}_n)$$

(iii) $L(-\mathbf{v}) = -L(\mathbf{v})$ for all $\mathbf{v} \in V$.

Statement (i) follows from the condition $L(\alpha\mathbf{v}) = \alpha L(\mathbf{v})$ with $\alpha = 0$. Statement (ii) can easily be proved by mathematical induction. We leave this to the reader as an exercise. To prove (iii), note that

$$\mathbf{0}_W = L(\mathbf{0}_V) = L(\mathbf{v} + (-\mathbf{v})) = L(\mathbf{v}) + L(-\mathbf{v})$$

Therefore, $L(-\mathbf{v})$ is the additive inverse of $L(\mathbf{v})$; that is,

$$L(-\mathbf{v}) = -L(\mathbf{v})$$

EXAMPLE 8 If V is any vector space, then the identity operator $\mathcal{I}$ is defined by

$$\mathcal{I}(\mathbf{v}) = \mathbf{v}$$

for all $\mathbf{v} \in V$. Clearly, $\mathcal{I}$ is a linear transformation that maps V into itself:

$$\mathcal{I}(\alpha\mathbf{v}_1 + \beta\mathbf{v}_2) = \alpha\mathbf{v}_1 + \beta\mathbf{v}_2 = \alpha\mathcal{I}(\mathbf{v}_1) + \beta\mathcal{I}(\mathbf{v}_2)$$

EXAMPLE 9 Let L be the mapping from $C[a, b]$ to $\mathbb{R}^1$ defined by

$$L(f) = \int_a^b f(x)\, dx$$

If f and g are any vectors in $C[a, b]$, then

$$L(\alpha f + \beta g) = \int_a^b (\alpha f + \beta g)(x)\, dx$$

$$= \alpha \int_a^b f(x)\, dx + \beta \int_a^b g(x)\, dx$$

$$= \alpha L(f) + \beta L(g)$$

Therefore, L is a linear transformation. ∎

EXAMPLE 10 Let D be the linear transformation mapping $C^1[a, b]$ into $C[a, b]$ defined by

$$D(f) = f' \qquad \text{(the derivative of } f)$$

D is a linear transformation, since

$$D(\alpha f + \beta g) = \alpha f' + \beta g' = \alpha D(f) + \beta D(g)$$ ∎

The Image and Kernel

Let $L \colon V \to W$ be a linear transformation. We close this section by considering the effect that L has on subspaces of V. Of particular importance is the set of vectors in V that get mapped into the zero vector of W.

Definition

> Let $L \colon V \to W$ be a linear transformation. The **kernel** of L, denoted $\ker(L)$, is defined by
>
> $$\ker(L) = \{\mathbf{v} \in V \mid L(\mathbf{v}) = \mathbf{0}_W\}$$

Definition

> Let $L \colon V \to W$ be a linear transformation and let S be a subspace of V. The **image** of S, denoted $L(S)$, is defined by
>
> $$L(S) = \{\mathbf{w} \in W \mid \mathbf{w} = L(\mathbf{v}) \quad \text{for some} \quad \mathbf{v} \in S\}$$
>
> The image of the entire vector space, $L(V)$, is called the **range** of L.

Let $L \colon V \to W$ be a linear transformation. It is easily seen that $\ker(L)$ is a subspace of V, and if S is any subspace of V, then $L(S)$ is a subspace of W. In particular, $L(V)$ is a subspace of W. Indeed, we have the following theorem.

Theorem 4.1.1 *If $L \colon V \to W$ is a linear transformation and S is a subspace of V, then*

> **(i)** $\ker(L)$ *is a subspace of V.*
> **(ii)** $L(S)$ *is a subspace of W.*

Proof We see that $\ker(L)$ is nonempty since $\mathbf{0}_V$, the zero vector of V, is in $\ker(L)$. To prove **(i)**, we must show that $\ker(L)$ is closed under scalar multiplication and addition of vectors.

For closure under scalar multiplication, let $\mathbf{v} \in \ker(L)$ and α be a scalar. Then

$$L(\alpha \mathbf{v}) = \alpha L(\mathbf{v}) = \alpha \mathbf{0}_W = \mathbf{0}_W$$

Therefore, $\alpha \mathbf{v} \in \ker(L)$.

For closure under addition, let $\mathbf{v}_1, \mathbf{v}_2 \in \ker(L)$. Then

$$L(\mathbf{v}_1 + \mathbf{v}_2) = L(\mathbf{v}_1) + L(\mathbf{v}_2) = \mathbf{0}_W + \mathbf{0}_W = \mathbf{0}_W$$

Therefore, $\mathbf{v}_1 + \mathbf{v}_2 \in \ker(L)$ and hence $\ker(L)$ is a subspace of V.

The proof of (ii) is similar. $L(S)$ is nonempty, since $\mathbf{0}_W = L(\mathbf{0}_V) \in L(S)$. If $\mathbf{w} \in L(S)$, then $\mathbf{w} = L(\mathbf{v})$ for some $\mathbf{v} \in S$. For any scalar α,

$$\alpha \mathbf{w} = \alpha L(\mathbf{v}) = L(\alpha \mathbf{v})$$

Since $\alpha \mathbf{v} \in S$, it follows that $\alpha \mathbf{w} \in L(S)$, and hence $L(S)$ is closed under scalar multiplication. If $\mathbf{w}_1, \mathbf{w}_2 \in L(S)$, then there exist $\mathbf{v}_1, \mathbf{v}_2 \in S$ such that $L(\mathbf{v}_1) = \mathbf{w}_1$ and $L(\mathbf{v}_2) = \mathbf{w}_2$. Thus,

$$\mathbf{w}_1 + \mathbf{w}_2 = L(\mathbf{v}_1) + L(\mathbf{v}_2) = L(\mathbf{v}_1 + \mathbf{v}_2)$$

and hence $L(S)$ is closed under addition. It follows that $L(S)$ is a subspace of W.   ■

EXAMPLE 11   Let L be the linear operator on $\mathbb{R}^2$ defined by

$$L(\mathbf{x}) = \begin{bmatrix} x_1 \\ 0 \end{bmatrix}$$

A vector $\mathbf{x}$ is in $\ker(L)$ if and only if $x_1 = 0$. Thus, $\ker(L)$ is the one-dimensional subspace of $\mathbb{R}^2$ spanned by $\mathbf{e}_2$. A vector $\mathbf{y}$ is in the range of L if and only if $\mathbf{y}$ is a multiple of $\mathbf{e}_1$. Hence, $L(\mathbb{R}^2)$ is the one-dimensional subspace of $\mathbb{R}^2$ spanned by $\mathbf{e}_1$.   ■

EXAMPLE 12   Let $L: \mathbb{R}^3 \to \mathbb{R}^2$ be the linear transformation defined by

$$L(\mathbf{x}) = (x_1 + x_2, \ x_2 + x_3)^T$$

and let S be the subspace of $\mathbb{R}^3$ spanned by $\mathbf{e}_1$ and $\mathbf{e}_3$.

If $\mathbf{x} \in \ker(L)$, then

$$x_1 + x_2 = 0 \quad \text{and} \quad x_2 + x_3 = 0$$

Setting the free variable $x_3 = a$, we get

$$x_2 = -a, \quad x_1 = a$$

and hence $\ker(L)$ is the one-dimensional subspace of $\mathbb{R}^3$ consisting of all vectors of the form $a(1, -1, 1)^T$.

If $\mathbf{x} \in S$, then $\mathbf{x}$ must be of the form $(a, 0, b)^T$, and hence $L(\mathbf{x}) = (a, b)^T$. Clearly, $L(S) = \mathbb{R}^2$. Since the image of the subspace S is all of $\mathbb{R}^2$, it follows that the entire range of L must be $\mathbb{R}^2$ [i.e., $L(\mathbb{R}^3) = \mathbb{R}^2$].   ■

EXAMPLE 13 Let $D: P_3 \to P_3$ be the differentiation operator, defined by

$$D(p(x)) = p'(x)$$

The kernel of D consists of all polynomials of degree 0. Thus, $\ker(D) = P_1$. The derivative of any polynomial in P_3 will be a polynomial of degree 1 or less. Conversely, any polynomial in P_2 will have antiderivatives in P_3, so each polynomial in P_2 will be the image of polynomials in P_3 under the operator D. It then follows that $D(P_3) = P_2$. ∎

SECTION 4.1 EXERCISES

1. Show that each of the following are linear operators on $\mathbb{R}^2$. Describe geometrically what each linear transformation accomplishes.

   (a) $L(\mathbf{x}) = (-x_1, x_2)^T$ **(b)** $L(\mathbf{x}) = -\mathbf{x}$
   (c) $L(\mathbf{x}) = (x_2, x_1)^T$ **(d)** $L(\mathbf{x}) = \frac{1}{2}\mathbf{x}$
   (e) $L(\mathbf{x}) = x_2\mathbf{e}_2$

2. Let L be the linear operator on $\mathbb{R}^2$ defined by

   $$L(\mathbf{x}) = (x_1 \cos \alpha - x_2 \sin \alpha, \ x_1 \sin \alpha + x_2 \cos \alpha)^T$$

   Express x_1, x_2, and $L(\mathbf{x})$ in terms of polar coordinates. Describe geometrically the effect of the linear transformation.

3. Let $\mathbf{a}$ be a fixed nonzero vector in $\mathbb{R}^2$. A mapping of the form

   $L(1.x) = 1(x+a)$

   ⟶ $L(\mathbf{x}) = \mathbf{x} + \mathbf{a}$ $L(d.x) = d(x+a)$

   is called a *translation*. Show that a translation is not a linear operator. Illustrate geometrically the effect of a translation.

4. Let $L: \mathbb{R}^2 \to \mathbb{R}^2$ be a linear operator. If

   $$L((1,2)^T) = (-2,3)^T$$

   and

   $$L((1,-1)^T) = (5,2)^T$$

   find the value of $L((7,5)^T)$.

5. Determine whether the following are linear transformations from $\mathbb{R}^3$ into $\mathbb{R}^2$:

   (a) $L(\mathbf{x}) = (x_2, x_3)^T$ **(b)** $L(\mathbf{x}) = (0,0)^T$
   (c) $L(\mathbf{x}) = (1 + x_1, x_2)^T$
   (d) $L(\mathbf{x}) = (x_3, x_1 + x_2)^T$

6. Determine whether the following are linear transformations from $\mathbb{R}^2$ into $\mathbb{R}^3$:

   (a) $L(\mathbf{x}) = (x_1, x_2, 1)^T$
   (b) $L(\mathbf{x}) = (x_1, x_2, x_1 + 2x_2)^T$
   (c) $L(\mathbf{x}) = (x_1, 0, 0)^T$

   (d) $L(\mathbf{x}) = (x_1, x_2, x_1^2 + x_2^2)^T$

7. Determine whether the following are linear operators on $\mathbb{R}^{n \times n}$:

   (a) $L(A) = 2A$ **(b)** $L(A) = A^T$
   (c) $L(A) = A + I$ **(d)** $L(A) = A - A^T$

8. Let C be a fixed $n \times n$ matrix. Determine whether the following are linear operators on $\mathbb{R}^{n \times n}$:

   (a) $L(A) = CA + AC$ **(b)** $L(A) = C^2A$
   (c) $L(A) = A^2C$

9. Determine whether the following are linear transformations from P_2 to P_3:

   (a) $L(p(x)) = xp(x)$
   (b) $L(p(x)) = x^2 + p(x)$
   (c) $L(p(x)) = p(x) + xp(x) + x^2p'(x)$

10. For each $f \in C[0,1]$, define $L(f) = F$, where

    $$F(x) = \int_0^x f(t)\, dt \qquad 0 \le x \le 1$$

    Show that L is a linear operator on $C[0,1]$ and then find $L(e^x)$ and $L(x^2)$.

11. Determine whether the following are linear transformations from $C[0,1]$ into $\mathbb{R}^1$:

    (a) $L(f) = f(0)$ **(b)** $L(f) = |f(0)|$
    (c) $L(f) = [f(0) + f(1)]/2$

    (d) $L(f) = \left\{ \int_0^1 [f(x)]^2\, dx \right\}^{1/2}$

12. Use mathematical induction to prove that if L is a linear transformation from V to W, then

    $$L(\alpha_1\mathbf{v}_1 + \alpha_2\mathbf{v}_2 + \cdots + \alpha_n\mathbf{v}_n)$$
    $$= \alpha_1 L(\mathbf{v}_1) + \alpha_2 L(\mathbf{v}_2) + \cdots + \alpha_n L(\mathbf{v}_n)$$

13. Let $\{\mathbf{v}_1, \ldots, \mathbf{v}_n\}$ be a basis for a vector space V, and let L_1 and L_2 be two linear transformations mapping V into a vector space W. Show that if

$$L_1(\mathbf{v}_i) = L_2(\mathbf{v}_i)$$

for each $i = 1, \ldots, n$, then $L_1 = L_2$ [i.e., show that $L_1(\mathbf{v}) = L_2(\mathbf{v})$ for all $\mathbf{v} \in V$].

14. Let L be a linear operator on $\mathbb{R}^1$ and let $a = L(1)$. Show that $L(x) = ax$ for all $x \in \mathbb{R}^1$.

15. Let L be a linear operator on a vector space V. Define L^n, $n \geq 1$, recursively by

$$L^1 = L$$
$$L^{k+1}(\mathbf{v}) = L(L^k(\mathbf{v})) \qquad \text{for all } \mathbf{v} \in V$$

Show that L^n is a linear operator on V for each $n \geq 1$.

16. Let $L_1: U \to V$ and $L_2: V \to W$ be linear transformations, and let $L = L_2 \circ L_1$ be the mapping defined by

$$L(\mathbf{u}) = L_2(L_1(\mathbf{u}))$$

for each $\mathbf{u} \in U$. Show that L is a linear transformation mapping U into W.

17. Determine the kernel and range of each of the following linear operators on $\mathbb{R}^3$:

(a) $L(\mathbf{x}) = (x_3, x_2, x_1)^T$ (b) $L(\mathbf{x}) = (x_1, x_2, 0)^T$

(c) $L(\mathbf{x}) = (x_1, x_1, x_1)^T$

18. Let S be the subspace of $\mathbb{R}^3$ spanned by $\mathbf{e}_1$ and $\mathbf{e}_2$. For each linear operator L in Exercise 17, find $L(S)$.

19. Find the kernel and range of each of the following linear operators on P_3:

(a) $L(p(x)) = xp'(x)$ (b) $L(p(x)) = p(x) - p'(x)$

(c) $L(p(x)) = p(0)x + p(1)$

20. Let $L: V \to W$ be a linear transformation, and let T be a subspace of W. The *inverse image* of T, denoted $L^{-1}(T)$, is defined by

$$L^{-1}(T) = \{\mathbf{v} \in V \mid L(\mathbf{v}) \in T\}$$

Show that $L^{-1}(T)$ is a subspace of V.

21. A linear transformation $L: V \to W$ is said to be *one-to-one* if $L(\mathbf{v}_1) = L(\mathbf{v}_2)$ implies that $\mathbf{v}_1 = \mathbf{v}_2$ (i.e., no two distinct vectors $\mathbf{v}_1, \mathbf{v}_2$ in V get mapped into the same vector $\mathbf{w} \in W$). Show that L is one-to-one if and only if $\ker(L) = \{\mathbf{0}_V\}$.

22. A linear transformation $L: V \to W$ is said to map V *onto* W if $L(V) = W$. Show that the linear transformation L defined by

$$L(\mathbf{x}) = (x_1, x_1 + x_2, x_1 + x_2 + x_3)^T$$

maps $\mathbb{R}^3$ onto $\mathbb{R}^3$.

23. Which of the operators defined in Exercise 17 are one-to-one? Which map $\mathbb{R}^3$ onto $\mathbb{R}^3$?

24. Let A be a 2×2 matrix, and let L_A be the linear operator defined by

$$L_A(\mathbf{x}) = A\mathbf{x}$$

Show that

(a) L_A maps $\mathbb{R}^2$ onto the column space of A.

(b) if A is nonsingular, then L_A maps $\mathbb{R}^2$ onto $\mathbb{R}^2$.

25. Let D be the differentiation operator on P_3, and let

$$S = \{p \in P_3 \mid p(0) = 0\}$$

Show that

(a) D maps P_3 onto the subspace P_2, but $D: P_3 \to P_2$ is not one-to-one.

(b) $D: S \to P_3$ is one-to-one but not onto.

4.2   Matrix Representations of Linear Transformations

In Section 4.1, it was shown that each $m \times n$ matrix A defines a linear transformation L_A from $\mathbb{R}^n$ to $\mathbb{R}^m$, where

$$L_A(\mathbf{x}) = A\mathbf{x}$$

for each $\mathbf{x} \in \mathbb{R}^n$. In this section, we will see that, for each linear transformation L mapping $\mathbb{R}^n$ into $\mathbb{R}^m$, there is an $m \times n$ matrix A such that

$$L(\mathbf{x}) = A\mathbf{x}$$

We will also see how any linear transformation between finite dimensional spaces can be represented by a matrix.

Theorem 4.2.1   *If L is a linear transformation mapping $\mathbb{R}^n$ into $\mathbb{R}^m$, there is an $m \times n$ matrix A such that*

$$L(\mathbf{x}) = A\mathbf{x}$$

for each $\mathbf{x} \in \mathbb{R}^n$. In fact, the jth column vector of A is given by

$$\mathbf{a}_j = L(\mathbf{e}_j) \qquad j = 1, 2, \ldots, n$$

Proof   For $j = 1, \ldots, n$, define

$$\mathbf{a}_j = L(\mathbf{e}_j)$$

and let

$$A = (a_{ij}) = (\mathbf{a}_1, \mathbf{a}_2, \ldots, \mathbf{a}_n)$$

If

$$\mathbf{x} = x_1 \mathbf{e}_1 + x_2 \mathbf{e}_2 + \cdots + x_n \mathbf{e}_n$$

is an arbitrary element of $\mathbb{R}^n$, then

$$
\begin{aligned}
L(\mathbf{x}) &= x_1 L(\mathbf{e}_1) + x_2 L(\mathbf{e}_2) + \cdots + x_n L(\mathbf{e}_n) \\
&= x_1 \mathbf{a}_1 + x_2 \mathbf{a}_2 + \cdots + x_n \mathbf{a}_n \\
&= (\mathbf{a}_1, \mathbf{a}_2, \ldots, \mathbf{a}_n) \begin{bmatrix} x_1 \\ x_2 \\ \vdots \\ x_n \end{bmatrix} \\
&= A\mathbf{x}
\end{aligned}
$$

We have established that each linear transformation from $\mathbb{R}^n$ into $\mathbb{R}^m$ can be represented in terms of an $m \times n$ matrix. Theorem 4.2.1 tells us how to construct the matrix A corresponding to a particular linear transformation L. To get the first column of A, see what L does to the first basis element $\mathbf{e}_1$ of $\mathbb{R}^n$. Set $\mathbf{a}_1 = L(\mathbf{e}_1)$. To get the second column of A, determine the effect of L on $\mathbf{e}_2$ and set $\mathbf{a}_2 = L(\mathbf{e}_2)$, and so on. Since the standard basis elements $\mathbf{e}_1, \mathbf{e}_2, \ldots, \mathbf{e}_n$ (the column vectors of the $n \times n$ identity matrix) are used for $\mathbb{R}^n$, and the column vectors of the $m \times m$ identity matrix are being used as a basis for $\mathbb{R}^m$, we refer to A as the *standard matrix representation* of L. Later (Theorem 4.2.3) we will see how to represent linear transformations with respect to other bases.

EXAMPLE 1   Define the linear transformation $L \colon \mathbb{R}^3 \to \mathbb{R}^2$ by

$$L(\mathbf{x}) = (x_1 + x_2, x_2 + x_3)^T$$

for each $\mathbf{x} = (x_1, x_2, x_3)^T$ in $\mathbb{R}^3$. It is easily verified that L is a linear operator. We wish to find a matrix A such that $L(\mathbf{x}) = A\mathbf{x}$ for each $\mathbf{x} \in \mathbb{R}^3$. To do this, we must calculate $L(\mathbf{e}_1)$, $L(\mathbf{e}_2)$, and $L(\mathbf{e}_3)$:

$$L(\mathbf{e}_1) = L((1,0,0)^T) = \begin{bmatrix} 1 \\ 0 \end{bmatrix}$$

$$L(\mathbf{e}_2) = L((0,1,0)^T) = \begin{bmatrix} 1 \\ 1 \end{bmatrix}$$

$$L(\mathbf{e}_3) = L((0,0,1)^T) = \begin{bmatrix} 0 \\ 1 \end{bmatrix}$$

We choose these vectors to be the columns of the matrix

$$A = \begin{bmatrix} 1 & 1 & 0 \\ 0 & 1 & 1 \end{bmatrix}$$

To check the result, we compute $A\mathbf{x}$:

$$A\mathbf{x} = \begin{bmatrix} 1 & 1 & 0 \\ 0 & 1 & 1 \end{bmatrix} \begin{bmatrix} x_1 \\ x_2 \\ x_3 \end{bmatrix} = \begin{bmatrix} x_1 + x_2 \\ x_2 + x_3 \end{bmatrix} \qquad \blacksquare$$

EXAMPLE 2   Let L be the linear transformation operator $\mathbb{R}^2$ that rotates each vector by an angle θ in the counterclockwise direction. We can see from Figure 4.2.1(a) that $\mathbf{e}_1$ is mapped into $(\cos\theta, \sin\theta)^T$ and the image of $\mathbf{e}_2$ is $(-\sin\theta, \cos\theta)^T$. The matrix A representing the transformation will have $(\cos\theta, \sin\theta)^T$ as its first column and $(-\sin\theta, \cos\theta)^T$ as its second column.

$$A = \begin{bmatrix} \cos\theta & -\sin\theta \\ \sin\theta & \cos\theta \end{bmatrix}$$

If $\mathbf{x}$ is any vector in $\mathbb{R}^2$, then, to rotate $\mathbf{x}$ counterclockwise by an angle θ, we simply multiply by A [see Figure 4.2.1(b)]. $\blacksquare$

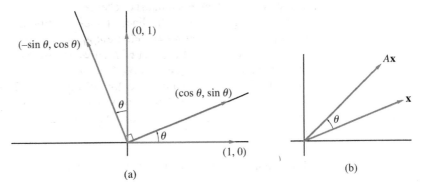

(a)   (b)

Figure 4.2.1.

Now that we have seen how matrices are used to represent linear transformations from $\mathbb{R}^n$ to $\mathbb{R}^m$, we may ask whether it is possible to find a similar representation for linear transformations from V into W, where V and W are vector spaces of dimension n and m, respectively. To see how this is done, let $E = \{\mathbf{v}_1, \mathbf{v}_2, \ldots, \mathbf{v}_n\}$ be an ordered basis for V and $F = \{\mathbf{w}_1, \mathbf{w}_2, \ldots, \mathbf{w}_m\}$ be an ordered basis for W. Let L be a linear transformation mapping V into W. If $\mathbf{v}$ is any vector in V, then we can express $\mathbf{v}$ in terms of the basis E:

$$\mathbf{v} = x_1 \mathbf{v}_1 + x_2 \mathbf{v}_2 + \cdots + x_n \mathbf{v}_n$$

We will show that there exists an $m \times n$ matrix A representing the linear transformation L, in the sense that

$$A\mathbf{x} = \mathbf{y} \quad \text{if and only if} \quad L(\mathbf{v}) = y_1 \mathbf{w}_1 + y_2 \mathbf{w}_2 + \cdots + y_m \mathbf{w}_m$$

The matrix A characterizes the effect of the linear transformation L. If $\mathbf{x}$ is the coordinate vector of $\mathbf{v}$ with respect to E, then the coordinate vector of $L(\mathbf{v})$ with respect to F is given by

$$[L(\mathbf{v})]_F = A\mathbf{x}$$

The procedure for determining the matrix representation A is essentially the same as before. For $j = 1, \ldots, n$, let $\mathbf{a}_j = (a_{1j}, a_{2j}, \ldots, a_{mj})^T$ be the coordinate vector of $L(\mathbf{v}_j)$ with respect to $\{\mathbf{w}_1, \mathbf{w}_2, \ldots, \mathbf{w}_m\}$; that is,

$$L(\mathbf{v}_j) = a_{1j} \mathbf{w}_1 + a_{2j} \mathbf{w}_2 + \cdots + a_{mj} \mathbf{w}_m \qquad 1 \le j \le n$$

Let $A = (a_{ij}) = (\mathbf{a}_1, \ldots, \mathbf{a}_n)$. If

$$\mathbf{v} = x_1 \mathbf{v}_1 + x_2 \mathbf{v}_2 + \cdots + x_n \mathbf{v}_n$$

then

$$
\begin{aligned}
L(\mathbf{v}) &= L\left(\sum_{j=1}^{n} x_j \mathbf{v}_j\right) \\
&= \sum_{j=1}^{n} x_j L(\mathbf{v}_j) \\
&= \sum_{j=1}^{n} x_j \left(\sum_{i=1}^{m} a_{ij} \mathbf{w}_i\right) \\
&= \sum_{i=1}^{m} \left(\sum_{j=1}^{n} a_{ij} x_j\right) \mathbf{w}_i
\end{aligned}
$$

For $i = 1, \ldots, m$, let

$$y_i = \sum_{j=1}^{n} a_{ij} x_j$$

Thus,

$$\mathbf{y} = (y_1, y_2, \ldots, y_m)^T = A\mathbf{x}$$

is the coordinate vector of $L(\mathbf{v})$ with respect to $\{\mathbf{w}_1, \mathbf{w}_2, \ldots, \mathbf{w}_m\}$. We have established the following theorem.

Theorem 4.2.2   Matrix Representation Theorem

If $E = \{\mathbf{v}_1, \mathbf{v}_2, \ldots, \mathbf{v}_n\}$ and $F = \{\mathbf{w}_1, \mathbf{w}_2, \ldots, \mathbf{w}_m\}$ are ordered bases for vector spaces V and W, respectively, then, corresponding to each linear transformation $L\colon V \to W$, there is an $m \times n$ matrix A such that

$$[L(\mathbf{v})]_F = A[\mathbf{v}]_E \quad \text{for each } \mathbf{v} \in V$$

A is the matrix representing L relative to the ordered bases E and F. In fact,

$$\mathbf{a}_j = \left[L(\mathbf{v}_j)\right]_F \quad j = 1, 2, \ldots, n$$

Theorem 4.2.2 is illustrated in Figure 4.2.2. If A is the matrix representing L with respect to the bases E and F, and if

$$\mathbf{x} = [\mathbf{v}]_E \quad \text{(the coordinate vector of } \mathbf{v} \text{ with respect to } E)$$
$$\mathbf{y} = [\mathbf{w}]_F \quad \text{(the coordinate vector of } \mathbf{w} \text{ with respect to } F)$$

then L maps $\mathbf{v}$ into $\mathbf{w}$ if and only if A maps $\mathbf{x}$ into $\mathbf{y}$.

Figure 4.2.2.

EXAMPLE 3   Let L be the linear transformation mapping $\mathbb{R}^3$ into $\mathbb{R}^2$ defined by

$$L(\mathbf{x}) = x_1 \mathbf{b}_1 + (x_2 + x_3) \mathbf{b}_2$$

for each $\mathbf{x} \in \mathbb{R}^3$, where

$$\mathbf{b}_1 = \begin{pmatrix} 1 \\ 1 \end{pmatrix} \quad \text{and} \quad \mathbf{b}_2 = \begin{pmatrix} -1 \\ 1 \end{pmatrix}$$

Find the matrix A representing L with respect to the ordered bases $\{\mathbf{e}_1, \mathbf{e}_2, \mathbf{e}_3\}$ and $\{\mathbf{b}_1, \mathbf{b}_2\}$.

Solution

$$L(\mathbf{e}_1) = 1\mathbf{b}_1 + 0\mathbf{b}_2$$
$$L(\mathbf{e}_2) = 0\mathbf{b}_1 + 1\mathbf{b}_2$$
$$L(\mathbf{e}_3) = 0\mathbf{b}_1 + 1\mathbf{b}_2$$

The ith column of A is determined by the coordinates of $L(\mathbf{e}_i)$ with respect to $\{\mathbf{b}_1, \mathbf{b}_2\}$ for $i = 1, 2, 3$. Thus,

$$A = \begin{bmatrix} 1 & 0 & 0 \\ 0 & 1 & 1 \end{bmatrix}$$

EXAMPLE 4   Let L be a linear transformation mapping $\mathbb{R}^2$ into itself defined by

$$L(\alpha\mathbf{b}_1 + \beta\mathbf{b}_2) = (\alpha + \beta)\mathbf{b}_1 + 2\beta\mathbf{b}_2$$

where $\{\mathbf{b}_1, \mathbf{b}_2\}$ is the ordered basis defined in Example 3. Find the matrix A representing L with respect to $\{\mathbf{b}_1, \mathbf{b}_2\}$.

Solution

$$L(\mathbf{b}_1) = 1\mathbf{b}_1 + 0\mathbf{b}_2$$
$$L(\mathbf{b}_2) = 1\mathbf{b}_1 + 2\mathbf{b}_2$$

Thus,

$$A = \begin{bmatrix} 1 & 1 \\ 0 & 2 \end{bmatrix}$$
■

EXAMPLE 5   The linear transformation D defined by $D(p) = p'$ maps P_3 into P_2. Given the ordered bases $[x^2, x, 1]$ and $[x, 1]$ for P_3 and P_2, respectively, we wish to determine a matrix representation for D. To do this, we apply D to each of the basis elements of P_3.

$$D(x^2) = 2x + 0 \cdot 1$$
$$D(x) = 0x + 1 \cdot 1$$
$$D(1) = 0x + 0 \cdot 1$$

In P_2, the coordinate vectors for $D(x^2), D(x)$, and $D(1)$ are $(2, 0)^T$, $(0, 1)^T$, and $(0, 0)^T$, respectively. The matrix A is formed with these vectors as its columns.

$$A = \begin{bmatrix} 2 & 0 & 0 \\ 0 & 1 & 0 \end{bmatrix}$$

If $p(x) = ax^2 + bx + c$, then the coordinate vector of p with respect to the ordered basis of P_3 is $(a, b, c)^T$. To find the coordinate vector of $D(p)$ with respect to the ordered basis of P_2, we simply multiply

$$\begin{bmatrix} 2 & 0 & 0 \\ 0 & 1 & 0 \end{bmatrix} \begin{bmatrix} a \\ b \\ c \end{bmatrix} = \begin{bmatrix} 2a \\ b \end{bmatrix}$$

Thus,

$$D(ax^2 + bx + c) = 2ax + b$$
■

To find the matrix representation A for a linear transformation $L: \mathbb{R}^n \rightarrow \mathbb{R}^m$ with respect to the ordered bases $E = \{\mathbf{u}_1, \ldots, \mathbf{u}_n\}$ and $F = \{\mathbf{b}_1, \ldots, \mathbf{b}_m\}$, we must represent each vector $L(\mathbf{u}_j)$ as a linear combination of $\mathbf{b}_1, \ldots, \mathbf{b}_m$. The following theorem shows that determining this representation of $L(\mathbf{u}_j)$ is equivalent to solving the linear system $B\mathbf{x} = L(\mathbf{u}_j)$.

Theorem 4.2.3 *Let $E = \{\mathbf{u}_1, \ldots, \mathbf{u}_n\}$ and $F = \{\mathbf{b}_1, \ldots, \mathbf{b}_m\}$ be ordered bases for $\mathbb{R}^n$ and $\mathbb{R}^m$, respectively. If $L: \mathbb{R}^n \to \mathbb{R}^m$ is a linear transformation and A is the matrix representing L with respect to E and F, then*

$$\mathbf{a}_j = B^{-1}L(\mathbf{u}_j) \qquad for \ j = 1, \ldots, n$$

where $B = (\mathbf{b}_1, \ldots, \mathbf{b}_m)$.

Proof If A is representing L with respect to E and F, then, for $j = 1, \ldots, n$,

$$L(\mathbf{u}_j) = a_{1j}\mathbf{b}_1 + a_{2j}\mathbf{b}_2 + \cdots + a_{mj}\mathbf{b}_m$$
$$= B\mathbf{a}_j$$

The matrix B is nonsingular since its column vectors form a basis for $\mathbb{R}^m$. Hence,

$$\mathbf{a}_j = B^{-1}L(\mathbf{u}_j) \qquad j = 1, \ldots, n \qquad \blacksquare$$

One consequence of this theorem is that we can determine the matrix representation of the transformation by computing the reduced row echelon form of an augmented matrix. The following corollary shows how this is done.

Corollary 4.2.4 *If A is the matrix representing the linear transformation $L: \mathbb{R}^n \to \mathbb{R}^m$ with respect to the bases*

$$E = \{\mathbf{u}_1, \ldots, \mathbf{u}_n\} \quad and \quad F = \{\mathbf{b}_1, \ldots, \mathbf{b}_m\}$$

then the reduced row echelon form of $(\mathbf{b}_1, \ldots, \mathbf{b}_m \mid L(\mathbf{u}_1), \ldots, L(\mathbf{u}_n))$ is $(I \mid A)$.

Proof Let $B = (\mathbf{b}_1, \ldots, \mathbf{b}_m)$. The matrix $(B \mid L(\mathbf{u}_1), \ldots, L(\mathbf{u}_n))$ is row equivalent to

$$B^{-1}(B \mid L(\mathbf{u}_1), \ldots, L(\mathbf{u}_n)) = (I \mid B^{-1}L(\mathbf{u}_1), \ldots, B^{-1}L(\mathbf{u}_n))$$
$$= (I \mid \mathbf{a}_1, \ldots, \mathbf{a}_n)$$
$$= (I \mid A) \qquad \blacksquare$$

EXAMPLE 6 Let $L: \mathbb{R}^2 \to \mathbb{R}^3$ be the linear transformation defined by

$$L(\mathbf{x}) = (x_2, x_1 + x_2, x_1 - x_2)^T$$

Find the matrix representations of L with respect to the ordered bases $\{\mathbf{u}_1, \mathbf{u}_2\}$ and $\{\mathbf{b}_1, \mathbf{b}_2, \mathbf{b}_3\}$, where

$$\mathbf{u}_1 = (1, 2)^T, \qquad \mathbf{u}_2 = (3, 1)^T$$

and

$$\mathbf{b}_1 = (1, 0, 0)^T, \qquad \mathbf{b}_2 = (1, 1, 0)^T, \qquad \mathbf{b}_3 = (1, 1, 1)^T$$

Solution ›

We must compute $L(\mathbf{u}_1)$ and $L(\mathbf{u}_2)$ and then transform the augmented matrix $(\mathbf{b}_1, \mathbf{b}_2, \mathbf{b}_3 \mid L(\mathbf{u}_1), L(\mathbf{u}_2))$ to reduced row echelon form:

$$L(\mathbf{u}_1) = (2, 3, -1)^T \qquad and \qquad L(\mathbf{u}_2) = (1, 4, 2)^T$$

$$\begin{bmatrix} 1 & 1 & 1 & 2 & 1 \\ 0 & 1 & 1 & 3 & 4 \\ 0 & 0 & 1 & -1 & 2 \end{bmatrix} \to \begin{bmatrix} 1 & 0 & 0 & -1 & -3 \\ 0 & 1 & 0 & 4 & 2 \\ 0 & 0 & 1 & -1 & 2 \end{bmatrix}$$

The matrix representing L with respect to the given ordered bases is

$$A = \begin{pmatrix} -1 & -3 \\ 4 & 2 \\ -1 & 2 \end{pmatrix}$$

The reader may verify that

$$L(\mathbf{u}_1) = -\mathbf{b}_1 + 4\mathbf{b}_2 - \mathbf{b}_3$$

$$L(\mathbf{u}_2) = -3\mathbf{b}_1 + 2\mathbf{b}_2 + 2\mathbf{b}_3$$

■

APPLICATION 1   Computer Graphics and Animation

A picture in the plane can be stored in the computer as a set of vertices. The vertices can then be plotted and connected by lines to produce the picture. If there are n vertices, they are stored in a $2 \times n$ matrix. The x-coordinates of the vertices are stored in the first row and the y-coordinates in the second. Each successive pair of points is connected by a straight line.

For example, to generate a triangle with vertices $(0,0)$, $(1,1)$, and $(1,-1)$, we store the pairs as columns of a matrix:

$$T = \begin{bmatrix} 0 & 1 & 1 & 0 \\ 0 & 1 & -1 & 0 \end{bmatrix}$$

An additional copy of the vertex $(0,0)$ is stored in the last column of T so that the previous point $(1,-1)$ will be connected back to $(0,0)$ [see Figure 4.2.3(a)].

We can transform a figure by changing the positions of the vertices and then redrawing the figure. If the transformation is linear, it can be carried out as a matrix multiplication. Viewing a succession of such drawings will produce the effect of animation.

The four primary geometric transformations that are used in computer graphics are as follows:

1. *Dilations and contractions.* A linear operator of the form

$$L(\mathbf{x}) = c\mathbf{x}$$

   is a *dilation* if $c > 1$ and a *contraction* if $0 < c < 1$. The operator L is represented by the matrix cI, where I is the 2×2 identity matrix. A dilation increases the size of the figure by a factor $c > 1$, and a contraction shrinks the figure by a factor $c < 1$. Figure 4.2.3(b) shows a dilation by a factor of 1.5 of the triangle stored in the matrix T.

2. *Reflections about an axis.* If L_x is a transformation that reflects a vector $\mathbf{x}$ about the x-axis, then L_x is a linear operator and hence it can be represented by a 2×2 matrix A. Since

$$L_x(\mathbf{e}_1) = \mathbf{e}_1 \qquad \text{and} \qquad L_x(\mathbf{e}_2) = -\mathbf{e}_2$$

   it follows that

$$A = \begin{bmatrix} 1 & 0 \\ 0 & -1 \end{bmatrix}$$

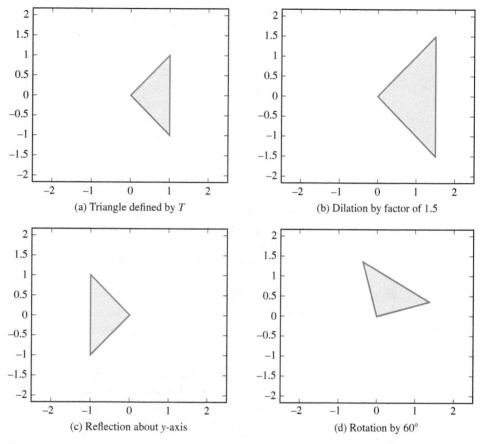

Figure 4.2.3.

Similarly, if L_y is the linear operator that reflects a vector about the y-axis, then L_y is represented by the matrix

$$\begin{pmatrix} -1 & 0 \\ 0 & 1 \end{pmatrix}$$

Figure 4.2.3(c) shows the image of the triangle T after a reflection about the y-axis. In Chapter 7, we will learn a simple method for constructing reflection matrices that have the effect of reflecting a vector about any line through the origin.

3. *Rotations.* Let L be a transformation that rotates a vector about the origin by an angle θ in the counterclockwise direction. We saw in Example 2 that L is a linear operator and that $L(\mathbf{x}) = A\mathbf{x}$, where

$$A = \begin{bmatrix} \cos\theta & -\sin\theta \\ \sin\theta & \cos\theta \end{bmatrix}$$

Figure 4.2.3(d) shows the result of rotating the triangle T by $60°$ in the counterclockwise direction.

4. *Translations.* A *translation* by a vector **a** is a transformation of the form

$$L(\mathbf{x}) = \mathbf{x} + \mathbf{a}$$

If $\mathbf{a} \neq \mathbf{0}$, then L is not a linear transformation and hence L cannot be represented by a 2×2 matrix. However, in computer graphics it is desirable to do all transformations as matrix multiplications. The way around the problem is to introduce a new system of coordinates called *homogeneous coordinates. This new system will allow us to perform translations as linear transformations.*

Homogeneous Coordinates

The *homogeneous coordinate system* is formed by equating each vector in $\mathbb{R}^2$ with a vector in $\mathbb{R}^3$ having the same first two coordinates and having 1 as its third coordinate.

$$\begin{bmatrix} x_1 \\ x_2 \end{bmatrix} \leftrightarrow \begin{bmatrix} x_1 \\ x_2 \\ 1 \end{bmatrix}$$

When we want to plot a point represented by the homogeneous coordinate vector $(x_1, x_2, 1)^T$, we simply ignore the third coordinate and plot the ordered pair (x_1, x_2).

The linear transformations discussed earlier must now be represented by 3×3 matrices. To do this, we take the 2×2 matrix representation and augment it by attaching the third row and third column of the 3×3 identity matrix. For example, in place of the 2×2 dilation matrix

$$\begin{bmatrix} 3 & 0 \\ 0 & 3 \end{bmatrix}$$

we have the 3×3 matrix

$$\begin{bmatrix} 3 & 0 & 0 \\ 0 & 3 & 0 \\ 0 & 0 & 1 \end{bmatrix}$$

Note that

$$\begin{bmatrix} 3 & 0 & 0 \\ 0 & 3 & 0 \\ 0 & 0 & 1 \end{bmatrix} \begin{bmatrix} x_1 \\ x_2 \\ 1 \end{bmatrix} = \begin{bmatrix} 3x_1 \\ 3x_2 \\ 1 \end{bmatrix}$$

If L is a translation by a vector **a** in $\mathbb{R}^2$, we can find a matrix representation for L with respect to the homogeneous coordinate system. We simply take the 3×3 identity matrix and replace the first two entries of its third column with the entries of **a**. To see that this works, consider, for example, a translation corresponding to the vector $\mathbf{a} = (6, 2)^T$. In homogeneous coordinates, this transformation is accomplished by the matrix multiplication

$$A\mathbf{x} = \begin{bmatrix} 1 & 0 & 6 \\ 0 & 1 & 2 \\ 0 & 0 & 1 \end{bmatrix} \begin{bmatrix} x_1 \\ x_2 \\ 1 \end{bmatrix} = \begin{bmatrix} x_1 + 6 \\ x_2 + 2 \\ 1 \end{bmatrix}$$

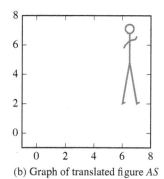

(a) Graph of 3 × 81 matrix S (b) Graph of translated figure AS

Figure 4.2.4.

Figure 4.2.4(a) shows a stick figure generated from a 3×81 matrix S. If we multiply S by the translation matrix A, the graph of AS is the translated image given in Figure 4.2.4(b).

APPLICATION 2   The Yaw, Pitch, and Roll of an Airplane

The terms *yaw*, *pitch*, and *roll* are commonly used in the aerospace industry to describe the maneuvering of an aircraft. Figure 4.2.5(a) shows the initial position of a model airplane. In describing *yaw*, *pitch*, and *roll*, the current coordinate system is given in terms of the position of the vehicle. It is always assumed that the craft is situated on the *xy*-plane with its nose pointing in the direction of the positive *x*-axis and the left wing pointing in the direction of the positive *y*-axis. Furthermore, when the plane moves, the three coordinate axes move with the vehicle (see Figure 4.2.5).

A *yaw* is a rotation in the *xy*-plane. Figure 4.2.5(b) illustrates a yaw of 45°. In this case, the craft has been rotated 45° to the right (clockwise). Viewed as a linear transformation in 3-space, a yaw is simply a rotation about the *z*-axis. Note that if the initial coordinates of the nose of the model plane are represented by the vector $(1, 0, 0)$, then its *xyz* coordinates after the yaw transformation will still be $(1, 0, 0)$, since the coordinate axis rotated with the craft. In the initial position of the airplane, the *x*, *y*, and *z* axes are in the same directions as the front-back, left-right, and top-bottom axes shown in the figure. We will refer to this initial front, left, top axis system as the FLT axis system. After the 45° yaw, the position of the nose of the craft with respect to the FLT axis system is $\left(\frac{1}{\sqrt{2}}, -\frac{1}{\sqrt{2}}, 0\right)$.

If we view a yaw transformation L in terms of the FLT axis system, it is easy to find a matrix representation. If L corresponds to yaw by an angle u, then L will rotate the points $(1, 0, 0)$ and $(0, 1, 0)$ to the positions $(\cos u, -\sin u, 0)$ and $(\sin u, \cos u, 0)$, respectively. The point $(0, 0, 1)$ will remained unchanged by the yaw since it is on the axis of rotation. In terms of column vectors, if $\mathbf{y}_1$, $\mathbf{y}_2$, and $\mathbf{y}_3$ are the images of the standard basis vectors for $\mathbb{R}^3$ under L, then

$$\mathbf{y}_1 = L(\mathbf{e}_1) = \begin{bmatrix} \cos u \\ -\sin u \\ 0 \end{bmatrix}, \quad \mathbf{y}_2 = L(\mathbf{e}_2) = \begin{bmatrix} \sin u \\ \cos u \\ 0 \end{bmatrix}, \quad \mathbf{y}_3 = L(\mathbf{e}_3) = \begin{bmatrix} 0 \\ 0 \\ 1 \end{bmatrix}$$

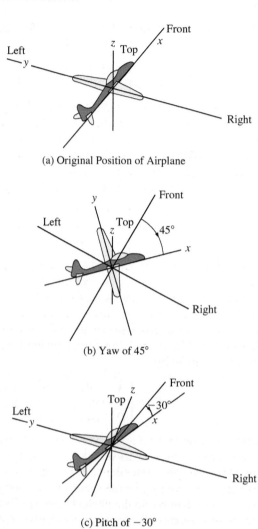

(a) Original Position of Airplane

(b) Yaw of 45°

(c) Pitch of −30°

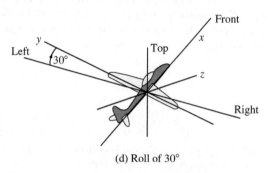

(d) Roll of 30°

Figure 4.2.5.

Therefore, the matrix representation of the yaw transformation is

$$Y = \begin{bmatrix} \cos u & \sin u & 0 \\ -\sin u & \cos u & 0 \\ 0 & 0 & 1 \end{bmatrix} \tag{1}$$

A *pitch* is a rotation of the aircraft in the *xz*-plane. Figure 4.2.5(c) illustrates a pitch of $-30°$. Since the angle is negative, the nose of the craft is rotated $30°$ downward, toward the bottom axis of the figure. Viewed as a linear transformation in 3-space, a pitch is simply a rotation about the *y*-axis. As with the yaw, we can find the matrix for a pitch transformation with respect to the FLT axis system. If L is a pitch transformation with angle of rotation v, the matrix representation of L is given by

$$P = \begin{bmatrix} \cos v & 0 & -\sin v \\ 0 & 1 & 0 \\ \sin v & 0 & \cos v \end{bmatrix} \tag{2}$$

A *roll* is a rotation of the aircraft in the *yz*-plane. Figure 4.2.5(d) illustrates a roll of $30°$. In this case, the left wing is rotated up $30°$ toward the top axis in the figure and the right wing is rotated $30°$ downward toward the bottom axis. Viewed as a linear transformation in 3-space, a roll is simply a rotation about the *x*-axis. As with the yaw and pitch, we can find the matrix representation for a roll transformation with respect to the FLT axis system. If L is a roll transformation with angle of rotation w, the matrix representation of L is given by

$$R = \begin{bmatrix} 1 & 0 & 0 \\ 0 & \cos w & -\sin w \\ 0 & \sin w & \cos w \end{bmatrix} \tag{3}$$

If we perform a yaw by an angle u and then a pitch by an angle v, the composite transformation is linear; however, its matrix representation is *not* equal to the product PY. The effect of the yaw on the standard basis vectors $\mathbf{e}_1$, $\mathbf{e}_2$, and $\mathbf{e}_3$ is to rotate them to the new directions $\mathbf{y}_1$, $\mathbf{y}_2$, and $\mathbf{y}_3$. So the vectors $\mathbf{y}_1$, $\mathbf{y}_2$, and $\mathbf{y}_3$ will define the directions of the x, y, and z axes when we do the pitch. The desired pitch transformation is then a rotation about the new y-axis (i.e., the axis in the direction of the vector $\mathbf{y}_2$). The vectors $\mathbf{y}_1$ and $\mathbf{y}_3$ form a plane, and when the pitch is applied, they are both rotated by an angle v in that plane. The vector $\mathbf{y}_2$ will remain unaffected by the pitch, since it lies on the axis of rotation. Thus, the composite transformation L has the following effect on the standard basis vectors:

$$\mathbf{e}_1 \overset{\text{yaw}}{\rightarrow} \mathbf{y}_1 \overset{\text{pitch}}{\rightarrow} \cos v\, \mathbf{y}_1 + \sin v\, \mathbf{y}_3$$
$$\mathbf{e}_2 \overset{\text{yaw}}{\rightarrow} \mathbf{y}_2 \overset{\text{pitch}}{\rightarrow} \mathbf{y}_2$$
$$\mathbf{e}_3 \overset{\text{yaw}}{\rightarrow} \mathbf{y}_3 \overset{\text{pitch}}{\rightarrow} -\sin v\, \mathbf{y}_1 + \cos v\, \mathbf{y}_3$$

The images of the standard basis vectors form the columns of the matrix representing the composite transformation:

$$(\cos v\, \mathbf{y}_1 + \sin v\, \mathbf{y}_3,\ \mathbf{y}_2,\ -\sin v\, \mathbf{y}_1 + \cos v\, \mathbf{y}_3) = (\mathbf{y}_1, \mathbf{y}_2, \mathbf{y}_3) \begin{bmatrix} \cos v & 0 & -\sin v \\ 0 & 1 & 0 \\ \sin v & 0 & \cos v \end{bmatrix}$$

$$= YP$$

It follows that matrix representation of the composite is a product of the two individual matrices representing the yaw and the pitch, but the product must be taken in the reverse order, with the yaw matrix Y on the left and the pitch matrix P on the right. Similarly, for a composite transformation of a yaw with angle u, followed by a pitch with angle v, and then a roll with angle w, the matrix representation of the composite transformation would be the product YPR.

SECTION 4.2 EXERCISES

1. Refer to Exercise 1 of Section 4.1. For each linear transformation L, find the standard matrix representation of L.

2. For each of the following linear transformations L mapping $\mathbb{R}^3$ into $\mathbb{R}^2$, find a matrix A such that $L(\mathbf{x}) = A\mathbf{x}$ for every $\mathbf{x}$ in $\mathbb{R}^3$:
   (a) $L((x_1, x_2, x_3)^T) = (x_1 + x_2, 0)^T$
   (b) $L((x_1, x_2, x_3)^T) = (x_1, x_2)^T$
   (c) $L((x_1, x_2, x_3)^T) = (x_2 - x_1, x_3 - x_2)^T$

3. For each of the following linear operators L on $\mathbb{R}^3$, find a matrix A such that $L(\mathbf{x}) = A\mathbf{x}$ for every $\mathbf{x}$ in $\mathbb{R}^3$:
   (a) $L((x_1, x_2, x_3)^T) = (x_3, x_2, x_1)^T$
   (b) $L((x_1, x_2, x_3)^T) = (x_1, x_1 + x_2, x_1 + x_2 + x_3)^T$
   (c) $L((x_1, x_2, x_3)^T) = (2x_3, x_2 + 3x_1, 2x_1 - x_3)^T$

4. Let L be the linear operator on $\mathbb{R}^3$ defined by
$$L(\mathbf{x}) = \begin{pmatrix} 2x_1 - x_2 - x_3 \\ 2x_2 - x_1 - x_3 \\ 2x_3 - x_1 - x_2 \end{pmatrix}$$
Determine the standard matrix representation A of L, and use A to find $L(\mathbf{x})$ for each of the following vectors $\mathbf{x}$:
   (a) $\mathbf{x} = (1, 1, 1)^T$ (b) $\mathbf{x} = (2, 1, 1)^T$
   (c) $\mathbf{x} = (-5, 3, 2)^T$

5. Find the standard matrix representation for each of the following linear operators:
   (a) L is the linear operator that rotates each $\mathbf{x}$ in $\mathbb{R}^2$ by $45°$ in the clockwise direction.
   (b) L is the linear operator that reflects each vector $\mathbf{x}$ in $\mathbb{R}^2$ about the x_1-axis and then rotates it $90°$ in the counterclockwise direction.
   (c) L doubles the length of $\mathbf{x}$ and then rotates it $30°$ in the counterclockwise direction.
   (d) L reflects each vector $\mathbf{x}$ about the line $x_2 = x_1$ and then projects it onto the x_1-axis.

6. Let
$$\mathbf{b}_1 = \begin{pmatrix} 1 \\ 1 \\ 0 \end{pmatrix}, \quad \mathbf{b}_2 = \begin{pmatrix} 1 \\ 0 \\ 1 \end{pmatrix}, \quad \mathbf{b}_3 = \begin{pmatrix} 0 \\ 1 \\ 1 \end{pmatrix}$$

and let L be the linear transformation from $\mathbb{R}^2$ into $\mathbb{R}^3$ defined by
$$L(\mathbf{x}) = x_1 \mathbf{b}_1 + x_2 \mathbf{b}_2 + (x_1 + x_2) \mathbf{b}_3$$
Find the matrix A representing L with respect to the ordered bases $\{\mathbf{e}_1, \mathbf{e}_2\}$ and $\{\mathbf{b}_1, \mathbf{b}_2, \mathbf{b}_3\}$.

7. Let
$$\mathbf{y}_1 = \begin{pmatrix} 1 \\ 1 \\ 1 \end{pmatrix}, \quad \mathbf{y}_2 = \begin{pmatrix} 1 \\ 1 \\ 0 \end{pmatrix}, \quad \mathbf{y}_3 = \begin{pmatrix} 1 \\ 0 \\ 0 \end{pmatrix}$$
and let $\mathcal{I}$ be the identity operator on $\mathbb{R}^3$.
   (a) Find the coordinates of $\mathcal{I}(\mathbf{e}_1)$, $\mathcal{I}(\mathbf{e}_2)$, and $\mathcal{I}(\mathbf{e}_3)$ with respect to $\{\mathbf{y}_1, \mathbf{y}_2, \mathbf{y}_3\}$.
   (b) Find a matrix A such that $A\mathbf{x}$ is the coordinate vector of $\mathbf{x}$ with respect to $\{\mathbf{y}_1, \mathbf{y}_2, \mathbf{y}_3\}$.

8. Let $\mathbf{y}_1, \mathbf{y}_2$, and $\mathbf{y}_3$ be defined as in Exercise 7, and let L be the linear operator on $\mathbb{R}^3$ defined by
$$L(c_1 \mathbf{y}_1 + c_2 \mathbf{y}_2 + c_3 \mathbf{y}_3)$$
$$= (c_1 + c_2 + c_3) \mathbf{y}_1 + (2c_1 + c_3) \mathbf{y}_2 - (2c_2 + c_3) \mathbf{y}_3$$
   (a) Find a matrix representing L with respect to the ordered basis $\{\mathbf{y}_1, \mathbf{y}_2, \mathbf{y}_3\}$.
   (b) For each of the following, write the vector $\mathbf{x}$ as a linear combination of $\mathbf{y}_1, \mathbf{y}_2$, and $\mathbf{y}_3$ and use the matrix from part (a) to determine $L(\mathbf{x})$:
   (i) $\mathbf{x} = (7, 5, 2)^T$ (ii) $\mathbf{x} = (3, 2, 1)^T$
   (iii) $\mathbf{x} = (1, 2, 3)^T$

9. Let
$$R = \begin{bmatrix} 0 & 0 & 1 & 1 & 0 \\ 0 & 1 & 1 & 0 & 0 \\ 1 & 1 & 1 & 1 & 1 \end{bmatrix}$$
The column vectors of R represent the homogeneous coordinates of points in the plane.
   (a) Draw the figure whose vertices correspond to the column vectors of R. What type of figure is it?

(b) For each of the following choices of A, sketch the graph of the figure represented by AR and describe geometrically the effect of the linear transformation:

(i) $A = \begin{bmatrix} \frac{1}{2} & 0 & 0 \\ 0 & \frac{1}{2} & 0 \\ 0 & 0 & 1 \end{bmatrix}$ $\begin{bmatrix} 0 & 0 & 1 & 1 & 0 \\ 0 & 1 & 1 & 0 & 0 \\ 1 & 1 & 1 & 1 & 1 \end{bmatrix}$

(ii) $A = \begin{bmatrix} \frac{1}{\sqrt{2}} & \frac{1}{\sqrt{2}} & 0 \\ -\frac{1}{\sqrt{2}} & \frac{1}{\sqrt{2}} & 0 \\ 0 & 0 & 1 \end{bmatrix}$

(iii) $A = \begin{bmatrix} 1 & 0 & 2 \\ 0 & 1 & -3 \\ 0 & 0 & 1 \end{bmatrix}$

10. For each of the following linear operators on $\mathbb{R}^2$, find the matrix representation of the transformation with respect to the homogeneous coordinate system:

(a) The transformation L that rotates each vector by $120°$ in the counterclockwise direction

(b) The transformation L that translates each point 3 units to the left and 5 units up

(c) The transformation L that contracts each vector by a factor of one-third

(d) The transformation that reflects a vector about the y-axis and then translates it up 2 units

11. Determine the matrix representation of each of the following composite transformations.

(a) A yaw of $90°$, followed by a pitch of $90°$

(b) A pitch of $90°$, followed by a yaw of $90°$

(c) A pitch of $45°$, followed by a roll of $-90°$

(d) A roll of $-90°$, followed by a pitch of $45°$

(e) A yaw of $45°$, followed by a pitch of $-90°$ and then a roll of $-45°$

(f) A roll of $-45°$, followed by a pitch of $-90°$ and then a yaw of $45°$

12. Let Y, P, and R be the yaw, pitch, and roll matrices given in equations (1), (2), and (3), respectively, and let $Q = YPR$.

(a) Show that Y, P, and R all have determinants equal to 1.

(b) The matrix Y represents a yaw with angle u. The inverse transformation should be a yaw with angle $-u$. Show that the matrix representation of the inverse transformation is Y^T and that $Y^T = Y^{-1}$.

(c) Show that Q is nonsingular and express Q^{-1} in terms of the transposes of Y, P, and R.

13. Let L be the linear transformation mapping P_2 into $\mathbb{R}^2$ defined by

$$L(p(x)) = \begin{bmatrix} \int_0^1 p(x)\, dx \\ p(0) \end{bmatrix}$$

Find a matrix A such that

$$L(\alpha + \beta x) = A \begin{bmatrix} \alpha \\ \beta \end{bmatrix}$$

14. The linear transformation L defined by

$$L(p(x)) = p'(x) + p(0)$$

maps P_3 into P_2. Find the matrix representation of L with respect to the ordered bases $[x^2, x, 1]$ and $[2, 1 - x]$. For each of the following vectors $p(x)$ in P_3, find the coordinates of $L(p(x))$ with respect to the ordered basis $[2, 1 - x]$:

(a) $x^2 + 2x - 3$ **(b)** $x^2 + 1$
(c) $3x$ **(d)** $4x^2 + 2x$

15. Let S be the subspace of $C[a, b]$ spanned by e^x, xe^x, and $x^2 e^x$. Let D be the differentiation operator of S. Find the matrix representing D with respect to $[e^x, xe^x, x^2 e^x]$.

16. Let L be a linear operator on $\mathbb{R}^n$. Suppose that $L(\mathbf{x}) = \mathbf{0}$ for some $\mathbf{x} \neq \mathbf{0}$. Let A be the matrix representing L with respect to the standard basis $\{\mathbf{e}_1, \mathbf{e}_2, \ldots, \mathbf{e}_n\}$. Show that A is singular.

17. Let L be a linear operator on a vector space V. Let A be the matrix representing L with respect to an ordered basis $\{\mathbf{v}_1, \ldots, \mathbf{v}_n\}$ of V [i.e.,

$$L(\mathbf{v}_j) = \sum_{i=1}^{n} a_{ij} \mathbf{v}_i, j = 1, \ldots, n].$$ Show that A^m is the matrix representing L^m with respect to $\{\mathbf{v}_1, \ldots, \mathbf{v}_n\}$.

18. Let $E = \{\mathbf{u}_1, \mathbf{u}_2, \mathbf{u}_3\}$ and $F = \{\mathbf{b}_1, \mathbf{b}_2\}$, where

$$\mathbf{u}_1 = \begin{bmatrix} 1 \\ 0 \\ -1 \end{bmatrix}, \quad \mathbf{u}_2 = \begin{bmatrix} 1 \\ 2 \\ 1 \end{bmatrix}, \quad \mathbf{u}_3 = \begin{bmatrix} -1 \\ 1 \\ 1 \end{bmatrix}$$

and

$$\mathbf{b}_1 = (1, -1)^T, \qquad \mathbf{b}_2 = (2, -1)^T$$

For each of the following linear transformations L from $\mathbb{R}^3$ into $\mathbb{R}^2$, find the matrix representing L with respect to the ordered bases E and F:

(a) $L(\mathbf{x}) = (x_3, x_1)^T$

(b) $L(\mathbf{x}) = (x_1 + x_2, x_1 - x_3)^T$

(c) $L(\mathbf{x}) = (2x_2, -x_1)^T$

19. Suppose that $L_1: V \rightarrow W$ and $L_2: W \rightarrow Z$ are linear transformations and E, F, and G are ordered bases for V, W, and Z, respectively. Show that, if A represents L_1 relative to E and F and B represents L_2 relative to F and G, then the matrix $C = BA$ represents $L_2 \circ L_1 : V \to Z$ relative to E and G. *Hint*: Show that $BA[\mathbf{v}]_E = [(L_2 \circ L_1)(\mathbf{v})]_G$ for all $\mathbf{v} \in V$.

20. Let V and W be vector spaces with ordered bases E and F, respectively. If $L: V \to W$ is a linear transformation

and A is the matrix representing L relative to E and F, show that

(a) $\mathbf{v} \in \ker(L)$ if and only if $[\mathbf{v}]_E \in N(A)$.

(b) $\mathbf{w} \in L(V)$ if and only if $[\mathbf{w}]_F$ is in the column space of A.

4.3 Similarity

If L is a linear operator on an n-dimensional vector space V, the matrix representation of L will depend on the ordered basis chosen for V. By using different bases, it is possible to represent L by different $n \times n$ matrices. In this section, we consider different matrix representations of linear operators and characterize the relationship between matrices representing the same linear operator.

Let us begin by considering an example in $\mathbb{R}^2$. Let L be the linear transformation mapping $\mathbb{R}^2$ into itself defined by

$$L(\mathbf{x}) = (2x_1, x_1 + x_2)^T$$

Since

$$L(\mathbf{e}_1) = \begin{bmatrix} 2 \\ 1 \end{bmatrix} \quad \text{and} \quad L(\mathbf{e}_2) = \begin{bmatrix} 0 \\ 1 \end{bmatrix}$$

it follows that the matrix representing L with respect to $\{\mathbf{e}_1, \mathbf{e}_2\}$ is

$$A = \begin{bmatrix} 2 & 0 \\ 1 & 1 \end{bmatrix}$$

If we use a different basis for $\mathbb{R}^2$, the matrix representation of L will change. If, for example, we use

$$\mathbf{u}_1 = \begin{bmatrix} 1 \\ 1 \end{bmatrix} \quad \text{and} \quad \mathbf{u}_2 = \begin{bmatrix} -1 \\ 1 \end{bmatrix}$$

for a basis, then to determine the matrix representation of L with respect to $\{\mathbf{u}_1, \mathbf{u}_2\}$, we must determine $L(\mathbf{u}_1)$ and $L(\mathbf{u}_2)$ and express these vectors as linear combinations of $\mathbf{u}_1$ and $\mathbf{u}_2$. We can use the matrix A to determine $L(\mathbf{u}_1)$ and $L(\mathbf{u}_2)$:

$$L(\mathbf{u}_1) = A\mathbf{u}_1 = \begin{bmatrix} 2 & 0 \\ 1 & 1 \end{bmatrix} \begin{bmatrix} 1 \\ 1 \end{bmatrix} = \begin{bmatrix} 2 \\ 2 \end{bmatrix}$$

$$L(\mathbf{u}_2) = A\mathbf{u}_2 = \begin{bmatrix} 2 & 0 \\ 1 & 1 \end{bmatrix} \begin{bmatrix} -1 \\ 1 \end{bmatrix} = \begin{bmatrix} -2 \\ 0 \end{bmatrix}$$

To express these vectors in terms of $\mathbf{u}_1$ and $\mathbf{u}_2$, we use a transition matrix to change from the ordered basis $\{\mathbf{e}_1, \mathbf{e}_2\}$ to $\{\mathbf{u}_1, \mathbf{u}_2\}$. Let us first compute the transition matrix from $\{\mathbf{u}_1, \mathbf{u}_2\}$ to $\{\mathbf{e}_1, \mathbf{e}_2\}$. This is simply

$$U = (\mathbf{u}_1, \mathbf{u}_2) = \begin{bmatrix} 1 & -1 \\ 1 & 1 \end{bmatrix}$$

The transition matrix from $\{\mathbf{e}_1, \mathbf{e}_2\}$ to $\{\mathbf{u}_1, \mathbf{u}_2\}$ will then be

$$U^{-1} = \begin{pmatrix} \frac{1}{2} & \frac{1}{2} \\ -\frac{1}{2} & \frac{1}{2} \end{pmatrix}$$

To determine the coordinates of $L(\mathbf{u}_1)$ and $L(\mathbf{u}_2)$ with respect to $\{\mathbf{u}_1, \mathbf{u}_2\}$, we multiply the vectors by U^{-1}:

$$U^{-1}L(\mathbf{u}_1) = U^{-1}A\mathbf{u}_1 = \begin{pmatrix} \frac{1}{2} & \frac{1}{2} \\ -\frac{1}{2} & \frac{1}{2} \end{pmatrix} \begin{pmatrix} 2 \\ 2 \end{pmatrix} = \begin{pmatrix} 2 \\ 0 \end{pmatrix}$$

$$U^{-1}L(\mathbf{u}_2) = U^{-1}A\mathbf{u}_2 = \begin{pmatrix} \frac{1}{2} & \frac{1}{2} \\ -\frac{1}{2} & \frac{1}{2} \end{pmatrix} \begin{pmatrix} -2 \\ 0 \end{pmatrix} = \begin{pmatrix} -1 \\ 1 \end{pmatrix}$$

Thus,

$$L(\mathbf{u}_1) = \quad 2\mathbf{u}_1 + 0\mathbf{u}_2$$
$$L(\mathbf{u}_2) = -1\mathbf{u}_1 + 1\mathbf{u}_2$$

and the matrix representing L with respect to $\{\mathbf{u}_1, \mathbf{u}_2\}$ is

$$B = \begin{pmatrix} 2 & -1 \\ 0 & 1 \end{pmatrix}$$

How are A and B related? Note that the columns of B are

$$\begin{pmatrix} 2 \\ 0 \end{pmatrix} = U^{-1}A\mathbf{u}_1 \quad \text{and} \quad \begin{pmatrix} -1 \\ 1 \end{pmatrix} = U^{-1}A\mathbf{u}_2$$

Hence,

$$B = (U^{-1}A\mathbf{u}_1, U^{-1}A\mathbf{u}_2) = U^{-1}A(\mathbf{u}_1, \mathbf{u}_2) = U^{-1}AU$$

Thus, if

   (i) B is the matrix representing L with respect to $\{\mathbf{u}_1, \mathbf{u}_2\}$,
   (ii) A is the matrix representing L with respect to $\{\mathbf{e}_1, \mathbf{e}_2\}$,
   (iii) U is the transition matrix corresponding to the change of basis from $\{\mathbf{u}_1, \mathbf{u}_2\}$ to $\{\mathbf{e}_1, \mathbf{e}_2\}$,

then

$$B = U^{-1}AU \tag{1}$$

The results that we have established for this particular linear operator on $\mathbb{R}^2$ are typical of what happens in a much more general setting. We will show next that the same sort of relationship as that given in (1) will hold for any two matrix representations of a linear operator that maps an n-dimensional vector space into itself.

Theorem 4.3.1 *Let $E = \{\mathbf{v}_1, \ldots, \mathbf{v}_n\}$ and $F = \{\mathbf{w}_1, \ldots, \mathbf{w}_n\}$ be two ordered bases for a vector space V, and let L be a linear operator on V. Let S be the transition matrix representing the change from F to E. If A is the matrix representing L with respect to E, and B is the matrix representing L with respect to F, then $B = S^{-1}AS$.*

Proof Let $\mathbf{x}$ be any vector in $\mathbb{R}^n$ and let

$$\mathbf{v} = x_1\mathbf{w}_1 + x_2\mathbf{w}_2 + \cdots + x_n\mathbf{w}_n$$

Let

$$\mathbf{y} = S\mathbf{x}, \qquad \mathbf{t} = A\mathbf{y}, \qquad \mathbf{z} = B\mathbf{x} \qquad (2)$$

It follows from the definition of S that $\mathbf{y} = [\mathbf{v}]_E$ and hence

$$\mathbf{v} = y_1\mathbf{v}_1 + \cdots + y_n\mathbf{v}_n$$

Since A represents L with respect to E, and B represents L with respect to F, we have

$$\mathbf{t} = [L(\mathbf{v})]_E \qquad \text{and} \qquad \mathbf{z} = [L(\mathbf{v})]_F$$

The transition matrix from E to F is S^{-1}. Therefore,

$$S^{-1}\mathbf{t} = \mathbf{z} \qquad (3)$$

It follows from (2) and (3) that

$$S^{-1}AS\mathbf{x} = S^{-1}A\mathbf{y} = S^{-1}\mathbf{t} = \mathbf{z} = B\mathbf{x}$$

(see Figure 4.3.1). Thus,

$$S^{-1}AS\mathbf{x} = B\mathbf{x}$$

for every $\mathbf{x} \in \mathbb{R}^n$, and hence $S^{-1}AS = B$.

◼

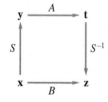

Figure 4.3.1.

Another way of viewing Theorem 4.3.1 is to consider S as the matrix representing the identity transformation $\mathcal{I}$ with respect to the ordered bases

$$F = \{\mathbf{w}_1, \ldots, \mathbf{w}_n\} \qquad \text{and} \qquad E = \{\mathbf{v}_1, \ldots, \mathbf{v}_n\}$$

If

S represents $\mathcal{I}$ relative to F and E,
A represents L relative to E,
S^{-1} represents $\mathcal{I}$ relative to E and F,

then L can be expressed as a composite operator $\mathcal{I} \circ L \circ \mathcal{I}$, and the matrix representation of the composite will be the product of the matrix representations of the components.

Thus, the matrix representation of $\mathcal{I} \circ L \circ \mathcal{I}$ relative to F is $S^{-1}AS$. If B is the matrix representing L relative to F, then B must equal $S^{-1}AS$ (see Figure 4.3.2).

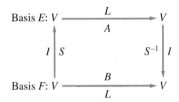

Figure 4.3.2.

Definition

Let A and B be $n \times n$ matrices. B is said to be **similar** to A if there exists a nonsingular matrix S such that $B = S^{-1}AS$.

Note that if B is similar to A, then $A = (S^{-1})^{-1}BS^{-1}$ is similar to B. Thus, we may simply say that A and B are similar matrices.

It follows from Theorem 4.3.1 that, if A and B are $n \times n$ matrices representing the same operator L, then A and B are similar. Conversely, suppose that A represents L with respect to the ordered basis $\{\mathbf{v}_1, \ldots, \mathbf{v}_n\}$ and $B = S^{-1}AS$ for some nonsingular matrix S. If $\mathbf{w}_1, \ldots, \mathbf{w}_n$ are defined by

$$\mathbf{w}_1 = s_{11}\mathbf{v}_1 + s_{21}\mathbf{v}_2 + \cdots + s_{n1}\mathbf{v}_n$$
$$\mathbf{w}_2 = s_{12}\mathbf{v}_1 + s_{22}\mathbf{v}_2 + \cdots + s_{n2}\mathbf{v}_n$$
$$\vdots$$
$$\mathbf{w}_n = s_{1n}\mathbf{v}_1 + s_{2n}\mathbf{v}_2 + \cdots + s_{nn}\mathbf{v}_n$$

then $\{\mathbf{w}_1, \ldots, \mathbf{w}_n\}$ is an ordered basis for V, and B is the matrix representing L with respect to $\{\mathbf{w}_1, \ldots, \mathbf{w}_n\}$.

EXAMPLE 1   Let D be the differentiation operator on P_3. Find the matrix B representing D with respect to $[1, x, x^2]$ and the matrix A representing D with respect to $[1, 2x, 4x^2 - 2]$.

Solution

$$D(1) = 0 \cdot 1 + 0 \cdot x + 0 \cdot x^2$$
$$D(x) = 1 \cdot 1 + 0 \cdot x + 0 \cdot x^2$$
$$D(x^2) = 0 \cdot 1 + 2 \cdot x + 0 \cdot x^2$$

The matrix B is then given by

$$B = \begin{pmatrix} 0 & 1 & 0 \\ 0 & 0 & 2 \\ 0 & 0 & 0 \end{pmatrix}$$

Applying D to 1, $2x$, and $4x^2 - 2$, we obtain

$$D(1) = 0 \cdot 1 + 0 \cdot 2x + 0 \cdot (4x^2 - 2)$$
$$D(2x) = 2 \cdot 1 + 0 \cdot 2x + 0 \cdot (4x^2 - 2)$$
$$D(4x^2 - 2) = 0 \cdot 1 + 4 \cdot 2x + 0 \cdot (4x^2 - 2)$$

Thus,

$$A = \begin{pmatrix} 0 & 2 & 0 \\ 0 & 0 & 4 \\ 0 & 0 & 0 \end{pmatrix}$$

The transition matrix S corresponding to the change of basis from $[1, 2x, 4x^2 - 2]$ to $[1, x, x^2]$ and its inverse are given by

$$S = \begin{pmatrix} 1 & 0 & -2 \\ 0 & 2 & 0 \\ 0 & 0 & 4 \end{pmatrix} \quad \text{and} \quad S^{-1} = \begin{pmatrix} 1 & 0 & \frac{1}{2} \\ 0 & \frac{1}{2} & 0 \\ 0 & 0 & \frac{1}{4} \end{pmatrix}$$

(See Example 6 from Section 3.5.) The reader may verify that $A = S^{-1}BS$. ∎

EXAMPLE 2   Let L be the linear operator mapping $\mathbb{R}^3$ into $\mathbb{R}^3$ defined by $L(\mathbf{x}) = A\mathbf{x}$, where

$$A = \begin{pmatrix} 2 & 2 & 0 \\ 1 & 1 & 2 \\ 1 & 1 & 2 \end{pmatrix}$$

Thus, the matrix A represents L with respect to $\{\mathbf{e}_1, \mathbf{e}_2, \mathbf{e}_3\}$. Find the matrix representing L with respect to $\{\mathbf{y}_1, \mathbf{y}_2, \mathbf{y}_3\}$, where

$$\mathbf{y}_1 = \begin{pmatrix} 1 \\ -1 \\ 0 \end{pmatrix}, \qquad \mathbf{y}_2 = \begin{pmatrix} -2 \\ 1 \\ 1 \end{pmatrix}, \qquad \mathbf{y}_3 = \begin{pmatrix} 1 \\ 1 \\ 1 \end{pmatrix}$$

Solution

$$L(\mathbf{y}_1) = A\mathbf{y}_1 = \mathbf{0} = 0\mathbf{y}_1 + 0\mathbf{y}_2 + 0\mathbf{y}_3$$
$$L(\mathbf{y}_2) = A\mathbf{y}_2 = \mathbf{y}_2 = 0\mathbf{y}_1 + 1\mathbf{y}_2 + 0\mathbf{y}_3$$
$$L(\mathbf{y}_3) = A\mathbf{y}_3 = 4\mathbf{y}_3 = 0\mathbf{y}_1 + 0\mathbf{y}_2 + 4\mathbf{y}_3$$

Thus, the matrix representing L with respect to $\{\mathbf{y}_1, \mathbf{y}_2, \mathbf{y}_3\}$ is

$$D = \begin{pmatrix} 0 & 0 & 0 \\ 0 & 1 & 0 \\ 0 & 0 & 4 \end{pmatrix}$$

We could have found D by using the transition matrix $Y = (\mathbf{y}_1, \mathbf{y}_2, \mathbf{y}_3)$ and computing

$$D = Y^{-1}AY$$

This was unnecessary due to the simplicity of the action of L on the basis $\{\mathbf{y}_1, \mathbf{y}_2, \mathbf{y}_3\}$. ∎

In Example 2, the linear operator L is represented by a diagonal matrix D with respect to the basis $\{\mathbf{y}_1, \mathbf{y}_2, \mathbf{y}_3\}$. It is much simpler to work with D than with A. For example, it is easier to compute $D\mathbf{x}$ and $D^n\mathbf{x}$ than $A\mathbf{x}$ and $A^n\mathbf{x}$. Generally, it is desirable to find as simple a representation as possible for a linear operator. In particular, if the operator can be represented by a diagonal matrix, this is usually the preferred representation. The problem of finding a diagonal representation for a linear operator will be studied in Chapter 6.

SECTION 4.3 EXERCISES

1. For each of the following linear operators L on $\mathbb{R}^2$, determine the matrix A representing L with respect to $\{\mathbf{e}_1, \mathbf{e}_2\}$ (see Exercise 1 of Section 1.2) and the matrix B representing L with respect to $\{\mathbf{u}_1 = (1, 1)^T, \mathbf{u}_2 = (-1, 1)^T\}$:

   (a) $L(\mathbf{x}) = (-x_1, x_2)^T$ (b) $L(\mathbf{x}) = -\mathbf{x}$
   (c) $L(\mathbf{x}) = (x_2, x_1)^T$ (d) $L(\mathbf{x}) = \frac{1}{2}\mathbf{x}$
   (e) $L(\mathbf{x}) = x_2\mathbf{e}_2$

2. Let $\{\mathbf{u}_1, \mathbf{u}_2\}$ and $\{\mathbf{v}_1, \mathbf{v}_2\}$ be ordered bases for $\mathbb{R}^2$, where

   $$\mathbf{u}_1 = \begin{bmatrix} 1 \\ 1 \end{bmatrix}, \quad \mathbf{u}_2 = \begin{bmatrix} -1 \\ 1 \end{bmatrix}$$

   and

   $$\mathbf{v}_1 = \begin{bmatrix} 2 \\ 1 \end{bmatrix}, \quad \mathbf{v}_2 = \begin{bmatrix} 1 \\ 0 \end{bmatrix}$$

   Let L be the linear transformation defined by
   $$L(\mathbf{x}) = (-x_1, x_2)^T$$
   and let B be the matrix representing L with respect to $\{\mathbf{u}_1, \mathbf{u}_2\}$ [from Exercise 1(a)].

   (a) Find the transition matrix S corresponding to the change of basis from $\{\mathbf{u}_1, \mathbf{u}_2\}$ to $\{\mathbf{v}_1, \mathbf{v}_2\}$.
   (b) Find the matrix A representing L with respect to $\{\mathbf{v}_1, \mathbf{v}_2\}$ by computing SBS^{-1}.
   (c) Verify that
   $$L(\mathbf{v}_1) = a_{11}\mathbf{v}_1 + a_{21}\mathbf{v}_2$$
   $$L(\mathbf{v}_2) = a_{12}\mathbf{v}_1 + a_{22}\mathbf{v}_2$$

3. Let L be the linear transformation on $\mathbb{R}^3$ defined by
   $$L(\mathbf{x}) = \begin{Bmatrix} 2x_1 - x_2 - x_3 \\ 2x_2 - x_1 - x_3 \\ 2x_3 - x_1 - x_2 \end{Bmatrix}$$

   and let A be the standard matrix representation of L (see Exercise 4 of Section 4.2). If $\mathbf{u}_1 = (1, 1, 0)^T$, $\mathbf{u}_2 = (1, 0, 1)^T$, and $\mathbf{u}_3 = (0, 1, 1)^T$, then $\{\mathbf{u}_1, \mathbf{u}_2, \mathbf{u}_3\}$ is an ordered basis for $\mathbb{R}^3$ and $U = (\mathbf{u}_1, \mathbf{u}_2, \mathbf{u}_3)$ is the transition matrix corresponding to a change of basis from $\{\mathbf{u}_1, \mathbf{u}_2, \mathbf{u}_3\}$ to the standard basis $\{\mathbf{e}_1, \mathbf{e}_2, \mathbf{e}_3\}$. Determine the matrix B representing L with respect to the basis $\{\mathbf{u}_1, \mathbf{u}_2, \mathbf{u}_3\}$ by calculating $U^{-1}AU$.

4. Let L be the linear operator mapping $\mathbb{R}^3$ into $\mathbb{R}^3$ defined by $L(\mathbf{x}) = A\mathbf{x}$, where

   $$A = \begin{bmatrix} 3 & -1 & -2 \\ 2 & 0 & -2 \\ 2 & -1 & -1 \end{bmatrix}$$

   and let

   $$\mathbf{v}_1 = \begin{bmatrix} 1 \\ 1 \\ 1 \end{bmatrix}, \quad \mathbf{v}_2 = \begin{bmatrix} 1 \\ 2 \\ 0 \end{bmatrix}, \quad \mathbf{v}_3 = \begin{bmatrix} 0 \\ -2 \\ 1 \end{bmatrix}$$

   Find the transition matrix V corresponding to a change of basis from $\{\mathbf{v}_1, \mathbf{v}_2, \mathbf{v}_3\}$ to $\{\mathbf{e}_1, \mathbf{e}_2, \mathbf{e}_3\}$, and use it to determine the matrix B representing L with respect to $\{\mathbf{v}_1, \mathbf{v}_2, \mathbf{v}_3\}$.

5. Let L be the operator on P_3 defined by
   $$L(p(x)) = xp'(x) + p''(x)$$
   (a) Find the matrix A representing L with respect to $[1, x, x^2]$.
   (b) Find the matrix B representing L with respect to $[1, x, 1 + x^2]$.
   (c) Find the matrix S such that $B = S^{-1}AS$.
   (d) If $p(x) = a_0 + a_1x + a_2(1 + x^2)$, calculate $L^n(p(x))$.

6. Let V be the subspace of $C[a, b]$ spanned by $1, e^x, e^{-x}$, and let D be the differentiation operator on V.

(a) Find the transition matrix S representing the change of coordinates from the ordered basis $[1, e^x, e^{-x}]$ to the ordered basis $[1, \cosh x, \sinh x]$. $[\cosh x = \frac{1}{2}(e^x + e^{-x}), \sinh x = \frac{1}{2}(e^x - e^{-x}).]$

(b) Find the matrix A representing D with respect to the ordered basis $[1, \cosh x, \sinh x]$.

(c) Find the matrix B representing D with respect to $[1, e^x, e^{-x}]$.

(d) Verify that $B = S^{-1}AS$.

7. Prove that if A is similar to B and B is similar to C, then A is similar to C.

8. Suppose that $A = S\Lambda S^{-1}$, where Λ is a diagonal matrix with diagonal elements $\lambda_1, \lambda_2, \ldots, \lambda_n$.

(a) Show that $A\mathbf{s}_i = \lambda_i \mathbf{s}_i, i = 1, \ldots, n$.

(b) Show that if $\mathbf{x} = \alpha_1 \mathbf{s}_1 + \alpha_2 \mathbf{s}_2 + \cdots + \alpha_n \mathbf{s}_n$, then

$$A^k \mathbf{x} = \alpha_1 \lambda_1^k \mathbf{s}_1 + \alpha_2 \lambda_2^k \mathbf{s}_2 + \cdots + \alpha_n \lambda_n^k \mathbf{s}_n$$

(c) Suppose that $|\lambda_i| < 1$ for $i = 1, \ldots, n$. What happens to $A^k \mathbf{x}$ as $k \to \infty$? Explain.

9. Suppose that $A = ST$, where S is nonsingular. Let $B = TS$. Show that B is similar to A.

10. Let A and B be $n \times n$ matrices. Show that if A is similar to B, then there exist $n \times n$ matrices S and T, with S nonsingular, such that

$$A = ST \quad \text{and} \quad B = TS$$

11. Show that if A and B are similar matrices, then $\det(A) = \det(B)$.

12. Let A and B be similar matrices. Show that

(a) A^T and B^T are similar.

(b) A^k and B^k are similar for each positive integer k.

13. Show that if A is similar to B and A is nonsingular, then B must also be nonsingular and A^{-1} and B^{-1} are similar.

14. Let A and B be similar matrices and let λ be any scalar. Show that

(a) $A - \lambda I$ and $B - \lambda I$ are similar.

(b) $\det(A - \lambda I) = \det(B - \lambda I)$.

15. The *trace* of an $n \times n$ matrix A, denoted $\text{tr}(A)$, is the sum of its diagonal entries; that is,

$$\text{tr}(A) = a_{11} + a_{22} + \cdots + a_{nn}$$

Show that

(a) $\text{tr}(AB) = \text{tr}(BA)$.

(b) if A is similar to B, then $\text{tr}(A) = \text{tr}(B)$.

Chapter 4 Exercises

MATLAB EXERCISES

1. Use MATLAB to generate a matrix W and a vector $\mathbf{x}$ by setting

$$W = \text{triu}(\text{ones}(5)) \quad \text{and} \quad \mathbf{x} = [1:5]'$$

The columns of W can be used to form an ordered basis:

$$F = \{\mathbf{w}_1, \mathbf{w}_2, \mathbf{w}_3, \mathbf{w}_4, \mathbf{w}_5\}$$

Let $L: \mathbb{R}^5 \to \mathbb{R}^5$ be a linear operator such that

$$L(\mathbf{w}_1) = \mathbf{w}_2, \quad L(\mathbf{w}_2) = \mathbf{w}_3, \quad L(\mathbf{w}_3) = \mathbf{w}_4$$

and

$$L(\mathbf{w}_4) = 4\mathbf{w}_1 + 3\mathbf{w}_2 + 2\mathbf{w}_3 + \mathbf{w}_4$$
$$L(\mathbf{w}_5) = \mathbf{w}_1 + \mathbf{w}_2 + \mathbf{w}_3 + 3\mathbf{w}_4 + \mathbf{w}_5$$

(a) Determine the matrix A representing L with respect to F, and enter it in MATLAB.

(b) Use MATLAB to compute the coordinate vector $\mathbf{y} = W^{-1}\mathbf{x}$ of $\mathbf{x}$ with respect to F.

(c) Use A to compute the coordinate vector $\mathbf{z}$ of $L(\mathbf{x})$ with respect to F.

(d) W is the transition matrix from F to the standard basis for $\mathbb{R}^5$. Use W to compute the coordinate vector of $L(\mathbf{x})$ with respect to the standard basis.

2. Set $A = \text{triu}(\text{ones}(5)) * \text{tril}(\text{ones}(5))$. If L denotes the linear operator defined by $L(\mathbf{x}) = A\mathbf{x}$ for all $\mathbf{x}$ in $\mathbb{R}^n$, then A is the matrix representing L with respect to the standard basis for $\mathbb{R}^5$. Construct a 5×5 matrix U by setting

$$U = \text{hankel}(\text{ones}(5, 1), 1:5)$$

Use the MATLAB function **rank** to verify that the column vectors of U are linearly independent. Thus, $E = \{\mathbf{u}_1, \mathbf{u}_2, \mathbf{u}_3, \mathbf{u}_4, \mathbf{u}_5\}$ is an ordered basis for $\mathbb{R}^5$. The matrix U is the transition matrix from E to the standard basis.

(a) Use MATLAB to compute the matrix B representing L with respect to E. (The matrix B should be computed in terms of A, U, and U^{-1}.)

(b) Generate another matrix by setting

$$V = \text{toeplitz}([1, 0, 1, 1, 1])$$

Use MATLAB to check that V is nonsingular. It follows that the column vectors of V are linearly independent and hence form an ordered basis F for $\mathbb{R}^5$. Use MATLAB to compute the matrix C, which represents L with respect to F. (The matrix C should be computed in terms of A, V, and V^{-1}.)

(c) The matrices B and C from parts (a) and (b) should be similar. Why? Explain. Use MATLAB to compute the transition matrix S from F to E. Compute the matrix C in terms of B, S, and S^{-1}. Compare your result with the result from part (b).

3. Let

$$A = \mathbf{toeplitz}(1:7),$$
$$S = \mathbf{compan}(\mathbf{ones}(8,1))$$

CHAPTER TEST A   True or False

For each statement that follows, answer true *if the statement is always true and* false *otherwise. In the case of a true statement, explain or prove your answer. In the case of a false statement, give an example to show that the statement is not always true.*

1. Let $L: \mathbb{R}^n \to \mathbb{R}^n$ be a linear transformation. If $L(\mathbf{x}_1) = L(\mathbf{x}_2)$, then the vectors $\mathbf{x}_1$ and $\mathbf{x}_2$ must be equal.

2. If L_1 and L_2 are both linear operators on a vector space V, then $L_1 + L_2$ is also a linear operator on V, where $L_1 + L_2$ is the mapping defined by

$$(L_1 + L_2)(\mathbf{v}) = L_1(\mathbf{v}) + L_2(\mathbf{v}) \text{ for all } \mathbf{v} \in V$$

3. If $L: V \to V$ is a linear transformation and $\mathbf{x} \in \ker(L)$, then $L(\mathbf{v} + \mathbf{x}) = L(\mathbf{v})$ for all $\mathbf{v} \in V$.

4. If L_1 rotates each vector $\mathbf{x}$ in $\mathbb{R}^2$ by $60°$ and then reflects the resulting vector about the x-axis, and if L_2 is a transformation that does the same two operations, but in the reverse order, then $L_1 = L_2$.

5. The set of all vectors $\mathbf{x}$ used in the homogeneous coordinate system (see the application on computer graphics and animation in Section 4.2) forms a subspace of $\mathbb{R}^3$.

CHAPTER TEST B

1. Determine whether the following are linear operators on $\mathbb{R}^2$:

(a) L is the operator defined by $L(\mathbf{x}) = (x_1 + x_2, x_1)^T$.

(b) L is the operator defined by $L(\mathbf{x}) = (x_1 x_2, x_1)^T$.

and set $B = S^{-1} * A * S$. The matrices A and B are similar. Use MATLAB to verify that the following properties hold for these two matrices:

(a) $\det(B) = \det(A)$

(b) $B^T = S^T A^T (S^T)^{-1}$

(c) $B^{-1} = S^{-1} A^{-1} S$

(d) $B^9 = S^{-1} A^9 S$

(e) $B - 3I = S^{-1}(A - 3I)S$

(f) $\det(B - 3I) = \det(A - 3I)$

(g) $\mathrm{tr}(B) = \mathrm{tr}(A)$ (Note that the trace of a matrix A can be computed with the MATLAB command **trace**.)

These properties will hold in general for any pair of similar matrices (see Exercises 11–15 of Section 4.3).

6. Let $L : \mathbb{R}^2 \to \mathbb{R}^2$ be a linear transformation, and let A be the standard matrix representation of L. If L^2 is defined by

$$L^2(\mathbf{x}) = L(L(\mathbf{x})) \text{ for all } \mathbf{x} \in \mathbb{R}^2$$

then L^2 is a linear transformation and its standard matrix representation is A^2.

7. Let $E = \{\mathbf{x}_1, \mathbf{x}_2, \dots, \mathbf{x}_n\}$ be an ordered basis for $\mathbb{R}^n$. If $L_1 : \mathbb{R}^n \to \mathbb{R}^n$ and $L_2 : \mathbb{R}^n \to \mathbb{R}^n$ have the same matrix representation with respect to E, then $L_1 = L_2$.

8. Let $L: \mathbb{R}^n \to \mathbb{R}^n$ be a linear transformation. If A is the standard matrix representation of L, then an $n \times n$ matrix B will also be a matrix representation of L if and only if B is similar to A.

9. Let A, B, and C be $n \times n$ matrices. If A is similar to B and B is similar to C, then A is similar to C.

10. Any two matrices with the same trace are similar. [This statement is the converse of part (b) of Exercise 15 in Section 4.3.]

2. Let L be a linear operator on $\mathbb{R}^2$ and let

If

$$\mathbf{v}_1 = \begin{bmatrix} 1 \\ 1 \end{bmatrix}, \quad \mathbf{v}_2 = \begin{bmatrix} -1 \\ 2 \end{bmatrix}, \quad \mathbf{v}_3 = \begin{bmatrix} 1 \\ 7 \end{bmatrix}$$

$$L(\mathbf{v}_1) = \begin{bmatrix} 2 \\ 5 \end{bmatrix} \quad \text{and} \quad L(\mathbf{v}_2) = \begin{bmatrix} -3 \\ 1 \end{bmatrix}$$

find the value of $L(\mathbf{v}_3)$.

3. Let L be the linear operator on $\mathbb{R}^3$ defined by

$$L(\mathbf{x}) = \begin{bmatrix} x_2 - x_1 \\ x_3 - x_2 \\ x_3 - x_1 \end{bmatrix}$$

and let $S = \text{Span}((1, 0, 1)^T)$.

(a) Find the kernel of L.

(b) Determine $L(S)$.

4. Let L be the linear operator on $\mathbb{R}^3$ defined by

$$L(\mathbf{x}) = \begin{bmatrix} x_2 \\ x_1 \\ x_1 + x_2 \end{bmatrix}$$

Determine the range of L.

5. Let $L: \mathbb{R}^2 \to \mathbb{R}^3$ be defined by

$$L(\mathbf{x}) = \begin{bmatrix} x_1 + x_2 \\ x_1 - x_2 \\ 3x_1 + 2x_2 \end{bmatrix}$$

Find a matrix A such that $L(\mathbf{x}) = A\mathbf{x}$ for each $\mathbf{x}$ in $\mathbb{R}^2$.

6. Let L be the linear operator on $\mathbb{R}^2$ that rotates a vector by $30°$ in the counterclockwise direction and then reflects the resulting vector about the y-axis. Find the standard matrix representation of L.

7. Let L be the translation operator on $\mathbb{R}^2$ defined by

$$L(\mathbf{x}) = \mathbf{x} + \mathbf{a}, \quad \text{where } \mathbf{a} = \begin{bmatrix} 2 \\ 5 \end{bmatrix}$$

Find the matrix representation of L with respect to the homogeneous coordinate system.

8. Let

$$\mathbf{u}_1 = \begin{bmatrix} 3 \\ 1 \end{bmatrix}, \quad \mathbf{u}_2 = \begin{bmatrix} 5 \\ 2 \end{bmatrix}$$

and let L be the linear operator that rotates vectors in $\mathbb{R}^2$ by $45°$ in the counterclockwise direction. Find the matrix representation of L with respect to the ordered basis $[\mathbf{u}_1, \mathbf{u}_2]$.

9. Let

$$\mathbf{u}_1 = \begin{bmatrix} 3 \\ 1 \end{bmatrix}, \quad \mathbf{u}_2 = \begin{bmatrix} 5 \\ 2 \end{bmatrix}$$

and

$$\mathbf{v}_1 = \begin{bmatrix} 1 \\ -2 \end{bmatrix}, \quad \mathbf{v}_2 = \begin{bmatrix} 1 \\ -1 \end{bmatrix}$$

and let L be a linear operator on $\mathbb{R}^2$ whose matrix representation with respect to the ordered basis $\{\mathbf{u}_1, \mathbf{u}_2\}$ is

$$A = \begin{bmatrix} 2 & 1 \\ 3 & 2 \end{bmatrix}$$

(a) Determine the transition matrix from the basis $\{\mathbf{v}_1, \mathbf{v}_2\}$ to the basis $\{\mathbf{u}_1, \mathbf{u}_2\}$.

(b) Find the matrix representation of L with respect to $\{\mathbf{v}_1, \mathbf{v}_2\}$.

10. Let A and B be similar matrices.

(a) Show that $\det(A) = \det(B)$.

(b) Show that if λ is any scalar, then $\det(A - \lambda I) = \det(B - \lambda I)$.

CHAPTER

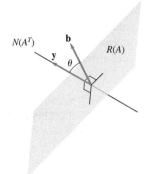

$$5$$

Orthogonality

We can add to the structure of a vector space by defining a scalar or inner product. Such a product is not a true vector multiplication, since to every pair of vectors it associates a scalar rather than a third vector. For example, in $\mathbb{R}^2$, we can define the scalar product of two vectors $\mathbf{x}$ and $\mathbf{y}$ to be $\mathbf{x}^T\mathbf{y}$. We can think of vectors in $\mathbb{R}^2$ as directed line segments beginning at the origin. It is not difficult to show that the angle between two line segments will be a right angle if and only if the scalar product of the corresponding vectors is zero. In general, if V is a vector space with a scalar product, then two vectors in V are said to be *orthogonal* if their scalar product is zero.

We can think of orthogonality as a generalization of the concept of *perpendicularity* to any vector space with an inner product. To see the significance of this, consider the following problem: Let l be a line passing through the origin, and let Q be a point not on l. Find the point P on l that is closest to Q. The solution P to this problem is characterized by the condition that QP is perpendicular to OP (see Figure 5.0.1). If we think of the line l as corresponding to a subspace of $\mathbb{R}^2$ and $\mathbf{v} = OQ$ as a vector in $\mathbb{R}^2$, then the problem is to find a vector in the subspace that is "closest" to $\mathbf{v}$. The solution $\mathbf{p}$ will then be characterized by the property that $\mathbf{p}$ is orthogonal to $\mathbf{v} - \mathbf{p}$ (see Figure 5.0.1). In the setting of a vector space with an inner product, we are able to consider general *least squares* problems. In these problems, we are given a vector $\mathbf{v}$ in V and a subspace

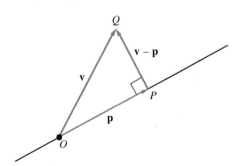

Figure 5.0.1.

W. We wish to find a vector in W that is "closest" to $\mathbf{v}$. A solution $\mathbf{p}$ must be orthogonal to $\mathbf{v} - \mathbf{p}$. This orthogonality condition provides the key to solving the least squares problem. Least squares problems occur in many statistical applications involving data fitting.

5.1 The Scalar Product in $\mathbb{R}^n$

Two vectors $\mathbf{x}$ and $\mathbf{y}$ in $\mathbb{R}^n$ may be regarded as $n \times 1$ matrices. We can then form the matrix product $\mathbf{x}^T\mathbf{y}$. This product is a 1×1 matrix that may be regarded as a vector in $\mathbb{R}^1$ or, more simply, as a real number. The product $\mathbf{x}^T\mathbf{y}$ is called the *scalar product* of $\mathbf{x}$ and $\mathbf{y}$. In particular, if $\mathbf{x} = (x_1, \ldots, x_n)^T$ and $\mathbf{y} = (y_1, \ldots, y_n)^T$, then

$$\mathbf{x}^T\mathbf{y} = x_1 y_1 + x_2 y_2 + \cdots + x_n y_n$$

EXAMPLE I   If

$$\mathbf{x} = \begin{bmatrix} 3 \\ -2 \\ 1 \end{bmatrix} \quad \text{and} \quad \mathbf{y} = \begin{bmatrix} 4 \\ 3 \\ 2 \end{bmatrix}$$

then

$$\mathbf{x}^T\mathbf{y} = (3, -2, 1) \begin{bmatrix} 4 \\ 3 \\ 2 \end{bmatrix} = 3 \cdot 4 - 2 \cdot 3 + 1 \cdot 2 = 8 \qquad \blacksquare$$

The Scalar Product in $\mathbb{R}^2$ and $\mathbb{R}^3$

In order to see the geometric significance of the scalar product, let us begin by restricting our attention to $\mathbb{R}^2$ and $\mathbb{R}^3$. Vectors in $\mathbb{R}^2$ and $\mathbb{R}^3$ can be represented by directed line segments. Given a vector $\mathbf{x}$ in either $\mathbb{R}^2$ or $\mathbb{R}^3$, its *Euclidean length* can be defined in terms of the scalar product.

$$\|\mathbf{x}\| = (\mathbf{x}^T\mathbf{x})^{1/2} = \begin{cases} \sqrt{x_1^2 + x_2^2} & \text{if } \mathbf{x} \in \mathbb{R}^2 \\ \sqrt{x_1^2 + x_2^2 + x_3^2} & \text{if } \mathbf{x} \in \mathbb{R}^3 \end{cases}$$

Given two nonzero vectors $\mathbf{x}$ and $\mathbf{y}$, we can think of them as directed line segments starting at the same point. The angle between the two vectors is then defined as the angle θ between the line segments. We can measure the distance between the vectors by measuring the length of the vector joining the terminal point of $\mathbf{x}$ to the terminal point of $\mathbf{y}$ (see Figure 5.1.1). Thus, we have the following definition.

Definition   Let $\mathbf{x}$ and $\mathbf{y}$ be vectors in either $\mathbb{R}^2$ or $\mathbb{R}^3$. The distance between $\mathbf{x}$ and $\mathbf{y}$ is defined to be the number $\|\mathbf{x} - \mathbf{y}\|$.

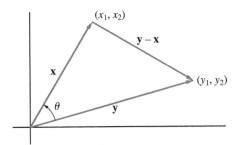

Figure 5.1.1.

EXAMPLE 2 If $\mathbf{x} = (3, 4)^T$ and $\mathbf{y} = (-1, 7)^T$, then the distance between $\mathbf{x}$ and $\mathbf{y}$ is given by

$$\|\mathbf{y} - \mathbf{x}\| = \sqrt{(-1 - 3)^2 + (7 - 4)^2} = 5$$ ■

The angle between two vectors can be computed using the following theorem.

Theorem 5.1.1 *If $\mathbf{x}$ and $\mathbf{y}$ are two nonzero vectors in either $\mathbb{R}^2$ or $\mathbb{R}^3$ and θ is the angle between them, then*

$$\mathbf{x}^T\mathbf{y} = \|\mathbf{x}\| \, \|\mathbf{y}\| \cos\theta \tag{1}$$

Proof The vectors $\mathbf{x}$, $\mathbf{y}$, and $\mathbf{y} - \mathbf{x}$ may be used to form a triangle as in Figure 5.1.1. By the law of cosines, we have

$$\|\mathbf{y} - \mathbf{x}\|^2 = \|\mathbf{x}\|^2 + \|\mathbf{y}\|^2 - 2\|\mathbf{x}\| \, \|\mathbf{y}\| \cos\theta$$

and hence it follows that

$$\begin{aligned}
\|\mathbf{x}\| \, \|\mathbf{y}\| \cos\theta &= \tfrac{1}{2}(\|\mathbf{x}\|^2 + \|\mathbf{y}\|^2 - \|\mathbf{y} - \mathbf{x}\|^2) \\
&= \tfrac{1}{2}(\|\mathbf{x}\|^2 + \|\mathbf{y}\|^2 - (\mathbf{y} - \mathbf{x})^T(\mathbf{y} - \mathbf{x})) \\
&= \tfrac{1}{2}(\|\mathbf{x}\|^2 + \|\mathbf{y}\|^2 - (\mathbf{y}^T\mathbf{y} - \mathbf{y}^T\mathbf{x} - \mathbf{x}^T\mathbf{y} + \mathbf{x}^T\mathbf{x})) \\
&= \mathbf{x}^T\mathbf{y}
\end{aligned}$$ ■

If $\mathbf{x}$ and $\mathbf{y}$ are nonzero vectors, then we can specify their directions by forming unit vectors

$$\mathbf{u} = \frac{1}{\|\mathbf{x}\|}\mathbf{x} \quad \text{and} \quad \mathbf{v} = \frac{1}{\|\mathbf{y}\|}\mathbf{y}$$

If θ is the angle between $\mathbf{x}$ and $\mathbf{y}$, then

$$\cos\theta = \frac{\mathbf{x}^T\mathbf{y}}{\|\mathbf{x}\|\|\mathbf{y}\|} = \mathbf{u}^T\mathbf{v}$$

The cosine of the angle between the vectors $\mathbf{x}$ and $\mathbf{y}$ is the scalar product of the corresponding direction vectors $\mathbf{u}$ and $\mathbf{v}$.

EXAMPLE 3   Let $\mathbf{x}$ and $\mathbf{y}$ be the vectors in Example 2. The directions of these vectors are given by the unit vectors

$$\mathbf{u} = \frac{1}{\|\mathbf{x}\|}\mathbf{x} = \begin{pmatrix} \frac{3}{5} \\ \frac{4}{5} \end{pmatrix} \quad \text{and} \quad \mathbf{v} = \frac{1}{\|\mathbf{y}\|}\mathbf{y} = \begin{pmatrix} -\frac{1}{5\sqrt{2}} \\ \frac{7}{5\sqrt{2}} \end{pmatrix}$$

The cosine of the angle θ between the two vectors is

$$\cos\theta = \mathbf{u}^T\mathbf{v} = \frac{1}{\sqrt{2}}$$

and hence $\theta = \frac{\pi}{4}$. ∎

Corollary 5.1.2   Cauchy--Schwarz Inequality

If $\mathbf{x}$ and $\mathbf{y}$ are vectors in either $\mathbb{R}^2$ or $\mathbb{R}^3$, then

$$|\mathbf{x}^T\mathbf{y}| \le \|\mathbf{x}\|\,\|\mathbf{y}\| \tag{2}$$

with equality holding if and only if one of the vectors is $\mathbf{0}$ or one vector is a multiple of the other.

Proof   The inequality follows from (1). If one of the vectors is $\mathbf{0}$, then both sides of (2) are 0. If both vectors are nonzero, it follows from (1) that equality can hold in (2) if and only if $\cos\theta = \pm 1$. But this would imply that the vectors are either in the same or opposite directions and hence that one vector must be a multiple of the other. ∎

If $\mathbf{x}^T\mathbf{y} = 0$, it follows from Theorem 5.1.1 that either one of the vectors is the zero vector or $\cos\theta = 0$. If $\cos\theta = 0$, the angle between the vectors is a right angle.

Definition | The vectors $\mathbf{x}$ and $\mathbf{y}$ in $\mathbb{R}^2$ (or $\mathbb{R}^3$) are said to be **orthogonal** if $\mathbf{x}^T\mathbf{y} = 0$.

EXAMPLE 4   **(a)** The vector $\mathbf{0}$ is orthogonal to every vector in $\mathbb{R}^2$.

(b) The vectors $\begin{bmatrix} 3 \\ 2 \end{bmatrix}$ and $\begin{bmatrix} -4 \\ 6 \end{bmatrix}$ are orthogonal in $\mathbb{R}^2$.

(c) The vectors $\begin{bmatrix} 2 \\ -3 \\ 1 \end{bmatrix}$ and $\begin{bmatrix} 1 \\ 1 \\ 1 \end{bmatrix}$ are orthogonal in $\mathbb{R}^3$. ∎

Scalar and Vector Projections

The scalar product can be used to find the component of one vector in the direction of another. Let $\mathbf{x}$ and $\mathbf{y}$ be nonzero vectors in either $\mathbb{R}^2$ or $\mathbb{R}^3$. We would like to write $\mathbf{x}$ as a sum of the form $\mathbf{p} + \mathbf{z}$, where $\mathbf{p}$ is in the direction of $\mathbf{y}$ and $\mathbf{z}$ is orthogonal to $\mathbf{p}$ (see Figure 5.1.2). To do this, let $\mathbf{u} = (1/\|\mathbf{y}\|)\mathbf{y}$. Thus, $\mathbf{u}$ is a unit vector (length 1) in the

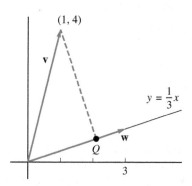

Figure 5.1.2.

direction of **y**. We wish to find α such that $\mathbf{p} = \alpha\mathbf{u}$ is orthogonal to $\mathbf{z} = \mathbf{x} - \alpha\mathbf{u}$. For **p** and **z** to be orthogonal, the scalar α must satisfy

$$\alpha = \|\mathbf{x}\| \cos\theta$$

$$= \frac{\|\mathbf{x}\| \, \|\mathbf{y}\| \cos\theta}{\|\mathbf{y}\|}$$

$$= \frac{\mathbf{x}^T\mathbf{y}}{\|\mathbf{y}\|}$$

The scalar α is called the *scalar projection* of **x** onto **y**, and the vector **p** is called the *vector projection* of **x** onto **y**.

Scalar projection of **x** onto **y**:

$$\alpha = \frac{\mathbf{x}^T\mathbf{y}}{\|\mathbf{y}\|}$$

Vector projection of **x** onto **y**:

$$\mathbf{p} = \alpha\mathbf{u} = \alpha\frac{1}{\|\mathbf{y}\|}\mathbf{y} = \frac{\mathbf{x}^T\mathbf{y}}{\mathbf{y}^T\mathbf{y}}\mathbf{y}$$

EXAMPLE 5   The point Q in Figure 5.1.3 is the point on the line $y = \frac{1}{3}x$ that is closest to the point $(1, 4)$. Determine the coordinates of Q.

Figure 5.1.3.

Solution

The vector $\mathbf{w} = (3, 1)^T$ is a vector in the direction of the line $y = \frac{1}{3}x$. Let $\mathbf{v} = (1, 4)^T$. If Q is the desired point, then Q^T is the vector projection of $\mathbf{v}$ onto $\mathbf{w}$.

$$Q^T = \left(\frac{\mathbf{v}^T \mathbf{w}}{\mathbf{w}^T \mathbf{w}} \right) \mathbf{w} = \frac{7}{10} \begin{bmatrix} 3 \\ 1 \end{bmatrix} = \begin{bmatrix} 2.1 \\ 0.7 \end{bmatrix}$$

Thus, $Q = (2.1, 0.7)$ is the closest point. ∎

Notation

If P_1 and P_2 are two points in 3-space, we will denote the vector from P_1 to P_2 by $\overrightarrow{P_1 P_2}$.

If $\mathbf{N}$ is a nonzero vector and P_0 is a fixed point, the set of points P such that $\overrightarrow{P_0 P}$ is orthogonal to $\mathbf{N}$ forms a plane π in 3-space that passes through P_0. The vector $\mathbf{N}$ and the plane π are said to be *normal* to each other. A point $P = (x, y, z)$ will lie on π if and only if

$$(\overrightarrow{P_0 P})^T \mathbf{N} = 0$$

If $\mathbf{N} = (a, b, c)^T$ and $P_0 = (x_0, y_0, z_0)$, this equation can be written in the form

$$a(x - x_0) + b(y - y_0) + c(z - z_0) = 0$$

EXAMPLE 6 Find the equation of the plane passing through the point $(2, -1, 3)$ and normal to the vector $\mathbf{N} = (2, 3, 4)^T$.

Solution

$\overrightarrow{P_0 P} = (x - 2, y + 1, z - 3)^T$. The equation is $(\overrightarrow{P_0 P})^T \mathbf{N} = 0$, or

$$2(x - 2) + 3(y + 1) + 4(z - 3) = 0$$ ∎

The span of two linearly independent vectors $\mathbf{x}$ and $\mathbf{y}$ in $\mathbb{R}^3$ corresponds to a plane through the origin in 3-space. To determine the equation of the plane, we must find a vector normal to the plane. In Section 2.3, it was shown that the cross product of the two vectors is orthogonal to each vector. If we take $\mathbf{N} = \mathbf{x} \times \mathbf{y}$ as our normal vector, then the equation of the plane is given by

$$n_1 x + n_2 y + n_3 z = 0$$

EXAMPLE 7 Find the equation of the plane that passes through the points

$$P_1 = (1, 1, 2), \quad P_2 = (2, 3, 3), \quad P_3 = (3, -3, 3)$$

Solution

Let

$$\mathbf{x} = \overrightarrow{P_1 P_2} = \begin{bmatrix} 1 \\ 2 \\ 1 \end{bmatrix} \quad \text{and} \quad \mathbf{y} = \overrightarrow{P_1 P_3} = \begin{bmatrix} 2 \\ -4 \\ 1 \end{bmatrix}$$

The normal vector **N** must be orthogonal to both **x** and **y**. If we set

$$\mathbf{N} = \mathbf{x} \times \mathbf{y} = \begin{bmatrix} 6 \\ 1 \\ -8 \end{bmatrix}$$

then **N** will be a normal vector to the plane that passes through the given points. We can then use any one of the points to determine the equation of the plane. Using the point P_1, we see that the equation of the plane is

$$6(x - 1) + (y - 1) - 8(z - 2) = 0$$

EXAMPLE 8   Find the distance from the point $(2, 0, 0)$ to the plane $x + 2y + 2z = 0$.

Solution

The vector $\mathbf{N} = (1, 2, 2)^T$ is normal to the plane and the plane passes through the origin. Let $\mathbf{v} = (2, 0, 0)^T$. The distance d from $(2, 0, 0)$ to the plane is simply the absolute value of the scalar projection of **v** onto **N**. Thus,

$$d = \frac{|\mathbf{v}^T \mathbf{N}|}{\|\mathbf{N}\|} = \frac{2}{3}$$

If **x** and **y** are nonzero vectors in $\mathbb{R}^3$ and θ is the angle between the vectors, then

$$\cos \theta = \frac{\mathbf{x}^T \mathbf{y}}{\|\mathbf{x}\| \|\mathbf{y}\|}$$

It then follows that

$$\sin \theta = \sqrt{1 - \cos^2 \theta} = \sqrt{1 - \frac{(\mathbf{x}^T \mathbf{y})^2}{\|\mathbf{x}\|^2 \|\mathbf{y}\|^2}} = \frac{\sqrt{\|\mathbf{x}\|^2 \|\mathbf{y}\|^2 - (\mathbf{x}^T \mathbf{y})^2}}{\|\mathbf{x}\| \|\mathbf{y}\|}$$

and hence

$$\begin{aligned} \|\mathbf{x}\| \|\mathbf{y}\| \sin \theta &= \sqrt{\|\mathbf{x}\|^2 \|\mathbf{y}\|^2 - (\mathbf{x}^T \mathbf{y})^2} \\ &= \sqrt{(x_1^2 + x_2^2 + x_3^2)(y_1^2 + y_2^2 + y_3^2) - (x_1 y_1 + x_2 y_2 + x_3 y_3)^2} \\ &= \sqrt{(x_2 y_3 - x_3 y_2)^2 + (x_3 y_1 - x_1 y_3)^2 + (x_1 y_2 - x_2 y_1)^2} \\ &= \|\mathbf{x} \times \mathbf{y}\| \end{aligned}$$

Thus, we have, for any nonzero vectors **x** and **y** in $\mathbb{R}^3$,

$$\|\mathbf{x} \times \mathbf{y}\| = \|\mathbf{x}\| \|\mathbf{y}\| \sin \theta$$

If either **x** or **y** is the zero vector, then $\mathbf{x} \times \mathbf{y} = \mathbf{0}$ and hence the norm of $\mathbf{x} \times \mathbf{y}$ will be 0.

Orthogonality in $\mathbb{R}^n$

The definitions that have been given for $\mathbb{R}^2$ and $\mathbb{R}^3$ can all be generalized to $\mathbb{R}^n$. Indeed, if $\mathbf{x} \in \mathbb{R}^n$, then the *Euclidean length* of $\mathbf{x}$ is defined by

$$\|\mathbf{x}\| = (\mathbf{x}^T \mathbf{x})^{1/2} = (x_1^2 + x_2^2 + \cdots + x_n^2)^{1/2}$$

If $\mathbf{x}$ and $\mathbf{y}$ are two vectors in $\mathbb{R}^n$, then the distance between the vectors is $\|\mathbf{y} - \mathbf{x}\|$.

The Cauchy–Schwarz inequality holds in $\mathbb{R}^n$. (We will prove this in Section 5.4.) Consequently,

$$-1 \leq \frac{\mathbf{x}^T \mathbf{y}}{\|\mathbf{x}\| \, \|\mathbf{y}\|} \leq 1 \tag{3}$$

for any nonzero vectors $\mathbf{x}$ and $\mathbf{y}$ in $\mathbb{R}^n$. In view of (3), the definition of the angle between two vectors that was used for $\mathbb{R}^2$ can be generalized to $\mathbb{R}^n$. Thus, the angle θ between two nonzero vectors $\mathbf{x}$ and $\mathbf{y}$ in $\mathbb{R}^n$ is given by

$$\cos \theta = \frac{\mathbf{x}^T \mathbf{y}}{\|\mathbf{x}\| \, \|\mathbf{y}\|}, \quad 0 \leq \theta \leq \pi$$

In talking about angles between vectors, it is usually more convenient to scale the vectors so as to make them unit vectors. If we set

$$\mathbf{u} = \frac{1}{\|\mathbf{x}\|}\mathbf{x} \quad \text{and} \quad \mathbf{v} = \frac{1}{\|\mathbf{y}\|}\mathbf{y}$$

then the angle θ between $\mathbf{u}$ and $\mathbf{v}$ is clearly the same as the angle between $\mathbf{x}$ and $\mathbf{y}$, and its cosine can be computed simply by taking the scalar product of the two unit vectors:

$$\cos \theta = \frac{\mathbf{x}^T \mathbf{y}}{\|\mathbf{x}\| \, \|\mathbf{y}\|} = \mathbf{u}^T \mathbf{v}$$

The vectors $\mathbf{x}$ and $\mathbf{y}$ are said to be *orthogonal* if $\mathbf{x}^T \mathbf{y} = 0$. Often the symbol $\perp$ is used to indicate orthogonality. Thus, if $\mathbf{x}$ and $\mathbf{y}$ are orthogonal, we will write $\mathbf{x} \perp \mathbf{y}$. Vector and scalar projections are defined in $\mathbb{R}^n$ in the same way that they were defined for $\mathbb{R}^2$.

If $\mathbf{x}$ and $\mathbf{y}$ are vectors in $\mathbb{R}^n$, then

$$\|\mathbf{x} + \mathbf{y}\|^2 = (\mathbf{x} + \mathbf{y})^T(\mathbf{x} + \mathbf{y}) = \|\mathbf{x}\|^2 + 2\mathbf{x}^T \mathbf{y} + \|\mathbf{y}\|^2 \tag{4}$$

In the case that $\mathbf{x}$ and $\mathbf{y}$ are orthogonal, equation (4) becomes the *Pythagorean law*

$$\|\mathbf{x} + \mathbf{y}\|^2 = \|\mathbf{x}\|^2 + \|\mathbf{y}\|^2$$

The Pythagorean law is a generalization of the Pythagorean theorem. When $\mathbf{x}$ and $\mathbf{y}$ are nonzero orthogonal vectors in $\mathbb{R}^2$, we can use these vectors and their sum $\mathbf{x} + \mathbf{y}$ to form a right triangle as in Figure 5.1.4. The Pythagorean law relates the lengths of the sides of the triangle. Indeed, if we set

$$a = \|\mathbf{x}\|, \quad b = \|\mathbf{y}\|, \quad c = \|\mathbf{x} + \mathbf{y}\|$$

then

$$c^2 = a^2 + b^2 \quad \text{(the famous Pythagorean theorem)}$$

Figure 5.1.4.

In many applications, the cosine of the angle between two nonzero vectors is used as a measure of how closely the directions of the vectors match up. If $\cos\theta$ is near 1, then the angle between the vectors is small and hence the vectors are in nearly the same direction. A cosine value near zero would indicate that the angle between the vectors is nearly a right angle.

APPLICATION 1   Information Retrieval Revisited

In Section 1.3, we considered the problem of searching a database for documents that contain certain keywords. If there are m possible key search words and a total of n documents in the collection, then the database can be represented by an $m \times n$ matrix A. Each column of A represents a document in the database. The entries of the jth column correspond to the relative frequencies of the keywords in the jth document.

Refined search techniques must deal with vocabulary disparities and the complexities of language. Two of the main problems are *polysemy* (words having multiple meanings) and *synonymy* (multiple words having the same meaning). On the one hand, some of the words that you are searching for may have multiple meanings and could appear in contexts that are completely irrelevant to your particular search. For example, the word *calculus* would occur frequently in both mathematical papers and in dentistry papers. On the other hand, most words have synonyms, and it is possible that many of the documents may use the synonyms rather than the specified search words. For example, you could search for an article on rabies using the keyword *dogs*; however, the author of the article may have preferred to use the word *canines* throughout the paper. To handle these problems, we need a technique to find the documents that best match the list of search words without necessarily matching every word on the list. We want to pick out the column vectors of the database matrix that most closely match a given search vector. To do this, we use the cosine of the angle between two vectors as a measure of how closely the vectors match up.

In practice, both m and n are quite large, as there are many possible keywords and many documents to search. For simplicity, let us consider an example where $m = 10$ and $n = 8$. Suppose that a Web site has eight modules for learning linear algebra and each module is located on a separate Web page. Our list of possible search words consists of

> *determinants, eigenvalues, linear, matrices, numerical,*
> *orthogonality, spaces, systems, transformations, vector*

(This list of keywords was compiled from the chapter headings for this book.) Table 5.1.1 shows the frequencies of the keywords in each of the modules. The $(2, 6)$ entry of the table is 5, which indicates that the keyword *eigenvalues* appears five times in the sixth module.

Table 5.1.1   Frequency of Keywords

Keywords	Modules							
	M1	**M2**	**M3**	**M4**	**M5**	**M6**	**M7**	**M8**
determinants	0	6	3	0	1	0	1	1
eigenvalues	0	0	0	0	0	5	3	2
linear	5	4	4	5	4	0	3	3
matrices	6	5	3	3	4	4	3	2
numerical	0	0	0	0	3	0	4	3
orthogonality	0	0	0	0	4	6	0	2
spaces	0	0	5	2	3	3	0	1
systems	5	3	3	2	4	2	1	1
transformations	0	0	0	5	1	3	1	0
vector	0	4	4	3	4	1	0	3

The database matrix is formed by scaling each column of the table so that all column vectors are unit vectors. Thus, if A is the matrix corresponding to Table 5.1.1, then the columns of the database matrix Q are determined by setting

$$\mathbf{q}_j = \frac{1}{\|\mathbf{a}_j\|}\mathbf{a}_j \quad j = 1,\ldots,8$$

To do a search for the keywords *orthogonality, spaces,* and *vector,* we form a search vector $\mathbf{x}$ whose entries are all 0 except for the three rows corresponding to the search rows. To obtain a unit search vector, we put $\frac{1}{\sqrt{3}}$ in each of the rows corresponding to the search words. For this example, the database matrix Q and search vector $\mathbf{x}$ (with entries rounded to three decimal places) are given by

$$Q = \begin{bmatrix} 0.000 & 0.594 & 0.327 & 0.000 & 0.100 & 0.000 & 0.147 & 0.154 \\ 0.000 & 0.000 & 0.000 & 0.000 & 0.000 & 0.500 & 0.442 & 0.309 \\ 0.539 & 0.396 & 0.436 & 0.574 & 0.400 & 0.000 & 0.442 & 0.463 \\ 0.647 & 0.495 & 0.327 & 0.344 & 0.400 & 0.400 & 0.442 & 0.309 \\ 0.000 & 0.000 & 0.000 & 0.000 & 0.300 & 0.000 & 0.590 & 0.463 \\ 0.000 & 0.000 & 0.000 & 0.000 & 0.400 & 0.600 & 0.000 & 0.309 \\ 0.000 & 0.000 & 0.546 & 0.229 & 0.300 & 0.300 & 0.000 & 0.154 \\ 0.539 & 0.297 & 0.327 & 0.229 & 0.400 & 0.200 & 0.147 & 0.154 \\ 0.000 & 0.000 & 0.000 & 0.574 & 0.100 & 0.300 & 0.147 & 0.000 \\ 0.000 & 0.396 & 0.436 & 0.344 & 0.400 & 0.100 & 0.000 & 0.463 \end{bmatrix}, \mathbf{x} = \begin{bmatrix} 0.000 \\ 0.000 \\ 0.000 \\ 0.000 \\ 0.000 \\ 0.577 \\ 0.577 \\ 0.000 \\ 0.000 \\ 0.577 \end{bmatrix}$$

If we set $\mathbf{y} = Q^T\mathbf{x}$, then

$$y_i = \mathbf{q}_i^T\mathbf{x} = \cos\theta_i$$

where θ_i is the angle between the unit vectors $\mathbf{x}$ and $\mathbf{q}_i$. For our example,

$$\mathbf{y} = (0.000, 0.229, 0.567, 0.331, 0.635, 0.577, 0.000, 0.535)^T$$

Since $y_5 = 0.635$ is the entry of $\mathbf{y}$ that is closest to 1, the direction of the search vector $\mathbf{x}$ is closest to the direction of $\mathbf{q}_5$ and hence module 5 is the one that best matches our search criteria. The next-best matches come from modules 6 ($y_6 = 0.577$) and 3 ($y_3 = 0.567$). If a document doesn't contain any of the search words, then the corresponding column vector of the database matrix will be orthogonal to the search vector. Note that modules 1 and 7 do not have any of the three search words and consequently

$$y_1 = \mathbf{q}_1^T \mathbf{x} = 0 \quad \text{and} \quad y_7 = \mathbf{q}_7^T \mathbf{x} = 0$$

This example illustrates some of the basic ideas behind database searches. Using modern matrix techniques, we can improve the search process significantly. We can speed up searches and at the same time correct for errors due to polysemy and synonymy. These advanced techniques are referred to as *latent semantic indexing* (LSI) and depend on a matrix factorization, the *singular value decomposition*, which we will discuss in Section 6.5.

There are many other important applications involving angles between vectors. In particular, statisticians use the cosine of the angle between two vectors as a measure of how closely the two vectors are correlated.

APPLICATION 2   Statistics—Correlation and Covariance Matrices

Suppose that we wanted to compare how closely exam scores for a class correlate with scores on homework assignments. As an example, we consider the total scores on assignments and tests of a mathematics class at the University of Massachusetts Dartmouth. The total scores for homework assignments during the semester for the class are given in the second column of Table 5.1.2. The third column represents the total scores for the two exams given during the semester, and the last column contains the scores on the final exam. In each case, a perfect score would be 200 points. The last row of the table summarizes the class averages.

Table 5.1.2   Math Scores Fall 1996

Student	Scores		
	Assignments	**Exams**	**Final**
S1	198	200	196
S2	160	165	165
S3	158	158	133
S4	150	165	91
S5	175	182	151
S6	134	135	101
S7	152	136	80
Average	161	163	131

We would like to measure how student performance compares between each set of exam or assignment scores. To see how closely the two sets of scores are correlated and allow for any differences in difficulty, we need to adjust the scores so that each test has a mean of 0. If, in each column, we subtract the average score from each of the test scores, then the translated scores will each have an average of 0. Let us store these translated scores in a matrix:

$$X = \begin{pmatrix} 37 & 37 & 65 \\ -1 & 2 & 34 \\ -3 & -5 & 2 \\ -11 & 2 & -40 \\ 14 & 19 & 20 \\ -27 & -28 & -30 \\ -9 & -27 & -51 \end{pmatrix}$$

The column vectors of X represent the deviations from the mean for each of the three sets of scores. The three sets of translated data specified by the column vectors of X all have mean 0, and all sum to 0. To compare two sets of scores, we compute the cosine of the angle between the corresponding column vectors of X. A cosine value near 1 indicates that the two sets of scores are highly correlated. For example, correlation between the assignment scores and the exam scores is given by

$$\cos \theta = \frac{\mathbf{x}_1^T \mathbf{x}_2}{\|\mathbf{x}_1\| \, \|\mathbf{x}_2\|} \approx 0.92$$

A perfect correlation of 1 would correspond to the case where the two sets of translated scores are proportional. Thus, for a perfect correlation, the translated vectors would satisfy

$$\mathbf{x}_2 = \alpha \mathbf{x}_1 \qquad (\alpha > 0)$$

and if the corresponding coordinates of $\mathbf{x}_1$ and $\mathbf{x}_2$ were paired off, then each ordered pair would lie on the line $y = \alpha x$. Although the vectors $\mathbf{x}_1$ and $\mathbf{x}_2$ in our example are not perfectly correlated, the coefficient of 0.92 does indicate that the two sets of scores are highly correlated. Figure 5.1.5 shows how close the actual pairs are to lying on a line $y = \alpha x$. The slope of the line in the figure was determined by setting

$$\alpha = \frac{\mathbf{x}_1^T \mathbf{x}_2}{\mathbf{x}_1^T \mathbf{x}_1} = \frac{2625}{2506} \approx 1.05$$

This choice of slope yields an optimal *least squares* fit to the data points. (See Exercise 7 of Section 5.3.)

If we scale $\mathbf{x}_1$ and $\mathbf{x}_2$ to make them unit vectors

$$\mathbf{u}_1 = \frac{1}{\|\mathbf{x}_1\|} \mathbf{x}_1 \quad \text{and} \quad \mathbf{u}_2 = \frac{1}{\|\mathbf{x}_2\|} \mathbf{x}_2$$

then the cosine of the angle between the vectors will remain unchanged, and it can be computed simply by taking the scalar product $\mathbf{u}_1^T \mathbf{u}_2$. Let us scale all three sets of translated scores in this way and store the results in a matrix:

$$U = \begin{pmatrix} 0.74 & 0.65 & 0.62 \\ -0.02 & 0.03 & 0.33 \\ -0.06 & -0.09 & 0.02 \\ -0.22 & 0.03 & -0.38 \\ 0.28 & 0.33 & 0.19 \\ -0.54 & -0.49 & -0.29 \\ -0.18 & -0.47 & -0.49 \end{pmatrix}$$

Figure 5.1.5.

If we set $C = U^T U$, then

$$C = \begin{bmatrix} 1 & 0.92 & 0.83 \\ 0.92 & 1 & 0.83 \\ 0.83 & 0.83 & 1 \end{bmatrix}$$

and the (i, j) entry of C represents the correlation between the ith and jth sets of scores. The matrix C is referred to as a *correlation matrix*.

The three sets of scores in our example are all *positively correlated*, since the correlation coefficients are all positive. A negative coefficient would indicate that two data sets were *negatively correlated*, and a coefficient of 0 would indicate that they were *uncorrelated*. Thus, two sets of test scores would be uncorrelated if the corresponding vectors of deviations from the mean were orthogonal.

Another statistically important quantity that is closely related to the correlation matrix is the *covariance matrix*. Given a collection of n data points representing values of some variable x, we compute the mean $\bar{x}$ of the data points and form a vector $\mathbf{x}$ of the deviations from the mean. The *variance*, s^2, is defined by

$$s^2 = \frac{1}{n-1} \sum_{1}^{n} x_i^2 = \frac{\mathbf{x}^T \mathbf{x}}{n-1}$$

and the standard deviation s is the square root of the variance. If we have two data sets X_1 and X_2, each containing n values of a variable, we can form vectors $\mathbf{x}_1$ and $\mathbf{x}_2$ of deviations from the mean for both sets. The *covariance* is defined by

$$\text{cov}(X_1, X_2) = \frac{\mathbf{x}_1^T \mathbf{x}_2}{n-1}$$

If we have more than two data sets, we can form a matrix X whose columns represent the deviations from the mean for each data set and then form a *covariance matrix S* by setting

$$S = \frac{1}{n-1}X^T X$$

The covariance matrix for the three sets of mathematics scores is

$$S = \frac{1}{6} \begin{bmatrix} 37 & -1 & -3 & -11 & 14 & -27 & -9 \\ 37 & 2 & -5 & 2 & 19 & -28 & -27 \\ 65 & 34 & 2 & -40 & 20 & -30 & -51 \end{bmatrix} \begin{bmatrix} 37 & 37 & 65 \\ -1 & 2 & 34 \\ -3 & -5 & 2 \\ -11 & 2 & -40 \\ 14 & 19 & 20 \\ -27 & -28 & -30 \\ -9 & -27 & -51 \end{bmatrix}$$

$$= \begin{bmatrix} 417.7 & 437.5 & 725.7 \\ 437.5 & 546.0 & 830.0 \\ 725.7 & 830.0 & 1814.3 \end{bmatrix}$$

The diagonal entries of S are the variances for the three sets of scores, and the off-diagonal entries are the covariances.

To illustrate the importance of the correlation and covariance matrices, we will consider an application to the field of psychology.

APPLICATION 3   Psychology—Factor Analysis and Principal Component Analysis

Factor analysis had its start at the beginning of the 20th century with the efforts of psychologists to identify the factor or factors that make up intelligence. The person most responsible for pioneering this field was the psychologist Charles Spearman. In a 1904 paper, Spearman analyzed a series of exam scores at a preparatory school. The exams were taken by a class of 23 pupils in a number of standard subject areas and also in pitch discrimination. The correlation matrix reported by Spearman is summarized in Table 5.1.3.

Table 5.1.3   Spearman's Correlation Matrix

	Classics	French	English	Math	Discrim.	Music
Classics	1	0.83	0.78	0.70	0.66	0.63
French	0.83	1	0.67	0.67	0.65	0.57
English	0.78	0.67	1	0.64	0.54	0.51
Math	0.70	0.67	0.64	1	0.45	0.51
Discrim.	0.66	0.65	0.54	0.45	1	0.40
Music	0.63	0.57	0.51	0.51	0.40	1

Using this and other sets of data, Spearman observed a hierarchy of correlations among the test scores for the various disciplines. This led him to conclude that "all branches of intellectual activity have in common one fundamental function (or group of fundamental functions), ..." Although Spearman did not assign names to these functions, others have used terms such as *verbal comprehension, spatial, perceptual,* and *associative memory* to describe the hypothetical factors.

The hypothetical factors can be isolated mathematically using a method known as *principal component analysis*. The basic idea is to form a matrix X of deviations from the mean and then factor it into a product UW, where the columns of U correspond to the hypothetical factors. While in practice the columns of X are positively correlated, the hypothetical factors should be uncorrelated. Thus, the column vectors of U should be mutually orthogonal (i.e., $\mathbf{u}_i^T \mathbf{u}_j = 0$ whenever $i \neq j$). The entries in each column of U measure how well the individual students exhibit the particular intellectual ability represented by that column. The matrix W measures to what extent each test depends on the hypothetical factors.

The construction of the principal component vectors relies on the covariance matrix $S = \frac{1}{n-1} X^T X$. Since it depends on the *eigenvalues* and *eigenvectors* of S, we will defer the details of the method until Chapter 6. In Section 6.5, we will revisit this application and learn an important factorization called the *singular value decomposition*, which is the main tool of principal component analysis.

References

1. Spearman, C., "'General Intelligence,' Objectively Determined and Measured," *American Journal of Psychology*, **15**, 1904.

2. Hotelling, H., "Analysis of a Complex of Statistical Variables in Principal Components," *Journal of Educational Psychology*, **26**, 1933.

3. Maxwell, A. E., *Multivariate Analysis in Behavioral Research*, Chapman & Hall, London, 1977.

SECTION 5.1 EXERCISES

1. Find the angle between the vectors $\mathbf{v}$ and $\mathbf{w}$ in each of the following:

   (a) $\mathbf{v} = (2, 1, 3)^T$, $\mathbf{w} = (6, 3, 9)^T$

   (b) $\mathbf{v} = (2, -3)^T$, $\mathbf{w} = (3, 2)^T$

   (c) $\mathbf{v} = (4, 1)^T$, $\mathbf{w} = (3, 2)^T$

   (d) $\mathbf{v} = (-2, 3, 1)^T$, $\mathbf{w} = (1, 2, 4)^T$

2. For each pair of vectors in Exercise 1, find the scalar projection of $\mathbf{v}$ onto $\mathbf{w}$. Also find the vector projection of $\mathbf{v}$ onto $\mathbf{w}$.

3. For each of the following pairs of vectors $\mathbf{x}$ and $\mathbf{y}$, find the vector projection $\mathbf{p}$ of $\mathbf{x}$ onto $\mathbf{y}$ and verify that $\mathbf{p}$ and $\mathbf{x} - \mathbf{p}$ are orthogonal:

   (a) $\mathbf{x} = (3, 4)^T$, $\mathbf{y} = (1, 0)^T$

   (b) $\mathbf{x} = (3, 5)^T$, $\mathbf{y} = (1, 1)^T$

   (c) $\mathbf{x} = (2, 4, 3)^T$, $\mathbf{y} = (1, 1, 1)^T$

   (d) $\mathbf{x} = (2, -5, 4)^T$, $\mathbf{y} = (1, 2, -1)^T$

4. Let $\mathbf{x}$ and $\mathbf{y}$ be linearly independent vectors in $\mathbb{R}^2$. If $\|\mathbf{x}\| = 2$ and $\|\mathbf{y}\| = 3$, what, if anything, can we conclude about the possible values of $|\mathbf{x}^T\mathbf{y}|$?

5. Find the point on the line $y = 2x$ that is closest to the point $(5, 2)$.

6. Find the point on the line $y = 2x + 1$ that is closest to the point $(5, 2)$.

7. Find the distance from the point $(1, 2)$ to the line $4x - 3y = 0$.

8. In each of the following, find the equation of the plane normal to the given vector $\mathbf{N}$ and passing through the point P_0:

   (a) $\mathbf{N} = (2, 4, 3)^T$, $P_0 = (0, 0, 0)$

   (b) $\mathbf{N} = (-3, 6, 2)^T$, $P_0 = (4, 2, -5)$

   (c) $\mathbf{N} = (0, 0, 1)^T$, $P_0 = (3, 2, 4)$

9. Find the equation of the plane that passes through the points

$$P_1 = (2, 3, 1), \quad P_2 = (5, 4, 3), \quad P_3 = (3, 4, 4)$$

10. Find the distance from the point $(1, 1, 1)$ to the plane $2x + 2y + z = 0$.

11. Find the distance from the point $(2, 1, -2)$ to the plane
$$6(x - 1) + 2(y - 3) + 3(z + 4) = 0$$

12. If $\mathbf{x} = (x_1, x_2)^T$, $\mathbf{y} = (y_1, y_2)^T$, and $\mathbf{z} = (z_1, z_2)^T$ are arbitrary vectors in $\mathbb{R}^2$, prove that
(a) $\mathbf{x}^T\mathbf{x} \geq 0$ (b) $\mathbf{x}^T\mathbf{y} = \mathbf{y}^T\mathbf{x}$
(c) $\mathbf{x}^T(\mathbf{y} + \mathbf{z}) = \mathbf{x}^T\mathbf{y} + \mathbf{x}^T\mathbf{z}$

13. Show that if $\mathbf{u}$ and $\mathbf{v}$ are any vectors in $\mathbb{R}^2$, then $\|\mathbf{u} + \mathbf{v}\|^2 \leq (\|\mathbf{u}\| + \|\mathbf{v}\|)^2$ and hence $\|\mathbf{u} + \mathbf{v}\| \leq \|\mathbf{u}\| + \|\mathbf{v}\|$. When does equality hold? Give a geometric interpretation of the inequality.

14. Let $\mathbf{x}_1, \mathbf{x}_2$, and $\mathbf{x}_3$ be vectors in $\mathbb{R}^3$. If $\mathbf{x}_1 \perp \mathbf{x}_2$ and $\mathbf{x}_2 \perp \mathbf{x}_3$, is it necessarily true that $\mathbf{x}_1 \perp \mathbf{x}_3$? Prove your answer.

15. Let A be a 2×2 matrix with linearly independent column vectors $\mathbf{a}_1$ and $\mathbf{a}_2$. If $\mathbf{a}_1$ and $\mathbf{a}_2$ are used to form a parallelogram P with altitude h (see the figure), show that
(a) $h^2\|\mathbf{a}_2\|^2 = \|\mathbf{a}_1\|^2\|\mathbf{a}_2\|^2 - (\mathbf{a}_1^T\mathbf{a}_2)^2$
(b) Area of $P = |\det(A)|$

16. If $\mathbf{x}$ and $\mathbf{y}$ are linearly independent vectors in $\mathbb{R}^3$, then they can be used to form a parallelogram P in the plane through the origin corresponding to Span$(\mathbf{x}, \mathbf{y})$. Show that
$$\text{Area of } P = \|\mathbf{x} \times \mathbf{y}\|$$

17. Let
$$\mathbf{x} = \begin{bmatrix} 4 \\ 4 \\ -4 \\ 4 \end{bmatrix} \quad \text{and} \quad \mathbf{y} = \begin{bmatrix} 4 \\ 2 \\ 2 \\ 1 \end{bmatrix}$$

(a) Determine the angle between $\mathbf{x}$ and $\mathbf{y}$.
(b) Determine the distance between $\mathbf{x}$ and $\mathbf{y}$.

18. Let $\mathbf{x}$ and $\mathbf{y}$ be vectors in $\mathbb{R}^n$ and define
$$\mathbf{p} = \frac{\mathbf{x}^T\mathbf{y}}{\mathbf{y}^T\mathbf{y}}\mathbf{y} \quad \text{and} \quad \mathbf{z} = \mathbf{x} - \mathbf{p}$$

(a) Show that $\mathbf{p} \perp \mathbf{z}$. Thus, $\mathbf{p}$ is the *vector projection* of $\mathbf{x}$ onto $\mathbf{y}$; that is, $\mathbf{x} = \mathbf{p} + \mathbf{z}$, where $\mathbf{p}$ and $\mathbf{z}$ are orthogonal components of $\mathbf{x}$, and $\mathbf{p}$ is a scalar multiple of $\mathbf{y}$.

(b) If $\|\mathbf{p}\| = 6$ and $\|\mathbf{z}\| = 8$, determine the value of $\|\mathbf{x}\|$.

19. Use the database matrix U from Application 1 and search for the keywords *orthogonality, spaces, vector*; only this time, give the keyword *orthogonality* twice the weight of the other two key search vector words. Which of the eight modules best matches the search criteria? [*Hint:* Form the search vector using the weights 2, 1, 1 in the rows corresponding to the search words and then scale the vector to make it a unit vector.]

20. Five students in an elementary school take aptitude tests in English, mathematics, and science. Their scores are given in the following table. Determine the correlation matrix and describe how the three sets of scores are correlated.

| Student | Scores | | |
	English	Mathematics	Science
S1	61	53	53
S2	63	73	78
S3	78	61	82
S4	65	84	96
S5	63	59	71
Average	66	66	76

21. Let t be a fixed real number and let
$$c = \cos t, \quad s = \sin t,$$
$$\mathbf{x} = (c, cs, cs^2, \ldots, cs^{n-1}, s^n)^T$$

Show that $\mathbf{x}$ is a unit vector in $\mathbb{R}^{n+1}$.

Hint:
$$1 + s^2 + s^4 + \cdots + s^{2n-2} = \frac{1 - s^{2n}}{1 - s^2}$$

5.2   Orthogonal Subspaces

Let A be an $m \times n$ matrix and let $\mathbf{x} \in N(A)$, the null space of A. Since $A\mathbf{x} = \mathbf{0}$, we have

$$a_{i1}x_1 + a_{i2}x_2 + \cdots + a_{in}x_n = 0 \tag{1}$$

for $i = 1, \ldots, m$. Equation (1) says that $\mathbf{x}$ is orthogonal to the ith column vector of A^T for $i = 1, \ldots, m$. Since $\mathbf{x}$ is orthogonal to each column vector of A^T, it is orthogonal to any linear combination of the column vectors of A^T. So if $\mathbf{y}$ is any vector in the column space of A^T, then $\mathbf{x}^T\mathbf{y} = 0$. Thus, each vector in $N(A)$ is orthogonal to every vector in the column space of A^T. When two subspaces of $\mathbb{R}^n$ have this property, we say that they are orthogonal.

> **Definition**   Two subspaces X and Y of $\mathbb{R}^n$ are said to be **orthogonal** if $\mathbf{x}^T\mathbf{y} = 0$ for every $\mathbf{x} \in X$ and every $\mathbf{y} \in Y$. If X and Y are orthogonal, we write $X \perp Y$.

EXAMPLE I   Let X be the subspace of $\mathbb{R}^3$ spanned by $\mathbf{e}_1$, and let Y be the subspace spanned by $\mathbf{e}_2$. If $\mathbf{x} \in X$ and $\mathbf{y} \in Y$, these vectors must be of the form

$$\mathbf{x} = \begin{bmatrix} x_1 \\ 0 \\ 0 \end{bmatrix} \quad \text{and} \quad \mathbf{y} = \begin{bmatrix} 0 \\ y_2 \\ 0 \end{bmatrix}$$

Thus,

$$\mathbf{x}^T\mathbf{y} = x_1 \cdot 0 + 0 \cdot y_2 + 0 \cdot 0 = 0$$

Therefore, $X \perp Y$.   ◾

The concept of orthogonal subspaces does not always agree with our intuitive idea of perpendicularity. For example, the floor and wall of the classroom "look" orthogonal, but the xy-plane and the yz-plane are not orthogonal subspaces. Indeed, we can think of the vectors $\mathbf{x}_1 = (1, 1, 0)^T$ and $\mathbf{x}_2 = (0, 1, 1)^T$ as lying in the xy- and yz-planes, respectively. Since

$$\mathbf{x}_1^T\mathbf{x}_2 = 1 \cdot 0 + 1 \cdot 1 + 0 \cdot 1 = 1$$

the subspaces are not orthogonal. The next example shows that the subspace corresponding to the z-axis is orthogonal to the subspace corresponding to the xy-plane.

EXAMPLE 2   Let X be the subspace of $\mathbb{R}^3$ spanned by $\mathbf{e}_1$ and $\mathbf{e}_2$, and let Y be the subspace spanned by $\mathbf{e}_3$. If $\mathbf{x} \in X$ and $\mathbf{y} \in Y$, then

$$\mathbf{x}^T\mathbf{y} = x_1 \cdot 0 + x_2 \cdot 0 + 0 \cdot y_3 = 0$$

Thus, $X \perp Y$. Furthermore, if $\mathbf{z}$ is any vector in $\mathbb{R}^3$ that is orthogonal to every vector in Y, then $\mathbf{z} \perp \mathbf{e}_3$, and hence

$$z_3 = \mathbf{z}^T\mathbf{e}_3 = 0$$

But if $z_3 = 0$, then $\mathbf{z} \in X$. Therefore, X is the set of all vectors in $\mathbb{R}^3$ that are orthogonal to every vector in Y (see Figure 5.2.1).   ◾

Figure 5.2.1.

Definition

Let Y be a subspace of $\mathbb{R}^n$. The set of all vectors in $\mathbb{R}^n$ that are orthogonal to every vector in Y will be denoted $Y^\perp$. Thus,

$$Y^\perp = \left\{ \mathbf{x} \in \mathbb{R}^n \mid \mathbf{x}^T \mathbf{y} = 0 \quad \text{for every} \quad \mathbf{y} \in Y \right\}$$

The set $Y^\perp$ is called the **orthogonal complement** of Y.

Note

The subspaces $X = \text{Span}(\mathbf{e}_1)$ and $Y = \text{Span}(\mathbf{e}_2)$ of $\mathbb{R}^3$ given in Example 1 are orthogonal, but they are not orthogonal complements. Indeed,

$$X^\perp = \text{Span}(\mathbf{e}_2, \mathbf{e}_3) \qquad \text{and} \qquad Y^\perp = \text{Span}(\mathbf{e}_1, \mathbf{e}_3)$$

Remarks

1. If X and Y are orthogonal subspaces of $\mathbb{R}^n$, then $X \cap Y = \{\mathbf{0}\}$.
2. If Y is a subspace of $\mathbb{R}^n$, then $Y^\perp$ is also a subspace of $\mathbb{R}^n$.

Proof of (1)   If $\mathbf{x} \in X \cap Y$ and $X \perp Y$, then $\|\mathbf{x}\|^2 = \mathbf{x}^T \mathbf{x} = 0$ and hence $\mathbf{x} = \mathbf{0}$. ∎

Proof of (2)   If $\mathbf{x} \in Y^\perp$ and α is a scalar, then for any $\mathbf{y} \in Y$,

$$(\alpha \mathbf{x})^T \mathbf{y} = \alpha(\mathbf{x}^T \mathbf{y}) = \alpha \cdot 0 = 0$$

Therefore, $\alpha \mathbf{x} \in Y^\perp$. If $\mathbf{x}_1$ and $\mathbf{x}_2$ are elements of $Y^\perp$, then

$$(\mathbf{x}_1 + \mathbf{x}_2)^T \mathbf{y} = \mathbf{x}_1^T \mathbf{y} + \mathbf{x}_2^T \mathbf{y} = 0 + 0 = 0$$

for each $\mathbf{y} \in Y$. Hence, $\mathbf{x}_1 + \mathbf{x}_2 \in Y^\perp$. Therefore, $Y^\perp$ is a subspace of $\mathbb{R}^n$. ∎

Fundamental Subspaces

Let A be an $m \times n$ matrix. We saw in Chapter 3 that a vector $\mathbf{b} \in \mathbb{R}^m$ is in the column space of A if and only if $\mathbf{b} = A\mathbf{x}$ for some $\mathbf{x} \in \mathbb{R}^n$. If we think of A as a linear transformation mapping $\mathbb{R}^n$ into $\mathbb{R}^m$, then the column space of A is the same as the range of A. Let us denote the range of A by $R(A)$. Thus,

$$R(A) = \{\mathbf{b} \in \mathbb{R}^m \mid \mathbf{b} = A\mathbf{x} \quad \text{for some} \quad \mathbf{x} \in \mathbb{R}^n\}$$
$$= \text{the column space of } A$$

The column space of A^T, $R(A^T)$, is a subspace of $\mathbb{R}^n$:

$$R(A^T) = \left\{\mathbf{y} \in \mathbb{R}^n \mid \mathbf{y} = A^T\mathbf{x} \quad \text{for some} \quad \mathbf{x} \in \mathbb{R}^m\right\}$$

The column space of $R(A^T)$ is essentially the same as the row space of A, except that it consists of vectors in $\mathbb{R}^n$ ($n \times 1$ matrices) rather than n-tuples. Thus, $\mathbf{y} \in R(A^T)$ if and only if $\mathbf{y}^T$ is in the row space of A. We have seen that $R(A^T) \perp N(A)$. The following theorem shows that $N(A)$ is actually the orthogonal complement of $R(A^T)$.

Theorem 5.2.1   Fundamental Subspaces Theorem

If A is an $m \times n$ matrix, then $N(A) = R(A^T)^\perp$ and $N(A^T) = R(A)^\perp$.

Proof   On the one hand, we have already seen that $N(A) \perp R(A^T)$, and this implies that $N(A) \subset R(A^T)^\perp$. On the other hand, if $\mathbf{x}$ is any vector in $R(A^T)^\perp$, then $\mathbf{x}$ is orthogonal to each of the column vectors of A^T and, consequently, $A\mathbf{x} = \mathbf{0}$. Thus, $\mathbf{x}$ must be an element of $N(A)$ and hence $N(A) = R(A^T)^\perp$. This proof does not depend on the dimensions of A. In particular, the result will also hold for the matrix $B = A^T$. Consequently,

$$N(A^T) = N(B) = R(B^T)^\perp = R(A)^\perp \qquad \blacksquare$$

EXAMPLE 3   Let

$$A = \begin{pmatrix} 1 & 0 \\ 2 & 0 \end{pmatrix}$$

The column space of A consists of all vectors of the form

$$\begin{bmatrix} \alpha \\ 2\alpha \end{bmatrix} = \alpha \begin{bmatrix} 1 \\ 2 \end{bmatrix}$$

Note that if $\mathbf{x}$ is any vector in $\mathbb{R}^2$ and $\mathbf{b} = A\mathbf{x}$, then

$$\mathbf{b} = \begin{bmatrix} 1 & 0 \\ 2 & 0 \end{bmatrix} \begin{bmatrix} x_1 \\ x_2 \end{bmatrix} = \begin{bmatrix} 1x_1 \\ 2x_1 \end{bmatrix} = x_1 \begin{bmatrix} 1 \\ 2 \end{bmatrix}$$

The null space of A^T consists of all vectors of the form $\beta(-2, 1)^T$. Since $(1, 2)^T$ and $(-2, 1)^T$ are orthogonal, it follows that every vector in $R(A)$ will be orthogonal to every vector in $N(A^T)$. The same relationship holds between $R(A^T)$ and $N(A)$. $R(A^T)$ consists of vectors of the form $\alpha\mathbf{e}_1$, and $N(A)$ consists of all vectors of the form $\beta\mathbf{e}_2$. Since $\mathbf{e}_1$ and $\mathbf{e}_2$ are orthogonal, it follows that each vector in $R(A^T)$ is orthogonal to every vector in $N(A)$. $\qquad \blacksquare$

Theorem 5.2.1 is one of the most important theorems in this chapter. In Section 5.3, we will see that the result $N(A^T) = R(A)^\perp$ provides a key to solving least squares problems. For the present, we will use Theorem 5.2.1 to prove the following theorem, which, in turn, will be used to establish two more important results about orthogonal subspaces.

Theorem 5.2.2 *If S is a subspace of $\mathbb{R}^n$, then $\dim S + \dim S^\perp = n$. Furthermore, if $\{\mathbf{x}_1, \ldots, \mathbf{x}_r\}$ is a basis for S and $\{\mathbf{x}_{r+1}, \ldots, \mathbf{x}_n\}$ is a basis for $S^\perp$, then $\{\mathbf{x}_1, \ldots, \mathbf{x}_r, \mathbf{x}_{r+1}, \ldots, \mathbf{x}_n\}$ is a basis for $\mathbb{R}^n$.*

Proof If $S = \{\mathbf{0}\}$, then $S^\perp = \mathbb{R}^n$ and

$$\dim S + \dim S^\perp = 0 + n = n$$

If $S \neq \{\mathbf{0}\}$, then let $\{\mathbf{x}_1, \ldots, \mathbf{x}_r\}$ be a basis for S and define X to be an $r \times n$ matrix whose ith row is $\mathbf{x}_i^T$ for each i. By construction, the matrix X has rank r and $R(X^T) = S$. By Theorem 5.2.1,

$$S^\perp = R(X^T)^\perp = N(X)$$

It follows from Theorem 3.6.5 that

$$\dim S^\perp = \dim N(X) = n - r$$

To show that $\{\mathbf{x}_1, \ldots, \mathbf{x}_r, \mathbf{x}_{r+1}, \ldots, \mathbf{x}_n\}$ is a basis for $\mathbb{R}^n$, it suffices to show that the n vectors are linearly independent. Suppose that

$$c_1\mathbf{x}_1 + \cdots + c_r\mathbf{x}_r + c_{r+1}\mathbf{x}_{r+1} + \cdots + c_n\mathbf{x}_n = \mathbf{0}$$

Let $\mathbf{y} = c_1\mathbf{x}_1 + \cdots + c_r\mathbf{x}_r$ and $\mathbf{z} = c_{r+1}\mathbf{x}_{r+1} + \cdots + c_n\mathbf{x}_n$. We then have

$$\mathbf{y} + \mathbf{z} = \mathbf{0}$$
$$\mathbf{y} = -\mathbf{z}$$

Thus, $\mathbf{y}$ and $\mathbf{z}$ are both elements of $S \cap S^\perp$. But $S \cap S^\perp = \{\mathbf{0}\}$. Therefore,

$$c_1\mathbf{x}_1 + \cdots + c_r\mathbf{x}_r = \mathbf{0}$$
$$c_{r+1}\mathbf{x}_{r+1} + \cdots + c_n\mathbf{x}_n = \mathbf{0}$$

Since $\mathbf{x}_1, \ldots, \mathbf{x}_r$ are linearly independent,

$$c_1 = c_2 = \cdots = c_r = 0$$

Similarly, $\mathbf{x}_{r+1}, \ldots, \mathbf{x}_n$ are linearly independent and hence

$$c_{r+1} = c_{r+2} = \cdots = c_n = 0$$

So $\mathbf{x}_1, \mathbf{x}_2, \ldots, \mathbf{x}_n$ are linearly independent and form a basis for $\mathbb{R}^n$. ∎

Given a subspace S of $\mathbb{R}^n$, we will use Theorem 5.2.2 to prove that each $\mathbf{x} \in \mathbb{R}^n$ can be expressed uniquely as a sum $\mathbf{y} + \mathbf{z}$, where $\mathbf{y} \in S$ and $\mathbf{z} \in S^\perp$.

Definition   If U and V are subspaces of a vector space W and each $\mathbf{w} \in W$ can be written uniquely as a sum $\mathbf{u} + \mathbf{v}$, where $\mathbf{u} \in U$ and $\mathbf{v} \in V$, then we say that W is a **direct sum** of U and V, and we write $W = U \oplus V$.

Theorem 5.2.3   *If S is a subspace of $\mathbb{R}^n$, then*

$$\mathbb{R}^n = S \oplus S^\perp$$

Proof   The result is trivial if either $S = \{\mathbf{0}\}$ or $S = \mathbb{R}^n$. In the case where $\dim S = r, 0 < r < n$, it follows from Theorem 5.2.2 that each vector $\mathbf{x} \in \mathbb{R}^n$ can be represented in the form

$$\mathbf{x} = c_1\mathbf{x}_1 + \cdots + c_r\mathbf{x}_r + c_{r+1}\mathbf{x}_{r+1} + \cdots + c_n\mathbf{x}_n$$

where $\{\mathbf{x}_1, \ldots, \mathbf{x}_r\}$ is a basis for S and $\{\mathbf{x}_{r+1}, \ldots, \mathbf{x}_n\}$ is a basis for $S^\perp$. If we let

$$\mathbf{u} = c_1\mathbf{x}_1 + \cdots + c_r\mathbf{x}_r \qquad \text{and} \qquad \mathbf{v} = c_{r+1}\mathbf{x}_{r+1} + \cdots + c_n\mathbf{x}_n$$

then $\mathbf{u} \in S, \mathbf{v} \in S^\perp$, and $\mathbf{x} = \mathbf{u} + \mathbf{v}$. To show uniqueness, suppose that $\mathbf{x}$ can also be written as a sum $\mathbf{y} + \mathbf{z}$, where $\mathbf{y} \in S$ and $\mathbf{z} \in S^\perp$. Thus,

$$\mathbf{u} + \mathbf{v} = \mathbf{x} = \mathbf{y} + \mathbf{z}$$
$$\mathbf{u} - \mathbf{y} = \mathbf{z} - \mathbf{v}$$

But $\mathbf{u} - \mathbf{y} \in S$ and $\mathbf{z} - \mathbf{v} \in S^\perp$, so each is in $S \cap S^\perp$. Since

$$S \cap S^\perp = \{\mathbf{0}\}$$

it follows that

$$\mathbf{u} = \mathbf{y} \qquad \text{and} \qquad \mathbf{v} = \mathbf{z} \qquad\qquad \blacksquare$$

Theorem 5.2.4   *If S is a subspace of $\mathbb{R}^n$, then $(S^\perp)^\perp = S$.*

Proof   On the one hand, if $\mathbf{x} \in S$, then $\mathbf{x}$ is orthogonal to each $\mathbf{y}$ in $S^\perp$. Therefore, $\mathbf{x} \in (S^\perp)^\perp$ and hence $S \subset (S^\perp)^\perp$. On the other hand, suppose that $\mathbf{z}$ is an arbitrary element of $(S^\perp)^\perp$. By Theorem 5.2.3, we can write $\mathbf{z}$ as a sum $\mathbf{u} + \mathbf{v}$, where $\mathbf{u} \in S$ and $\mathbf{v} \in S^\perp$. Since $\mathbf{v} \in S^\perp$, it is orthogonal to both $\mathbf{u}$ and $\mathbf{z}$. It then follows that

$$0 = \mathbf{v}^T\mathbf{z} = \mathbf{v}^T\mathbf{u} + \mathbf{v}^T\mathbf{v} = \mathbf{v}^T\mathbf{v}$$

and, consequently, $\mathbf{v} = \mathbf{0}$. Therefore, $\mathbf{z} = \mathbf{u} \in S$ and hence $S = (S^\perp)^\perp$. $\qquad\qquad \blacksquare$

It follows from Theorem 5.2.4 that if T is the orthogonal complement of a subspace S, then S is the orthogonal complement of T, and we may say simply that S and T are orthogonal complements. In particular, it follows from Theorem 5.2.1 that $N(A)$ and $R(A^T)$ are orthogonal complements of each other and that $N(A^T)$ and $R(A)$ are orthogonal complements. Hence, we may write

$$N(A)^\perp = R(A^T) \qquad \text{and} \qquad N(A^T)^\perp = R(A)$$

Recall that the system $A\mathbf{x} = \mathbf{b}$ is consistent if and only if $\mathbf{b} \in R(A)$. Since $R(A) = N(A^T)^\perp$, we have the following result, which may be considered a corollary to Theorem 5.2.1.

Corollary 5.2.5   *If A is an $m \times n$ matrix and $\mathbf{b} \in \mathbb{R}^m$, then either there is a vector $\mathbf{x} \in \mathbb{R}^n$ such that $A\mathbf{x} = \mathbf{b}$ or there is a vector $\mathbf{y} \in \mathbb{R}^m$ such that $A^T\mathbf{y} = \mathbf{0}$ and $\mathbf{y}^T\mathbf{b} \neq 0$.*

Corollary 5.2.5 is illustrated in Figure 5.2.2 for the case where $R(A)$ is a two-dimensional subspace of $\mathbb{R}^3$. The angle θ in the figure will be a right angle if and only if $\mathbf{b} \in R(A)$.

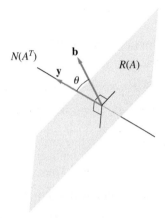

Figure 5.2.2.

EXAMPLE 4   Let

$$A = \begin{bmatrix} 1 & 1 & 2 \\ 0 & 1 & 1 \\ 1 & 3 & 4 \end{bmatrix}$$

Find the bases for $N(A)$, $R(A^T)$, $N(A^T)$, and $R(A)$.

Solution

We can find bases for $N(A)$ and $R(A^T)$ by transforming A into reduced row echelon form:

$$\begin{bmatrix} 1 & 1 & 2 \\ 0 & 1 & 1 \\ 1 & 3 & 4 \end{bmatrix} \rightarrow \begin{bmatrix} 1 & 1 & 2 \\ 0 & 1 & 1 \\ 0 & 2 & 2 \end{bmatrix} \rightarrow \begin{bmatrix} 1 & 0 & 1 \\ 0 & 1 & 1 \\ 0 & 0 & 0 \end{bmatrix}$$

Since $(1, 0, 1)$ and $(0, 1, 1)$ form a basis for the row space of A, it follows that $(1, 0, 1)^T$ and $(0, 1, 1)^T$ form a basis for $R(A^T)$. If $\mathbf{x} \in N(A)$, it follows from the reduced row echelon form of A that

$$x_1 + x_3 = 0$$
$$x_2 + x_3 = 0$$

Thus,

$$x_1 = x_2 = -x_3$$

Setting $x_3 = \alpha$, we see that $N(A)$ consists of all vectors of the form $\alpha(-1, -1, 1)^T$. Note that $(-1, -1, 1)^T$ is orthogonal to $(1, 0, 1)^T$ and $(0, 1, 1)^T$.

To find bases for $R(A)$ and $N(A^T)$, transform A^T to reduced row echelon form.

$$\begin{bmatrix} 1 & 0 & 1 \\ 1 & 1 & 3 \\ 2 & 1 & 4 \end{bmatrix} \rightarrow \begin{bmatrix} 1 & 0 & 1 \\ 0 & 1 & 2 \\ 0 & 1 & 2 \end{bmatrix} \rightarrow \begin{bmatrix} 1 & 0 & 1 \\ 0 & 1 & 2 \\ 0 & 0 & 0 \end{bmatrix}$$

Thus, $(1, 0, 1)^T$ and $(0, 1, 2)^T$ form a basis for $R(A)$. If $\mathbf{x} \in N(A^T)$, then $x_1 = -x_3$, $x_2 = -2x_3$. Hence, $N(A^T)$ is the subspace of $\mathbb{R}^3$ spanned by $(-1, -2, 1)^T$. Note that $(-1, -2, 1)^T$ is orthogonal to $(1, 0, 1)^T$ and $(0, 1, 2)^T$. ∎

We saw in Chapter 3 that the row space and the column space have the same dimension. If A has rank r, then

$$\dim R(A) = \dim R(A^T) = r$$

Actually, A can be used to establish a one-to-one correspondence between $R(A^T)$ and $R(A)$.

We can think of an $m \times n$ matrix A as a linear transformation from $\mathbb{R}^n$ to $\mathbb{R}^m$:

$$\mathbf{x} \in \mathbb{R}^n \rightarrow A\mathbf{x} \in \mathbb{R}^m$$

Since $R(A^T)$ and $N(A)$ are orthogonal complements in $\mathbb{R}^n$,

$$\mathbb{R}^n = R(A^T) \oplus N(A)$$

Each vector $\mathbf{x} \in \mathbb{R}^n$ can be written as a sum

$$\mathbf{x} = \mathbf{y} + \mathbf{z}, \qquad \mathbf{y} \in R(A^T), \qquad \mathbf{z} \in N(A)$$

It follows that

$$A\mathbf{x} = A\mathbf{y} + A\mathbf{z} = A\mathbf{y} \qquad \text{for each } \mathbf{x} \in \mathbb{R}^n$$

and hence

$$R(A) = \left\{ A\mathbf{x} \mid \mathbf{x} \in \mathbb{R}^n \right\} = \left\{ A\mathbf{y} \mid \mathbf{y} \in R(A^T) \right\}$$

Thus, if we restrict the domain of A to $R(A^T)$, then A maps $R(A^T)$ onto $R(A)$. Furthermore, the mapping is one-to-one. Indeed, if $\mathbf{x}_1, \mathbf{x}_2 \in R(A^T)$ and

$$A\mathbf{x}_1 = A\mathbf{x}_2$$

then

$$A(\mathbf{x}_1 - \mathbf{x}_2) = \mathbf{0}$$

and hence

$$\mathbf{x}_1 - \mathbf{x}_2 \in R(A^T) \cap N(A)$$

Since $R(A^T) \cap N(A) = \{\mathbf{0}\}$, it follows that $\mathbf{x}_1 = \mathbf{x}_2$. Therefore, we can think of A as determining a one-to-one correspondence between $R(A^T)$ and $R(A)$. Since each $\mathbf{b} \in R(A)$ corresponds to exactly one $\mathbf{y} \in R(A^T)$, we can define an inverse transformation from $R(A)$ to $R(A^T)$. Indeed, every $m \times n$ matrix A is invertible when viewed as a linear transformation from $R(A^T)$ to $R(A)$.

EXAMPLE 5   Let $A = \begin{bmatrix} 2 & 0 & 0 \\ 0 & 3 & 0 \end{bmatrix}$. $R(A^T)$ is spanned by e_1 and e_2, and $N(A)$ is spanned by e_3. Any vector $\mathbf{x} \in \mathbb{R}^3$ can be written as a sum

$$\mathbf{x} = \mathbf{y} + \mathbf{z}$$

where

$$\mathbf{y} = (x_1, x_2, 0)^T \in R(A^T) \qquad \text{and} \qquad \mathbf{z} = (0, 0, x_3)^T \in N(A)$$

If we restrict ourselves to vectors $\mathbf{y} \in R(A^T)$, then

$$\mathbf{y} = \begin{bmatrix} x_1 \\ x_2 \\ 0 \end{bmatrix} \rightarrow A\mathbf{y} = \begin{bmatrix} 2x_1 \\ 3x_2 \end{bmatrix}$$

In this case, $R(A) = \mathbb{R}^2$ and the inverse transformation from $R(A)$ to $R(A^T)$ is defined by

$$\mathbf{b} = \begin{bmatrix} b_1 \\ b_2 \end{bmatrix} \rightarrow \begin{bmatrix} \frac{1}{2} b_1 \\ \frac{1}{3} b_2 \\ 0 \end{bmatrix}$$ ∎

SECTION 5.2 EXERCISES

1. For each of the following matrices, determine a basis for each of the subspaces $R(A^T)$, $N(A)$, $R(A)$, and $N(A^T)$.

 (a) $A = \begin{bmatrix} 3 & 4 \\ 6 & 8 \end{bmatrix}$ (b) $A = \begin{bmatrix} 1 & 3 & 1 \\ 2 & 4 & 0 \end{bmatrix}$

 (c) $A = \begin{bmatrix} 4 & -2 \\ 1 & 3 \\ 2 & 1 \\ 3 & 4 \end{bmatrix}$ (d) $A = \begin{bmatrix} 1 & 0 & 0 & 0 \\ 0 & 1 & 1 & 1 \\ 0 & 0 & 1 & 1 \\ 1 & 1 & 2 & 2 \end{bmatrix}$

2. Let S be the subspace of $\mathbb{R}^3$ spanned by $\mathbf{x} = (1, -1, 1)^T$.

 (a) Find a basis for $S^{\perp}$.

 (b) Give a geometrical description of S and $S^{\perp}$.

3. (a) Let S be the subspace of $\mathbb{R}^3$ spanned by the vectors $\mathbf{x} = (x_1, x_2, x_3)^T$ and $\mathbf{y} = (y_1, y_2, y_3)^T$. Let

$$A = \begin{bmatrix} x_1 & x_2 & x_3 \\ y_1 & y_2 & y_3 \end{bmatrix}$$

 Show that $S^{\perp} = N(A)$.

 (b) Find the orthogonal complement of the subspace of $\mathbb{R}^3$ spanned by $(1, 2, 1)^T$ and $(1, -1, 2)^T$.

4. Let S be the subspace of $\mathbb{R}^4$ spanned by $\mathbf{x}_1 = (1, 0, -2, 1)^T$ and $\mathbf{x}_2 = (0, 1, 3, -2)^T$. Find a basis for $S^{\perp}$.

5. Let A be a 3×2 matrix with rank 2. Give geometric descriptions of $R(A)$ and $N(A^T)$, and describe geometrically how the subspaces are related.

6. Is it possible for a matrix to have the vector $(3, 1, 2)$ in its row space and $(2, 1, 1)^T$ in its null space? Explain.

7. Let $\mathbf{a}_j$ be a nonzero column vector of an $m \times n$ matrix A. Is it possible for $\mathbf{a}_j$ to be in $N(A^T)$? Explain.

8. Let S be the subspace of $\mathbb{R}^n$ spanned by the vectors $\mathbf{x}_1, \mathbf{x}_2, \ldots, \mathbf{x}_k$. Show that $\mathbf{y} \in S^{\perp}$ if and only if $\mathbf{y} \perp \mathbf{x}_i$ for $i = 1, \ldots, k$.

9. If A is an $m \times n$ matrix of rank r, what are the dimensions of $N(A)$ and $N(A^T)$? Explain.

10. Prove Corollary 5.2.5.

11. Prove: If A is an $m \times n$ matrix and $\mathbf{x} \in \mathbb{R}^n$, then either $A\mathbf{x} = \mathbf{0}$ or there exists $\mathbf{y} \in R(A^T)$ such that $\mathbf{x}^T \mathbf{y} \neq 0$. Draw a picture similar to Figure 5.2.2 to illustrate this result geometrically for the case where $N(A)$ is a two-dimensional subspace of $\mathbb{R}^3$.

12. Let A be an $m \times n$ matrix. Explain why the following are true.

   (a) Any vector $\mathbf{x}$ in $\mathbb{R}^n$ can be uniquely written as a sum $\mathbf{y} + \mathbf{z}$, where $\mathbf{y} \in N(A)$ and $\mathbf{z} \in R(A^T)$.

   (b) Any vector $\mathbf{b} \in \mathbb{R}^m$ can be uniquely written as a sum $\mathbf{u} + \mathbf{v}$, where $\mathbf{u} \in N(A^T)$ and $\mathbf{v} \in R(A)$.

13. Let A be an $m \times n$ matrix. Show that

   (a) if $\mathbf{x} \in N(A^TA)$, then $A\mathbf{x}$ is in both $R(A)$ and $N(A^T)$.

   (b) $N(A^TA) = N(A)$.

   (c) A and A^TA have the same rank.

   (d) if A has linearly independent columns, then A^TA is nonsingular.

14. Let A be an $m \times n$ matrix, B an $n \times r$ matrix, and $C = AB$. Show that

   (a) $N(B)$ is a subspace of $N(C)$.

   (b) $N(C)^{\perp}$ is a subspace of $N(B)^{\perp}$ and, consequently, $R(C^T)$ is a subspace of $R(B^T)$.

15. Let U and V be subspaces of a vector space W. Show that if $W = U \oplus V$, then $U \cap V = \{\mathbf{0}\}$.

16. Let A be an $m \times n$ matrix of rank r and let $\{\mathbf{x}_1, \ldots, \mathbf{x}_r\}$ be a basis for $R(A^T)$. Show that $\{A\mathbf{x}_1, \ldots, A\mathbf{x}_r\}$ is a basis for $R(A)$.

17. Let $\mathbf{x}$ and $\mathbf{y}$ be linearly independent vectors in $\mathbb{R}^n$ and let $S = \text{Span}(\mathbf{x}, \mathbf{y})$. We can use $\mathbf{x}$ and $\mathbf{y}$ to define a matrix A by setting

$$A = \mathbf{xy}^T + \mathbf{yx}^T$$

   (a) Show that A is symmetric.

   (b) Show that $N(A) = S^{\perp}$.

   (c) Show that the rank of A must be 2.

5.3   Least Squares Problems

A standard technique in mathematical and statistical modeling is to find a *least squares* fit to a set of data points in the plane. The least squares curve is usually the graph of a standard type of function, such as a linear function, a polynomial, or a trigonometric polynomial. Since the data may include errors in measurement or experiment-related inaccuracies, we do not require the curve to pass through all the data points. Instead, we require the curve to provide an optimal approximation in the sense that the sum of squares of errors between the y values of the data points and the corresponding y values of the approximating curve are minimized.

The technique of least squares was developed independently by Adrien-Marie Legendre and Carl Friedrich Gauss. The first paper on the subject was published by Legendre in 1806, although there is clear evidence that Gauss had discovered it as a student nine years prior to Legendre's paper and had used the method to do astronomical calculations. Figure 5.3.1 is a portrait of Gauss.

Pearson Education, Inc.

Figure 5.3.1. Carl Friedrich Gauss

On January 1, 1801, the Italian astronomer Giuseppe Piazzi discovered the asteroid Ceres. He was able to track the asteroid for six weeks, but it was lost due to interference caused by the sun. A number of leading astronomers published papers predicting the orbit of the asteroid. Gauss also published a forecast, but his predicted orbit differed considerably from the others. Ceres was relocated by one observer on December 7 and by another on January 1, 1802. In both cases, the position was very close to that predicted by Gauss. Gauss won instant fame in astronomical circles and for a time was more well known as an astronomer than as a mathematician. The key to his success was the use of the method of least squares.

Least Squares Solutions of Overdetermined Systems

A least squares problem can generally be formulated as an overdetermined linear system of equations. Recall that an overdetermined system is one involving more equations than unknowns. Such systems are usually inconsistent. Thus, given an $m \times n$ system $A\mathbf{x} = \mathbf{b}$ with $m > n$, we cannot expect in general to find a vector $\mathbf{x} \in \mathbb{R}^n$ for which $A\mathbf{x}$ equals $\mathbf{b}$. Instead, we can look for a vector $\mathbf{x}$ for which $A\mathbf{x}$ is "closest" to $\mathbf{b}$. As you might expect, orthogonality plays an important role in finding such an $\mathbf{x}$.

If we are given a system of equations $A\mathbf{x} = \mathbf{b}$, where A is an $m \times n$ matrix with $m > n$ and $\mathbf{b} \in \mathbb{R}^m$, then, for each $\mathbf{x} \in \mathbb{R}^n$, we can form a *residual*

$$r(\mathbf{x}) = \mathbf{b} - A\mathbf{x}$$

The distance between $\mathbf{b}$ and $A\mathbf{x}$ is given by

$$\|\mathbf{b} - A\mathbf{x}\| = \|r(\mathbf{x})\|$$

We wish to find a vector $\mathbf{x} \in \mathbb{R}^n$ for which $\|r(\mathbf{x})\|$ will be a minimum. Minimizing $\|r(\mathbf{x})\|$ is equivalent to minimizing $\|r(\mathbf{x})\|^2$. A vector $\hat{\mathbf{x}}$ that accomplishes this is said to be a *least squares solution* of the system $A\mathbf{x} = \mathbf{b}$.

If $\hat{\mathbf{x}}$ is a least squares solution of the system $A\mathbf{x} = \mathbf{b}$ and $\mathbf{p} = A\hat{\mathbf{x}}$, then $\mathbf{p}$ is a vector in the column space of A that is closest to $\mathbf{b}$. The next theorem guarantees that such a closest vector $\mathbf{p}$ not only exists, but is unique. Additionally, it provides an important characterization of the closest vector.

Theorem 5.3.1   *Let S be a subspace of $\mathbb{R}^m$. For each $\mathbf{b} \in \mathbb{R}^m$, there is a unique element $\mathbf{p}$ of S that is closest to $\mathbf{b}$; that is,*

$$\|\mathbf{b} - \mathbf{y}\| > \|\mathbf{b} - \mathbf{p}\|$$

for any $\mathbf{y} \neq \mathbf{p}$ in S. Furthermore, a given vector $\mathbf{p}$ in S will be closest to a given vector $\mathbf{b} \in \mathbb{R}^m$ if and only if $\mathbf{b} - \mathbf{p} \in S^{\perp}$.

Proof   Since $\mathbb{R}^m = S \oplus S^{\perp}$, each element $\mathbf{b}$ in $\mathbb{R}^m$ can be expressed uniquely as a sum

$$\mathbf{b} = \mathbf{p} + \mathbf{z}$$

where $\mathbf{p} \in S$ and $\mathbf{z} \in S^{\perp}$. If $\mathbf{y}$ is any other element of S, then

$$\|\mathbf{b} - \mathbf{y}\|^2 = \|(\mathbf{b} - \mathbf{p}) + (\mathbf{p} - \mathbf{y})\|^2$$

Since $\mathbf{p} - \mathbf{y} \in S$ and $\mathbf{b} - \mathbf{p} = \mathbf{z} \in S^{\perp}$, it follows from the Pythagorean law that

$$\|\mathbf{b} - \mathbf{y}\|^2 = \|\mathbf{b} - \mathbf{p}\|^2 + \|\mathbf{p} - \mathbf{y}\|^2$$

Therefore,

$$\|\mathbf{b} - \mathbf{y}\| > \|\mathbf{b} - \mathbf{p}\|$$

Thus, if $\mathbf{p} \in S$ and $\mathbf{b} - \mathbf{p} \in S^{\perp}$, then $\mathbf{p}$ is the element of S that is closest to $\mathbf{b}$. Conversely, if $\mathbf{q} \in S$ and $\mathbf{b} - \mathbf{q} \notin S^{\perp}$, then $\mathbf{q} \neq \mathbf{p}$, and it follows from the preceding argument (with $\mathbf{y} = \mathbf{q}$) that

$$\|\mathbf{b} - \mathbf{q}\| > \|\mathbf{b} - \mathbf{p}\|$$ ∎

In the special case that $\mathbf{b}$ is in the subspace S to begin with, we have

$$\mathbf{b} = \mathbf{p} + \mathbf{z}, \qquad \mathbf{p} \in S, \quad \mathbf{z} \in S^{\perp}$$

and

$$\mathbf{b} = \mathbf{b} + \mathbf{0}$$

By the uniqueness of the direct sum representation,

$$\mathbf{p} = \mathbf{b} \quad \text{and} \quad \mathbf{z} = \mathbf{0}$$

A vector $\hat{\mathbf{x}}$ will be a solution of the least squares problem $A\mathbf{x} = \mathbf{b}$ if and only if $\mathbf{p} = A\hat{\mathbf{x}}$ is the vector in $R(A)$ that is closest to $\mathbf{b}$. The vector $\mathbf{p}$ is said to be the *projection of $\mathbf{b}$ onto $R(A)$*. It follows from Theorem 5.3.1 that

$$\mathbf{b} - \mathbf{p} = \mathbf{b} - A\hat{\mathbf{x}} = r(\hat{\mathbf{x}})$$

must be an element of $R(A)^{\perp}$. Thus, $\hat{\mathbf{x}}$ is a solution of the least squares problem if and only if

$$r(\hat{\mathbf{x}}) \in R(A)^{\perp} \tag{1}$$

(see Figure 5.3.2).

(a) $\mathbf{b} \in R^2$ and A is a 2×1 matrix of rank 1.   (b) $\mathbf{b} \in R^2$ and A is a 3×2 matrix of rank 2.

Figure 5.3.2.

How do we find a vector $\hat{\mathbf{x}}$ satisfying (1)? The key to solving the least squares problem is provided by Theorem 5.2.1, which states that

$$R(A)^{\perp} = N(A^T)$$

A vector $\hat{\mathbf{x}}$ will be a least squares solution to the system $A\mathbf{x} = \mathbf{b}$ if and only if

$$r(\hat{\mathbf{x}}) \in N(A^T)$$

or, equivalently,

$$\mathbf{0} = A^T r(\hat{\mathbf{x}}) = A^T(\mathbf{b} - A\hat{\mathbf{x}})$$

Thus, to solve the least squares problem $A\mathbf{x} = \mathbf{b}$, we must solve

$$A^T A\mathbf{x} = A^T\mathbf{b} \tag{2}$$

Equation (2) represents an $n \times n$ system of linear equations. These equations are called the *normal equations*. In general, it is possible to have more than one solution of the normal equations; however, if $\hat{\mathbf{x}}$ and $\hat{\mathbf{y}}$ are both solutions, then, since the projection $\mathbf{p}$ of $\mathbf{b}$ onto $R(A)$ is unique,

$$A\hat{\mathbf{x}} = A\hat{\mathbf{y}} = \mathbf{p}$$

The following theorem characterizes the conditions under which the least squares problem $A\mathbf{x} = \mathbf{b}$ will have a unique solution.

Theorem 5.3.2 *If A is an $m \times n$ matrix of rank n, the normal equations*

$$A^T A\mathbf{x} = A^T\mathbf{b}$$

have a unique solution

$$\hat{\mathbf{x}} = (A^T A)^{-1} A^T\mathbf{b}$$

and $\hat{\mathbf{x}}$ is the unique least squares solution of the system $A\mathbf{x} = \mathbf{b}$.

Proof We will first show that $A^T A$ is nonsingular. To prove this, let $\mathbf{z}$ be a solution of

$$A^T A\mathbf{x} = \mathbf{0} \tag{3}$$

Then $A\mathbf{z} \in N(A^T)$. Clearly, $A\mathbf{z} \in R(A) = N(A^T)^{\perp}$. Since $N(A^T) \cap N(A^T)^{\perp} = \{\mathbf{0}\}$, it follows that $A\mathbf{z} = \mathbf{0}$. If A has rank n, the column vectors of A are linearly independent and, consequently, $A\mathbf{x} = \mathbf{0}$ has only the trivial solution. Thus, $\mathbf{z} = \mathbf{0}$ and (3) has only the trivial solution. Therefore, by Theorem 1.5.2, $A^T A$ is nonsingular. It follows that $\hat{\mathbf{x}} = (A^T A)^{-1} A^T\mathbf{b}$ is the unique solution of the normal equations and, consequently, the unique least squares solution of the system $A\mathbf{x} = \mathbf{b}$. ∎

The projection vector

$$\mathbf{p} = A\hat{\mathbf{x}} = A(A^T A)^{-1} A^T\mathbf{b}$$

is the element of $R(A)$ that is closest to $\mathbf{b}$ in the least squares sense. The matrix $P = A(A^T A)^{-1} A^T$ is called the *projection matrix*.

APPLICATION 2 Spring Constants

Hooke's law states that the force applied to a spring is proportional to the distance that the spring is stretched. Thus, if F is the force applied and x is the distance that the spring has been stretched, then $F = kx$. The proportionality constant k is called the *spring constant*.

Some physics students want to determine the spring constant for a given spring. They apply forces of 3, 5, and 8 pounds, which have the effect of stretching the spring

4, 7, and 11 inches, respectively. Using Hooke's law, they derive the following system of equations:

$$4k = 3$$
$$7k = 5$$
$$11k = 8$$

The system is clearly inconsistent, since each equation yields a different value of k. Rather than use any one of these values, the students decide to compute the least squares solution of the system.

$$(4, 7, 11) \begin{bmatrix} 4 \\ 7 \\ 11 \end{bmatrix} (k) = (4, 7, 11) \begin{bmatrix} 3 \\ 5 \\ 8 \end{bmatrix}$$
$$186k = 135$$
$$k \approx 0.726$$

EXAMPLE 1 Find the least squares solution of the system

$$x_1 + x_2 = 3$$
$$-2x_1 + 3x_2 = 1$$
$$2x_1 - x_2 = 2$$

Solution

The normal equations for this system are

$$\begin{bmatrix} 1 & -2 & 2 \\ 1 & 3 & -1 \end{bmatrix} \begin{bmatrix} 1 & 1 \\ -2 & 3 \\ 2 & -1 \end{bmatrix} \begin{bmatrix} x_1 \\ x_2 \end{bmatrix} = \begin{bmatrix} 1 & -2 & 2 \\ 1 & 3 & -1 \end{bmatrix} \begin{bmatrix} 3 \\ 1 \\ 2 \end{bmatrix}$$

This simplifies to the 2×2 system

$$\begin{bmatrix} 9 & -7 \\ -7 & 11 \end{bmatrix} \begin{bmatrix} x_1 \\ x_2 \end{bmatrix} = \begin{bmatrix} 5 \\ 4 \end{bmatrix}$$

The solution of the 2×2 system is $\left(\frac{83}{50}, \frac{71}{50} \right)^T$. ∎

Scientists often collect data and try to find a functional relationship among the variables. For example, the data may involve temperatures $T_0, T_1, \ldots, T_n$ of a liquid measured at times $t_0, t_1, \ldots, t_n$, respectively. If the temperature T can be represented as a function of the time t, this function can be used to predict the temperatures at future times. If the data consist of $n + 1$ points in the plane, it is possible to find a polynomial of degree n or less passing through all the points. Such a polynomial is called an *interpolating polynomial*. Actually, since the data usually involve experimental error, there is no reason to require that the function pass through all the points. Indeed, lower degree polynomials that do not pass through the points exactly usually give a truer description of the relationship between the variables. If, for example, the relationship between the variables is actually linear and the data involve slight errors, it would be disastrous to use an interpolating polynomial (see Figure 5.3.3).

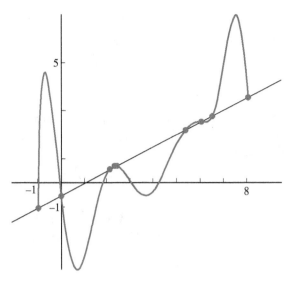

x	−1.00	0.00	2.10	2.30	2.40	5.30	6.00	6.50	8.00
y	−1.02	−0.52	0.55	0.70	0.70	2.13	2.52	2.82	3.54

Figure 5.3.3.

Given a table of data

x	x_1	x_2	$\cdots$	x_m
y	y_1	y_2	$\cdots$	y_m

we wish to find a linear function

$$y = c_0 + c_1 x$$

that best fits the data in the least squares sense. If we require that

$$y_i = c_0 + c_1 x_i \qquad \text{for} \qquad i = 1, \ldots, m$$

we get a system of m equations in two unknowns.

$$\begin{bmatrix} 1 & x_1 \\ 1 & x_2 \\ \vdots & \vdots \\ 1 & x_m \end{bmatrix} \begin{bmatrix} c_0 \\ c_1 \end{bmatrix} = \begin{bmatrix} y_1 \\ y_2 \\ \vdots \\ y_m \end{bmatrix} \tag{4}$$

The linear function whose coefficients are the least squares solution of (4) is said to be the best least squares fit to the data by a linear function.

EXAMPLE 2   Given the data

x	0	3	6
y	1	4	5

find the best least squares fit by a linear function.

Solution

For this example, the system (4) becomes

$$A\mathbf{c} = \mathbf{y}$$

where

$$A = \begin{bmatrix} 1 & 0 \\ 1 & 3 \\ 1 & 6 \end{bmatrix}, \quad \mathbf{c} = \begin{bmatrix} c_0 \\ c_1 \end{bmatrix}, \quad \text{and} \quad \mathbf{y} = \begin{bmatrix} 1 \\ 4 \\ 5 \end{bmatrix}$$

The normal equations

$$A^T A \mathbf{c} = A^T \mathbf{y}$$

simplify to

$$\begin{bmatrix} 3 & 9 \\ 9 & 45 \end{bmatrix} \begin{bmatrix} c_0 \\ c_1 \end{bmatrix} = \begin{bmatrix} 10 \\ 42 \end{bmatrix} \tag{5}$$

The solution of this system is $\left(\frac{4}{3}, \frac{2}{3}\right)$. Thus, the best linear least squares fit is given by

$$y = \tfrac{4}{3} + \tfrac{2}{3}x \qquad \blacksquare$$

Example 2 could also have been solved using calculus. The residual $r(\mathbf{c})$ is given by

$$r(\mathbf{c}) = \mathbf{y} - A\mathbf{c}$$

and

$$\begin{aligned} \|r(\mathbf{c})\|^2 &= \|\mathbf{y} - A\mathbf{c}\|^2 \\ &= [1 - (c_0 + 0c_1)]^2 + [4 - (c_0 + 3c_1)]^2 + [5 - (c_0 + 6c_1)]^2 \\ &= f(c_0, c_1) \end{aligned}$$

Thus, $\|r(\mathbf{c})\|^2$ can be thought of as a function of two variables, $f(c_0, c_1)$. The minimum of this function will occur when its partial derivatives are zero:

$$\frac{\partial f}{\partial c_0} = -2(10 - 3c_0 - 9c_1) = 0$$

$$\frac{\partial f}{\partial c_1} = -6(14 - 3c_0 - 15c_1) = 0$$

Dividing both equations through by -2 gives the same system as (5) (see Figure 5.3.4).

If the data do not resemble a linear function, we could use a higher degree polynomial. To find the coefficients $c_0, c_1, \ldots, c_n$ of the best least squares fit to the data

x	x_1	x_2	$\cdots$	x_m
y	y_1	y_2	$\cdots$	y_m

by a polynomial of degree n, we must find the least squares solution the system:

$$\begin{bmatrix} 1 & x_1 & x_1^2 & \cdots & x_1^n \\ 1 & x_2 & x_2^2 & \cdots & x_2^n \\ \vdots & & & & \\ 1 & x_m & x_m^2 & \cdots & x_m^n \end{bmatrix} \begin{bmatrix} c_0 \\ c_1 \\ \vdots \\ c_n \end{bmatrix} = \begin{bmatrix} y_1 \\ y_2 \\ \vdots \\ y_m \end{bmatrix} \tag{6}$$

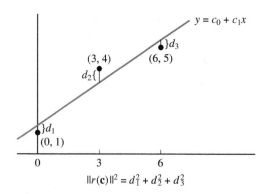

$$\|r(\mathbf{c})\|^2 = d_1^2 + d_2^2 + d_3^2$$

Figure 5.3.4.

EXAMPLE 3   Find the best quadratic least squares fit to the data

x	0	1	2	3
y	3	2	4	4

Solution

For this example, the system (6) becomes

$$\begin{pmatrix} 1 & 0 & 0 \\ 1 & 1 & 1 \\ 1 & 2 & 4 \\ 1 & 3 & 9 \end{pmatrix} \begin{pmatrix} c_0 \\ c_1 \\ c_2 \end{pmatrix} = \begin{pmatrix} 3 \\ 2 \\ 4 \\ 4 \end{pmatrix}$$

Thus, the normal equations are

$$\begin{pmatrix} 1 & 1 & 1 & 1 \\ 0 & 1 & 2 & 3 \\ 0 & 1 & 4 & 9 \end{pmatrix} \begin{pmatrix} 1 & 0 & 0 \\ 1 & 1 & 1 \\ 1 & 2 & 4 \\ 1 & 3 & 9 \end{pmatrix} \begin{pmatrix} c_0 \\ c_1 \\ c_2 \end{pmatrix} = \begin{pmatrix} 1 & 1 & 1 & 1 \\ 0 & 1 & 2 & 3 \\ 0 & 1 & 4 & 9 \end{pmatrix} \begin{pmatrix} 3 \\ 2 \\ 4 \\ 4 \end{pmatrix}$$

These simplify to

$$\begin{pmatrix} 4 & 6 & 14 \\ 6 & 14 & 36 \\ 14 & 36 & 98 \end{pmatrix} \begin{pmatrix} c_0 \\ c_1 \\ c_2 \end{pmatrix} = \begin{pmatrix} 13 \\ 22 \\ 54 \end{pmatrix}$$

The solution of this system is $(2.75, -0.25, 0.25)$. The quadratic polynomial that gives the best least squares fit to the data is

$$p(x) = 2.75 - 0.25x + 0.25x^2$$ ∎

APPLICATION 3   Coordinate Metrology

Many manufactured goods, such as rods, disks, and pipes, are circular in shape. A company will often employ quality control engineers to test whether items produced on the production line are meeting industrial standards. Sensing machines are used to record the coordinates of points on the perimeter of the manufactured products. To determine

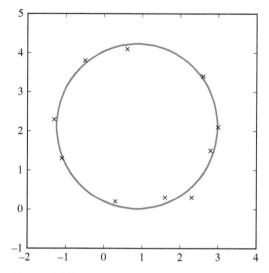

x	y
3.0	2.1
2.6	3.4
0.6	4.1
−0.5	3.8
−1.3	2.3
−1.1	1.3
0.3	0.2
1.6	0.3
2.3	0.3
2.8	1.5

Figure 5.3.5.

how close these points are to being circular, we can fit a least squares circle to the data and check to see how close the measured points are to the circle. (See Figure 5.3.5.)

To fit a circle

$$(x - c_1)^2 + (y - c_2)^2 = r^2 \tag{7}$$

to n sample pairs of coordinates $(x_1, y_1), (x_2, y_2), \ldots, (x_n, y_n)$, we must determine the center (c_1, c_2) and the radius r. Rewriting equation (7), we get

$$2xc_1 + 2yc_2 + (r^2 - c_1^2 - c_2^2) = x^2 + y^2$$

If we set $c_3 = r^2 - c_1^2 - c_2^2$, then the equation takes the form

$$2xc_1 + 2yc_2 + c_3 = x^2 + y^2$$

Substituting each of the data points into this equation, we obtain the overdetermined system

$$\begin{bmatrix} 2x_1 & 2y_1 & 1 \\ 2x_2 & 2y_2 & 1 \\ \vdots & \vdots & \vdots \\ 2x_n & 2y_n & 1 \end{bmatrix} \begin{bmatrix} c_1 \\ c_2 \\ c_3 \end{bmatrix} = \begin{bmatrix} x_1^2 + y_1^2 \\ x_2^2 + y_2^2 \\ \vdots \\ x_n^2 + y_n^2 \end{bmatrix}$$

Once we find the least squares solution $\mathbf{c}$, the center of the least squares circle is (c_1, c_2), and the radius is determined by setting

$$r = \sqrt{c_3 + c_1^2 + c_2^2}$$

To measure how close the sampled points are to the circle, we can form a residual vector $\mathbf{r}$ by setting

$$r_i = r^2 - (x_i - c_1)^2 - (y_i - c_2)^2 \quad i = 1, \ldots, n$$

We can then use $\|\mathbf{r}\|$ as a measure of how close the points are to the circle.

APPLICATION 4   Management Science: The Analytic Hierarchy Process Revisited

In Section 1.3, we looked at an example of how one can use the analytic hierarchy process from management science as a tool for making hiring decisions in a mathematics department. The process involves selecting the criteria upon which the decision is based and assigning weights to the criteria. In the example, hiring decisions were based on rating the candidates in the areas of Research, Teaching, and Professional Activities. For each of these areas, the committee assigned weights to all of candidates. The weights are measurements of the relative strengths of the candidates in each area. Once all of the weights have been assigned, the overall ranking of the candidates can be determined by multiplying a matrix times a vector.

The key to the whole process is the assignment of weights. In our example, the evaluation of teaching will involve qualitative judgments by the search committee. These judgments must then be translated into weights. The evaluation of research can be both quantitative based on the number of pages the candidates have published in journals and qualitative based on the quality of the papers published. A standard technique for determining weights based on qualitative judgments is to first make pairwise comparisons between the candidates, and then use those comparisons to determine weights. The method we describe here leads to an overdetermined linear system. We will compute the weights by finding the least squares solution to the system.

Later in Chapter 6 (Section 8), we will examine an alternative "eigenvector" method that is commonly used to determine weights based on pairwise comparisons. In that method, one forms a comparison matrix C whose (i, j) entry represents the weight of the ith characteristic or alternative relative to the jth characteristic or alternative. The method depends upon an important theorem about positive matrices (i.e., matrices whose entries are all positive real numbers) that we will study in Section 6.8. The "eigenvector" method was recommended by T. L. Saaty, the developer of the analytic hierarchy process theory.

For our search example, the committee assigned weights for the three criteria based on the qualitative judgments that Teaching and Research were equally important and that both were twice as important as Professional Activities. To reflect these judgments the weights w_1, w_2, w_3 for Research, Teaching, and Professional Activities must satisfy,

$$w_1 = w_2, \quad w_1 = 2w_3, \quad w_2 = 2w_3$$

Additionally, the weights must all add up to 1. Thus, the weights must be solutions to the system

$$w_1 - w_2 + 0w_3 = 0$$
$$w_1 + 0w_2 - 2w_3 = 0$$
$$0w_1 + w_2 - 2w_3 = 0$$
$$w_1 + w_2 + w_3 = 1$$

Although the system is overdetermined, it does have a unique solution $\mathbf{w} = (0.4, 0.4, 0.2)^T$. Usually, overdetermined systems turn out to be inconsistent. In fact, had the committee used four criteria and made pairwise comparisons based on their human judgments, it is quite likely that the system they would end up with (seven equations and four unknowns) would be inconsistent. For an inconsistent system, one could determine weights that add up to 1 by finding the least squares solution to a linear system. We illustrate how this is done in the next example.

EXAMPLE 4   Suppose the search committee for the mathematics position has narrowed the field down to four candidates: Dr. Gauss, Dr. Ipsen, Dr. O'Leary, and Dr. Taussky. To determine the weights for research, the committee decides to evaluate both the quantity and quality of the publications. The committee feels that quality is more important than quantity so in comparing the two, they give quantity of publications a weight of 0.4 and quality a weight of 0.6. The hierarchy structure of the decision process is shown in Figure 5.3.6. All of the weights computed by the committee are included in the figure. We will examine how the weights for quantity and quality of publications were determined and then combine all of the weights in the figure to calculate a vector **r** containing the overall ratings of the candidates.

The quantitative research weights are computed by taking the number of pages published by a candidate and dividing by the total number of pages published by all candidates combined. These weights are given in Table 5.3.1.

Table 5.3.1   Quantity of Research Weights

Candidate	Pages	Weights
Gauss	700	0.35
Ipsen	400	0.20
O'Leary	500	0.25
Taussky	400	0.20
Total	2000	1.00

Figure 5.3.6.   Analytic Hierarchy Process Chart

To rate the quality of research, the committee did comparisons of the quality of publications for each pair of candidates. If for a particular pair the quality was rated equal, then the candidates were given equal weights. It was agreed that no candidate would receive a quality weight that was more than twice the rate of another candidate. Thus, if candidate i had more impressive publications than candidate j, then weights would be assigned so that

$$w_i = \beta w_j \ \text{ or } \ w_j = \frac{1}{\beta}w_i \ \text{ where } \ 1 < \beta \le 2$$

After studying the publications of all the candidates, the committee agreed upon the following pairwise comparisons of the weights:

$$w_1 = 1.75w_2, \ w_1 = 1.5w_3, \ w_1 = 1.25w_4, \ w_2 = 0.75w_3, \ w_2 = 0.50w_4, \ w_3 = 0.75w_4$$

These conditions lead to the linear system

$$
\begin{aligned}
1w_1 - 1.75w_2 + 0w_3 + 0w_4 &= 0 \\
1w_1 + 0w_2 - 1.5w_3 + 0w_4 &= 0 \\
1w_1 + 0w_2 + 0w_3 - 1.25w_4 &= 0 \\
0w_1 + 1w_2 - 0.75w_3 + 0w_4 &= 0 \\
0w_1 + 1w_2 + 0w_3 - 0.50w_4 &= 0 \\
0w_1 + 0w_2 + 1w_3 - 0.75w_4 &= 0
\end{aligned}
$$

For our solution $\mathbf{w}$ to be a weight vector, its entries must add up to 1.

$$w_1 + w_2 + w_3 + w_4 = 1$$

Given that the AHP weights must satisfy this last equation exactly, we can solve for w_4:

$$w_4 = 1 - w_1 - w_2 - w_3 \tag{8}$$

and rewrite the other equations to form a 6×3 system

$$
\begin{aligned}
1w_1 - 1.75w_2 + 0w_3 &= 0 \\
1w_1 + 0w_2 - 1.5w_3 &= 0 \\
2.25w_1 + 1.25w_2 + 1.25w_3 &= 1.25 \\
0w_1 + 1w_2 - 0.75w_3 &= 0 \\
0.5w_1 + 1.5w_2 + 0.5w_3 &= 0.5 \\
0.75w_1 + 0.75w_2 + 1.75w_3 &= 0.75
\end{aligned}
$$

Although this system is inconsistent, it does have a unique least squares solution $w_1 = 0.3289$, $w_2 = 0.1739$, $w_3 = 0.2188$. It follows from equation (8) that $w_4 = 0.2784$.

The final step in our decision process is to combine the rating vectors from the categories and subcategories of evaluation. We multiply each of these vectors by the appropriate weight given in the chart and then combine them to form the overall rating vector $\mathbf{r}$.

$$
\mathbf{r} = 0.40 \left[0.40 \begin{Bmatrix} 0.35 \\ 0.20 \\ 0.25 \\ 0.20 \end{Bmatrix} + 0.60 \begin{Bmatrix} 0.3289 \\ 0.1739 \\ 0.2188 \\ 0.2784 \end{Bmatrix} \right] + 0.40 \begin{Bmatrix} 0.21 \\ 0.29 \\ 0.33 \\ 0.17 \end{Bmatrix} + 0.20 \begin{Bmatrix} 0.23 \\ 0.28 \\ 0.28 \\ 0.21 \end{Bmatrix}
$$

$$
= 0.40 \begin{Bmatrix} 0.3373 \\ 0.1843 \\ 0.2313 \\ 0.2470 \end{Bmatrix} + 0.40 \begin{Bmatrix} 0.21 \\ 0.29 \\ 0.33 \\ 0.17 \end{Bmatrix} + 0.20 \begin{Bmatrix} 0.23 \\ 0.28 \\ 0.28 \\ 0.21 \end{Bmatrix} = \begin{Bmatrix} 0.2649 \\ 0.2457 \\ 0.2805 \\ 0.2088 \end{Bmatrix}
$$

The candidate with the highest rating is O'Leary. Gauss comes in second. Ipsen and Taussky are third and fourth, respectively. ∎

SECTION 5.3 EXERCISES

1. Find the least squares solution of each of the following systems:

   (a) $\begin{aligned} x_1 + x_2 &= 3 \\ 2x_1 - 3x_2 &= 1 \\ 0x_1 + 0x_2 &= 2 \end{aligned}$ (b) $\begin{aligned} -x_1 + x_2 &= 10 \\ 2x_1 + x_2 &= 5 \\ x_1 - 2x_2 &= 20 \end{aligned}$

   (c) $\begin{aligned} x_1 + x_2 + x_3 &= 4 \\ -x_1 + x_2 + x_3 &= 0 \\ - x_2 + x_3 &= 1 \\ x_1 \qquad + x_3 &= 2 \end{aligned}$

2. For each of your solutions $\hat{\mathbf{x}}$ in Exercise 1:
   (a) determine the projection $\mathbf{p} = A\hat{\mathbf{x}}$.
   (b) calculate the residual $r(\hat{\mathbf{x}})$.
   (c) verify that $r(\hat{\mathbf{x}}) \in N(A^T)$.

3. For each of the following systems $A\mathbf{x} = \mathbf{b}$, find all least squares solutions:

   (a) $A = \begin{bmatrix} 1 & 2 \\ 2 & 4 \\ -1 & -2 \end{bmatrix}$, $\mathbf{b} = \begin{bmatrix} 3 \\ 2 \\ 1 \end{bmatrix}$

   (b) $A = \begin{bmatrix} 1 & 1 & 3 \\ -1 & 3 & 1 \\ 1 & 2 & 4 \end{bmatrix}$, $\mathbf{b} = \begin{bmatrix} -2 \\ 0 \\ 8 \end{bmatrix}$

4. For each of the systems in Exercise 3, determine the projection $\mathbf{p}$ of $\mathbf{b}$ onto $R(A)$ and verify that $\mathbf{b} - \mathbf{p}$ is orthogonal to each of the column vectors of A.

5. (a) Find the best least squares fit by a linear function to the data

x	−1	0	1	2
y	0	1	3	9

   (b) Plot your linear function from part (a) along with the data on a coordinate system.

6. Find the best least squares fit to the data in Exercise 5 by a quadratic polynomial. Plot the points $x = -1, 0, 1, 2$ for your function and sketch the graph.

7. Given a collection of points $(x_1, y_1), (x_2, y_2), \ldots,$ (x_n, y_n), let

   $$\mathbf{x} = (x_1, x_2, \ldots, x_n)^T \qquad \mathbf{y} = (y_1, y_2, \ldots, y_n)^T$$

   $$\bar{x} = \frac{1}{n} \sum_{i=1}^{n} x_i \qquad \bar{y} = \frac{1}{n} \sum_{i=1}^{n} y_i$$

   and let $y = c_0 + c_1 x$ be the linear function that gives the best least squares fit to the points. Show that if $\bar{x} = 0$, then

   $$c_0 = \bar{y} \qquad \text{and} \qquad c_1 = \frac{\mathbf{x}^T \mathbf{y}}{\mathbf{x}^T \mathbf{x}}$$

8. The point $(\bar{x}, \bar{y})$ is the *center of mass* for the collection of points in Exercise 7. Show that the least squares line must pass through the center of mass. [*Hint*: Use a change of variables $z = x - \bar{x}$ to translate the problem so that the new independent variable has mean 0.]

9. Let A be an $m \times n$ matrix of rank n and let $P = A(A^TA)^{-1}A^T$.
   (a) Show that $P\mathbf{b} = \mathbf{b}$ for every $\mathbf{b} \in R(A)$. Explain this property in terms of projections.
   (b) If $\mathbf{b} \in R(A)^{\perp}$, show that $P\mathbf{b} = \mathbf{0}$.
   (c) Give a geometric illustration of parts (a) and (b) if $R(A)$ is a plane through the origin in $\mathbb{R}^3$.

10. Let A be an 8×5 matrix of rank 3, and let $\mathbf{b}$ be a nonzero vector in $N(A^T)$.

    (a) Show that the system $A\mathbf{x} = \mathbf{b}$ must be inconsistent.

    (b) How many least squares solutions will the system $A\mathbf{x} = \mathbf{b}$ have? Explain.

11. Let $P = A(A^T A)^{-1} A^T$, where A is an $m \times n$ matrix of rank n.

    (a) Show that $P^2 = P$.

    (b) Prove that $P^k = P$ for $k = 1, 2, \ldots$.

    (c) Show that P is symmetric. [*Hint*: If B is nonsingular, then $(B^{-1})^T = (B^T)^{-1}$.]

12. Show that if

$$\begin{bmatrix} A & I \\ O & A^T \end{bmatrix} \begin{bmatrix} \hat{\mathbf{x}} \\ \mathbf{r} \end{bmatrix} = \begin{bmatrix} \mathbf{b} \\ \mathbf{0} \end{bmatrix}$$

    then $\hat{\mathbf{x}}$ is a least squares solution of the system $A\mathbf{x} = \mathbf{b}$ and $\mathbf{r}$ is the residual vector.

13. Let $A \in \mathbb{R}^{m \times n}$ and let $\hat{\mathbf{x}}$ be a solution of the least squares problem $A\mathbf{x} = \mathbf{b}$. Show that a vector $\mathbf{y} \in \mathbb{R}^n$ will also be a solution if and only if $\mathbf{y} = \hat{\mathbf{x}} + \mathbf{z}$, for some vector $\mathbf{z} \in N(A)$. [*Hint*: $N(A^T A) = N(A)$.]

14. Find the equation of the circle that gives the best least squares circle fit to the points $(-1, -2)$, $(0, 2.4)$, $(1.1, -4)$, and $(2.4, -1.6)$.

15. Suppose that in the search procedure described in Example 4, the search committee made the following judgments in evaluating the teaching credentials of the candidates:

    (i) Gauss and Taussky have equal teaching credentials.

    (ii) O'Leary's teaching credentials should be given 1.25 times the weight of Ipsen's credentials and 1.75 times the weight given to the credentials of both Gauss and Taussky.

    (iii) Ipsen's teaching credentials should be given 1.25 times the weight given to the credentials of both Gauss and Taussky.

    (a) Use the method given in Application 4 to determine a weight vector for rating the teaching credentials of the candidates.

    (b) Use the weight vector from part (a) to obtain overall ratings of the candidates.

5.4   Inner Product Spaces

Scalar products are useful not only in $\mathbb{R}^n$, but also in a wide variety of contexts. To generalize this concept to other vector spaces, we introduce the following definition.

Definition and Examples

Definition

> An **inner product** on a vector space V is an operation on V that assigns, to each pair of vectors $\mathbf{x}$ and $\mathbf{y}$ in V, a real number $\langle \mathbf{x}, \mathbf{y} \rangle$ satisfying the following conditions:
>
> **I.** $\langle \mathbf{x}, \mathbf{x} \rangle \geq 0$ with equality if and only if $\mathbf{x} = \mathbf{0}$
>
> **II.** $\langle \mathbf{x}, \mathbf{y} \rangle = \langle \mathbf{y}, \mathbf{x} \rangle$ for all $\mathbf{x}$ and $\mathbf{y}$ in V
>
> **III.** $\langle \alpha \mathbf{x} + \beta \mathbf{y}, \mathbf{z} \rangle = \alpha \langle \mathbf{x}, \mathbf{z} \rangle + \beta \langle \mathbf{y}, \mathbf{z} \rangle$ for all $\mathbf{x}, \mathbf{y}, \mathbf{z}$ in V and all scalars α and β

A vector space V with an inner product is called an **inner product space**.

The Vector Space $\mathbb{R}^n$

The standard inner product for $\mathbb{R}^n$ is the scalar product

$$\langle \mathbf{x}, \mathbf{y} \rangle = \mathbf{x}^T \mathbf{y}$$

Given a vector $\mathbf{w}$ with positive entries, we could also define an inner product on $\mathbb{R}^n$ by

$$\langle \mathbf{x}, \mathbf{y} \rangle = \sum_{i=1}^{n} x_i y_i w_i \tag{1}$$

The entries w_i are referred to as *weights*.

The Vector Space $\mathbb{R}^{m \times n}$

Given A and B in $\mathbb{R}^{m \times n}$, we can define an inner product by

$$\langle A, B \rangle = \sum_{i=1}^{m} \sum_{j=1}^{n} a_{ij} b_{ij} \tag{2}$$

We leave it to the reader to verify that (2) does indeed define an inner product on $\mathbb{R}^{m \times n}$.

The Vector Space $C[a, b]$

We may define an inner product on $C[a, b]$ by

$$\langle f, g \rangle = \int_{a}^{b} f(x)g(x)\, dx \tag{3}$$

Note that

$$\langle f, f \rangle = \int_{a}^{b} (f(x))^2 \, dx \geq 0$$

If $f(x_0) \neq 0$ for some x_0 in $[a, b]$, then, since $(f(x))^2$ is continuous, there exists a subinterval I of $[a, b]$ containing x_0 such that $(f(x))^2 \geq (f(x_0))^2/2$ for all x in I. If we let p represent the length of I, then it follows that

$$\langle f, f \rangle = \int_{a}^{b} (f(x))^2 \, dx \geq \int_{I} (f(x))^2 \, dx \geq \frac{(f(x_0))^2 p}{2} > 0$$

So if $\langle f, f \rangle = 0$, then $f(x)$ must be identically zero on $[a, b]$. We leave it to the reader to verify that (3) satisfies the other two conditions specified in the definition of an inner product.

If $w(x)$ is a positive continuous function on $[a, b]$, then

$$\langle f, g \rangle = \int_{a}^{b} f(x)g(x)w(x)\, dx \tag{4}$$

also defines an inner product on $C[a, b]$. The function $w(x)$ is called a *weight function*. Thus, it is possible to define many different inner products on $C[a, b]$.

The Vector Space P_n

Let $x_1, x_2, \ldots, x_n$ be distinct real numbers. For each pair of polynomials in P_n, define

$$\langle p, q \rangle = \sum_{i=1}^{n} p(x_i) q(x_i) \tag{5}$$

It is easily seen that (5) satisfies conditions (ii) and (iii) of the definition of an inner product. To show that (i) holds, note that

$$\langle p, p \rangle = \sum_{i=1}^{n} (p(x_i))^2 \geq 0$$

If $\langle p, p \rangle = 0$, then $x_1, x_2, \ldots, x_n$ must be roots of $p(x) = 0$. Since $p(x)$ is of degree less than n, it must be the zero polynomial.

If $w(x)$ is a positive function, then

$$\langle p, q \rangle = \sum_{i=1}^{n} p(x_i)q(x_i)w(x_i)$$

also defines an inner product on P_n.

Basic Properties of Inner Product Spaces

The results presented in Section 5.1 for scalar products in $\mathbb{R}^n$ all generalize to inner product spaces. In particular, if $\mathbf{v}$ is a vector in an inner product space V, the *length*, or *norm* of $\mathbf{v}$ is given by

$$\|\mathbf{v}\| = \sqrt{\langle \mathbf{v}, \mathbf{v} \rangle}$$

Two vectors $\mathbf{u}$ and $\mathbf{v}$ are said to be *orthogonal* if $\langle \mathbf{u}, \mathbf{v} \rangle = 0$. As in $\mathbb{R}^n$, a pair of orthogonal vectors will satisfy the Pythagorean law.

Theorem 5.4.1   The Pythagorean Law

If $\mathbf{u}$ and $\mathbf{v}$ are orthogonal vectors in an inner product space V, then

$$\|\mathbf{u} + \mathbf{v}\|^2 = \|\mathbf{u}\|^2 + \|\mathbf{v}\|^2$$

Proof

$$\begin{aligned}
\|\mathbf{u} + \mathbf{v}\|^2 &= \langle \mathbf{u} + \mathbf{v}, \mathbf{u} + \mathbf{v} \rangle \\
&= \langle \mathbf{u}, \mathbf{u} \rangle + 2\langle \mathbf{u}, \mathbf{v} \rangle + \langle \mathbf{v}, \mathbf{v} \rangle \\
&= \|\mathbf{u}\|^2 + \|\mathbf{v}\|^2
\end{aligned}$$

Interpreted in $\mathbb{R}^2$, this is just the familiar Pythagorean theorem as shown in Figure 5.4.1.

Figure 5.4.1.

EXAMPLE 1   Consider the vector space $C[-1, 1]$ with an inner product defined by (3). The vectors 1 and x are orthogonal, since

$$\langle 1, x \rangle = \int_{-1}^{1} 1 \cdot x \, dx = 0$$

To determine the lengths of these vectors, we compute

$$\langle 1, 1 \rangle = \int_{-1}^{1} 1 \cdot 1 \, dx = 2$$

$$\langle x, x \rangle = \int_{-1}^{1} x^2 \, dx = \frac{2}{3}$$

It follows that

$$\|1\| = (\langle 1, 1 \rangle)^{1/2} = \sqrt{2}$$

$$\|x\| = (\langle x, x \rangle)^{1/2} = \frac{\sqrt{6}}{3}$$

Since 1 and x are orthogonal, they satisfy the Pythagorean law:

$$\|1 + x\|^2 = \|1\|^2 + \|x\|^2 = 2 + \frac{2}{3} = \frac{8}{3}$$

The reader may verify that

$$\|1 + x\|^2 = \langle 1 + x, 1 + x \rangle = \int_{-1}^{1} (1 + x)^2 \, dx = \frac{8}{3}$$ ■

EXAMPLE 2   For the vector space $C[-\pi, \pi]$, if we use a constant weight function $w(x) = 1/\pi$ to define an inner product

$$\langle f, g \rangle = \frac{1}{\pi} \int_{-\pi}^{\pi} f(x)g(x) \, dx \tag{6}$$

then

$$\langle \cos x, \sin x \rangle = \frac{1}{\pi} \int_{-\pi}^{\pi} \cos x \sin x \, dx = 0$$

$$\langle \cos x, \cos x \rangle = \frac{1}{\pi} \int_{-\pi}^{\pi} \cos x \cos x \, dx = 1$$

$$\langle \sin x, \sin x \rangle = \frac{1}{\pi} \int_{-\pi}^{\pi} \sin x \sin x \, dx = 1$$

Thus, $\cos x$ and $\sin x$ are orthogonal unit vectors with respect to this inner product. It follows from the Pythagorean law that

$$\| \cos x + \sin x \| = \sqrt{2}$$ ■

The inner product (6) plays a key role in Fourier analysis applications involving a trigonometric approximation of functions. We will look at some of these applications in Section 5.5.

For the vector space $\mathbb{R}^{m \times n}$, the norm derived from the inner product (2) is called the *Frobenius norm* and is denoted by $\| \cdot \|_F$. Thus, if $A \in \mathbb{R}^{m \times n}$, then

$$\|A\|_F = (\langle A, A \rangle)^{1/2} = \left(\sum_{i=1}^{m} \sum_{j=1}^{n} a_{ij}^2 \right)^{1/2}$$

EXAMPLE 3   If

$$A = \begin{bmatrix} 1 & 1 \\ 1 & 2 \\ 3 & 3 \end{bmatrix} \quad \text{and} \quad B = \begin{bmatrix} -1 & 1 \\ 3 & 0 \\ -3 & 4 \end{bmatrix}$$

then

$$\langle A, B \rangle = 1 \cdot -1 + 1 \cdot 1 + 1 \cdot 3 + 2 \cdot 0 + 3 \cdot -3 + 3 \cdot 4 = 6$$

Hence, A is not orthogonal to B. The norms of these matrices are given by

$$\|A\|_F = (1 + 1 + 1 + 4 + 9 + 9)^{1/2} = 5$$
$$\|B\|_F = (1 + 1 + 9 + 0 + 9 + 16)^{1/2} = 6$$

EXAMPLE 4 In P_5, define an inner product by (5) with $x_i = (i - 1)/4$ for $i = 1, 2, \ldots, 5$. The length of the function $p(x) = 4x$ is given by

$$\|4x\| = (\langle 4x, 4x \rangle)^{1/2} = \left(\sum_{i=1}^{5} 16x_i^2 \right)^{1/2} = \left(\sum_{i=1}^{5} (i - 1)^2 \right)^{1/2} = \sqrt{30}$$

Definition

If $\mathbf{u}$ and $\mathbf{v}$ are vectors in an inner product space V and $\mathbf{v} \neq \mathbf{0}$, then the **scalar projection** of $\mathbf{u}$ onto $\mathbf{v}$ is given by

$$\alpha = \frac{\langle \mathbf{u}, \mathbf{v} \rangle}{\|\mathbf{v}\|}$$

and the **vector projection** of $\mathbf{u}$ onto $\mathbf{v}$ is given by

$$\mathbf{p} = \alpha \left(\frac{1}{\|\mathbf{v}\|} \mathbf{v} \right) = \frac{\langle \mathbf{u}, \mathbf{v} \rangle}{\langle \mathbf{v}, \mathbf{v} \rangle} \mathbf{v} \tag{7}$$

Observations

If $\mathbf{v} \neq \mathbf{0}$ and $\mathbf{p}$ is the vector projection of $\mathbf{u}$ onto $\mathbf{v}$, then

    I. $\mathbf{u} - \mathbf{p}$ and $\mathbf{p}$ are orthogonal.

    II. $\mathbf{u} = \mathbf{p}$ if and only if $\mathbf{u}$ is a scalar multiple of $\mathbf{v}$.

Proof of Observation I Since

$$\langle \mathbf{p}, \mathbf{p} \rangle = \left\langle \frac{\alpha}{\|\mathbf{v}\|} \mathbf{v}, \frac{\alpha}{\|\mathbf{v}\|} \mathbf{v} \right\rangle = \left(\frac{\alpha}{\|\mathbf{v}\|} \right)^2 \langle \mathbf{v}, \mathbf{v} \rangle = \alpha^2$$

and

$$\langle \mathbf{u}, \mathbf{p} \rangle = \frac{(\langle \mathbf{u}, \mathbf{v} \rangle)^2}{\langle \mathbf{v}, \mathbf{v} \rangle} = \alpha^2$$

it follows that

$$\langle \mathbf{u} - \mathbf{p}, \mathbf{p} \rangle = \langle \mathbf{u}, \mathbf{p} \rangle - \langle \mathbf{p}, \mathbf{p} \rangle = \alpha^2 - \alpha^2 = 0$$

Therefore, $\mathbf{u} - \mathbf{p}$ and $\mathbf{p}$ are orthogonal.

Proof of Observation II If $\mathbf{u} = \beta \mathbf{v}$, then the vector projection of $\mathbf{u}$ onto $\mathbf{v}$ is given by

$$\mathbf{p} = \frac{\langle \beta \mathbf{v}, \mathbf{v} \rangle}{\langle \mathbf{v}, \mathbf{v} \rangle} \mathbf{v} = \beta \mathbf{v} = \mathbf{u}$$

Conversely, if $\mathbf{u} = \mathbf{p}$, it follows from (7) that

$$\mathbf{u} = \beta\mathbf{v} \qquad \text{where} \quad \beta = \frac{\alpha}{\|\mathbf{v}\|}$$

∎

Observations I and II are useful for establishing the following theorem.

Theorem 5.4.2   The Cauchy–Schwarz Inequality

If $\mathbf{u}$ and $\mathbf{v}$ are any two vectors in an inner product space V, then

$$| \langle \mathbf{u}, \mathbf{v} \rangle | \leq \|\mathbf{u}\| \, \|\mathbf{v}\| \tag{8}$$

Equality holds if and only if $\mathbf{u}$ and $\mathbf{v}$ are linearly dependent.

Proof   If $\mathbf{v} = \mathbf{0}$, then

$$| \langle \mathbf{u}, \mathbf{v} \rangle | = 0 = \|\mathbf{u}\| \, \|\mathbf{v}\|$$

If $\mathbf{v} \neq \mathbf{0}$, then let $\mathbf{p}$ be the vector projection of $\mathbf{u}$ onto $\mathbf{v}$. Since $\mathbf{p}$ is orthogonal to $\mathbf{u} - \mathbf{p}$, it follows from the Pythagorean law that

$$\|\mathbf{p}\|^2 + \|\mathbf{u} - \mathbf{p}\|^2 = \|\mathbf{u}\|^2$$

Thus,

$$\frac{(\langle \mathbf{u}, \mathbf{v} \rangle)^2}{\|\mathbf{v}\|^2} = \|\mathbf{p}\|^2 = \|\mathbf{u}\|^2 - \|\mathbf{u} - \mathbf{p}\|^2$$

and hence

$$(\langle \mathbf{u}, \mathbf{v} \rangle)^2 = \|\mathbf{u}\|^2 \|\mathbf{v}\|^2 - \|\mathbf{u} - \mathbf{p}\|^2 \|\mathbf{v}\|^2 \leq \|\mathbf{u}\|^2 \|\mathbf{v}\|^2 \tag{9}$$

Therefore,

$$| \langle \mathbf{u}, \mathbf{v} \rangle | \leq \|\mathbf{u}\| \, \|\mathbf{v}\|$$

Equality holds in (9) if and only if $\mathbf{u} = \mathbf{p}$. It follows from observation II that equality will hold in (8) if and only if $\mathbf{v} = \mathbf{0}$ or $\mathbf{u}$ is a multiple of $\mathbf{v}$. More simply stated, equality will hold if and only if $\mathbf{u}$ and $\mathbf{v}$ are linearly dependent.   ∎

One consequence of the Cauchy–Schwarz inequality is that if $\mathbf{u}$ and $\mathbf{v}$ are nonzero vectors, then

$$-1 \leq \frac{\langle \mathbf{u}, \mathbf{v} \rangle}{\|\mathbf{u}\| \|\mathbf{v}\|} \leq 1$$

and hence there is a unique angle θ in $[0, \pi]$ such that

$$\cos \theta = \frac{\langle \mathbf{u}, \mathbf{v} \rangle}{\|\mathbf{u}\| \|\mathbf{v}\|} \tag{10}$$

Thus, equation (10) can be used to define the angle θ between two nonzero vectors $\mathbf{u}$ and $\mathbf{v}$.

Norms

The word *norm* in mathematics has its own meaning that is independent of an inner product and its use here should be justified.

Figure 5.4.2.

Definition

> A vector space V is said to be a **normed linear space** if, to each vector $\mathbf{v} \in V$, there is associated a real number $\|\mathbf{v}\|$, called the **norm** of $\mathbf{v}$, satisfying
>
> **I.** $\|\mathbf{v}\| \geq 0$ with equality if and only if $\mathbf{v} = \mathbf{0}$.
> **II.** $\|\alpha\mathbf{v}\| = |\alpha|\,\|\mathbf{v}\|$ for any scalar α.
> **III.** $\|\mathbf{v} + \mathbf{w}\| \leq \|\mathbf{v}\| + \|\mathbf{w}\|$ for all $\mathbf{v}, \mathbf{w} \in V$.

The third condition is called the *triangle inequality* (see Figure 5.4.2).

Theorem 5.4.3   *If V is an inner product space, then the equation*

$$\|\mathbf{v}\| = \sqrt{\langle \mathbf{v}, \mathbf{v} \rangle} \qquad \text{for all} \quad \mathbf{v} \in V$$

defines a norm on V.

Proof   It is easily seen that conditions **I** and **II** of the definition are satisfied. We leave this for the reader to verify and proceed to show that condition **III** is satisfied.

$$\begin{aligned}
\|\mathbf{u} + \mathbf{v}\|^2 &= \langle \mathbf{u} + \mathbf{v}, \mathbf{u} + \mathbf{v} \rangle \\
&= \langle \mathbf{u}, \mathbf{u} \rangle + 2\langle \mathbf{u}, \mathbf{v} \rangle + \langle \mathbf{v}, \mathbf{v} \rangle \\
&\leq \|\mathbf{u}\|^2 + 2\|\mathbf{u}\|\,\|\mathbf{v}\| + \|\mathbf{v}\|^2 \quad \text{(Cauchy–Schwarz)} \\
&= (\|\mathbf{u}\| + \|\mathbf{v}\|)^2
\end{aligned}$$

Thus,

$$\|\mathbf{u} + \mathbf{v}\| \leq \|\mathbf{u}\| + \|\mathbf{v}\| \qquad\qquad \blacksquare$$

It is possible to define many different norms on a given vector space. For example, in $\mathbb{R}^n$ we could define

$$\|\mathbf{x}\|_1 = \sum_{i=1}^{n} |x_i|$$

for every $\mathbf{x} = (x_1, x_2, \ldots, x_n)^T$. It is easily verified that $\|\cdot\|_1$ defines a norm on $\mathbb{R}^n$. Another important norm on $\mathbb{R}^n$ is the *uniform norm* or *infinity norm*, which is defined by

$$\|\mathbf{x}\|_\infty = \max_{1 \leq i \leq n} |x_i|$$

More generally, we could define a norm on $\mathbb{R}^n$ by

$$\|\mathbf{x}\|_p = \left(\sum_{i=1}^{n} |x_i|^p \right)^{1/p}$$

for any real number $p \geq 1$. In particular, if $p = 2$, then

$$\|\mathbf{x}\|_2 = \left(\sum_{i=1}^{n} |x_i|^2 \right)^{1/2} = \sqrt{\langle \mathbf{x}, \mathbf{x} \rangle}$$

The norm $\| \cdot \|_2$ is the norm on $\mathbb{R}^n$ derived from the inner product. If $p \neq 2$, $\| \cdot \|_p$ does not correspond to any inner product. In the case of a norm that is not derived from an inner product, the Pythagorean law will not hold. For example,

$$\mathbf{x}_1 = \begin{bmatrix} 1 \\ 2 \end{bmatrix} \quad \text{and} \quad \mathbf{x}_2 = \begin{bmatrix} -4 \\ 2 \end{bmatrix}$$

are orthogonal; however,

$$\|\mathbf{x}_1\|_\infty^2 + \|\mathbf{x}_2\|_\infty^2 = 4 + 16 = 20$$

while

$$\|\mathbf{x}_1 + \mathbf{x}_2\|_\infty^2 = 16$$

If, however, $\| \cdot \|_2$ is used, then

$$\|\mathbf{x}_1\|_2^2 + \|\mathbf{x}_2\|_2^2 = 5 + 20 = 25 = \|\mathbf{x}_1 + \mathbf{x}_2\|_2^2$$

EXAMPLE 5   Let $\mathbf{x}$ be the vector $(4, -5, 3)^T$ in $\mathbb{R}^3$. Compute $\|\mathbf{x}\|_1$, $\|\mathbf{x}\|_2$, and $\|\mathbf{x}\|_\infty$.

$$\|\mathbf{x}\|_1 = |4| + |-5| + |3| = 12$$
$$\|\mathbf{x}\|_2 = \sqrt{16 + 25 + 9} = 5\sqrt{2}$$
$$\|\mathbf{x}\|_\infty = \max(|4|, |-5|, |3|) = 5$$

It is also possible to define different matrix norms for $\mathbb{R}^{m \times n}$. In Chapter 7, we will study other types of matrix norms that are useful in determining the sensitivity of linear systems.

In general, a norm provides a way of measuring the distance between vectors.

Definition   Let $\mathbf{x}$ and $\mathbf{y}$ be vectors in a normed linear space. The distance between $\mathbf{x}$ and $\mathbf{y}$ is defined to be the number $\|\mathbf{y} - \mathbf{x}\|$.

Many applications involve finding a unique closest vector in a subspace S to a given vector $\mathbf{v}$ in a vector space V. If the norm used for V is derived from an inner product, then the closest vector can be computed as a vector projection of $\mathbf{v}$ onto the subspace S. This type of approximation problem is discussed further in the next section.

SECTION 5.4 EXERCISES

1. Let $\mathbf{x} = (-1, -1, 1, 1)^T$ and $\mathbf{y} = (1, 1, 5, -3)^T$. Show that $\mathbf{x} \perp \mathbf{y}$. Calculate $\|\mathbf{x}\|_2$, $\|\mathbf{y}\|_2$, $\|\mathbf{x} + \mathbf{y}\|_2$ and verify that the Pythagorean law holds.

2. Let $\mathbf{x} = (1, 1, 1, 1)^T$ and $\mathbf{y} = (8, 2, 2, 0)^T$.
   (a) Determine the angle θ between $\mathbf{x}$ and $\mathbf{y}$.

   (b) Find the vector projection $\mathbf{p}$ of $\mathbf{x}$ onto $\mathbf{y}$.

   (c) Verify that $\mathbf{x} - \mathbf{p}$ is orthogonal to $\mathbf{p}$.

   (d) Compute $\|\mathbf{x} - \mathbf{p}\|_2$, $\|\mathbf{p}\|_2$, $\|\mathbf{x}\|_2$ and verify that the Pythagorean law is satisfied.

3. Use equation (1) with weight vector $\mathbf{w} = \left(\frac{1}{4}, \frac{1}{2}, \frac{1}{4}\right)^T$ to define an inner product for $\mathbb{R}^3$, and let $\mathbf{x} = (1, 1, 1)^T$ and $\mathbf{y} = (-5, 1, 3)^T$.
   (a) Show that $\mathbf{x}$ and $\mathbf{y}$ are orthogonal with respect to this inner product.

   (b) Compute the values of $\|\mathbf{x}\|$ and $\|\mathbf{y}\|$ with respect to this inner product.

4. Given
$$A = \begin{bmatrix} 1 & 2 & 2 \\ 1 & 0 & 2 \\ 3 & 1 & 1 \end{bmatrix} \quad \text{and} \quad B = \begin{bmatrix} -4 & 1 & 1 \\ -3 & 3 & 2 \\ 1 & -2 & -2 \end{bmatrix}$$
determine the value of each of the following:
   (a) $\langle A, B \rangle$ (b) $\|A\|_F$

   (c) $\|B\|_F$ (d) $\|A + B\|_F$

5. Show that equation (2) defines an inner product on $\mathbb{R}^{m \times n}$.

6. Show that the inner product defined by equation (3) satisfies the last two conditions of the definition of an inner product.

7. In $C[0, 1]$, with inner product defined by (3), compute
   (a) $\langle e^x, e^{-x} \rangle$ (b) $\langle x, \sin \pi x \rangle$ (c) $\langle x^2, x^3 \rangle$

8. In $C[0, 1]$, with inner product defined by (3), consider the vectors 1 and x.
   (a) Find the angle θ between 1 and x.

   (b) Determine the vector projection $\mathbf{p}$ of 1 onto x and verify that $1 - \mathbf{p}$ is orthogonal to $\mathbf{p}$.

   (c) Compute $\|1 - \mathbf{p}\|$, $\|\mathbf{p}\|$, $\|1\|$ and verify that the Pythagorean law holds.

9. In $C[-\pi, \pi]$ with inner product defined by (6), show that $\cos mx$ and $\sin nx$ are orthogonal and that both are

unit vectors. Determine the distance between the two vectors.

10. Show that the functions x and x^2 are orthogonal in P_5 with the inner product defined by (5), where $x_i = (i - 3)/2$ for $i = 1, \ldots, 5$.

11. In P_5 with the inner product as in Exercise 10 and the norm defined by
$$\|p\| = \sqrt{\langle p, p \rangle} = \left\{ \sum_{i=1}^{5} [p(x_i)]^2 \right\}^{1/2}$$
compute
   (a) $\|x\|$ (b) $\|x^2\|$
   (c) the distance between x and x^2

12. If V is an inner product space, show that
$$\|\mathbf{v}\| = \sqrt{\langle \mathbf{v}, \mathbf{v} \rangle}$$
satisfies the first two conditions in the definition of a norm.

13. Show that
$$\|\mathbf{x}\|_1 = \sum_{i=1}^{n} |x_i|$$
defines a norm on $\mathbb{R}^n$.

14. Show that
$$\|\mathbf{x}\|_\infty = \max_{1 \le i \le n} |x_i|$$
defines a norm on $\mathbb{R}^n$.

15. Compute $\|\mathbf{x}\|_1$, $\|\mathbf{x}\|_2$, and $\|\mathbf{x}\|_\infty$ for each of the following vectors in $\mathbb{R}^3$:
   (a) $\mathbf{x} = (-3, 4, 0)^T$ (b) $\mathbf{x} = (-1, -1, 2)^T$
   (c) $\mathbf{x} = (1, 1, 1)^T$

16. Let $\mathbf{x} = (5, 2, 4)^T$ and $\mathbf{y} = (3, 3, 2)^T$. Compute $\|\mathbf{x} - \mathbf{y}\|_1$, $\|\mathbf{x} - \mathbf{y}\|_2$, and $\|\mathbf{x} - \mathbf{y}\|_\infty$. Under which norm are the two vectors closest together? Under which norm are they farthest apart?

17. Let $\mathbf{x}$ and $\mathbf{y}$ be vectors in an inner product space. Show that if $\mathbf{x} \perp \mathbf{y}$, then the distance between $\mathbf{x}$ and $\mathbf{y}$ is
$$\left(\|\mathbf{x}\|^2 + \|\mathbf{y}\|^2 \right)^{1/2}$$

18. Show that if $\mathbf{u}$ and $\mathbf{v}$ are vectors in an inner product space that satisfy the Pythagorean law
$$\|\mathbf{u} + \mathbf{v}\|^2 = \|\mathbf{u}\|^2 + \|\mathbf{v}\|^2$$
then $\mathbf{u}$ and $\mathbf{v}$ must be orthogonal.

19. In $\mathbb{R}^n$ with inner product

$$\langle \mathbf{x}, \mathbf{y} \rangle = \mathbf{x}^T \mathbf{y}$$

derive a formula for the distance between two vectors $\mathbf{x} = (x_1, \ldots, x_n)^T$ and $\mathbf{y} = (y_1, \ldots, y_n)^T$.

20. Let A be a nonsingular $n \times n$ matrix and for each vector $\mathbf{x}$ in $\mathbb{R}^n$ define

$$\|\mathbf{x}\|_A = \|A\mathbf{x}\|_2 \qquad (11)$$

Show that (11) defines a norm on $\mathbb{R}^n$.

21. Let $\mathbf{x} \in \mathbb{R}^n$. Show that $\|\mathbf{x}\|_\infty \leq \|\mathbf{x}\|_2$.

22. Let $\mathbf{x} \in \mathbb{R}^2$. Show that $\|\mathbf{x}\|_2 \leq \|\mathbf{x}\|_1$. [*Hint*: Write $\mathbf{x}$ in the form $x_1 \mathbf{e}_1 + x_2 \mathbf{e}_2$ and use the triangle inequality.]

23. Give an example of a nonzero vector $\mathbf{x} \in \mathbb{R}^2$ for which

$$\|\mathbf{x}\|_\infty = \|\mathbf{x}\|_2 = \|\mathbf{x}\|_1$$

24. Show that in any vector space with a norm,

$$\|-\mathbf{v}\| = \|\mathbf{v}\|$$

25. Show that for any $\mathbf{u}$ and $\mathbf{v}$ in a normed vector space,

$$\|\mathbf{u} + \mathbf{v}\| \geq |\, \|\mathbf{u}\| - \|\mathbf{v}\| \,|$$

26. Prove that, for any $\mathbf{u}$ and $\mathbf{v}$ in an inner product space V,

$$\|\mathbf{u} + \mathbf{v}\|^2 + \|\mathbf{u} - \mathbf{v}\|^2 = 2\|\mathbf{u}\|^2 + 2\|\mathbf{v}\|^2$$

Give a geometric interpretation of this result for the vector space $\mathbb{R}^2$.

27. The result of Exercise 26 is not valid for norms other than the norm derived from the inner product. Give an example of this in $\mathbb{R}^2$ using $\|\cdot\|_1$.

28. Determine whether the following define norms on $C[a, b]$:

(a) $\|f\| = |f(a)| + |f(b)|$

(b) $\|f\| = \int_a^b |f(x)|\, dx$

(c) $\|f\| = \max_{a \leq x \leq b} |f(x)|$

29. Let $\mathbf{x} \in \mathbb{R}^n$ and show that

(a) $\|\mathbf{x}\|_1 \leq n\|\mathbf{x}\|_\infty$ (b) $\|\mathbf{x}\|_2 \leq \sqrt{n}\,\|\mathbf{x}\|_\infty$

Give examples of vectors in $\mathbb{R}^n$ for which equality holds in parts (a) and (b).

30. Sketch the set of points $(x_1, x_2) = \mathbf{x}^T$ in $\mathbb{R}^2$ such that

(a) $\|\mathbf{x}\|_2 = 1$ (b) $\|\mathbf{x}\|_1 = 1$ (c) $\|\mathbf{x}\|_\infty = 1$

31. Let K be an $n \times n$ matrix of the form

$$K = \begin{pmatrix} 1 & -c & -c & \cdots & -c & -c \\ 0 & s & -sc & \cdots & -sc & -sc \\ 0 & 0 & s^2 & \cdots & -s^2 c & -s^2 c \\ \vdots & & & & & \\ 0 & 0 & 0 & \cdots & s^{n-2} & -s^{n-2}c \\ 0 & 0 & 0 & \cdots & 0 & s^{n-1} \end{pmatrix}$$

where $c^2 + s^2 = 1$. Show that $\|K\|_F = \sqrt{n}$.

32. The *trace* of an $n \times n$ matrix C, denoted $\text{tr}(C)$, is the sum of its diagonal entries; that is,

$$\text{tr}(C) = c_{11} + c_{22} + \cdots + c_{nn}$$

If A and B are $m \times n$ matrices, show that

(a) $\|A\|_F^2 = \text{tr}(A^T A)$

(b) $\|A + B\|_F^2 = \|A\|_F^2 + 2\,\text{tr}(A^T B) + \|B\|_F^2$

33. Consider the vector space $\mathbb{R}^n$ with inner product $\langle \mathbf{x}, \mathbf{y} \rangle = \mathbf{x}^T \mathbf{y}$. Show that for any $n \times n$ matrix A,

(a) $\langle A\mathbf{x}, \mathbf{y} \rangle = \langle \mathbf{x}, A^T \mathbf{y} \rangle$

(b) $\langle A^T A \mathbf{x}, \mathbf{x} \rangle = \|A\mathbf{x}\|^2$

5.5 Orthonormal Sets

In $\mathbb{R}^2$, it is generally more convenient to use the standard basis $\{\mathbf{e}_1, \mathbf{e}_2\}$ than to use some other basis, such as $\{(2, 1)^T, (3, 5)^T\}$. For example, it would be easier to find the coordinates of $(x_1, x_2)^T$ with respect to the standard basis. The elements of the standard basis are orthogonal unit vectors. In working with an inner product space V, it is generally desirable to have a basis of mutually orthogonal unit vectors. Such a basis is convenient not only in finding coordinates of vectors, but also in solving least squares problems.

Definition   Let $\mathbf{v}_1, \mathbf{v}_2, \ldots, \mathbf{v}_n$ be nonzero vectors in an inner product space V. If $\langle \mathbf{v}_i, \mathbf{v}_j \rangle = 0$ whenever $i \neq j$, then $\{\mathbf{v}_1, \mathbf{v}_2, \ldots, \mathbf{v}_n\}$ is said to be an **orthogonal set** of vectors.

EXAMPLE 1   The set $\{(1, 1, 1)^T, (2, 1, -3)^T, (4, -5, 1)^T\}$ is an orthogonal set in $\mathbb{R}^3$, since

$$(1, 1, 1)(2, 1, -3)^T = 0$$
$$(1, 1, 1)(4, -5, 1)^T = 0$$
$$(2, 1, -3)(4, -5, 1)^T = 0$$

∎

Theorem 5.5.1   *If $\{v_1, v_2, \ldots, v_n\}$ is an orthogonal set of nonzero vectors in an inner product space V, then $v_1, v_2, \ldots, v_n$ are linearly independent.*

Proof   Suppose that $v_1, v_2, \ldots, v_n$ are mutually orthogonal nonzero vectors and

$$c_1 v_1 + c_2 v_2 + \cdots + c_n v_n = 0 \tag{1}$$

If $1 \leq j \leq n$, then, taking the inner product of v_j with both sides of equation (1), we see that

$$c_1 \langle v_j, v_1 \rangle + c_2 \langle v_j, v_2 \rangle + \cdots + c_n \langle v_j, v_n \rangle = 0$$
$$c_j \|v_j\|^2 = 0$$

and hence all the scalars $c_1, c_2, \ldots, c_n$ must be 0.

∎

Definition

An **orthonormal** set of vectors is an orthogonal set of unit vectors.

The set $\{u_1, u_2, \ldots, u_n\}$ will be orthonormal if and only if

$$\langle u_i, u_j \rangle = \delta_{ij}$$

where

$$\delta_{ij} = \begin{cases} 1 & \text{if } i = j \\ 0 & \text{if } i \neq j \end{cases}$$

Given any orthogonal set of nonzero vectors $\{v_1, v_2, \ldots, v_n\}$, it is possible to form an orthonormal set by defining

$$u_i = \left(\frac{1}{\|v_i\|} \right) v_i \qquad \text{for} \quad i = 1, 2, \ldots, n$$

The reader may verify that $\{u_1, u_2, \ldots, u_n\}$ will be an orthonormal set.

EXAMPLE 2   We saw in Example 1 that if $v_1 = (1, 1, 1)^T$, $v_2 = (2, 1, -3)^T$, and $v_3 = (4, -5, 1)^T$, then $\{v_1, v_2, v_3\}$ is an orthogonal set in $\mathbb{R}^3$. To form an orthonormal set, let

$$u_1 = \left(\frac{1}{\|v_1\|} \right) v_1 = \frac{1}{\sqrt{3}}(1, 1, 1)^T$$

$$u_2 = \left(\frac{1}{\|v_2\|} \right) v_2 = \frac{1}{\sqrt{14}}(2, 1, -3)^T$$

$$u_3 = \left(\frac{1}{\|v_3\|} \right) v_3 = \frac{1}{\sqrt{42}}(4, -5, 1)^T$$

∎

EXAMPLE 3   In $C[-\pi, \pi]$ with inner product

$$\langle f, g \rangle = \frac{1}{\pi} \int_{-\pi}^{\pi} f(x)g(x)\, dx \tag{2}$$

the set $\{1, \cos x, \cos 2x, \ldots, \cos nx\}$ is an orthogonal set of vectors, since for any positive integers j and k

$$\langle 1, \cos kx \rangle = \frac{1}{\pi} \int_{-\pi}^{\pi} \cos kx\, dx = 0$$

$$\langle \cos jx, \cos kx \rangle = \frac{1}{\pi} \int_{-\pi}^{\pi} \cos jx \cos kx\, dx = 0 \qquad (j \neq k)$$

The functions $\cos x, \cos 2x, \ldots, \cos nx$ are already unit vectors since

$$\langle \cos kx, \cos kx \rangle = \frac{1}{\pi} \int_{-\pi}^{\pi} \cos^2 kx\, dx = 1 \qquad \text{for} \quad k = 1, 2, \ldots, n$$

To form an orthonormal set, we need only find a unit vector in the direction of 1.

$$\|1\|^2 = \langle 1, 1 \rangle = \frac{1}{\pi} \int_{-\pi}^{\pi} 1\, dx = 2$$

Thus, $1/\sqrt{2}$ is a unit vector, and hence $\{1/\sqrt{2}, \cos x, \cos 2x, \ldots, \cos nx\}$ is an orthonormal set of vectors. ∎

It follows from Theorem 5.5.1 that if $B = \{\mathbf{u}_1, \mathbf{u}_2, \ldots, \mathbf{u}_k\}$ is an orthonormal set in an inner product space V, then B is a basis for the subspace $S = \text{Span}(\mathbf{u}_1, \mathbf{u}_2, \ldots, \mathbf{u}_k)$. We say that B is an *orthonormal basis* for S. It is generally much easier to work with an orthonormal basis than with an ordinary basis. In particular, it is much easier to calculate the coordinates of a given vector $\mathbf{v}$ with respect to an orthonormal basis. Once these coordinates have been determined, they can be used to compute $\|\mathbf{v}\|$.

Theorem 5.5.2   *Let $\{\mathbf{u}_1, \mathbf{u}_2, \ldots, \mathbf{u}_n\}$ be an orthonormal basis for an inner product space V. If $\mathbf{v} = \sum_{i=1}^{n} c_i \mathbf{u}_i$, then $c_i = \langle \mathbf{v}, \mathbf{u}_i \rangle$.*

Proof

$$\langle \mathbf{v}, \mathbf{u}_i \rangle = \left\langle \sum_{j=1}^{n} c_j \mathbf{u}_j, \mathbf{u}_i \right\rangle = \sum_{j=1}^{n} c_j \langle \mathbf{u}_j, \mathbf{u}_i \rangle = \sum_{j=1}^{n} c_j \delta_{ji} = c_i \qquad ∎$$

As a consequence of Theorem 5.5.2, we can state two more important results.

Corollary 5.5.3   *Let $\{\mathbf{u}_1, \mathbf{u}_2, \ldots, \mathbf{u}_n\}$ be an orthonormal basis for an inner product space V. If $\mathbf{u} = \sum_{i=1}^{n} a_i \mathbf{u}_i$ and $\mathbf{v} = \sum_{i=1}^{n} b_i \mathbf{u}_i$, then*

$$\langle \mathbf{u}, \mathbf{v} \rangle = \sum_{i=1}^{n} a_i b_i$$

Proof   By Theorem 5.5.2,

$$\langle \mathbf{v}, \mathbf{u}_i \rangle = b_i \qquad i = 1, \ldots, n$$

Therefore,

$$\langle \mathbf{u}, \mathbf{v} \rangle = \left\langle \sum_{i=1}^{n} a_i \mathbf{u}_i, \mathbf{v} \right\rangle = \sum_{i=1}^{n} a_i \langle \mathbf{u}_i, \mathbf{v} \rangle = \sum_{i=1}^{n} a_i \langle \mathbf{v}, \mathbf{u}_i \rangle = \sum_{i=1}^{n} a_i b_i \qquad \blacksquare$$

Corollary 5.5.4   Parseval's Formula

If $\{\mathbf{u}_1, \ldots, \mathbf{u}_n\}$ *is an orthonormal basis for an inner product space V and* $\mathbf{v} = \sum_{i=1}^{n} c_i \mathbf{u}_i$,

then

$$\|\mathbf{v}\|^2 = \sum_{i=1}^{n} c_i^2$$

Proof   If $\mathbf{v} = \sum_{i=1}^{n} c_i \mathbf{u}_i$, then, by Corollary 5.5.3,

$$\|\mathbf{v}\|^2 = \langle \mathbf{v}, \mathbf{v} \rangle = \sum_{i=1}^{n} c_i^2 \qquad \blacksquare$$

EXAMPLE 4   The vectors

$$\mathbf{u}_1 = \left(\frac{1}{\sqrt{2}}, \frac{1}{\sqrt{2}} \right)^T \qquad \text{and} \qquad \mathbf{u}_2 = \left(\frac{1}{\sqrt{2}}, -\frac{1}{\sqrt{2}} \right)^T$$

form an orthonormal basis for $\mathbb{R}^2$. If $\mathbf{x} \in \mathbb{R}^2$, then

$$\mathbf{x}^T \mathbf{u}_1 = \frac{x_1 + x_2}{\sqrt{2}} \qquad \text{and} \qquad \mathbf{x}^T \mathbf{u}_2 = \frac{x_1 - x_2}{\sqrt{2}}$$

It follows from Theorem 5.5.2 that

$$\mathbf{x} = \frac{x_1 + x_2}{\sqrt{2}} \mathbf{u}_1 + \frac{x_1 - x_2}{\sqrt{2}} \mathbf{u}_2$$

and it follows from Corollary 5.5.4 that

$$\|\mathbf{x}\|^2 = \left(\frac{x_1 + x_2}{\sqrt{2}} \right)^2 + \left(\frac{x_1 - x_2}{\sqrt{2}} \right)^2 = x_1^2 + x_2^2 \qquad \blacksquare$$

EXAMPLE 5   Given that $\{1/\sqrt{2}, \cos 2x\}$ is an orthonormal set in $C[-\pi, \pi]$ (with an inner product as in Example 3), determine the value of $\int_{-\pi}^{\pi} \sin^4 x \, dx$ without computing antiderivatives.

Solution

Since

$$\sin^2 x = \frac{1 - \cos 2x}{2} = \frac{1}{\sqrt{2}} \frac{1}{\sqrt{2}} + \left(-\frac{1}{2} \right) \cos 2x$$

it follows from Parseval's formula that

$$\int_{-\pi}^{\pi} \sin^4 x \, dx = \pi \| \sin^2 x \|^2 = \pi \left(\frac{1}{2} + \frac{1}{4} \right) = \frac{3\pi}{4}$$

Orthogonal Matrices

Of particular importance are $n \times n$ matrices whose column vectors form an orthonormal set in $\mathbb{R}^n$.

Definition

An $n \times n$ matrix Q is said to be an **orthogonal matrix** if the column vectors of Q form an orthonormal set in $\mathbb{R}^n$.

Theorem 5.5.5   *An $n \times n$ matrix Q is orthogonal if and only if $Q^T Q = I$.*

Proof   It follows from the definition that an $n \times n$ matrix Q is orthogonal if and only if its column vectors satisfy

$$\mathbf{q}_i^T \mathbf{q}_j = \delta_{ij}$$

However, $\mathbf{q}_i^T \mathbf{q}_j$ is the (i,j) entry of the matrix $Q^T Q$. Thus, Q is orthogonal if and only if $Q^T Q = I$.

It follows from the theorem that if Q is an orthogonal matrix, then Q is invertible and $Q^{-1} = Q^T$.

EXAMPLE 6   For any fixed θ, the matrix

$$Q = \begin{bmatrix} \cos\theta & -\sin\theta \\ \sin\theta & \cos\theta \end{bmatrix}$$

is orthogonal and

$$Q^{-1} = Q^T = \begin{bmatrix} \cos\theta & \sin\theta \\ -\sin\theta & \cos\theta \end{bmatrix}$$

The matrix Q in Example 6 can be thought of as a linear transformation from $\mathbb{R}^2$ onto $\mathbb{R}^2$ that has the effect of rotating each vector by an angle θ while leaving the length of the vector unchanged (see Example 2 in Section 4.2). Similarly, Q^{-1} can be thought of as a rotation by the angle $-\theta$ (see Figure 5.5.1).

In general, inner products are preserved under multiplication by an orthogonal matrix [i.e., $\langle \mathbf{x}, \mathbf{y} \rangle = \langle Q\mathbf{x}, Q\mathbf{y} \rangle$]. Indeed,

$$\langle Q\mathbf{x}, Q\mathbf{y} \rangle = (Q\mathbf{y})^T Q\mathbf{x} = \mathbf{y}^T Q^T Q\mathbf{x} = \mathbf{y}^T \mathbf{x} = \langle \mathbf{x}, \mathbf{y} \rangle$$

In particular, if $\mathbf{x} = \mathbf{y}$, then $\| Q\mathbf{x} \|^2 = \| \mathbf{x} \|^2$ and hence $\| Q\mathbf{x} \| = \| \mathbf{x} \|$. Multiplication by an orthogonal matrix preserves the lengths of vectors.

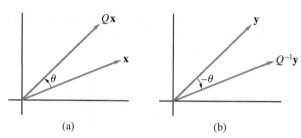

Figure 5.5.1.

Properties of Orthogonal Matrices
If Q is an $n \times n$ orthogonal matrix, then

    (a) the column vectors of Q form an orthonormal basis for $\mathbb{R}^n$
    (b) $Q^T Q = I$
    (c) $Q^T = Q^{-1}$
    (d) $\langle Q\mathbf{x}, Q\mathbf{y} \rangle = \langle \mathbf{x}, \mathbf{y} \rangle$
    (e) $\|Q\mathbf{x}\|_2 = \|\mathbf{x}\|_2$

Permutation Matrices

A *permutation matrix* is a matrix formed from the identity matrix by reordering its columns. Clearly, then, permutation matrices are orthogonal matrices. If P is the permutation matrix formed by reordering the columns of I in the order $(k_1, \ldots, k_n)$, then $P = (\mathbf{e}_{k_1}, \ldots, \mathbf{e}_{k_n})$. If A is an $m \times n$ matrix, then

$$AP = (A\mathbf{e}_{k_1}, \ldots, A\mathbf{e}_{k_n}) = (\mathbf{a}_{k_1}, \ldots, \mathbf{a}_{k_n})$$

Postmultiplication of A by P reorders the columns of A in the order $(k_1, \ldots, k_n)$. For example, if

$$A = \begin{bmatrix} 1 & 2 & 3 \\ 1 & 2 & 3 \end{bmatrix} \qquad \text{and} \qquad P = \begin{bmatrix} 0 & 1 & 0 \\ 0 & 0 & 1 \\ 1 & 0 & 0 \end{bmatrix}$$

then

$$AP = \begin{bmatrix} 3 & 1 & 2 \\ 3 & 1 & 2 \end{bmatrix}$$

Since $P = (\mathbf{e}_{k_1}, \ldots, \mathbf{e}_{k_n})$ is orthogonal, it follows that

$$P^{-1} = P^T = \begin{bmatrix} \mathbf{e}_{k_1}^T \\ \vdots \\ \mathbf{e}_{k_n}^T \end{bmatrix}$$

The k_1 column of P^T will be $\mathbf{e}_1$, the k_2 column will be $\mathbf{e}_2$, and so on. Thus, P^T is a permutation matrix. The matrix P^T can be formed directly from I by reordering its rows in the order $(k_1, k_2, \ldots, k_n)$. In general, a permutation matrix can be formed from I by reordering either its rows or its columns.

If Q is the permutation matrix formed by reordering the rows of I in the order $(k_1, k_2, \ldots, k_n)$ and B is an $n \times r$ matrix, then

$$QB = \begin{pmatrix} \mathbf{e}_{k_1}^T \\ \vdots \\ \mathbf{e}_{k_n}^T \end{pmatrix} B = \begin{pmatrix} \mathbf{e}_{k_1}^T B \\ \vdots \\ \mathbf{e}_{k_n}^T B \end{pmatrix} = \begin{pmatrix} \vec{\mathbf{b}}_{k_1} \\ \vdots \\ \vec{\mathbf{b}}_{k_n} \end{pmatrix}$$

Thus, QB is the matrix formed by reordering the rows of B in the order $(k_1, k_2, \ldots, k_n)$. For example, if

$$Q = \begin{pmatrix} 0 & 0 & 1 \\ 1 & 0 & 0 \\ 0 & 1 & 0 \end{pmatrix} \quad \text{and} \quad B = \begin{pmatrix} 1 & 1 \\ 2 & 2 \\ 3 & 3 \end{pmatrix}$$

then

$$QB = \begin{pmatrix} 3 & 3 \\ 1 & 1 \\ 2 & 2 \end{pmatrix}$$

In general, if P is an $n \times n$ permutation matrix, premultiplication of an $n \times r$ matrix B by P reorders the rows of B and postmultiplication of an $m \times n$ matrix A by P reorders the columns of A.

Orthonormal Sets and Least Squares

Orthogonality plays an important role in solving least squares problems. Recall that if A is an $m \times n$ matrix of rank n, then the least squares problem $A\mathbf{x} = \mathbf{b}$ has a unique solution $\hat{\mathbf{x}}$ that is determined by solving the normal equations $A^T A \mathbf{x} = A^T \mathbf{b}$. The projection $\mathbf{p} = A\hat{\mathbf{x}}$ is the vector in $R(A)$ that is closest to $\mathbf{b}$. The least squares problem is especially easy to solve in the case where the column vectors of A form an orthonormal set in $\mathbb{R}^m$.

Theorem 5.5.6   *If the column vectors of A form an orthonormal set of vectors in $\mathbb{R}^m$, then $A^T A = I$ and the solution to the least squares problem is*

$$\hat{\mathbf{x}} = A^T \mathbf{b}$$

Proof   The (i, j) entry of $A^T A$ is formed from the ith row of A^T and the jth column of A. Thus, the (i, j) entry is actually the scalar product of the ith and jth columns of A. Since the column vectors of A are orthonormal, it follows that

$$A^T A = (\delta_{ij}) = I$$

Consequently, the normal equations simplify to

$$\mathbf{x} = A^T \mathbf{b} \qquad \blacksquare$$

What if the columns of A are not orthonormal? In the next section, we will learn a method for finding an orthonormal basis for $R(A)$. From this method, we will obtain a factorization of A into a product QR, where Q has an orthonormal set of column vectors and R is upper triangular. With this factorization, the least squares problem is easily solved.

If we have an orthonormal basis for $R(A)$, the projection $\mathbf{p} = A\hat{\mathbf{x}}$ can be determined in terms of the basis elements. Indeed, this is a special case of the more general least squares problem of finding the element $\mathbf{p}$ in a subspace S of an inner product space V that is closest to a given element $\mathbf{x}$ in V. This problem is easily solved if S has an orthonormal basis. We first prove the following theorem.

Theorem 5.5.7 *Let S be a subspace of an inner product space V and let $\mathbf{x} \in V$. Let $\{\mathbf{u}_1, \mathbf{u}_2, \ldots, \mathbf{u}_n\}$ be an orthonormal basis for S. If*

$$\mathbf{p} = \sum_{i=1}^{n} c_i \mathbf{u}_i \tag{3}$$

where

$$c_i = \langle \mathbf{x}, \mathbf{u}_i \rangle \qquad \text{for each } i \tag{4}$$

then $\mathbf{p} - \mathbf{x} \in S^\perp$ (see Figure 5.5.2).

Figure 5.5.2.

Proof We will show first that $(\mathbf{p} - \mathbf{x}) \perp \mathbf{u}_i$ for each i.

$$\langle \mathbf{u}_i, \mathbf{p} - \mathbf{x} \rangle = \langle \mathbf{u}_i, \mathbf{p} \rangle - \langle \mathbf{u}_i, \mathbf{x} \rangle$$
$$= \left\langle \mathbf{u}_i, \sum_{j=1}^{n} c_j \mathbf{u}_j \right\rangle - c_i$$
$$= \sum_{j=1}^{n} c_j \langle \mathbf{u}_i, \mathbf{u}_j \rangle - c_i$$
$$= 0$$

So $\mathbf{p} - \mathbf{x}$ is orthogonal to all the $\mathbf{u}_i$'s. If $\mathbf{y} \in S$, then

$$\mathbf{y} = \sum_{i=1}^{n} \alpha_i \mathbf{u}_i$$

and hence

$$\langle \mathbf{p} - \mathbf{x}, \mathbf{y} \rangle = \left\langle \mathbf{p} - \mathbf{x}, \sum_{i=1}^{n} \alpha_i \mathbf{u}_i \right\rangle = \sum_{i=1}^{n} \alpha_i \langle \mathbf{p} - \mathbf{x}, \mathbf{u}_i \rangle = 0 \qquad \blacksquare$$

If $\mathbf{x} \in S$, the preceding result is trivial, since by Theorem 5.5.2, $\mathbf{p} - \mathbf{x} = \mathbf{0}$. If $\mathbf{x} \notin S$, then $\mathbf{p}$ is the element in S closest to $\mathbf{x}$.

Theorem 5.5.8   *Under the hypothesis of Theorem 5.5.7, $\mathbf{p}$ is the element of S that is closest to $\mathbf{x}$; that is,*

$$\|\mathbf{y} - \mathbf{x}\| > \|\mathbf{p} - \mathbf{x}\|$$

for any $\mathbf{y} \neq \mathbf{p}$ in S.

Proof   If $\mathbf{y} \in S$ and $\mathbf{y} \neq \mathbf{p}$, then

$$\|\mathbf{y} - \mathbf{x}\|^2 = \|(\mathbf{y} - \mathbf{p}) + (\mathbf{p} - \mathbf{x})\|^2$$

Since $\mathbf{y} - \mathbf{p} \in S$, it follows from Theorem 5.5.7 and the Pythagorean law that

$$\|\mathbf{y} - \mathbf{x}\|^2 = \|\mathbf{y} - \mathbf{p}\|^2 + \|\mathbf{p} - \mathbf{x}\|^2 > \|\mathbf{p} - \mathbf{x}\|^2$$

Therefore, $\|\mathbf{y} - \mathbf{x}\| > \|\mathbf{p} - \mathbf{x}\|$.   ∎

The vector $\mathbf{p}$ defined by (3) and (4) is said to be the *projection of $\mathbf{x}$ onto S*.

Corollary 5.5.9   *Let S be a nonzero subspace of $\mathbb{R}^m$ and let $\mathbf{b} \in \mathbb{R}^m$. If $\{\mathbf{u}_1, \mathbf{u}_2, \ldots, \mathbf{u}_k\}$ is an orthonormal basis for S and $U = (\mathbf{u}_1, \mathbf{u}_2, \ldots, \mathbf{u}_k)$, then the projection $\mathbf{p}$ of $\mathbf{b}$ onto S is given by*

$$\mathbf{p} = UU^T\mathbf{b}$$

Proof   It follows from Theorem 5.5.7 that the projection $\mathbf{p}$ of $\mathbf{b}$ onto S is given by

$$\mathbf{p} = c_1\mathbf{u}_1 + c_2\mathbf{u}_2 + \cdots + c_k\mathbf{u}_k = U\mathbf{c}$$

where

$$\mathbf{c} = \begin{pmatrix} c_1 \\ c_2 \\ \vdots \\ c_k \end{pmatrix} = \begin{pmatrix} \mathbf{u}_1^T\mathbf{b} \\ \mathbf{u}_2^T\mathbf{b} \\ \vdots \\ \mathbf{u}_k^T\mathbf{b} \end{pmatrix} = U^T\mathbf{b}$$

Therefore,

$$\mathbf{p} = UU^T\mathbf{b}$$ ∎

The matrix UU^T in Corollary 5.5.9 is the projection matrix corresponding to the subspace S of $\mathbb{R}^m$. To project any vector $\mathbf{b} \in \mathbb{R}^m$ onto S, we need only find an orthonormal basis $\{\mathbf{u}_1, \mathbf{u}_2, \ldots, \mathbf{u}_k\}$ for S, form the matrix UU^T, and then multiply UU^T times $\mathbf{b}$.

If P is a projection matrix corresponding to a subspace S of $\mathbb{R}^m$, then, for any $\mathbf{b} \in \mathbb{R}^m$, the projection $\mathbf{p}$ of $\mathbf{b}$ onto S is unique. If Q is also a projection matrix corresponding to S, then

$$Q\mathbf{b} = \mathbf{p} = P\mathbf{b}$$

It then follows that

$$\mathbf{q}_j = Q\mathbf{e}_j = P\mathbf{e}_j = \mathbf{p}_j \qquad \text{for} \quad j = 1, \ldots, m$$

and hence $Q = P$. Thus, the projection matrix for a subspace S of $\mathbb{R}^m$ is unique.

EXAMPLE 7   Let S be the set of all vectors in $\mathbb{R}^3$ of the form $(x, y, 0)^T$. Find the vector $\mathbf{p}$ in S that is closest to $\mathbf{w} = (5, 3, 4)^T$ (see Figure 5.5.3).

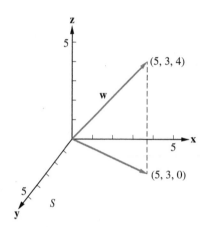

Figure 5.5.3.

Solution

Let $\mathbf{u}_1 = (1, 0, 0)^T$ and $\mathbf{u}_2 = (0, 1, 0)^T$. Clearly, $\mathbf{u}_1$ and $\mathbf{u}_2$ form an orthonormal basis for S. Now

$$c_1 = \mathbf{w}^T\mathbf{u}_1 = 5$$
$$c_2 = \mathbf{w}^T\mathbf{u}_2 = 3$$

The vector $\mathbf{p}$ turns out to be exactly what we would expect:

$$\mathbf{p} = 5\mathbf{u}_1 + 3\mathbf{u}_2 = (5, 3, 0)^T$$

Alternatively, $\mathbf{p}$ could have been calculated using the projection matrix UU^T.

$$\mathbf{p} = UU^T\mathbf{w} = \begin{bmatrix} 1 & 0 & 0 \\ 0 & 1 & 0 \\ 0 & 0 & 0 \end{bmatrix} \begin{bmatrix} 5 \\ 3 \\ 4 \end{bmatrix} = \begin{bmatrix} 5 \\ 3 \\ 0 \end{bmatrix} \qquad \blacksquare$$

Approximation of Functions

In many applications, it is necessary to approximate a continuous function in terms of functions from some special type of approximating set. Most commonly, we approximate by a polynomial of degree n or less. We can use Theorem 5.5.8 to obtain the best least squares approximation.

EXAMPLE 8   Find the best least squares approximation to e^x on the interval $[0, 1]$ by a linear function.

Solution

Let S be the subspace of all linear functions in $C[0, 1]$. Although the functions 1 and x span S, they are not orthogonal. We seek a function of the form $x - a$ that is orthogonal to 1.

$$\langle 1, x - a \rangle = \int_0^1 (x - a)\, dx = \frac{1}{2} - a$$

Thus, $a = \frac{1}{2}$. Since $\|x - \frac{1}{2}\| = 1/\sqrt{12}$, it follows that

$$u_1(x) = 1 \quad \text{and} \quad u_2(x) = \sqrt{12}\left(x - \tfrac{1}{2}\right)$$

form an orthonormal basis for S.

Let

$$c_1 = \int_0^1 u_1(x)\, e^x\, dx = e - 1$$

$$c_2 = \int_0^1 u_2(x)\, e^x\, dx = \sqrt{3}\,(3 - e)$$

The projection

$$
\begin{aligned}
p(x) &= c_1 u_1(x) + c_2 u_2(x) \\
&= (e - 1) \cdot 1 + \sqrt{3}(3 - e)\left[\sqrt{12}\left(x - \tfrac{1}{2}\right)\right] \\
&= (4e - 10) + 6(3 - e)x
\end{aligned}
$$

is the best linear least squares approximation to e^x on $[0, 1]$ (see Figure 5.5.4).

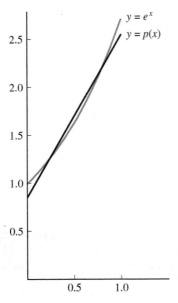

$y = e^x$

$y = p(x)$

Figure 5.5.4.

Approximation by Trigonometric Polynomials

Trigonometric polynomials are used to approximate periodic functions. By a *trigonometric polynomial* of degree n, we mean a function of the form

$$t_n(x) = \frac{a_0}{2} + \sum_{k=1}^{n}(a_k \cos kx + b_k \sin kx)$$

We have already seen that the collection of functions

$$\frac{1}{\sqrt{2}}, \cos x, \cos 2x, \ldots, \cos nx$$

forms an orthonormal set with respect to the inner product (2). We leave it to the reader to verify that if the functions

$$\sin x, \sin 2x, \ldots, \sin nx$$

are added to the collection, it will still be an orthonormal set. Thus, we can use Theorem 5.5.8 to find the best least squares approximation to a continuous 2π periodic function $f(x)$ by a trigonometric polynomial of degree n or less. Note that

$$\left\langle f, \frac{1}{\sqrt{2}} \right\rangle \frac{1}{\sqrt{2}} = \langle f, 1 \rangle \frac{1}{2}$$

so that if

$$a_0 = \langle f, 1 \rangle = \frac{1}{\pi} \int_{-\pi}^{\pi} f(x)\, dx$$

and

$$a_k = \langle f, \cos kx \rangle = \frac{1}{\pi} \int_{-\pi}^{\pi} f(x) \cos kx\, dx$$

$$b_k = \langle f, \sin kx \rangle = \frac{1}{\pi} \int_{-\pi}^{\pi} f(x) \sin kx\, dx$$

for $k = 1, 2, \ldots, n$, then these coefficients determine the best least squares approximation to f. The a_k's and the b_k's turn out to be the well-known *Fourier coefficients* that occur in many applications involving trigonometric series approximations of functions.

Let us think of $f(x)$ as representing the position at time x of an object moving along a line, and let t_n be the Fourier approximation of degree n to f. If we set

$$r_k = \sqrt{a_k^2 + b_k^2} \quad \text{and} \quad \theta_k = \mathrm{Tan}^{-1}\left(\frac{b_k}{a_k}\right)$$

then

$$a_k \cos kx + b_k \sin kx = r_k \left(\frac{a_k}{r_k} \cos kx + \frac{b_k}{r_k} \sin kx\right)$$
$$= r_k \cos(kx - \theta_k)$$

Thus, the motion $f(x)$ is being represented as a sum of simple harmonic motions.

For signal-processing applications, it is useful to express the trigonometric approximation in complex form. To this end, we define complex Fourier coefficients c_k in terms of the real Fourier coefficients a_k and b_k:

$$c_k = \frac{1}{2}(a_k - ib_k) = \frac{1}{2\pi}\int_{-\pi}^{\pi} f(x)(\cos kx - i\sin kx)\, dx$$

$$= \frac{1}{2\pi}\int_{-\pi}^{\pi} f(x)e^{-ikx}dx \quad (k \geq 0)$$

The latter equality follows from the identity

$$e^{i\theta} = \cos\theta + i\sin\theta$$

We also define the coefficient c_{-k} to be the complex conjugate of c_k. Thus,

$$c_{-k} = \overline{c_k} = \frac{1}{2}(a_k + ib_k) \quad (k \geq 0)$$

Alternatively, if we solve for a_k and b_k, then

$$a_k = c_k + c_{-k} \quad \text{and} \quad b_k = i(c_k - c_{-k})$$

From these identities, it follows that

$$c_k e^{ikx} + c_{-k}e^{-ikx} = (c_k + c_{-k})\cos kx + i(c_k - c_{-k})\sin kx$$
$$= a_k \cos kx + b_k \sin kx$$

and hence the trigonometric polynomial

$$t_n(x) = \frac{a_0}{2} + \sum_{k=1}^{n}(a_k \cos kx + b_k \sin kx)$$

can be rewritten in complex form as

$$t_n(x) = \sum_{k=-n}^{n} c_k e^{ikx}$$

APPLICATION I Signal Processing

The Discrete Fourier Transform

The function $f(x)$ pictured in Figure 5.5.5(a) corresponds to a noisy signal. Here, the independent variable x represents time and the signal values are plotted as a function of time. In this context, it is convenient to start with time 0. Thus, we will choose $[0, 2\pi]$, rather than $[-\pi, \pi]$, as the interval for our inner product.

Let us approximate $f(x)$ by a trigonometric polynomial

$$t_n(x) = \sum_{k=-n}^{n} c_k e^{ikx}$$

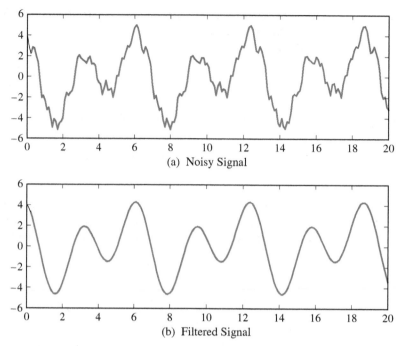

(a) Noisy Signal

(b) Filtered Signal

Figure 5.5.5.

As noted in the previous discussion, the trigonometric approximation allows us to represent the function as a sum of simple harmonics. The kth harmonic can be written as $r_k \cos(kx - \theta_k)$. It is said to have *angular frequency* k. A signal is *smooth* if the coefficients c_k approach 0 rapidly as k increases. If some of the coefficients corresponding to larger frequencies are not small, the graph will appear to be noisy as in Figure 5.5.5(a). We can filter the signal by setting these coefficients equal to 0. Figure 5.5.5(b) shows the smooth function obtained by suppressing some of the higher frequencies from the original signal.

In actual signal-processing applications, we do not have a mathematical formula for the signal function $f(x)$; rather, the signal is sampled over a sequence of times $x_0, x_1, \ldots, x_N$, where $x_j = \frac{2j\pi}{N}$. The function f is represented by the N sample values

$$y_0 = f(x_0), \ y_1 = f(x_1), \ldots, \ y_{N-1} = f(x_{N-1})$$

[*Note:* $y_N = f(2\pi) = f(0) = y_0$.] In this case, it is not possible to compute the Fourier coefficients as integrals. Instead of using

$$c_k = \frac{1}{2\pi} \int_0^{2\pi} f(x)e^{-ikx}dx$$

we use a numerical integration method, the trapezoid rule, to approximate the integral. The approximation is given by

$$d_k = \frac{1}{N} \sum_{j=0}^{N-1} f(x_j)e^{-ikx_j} \tag{5}$$

The d_k coefficients are approximations to the Fourier coefficients. The larger the sample size N, the closer d_k will be to c_k.

If we set

$$\omega_N = e^{-\frac{2\pi i}{N}} = \cos\frac{2\pi}{N} - i\sin\frac{2\pi}{N}$$

then equation (5) can be rewritten in the form

$$d_k = \frac{1}{N}\sum_{j=0}^{N-1} y_j\omega_N^{jk}$$

The finite sequence $\{d_0, d_1, \ldots, d_{N-1}\}$ is said to be the *discrete Fourier transform* of $\{y_0, y_1, \ldots, y_{N-1}\}$. The discrete Fourier transform can be determined by a single matrix vector multiplication. For example, if $N = 4$, the coefficients are given by

$$d_0 = \frac{1}{4}(y_0 + y_1 + y_2 + y_3)$$

$$d_1 = \frac{1}{4}(y_0 + \omega_4 y_1 + \omega_4^2 y_2 + \omega_4^3 y_3)$$

$$d_2 = \frac{1}{4}(y_0 + \omega_4^2 y_1 + \omega_4^4 y_2 + \omega_4^6 y_3)$$

$$d_3 = \frac{1}{4}(y_0 + \omega_4^3 y_1 + \omega_4^6 y_2 + \omega_4^9 y_3)$$

If we set

$$\mathbf{z} = \frac{1}{4}\mathbf{y} = \frac{1}{4}(y_0, y_1, y_2, y_3)^T$$

then the vector $\mathbf{d} = (d_0, d_1, d_2, d_3)^T$ is determined by multiplying $\mathbf{z}$ by the matrix

$$F_4 = \begin{pmatrix} 1 & 1 & 1 & 1 \\ 1 & \omega_4 & \omega_4^2 & \omega_4^3 \\ 1 & \omega_4^2 & \omega_4^4 & \omega_4^6 \\ 1 & \omega_4^3 & \omega_4^6 & \omega_4^9 \end{pmatrix} = \begin{pmatrix} 1 & 1 & 1 & 1 \\ 1 & -i & -1 & i \\ 1 & -1 & 1 & -1 \\ 1 & i & -1 & -i \end{pmatrix}$$

The matrix F_4 is called a *Fourier matrix*.

In the case of N sample values, $y_0, y_1, \ldots, y_{N-1}$, the coefficients are computed by setting

$$\mathbf{z} = \frac{1}{N}\mathbf{y} \qquad \text{and} \qquad \mathbf{d} = F_N\mathbf{z}$$

where $\mathbf{y} = (y_0, y_1, \ldots, y_{N-1})^T$ and F_N is the $N \times N$ matrix whose (j, k) entry is given by $f_{j,k} = \omega_N^{(j-1)(k-1)}$. The method of computing the discrete Fourier transform $\mathbf{d}$ by multiplying F_N times $\mathbf{z}$ will be referred to as the *DFT algorithm*. The DFT computation requires a multiple of N^2 arithmetic operations (roughly $8N^2$, since complex arithmetic is used).

In signal-processing applications, N is generally very large and consequently the DFT computation of the discrete Fourier transform can be prohibitively slow and costly even on modern high-powered computers. A revolution in signal processing occurred in 1965 with the introduction by James W. Cooley and John W. Tukey of a dramatically more efficient method for computing the discrete Fourier transform. Actually, it turns out that the 1965 Cooley–Tukey paper is a rediscovery of a method that was known to Gauss in 1805.

The Fast Fourier Transform

The method of Cooley and Tukey, known as the *fast Fourier transform* or simply the *FFT*, is an efficient algorithm for computing the discrete Fourier transform. It takes advantage of the special structure of the Fourier matrices. We illustrate this method in the case $N = 4$. To see the special structure, we rearrange the columns of F_4 so that its odd-numbered columns all come before the even-numbered columns. This rearrangement is equivalent to postmultiplying F_4 by the permutation matrix

$$P_4 = \begin{pmatrix} 1 & 0 & 0 & 0 \\ 0 & 0 & 1 & 0 \\ 0 & 1 & 0 & 0 \\ 0 & 0 & 0 & 1 \end{pmatrix}$$

If we set $\mathbf{w} = P_4^T \mathbf{z}$, then

$$F_4 \mathbf{z} = F_4 P_4 P_4^T \mathbf{z} = F_4 P_4 \mathbf{w}$$

Partitioning $F_4 P_4$ into 2×2 blocks, we get

$$F_4 P_4 = \left(\begin{array}{cc|cc} 1 & 1 & 1 & 1 \\ 1 & -1 & -i & i \\ \hline 1 & 1 & -1 & -1 \\ 1 & -1 & i & -i \end{array} \right)$$

The $(1,1)$ and $(2,1)$ blocks are both equal to the Fourier matrix F_2, and if we set

$$D_2 = \begin{bmatrix} 1 & 0 \\ 0 & -i \end{bmatrix}$$

then the $(1,2)$ and $(2,2)$ blocks are $D_2 F_2$ and $-D_2 F_2$, respectively. The computation of the Fourier transform can now be carried out as a block multiplication.

$$\mathbf{d}_4 = \begin{bmatrix} F_2 & D_2 F_2 \\ F_2 & -D_2 F_2 \end{bmatrix} \begin{bmatrix} \mathbf{w}_1 \\ \mathbf{w}_2 \end{bmatrix} = \begin{bmatrix} F_2 \mathbf{w}_1 + D_2 F_2 \mathbf{w}_2 \\ F_2 \mathbf{w}_1 - D_2 F_2 \mathbf{w}_2 \end{bmatrix}$$

The computation reduces to computing two Fourier transforms of length 2. If we set $\mathbf{q}_1 = F_2 \mathbf{w}_1$ and $\mathbf{q}_2 = D_2(F_2 \mathbf{w}_2)$, then

$$\mathbf{d}_4 = \begin{bmatrix} \mathbf{q}_1 + \mathbf{q}_2 \\ \mathbf{q}_1 - \mathbf{q}_2 \end{bmatrix}$$

The procedure we have just described will work in general whenever the number of sample points is even. If, say, $N = 2m$, and we permute the columns of F_{2m} so that the odd columns are first, then the reordered Fourier matrix $F_{2m}P_{2m}$ can be partitioned into $m \times m$ blocks

$$F_{2m}P_{2m} = \begin{bmatrix} F_m & D_m F_m \\ F_m & -D_m F_m \end{bmatrix}$$

where D_m is a diagonal matrix whose (j, j) entry is ω_{2m}^{j-1}. The discrete Fourier transform can then be computed in terms of two transforms of length m. Furthermore, if m is even, then each length m transform can be computed in terms of two transforms of length $\frac{m}{2}$, and so on.

If, initially, N is a power of 2, say, $N = 2^k$, then we can apply this procedure recursively through k levels of recursion. The amount of arithmetic required to compute the FFT is proportional to $Nk = N \log_2 N$. In fact, the actual amount of arithmetic operations required for the FFT is approximately $5N \log_2 N$. How dramatic of a speedup is this? If we consider, for example, the case where $N = 2^{20} = 1,048,576$, then the DFT algorithm requires $8N^2 = 8 \cdot 2^{40}$ operations, that is, approximately 8.8 trillion operations. On the other hand, the FFT algorithm requires only $100N = 100 \cdot 2^{20}$, or approximately 100 million, operations. The ratio of these two operations counts is

$$r = \frac{8N^2}{5N \log_2 N} = 0.08 \cdot 1,048,576 = 83,886$$

In this case, the FFT algorithm is approximately 84,000 times faster than the DFT algorithm.

SECTION 5.5 EXERCISES

1. Which of the following sets of vectors form an orthonormal basis for $\mathbb{R}^2$?

   (a) $\{(1, 0)^T, (0, 1)^T\}$

   (b) $\left\{\left(\frac{3}{5}, \frac{4}{5}\right)^T, \left(\frac{5}{13}, \frac{12}{13}\right)^T\right\}$

   (c) $\{(1, -1)^T, (1, 1)^T\}$

   (d) $\left\{\left(\frac{\sqrt{3}}{2}, \frac{1}{2}\right)^T, \left(-\frac{1}{2}, \frac{\sqrt{3}}{2}\right)^T\right\}$

2. Let

   $$\mathbf{u}_1 = \begin{bmatrix} \frac{1}{3\sqrt{2}} \\ \frac{1}{3\sqrt{2}} \\ -\frac{4}{3\sqrt{2}} \end{bmatrix}, \quad \mathbf{u}_2 = \begin{bmatrix} \frac{2}{3} \\ \frac{2}{3} \\ \frac{1}{3} \end{bmatrix}, \quad \mathbf{u}_3 = \begin{bmatrix} \frac{1}{\sqrt{2}} \\ -\frac{1}{\sqrt{2}} \\ 0 \end{bmatrix}$$

   (a) Show that $\{\mathbf{u}_1, \mathbf{u}_2, \mathbf{u}_3\}$ is an orthonormal basis for $\mathbb{R}^3$.

   (b) Let $\mathbf{x} = (1, 1, 1)^T$. Write $\mathbf{x}$ as a linear combination of $\mathbf{u}_1$, $\mathbf{u}_2$, and $\mathbf{u}_3$ using Theorem 5.5.2 and use Parseval's formula to compute $\|\mathbf{x}\|$.

3. Let S be the subspace of $\mathbb{R}^3$ spanned by the vectors $\mathbf{u}_2$ and $\mathbf{u}_3$ of Exercise 2. Let $\mathbf{x} = (1, 2, 2)^T$. Find the projection $\mathbf{p}$ of $\mathbf{x}$ onto S. Show that $(\mathbf{p} - \mathbf{x}) \perp \mathbf{u}_2$ and $(\mathbf{p} - \mathbf{x}) \perp \mathbf{u}_3$.

4. Let θ be a fixed real number and let

   $$\mathbf{x}_1 = \begin{bmatrix} \cos \theta \\ \sin \theta \end{bmatrix} \quad \text{and} \quad \mathbf{x}_2 = \begin{bmatrix} -\sin \theta \\ \cos \theta \end{bmatrix}$$

   (a) Show that $\{\mathbf{x}_1, \mathbf{x}_2\}$ is an orthonormal basis for $\mathbb{R}^2$.

   (b) Given a vector $\mathbf{y}$ in $\mathbb{R}^2$, write it as a linear combination $c_1\mathbf{x}_1 + c_2\mathbf{x}_2$.

   (c) Verify that

   $$c_1^2 + c_2^2 = \|\mathbf{y}\|^2 = y_1^2 + y_2^2$$

5. Let $\mathbf{u}_1$ and $\mathbf{u}_2$ form an orthonormal basis for $\mathbb{R}^2$ and let $\mathbf{u}$ be a unit vector in $\mathbb{R}^2$. If $\mathbf{u}^T\mathbf{u}_1 = \frac{1}{2}$, determine the value of $|\mathbf{u}^T\mathbf{u}_2|$.

6. Let $\{\mathbf{u}_1, \mathbf{u}_2, \mathbf{u}_3\}$ be an orthonormal basis for an inner product space V and let

$$\mathbf{u} = \mathbf{u}_1 + 2\mathbf{u}_2 + 2\mathbf{u}_3 \qquad \text{and} \qquad \mathbf{v} = \mathbf{u}_1 + 7\mathbf{u}_3$$

Determine the value of each of the following:

(a) $\langle \mathbf{u}, \mathbf{v} \rangle$ **(b)** $\|\mathbf{u}\|$ and $\|\mathbf{v}\|$

(c) The angle θ between $\mathbf{u}$ and $\mathbf{v}$

7. Let $\{\mathbf{u}_1, \mathbf{u}_2, \mathbf{u}_3\}$ be an orthonormal basis for an inner product space V. If $\mathbf{x} = c_1\mathbf{u}_1 + c_2\mathbf{u}_2 + c_3\mathbf{u}_3$ is a vector with the properties $\|\mathbf{x}\| = 5$, $\langle \mathbf{u}_1, \mathbf{x} \rangle = 4$, and $\mathbf{x} \perp \mathbf{u}_2$, then what are the possible values of c_1, c_2, c_3?

8. The functions $\cos x$ and $\sin x$ form an orthonormal set in $C[-\pi, \pi]$. If

$$f(x) = 3\cos x + 2\sin x \quad \text{and} \quad g(x) = \cos x - \sin x$$

use Corollary 5.5.3 to determine the value of

$$\langle f, g \rangle = \frac{1}{\pi} \int_{-\pi}^{\pi} f(x)g(x)\, dx$$

9. The set

$$S = \left\{ \frac{1}{\sqrt{2}}, \cos x, \cos 2x, \cos 3x, \cos 4x \right\}$$

is an orthonormal set of vectors in $C[-\pi, \pi]$ with the inner product defined by (2).

(a) Use trigonometric identities to write the function $\sin^4 x$ as a linear combination of elements of S.

(b) Use part (a) and Theorem 5.5.2 to find the values of the following integrals:

(i) $\int_{-\pi}^{\pi} \sin^4 x \cos x\, dx$ **(ii)** $\int_{-\pi}^{\pi} \sin^4 x \cos 2x\, dx$

(iii) $\int_{-\pi}^{\pi} \sin^4 x \cos 3x\, dx$ **(iv)** $\int_{-\pi}^{\pi} \sin^4 x \cos 4x\, dx$

10. Write out the Fourier matrix F_8. Show that $F_8 P_8$ can be partitioned into block form:

$$\begin{bmatrix} F_4 & D_4 F_4 \\ F_4 & -D_4 F_4 \end{bmatrix}$$

11. Prove that the transpose of an orthogonal matrix is an orthogonal matrix.

12. If Q is an $n \times n$ orthogonal matrix and $\mathbf{x}$ and $\mathbf{y}$ are nonzero vectors in $\mathbb{R}^n$, then how does the angle between $Q\mathbf{x}$ and $Q\mathbf{y}$ compare with the angle between $\mathbf{x}$ and $\mathbf{y}$? Prove your answer.

13. Let Q be an $n \times n$ orthogonal matrix. Use mathematical induction to prove each of the following:

(a) $(Q^m)^{-1} = (Q^T)^m = (Q^m)^T$ for any positive integer m

(b) $\|Q^m\mathbf{x}\| = \|\mathbf{x}\|$ for any $\mathbf{x} \in \mathbb{R}^n$

14. Let $\mathbf{u}$ be a unit vector in $\mathbb{R}^n$ and let $H = I - 2\mathbf{u}\mathbf{u}^T$. Show that H is both orthogonal and symmetric and hence is its own inverse.

15. Let Q be an orthogonal matrix and let $d = \det(Q)$. Show that $|d| = 1$.

16. Show that the product of two orthogonal matrices is also an orthogonal matrix. Is the product of two permutation matrices a permutation matrix? Explain.

17. How many $n \times n$ permutation matrices are there?

18. Show that if P is a symmetric permutation matrix, then $P^{2k} = I$ and $P^{2k+1} = P$.

19. Show that if U is an $n \times n$ orthogonal matrix, then

$$\mathbf{u}_1\mathbf{u}_1^T + \mathbf{u}_2\mathbf{u}_2^T + \cdots + \mathbf{u}_n\mathbf{u}_n^T = I$$

20. Use mathematical induction to show that if $Q \in \mathbb{R}^{n \times n}$ is both upper triangular and orthogonal, then $\mathbf{q}_j = \pm\mathbf{e}_j$, $j = 1, \ldots, n$.

21. Let

$$A = \begin{bmatrix} \frac{1}{2} & -\frac{1}{2} \\ \frac{1}{2} & -\frac{1}{2} \\ \frac{1}{2} & \frac{1}{2} \\ \frac{1}{2} & \frac{1}{2} \end{bmatrix}$$

(a) Show that the column vectors of A form an orthonormal set in $\mathbb{R}^4$.

(b) Solve the least squares problem $A\mathbf{x} = \mathbf{b}$ for each of the following choices of $\mathbf{b}$:

(i) $\mathbf{b} = (4, 0, 0, 0)^T$ **(ii)** $\mathbf{b} = (1, 2, 3, 4)^T$

(iii) $\mathbf{b} = (1, 1, 2, 2)^T$

22. Let A be the matrix given in Exercise 21.

(a) Find the projection matrix P that projects vectors in $\mathbb{R}^4$ onto $R(A)$.

(b) For each of your solutions $\mathbf{x}$ to Exercise 21(b), compute $A\mathbf{x}$ and compare it with $P\mathbf{b}$.

23. Let A be the matrix given in Exercise 21.

(a) Find an orthonormal basis for $N(A^T)$.

(b) Determine the projection matrix Q that projects vectors in $\mathbb{R}^4$ onto $N(A^T)$.

24. Let A be an $m \times n$ matrix, let P be the projection matrix that projects vectors in $\mathbb{R}^m$ onto $R(A)$, and let Q be the projection matrix that projects vectors in $\mathbb{R}^n$ onto $R(A^T)$. Show that

(a) $I - P$ is the projection matrix from $\mathbb{R}^m$ onto $N(A^T)$.

(b) $I - Q$ is the projection matrix from $\mathbb{R}^n$ onto $N(A)$.

25. Let P be the projection matrix corresponding to a subspace S of $\mathbb{R}^m$. Show that

(a) $P^2 = P$ (b) $P^T = P$

26. Let A be an $m \times n$ matrix whose column vectors are mutually orthogonal and let $\mathbf{b} \in \mathbb{R}^m$. Show that if $\mathbf{y}$ is the least squares solution of the system $A\mathbf{x} = \mathbf{b}$, then

$$y_i = \frac{\mathbf{b}^T \mathbf{a}_i}{\mathbf{a}_i^T \mathbf{a}_i} \qquad i = 1, \ldots, n$$

27. Let $\mathbf{v}$ be a vector in an inner product space V and let $\mathbf{p}$ be the projection of $\mathbf{v}$ onto an n-dimensional subspace S of V. Show that $\|\mathbf{p}\| \leq \|\mathbf{v}\|$. Under what conditions does equality occur?

28. Let $\mathbf{v}$ be a vector in an inner product space V and let $\mathbf{p}$ be the projection of $\mathbf{v}$ onto an n-dimensional subspace S of V. Show that $\|\mathbf{p}\|^2 = \langle \mathbf{p}, \mathbf{v} \rangle$.

29. Given the vector space $C[-1, 1]$ with inner product

$$\langle f, g \rangle = \int_{-1}^{1} f(x)g(x)\,dx$$

and norm

$$\|f\| = (\langle f, f \rangle)^{1/2}$$

(a) show that the vectors 1 and x are orthogonal.

(b) compute $\|1\|$ and $\|x\|$.

(c) find the best least squares approximation to $x^{1/3}$ on $[-1, 1]$ by a linear function $l(x) = c_1 1 + c_2 x$.

(d) sketch the graphs of $x^{1/3}$ and $l(x)$ on $[-1, 1]$.

30. Consider the inner product space $C[0, 1]$ with the inner product defined by

$$\langle f, g \rangle = \int_{0}^{1} f(x)g(x)\,dx$$

Let S be the subspace spanned by the vectors 1 and $2x-1$.

(a) Show that 1 and $2x - 1$ are orthogonal.

(b) Determine $\|1\|$ and $\|2x - 1\|$.

(c) Find the best least squares approximation to $\sqrt{x}$ by a function from the subspace S.

31. Let

$$S = \{1/\sqrt{2}, \cos x, \cos 2x, \ldots, \cos nx,$$

$$\sin x, \sin 2x, \ldots, \sin nx\}$$

Show that S is an orthonormal set in $C[-\pi, \pi]$ with the inner product defined by (2).

32. Find the best least squares approximation to $f(x) = |x|$ on $[-\pi, \pi]$ by a trigonometric polynomial of degree less than or equal to 2.

33. Let $\{\mathbf{x}_1, \mathbf{x}_2, \ldots, \mathbf{x}_k, \mathbf{x}_{k+1}, \ldots, \mathbf{x}_n\}$ be an orthonormal basis for an inner product space V. Let S_1 be the subspace of V spanned by $\mathbf{x}_1, \ldots, \mathbf{x}_k$, and let S_2 be the subspace spanned by $\mathbf{x}_{k+1}, \mathbf{x}_{k+2}, \ldots, \mathbf{x}_n$. Show that $S_1 \perp S_2$.

34. Let $\mathbf{x}$ be an element of the inner product space V in Exercise 33, and let $\mathbf{p}_1$ and $\mathbf{p}_2$ be the projections of $\mathbf{x}$ onto S_1 and S_2, respectively. Show that

(a) $\mathbf{x} = \mathbf{p}_1 + \mathbf{p}_2$.

(b) if $\mathbf{x} \in S_1^\perp$, then $\mathbf{p}_1 = \mathbf{0}$ and hence $S_1^\perp = S_2$.

35. Let S be a subspace of an inner product space V. Let $\{\mathbf{x}_1, \ldots, \mathbf{x}_n\}$ be an orthogonal basis for S and let $\mathbf{x} \in V$. Show that the best least squares approximation to $\mathbf{x}$ by elements of S is given by

$$\mathbf{p} = \sum_{i=1}^{n} \frac{\langle \mathbf{x}, \mathbf{x}_i \rangle}{\langle \mathbf{x}_i, \mathbf{x}_i \rangle} \mathbf{x}_i$$

36. A (real or complex) scalar u is said to be an nth root of unity if $u^n = 1$.

(a) Show that if u is an nth root of unity and $u \neq 1$, then

$$1 + u + +u^2 + \cdots + u^{n-1} = 0$$

[Hint: $1 - u^n = (1 - u)(1 + u + u^2 + \cdots + u^{n-1})$.]

(b) Let $\omega_n = e^{\frac{2\pi i}{n}}$. Use Euler's formula ($e^{i\theta} = \cos\theta + i\sin\theta$) to show that ω_n is an nth root of unity.

(c) Show that if j and k are positive integers and if $u_j = \omega_n^{j-1}$ and $z_k = \omega_n^{-(k-1)}$, then u_j, z_k, and $u_j z_k$ are all nth roots of unity.

37. Let ω_n, u_j, and z_k be defined as in Exercise 36. If F_n is the $n \times n$ Fourier matrix, then its (j, s) entry is

$$f_{js} = \omega_n^{(j-1)(s-1)} = u^{s-1}$$

Let G_n be the matrix defined by

$$g_{sk} = \frac{1}{f_{sk}} = \omega^{-(s-1)(k-1)} = z_k^{s-1}, \quad 1 \leq s \leq n,$$
$$1 \leq k \leq n$$

Show that the the (j, k) entry of $F_n G_n$ is

$$1 + u_j z_k + (u_j z_k)^2 + \cdots + (u_j z_k)^{n-1}$$

38. Use the results from Exercises 36 and 37 to show that F_n is nonsingular and

$$F_n^{-1} = \frac{1}{n} G_n = \frac{1}{n}\overline{F_n}$$

where $\overline{F_n}$ is the matrix whose (i, j) entry is the complex conjugate of f_{ij}.

5.6 The Gram–Schmidt Orthogonalization Process

In this section, we learn a process for constructing an orthonormal basis for an n-dimensional inner product space V. The method involves using projections to transform an ordinary basis $\{\mathbf{x}_1, \mathbf{x}_2, \ldots, \mathbf{x}_n\}$ into an orthonormal basis $\{\mathbf{u}_1, \mathbf{u}_2, \ldots, \mathbf{u}_n\}$.

We will construct the $\mathbf{u}_i$'s so that

$$\mathrm{Span}(\mathbf{u}_1, \ldots, \mathbf{u}_k) = \mathrm{Span}(\mathbf{x}_1, \ldots, \mathbf{x}_k)$$

for $k = 1, \ldots, n$. To begin the process, let

$$\mathbf{u}_1 = \left(\frac{1}{\|\mathbf{x}_1\|} \right) \mathbf{x}_1 \tag{1}$$

$\mathrm{Span}(\mathbf{u}_1) = \mathrm{Span}(\mathbf{x}_1)$, since $\mathbf{u}_1$ is a unit vector in the direction of $\mathbf{x}_1$. Let $\mathbf{p}_1$ denote the projection of $\mathbf{x}_2$ onto $\mathrm{Span}(\mathbf{x}_1) = \mathrm{Span}(\mathbf{u}_1)$; that is,

$$\mathbf{p}_1 = \langle \mathbf{x}_2, \mathbf{u}_1 \rangle \, \mathbf{u}_1$$

By Theorem 5.5.7,

$$(\mathbf{x}_2 - \mathbf{p}_1) \perp \mathbf{u}_1$$

Note that $\mathbf{x}_2 - \mathbf{p}_1 \neq \mathbf{0}$, since

$$\mathbf{x}_2 - \mathbf{p}_1 = \frac{-\langle \mathbf{x}_2, \mathbf{u}_1 \rangle}{\|\mathbf{x}_1\|} \mathbf{x}_1 + \mathbf{x}_2 \tag{2}$$

and $\mathbf{x}_1$ and $\mathbf{x}_2$ are linearly independent. If we set

$$\mathbf{u}_2 = \frac{1}{\|\mathbf{x}_2 - \mathbf{p}_1\|}(\mathbf{x}_2 - \mathbf{p}_1) \tag{3}$$

then $\mathbf{u}_2$ is a unit vector orthogonal to $\mathbf{u}_1$. It follows from (1), (2), and (3) that $\mathrm{Span}(\mathbf{u}_1, \mathbf{u}_2) \subset \mathrm{Span}(\mathbf{x}_1, \mathbf{x}_2)$. Since $\mathbf{u}_1$ and $\mathbf{u}_2$ are linearly independent, it also follows that $\{\mathbf{u}_1, \mathbf{u}_2\}$ is an orthonormal basis for $\mathrm{Span}(\mathbf{x}_1, \mathbf{x}_2)$, and hence

$$\mathrm{Span}(\mathbf{x}_1, \mathbf{x}_2) = \mathrm{Span}(\mathbf{u}_1, \mathbf{u}_2)$$

To construct $\mathbf{u}_3$, continue in the same manner: Let $\mathbf{p}_2$ be the projection of $\mathbf{x}_3$ onto $\mathrm{Span}(\mathbf{x}_1, \mathbf{x}_2) = \mathrm{Span}(\mathbf{u}_1, \mathbf{u}_2)$; that is,

$$\mathbf{p}_2 = \langle \mathbf{x}_3, \mathbf{u}_1 \rangle \, \mathbf{u}_1 + \langle \mathbf{x}_3, \mathbf{u}_2 \rangle \, \mathbf{u}_2$$

and set

$$\mathbf{u}_3 = \frac{1}{\|\mathbf{x}_3 - \mathbf{p}_2\|}(\mathbf{x}_3 - \mathbf{p}_2)$$

and so on (see Figure 5.6.1).

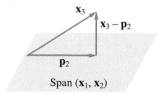

Figure 5.6.1.

Theorem 5.6.1   The Gram–Schmidt Process

Let $\{\mathbf{x}_1, \mathbf{x}_2, \ldots, \mathbf{x}_n\}$ be a basis for the inner product space V. Let

$$\mathbf{u}_1 = \left(\frac{1}{\|\mathbf{x}_1\|}\right) \mathbf{x}_1$$

and define $\mathbf{u}_2, \ldots, \mathbf{u}_n$ recursively by

$$\mathbf{u}_{k+1} = \frac{1}{\|\mathbf{x}_{k+1} - \mathbf{p}_k\|}(\mathbf{x}_{k+1} - \mathbf{p}_k) \quad \text{for } k = 1, \ldots, n-1$$

where

$$\mathbf{p}_k = \langle \mathbf{x}_{k+1}, \mathbf{u}_1 \rangle \, \mathbf{u}_1 + \langle \mathbf{x}_{k+1}, \mathbf{u}_2 \rangle \, \mathbf{u}_2 + \cdots + \langle \mathbf{x}_{k+1}, \mathbf{u}_k \rangle \, \mathbf{u}_k$$

is the projection of $\mathbf{x}_{k+1}$ onto $\mathrm{Span}(\mathbf{u}_1, \mathbf{u}_2, \ldots, \mathbf{u}_k)$. Then the set

$$\{\mathbf{u}_1, \mathbf{u}_2, \ldots, \mathbf{u}_n\}$$

is an orthonormal basis for V.

Proof   We will argue inductively. Clearly, $\mathrm{Span}(\mathbf{u}_1) = \mathrm{Span}(\mathbf{x}_1)$. Suppose that $\mathbf{u}_1, \mathbf{u}_2, \ldots, \mathbf{u}_k$ have been constructed so that $\{\mathbf{u}_1, \mathbf{u}_2, \ldots, \mathbf{u}_k\}$ is an orthonormal set and

$$\mathrm{Span}(\mathbf{u}_1, \mathbf{u}_2, \ldots, \mathbf{u}_k) = \mathrm{Span}(\mathbf{x}_1, \mathbf{x}_2, \ldots, \mathbf{x}_k)$$

Since $\mathbf{p}_k$ is a linear combination of $\mathbf{u}_1, \ldots, \mathbf{u}_k$, it follows that $\mathbf{p}_k \in \mathrm{Span}(\mathbf{x}_1, \ldots, \mathbf{x}_k)$ and $\mathbf{x}_{k+1} - \mathbf{p}_k \in \mathrm{Span}(\mathbf{x}_1, \ldots, \mathbf{x}_{k+1})$.

$$\mathbf{x}_{k+1} - \mathbf{p}_k = \mathbf{x}_{k+1} - \sum_{i=1}^{k} c_i \mathbf{x}_i$$

Since $\mathbf{x}_1, \ldots, \mathbf{x}_{k+1}$ are linearly independent, it follows that $\mathbf{x}_{k+1} - \mathbf{p}_k$ is nonzero and, by Theorem 5.5.7, it is orthogonal to each $\mathbf{u}_i$, $1 \le i \le k$. Thus, $\{\mathbf{u}_1, \mathbf{u}_2, \ldots, \mathbf{u}_{k+1}\}$ is an orthonormal set of vectors in $\mathrm{Span}(\mathbf{x}_1, \ldots, \mathbf{x}_{k+1})$. Since $\mathbf{u}_1, \ldots, \mathbf{u}_{k+1}$ are linearly independent, they form a basis for $\mathrm{Span}(\mathbf{x}_1, \ldots, \mathbf{x}_{k+1})$ and, consequently,

$$\mathrm{Span}(\mathbf{u}_1, \ldots, \mathbf{u}_{k+1}) = \mathrm{Span}(\mathbf{x}_1, \ldots, \mathbf{x}_{k+1})$$

It follows by mathematical induction that $\{\mathbf{u}_1, \mathbf{u}_2, \ldots, \mathbf{u}_n\}$ is an orthonormal basis for V.

EXAMPLE 1 Find an orthonormal basis for P_3 if the inner product on P_3 is defined by

$$\langle p, q \rangle = \sum_{i=1}^{3} p(x_i)q(x_i)$$

where $x_1 = -1$, $x_2 = 0$, and $x_3 = 1$.

Solution

Starting with the basis $\{1, x, x^2\}$, we can use the Gram–Schmidt process to generate an orthonormal basis:

$$\|1\|^2 = \langle 1, 1 \rangle = 3$$

so

$$\mathbf{u}_1 = \left(\frac{1}{\|1\|} \right) 1 = \frac{1}{\sqrt{3}}$$

Set

$$p_1 = \left\langle x, \frac{1}{\sqrt{3}} \right\rangle \frac{1}{\sqrt{3}} = \left(-1 \cdot \frac{1}{\sqrt{3}} + 0 \cdot \frac{1}{\sqrt{3}} + 1 \cdot \frac{1}{\sqrt{3}} \right) \frac{1}{\sqrt{3}} = 0$$

Therefore,

$$x - p_1 = x \quad \text{and} \quad \|x - p_1\|^2 = \langle x, x \rangle = 2$$

Hence,

$$\mathbf{u}_2 = \frac{1}{\sqrt{2}} x$$

Finally,

$$p_2 = \left\langle x^2, \frac{1}{\sqrt{3}} \right\rangle \frac{1}{\sqrt{3}} + \left\langle x^2, \frac{1}{\sqrt{2}} x \right\rangle \frac{1}{\sqrt{2}} x = \frac{2}{3}$$

$$\|x^2 - p_2\|^2 = \left\langle x^2 - \frac{2}{3}, x^2 - \frac{2}{3} \right\rangle = \frac{2}{3}$$

and hence

$$\mathbf{u}_3 = \frac{\sqrt{6}}{2} \left(x^2 - \frac{2}{3} \right)$$

Orthogonal polynomials will be studied in more detail in Section 5.7.

EXAMPLE 2 Let

$$A = \begin{bmatrix} 1 & -1 & 4 \\ 1 & 4 & -2 \\ 1 & 4 & 2 \\ 1 & -1 & 0 \end{bmatrix}$$

Find an orthonormal basis for the column space of A.

Solution

The column vectors of A are linearly independent and hence form a basis for a three-dimensional subspace of $\mathbb{R}^4$. The Gram–Schmidt process can be used to construct an orthonormal basis as follows: Set

$$r_{11} = \|\mathbf{a}_1\| = 2$$

$$\mathbf{q}_1 = \frac{1}{r_{11}}\mathbf{a}_1 = \left(\frac{1}{2}, \frac{1}{2}, \frac{1}{2}, \frac{1}{2}\right)^T$$
$$r_{12} = \langle \mathbf{a}_2, \mathbf{q}_1 \rangle = \mathbf{q}_1^T \mathbf{a}_2 = 3$$
$$\mathbf{p}_1 = r_{12}\mathbf{q}_1 = 3\mathbf{q}_1$$

$$\mathbf{a}_2 - \mathbf{p}_1 = \left(-\frac{5}{2}, \frac{5}{2}, \frac{5}{2}, -\frac{5}{2}\right)^T$$
$$r_{22} = \|\mathbf{a}_2 - \mathbf{p}_1\| = 5$$

$$\mathbf{q}_2 = \frac{1}{r_{22}}(\mathbf{a}_2 - \mathbf{p}_1) = \left(-\frac{1}{2}, \frac{1}{2}, \frac{1}{2}, -\frac{1}{2}\right)^T$$
$$r_{13} = \langle \mathbf{a}_3, \mathbf{q}_1 \rangle = \mathbf{q}_1^T \mathbf{a}_3 = 2, \qquad r_{23} = \langle \mathbf{a}_3, \mathbf{q}_2 \rangle = \mathbf{q}_2^T \mathbf{a}_3 = -2$$
$$\mathbf{p}_2 = r_{13}\mathbf{q}_1 + r_{23}\mathbf{q}_2 = (2, 0, 0, 2)^T$$

$$\mathbf{a}_3 - \mathbf{p}_2 = (2, -2, 2, -2)^T$$
$$r_{33} = \|\mathbf{a}_3 - \mathbf{p}_2\| = 4$$
$$\mathbf{q}_3 = \frac{1}{r_{33}}(\mathbf{a}_3 - \mathbf{p}_2) = \left(\frac{1}{2}, -\frac{1}{2}, \frac{1}{2}, -\frac{1}{2}\right)^T$$

The vectors $\mathbf{q}_1, \mathbf{q}_2, \mathbf{q}_3$ form an orthonormal basis for $R(A)$.   ∎

We can obtain a useful factorization of the matrix A if we keep track of all the inner products and norms computed in the Gram–Schmidt process. For the matrix in Example 2, if the r_{ij}'s are used to form a matrix

$$R = \begin{bmatrix} r_{11} & r_{12} & r_{13} \\ 0 & r_{22} & r_{23} \\ 0 & 0 & r_{33} \end{bmatrix} = \begin{bmatrix} 2 & 3 & 2 \\ 0 & 5 & -2 \\ 0 & 0 & 4 \end{bmatrix}$$

and we set

$$Q = (\mathbf{q}_1, \mathbf{q}_2, \mathbf{q}_3) = \begin{bmatrix} \frac{1}{2} & -\frac{1}{2} & \frac{1}{2} \\ \frac{1}{2} & \frac{1}{2} & -\frac{1}{2} \\ \frac{1}{2} & \frac{1}{2} & \frac{1}{2} \\ \frac{1}{2} & -\frac{1}{2} & -\frac{1}{2} \end{bmatrix}$$

then it is easily verified that $QR = A$. This result is proved in the following theorem.

Theorem 5.6.2   Gram–Schmidt QR Factorization

If A is an $m \times n$ matrix of rank n, then A can be factored into a product QR, where Q is an $m \times n$ matrix with orthonormal column vectors and R is an upper triangular $n \times n$ matrix whose diagonal entries are all positive. [Note: R must be nonsingular since $\det(R) > 0$.]

Proof Let $\mathbf{p}_1, \ldots, \mathbf{p}_{n-1}$ be the projection vectors defined in Theorem 5.6.1, and let $\{\mathbf{q}_1, \mathbf{q}_2, \ldots, \mathbf{q}_n\}$ be the orthonormal basis of $R(A)$ derived from the Gram–Schmidt process. Define

$$r_{11} = \|\mathbf{a}_1\|$$
$$r_{kk} = \|\mathbf{a}_k - \mathbf{p}_{k-1}\| \qquad \text{for} \qquad k = 2, \ldots, n$$

and

$$r_{ik} = \mathbf{q}_i^T \mathbf{a}_k \qquad \text{for} \quad i = 1, \ldots, k-1 \qquad \text{and} \qquad k = 2, \ldots, n$$

By the Gram–Schmidt process,

$$r_{11}\mathbf{q}_1 = \mathbf{a}_1 \tag{4}$$
$$r_{kk}\mathbf{q}_k = \mathbf{a}_k - r_{1k}\mathbf{q}_1 - r_{2k}\mathbf{q}_2 - \cdots - r_{k-1,k}\mathbf{q}_{k-1} \quad \text{for} \quad k = 2, \ldots, n$$

System (4) may be rewritten in the form

$$\mathbf{a}_1 = r_{11}\mathbf{q}_1$$
$$\mathbf{a}_2 = r_{12}\mathbf{q}_1 + r_{22}\mathbf{q}_2$$
$$\vdots$$
$$\mathbf{a}_n = r_{1n}\mathbf{q}_1 + \cdots + r_{nn}\mathbf{q}_n$$

If we set

$$Q = (\mathbf{q}_1, \mathbf{q}_2, \ldots, \mathbf{q}_n)$$

and define R to be the upper triangular matrix

$$R = \begin{pmatrix} r_{11} & r_{12} & \cdots & r_{1n} \\ 0 & r_{22} & \cdots & r_{2n} \\ \vdots & & & \\ 0 & 0 & \cdots & r_{nn} \end{pmatrix}$$

then the jth column of the product QR will be

$$Q\mathbf{r}_j = r_{1j}\mathbf{q}_1 + r_{2j}\mathbf{q}_2 + \cdots + r_{jj}\mathbf{q}_j = \mathbf{a}_j$$

for $j = 1, \ldots, n$. Therefore,

$$QR = (\mathbf{a}_1, \mathbf{a}_2, \ldots, \mathbf{a}_n) = A \qquad \blacksquare$$

EXAMPLE 3 Compute the Gram–Schmidt QR factorization of the matrix

$$A = \begin{pmatrix} 1 & -2 & -1 \\ 2 & 0 & 1 \\ 2 & -4 & 2 \\ 4 & 0 & 0 \end{pmatrix}$$

Solution

Step 1. Set

$$r_{11} = \|\mathbf{a}_1\| = 5$$

$$\mathbf{q}_1 = \frac{1}{r_{11}}\mathbf{a}_1 = \left(\frac{1}{5}, \frac{2}{5}, \frac{2}{5}, \frac{4}{5}\right)^T$$

Step 2. Set

$$r_{12} = \mathbf{q}_1^T\mathbf{a}_2 = -2$$
$$\mathbf{p}_1 = r_{12}\mathbf{q}_1 = -2\mathbf{q}_1$$
$$\mathbf{a}_2 - \mathbf{p}_1 = \left(-\frac{8}{5}, \frac{4}{5}, -\frac{16}{5}, \frac{8}{5}\right)^T$$
$$r_{22} = \|\mathbf{a}_2 - \mathbf{p}_1\| = 4$$
$$\mathbf{q}_2 = \frac{1}{r_{22}}(\mathbf{a}_2 - \mathbf{p}_1) = \left(-\frac{2}{5}, \frac{1}{5}, -\frac{4}{5}, \frac{2}{5}\right)^T$$

Step 3. Set

$$r_{13} = \mathbf{q}_1^T\mathbf{a}_3 = 1, \qquad r_{23} = \mathbf{q}_2^T\mathbf{a}_3 = -1$$
$$\mathbf{p}_2 = r_{13}\mathbf{q}_1 + r_{23}\mathbf{q}_2 = \mathbf{q}_1 - \mathbf{q}_2 = \left(\frac{3}{5}, \frac{1}{5}, \frac{6}{5}, \frac{2}{5}\right)^T$$
$$\mathbf{a}_3 - \mathbf{p}_2 = \left(-\frac{8}{5}, \frac{4}{5}, \frac{4}{5}, -\frac{2}{5}\right)^T$$
$$r_{33} = \|\mathbf{a}_3 - \mathbf{p}_2\| = 2$$
$$\mathbf{q}_3 = \frac{1}{r_{33}}(\mathbf{a}_3 - \mathbf{p}_2) = \left(-\frac{4}{5}, \frac{2}{5}, \frac{2}{5}, -\frac{1}{5}\right)^T$$

At each step, we have determined a column of Q and a column of R. The factorization is given by

$$A = QR = \begin{bmatrix} \frac{1}{5} & -\frac{2}{5} & -\frac{4}{5} \\ \frac{2}{5} & \frac{1}{5} & \frac{2}{5} \\ \frac{2}{5} & -\frac{4}{5} & \frac{2}{5} \\ \frac{4}{5} & \frac{2}{5} & -\frac{1}{5} \end{bmatrix} \begin{bmatrix} 5 & -2 & 1 \\ 0 & 4 & -1 \\ 0 & 0 & 2 \end{bmatrix}$$ ■

We saw in Section 5.5 that if the columns of an $m \times n$ matrix A form an orthonormal set, then the least squares solution of $A\mathbf{x} = \mathbf{b}$ is simply $\hat{\mathbf{x}} = A^T\mathbf{b}$. If A has rank n, but its column vectors do not form an orthonormal set in $\mathbb{R}^m$, then the QR factorization can be used to solve the least squares problem.

Theorem 5.6.3   *If A is an $m \times n$ matrix of rank n, then the least squares solution of $A\mathbf{x} = \mathbf{b}$ is given by $\hat{\mathbf{x}} = R^{-1}Q^T\mathbf{b}$, where Q and R are the matrices obtained from the factorization given in Theorem 5.6.2. The solution $\hat{\mathbf{x}}$ may be obtained by using back substitution to solve $R\mathbf{x} = Q^T\mathbf{b}$.*

Proof   Let $\hat{\mathbf{x}}$ be the least squares solution of $A\mathbf{x} = \mathbf{b}$ guaranteed by Theorem 5.3.2. Thus, $\hat{\mathbf{x}}$ is the solution of the normal equations

$$A^T A\mathbf{x} = A^T \mathbf{b}$$

If A is factored into a product QR, these equations become

$$(QR)^T QR\mathbf{x} = (QR)^T \mathbf{b}$$

or

$$R^T (Q^T Q)R\mathbf{x} = R^T Q^T \mathbf{b}$$

Since Q has orthonormal columns, it follows that $Q^T Q = I$ and hence

$$R^T R\mathbf{x} = R^T Q^T \mathbf{b}$$

Since R^T is invertible, this equation simplifies to

$$R\mathbf{x} = Q^T \mathbf{b} \qquad \text{or} \qquad \mathbf{x} = R^{-1} Q^T \mathbf{b}$$ ∎

EXAMPLE 4   Find the least squares solution of

$$\begin{pmatrix} 1 & -2 & -1 \\ 2 & 0 & 1 \\ 2 & -4 & 2 \\ 4 & 0 & 0 \end{pmatrix} \begin{pmatrix} x_1 \\ x_2 \\ x_3 \end{pmatrix} = \begin{pmatrix} -1 \\ 1 \\ 1 \\ -2 \end{pmatrix}$$

Solution

The coefficient matrix of this system was factored in Example 3. Using that factorization, we have

$$Q^T \mathbf{b} = \begin{pmatrix} \frac{1}{5} & \frac{2}{5} & \frac{2}{5} & \frac{4}{5} \\ -\frac{2}{5} & \frac{1}{5} & -\frac{4}{5} & \frac{2}{5} \\ -\frac{4}{5} & \frac{2}{5} & \frac{2}{5} & -\frac{1}{5} \end{pmatrix} \begin{pmatrix} -1 \\ 1 \\ 1 \\ -2 \end{pmatrix} = \begin{pmatrix} -1 \\ -1 \\ 2 \end{pmatrix}$$

The system $R\mathbf{x} = Q^T \mathbf{b}$ is easily solved by back substitution:

$$\begin{pmatrix} 5 & -2 & 1 & | & -1 \\ 0 & 4 & -1 & | & -1 \\ 0 & 0 & 2 & | & 2 \end{pmatrix}$$

The solution is $\mathbf{x} = \left(-\frac{2}{5}, 0, 1\right)^T$.   ∎

The Modified Gram–Schmidt Process

In Chapter 7, we will consider computer methods for solving least squares problems. The QR factorization method of Example 4 does not, in general, produce accurate results when carried out with finite-precision arithmetic. In practice, there may be a loss of orthogonality due to roundoff error in computing $\mathbf{q}_1, \mathbf{q}_2, \ldots, \mathbf{q}_n$. We can achieve better numerical accuracy using a modified version of the Gram–Schmidt method. In the modified version, the vector $\mathbf{q}_1$ is constructed as before:

$$\mathbf{q}_1 = \frac{1}{\|\mathbf{a}_1\|}\mathbf{a}_1$$

However, the remaining vectors $\mathbf{a}_2, \ldots, \mathbf{a}_n$ are then modified so as to be orthogonal to $\mathbf{q}_1$. This can be done by subtracting from each vector $\mathbf{a}_k$ the projection of $\mathbf{a}_k$ onto $\mathbf{q}_1$:

$$\mathbf{a}_k^{(1)} = \mathbf{a}_k - (\mathbf{q}_1^T \mathbf{a}_k)\mathbf{q}_1 \qquad k = 2, \ldots, n$$

At the second step, we take

$$\mathbf{q}_2 = \frac{1}{\|\mathbf{a}_2^{(1)}\|}\mathbf{a}_2^{(1)}$$

The vector $\mathbf{q}_2$ is already orthogonal to $\mathbf{q}_1$. We then modify the remaining vectors to make them orthogonal to $\mathbf{q}_2$:

$$\mathbf{a}_k^{(2)} = \mathbf{a}_k^{(1)} - (\mathbf{q}_2^T \mathbf{a}_k^{(1)})\mathbf{q}_2 \qquad k = 3, \ldots, n$$

In a similar manner, $\mathbf{q}_3, \mathbf{q}_4, \ldots, \mathbf{q}_n$ are successively determined. At the last step, we need only set

$$\mathbf{q}_n = \frac{1}{\|\mathbf{a}_n^{(n-1)}\|}\mathbf{a}_n^{(n-1)}$$

to achieve an orthonormal set $\{\mathbf{q}_1, \ldots, \mathbf{q}_n\}$. The following algorithm summarizes the process:

Algorithm 5.6.1   Modified Gram–Schmidt Process

> *For $k = 1, 2, \ldots, n$, set*
> $$r_{kk} = \|\mathbf{a}_k\|$$
> $$\mathbf{q}_k = \frac{1}{r_{kk}}\mathbf{a}_k$$
> > *For $j = k+1, k+2, \ldots, n$, set*
> > $$r_{kj} = \mathbf{q}_k^T \mathbf{a}_j$$
> > $$\mathbf{a}_j = \mathbf{a}_j - r_{kj}\mathbf{q}_k$$
> > *End for loop*
> *End for loop*

If the modified Gram–Schmidt process is applied to the column vectors of an $m \times n$ matrix A having rank n, then, as before, we can obtain a QR factorization of A. This factorization may then be used computationally to determine the least squares solution to $A\mathbf{x} = \mathbf{b}$; however, in this case one should not compute $\mathbf{c} = Q^T\mathbf{b}$ directly. Instead, as each column vector $\mathbf{q}_k$ is determined, one modifies the right-hand side vector obtaining a modified vector $\mathbf{b}_k$ and then sets $c_k = \mathbf{q}_k^T\mathbf{b}_k$. An algorithm for solving least squares problems using the modified Gram–Schmidt QR factorization is given in Section 7.7.

SECTION 5.6 EXERCISES

1. For each of the following, use the Gram–Schmidt process to find an orthonormal basis for $R(A)$:

   (a) $A = \begin{bmatrix} -1 & 3 \\ 1 & 5 \end{bmatrix}$ 　(b) $A = \begin{bmatrix} 2 & 5 \\ 1 & 10 \end{bmatrix}$

2. Factor each of the matrices in Exercise 1 into a product QR, where Q is an orthogonal matrix and R is upper triangular.

3. Given the basis $\{(1, 2, -2)^T, (4, 3, 2)^T, (1, 2, 1)^T\}$ for $\mathbb{R}^3$, use the Gram–Schmidt process to obtain an orthonormal basis.

4. Consider the vector space $C[-1, 1]$ with the inner product defined by

   $$\langle f, g \rangle = \int_{-1}^{1} f(x)g(x)\, dx$$

   Find an orthonormal basis for the subspace spanned by 1, x, and x^2.

5. Let

   $$A = \begin{bmatrix} 2 & 1 \\ 1 & 1 \\ 2 & 1 \end{bmatrix} \quad \text{and} \quad \mathbf{b} = \begin{bmatrix} 12 \\ 6 \\ 18 \end{bmatrix}$$

   (a) Use the Gram–Schmidt process to find an orthonormal basis for the column space of A.

   (b) Factor A into a product QR, where Q has an orthonormal set of column vectors and R is upper triangular.

   (c) Solve the least squares problem $A\mathbf{x} = \mathbf{b}$.

6. Repeat Exercise 5 using

   $$A = \begin{bmatrix} 3 & -1 \\ 4 & 2 \\ 0 & 2 \end{bmatrix} \quad \text{and} \quad \mathbf{b} = \begin{bmatrix} 0 \\ 20 \\ 10 \end{bmatrix}$$

7. Given $\mathbf{x}_1 = \frac{1}{2}(1, 1, 1, -1)^T$ and $\mathbf{x}_2 = \frac{1}{6}(1, 1, 3, 5)^T$, verify that these vectors form an orthonormal set in $\mathbb{R}^4$. Extend this set to an orthonormal basis for $\mathbb{R}^4$ by finding an orthonormal basis for the null space of

   $$\begin{bmatrix} 1 & 1 & 1 & -1 \\ 1 & 1 & 3 & 5 \end{bmatrix}$$

   [*Hint*: First find a basis for the null space and then use the Gram–Schmidt process.]

8. Use the Gram–Schmidt process to find an orthonormal basis for the subspace of $\mathbb{R}^4$ spanned by $\mathbf{x}_1 = (4, 2, 2, 1)^T$, $\mathbf{x}_2 = (2, 0, 0, 2)^T$, and $\mathbf{x}_3 = (1, 1, -1, 1)^T$.

9. Repeat Exercise 8 using the modified Gram–Schmidt process and compare answers.

10. Let A be an $m \times 2$ matrix. Show that if both the classical Gram–Schmidt process and the modified Gram–Schmidt process are applied to the column vectors of A, then both algorithms will produce the exact same QR factorization, even when the computations are carried out in finite-precision arithmetic (i.e., show that both algorithms will perform the exact same arithmetic computations).

11. Let A be an $m \times 3$ matrix. Let QR be the QR factorization obtained when the classical Gram–Schmidt process is applied to the column vectors of A, and let $\tilde{Q}\tilde{R}$ be the factorization obtained when the modified Gram–Schmidt process is used. Show that if all computations were carried out using exact arithmetic, then we would have

    $$\tilde{Q} = Q \quad \text{and} \quad \tilde{R} = R$$

    and show that when the computations are done in finite-precision arithmetic, $\tilde{r}_{23}$ will not necessarily be equal to r_{23} and, consequently, $\tilde{r}_{33}$ and $\tilde{\mathbf{q}}_3$ will not necessarily be the same as r_{33} and $\mathbf{q}_3$.

12. What will happen if the Gram–Schmidt process is applied to a set of vectors $\{\mathbf{v}_1, \mathbf{v}_2, \mathbf{v}_3\}$, where $\mathbf{v}_1$ and $\mathbf{v}_2$ are linearly independent, but $\mathbf{v}_3 \in \text{Span}(\mathbf{v}_1, \mathbf{v}_2)$? Will the process fail? If so, how? Explain.

13. Let A be an $m \times n$ matrix of rank n and let $\mathbf{b} \in \mathbb{R}^m$. Show that if Q and R are the matrices derived from applying the Gram–Schmidt process to the column vectors of A and

    $$\mathbf{p} = c_1\mathbf{q}_1 + c_2\mathbf{q}_2 + \cdots + c_n\mathbf{q}_n$$

    is the projection of $\mathbf{b}$ onto $R(A)$, then

    (a) $\mathbf{c} = Q^T\mathbf{b}$ 　　　　(b) $\mathbf{p} = QQ^T\mathbf{b}$

    (c) $QQ^T = A(A^TA)^{-1}A^T$

14. Let U be an m-dimensional subspace of $\mathbb{R}^n$ and let V be a k-dimensional subspace of U, where $0 < k < m$.

    (a) Show that any orthonormal basis
$$\{\mathbf{v}_1, \mathbf{v}_2, \ldots, \mathbf{v}_k\}$$
for V can be expanded to form an orthonormal basis $\{\mathbf{v}_1, \mathbf{v}_2, \ldots, \mathbf{v}_k, \mathbf{v}_{k+1}, \ldots, \mathbf{v}_m\}$ for U.

    (b) Show that if $W = \text{Span}(\mathbf{v}_{k+1}, \mathbf{v}_{k+2} \ldots, \mathbf{v}_m)$, then $U = V \oplus W$.

15. (Dimension Theorem)   Let U and V be subspaces of $\mathbb{R}^n$. In the case that $U \cap V = \{\mathbf{0}\}$, we have the following dimension relation:

$$\dim(U + V) = \dim U + \dim V$$

(See Exercise 18 in Section 3.4.) Make use of the result from Exercise 14 to prove the more general theorem

$$\dim(U + V) = \dim U + \dim V - \dim(U \cap V)$$

5.7 Orthogonal Polynomials

We have already seen how polynomials can be used for data fitting and for approximating continuous functions. Since both of these problems are least squares problems, they can be simplified by selecting an orthogonal basis for the class of approximating polynomials. This leads us to the concept of orthogonal polynomials.

In this section, we study families of orthogonal polynomials associated with various inner products on $C[a, b]$. We will see that the polynomials in each of these classes satisfy a three-term recursion relation. This recursion relation is particularly useful in computer applications. Certain families of orthogonal polynomials have important applications in many areas of mathematics. We will refer to these polynomials as *classical polynomials* and examine them in more detail. In particular, the classical polynomials are solutions of certain classes of second-order linear differential equations that arise in the solution of many partial differential equations from mathematical physics.

Orthogonal Sequences

Since the proof of Theorem 5.6.1 was by induction, the Gram–Schmidt process is valid for a denumerable set. Thus, if $\mathbf{x}_1, \mathbf{x}_2, \ldots$ is a sequence of vectors in an inner product space V and $\mathbf{x}_1, \mathbf{x}_2, \ldots, \mathbf{x}_n$ are linearly independent for each n, then the Gram–Schmidt process may be used to form a sequence $\mathbf{u}_1, \mathbf{u}_2, \ldots$, where $\{\mathbf{u}_1, \mathbf{u}_2, \ldots\}$ is an orthonormal set and

$$\text{Span}(\mathbf{x}_1, \mathbf{x}_2, \ldots, \mathbf{x}_n) = \text{Span}(\mathbf{u}_1, \mathbf{u}_2, \ldots, \mathbf{u}_n)$$

for each n. In particular, from the sequence $1, x, x^2, \ldots$, it is possible to construct an *orthonormal sequence* $p_0(x), p_1(x), \ldots$.

Let P be the vector space of all polynomials and define the inner product $\langle , \rangle$ on P by

$$\langle p, q \rangle = \int_a^b p(x)q(x)w(x)\, dx \tag{1}$$

where $w(x)$ is a positive continuous function. The interval can be taken as either open or closed and may be finite or infinite. If, however,

$$\int_a^b p(x)w(x)\, dx$$

is improper, we require that it converge for every $p \in P$.

Definition

> Let $p_0(x), p_1(x), \ldots$ be a sequence of polynomials with $\deg p_i(x) = i$ for each i. If $\langle p_i(x), p_j(x) \rangle = 0$ whenever $i \neq j$, then $\{p_n(x)\}$ is said to be a **sequence of orthogonal polynomials**. If $\langle p_i, p_j \rangle = \delta_{ij}$, then $\{p_n(x)\}$ is said to be a **sequence of orthonormal polynomials**.

Theorem 5.7.1   *If $p_0, p_1, \ldots$ is a sequence of orthogonal polynomials, then*

   I. $p_0, \ldots, p_{n-1}$ *form a basis for P_n.*
   II. $p_n \in P_n^\perp$ *(i.e., p_n is orthogonal to every polynomial of degree less than n).*

Proof   It follows from Theorem 5.5.1 that $p_0, p_1, \ldots, p_{n-1}$ are linearly independent in P_n. Since $\dim P_n = n$, these n vectors must form a basis for P_n. Let $p(x)$ be any polynomial of degree less than n. Then

$$p(x) = \sum_{i=0}^{n-1} c_i p_i(x)$$

and hence

$$\langle p_n, p \rangle = \left\langle p_n, \sum_{i=0}^{n-1} c_i p_i \right\rangle = \sum_{i=0}^{n-1} c_i \langle p_n, p_i \rangle = 0$$

Therefore, $p_n \in P_n^\perp$.   ∎

If $\{p_0, p_1, \ldots, p_{n-1}\}$ is an orthogonal set in P_n and

$$u_i = \left(\frac{1}{\|p_i\|} \right) p_i \quad \text{for} \quad i = 0, \ldots, n-1$$

then $\{u_0, \ldots, u_{n-1}\}$ is an orthonormal basis for P_n. Hence, if $p \in P_n$, then

$$p = \sum_{i=0}^{n-1} \langle p, u_i \rangle \, u_i$$

$$= \sum_{i=0}^{n-1} \left\langle p, \left(\frac{1}{\|p_i\|} \right) p_i \right\rangle \left(\frac{1}{\|p_i\|} \right) p_i$$

$$= \sum_{i=0}^{n-1} \frac{\langle p, p_i \rangle}{\langle p_i, p_i \rangle} p_i$$

Similarly, if $f \in C[a, b]$, then the best least squares approximation to f by the elements of P_n is given by

$$p = \sum_{i=0}^{n-1} \frac{\langle f, p_i \rangle}{\langle p_i, p_i \rangle} p_i$$

where $p_0, p_1, \ldots, p_{n-1}$ are orthogonal polynomials.

Another nice feature of sequences of orthogonal polynomials is that they satisfy a three-term recursion relation.

Theorem 5.7.2   *Let $p_0, p_1, \ldots$ be a sequence of orthogonal polynomials. Let a_i denote the lead coefficient of p_i for each i, and define $p_{-1}(x)$ to be the zero polynomial. Then*

$$\alpha_{n+1}p_{n+1}(x) = (x - \beta_{n+1})p_n(x) - \alpha_n\gamma_n p_{n-1}(x) \qquad (n \geq 0)$$

where $\alpha_0 = \gamma_0 = 1$ and

$$\alpha_n = \frac{a_{n-1}}{a_n}, \qquad \beta_n = \frac{\langle p_{n-1}, xp_{n-1}\rangle}{\langle p_{n-1}, p_{n-1}\rangle}, \qquad \gamma_n = \frac{\langle p_n, p_n\rangle}{\langle p_{n-1}, p_{n-1}\rangle} \qquad (n \geq 1)$$

Proof   Since $p_0, p_1, \ldots, p_{n+1}$ form a basis for P_{n+2}, we can write

$$xp_n(x) = \sum_{k=0}^{n+1} c_{nk}p_k(x) \tag{2}$$

where

$$c_{nk} = \frac{\langle xp_n, p_k\rangle}{\langle p_k, p_k\rangle} \tag{3}$$

For any inner product defined by (1),

$$\langle xf, g\rangle = \langle f, xg\rangle$$

In particular,

$$\langle xp_n, p_k\rangle = \langle p_n, xp_k\rangle$$

It follows from Theorem 5.7.1 that if $k < n - 1$, then

$$c_{nk} = \frac{\langle xp_n, p_k\rangle}{\langle p_k, p_k\rangle} = \frac{\langle p_n, xp_k\rangle}{\langle p_k, p_k\rangle} = 0$$

Therefore, (2) simplifies to

$$xp_n(x) = c_{n,n-1}p_{n-1}(x) + c_{n,n}p_n(x) + c_{n,n+1}p_{n+1}(x)$$

This equation can be rewritten in the form

$$c_{n,n+1}p_{n+1}(x) = (x - c_{n,n})p_n(x) - c_{n,n-1}p_{n-1}(x) \tag{4}$$

Comparing the lead coefficients of the polynomials on each side of (4), we see that

$$c_{n,n+1}a_{n+1} = a_n$$

or

$$c_{n,n+1} = \frac{a_n}{a_{n+1}} = \alpha_{n+1} \tag{5}$$

It follows from (4) that

$$c_{n,n+1}\langle p_n, p_{n+1}\rangle = \langle p_n, (x - c_{n,n})p_n\rangle - c_{n,n-1}\langle p_n, p_{n-1}\rangle$$
$$0 = \langle p_n, xp_n\rangle - c_{nn}\langle p_n, p_n\rangle$$

Thus,

$$c_{nn} = \frac{\langle p_n, xp_n \rangle}{\langle p_n, p_n \rangle} = \beta_{n+1}$$

It follows from (3) that

$$\begin{aligned} \langle p_{n-1}, p_{n-1} \rangle \, c_{n,n-1} &= \langle xp_n, p_{n-1} \rangle \\ &= \langle p_n, xp_{n-1} \rangle \\ &= \langle p_n, p_n \rangle \, c_{n-1,n} \end{aligned}$$

and hence, by (5), we have

$$c_{n,n-1} = \frac{\langle p_n, p_n \rangle}{\langle p_{n-1}, p_{n-1} \rangle} \alpha_n = \gamma_n \alpha_n \qquad\qquad \blacksquare$$

In generating a sequence of orthogonal polynomials by the recursion relation in Theorem 5.7.2, we are free to choose any nonzero lead coefficient a_{n+1} that we want at each step. This is reasonable, since any nonzero multiple of a particular p_{n+1} will also be orthogonal to $p_0, \ldots, p_n$. If we were to choose our a_i's to be 1, for example, then the recursion relation would simplify to

$$p_{n+1}(x) = (x - \beta_{n+1})p_n(x) - \gamma_n p_{n-1}(x)$$

Classical Orthogonal Polynomials

Let us now look at some examples. Because of their importance, we will consider the classical polynomials beginning with the simplest, the Legendre polynomials.

Legendre Polynomials

The Legendre polynomials are orthogonal with respect to the inner product

$$\langle p, q \rangle = \int_{-1}^{1} p(x)q(x)\,dx$$

Let $P_n(x)$ denote the Legendre polynomial of degree n. If we choose the lead coefficients so that $P_n(1) = 1$ for each n, then the recursion formula for the Legendre polynomials is

$$(n + 1)P_{n+1}(x) = (2n + 1)xP_n(x) - nP_{n-1}(x)$$

By the use of this formula, the sequence of Legendre polynomials is easily generated. The first five polynomials of the sequence are

$$\begin{aligned} P_0(x) &= 1 \\ P_1(x) &= x \\ P_2(x) &= \tfrac{1}{2}(3x^2 - 1) \\ P_3(x) &= \tfrac{1}{2}(5x^3 - 3x) \\ P_4(x) &= \tfrac{1}{8}(35x^4 - 30x^2 + 3) \end{aligned}$$

Chebyshev Polynomials

The Chebyshev polynomials are orthogonal with respect to the inner product

$$\langle p, q \rangle = \int_{-1}^{1} p(x)q(x)(1-x^2)^{-1/2} \, dx$$

It is customary to normalize the lead coefficients so that $a_0 = 1$ and $a_k = 2^{k-1}$ for $k = 1, 2, \ldots$. The Chebyshev polynomials are denoted by $T_n(x)$ and have the interesting property that

$$T_n(\cos \theta) = \cos n\theta$$

This property, together with the trigonometric identity

$$\cos(n+1)\theta = 2\cos\theta\cos n\theta - \cos(n-1)\theta$$

can be used to derive the recursion relations

$$T_1(x) = xT_0(x)$$
$$T_{n+1}(x) = 2xT_n(x) - T_{n-1}(x) \quad \text{for } n \geq 1$$

Jacobi Polynomials

The Legendre and Chebyshev polynomials are both special cases of the Jacobi polynomials. The Jacobi polynomials $P_n^{(\lambda,\mu)}$ are orthogonal with respect to the inner product

$$\langle p, q \rangle = \int_{-1}^{1} p(x)q(x)(1-x)^{\lambda}(1+x)^{\mu} \, dx$$

where $\lambda, \mu > -1$.

Hermite Polynomials

The Hermite polynomials are defined on the interval $(-\infty, \infty)$. They are orthogonal with respect to the inner product

$$\langle p, q \rangle = \int_{-\infty}^{\infty} p(x)q(x)e^{-x^2} \, dx$$

The recursion relation for Hermite polynomials is given by
$$H_{n+1}(x) = 2xH_n(x) - 2nH_{n-1}(x)$$

Laguerre Polynomials

The Laguerre polynomials are defined on the interval $(0, \infty)$ and are orthogonal with respect to the inner product

$$\langle p, q \rangle = \int_{0}^{\infty} p(x)q(x)x^{\lambda}e^{-x} \, dx$$

where $\lambda > -1$. The recursion relation for the Laguerre polynomials is given by

$$(n+1)L_{n+1}^{(\lambda)}(x) = (2n + \lambda + 1 - x)L_n^{(\lambda)}(x) - (n+\lambda)L_{n-1}^{(\lambda)}(x)$$

The Chebyshev, Hermite, and Laguerre polynomials are compared in Table 5.7.1.

Table 5.7.1 Chebyshev, Hermite, and Laguerre Polynomials

Chebyshev	Hermite	Laguerre ($\lambda = 0$)
$T_{n+1} = 2xT_n - T_{n-1}, n \geq 1$	$H_{n+1} = 2xH_n - 2nH_{n-1}$	$(n+1)L_{n+1}^{(0)} = (2n+1-x)L_n^{(0)} - nL_{n-1}^{(0)}$
$T_0 = 1$	$H_0 = 1$	$L_0^{(0)} = 1$
$T_1 = x$	$H_1 = 2x$	$L_1^{(0)} = 1 - x$
$T_2 = 2x^2 - 1$	$H_2 = 4x^2 - 2$	$L_2^{(0)} = \frac{1}{2}x^2 - x + 2$
$T_3 = 4x^3 - 3x$	$H_3 = 8x^3 - 12x$	$L_3^{(0)} = \frac{1}{6}x^3 + 9x^2 - 18x + 6$

APPLICATION 1   Numerical Integration

One important application of orthogonal polynomials occurs in numerical integration. To approximate

$$\int_a^b f(x)w(x)\,dx \tag{6}$$

we first approximate $f(x)$ by an interpolating polynomial. Using *Lagrange's interpolation formula*,

$$P(x) = \sum_{i=1}^n f(x_i)L_i(x)$$

where the Lagrange functions L_i are defined by

$$L_i(x) = \frac{\displaystyle\prod_{\substack{j=1 \\ j \neq i}}^n (x - x_j)}{\displaystyle\prod_{\substack{j=1 \\ j \neq i}}^n (x_i - x_j)}$$

we can determine a polynomial $P(x)$ that agrees with $f(x)$ at n points $x_1, \ldots, x_n$ in $[a, b]$. The integral (6) is then approximated by

$$\int_a^b P(x)w(x)\,dx = \sum_{i=1}^n A_i f(x_i) \tag{7}$$

where

$$A_i = \int_a^b L_i(x)w(x)\,dx \qquad i = 1, \ldots, n$$

It can be shown that (7) will give the exact value of the integral whenever $f(x)$ is a polynomial of degree less than n. If the points $x_1, \ldots, x_n$ are chosen properly, formula (7) will be exact for higher degree polynomials. Indeed, it can be shown that if $p_0, p_1, p_2, \ldots$ is a sequence of orthogonal polynomials with respect to the inner product (1) and $x_1, \ldots, x_n$ are the zeros of $p_n(x)$, then formula (7) will be exact for all polynomials of degree less than $2n$. The following theorem guarantees that the roots of p_n are all real and lie in the open interval (a, b).

Theorem 5.7.3   *If $p_0, p_1, p_2, \ldots$ is a sequence of orthogonal polynomials with respect to the inner product (1), then the zeros of $p_n(x)$ are all real and distinct and lie in the interval (a, b).*

Proof   Let $x_1, \ldots, x_m$ be the zeros of $p_n(x)$ that lie in (a, b) and for which $p_n(x)$ changes sign. Thus, $p_n(x)$ must have a factor of $(x - x_i)^{k_i}$, where k_i is odd, for $i = 1, \ldots, m$. We may write

$$p_n(x) = (x - x_1)^{k_1}(x - x_2)^{k_2} \cdots (x - x_m)^{k_m} q(x)$$

where $q(x)$ does not change sign on (a, b) and $q(x_i) \neq 0$ for $i = 1, \ldots, m$. Clearly, $m \leq n$. We will show that $m = n$. Let

$$r(x) = (x - x_1)(x - x_2) \cdots (x - x_m)$$

The product

$$p_n(x)r(x) = (x - x_1)^{k_1+1}(x - x_2)^{k_2+1} \cdots (x - x_m)^{k_m+1} q(x)$$

will involve only even powers of $(x - x_i)$ for each i and hence will not change sign on (a, b). Therefore,

$$\langle p_n, r \rangle = \int_a^b p_n(x)r(x)w(x)\,dx \neq 0$$

Since p_n is orthogonal to all polynomials of degree less than n, it follows that $\deg(r(x)) = m \geq n$. ∎

Numerical integration formulas of the form (7), where the x_i's are roots of orthogonal polynomials, are called *Gaussian quadrature formulas*. The proof of exactness for polynomials of degree less than $2n$ can be found in most undergraduate numerical analysis textbooks.

Actually, it is not necessary to perform n integrations to calculate the quadrature coefficients $A_1, \ldots, A_n$. They can be determined by solving an $n \times n$ linear system. Exercise 16 illustrates how this is done when the roots of the Legendre polynomial P_n are used in a quadrature rule for approximating $\int_{-1}^{1} f(x)\,dx$.

SECTION 5.7 EXERCISES

1. Use the recursion formulas to calculate (a) T_4, T_5 and (b) H_4, H_5.

2. Let $p_0(x)$, $p_1(x)$, and $p_2(x)$ be orthogonal with respect to the inner product

$$\langle p(x), q(x) \rangle = \int_{-1}^{1} \frac{p(x)q(x)}{1 + x^2}\,dx$$

Use Theorem 5.7.2 to calculate $p_1(x)$ and $p_2(x)$ if all polynomials have lead coefficient 1.

3. Show that the Chebyshev polynomials have the following properties:

    (a) $2T_m(x)T_n(x) = T_{m+n}(x) + T_{m-n}(x)$, for $m > n$

    (b) $T_m(T_n(x)) = T_{mn}(x)$

4. Find the best quadratic least squares approximation to e^x on $[-1, 1]$ with respect to the inner product

$$\langle f, g \rangle = \int_{-1}^{1} f(x)g(x)\,dx$$

5. Let $p_0, p_1, \ldots$ be a sequence of orthogonal polynomials and let a_n denote the lead coefficient of p_n. Prove that

$$\|p_n\|^2 = a_n \langle x^n, p_n \rangle$$

6. Let $T_n(x)$ denote the Chebyshev polynomial of degree n and define

$$U_{n-1}(x) = \frac{1}{n} T_n'(x)$$

for $n = 1, 2, \ldots$.

(a) Compute $U_0(x)$, $U_1(x)$, and $U_2(x)$.

(b) Show that if $x = \cos\theta$, then

$$U_{n-1}(x) = \frac{\sin n\theta}{\sin\theta}$$

7. Let $U_{n-1}(x)$ be defined as in Exercise 6 for $n \geq 1$ and define $U_{-1}(x) = 0$. Show that

(a) $T_n(x) = U_n(x) - xU_{n-1}(x)$, for $n \geq 0$

(b) $U_n(x) = 2xU_{n-1}(x) - U_{n-2}(x)$, for $n \geq 1$

8. Show that the U_i's defined in Exercise 6 are orthogonal with respect to the inner product

$$\langle p, q \rangle = \int_{-1}^{1} p(x)q(x)(1 - x^2)^{1/2}\, dx$$

The U_i's are called *Chebyshev polynomials of the second kind.*

9. Verify that the Legendre polynomial $P_n(x)$ satisfies the second-order equation

$$(1 - x^2)y'' - 2xy' + n(n+1)y = 0$$

for $n = 0, 1, 2$.

10. Prove each of the following:

(a) $H_n'(x) = 2nH_{n-1}(x), \quad n = 0, 1, \ldots$

(b) $H_n''(x) - 2xH_n'(x) + 2nH_n(x) = 0, \quad n = 0, 1, \ldots$

11. Given a function $f(x)$ that passes through the points $(1, 2)$, $(2, -1)$, and $(3, 4)$, use the Lagrange interpolating formula to construct a second-degree polynomial that interpolates f at the given points.

12. Show that if $f(x)$ is a polynomial of degree less than n, then $f(x)$ must equal the interpolating polynomial $P(x)$ in (7) and hence the sum in (7) gives the exact value for $\int_a^b f(x)w(x)\, dx$.

13. Use the zeros of the Legendre polynomial $P_2(x)$ to obtain a two-point quadrature formula:

$$\int_{-1}^{1} f(x)\, dx \approx A_1 f(x_1) + A_2 f(x_2)$$

14. (a) For what degree polynomials will the quadrature formula in Exercise 13 be exact?

(b) Use the formula from Exercise 13 to approximate

$$\int_{-1}^{1} (x^3 + 3x^2 + 1)\, dx \quad \text{and} \quad \int_{-1}^{1} \frac{1}{1 + x^2}\, dx$$

How do the approximations compare with the actual values?

15. Let $x_1, x_2, \ldots, x_n$ be distinct points in the interval $[-1, 1]$ and let

$$A_i = \int_{-1}^{1} L_i(x)dx, \quad i = 1, \ldots, n$$

where the L_i's are the Lagrange functions for the points $x_1, x_2, \ldots, x_n$.

(a) Explain why the quadrature formula

$$\int_{-1}^{1} f(x)dx = A_1 f(x_1) + A_2 f(x_2) + \cdots + A_n f(x_n)$$

will yield the exact value of the integral whenever $f(x)$ is a polynomial of degree less than n.

(b) Apply the quadrature formula to a polynomial of degree 0 and show that

$$A_1 + A_2 + \cdots + A_n = 2$$

16. Let $x_1, x_2, \ldots, x_n$ be the roots of the Legendre polynomial P_n. If the A_i's are defined as in Exercise 15, then the quadrature formula

$$\int_{-1}^{1} f(x)dx = A_1 f(x_1) + A_2 f(x_2) + \cdots + A_n f(x_n)$$

will be exact for all polynomials of degree less than $2n$.

(a) Show that if $1 \leq j < 2n$, then

$$P_j(x_1)A_1 + P_j(x_2)A_2 + \cdots + P_j(x_n)A_n = \langle 1, P_j \rangle = 0$$

(b) Use the results from part (a) and from Exercise 15 to set up a nonhomogeneous $n \times n$ linear system for determining the coefficients $A_1, A_2, \ldots, A_n$.

17. Let $Q_0(x), Q_1(x), \ldots$ be an orthonormal sequence of polynomials, that is, it is an orthogonal sequence of polynomials and $\|Q_k\| = 1$ for each k.

(a) How can the recursion relation in Theorem 5.7.2 be simplified in the case of an orthonormal sequence of polynomials?

(b) Let λ be a root of Q_n. Show that λ must satisfy the matrix equation

$$
\left\{
\begin{array}{ccccc}
\beta_1 & \alpha_1 & & & \\
\alpha_1 & \beta_2 & \alpha_2 & & \\
& \ddots & \ddots & \ddots & \\
& & \alpha_{n-2} & \beta_{n-1} & \alpha_{n-1} \\
& & & \alpha_{n-1} & \beta_n
\end{array}
\right\}
\left\{
\begin{array}{c}
Q_0(\lambda) \\
Q_1(\lambda) \\
\vdots \\
Q_{n-2}(\lambda) \\
Q_{n-1}(\lambda)
\end{array}
\right\}
= \lambda
\left\{
\begin{array}{c}
Q_0(\lambda) \\
Q_1(\lambda) \\
\vdots \\
Q_{n-2}(\lambda) \\
Q_{n-1}(\lambda)
\end{array}
\right\}
$$

where the α_i's and β_j's are the coefficients from the recursion equations.

Chapter 5 Exercises

MATLAB EXERCISES

1. Set

$$\mathbf{x} = [\,0:4, 4, -4, 1, 1\,]' \qquad \text{and} \qquad \mathbf{y} = \mathbf{ones}(9,1)$$

(a) Use the MATLAB function **norm** to compute the values of $\|\mathbf{x}\|$, $\|\mathbf{y}\|$, $\|\mathbf{x}+\mathbf{y}\|$ and to verify that the triangle inequality holds. Use MATLAB also to verify that the parallelogram law

$$\|\mathbf{x}+\mathbf{y}\|^2 + \|\mathbf{x}-\mathbf{y}\|^2 = 2(\|\mathbf{x}\|^2 + \|\mathbf{y}\|^2)$$

is satisfied.

(b) If

$$t = \frac{\mathbf{x}^T \mathbf{y}}{\|\mathbf{x}\|\,\|\mathbf{y}\|}$$

then why do we know that $|t|$ must be less than or equal to 1? Use MATLAB to compute the value of t and use the MATLAB function **acos** to compute the angle between $\mathbf{x}$ and $\mathbf{y}$. Convert the angle to degrees by multiplying by $180/\pi$. (Note that the number π is given by **pi** in MATLAB.)

(c) Use MATLAB to compute the vector projection $\mathbf{p}$ of $\mathbf{x}$ onto $\mathbf{y}$. Set $\mathbf{z} = \mathbf{x} - \mathbf{p}$ and verify that $\mathbf{z}$ is orthogonal to $\mathbf{p}$ by computing the scalar product of the two vectors. Compute $\|\mathbf{x}\|^2$ and $\|\mathbf{z}\|^2 + \|\mathbf{p}\|^2$ and verify that the Pythagorean law is satisfied.

2. (Least Squares Fit to a Data Set by a Linear Function) The following table of x and y values was given in Section 5.3 of this chapter (see Figure 5.3.3):

x	-1.0	0.0	2.1	2.3	2.4	5.3	6.0	6.5	8.0
y	-1.02	-0.52	0.55	0.70	0.70	2.13	2.52	2.82	3.54

The nine data points are nearly linear and hence the data can be approximated by a linear function $z = c_1 x + c_2$. Enter the x and y coordinates of the data points as column vectors $\mathbf{x}$ and $\mathbf{y}$, respectively. Set $V =$

$[\,\mathbf{x}, \mathbf{ones}(\mathbf{size}(\mathbf{x}))\,]$ and use the MATLAB "\" operation to compute the coefficients c_1 and c_2 as the least squares solution to the 9×2 linear system $V\mathbf{c} = \mathbf{y}$. To see the results graphically, set

$$\mathbf{w} = -1:0.1:8$$

and

$$\mathbf{z} = c(1) * \mathbf{w} + c(2) * \mathbf{ones}(\mathbf{size}(\mathbf{w}))$$

and plot the original data points and the least squares linear fit, using the MATLAB command

$$\mathbf{plot}(\mathbf{x}, \mathbf{y}, \text{`}x\text{'}, \mathbf{w}, \mathbf{z})$$

3. (Construction of Temperature Profiles by Least Squares Polynomials) Among the important inputs in weather forecasting models are data sets consisting of temperature values at various parts of the atmosphere. These values are either measured directly using weather balloons or inferred from remote soundings taken by weather satellites. A typical set of RAOB (weather balloon) data is given next. The temperature T in kelvins may be considered as a function of p, the atmospheric pressure measured in decibars. Pressures in the range from 1 to 3 decibars correspond to the top of the atmosphere, and those in the range from 9 to 10 decibars correspond to the lower part of the atmosphere.

p	1	2	3	4	5	6	7	8	9	10
T	222	227	223	233	244	253	260	266	270	266

(a) Enter the pressure values as a column vector $\mathbf{p}$ by setting $\mathbf{p} = [1:10]'$, and enter the temperature values as a column vector $\mathbf{T}$. To find the best least squares fit to the data by a linear function $c_1 x + c_2$, set up an overdetermined system $V\mathbf{c} = \mathbf{T}$. The coefficient matrix V can be generated in MATLAB by setting

$$V = [\,\mathbf{p}, \mathbf{ones}(10, 1)\,]$$

or, alternatively, by setting

$$A = \mathbf{vander}(\mathbf{p}); \qquad V = A(:, 9 : 10)$$

Note: For any vector $\mathbf{x} = (x_1, x_2, \ldots, x_{n+1})^T$, the MATLAB command $\mathbf{vander}(\mathbf{x})$ generates a full Vandermonde matrix of the form

$$\begin{bmatrix} x_1^n & x_1^{n-1} & \cdots & x_1 & 1 \\ x_2^n & x_2^{n-1} & \cdots & x_2 & 1 \\ \vdots & & & & \\ x_{n+1}^n & x_{n+1}^{n-1} & \cdots & x_{n+1} & 1 \end{bmatrix}$$

For a linear fit, only the last two columns of the full Vandermonde matrix are used. More information on the **vander** function can be obtained by typing **help vander**. Once V has been constructed, the least squares solution $\mathbf{c}$ of the system can be calculated using the MATLAB "\" operation.

(b) To see how well the linear function fits the data, define a range of pressure values by setting

$$\mathbf{q} = 1 : 0.1 : 10;$$

The corresponding function values can be determined by setting

$$\mathbf{z} = \mathbf{polyval}(\mathbf{c}, \mathbf{q});$$

We can plot the function and the data points with the command

$$\mathbf{plot}(\mathbf{q}, \mathbf{z}, \mathbf{p}, \mathbf{T}, `x')$$

(c) Let us now try to obtain a better fit by using a cubic polynomial approximation. Again, we can calculate the coefficients of the cubic polynomial

$$c_1 x^3 + c_2 x^2 + c_3 x + c_4$$

that gives the best least squares fit to the data by finding the least squares solution of an overdetermined system $V\mathbf{c} = \mathbf{T}$. The coefficient matrix V is determined by taking the last four columns of the matrix $A = \mathbf{vander}(\mathbf{p})$. To see the results graphically, again set

$$\mathbf{z} = \mathbf{polyval}(\mathbf{c}, \mathbf{q})$$

and plot the cubic function and data points, using the same plot command as before. Where do you get the better fit, at the top or bottom of the atmosphere?

(d) To obtain a good fit at both the top and bottom of the atmosphere, try using a sixth-degree polynomial. Determine the coefficients as before using the last seven columns of A. Set $\mathbf{z} = \mathbf{polyval}(\mathbf{c}, \mathbf{q})$ and plot the results.

4. (Least Squares Circles) The parametric equations for a circle with center $(3, 1)$ and radius 2 are

$$x = 3 + 2 \cos t \quad y = 1 + 2 \sin t$$

Set $\mathbf{t} = 0 : .5 : 6$ and use MATLAB to generate vectors of x and y coordinates for the corresponding points on the circle. Next, add some noise to your points by setting

$$\mathbf{x} = \mathbf{x} + 0.1 * \mathbf{rand}(1, 13)$$

and

$$\mathbf{y} = \mathbf{y} + 0.1 * \mathbf{rand}(1, 13)$$

Use MATLAB to determine the center $\mathbf{c}$ and radius r of the circle that gives the best least squares fit to the points. Set

$$\mathbf{t1} = 0 : 0.1 : 6.3$$
$$\mathbf{x1} = \mathbf{c}(1) + r * \cos(\mathbf{t1})$$
$$\mathbf{y1} = \mathbf{c}(2) + r * \sin(\mathbf{t1})$$

and use the command

$$\mathbf{plot}(\mathbf{x1}, \mathbf{y1}, \mathbf{x}, \mathbf{y}, `x')$$

to plot the circle and the data points.

5. (Fundamental Subspaces: Orthonormal Bases) The vector spaces $N(A)$, $R(A)$, $N(A^T)$, and $R(A^T)$ are the four fundamental subspaces associated with a matrix A. We can use MATLAB to construct orthonormal bases for each of the fundamental subspaces associated with a given matrix. We can then construct projection matrices corresponding to each subspace.

(a) Set

$$A = \mathbf{rand}(5, 2) * \mathbf{rand}(2, 5)$$

What would you expect the rank and nullity of A to be? Explain. Use MATLAB to check your answer by computing $\mathbf{rank}(A)$ and $Z = \mathbf{null}(A)$. The columns of Z form an orthonormal basis for $N(A)$.

(b) Next, set

$$Q = \mathbf{orth}(A), \qquad W = \mathbf{null}(A'),$$
$$S = [Q \quad W]$$

The matrix S should be orthogonal. Why? Explain. Compute $S * S'$ and compare your result to $\mathbf{eye}(5)$. In theory, $A^T W$ and $W^T A$ should both consist entirely of zeros. Why? Explain. Use MATLAB to compute $A^T W$ and $W^T A$.

(c) Prove that if Q and W had been computed in exact arithmetic, then we would have

$$I - WW^T = QQ^T \qquad \text{and} \qquad QQ^T A = A$$

[*Hint*: Write SS^T in terms of Q and W.] Use MATLAB to verify these identities.

(d) Prove that if Q had been calculated in exact arithmetic, then we would have $QQ^T\mathbf{b} = \mathbf{b}$ for all $\mathbf{b} \in R(A)$. Use MATLAB to verify this property by setting $\mathbf{b} = A * \mathbf{rand}(5, 1)$ and then computing $Q * Q' * \mathbf{b}$ and comparing it with $\mathbf{b}$.

(e) Since the column vectors of Q form an orthonormal basis for $R(A)$, it follows that QQ^T is the projection matrix corresponding to $R(A)$. Thus, for any $\mathbf{c} \in \mathbb{R}^5$, the vector $\mathbf{q} = QQ^T\mathbf{c}$ is the projection of $\mathbf{c}$ onto $R(A)$. Set $\mathbf{c} = \mathbf{rand}(5, 1)$ and compute the projection vector $\mathbf{q}$. The vector $\mathbf{r} = \mathbf{c} - \mathbf{q}$ should be in $N(A^T)$. Why? Explain. Use MATLAB to compute $A' * \mathbf{r}$.

(f) The matrix WW^T is the projection matrix corresponding to $N(A^T)$. Use MATLAB to compute the projection $\mathbf{w} = WW^T\mathbf{c}$ of $\mathbf{c}$ onto $N(A^T)$ and compare the result to $\mathbf{r}$.

(g) Set $Y = \mathbf{orth}(A')$ and use it to compute the projection matrix U corresponding to $R(A^T)$. Let $\mathbf{b} = \mathbf{rand}(5, 1)$ and compute the projection vector $\mathbf{y} = U * \mathbf{b}$ of $\mathbf{b}$ onto $R(A^T)$. Compute also $U * \mathbf{y}$ and compare it with $\mathbf{y}$. The vector $\mathbf{s} = \mathbf{b} - \mathbf{y}$ should be in $N(A)$. Why? Explain. Use MATLAB to compute $A * \mathbf{s}$.

(h) Use the matrix $Z = \mathbf{null}(A)$ to compute the projection matrix V corresponding to $N(A)$. Compute $V * \mathbf{b}$ and compare it with $\mathbf{s}$.

CHAPTER TEST A   True or False

For each statement that follows, answer true *if the statement is always true and* false *otherwise. In the case of a true statement, explain or prove your answer. In the case of a false statement, give an example to show that the statement is not always true.*

1. If $\mathbf{x}$ and $\mathbf{y}$ are nonzero vectors in $\mathbb{R}^n$, then the vector projection of $\mathbf{x}$ onto $\mathbf{y}$ is equal to the vector projection of $\mathbf{y}$ onto $\mathbf{x}$.

2. If $\mathbf{x}$ and $\mathbf{y}$ are unit vectors in $\mathbb{R}^n$ and $|\mathbf{x}^T\mathbf{y}| = 1$, then $\mathbf{x}$ and $\mathbf{y}$ are linearly independent.

3. If U, V, and W are subspaces of $\mathbb{R}^3$ and if $U \perp V$ and $V \perp W$, then $U \perp W$.

4. It is possible to find a nonzero vector $\mathbf{y}$ in the column space of A such that $A^T\mathbf{y} = \mathbf{0}$.

5. If A is an $m \times n$ matrix, then AA^T and A^TA have the same rank.

6. If an $m \times n$ matrix A has linearly dependent columns and $\mathbf{b}$ is a vector in $\mathbb{R}^m$, then $\mathbf{b}$ does not have a unique projection onto the column space of A.

7. If $N(A) = \{\mathbf{0}\}$, then the system $A\mathbf{x} = \mathbf{b}$ will have a unique least squares solution.

8. If Q_1 and Q_2 are orthogonal matrices, then Q_1Q_2 also is an orthogonal matrix.

9. If $\{\mathbf{u}_1, \mathbf{u}_2, \dots, \mathbf{u}_k\}$ is an orthonormal set of vectors in $\mathbb{R}^n$ and

$$U = (\mathbf{u}_1, \mathbf{u}_2, \dots, \mathbf{u}_k)$$

then $U^TU = I_k$ (the $k \times k$ identity matrix).

10. If $\{\mathbf{u}_1, \mathbf{u}_2, \dots, \mathbf{u}_k\}$ is an orthonormal set of vectors in $\mathbb{R}^n$ and

$$U = (\mathbf{u}_1, \mathbf{u}_2, \dots, \mathbf{u}_k)$$

then $UU^T = I_n$ (the $n \times n$ identity matrix).

CHAPTER TEST B

1. Let

$$\mathbf{x} = \begin{Bmatrix} 1 \\ 1 \\ 2 \\ 2 \end{Bmatrix} \quad \text{and} \quad \mathbf{y} = \begin{Bmatrix} -2 \\ 1 \\ 2 \\ 0 \end{Bmatrix}$$

(a) Find the vector projection $\mathbf{p}$ of $\mathbf{x}$ onto $\mathbf{y}$.

(b) Verify that $\mathbf{x} - \mathbf{p}$ is orthogonal to $\mathbf{p}$.

(c) Verify that the Pythagorean law holds for $\mathbf{x}$, $\mathbf{p}$, and $\mathbf{x} - \mathbf{p}$.

2. Let $\mathbf{v}_1$ and $\mathbf{v}_2$ be vectors in an inner product space V.

(a) Is it possible for $|\langle \mathbf{v}_1, \mathbf{v}_2 \rangle|$ to be greater than $\|\mathbf{v}_1\| \|\mathbf{v}_2\|$? Explain.

(b) If

$$|\langle \mathbf{v}_1, \mathbf{v}_2 \rangle| = \|\mathbf{v}_1\| \|\mathbf{v}_2\|$$

what can you conclude about the vectors $\mathbf{v}_1$ and $\mathbf{v}_2$? Explain.

3. Let $\mathbf{v}_1$ and $\mathbf{v}_2$ be vectors in an inner product space V. Show that

$$\|\mathbf{v}_1 + \mathbf{v}_2\|^2 \le (\|\mathbf{v}_1\| + \|\mathbf{v}_2\|)^2$$

4. Let A be a 7×5 matrix with rank equal to 4 and let $\mathbf{b}$ be a vector in $\mathbb{R}^7$. The four fundamental subspaces associated with A are $R(A)$, $N(A^T)$, $R(A^T)$, and $N(A)$.

(a) What is the dimension of $N(A^T)$, and which of the other fundamental subspaces is the orthogonal complement of $N(A^T)$?

(b) If $\mathbf{x}$ is a vector in $R(A)$ and $A^T\mathbf{x} = \mathbf{0}$, then what can you conclude about the value of $\|\mathbf{x}\|$? Explain.

(c) What is the dimension of $N(A^TA)$? How many solutions will the least squares system $A\mathbf{x} = \mathbf{b}$ have? Explain.

5. Let $\mathbf{x}$ and $\mathbf{y}$ be vectors in $\mathbb{R}^n$ and let Q be an $n \times n$ orthogonal matrix. Show that if

$$\mathbf{z} = Q\mathbf{x} \quad \text{and} \quad \mathbf{w} = Q\mathbf{y}$$

then the angle between $\mathbf{z}$ and $\mathbf{w}$ is equal to the angle between $\mathbf{x}$ and $\mathbf{y}$.

6. Let S be the two-dimensional subspace of $\mathbb{R}^3$ spanned by

$$\mathbf{x}_1 = \begin{bmatrix} 1 \\ 0 \\ 2 \end{bmatrix} \quad \text{and} \quad \mathbf{x}_2 = \begin{bmatrix} 0 \\ 1 \\ -2 \end{bmatrix}$$

(a) Find a basis for $S^\perp$.

(b) Give a geometric description of S and $S^\perp$.

(c) Determine the projection matrix P that projects vectors in $\mathbb{R}^3$ onto $S^\perp$.

7. Given the table of data points

x	-1	1	2
y	1	3	3

find the best least squares fit by a linear function $f(x) = c_1 + c_2x$.

8. Let $\{\mathbf{u}_1, \mathbf{u}_2, \mathbf{u}_3\}$ be an orthonormal basis for a three-dimensional subspace S of an inner product space V, and let

$$\mathbf{x} = 2\mathbf{u}_1 - 2\mathbf{u}_2 + \mathbf{u}_3 \quad \text{and} \quad \mathbf{y} = 3\mathbf{u}_1 + \mathbf{u}_2 - 4\mathbf{u}_3$$

(a) Determine the value of $\langle \mathbf{x}, \mathbf{y} \rangle$.

(b) Determine the value of $\|\mathbf{x}\|$.

9. Let A be a 7×5 matrix of rank 4. Let P and Q be the projection matrices that project vectors in $\mathbb{R}^7$ onto $R(A)$ and $N(A^T)$, respectively.

(a) Show that $PQ = O$.

(b) Show that $P + Q = I$.

10. Given

$$A = \begin{bmatrix} 1 & -3 & -5 \\ 1 & 1 & -2 \\ 1 & -3 & 1 \\ 1 & 1 & 4 \end{bmatrix} \quad \text{and} \quad \mathbf{b} = \begin{bmatrix} -6 \\ 1 \\ 1 \\ 6 \end{bmatrix}$$

If the Gram–Schmidt process is applied to determine an orthonormal basis for $R(A)$ and a QR factorization of A, then after the first two orthonormal vectors $\mathbf{q}_1$ and $\mathbf{q}_2$ are computed, we have

$$Q = \begin{bmatrix} \frac{1}{2} & -\frac{1}{2} & - \\ \frac{1}{2} & \frac{1}{2} & - \\ \frac{1}{2} & -\frac{1}{2} & - \\ \frac{1}{2} & \frac{1}{2} & - \end{bmatrix} \quad R = \begin{bmatrix} 2 & -2 & - \\ 0 & 4 & - \\ 0 & 0 & - \end{bmatrix}$$

(a) Finish the process. Determine $\mathbf{q}_3$ and fill in the third columns of Q and R.

(b) Use the QR factorization to find the least squares solution of $A\mathbf{x} = \mathbf{b}$

11. The functions $\cos x$ and $\sin x$ are both unit vectors in $C[-\pi, \pi]$ with the inner product defined by

$$\langle f, g \rangle = \frac{1}{\pi} \int_{-\pi}^{\pi} f(x)g(x)dx$$

(a) Show that $\cos x \perp \sin x$.

(b) Determine the value of $\|\cos x + \sin x\|_2$.

12. Consider the vector space $C[-1, 1]$ with the inner product defined by

$$\langle f, g \rangle = \int_{-1}^{1} f(x)g(x)dx$$

(a) Show that

$$u_1(x) = \frac{1}{\sqrt{2}} \quad \text{and} \quad u_2(x) = \frac{\sqrt{6}}{2}x$$

form an orthonormal set of vectors.

(b) Use the result from part (a) to find the best least squares approximation to $h(x) = x^{1/3} + x^{2/3}$ by a linear function.

6

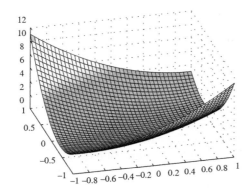

Eigenvalues

In Section 6.1, we will be concerned with the equation $A\mathbf{x} = \lambda\mathbf{x}$. This equation occurs in many applications of linear algebra. If the equation has a nonzero solution $\mathbf{x}$, then λ is said to be an *eigenvalue* of A and $\mathbf{x}$ is said to be an *eigenvector* belonging to λ.

Eigenvalues are a common part of our life whether we realize it or not. Wherever there are vibrations, there are eigenvalues, the natural frequencies of the vibrations. If you have ever tuned a guitar, you have solved an eigenvalue problem. When engineers design structures, they are concerned with the frequencies of vibration of the structure. This concern is particularly important in earthquake-prone regions such as California. The eigenvalues of a boundary value problem can be used to determine the energy states of an atom or critical loads that cause buckling in a beam. This latter application is presented in Section 6.1.

In Section 6.2, we will learn more about how to use eigenvalues and eigenvectors to solve systems of linear differential equations. We will consider a number of applications, including mixture problems, the harmonic motion of a system of springs, and the vibrations of a building. The motion of a building can be modeled by a second-order system of differential equations of the form

$$MY''(t) = KY(t)$$

where $\mathbf{Y}(t)$ is a vector whose entries are all functions of t and $\mathbf{Y}''(t)$ is the vector of functions formed by taking the second derivatives of each of the entries of $\mathbf{Y}(t)$. The solution of the equation is determined by the eigenvalues and eigenvectors of the matrix $A = M^{-1}K$.

In general, we can view eigenvalues as natural frequencies associated with linear operators. If A is an $n \times n$ matrix, we can think of A as representing a linear operator on $\mathbb{R}^n$. Eigenvalues and eigenvectors provide the key to understanding how the operator works. For example, if $\lambda > 0$, the effect of the operator on any eigenvector belonging to λ is simply a stretching or shrinking by a constant factor. Indeed, the effect of the operator is easily determined on any linear combination of eigenvectors. In particular, if it is possible to find a basis of eigenvectors for $\mathbb{R}^n$, the operator can be represented by a diagonal matrix D with respect to that basis and the matrix A can be factored into a product XDX^{-1}. In Section 6.3, we see how this is done and look at a number of applications.

In Section 6.4, we consider matrices with complex entries. In this setting, we will be concerned with matrices whose eigenvectors can be used to form an orthonormal basis for $\mathbb{C}^n$ (the vector space of all n-tuples of complex numbers). In Section 6.5, we introduce the singular value decomposition of a matrix and show four applications. Another important application of this factorization will be presented in Chapter 7.

Section 6.6 deals with the application of eigenvalues to quadratic equations in several variables and also with applications involving maxima and minima of functions of several variables. In Section 6.7, we consider symmetric positive definite matrices. The eigenvalues of such matrices are real and positive. These matrices occur in a wide variety of applications. Finally, in Section 6.8, we study matrices with nonnegative entries and some applications to economics.

6.1 Eigenvalues and Eigenvectors

Many application problems involve applying a linear transformation repeatedly to a given vector. The key to solving these problems is to choose a coordinate system or basis that is in some sense natural for the operator and for which it will be simpler to do calculations involving the operator. With respect to these new basis vectors (*eigenvectors*), we associate scaling factors (*eigenvalues*) that represent the natural frequencies of the operator. We illustrate with a simple example.

EXAMPLE I   Let us recall Application 1 from Section 1.4. In a certain town, 30 percent of the married women get divorced each year and 20 percent of the single women get married each year. There are 8000 married women and 2000 single women, and the total population remains constant. Let us investigate the long-range prospects if these percentages of marriages and divorces continue indefinitely into the future.

To find the number of married and single women after one year, we multiply the vector $\mathbf{w}_0 = (8000, 2000)^T$ by

$$A = \begin{bmatrix} 0.7 & 0.2 \\ 0.3 & 0.8 \end{bmatrix}$$

The number of married and single women after one year is given by

$$\mathbf{w}_1 = A\mathbf{w}_0 = \begin{bmatrix} 0.7 & 0.2 \\ 0.3 & 0.8 \end{bmatrix} \begin{bmatrix} 8000 \\ 2000 \end{bmatrix} = \begin{bmatrix} 6000 \\ 4000 \end{bmatrix}$$

To determine the number of married and single women after two years, we compute

$$\mathbf{w}_2 = A\mathbf{w}_1 = A^2\mathbf{w}_0$$

and in general for n years we must compute $\mathbf{w}_n = A^n\mathbf{w}_0$.

Let us compute $\mathbf{w}_{10}, \mathbf{w}_{20}, \mathbf{w}_{30}$ in this way and round the entries of each to the nearest integer.

$$\mathbf{w}_{10} = \begin{bmatrix} 4004 \\ 5996 \end{bmatrix}, \quad \mathbf{w}_{20} = \begin{bmatrix} 4000 \\ 6000 \end{bmatrix}, \quad \mathbf{w}_{30} = \begin{bmatrix} 4000 \\ 6000 \end{bmatrix}$$

After a certain point, we seem to always get the same answer. In fact, $\mathbf{w}_{12} = (4000, 6000)^T$ and since

$$A\mathbf{w}_{12} = \begin{bmatrix} 0.7 & 0.2 \\ 0.3 & 0.8 \end{bmatrix} \begin{bmatrix} 4000 \\ 6000 \end{bmatrix} = \begin{bmatrix} 4000 \\ 6000 \end{bmatrix}$$

it follows that all the succeeding vectors in the sequence remain unchanged. The vector $(4000, 6000)^T$ is said to be a *steady-state vector* for the process.

Suppose that initially we had different proportions of married and single women. If, for example, we had started with 10,000 married women and 0 single women, then $\mathbf{w}_0 = (10{,}000, 0)^T$ and we can compute $\mathbf{w}_n$ as before by multiplying $\mathbf{w}_0$ by A^n. In this case, it turns out that $\mathbf{w}_{14} = (4000, 6000)^T$, and hence we still end up with the same steady-state vector.

Why does this process converge, and why do we seem to get the same steady-state vector even when we change the initial vector? These questions are not difficult to answer if we choose a basis for $\mathbb{R}^2$ consisting of vectors for which the effect of the linear operator A is easily determined. In particular, if we choose a multiple of the steady-state vector, say, $\mathbf{x}_1 = (2, 3)^T$, as our first basis vector, then

$$A\mathbf{x}_1 = \begin{bmatrix} 0.7 & 0.2 \\ 0.3 & 0.8 \end{bmatrix} \begin{bmatrix} 2 \\ 3 \end{bmatrix} = \begin{bmatrix} 2 \\ 3 \end{bmatrix} = \mathbf{x}_1$$

Thus, $\mathbf{x}_1$ is also a steady-state vector. It is a natural basis vector to use since the effect of A on $\mathbf{x}_1$ could not be simpler. Although it would be nice to use another steady-state vector as the second basis vector, this is not possible, because all the steady-state vectors turn out to be multiples of $\mathbf{x}_1$. However, if we choose $\mathbf{x}_2 = (-1, 1)^T$, then the effect of A on $\mathbf{x}_2$ is also very simple:

$$A\mathbf{x}_2 = \begin{bmatrix} 0.7 & 0.2 \\ 0.3 & 0.8 \end{bmatrix} \begin{bmatrix} -1 \\ 1 \end{bmatrix} = \begin{bmatrix} -\frac{1}{2} \\ \frac{1}{2} \end{bmatrix} = \tfrac{1}{2}\mathbf{x}_2$$

Let us now analyze the process using $\mathbf{x}_1$ and $\mathbf{x}_2$ as our basis vectors. If we express the initial vector $\mathbf{w}_0 = (8000, 2000)^T$ as a linear combination of $\mathbf{x}_1$ and $\mathbf{x}_2$, then

$$\mathbf{w}_0 = 2000 \begin{bmatrix} 2 \\ 3 \end{bmatrix} - 4000 \begin{bmatrix} -1 \\ 1 \end{bmatrix} = 2000\mathbf{x}_1 - 4000\mathbf{x}_2$$

and it follows that

$$\mathbf{w}_1 = A\mathbf{w}_0 = 2000A\mathbf{x}_1 - 4000A\mathbf{x}_2 = 2000\mathbf{x}_1 - 4000\left(\frac{1}{2}\right)\mathbf{x}_2$$

$$\mathbf{w}_2 = A\mathbf{w}_1 = 2000\mathbf{x}_1 - 4000\left(\frac{1}{2}\right)^2 \mathbf{x}_2$$

In general,

$$\mathbf{w}_n = A^n\mathbf{w}_0 = 2000\mathbf{x}_1 - 4000\left(\frac{1}{2}\right)^n \mathbf{x}_2$$

The first component of this sum is the steady-state vector and the second component converges to the zero vector.

Will we always end up with the same steady-state vector for any choice of $\mathbf{w}_0$? Suppose that initially there are p married women. Since there are 10,000 women altogether, the number of single women must be $10{,}000 - p$. Our initial vector is then

$$\mathbf{w}_0 = \begin{bmatrix} p \\ 10{,}000 - p \end{bmatrix}$$

If we express $\mathbf{w}_0$ as a linear combination $c_1\mathbf{x}_1 + c_2\mathbf{x}_2$, then, as before,

$$\mathbf{w}_n = A^n\mathbf{w}_0 = c_1\mathbf{x}_1 + \left(\frac{1}{2}\right)^n c_2\mathbf{x}_2$$

The steady-state vector will be $c_1\mathbf{x}_1$. To determine c_1, we write the equation

$$c_1\mathbf{x}_1 + c_2\mathbf{x}_2 = \mathbf{w}_0$$

as a linear system:

$$\begin{aligned} 2c_1 - c_2 &= p \\ 3c_1 + c_2 &= 10{,}000 - p \end{aligned}$$

Adding the two equations, we see that $c_1 = 2000$. Thus, for any integer p in the range $0 \leq p \leq 10{,}000$, the steady-state vector turns out to be

$$2000\mathbf{x}_1 = \begin{bmatrix} 4000 \\ 6000 \end{bmatrix} \qquad \blacksquare$$

The vectors $\mathbf{x}_1$ and $\mathbf{x}_2$ were natural vectors to use in analyzing the process in Example 1, since the effect of the matrix A on each of these vectors was so simple:

$$A\mathbf{x}_1 = \mathbf{x}_1 = 1\mathbf{x}_1 \qquad \text{and} \qquad A\mathbf{x}_2 = \tfrac{1}{2}\mathbf{x}_2$$

For each of the two vectors, the effect of A was just to multiply the vector by a scalar. The two scalars 1 and $\frac{1}{2}$ can be thought of as the natural frequencies of the linear transformation.

In general, if a linear transformation is represented by an $n \times n$ matrix A and we can find a nonzero vector $\mathbf{x}$ so that $A\mathbf{x} = \lambda\mathbf{x}$, for some scalar λ, then, for this transformation, $\mathbf{x}$ is a natural choice to use as a basis vector for $\mathbb{R}^n$ and the scalar λ defines a natural frequency corresponding to that basis vector. More precisely, we use the following terminology to refer to $\mathbf{x}$ and λ.

Definition

Let A be an $n \times n$ matrix. A scalar λ is said to be an **eigenvalue** or a **characteristic value** of A if there exists a nonzero vector $\mathbf{x}$ such that $A\mathbf{x} = \lambda\mathbf{x}$. The vector $\mathbf{x}$ is said to be an **eigenvector** or a **characteristic vector** belonging to λ.

EXAMPLE 2   Let

$$A = \begin{bmatrix} 4 & -2 \\ 1 & 1 \end{bmatrix} \qquad \text{and} \qquad \mathbf{x} = \begin{bmatrix} 2 \\ 1 \end{bmatrix}$$

Since

$$A\mathbf{x} = \begin{bmatrix} 4 & -2 \\ 1 & 1 \end{bmatrix} \begin{bmatrix} 2 \\ 1 \end{bmatrix} = \begin{bmatrix} 6 \\ 3 \end{bmatrix} = 3 \begin{bmatrix} 2 \\ 1 \end{bmatrix} = 3\mathbf{x}$$

it follows that $\lambda = 3$ is an eigenvalue of A and $\mathbf{x} = (2, 1)^T$ is an eigenvector belonging to λ. Actually, any nonzero multiple of $\mathbf{x}$ will be an eigenvector, because

$$A(\alpha \mathbf{x}) = \alpha A\mathbf{x} = \alpha \lambda \mathbf{x} = \lambda(\alpha \mathbf{x})$$

For example, $(4, 2)^T$ is also an eigenvector belonging to $\lambda = 3$.

$$\begin{bmatrix} 4 & -2 \\ 1 & 1 \end{bmatrix} \begin{bmatrix} 4 \\ 2 \end{bmatrix} = \begin{bmatrix} 12 \\ 6 \end{bmatrix} = 3 \begin{bmatrix} 4 \\ 2 \end{bmatrix}$$

Geometric Visualization of Eigenvalues and Eigenvectors

If a positive real number λ_1 is an eigenvalue of a 2×2 matrix A, then to find the corresponding eigenvectors, we need to find vectors $\mathbf{x}$ such that $A\mathbf{x} = \lambda_1 \mathbf{x}$. The direction of an eigenvector $\mathbf{x}$ is specified by the unit vector

$$\mathbf{x}_1 = \alpha \mathbf{x} \quad \text{where} \quad \alpha = \frac{1}{\|\mathbf{x}\|}$$

Note that the direction vector $\mathbf{x}_1$ is itself an eigenvector belonging to λ_1 since it is a nonzero scalar multiple of an eigenvector $\mathbf{x}$. Since $\lambda_1 > 0$, the vector $A\mathbf{x}_1$ is in the same direction as $\mathbf{x}_1$ and $\|A\mathbf{x}_1\| = \lambda_1$. In the case that λ_1 is a negative real eigenvalue of A with unit eigenvector $\mathbf{x}_1$, the vectors $\mathbf{x}_1$ and $A\mathbf{x}_1$ will be in opposite directions and the length of $A\mathbf{x}_1$ will be $|\lambda_1|$. In general, for a real eigenvalue λ_1, we can view the problem of finding a corresponding eigenvector as one of finding a direction vector $\mathbf{x}_1$ for which $A\mathbf{x}_1$ and $\mathbf{x}_1$ lie along the same line through the origin in 2-space.

Unit vectors in $\mathbb{R}^2$ are vectors of the form

$$x = \begin{bmatrix} \cos t \\ \sin t \end{bmatrix} \quad 0 \le t \le 2\pi$$

Geometrically, the vectors start at the origin and have terminal points on the circle of radius 1 that is centered about the origin. One way to search for an eigenvector belonging to a real eigenvalue of a 2×2 matrix A is to move around the circumference of that circle (let t vary from 0 to 2π) and try to find points $(\cos t, \sin t)$ where the corresponding vectors $\mathbf{x}$ and $A\mathbf{x}$ both lie along the same line through the origin. Consider the following example.

EXAMPLE 3   Let

$$A = \begin{bmatrix} \frac{1}{2} & \frac{3}{2} \\ \frac{3}{2} & \frac{1}{2} \end{bmatrix}$$

The unit vector $\mathbf{x} = (1, 0)^T$ is not an eigenvector since $\mathbf{x}$ and $A\mathbf{x}$ do not lie on the same line through the origin. See Figure 6.1.1.

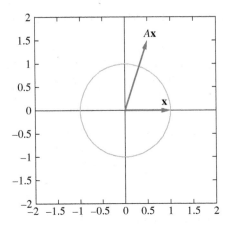

Figure 6.1.1.

To search for an eigenvector, we can rotate this initial unit vector counter-clockwise. As we rotate, we can compare the directions of $\mathbf{x}$ and $A\mathbf{x}$. If for some direction vector $\mathbf{x}$, the vector $A\mathbf{x}$ is in the same or opposite direction of $\mathbf{x}$, then we have found an eigenvector. For this example, the two vectors do not align until we have rotated the initial vector 45°. The unit vector $\mathbf{x}_1$ in this direction will be an eigenvector of A. Indeed,

$$\mathbf{x}_1 = \begin{bmatrix} \cos\frac{\pi}{4} \\ \sin\frac{\pi}{4} \end{bmatrix} = \begin{bmatrix} \frac{1}{\sqrt{2}} \\ \frac{1}{\sqrt{2}} \end{bmatrix} \quad \text{and} \quad A\mathbf{x}_1 = \begin{bmatrix} \frac{2}{\sqrt{2}} \\ \frac{2}{\sqrt{2}} \end{bmatrix} = 2\mathbf{x}_1$$

Thus, $\mathbf{x}_1$ is a unit eigenvector belonging to the eigenvalue $\lambda_1 = 2$. See Figure 6.1.2(a).

If we continue rotating an additional 90°, we discover a second unit eigenvector.

$$\mathbf{x}_2 = \begin{bmatrix} \cos\frac{3\pi}{4} \\ \sin\frac{3\pi}{4} \end{bmatrix} = \begin{bmatrix} \frac{-1}{\sqrt{2}} \\ \frac{1}{\sqrt{2}} \end{bmatrix} \quad \text{and} \quad A\mathbf{x}_2 = \begin{bmatrix} \frac{1}{\sqrt{2}} \\ \frac{-1}{\sqrt{2}} \end{bmatrix} = -1\mathbf{x}_2$$

(a)

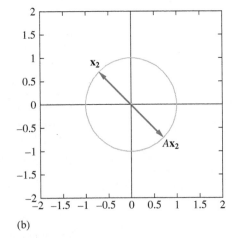

(b)

Figure 6.1.2.

The vector $\mathbf{x}_2$ is a unit eigenvector of A belonging to the eigenvalue $\lambda_2 = -1$. See Figure 6.1.2(b). ∎

Once a unit eigenvector $\mathbf{x}$ has been found, it is easy to determine the value of the corresponding eigenvalue. Since $\|\mathbf{x}\| = 1$, it follows that

$$\mathbf{x}^T A \mathbf{x} = \mathbf{x}^T(\lambda \mathbf{x}) = \lambda \|\mathbf{x}\|^2 = \lambda$$

Thus, one can compute the eigenvalue by setting $\lambda = \mathbf{x}^T A \mathbf{x}$.

Next, we present a method of finding the eigenvalues directly. Once the eigenvalues are known, there is a straightforward method to find the corresponding eigenvectors.

Finding Eigenvalues and Eigenvectors

The equation $A\mathbf{x} = \lambda \mathbf{x}$ can be written in the form

$$(A - \lambda I)\mathbf{x} = \mathbf{0} \tag{1}$$

Thus, λ is an eigenvalue of A if and only if (1) has a nontrivial solution. The set of solutions to (1) is $N(A - \lambda I)$, which is a subspace of $\mathbb{R}^n$. Hence, if λ is an eigenvalue of A, then $N(A - \lambda I) \neq \{\mathbf{0}\}$, and any nonzero vector in $N(A - \lambda I)$ is an eigenvector belonging to λ. The subspace $N(A - \lambda I)$ is called the *eigenspace* corresponding to the eigenvalue λ.

Equation (1) will have a nontrivial solution if and only if $A - \lambda I$ is singular, or, equivalently,

$$\det(A - \lambda I) = 0 \tag{2}$$

If the determinant in (2) is expanded, we obtain an nth-degree polynomial in the variable λ:

$$p(\lambda) = \det(A - \lambda I)$$

This polynomial is called the *characteristic polynomial*, and equation (2) is called the *characteristic equation*, for the matrix A. The roots of the characteristic polynomial are the eigenvalues of A. If roots are counted according to multiplicity, then the characteristic polynomial will have exactly n roots. Thus, A will have n eigenvalues, some of which may be repeated and some of which may be complex numbers. To take care of the latter case, it will be necessary to expand our field of scalars to the complex numbers and to allow complex entries for our vectors and matrices.

We have now established a number of equivalent conditions for λ to be an eigenvalue of A.

Let A be an $n \times n$ matrix and λ be a scalar. The following statements are equivalent:

(a) λ is an eigenvalue of A.

(b) $(A - \lambda I)\mathbf{x} = \mathbf{0}$ has a nontrivial solution.

(c) $N(A - \lambda I) \neq \{\mathbf{0}\}$

(d) $A - \lambda I$ is singular.

(e) $\det(A - \lambda I) = 0$

We will now use statement **(e)** to determine the eigenvalues in a number of examples.

EXAMPLE 4   Find the eigenvalues and the corresponding eigenvectors of the matrix

$$A = \begin{pmatrix} 3 & 2 \\ 3 & -2 \end{pmatrix}$$

Solution

The characteristic equation is

$$\begin{vmatrix} 3 - \lambda & 2 \\ 3 & -2 - \lambda \end{vmatrix} = 0 \quad \text{or} \quad \lambda^2 - \lambda - 12 = 0$$

Thus, the eigenvalues of A are $\lambda_1 = 4$ and $\lambda_2 = -3$. To find the eigenvectors belonging to $\lambda_1 = 4$, we must determine the null space of $A - 4I$.

$$A - 4I = \begin{bmatrix} -1 & 2 \\ 3 & -6 \end{bmatrix}$$

Solving $(A - 4I)\mathbf{x} = \mathbf{0}$, we get

$$\mathbf{x} = (2x_2, x_2)^T$$

Hence, any nonzero multiple of $(2, 1)^T$ is an eigenvector belonging to λ_1, and $\{(2, 1)^T\}$ is a basis for the eigenspace corresponding to λ_1. Similarly, to find the eigenvectors for λ_2, we must solve

$$(A + 3I)\mathbf{x} = \mathbf{0}$$

In this case, $\{(-1, 3)^T\}$ is a basis for $N(A + 3I)$ and any nonzero multiple of $(-1, 3)^T$ is an eigenvector belonging to λ_2.   ∎

EXAMPLE 5   Let

$$A = \begin{pmatrix} 2 & -3 & 1 \\ 1 & -2 & 1 \\ 1 & -3 & 2 \end{pmatrix}$$

Find the eigenvalues and the corresponding eigenspaces.

Solution

$$\begin{vmatrix} 2 - \lambda & -3 & 1 \\ 1 & -2 - \lambda & 1 \\ 1 & -3 & 2 - \lambda \end{vmatrix} = -\lambda(\lambda - 1)^2$$

Thus, the characteristic polynomial has roots $\lambda_1 = 0$, $\lambda_2 = \lambda_3 = 1$. The eigenspace corresponding to $\lambda_1 = 0$ is $N(A)$, which we determine in the usual manner:

$$\begin{pmatrix} 2 & -3 & 1 & | & 0 \\ 1 & -2 & 1 & | & 0 \\ 1 & -3 & 2 & | & 0 \end{pmatrix} \rightarrow \begin{pmatrix} 1 & 0 & -1 & | & 0 \\ 0 & 1 & -1 & | & 0 \\ 0 & 0 & 0 & | & 0 \end{pmatrix}$$

Setting $x_3 = \alpha$, we find that $x_1 = x_2 = x_3 = \alpha$. Consequently, the eigenspace corresponding to $\lambda_1 = 0$ consists of all vectors of the form $\alpha(1, 1, 1)^T$. To find the eigenspace corresponding to $\lambda = 1$, we solve the system $(A - I)\mathbf{x} = \mathbf{0}$:

$$\left(\begin{array}{ccc|c} 1 & -3 & 1 & 0 \\ 1 & -3 & 1 & 0 \\ 1 & -3 & 1 & 0 \end{array}\right) \rightarrow \left(\begin{array}{ccc|c} 1 & -3 & 1 & 0 \\ 0 & 0 & 0 & 0 \\ 0 & 0 & 0 & 0 \end{array}\right)$$

Setting $x_2 = \alpha$ and $x_3 = \beta$, we get $x_1 = 3\alpha - \beta$. Thus, the eigenspace corresponding to $\lambda = 1$ consists of all vectors of the form

$$\left(\begin{array}{c} 3\alpha - \beta \\ \alpha \\ \beta \end{array}\right) = \alpha \left(\begin{array}{c} 3 \\ 1 \\ 0 \end{array}\right) + \beta \left(\begin{array}{c} -1 \\ 0 \\ 1 \end{array}\right) \qquad \blacksquare$$

EXAMPLE 6   Let

$$A = \left(\begin{array}{cc} 1 & 2 \\ -2 & 1 \end{array}\right)$$

Compute the eigenvalues of A and find bases for the corresponding eigenspaces.

Solution

$$\left|\begin{array}{cc} 1 - \lambda & 2 \\ -2 & 1 - \lambda \end{array}\right| = (1 - \lambda)^2 + 4$$

The roots of the characteristic polynomial are $\lambda_1 = 1 + 2i$, $\lambda_2 = 1 - 2i$.

$$A - \lambda_1 I = \left(\begin{array}{cc} -2i & 2 \\ -2 & -2i \end{array}\right) = -2 \left(\begin{array}{cc} i & -1 \\ 1 & i \end{array}\right)$$

It follows that $\{(1, i)^T\}$ is a basis for the eigenspace corresponding to $\lambda_1 = 1 + 2i$. Similarly,

$$A - \lambda_2 I = \left(\begin{array}{cc} 2i & 2 \\ -2 & 2i \end{array}\right) = 2 \left(\begin{array}{cc} i & 1 \\ -1 & i \end{array}\right)$$

and $\{(1, -i)^T\}$ is a basis for $N(A - \lambda_2 I)$. $\blacksquare$

APPLICATION I   Structures—Buckling of a Beam

For an example of a physical eigenvalue problem, consider the case of a beam. If a force or load is applied to one end of the beam, the beam will buckle when the load reaches a critical value. If we continue increasing the load beyond the critical value, we can expect the beam to buckle again when the load reaches a second critical value, and so on. Assume that the beam has length L and that it is positioned along the x-axis in the plane with the left support of the beam at $x = 0$. Let $y(x)$ represent the vertical displacement of the beam for any point x, and assume that the beam is simply supported; that is, $y(0) = y(L) = 0$. (See Figure 6.1.3.)

Figure 6.1.3.

The physical system for the beam is modeled by the boundary value problem

$$R\frac{d^2y}{dx^2} = -Py \quad y(0) = y(L) = 0 \tag{3}$$

where R is the flexural rigidity of the beam and P is the load placed on the beam. A standard procedure to compute the solution $y(x)$ is to use a finite difference method to approximate the differential equation. Specifically, we partition the interval $[0, L]$ into n equal subintervals

$$0 = x_0 < x_1 < \cdots < x_n = L \quad \left(x_j = \frac{jL}{n}, j = 0, \ldots, n\right)$$

and, for each j, we approximate $y''(x_j)$ by a difference quotient. If we set $h = \frac{L}{n}$ and use the shorthand notation y_k for $y(x_k)$, then the standard difference approximation is given by

$$y''(x_j) \approx \frac{y_{j+1} - 2y_j + y_{j-1}}{h^2} \quad j = 1, \ldots, n$$

Substituting these approximations into equation (3), we end up with a system of n linear equations. If we multiply each equation through by $-\frac{h^2}{R}$ and set $\lambda = \frac{Ph^2}{R}$, then the system can be written as a matrix equation of the form $A\mathbf{y} = \lambda\mathbf{y}$, where

$$A = \begin{bmatrix} 2 & -1 & 0 & \cdots & 0 & 0 & 0 \\ -1 & 2 & -1 & \cdots & 0 & 0 & 0 \\ 0 & -1 & 2 & \cdots & 0 & 0 & 0 \\ \vdots & & & & & & \vdots \\ 0 & 0 & 0 & \cdots & -1 & 2 & -1 \\ 0 & 0 & 0 & \cdots & 0 & -1 & 2 \end{bmatrix}$$

The eigenvalues of this matrix will all be real and positive. (See MATLAB Exercise 14 at the end of the chapter.) For n sufficiently large, each eigenvalue λ of A can be used to approximate a critical load $P = \frac{R\lambda}{h^2}$ under which buckling may occur. The most important of these critical loads is the one corresponding to the smallest eigenvalue since the beam may actually break after this load is exceeded.

APPLICATION 2   Aerospace: The Orientation of a Space Shuttle

In Section 4.2, we saw how to determine the matrix representation corresponding to a yaw, pitch, or roll of an airplane in terms of 3×3 rotation matrices Y, P, and R. Recall that a yaw is a rotation of an aircraft about the z-axis, a pitch is a rotation about the y-axis, and a roll is a rotation about the x-axis. We also saw in the airplane application that a combination of a yaw followed by a pitch and then a roll could be represented by a product $Q = YPR$. The same terms—yaw, pitch, and roll—are used to describe the rotations of a space shuttle from its initial position to a new orientation. The only difference is that, for a space shuttle, it is customary to have the positive x and z axes pointing in the opposite directions. Figure 6.1.4 shows the axis system for the shuttle, compared with the axis system used for an airplane. The shuttle axes for the yaw, pitch, and roll are denoted Z_S, Y_S, and X_S, respectively. The origin for the axis system is at the center of mass of the space shuttle. We could use the yaw, pitch, and roll transformations, to reorient the shuttle from its initial position; however, rather than performing three separate rotations, it is more efficient to use only one rotation. Given the angles for the yaw, pitch, and roll, it is desirable to have the shuttle computer determine a new single axis of rotation R and an angle of rotation β about that axis.

In 2-space, a rotation in the plane of $45°$, followed by a $30°$ rotation, is equivalent to a single $75°$ rotation from the initial position. Likewise, in 3-space, a combination of two or more rotations is equivalent to a single rotation. In the case of the space shuttle, we would like to accomplish the combined rotations of yaw, pitch, and roll by performing a single rotation about a new axis R. The new axis can be determined by computing the eigenvectors of the transformation matrix Q.

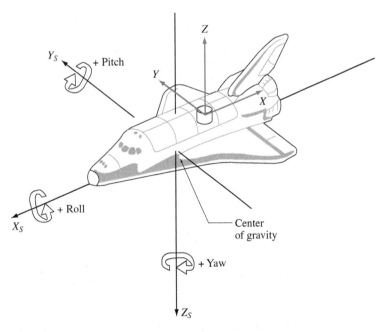

Figure 6.1.4.

The matrix Q representing the combined yaw, pitch, and roll transformations is a product of three orthogonal matrices, each having a determinant equal to 1. So Q is also orthogonal and $\det(Q) = 1$. It follows that Q must have $\lambda = 1$ as an eigenvalue. (See Exercise 23.) If $\mathbf{z}$ is a unit vector in the direction of the axis of rotation R, then $\mathbf{z}$ should remain unchanged by the transformation and hence we should have $Q\mathbf{z} = \mathbf{z}$. Thus, $\mathbf{z}$ is an unit eigenvector of Q belonging to the eigenvalue $\lambda = 1$. The eigenvector $\mathbf{z}$ determines the axis of rotation.

To determine the angle of rotation about the new axis R, note that $\mathbf{e}_1$ represents the initial direction of the X_S axis and $\mathbf{q}_1 = Q\mathbf{e}_1$ represents the direction after the transformation. If we project $\mathbf{e}_1$ and $\mathbf{q}_1$ onto the R-axis, they both will project onto the same vector

$$\mathbf{p} = (\mathbf{z}^T\mathbf{e}_1)\mathbf{z} = z_1\mathbf{z}$$

The vectors

$$\mathbf{v} = \mathbf{e}_1 - \mathbf{p} \qquad \text{and} \qquad \mathbf{w} = \mathbf{q}_1 - \mathbf{p}$$

have the same length and both are in the plane that is normal to the R-axis and passes through the origin. As $\mathbf{e}_1$ rotates to $\mathbf{q}_1$, the vector $\mathbf{v}$ gets rotated to $\mathbf{w}$. (See Figure 6.1.5.) The angle of rotation β can be computed by finding the angle between $\mathbf{v}$ and $\mathbf{w}$:

$$\beta = \arccos\left(\frac{\mathbf{v}^T\mathbf{w}}{\|\mathbf{v}\|^2}\right)$$

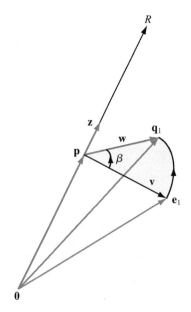

Figure 6.1.5.

Complex Eigenvalues

If A is an $n \times n$ matrix with real entries, then the characteristic polynomial of A will have real coefficients, and hence all its complex roots must occur in conjugate pairs. Thus, if $\lambda = a + bi$ $(b \neq 0)$ is an eigenvalue of A, then $\bar{\lambda} = a - bi$ must also be an eigenvalue of A. Here, the symbol $\bar{\lambda}$ (read *lambda bar*) is used to denote the complex conjugate of λ. A similar notation can be used for matrices. If $A = (a_{ij})$ is a matrix with complex entries, then $\bar{A} = (\overline{a_{ij}})$ is the matrix formed from A by conjugating each of its entries. We define a *real matrix* to be a matrix with the property that $\bar{A} = A$. In general, if A and B are matrices with complex entries and the multiplication AB is possible, then $\overline{AB} = \bar{A}\,\bar{B}$ (see Exercise 20).

Not only do the complex eigenvalues of a real matrix occur in conjugate pairs, but so do the eigenvectors. Indeed, if λ is a complex eigenvalue of a real $n \times n$ matrix A and $\mathbf{z}$ is an eigenvector belonging to λ, then

$$A\bar{\mathbf{z}} = \bar{A}\,\bar{\mathbf{z}} = \overline{A\mathbf{z}} = \overline{\lambda\mathbf{z}} = \bar{\lambda}\,\bar{\mathbf{z}}$$

Thus, $\bar{\mathbf{z}}$ is an eigenvector of A belonging to $\bar{\lambda}$. In Example 6, the eigenvector computed for the eigenvalue $\lambda = 1 + 2i$ was $\mathbf{z} = (1, i)^T$, and the eigenvector computed for $\bar{\lambda} = 1 - 2i$ was $\bar{\mathbf{z}} = (1, -i)^T$.

The Product and Sum of the Eigenvalues

It is easy to determine the product and sum of the eigenvalues of an $n \times n$ matrix A. If $p(\lambda)$ is the characteristic polynomial of A, then

$$p(\lambda) = \det(A - \lambda I) = \begin{vmatrix} a_{11} - \lambda & a_{12} & \cdots & a_{1n} \\ a_{21} & a_{22} - \lambda & & a_{2n} \\ \vdots & & & \\ a_{n1} & a_{n2} & & a_{nn} - \lambda \end{vmatrix} \tag{4}$$

Expanding along the first column, we get

$$\det(A - \lambda I) = (a_{11} - \lambda)\det(M_{11}) + \sum_{i=2}^{n} a_{i1}(-1)^{i+1}\det(M_{i1})$$

where the minors M_{i1}, $i = 2, \ldots, n$, do not contain the two diagonal elements $(a_{11} - \lambda)$ and $(a_{ii} - \lambda)$. Expanding $\det(M_{11})$ in the same manner, we conclude that

$$(a_{11} - \lambda)(a_{22} - \lambda)\cdots(a_{nn} - \lambda) \tag{5}$$

is the only term in the expansion of $\det(A - \lambda I)$ involving a product of more than $n - 2$ of the diagonal elements. When (5) is expanded, the coefficient of λ^n will be $(-1)^n$. Thus, the lead coefficient of $p(\lambda)$ is $(-1)^n$, and hence if $\lambda_1, \ldots, \lambda_n$ are the eigenvalues of A, then

$$\begin{aligned} p(\lambda) &= (-1)^n(\lambda - \lambda_1)(\lambda - \lambda_2)\cdots(\lambda - \lambda_n) \\ &= (\lambda_1 - \lambda)(\lambda_2 - \lambda)\cdots(\lambda_n - \lambda) \end{aligned} \tag{6}$$

It follows from (4) and (6) that

$$\lambda_1 \cdot \lambda_2 \cdots \lambda_n = p(0) = \det(A)$$

From (5), we also see that the coefficient of $(-\lambda)^{n-1}$ is $\sum\limits_{i=1}^{n} a_{ii}$. If we use (6) to determine this same coefficient, we obtain $\sum\limits_{i=1}^{n} \lambda_i$. It follows that

$$\sum_{i=1}^{n} \lambda_i = \sum_{i=1}^{n} a_{ii}$$

The sum of the diagonal elements of A is called the *trace* of A and is denoted by $\text{tr}(A)$.

EXAMPLE 7   If

$$A = \begin{pmatrix} 5 & -18 \\ 1 & -1 \end{pmatrix}$$

then

$$\det(A) = -5 + 18 = 13 \qquad \text{and} \qquad \text{tr}(A) = 5 - 1 = 4$$

The characteristic polynomial of A is given by

$$\begin{vmatrix} 5 - \lambda & -18 \\ 1 & -1 - \lambda \end{vmatrix} = \lambda^2 - 4\lambda + 13$$

and hence the eigenvalues of A are $\lambda_1 = 2 + 3i$ and $\lambda_2 = 2 - 3i$. Note that

$$\lambda_1 + \lambda_2 = 4 = \text{tr}(A)$$

and

$$\lambda_1 \lambda_2 = 13 = \det(A) \qquad\qquad \blacksquare$$

In the examples we have looked at so far, n has always been less than 4. For larger n, it is more difficult to find the roots of the characteristic polynomial. In Chapter 7, we will learn numerical methods for computing eigenvalues. (These methods will not involve the characteristic polynomial at all.) If the eigenvalues of A have been computed by some numerical method, one way to check their accuracy is to compare their sum with the trace of A.

Similar Matrices

We close this section with an important result about the eigenvalues of similar matrices. Recall that a matrix B is said to be *similar* to a matrix A if there exists a nonsingular matrix S such that $B = S^{-1}AS$.

Theorem 6.1.1   *Let A and B be $n \times n$ matrices. If B is similar to A, then the two matrices have the same characteristic polynomial and, consequently, the same eigenvalues.*

Proof   Let $p_A(x)$ and $p_B(x)$ denote the characteristic polynomials of A and B, respectively. If B is similar to A, then there exists a nonsingular matrix S such that $B = S^{-1}AS$. Thus,

$$
\begin{aligned}
p_B(\lambda) &= \det(B - \lambda I) \\
&= \det(S^{-1}AS - \lambda I) \\
&= \det(S^{-1}(A - \lambda I)S) \\
&= \det(S^{-1})\det(A - \lambda I)\det(S) \\
&= p_A(\lambda)
\end{aligned}
$$

The eigenvalues of a matrix are the roots of the characteristic polynomial. Since the two matrices have the same characteristic polynomial, they must have the same eigenvalues. ∎

EXAMPLE 8   Given

$$
T = \begin{bmatrix} 2 & 1 \\ 0 & 3 \end{bmatrix} \quad \text{and} \quad S = \begin{bmatrix} 5 & 3 \\ 3 & 2 \end{bmatrix}
$$

It is easily seen that the eigenvalues of T are $\lambda_1 = 2$ and $\lambda_2 = 3$. If we set $A = S^{-1}TS$, then the eigenvalues of A should be the same as those of T.

$$
A = \begin{bmatrix} 2 & -3 \\ -3 & 5 \end{bmatrix} \begin{bmatrix} 2 & 1 \\ 0 & 3 \end{bmatrix} \begin{bmatrix} 5 & 3 \\ 3 & 2 \end{bmatrix} = \begin{bmatrix} -1 & -2 \\ 6 & 6 \end{bmatrix}
$$

We leave it to the reader to verify that the eigenvalues of this matrix are $\lambda_1 = 2$ and $\lambda_2 = 3$. ∎

SECTION 6.1 EXERCISES

1. Find the eigenvalues and the corresponding eigenspaces for each of the following matrices:

(a) $\begin{bmatrix} 3 & 2 \\ 4 & 1 \end{bmatrix}$ **(b)** $\begin{bmatrix} 6 & -4 \\ 3 & -1 \end{bmatrix}$

(c) $\begin{bmatrix} 3 & -1 \\ 1 & 1 \end{bmatrix}$ **(d)** $\begin{bmatrix} 3 & -8 \\ 2 & 3 \end{bmatrix}$

(e) $\begin{bmatrix} 1 & 1 \\ -2 & 3 \end{bmatrix}$ **(f)** $\begin{bmatrix} 0 & 1 & 0 \\ 0 & 0 & 1 \\ 0 & 0 & 0 \end{bmatrix}$

(g) $\begin{bmatrix} 1 & 1 & 1 \\ 0 & 2 & 1 \\ 0 & 0 & 1 \end{bmatrix}$ **(h)** $\begin{bmatrix} 1 & 2 & 1 \\ 0 & 3 & 1 \\ 0 & 5 & -1 \end{bmatrix}$

(i) $\begin{bmatrix} 4 & -5 & 1 \\ 1 & 0 & -1 \\ 0 & 1 & -1 \end{bmatrix}$ **(j)** $\begin{bmatrix} -2 & 0 & 1 \\ 1 & 0 & -1 \\ 0 & 1 & -1 \end{bmatrix}$

(k) $\begin{bmatrix} 2 & 0 & 0 & 0 \\ 0 & 2 & 0 & 0 \\ 0 & 0 & 3 & 0 \\ 0 & 0 & 0 & 4 \end{bmatrix}$ **(l)** $\begin{bmatrix} 3 & 0 & 0 & 0 \\ 4 & 1 & 0 & 0 \\ 0 & 0 & 2 & 1 \\ 0 & 0 & 0 & 2 \end{bmatrix}$

2. Show that the eigenvalues of a triangular matrix are the diagonal elements of the matrix.

3. Let A be an $n \times n$ matrix. Prove that A is singular if and only if $\lambda = 0$ is an eigenvalue of A.

4. Let A be a nonsingular matrix and let λ be an eigenvalue of A. Show that $1/\lambda$ is an eigenvalue of A^{-1}.

5. Let A and B be $n \times n$ matrices. Show that if none of the eigenvalues of A are equal to 1, then the matrix equation

$$XA + B = X$$

will have a unique solution.

6. Let λ be an eigenvalue of A and let $\mathbf{x}$ be an eigenvector belonging to λ. Use mathematical induction to show that, for $m \geq 1$, λ^m is an eigenvalue of A^m and $\mathbf{x}$ is an eigenvector of A^m belonging to λ^m.

7. Let A be an $n \times n$ matrix and let $B = I - 2A + A^2$.
   (a) Show that if $\mathbf{x}$ is an eigenvector of A belonging to an eigenvalue λ, then $\mathbf{x}$ is also an eigenvector of B belonging to an eigenvalue μ of B. How are λ and μ related?
   (b) Show that if $\lambda = 1$ is an eigenvalue of A, then the matrix B will be singular.

8. An $n \times n$ matrix A is said to be *idempotent* if $A^2 = A$. Show that if λ is an eigenvalue of an idempotent matrix, then λ must be either 0 or 1.

9. An $n \times n$ matrix is said to be *nilpotent* if $A^k = O$ for some positive integer k. Show that all eigenvalues of a nilpotent matrix are 0.

10. Let A be an $n \times n$ matrix and let $B = A - \alpha I$ for some scalar α. How do the eigenvalues of A and B compare? Explain.

11. Let A be an $n \times n$ matrix and let $B = A + I$. Is it possible for A and B to be similar? Explain.

12. Show that A and A^T have the same eigenvalues. Do they necessarily have the same eigenvectors? Explain.

13. Show that the matrix

$$A = \begin{bmatrix} \cos\theta & -\sin\theta \\ \sin\theta & \cos\theta \end{bmatrix}$$

will have complex eigenvalues if θ is not a multiple of π. Give a geometric interpretation of this result.

14. Let A be a 2×2 matrix. If $\text{tr}(A) = 8$ and $\det(A) = 12$, what are the eigenvalues of A?

15. Let $A = (a_{ij})$ be an $n \times n$ matrix with eigenvalues $\lambda_1, \ldots, \lambda_n$. Show that

$$\lambda_j = a_{jj} + \sum_{i \neq j}(a_{ii} - \lambda_i) \quad \text{for} \quad j = 1, \ldots, n$$

16. Let A be a 2×2 matrix and let $p(\lambda) = \lambda^2 + b\lambda + c$ be the characteristic polynomial of A. Show that $b = -\text{tr}(A)$ and $c = \det(A)$.

17. Let λ be a nonzero eigenvalue of A and let $\mathbf{x}$ be an eigenvector belonging to λ. Show that $A^m\mathbf{x}$ is also an eigenvector belonging to λ for $m = 1, 2, \ldots$.

18. Let A be an $n \times n$ matrix and let λ be an eigenvalue of A. If $A - \lambda I$ has rank k, what is the dimension of the eigenspace corresponding to λ? Explain.

19. Let A be an $n \times n$ matrix. Show that a vector $\mathbf{x}$ in either $\mathbb{R}^n$ or $\mathbb{C}^n$ is an eigenvector belonging to A if and only if the subspace S spanned by $\mathbf{x}$ and $A\mathbf{x}$ has dimension 1.

20. Let $\alpha = a + bi$ and $\beta = c + di$ be complex scalars and let A and B be matrices with complex entries.
    (a) Show that
    $$\overline{\alpha + \beta} = \overline{\alpha} + \overline{\beta} \qquad \text{and} \qquad \overline{\alpha\beta} = \overline{\alpha}\,\overline{\beta}$$
    (b) Show that the (i, j) entries of $\overline{AB}$ and $\overline{A}\,\overline{B}$ are equal and hence that
    $$\overline{AB} = \overline{A}\,\overline{B}$$

21. Let Q be an orthogonal matrix.
    (a) Show that if λ is an eigenvalue of Q, then $|\lambda| = 1$.
    (b) Show that $|\det(Q)| = 1$.

22. Let Q be an orthogonal matrix with an eigenvalue $\lambda_1 = 1$ and let $\mathbf{x}$ be an eigenvector belonging to λ_1. Show that $\mathbf{x}$ is also an eigenvector of Q^T.

23. Let Q be a 3×3 orthogonal matrix whose determinant is equal to 1.
    (a) If the eigenvalues of Q are all real and if they are ordered so that $\lambda_1 \geq \lambda_2 \geq \lambda_3$, determine the values of all possible triples of eigenvalues $(\lambda_1, \lambda_2, \lambda_3)$.
    (b) In the case that the eigenvalues λ_2 and λ_3 are complex, what are the possible values for λ_1? Explain.
    (c) Explain why $\lambda = 1$ must be an eigenvalue of Q.

24. Let $\mathbf{x}_1, \ldots, \mathbf{x}_r$ be eigenvectors of an $n \times n$ matrix A and let S be the subspace of $\mathbb{R}^n$ spanned by $\mathbf{x}_1, \mathbf{x}_2, \ldots, \mathbf{x}_r$. Show that S is *invariant* under A (i.e., show that $A\mathbf{x} \in S$ whenever $\mathbf{x} \in S$).

25. Let A be an $n \times n$ matrix and let λ be an eigenvalue of A. Show that if B is any matrix that commutes with A, then the eigenspace $N(A - \lambda I)$ is invariant under B.

26. Let $B = S^{-1}AS$ and let $\mathbf{x}$ be an eigenvector of B belonging to an eigenvalue λ. Show that $S\mathbf{x}$ is an eigenvector of A belonging to λ.

27. Let A be an $n \times n$ matrix with an eigenvalue λ and let $\mathbf{x}$ be an eigenvector belonging to λ. Let S be a nonsingular $n \times n$ matrix and let α be a scalar. Show that if

$$B = \alpha I - SAS^{-1}, \quad \mathbf{y} = S\mathbf{x}$$

then $\mathbf{y}$ is an eigenvector of B. Determine the eigenvalue of B corresponding to $\mathbf{y}$?

28. Show that if two $n \times n$ matrices A and B have a common eigenvector $\mathbf{x}$ (but not necessarily a common eigenvalue), then $\mathbf{x}$ will also be an eigenvector of any matrix of the form $C = \alpha A + \beta B$.

29. Let A be an $n \times n$ matrix and let λ be a nonzero eigenvalue of A. Show that if $\mathbf{x}$ is an eigenvector belonging to λ, then $\mathbf{x}$ is in the column space of A. Hence, the eigenspace corresponding to λ is a subspace of the column space of A.

30. Let $\{\mathbf{u}_1, \mathbf{u}_2, \ldots, \mathbf{u}_n\}$ be an orthonormal basis for $\mathbb{R}^n$ and let A be a linear combination of the rank 1 matrices $\mathbf{u}_1\mathbf{u}_1^T, \mathbf{u}_2\mathbf{u}_2^T, \ldots, \mathbf{u}_n\mathbf{u}_n^T$. If

$$A = c_1\mathbf{u}_1\mathbf{u}_1^T + c_2\mathbf{u}_2\mathbf{u}_2^T + \cdots + c_n\mathbf{u}_n\mathbf{u}_n^T$$

show that A is a symmetric matrix with eigenvalues $c_1, c_2, \ldots, c_n$ and that $\mathbf{u}_i$ is an eigenvector belonging to c_i for each i.

31. Let A be a matrix whose columns all add up to a fixed constant δ. Show that δ is an eigenvalue of A.

32. Let λ_1 and λ_2 be distinct eigenvalues of A. Let $\mathbf{x}$ be an eigenvector of A belonging to λ_1 and let $\mathbf{y}$ be an eigenvector of A^T belonging to λ_2. Show that $\mathbf{x}$ and $\mathbf{y}$ are orthogonal.

33. Let A and B be $n \times n$ matrices. Show that

(a) if λ is a nonzero eigenvalue of AB, then it is also an eigenvalue of BA.

(b) if $\lambda = 0$ is an eigenvalue of AB, then $\lambda = 0$ is also an eigenvalue of BA.

34. Prove that there do not exist $n \times n$ matrices A and B such that

$$AB - BA = I$$

Hint: See Exercises 10 and 33.

35. Let $p(\lambda) = (-1)^n(\lambda^n - a_{n-1}\lambda^{n-1} - \cdots - a_1\lambda - a_0)$ be a polynomial of degree $n \geq 1$, and let

$$C = \begin{bmatrix} a_{n-1} & a_{n-2} & \cdots & a_1 & a_0 \\ 1 & 0 & \cdots & 0 & 0 \\ 0 & 1 & \cdots & 0 & 0 \\ \vdots & & & & \\ 0 & 0 & \cdots & 1 & 0 \end{bmatrix}$$

(a) Show that if λ_i is a root of $p(\lambda) = 0$, then λ_i is an eigenvalue of C with eigenvector $\mathbf{x} = (\lambda_i^{n-1}, \lambda_i^{n-2}, \ldots, \lambda_i, 1)^T$.

(b) Use part (a) to show that if $p(\lambda)$ has n distinct roots, then $p(\lambda)$ is the characteristic polynomial of C.

The matrix C is called the *companion matrix* of $p(\lambda)$.

36. The result given in Exercise 35(b) holds even if all the eigenvalues of $p(\lambda)$ are not distinct. Prove this as follows:

(a) Let

$$D_m(\lambda) = \begin{bmatrix} a_m & a_{m-1} & \cdots & a_1 & a_0 \\ 1 & -\lambda & \cdots & 0 & 0 \\ \vdots & & & & \\ 0 & 0 & \cdots & 1 & -\lambda \end{bmatrix}$$

and use mathematical induction to prove that

$$\det(D_m(\lambda)) = (-1)^m(a_m\lambda^m + a_{m-1}\lambda^{m-1} + \cdots + a_1\lambda + a_0)$$

(b) Show that

$$\det(C - \lambda I)$$
$$= (a_{n-1} - \lambda)(-\lambda)^{n-1} - \det(D_{n-2})$$
$$= p(\lambda)$$

6.2 Systems of Linear Differential Equations

Eigenvalues play an important role in the solution of systems of linear differential equations. In this section, we see how they are used in the solution of systems of linear differential equations with constant coefficients. We begin by considering systems of first-order equations of the form

$$y_1' = a_{11}y_1 + a_{12}y_2 + \cdots + a_{1n}y_n$$
$$y_2' = a_{21}y_1 + a_{22}y_2 + \cdots + a_{2n}y_n$$
$$\vdots$$
$$y_n' = a_{n1}y_1 + a_{n2}y_2 + \cdots + a_{nn}y_n$$

where $y_i = f_i(t)$ is a function in $C^1[a, b]$ for each i. If we let

$$\mathbf{Y} = \begin{pmatrix} y_1 \\ y_2 \\ \vdots \\ y_n \end{pmatrix} \quad \text{and} \quad \mathbf{Y}' = \begin{pmatrix} y_1' \\ y_2' \\ \vdots \\ y_n' \end{pmatrix}$$

then the system can be written in the form

$$\mathbf{Y}' = A\mathbf{Y}$$

$\mathbf{Y}$ and $\mathbf{Y}'$ are both vector functions of t. Let us consider the simplest case first. When $n = 1$, the system is simply

$$y' = ay \tag{1}$$

Clearly, any function of the form

$$y(t) = ce^{at} \quad (c \text{ an arbitrary constant})$$

satisfies equation (1). A natural generalization of this solution for the case $n > 1$ is to take

$$\mathbf{Y} = \begin{pmatrix} x_1 e^{\lambda t} \\ x_2 e^{\lambda t} \\ \vdots \\ x_n e^{\lambda t} \end{pmatrix} = e^{\lambda t} \mathbf{x}$$

where $\mathbf{x} = (x_1, x_2, \ldots, x_n)^T$. To verify that a vector function of this form does work, we compute the derivative

$$\mathbf{Y}' = \lambda e^{\lambda t} \mathbf{x} = \lambda \mathbf{Y}$$

Now, if we choose λ to be an eigenvalue of A and $\mathbf{x}$ to be an eigenvector belonging to λ, then

$$A\mathbf{Y} = e^{\lambda t} A\mathbf{x} = \lambda e^{\lambda t} \mathbf{x} = \lambda \mathbf{Y} = \mathbf{Y}'$$

Hence, $\mathbf{Y}$ is a solution of the system. Thus, if λ is an eigenvalue of A and $\mathbf{x}$ is an eigenvector belonging to λ, then $e^{\lambda t} \mathbf{x}$ is a solution of the system $\mathbf{Y}' = A\mathbf{Y}$. This will be true whether λ is real or complex. Note that if $\mathbf{Y}_1$ and $\mathbf{Y}_2$ are both solutions of $\mathbf{Y}' = A\mathbf{Y}$, then $\alpha \mathbf{Y}_1 + \beta \mathbf{Y}_2$ is also a solution, since

$$\begin{aligned} (\alpha \mathbf{Y}_1 + \beta \mathbf{Y}_2)' &= \alpha \mathbf{Y}_1' + \beta \mathbf{Y}_2' \\ &= \alpha A\mathbf{Y}_1 + \beta A\mathbf{Y}_2 \\ &= A(\alpha \mathbf{Y}_1 + \beta \mathbf{Y}_2) \end{aligned}$$

It follows by induction that if $\mathbf{Y}_1, \ldots, \mathbf{Y}_n$ are solutions of $\mathbf{Y}' = A\mathbf{Y}$, then any linear combination $c_1 \mathbf{Y}_1 + \cdots + c_n \mathbf{Y}_n$ will also be a solution.

In general, the solutions of an $n \times n$ first-order system of the form

$$\mathbf{Y}' = A\mathbf{Y}$$

will form an n-dimensional subspace of the vector space of all continuous vector-valued functions. If, in addition, we require that $\mathbf{Y}(t)$ take on a prescribed value $\mathbf{Y}_0$ when $t = 0$, then a standard theorem from differential equations guarantees that the problem will have a unique solution. A problem of the form

$$\mathbf{Y}' = A\mathbf{Y}, \qquad \mathbf{Y}(0) = \mathbf{Y}_0$$

is called an *initial value problem*.

EXAMPLE I Solve the system

$$y_1' = 3y_1 + 4y_2$$
$$y_2' = 3y_1 + 2y_2$$

Solution

$$A = \begin{pmatrix} 3 & 4 \\ 3 & 2 \end{pmatrix}$$

The eigenvalues of A are $\lambda_1 = 6$ and $\lambda_2 = -1$. Solving $(A - \lambda I)\mathbf{x} = \mathbf{0}$ with $\lambda = \lambda_1$ and $\lambda = \lambda_2$, we see that $\mathbf{x}_1 = (4, 3)^T$ is an eigenvector belonging to λ_1 and $\mathbf{x}_2 = (1, -1)^T$ is an eigenvector belonging to λ_2. Thus, any vector function of the form

$$\mathbf{Y} = c_1 e^{\lambda_1 t}\mathbf{x}_1 + c_2 e^{\lambda_2 t}\mathbf{x}_2 = \begin{pmatrix} 4c_1 e^{6t} + c_2 e^{-t} \\ 3c_1 e^{6t} - c_2 e^{-t} \end{pmatrix}$$

is a solution of the system.   ∎

In Example 1, suppose we require that $y_1 = 6$ and $y_2 = 1$ when $t = 0$. Then

$$\mathbf{Y}(0) = \begin{pmatrix} 4c_1 + c_2 \\ 3c_1 - c_2 \end{pmatrix} = \begin{pmatrix} 6 \\ 1 \end{pmatrix}$$

and it follows that $c_1 = 1$ and $c_2 = 2$. Hence, the solution to the initial value problem is given by

$$\mathbf{Y} = e^{6t}\mathbf{x}_1 + 2e^{-t}\mathbf{x}_2 = \begin{pmatrix} 4e^{6t} + 2e^{-t} \\ 3e^{6t} - 2e^{-t} \end{pmatrix}$$

APPLICATION I Mixtures

Two tanks are connected as shown in Figure 6.2.1. Initially, tank A contains 200 liters of water in which 60 grams of salt have been dissolved and tank B contains 200 liters of pure water. Liquid is pumped in and out of the two tanks at rates shown in the diagram. Determine the amount of salt in each tank at time t.

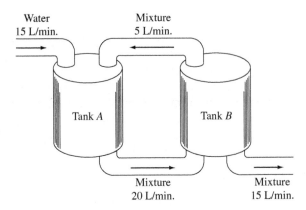

Figure 6.2.1.

Solution

Let $y_1(t)$ and $y_2(t)$ be the number of grams of salt in tanks A and B, respectively, at time t. Initially,

$$\mathbf{Y}(0) = \begin{bmatrix} y_1(0) \\ y_2(0) \end{bmatrix} = \begin{bmatrix} 60 \\ 0 \end{bmatrix}$$

The total amount of liquid in each tank will remain at 200 liters since the amount being pumped in equals the amount being pumped out. The rate of change in the amount of salt for each tank is equal to the rate at which it is being added minus the rate at which it is being pumped out. For tank A, the rate at which the salt is added is given by

$$(5 \text{ L/min.}) \cdot \left(\frac{y_2(t)}{200} \text{g/L} \right) = \frac{y_2(t)}{40} \text{g/min.}$$

and the rate at which the salt is being pumped out is

$$(20 \text{ L/min.}) \cdot \left(\frac{y_1(t)}{200} \text{g/L} \right) = \frac{y_1(t)}{10} \text{g/min.}$$

Thus, the rate of change for tank A is given by

$$y_1'(t) = \frac{y_2(t)}{40} - \frac{y_1(t)}{10}$$

Similarly, for tank B, the rate of change is given by

$$y_2'(t) = \frac{20y_1(t)}{200} - \frac{20y_2(t)}{200} = \frac{y_1(t)}{10} - \frac{y_2(t)}{10}$$

To determine $y_1(t)$ and $y_2(t)$, we must solve the initial value problem

$$\mathbf{Y}' = A\mathbf{Y}, \quad \mathbf{Y}(0) = \mathbf{Y}_0$$

where

$$A = \begin{bmatrix} -\frac{1}{10} & \frac{1}{40} \\ \frac{1}{10} & -\frac{1}{10} \end{bmatrix}, \qquad \mathbf{Y}_0 = \begin{bmatrix} 60 \\ 0 \end{bmatrix}$$

The eigenvalues of A are $\lambda_1 = -\frac{3}{20}$ and $\lambda_2 = -\frac{1}{20}$ with corresponding eigenvectors

$$\mathbf{x}_1 = \begin{bmatrix} 1 \\ -2 \end{bmatrix} \qquad \text{and} \qquad \mathbf{x}_2 = \begin{bmatrix} 1 \\ 2 \end{bmatrix}$$

The solution must then be of the form

$$\mathbf{Y} = c_1 e^{-3t/20}\mathbf{x}_1 + c_2 e^{-t/20}\mathbf{x}_2$$

When $t = 0$, $\mathbf{Y} = \mathbf{Y}_0$. Thus,

$$c_1\mathbf{x}_1 + c_2\mathbf{x}_2 = \mathbf{Y}_0$$

and we can find c_1 and c_2 by solving

$$\begin{bmatrix} 1 & 1 \\ -2 & 2 \end{bmatrix} \begin{bmatrix} c_1 \\ c_2 \end{bmatrix} = \begin{bmatrix} 60 \\ 0 \end{bmatrix}$$

The solution of this system is $c_1 = c_2 = 30$. Therefore, the solution of the initial value problem is

$$\mathbf{Y}(t) = \begin{bmatrix} y_1(t) \\ y_2(t) \end{bmatrix} = \begin{bmatrix} 30e^{-3t/20} + 30e^{-t/20} \\ -60e^{-3t/20} + 60e^{-t/20} \end{bmatrix} \qquad \blacksquare$$

Complex Eigenvalues

Let A be a real $n \times n$ matrix with a complex eigenvalue $\lambda = a + bi$, and let $\mathbf{x}$ be an eigenvector belonging to λ. The vector $\mathbf{x}$ can be split up into its real and imaginary parts.

$$\mathbf{x} = \begin{bmatrix} \operatorname{Re} x_1 + i\operatorname{Im} x_1 \\ \operatorname{Re} x_2 + i\operatorname{Im} x_2 \\ \vdots \\ \operatorname{Re} x_n + i\operatorname{Im} x_n \end{bmatrix} = \begin{bmatrix} \operatorname{Re} x_1 \\ \operatorname{Re} x_2 \\ \vdots \\ \operatorname{Re} x_n \end{bmatrix} + i \begin{bmatrix} \operatorname{Im} x_1 \\ \operatorname{Im} x_2 \\ \vdots \\ \operatorname{Im} x_n \end{bmatrix} = \operatorname{Re} \mathbf{x} + i\operatorname{Im} \mathbf{x}$$

Since the entries of A are all real, it follows that $\overline{\lambda} = a - bi$ is also an eigenvalue of A with eigenvector

$$\overline{\mathbf{x}} = \begin{bmatrix} \operatorname{Re} x_1 - i\operatorname{Im} x_1 \\ \operatorname{Re} x_2 - i\operatorname{Im} x_2 \\ \vdots \\ \operatorname{Re} x_n - i\operatorname{Im} x_n \end{bmatrix} = \operatorname{Re} \mathbf{x} - i\operatorname{Im} \mathbf{x}$$

and hence $e^{\lambda t}\mathbf{x}$ and $e^{\bar{\lambda} t}\bar{\mathbf{x}}$ are both solutions of the first-order system $\mathbf{Y}' = A\mathbf{Y}$. Any linear combination of these two solutions will also be a solution. Thus, if we set

$$\mathbf{Y}_1 = \frac{1}{2}(e^{\lambda t}\mathbf{x} + e^{\bar{\lambda} t}\bar{\mathbf{x}}) = \text{Re}(e^{\lambda t}\mathbf{x})$$

and

$$\mathbf{Y}_2 = \frac{1}{2i}(e^{\lambda t}\mathbf{x} - e^{\bar{\lambda} t}\bar{\mathbf{x}}) = \text{Im}(e^{\lambda t}\mathbf{x})$$

then the vector functions $\mathbf{Y}_1$ and $\mathbf{Y}_2$ are real-valued solutions of $\mathbf{Y}' = A\mathbf{Y}$. Taking the real and imaginary parts of

$$e^{\lambda t}\mathbf{x} = e^{(a+ib)t}\mathbf{x}$$
$$= e^{at}(\cos bt + i \sin bt)(\text{Re }\mathbf{x} + i \text{ Im }\mathbf{x})$$

we see that

$$\mathbf{Y}_1 = e^{at}\,[(\cos bt)\,\text{Re }\mathbf{x} - (\sin bt)\,\text{Im }\mathbf{x}]$$
$$\mathbf{Y}_2 = e^{at}\,[(\cos bt)\,\text{Im }\mathbf{x} + (\sin bt)\,\text{Re }\mathbf{x}]$$

EXAMPLE 2   Solve the system

$$\begin{aligned} y_1' &= y_1 + y_2 \\ y_2' &= -2y_1 + 3y_2 \end{aligned}$$

Solution

Let

$$A = \begin{bmatrix} 1 & 1 \\ -2 & 3 \end{bmatrix}$$

The eigenvalues of A are $\lambda = 2 + i$ and $\bar{\lambda} = 2 - i$, with eigenvectors $\mathbf{x} = (1, 1 + i)^T$ and $\bar{\mathbf{x}} = (1, 1 - i)^T$, respectively.

$$e^{\lambda t}\mathbf{x} = \begin{bmatrix} e^{2t}(\cos t + i \sin t) \\ e^{2t}(\cos t + i \sin t)(1 + i) \end{bmatrix}$$

$$= \begin{bmatrix} e^{2t}\cos t + ie^{2t}\sin t \\ e^{2t}(\cos t - \sin t) + ie^{2t}(\cos t + \sin t) \end{bmatrix}$$

Let

$$\mathbf{Y}_1 = \text{Re}(e^{\lambda t}\mathbf{x}) = \begin{bmatrix} e^{2t}\cos t \\ e^{2t}(\cos t - \sin t) \end{bmatrix}$$

and

$$\mathbf{Y}_2 = \text{Im}(e^{\lambda t}\mathbf{x}) = \begin{bmatrix} e^{2t}\sin t \\ e^{2t}(\cos t + \sin t) \end{bmatrix}$$

Any linear combination

$$\mathbf{Y} = c_1\mathbf{Y}_1 + c_2\mathbf{Y}_2$$

will be a solution of the system.   ■

If the $n \times n$ coefficient matrix A of the system $\mathbf{Y}' = A\mathbf{Y}$ has n linearly independent eigenvectors, the general solution can be obtained by the methods that have been presented. The case when A has fewer than n linearly independent eigenvectors is more complicated; consequently, we will defer discussion of this case to Section 6.3.

Higher-Order Systems

Given a second-order system of the form

$$\mathbf{Y}'' = A_1\mathbf{Y} + A_2\mathbf{Y}'$$

we may translate it into a first-order system by setting

$$y_{n+1}(t) = y_1'(t)$$
$$y_{n+2}(t) = y_2'(t)$$
$$\vdots$$
$$y_{2n}(t) = y_n'(t)$$

If we let

$$\mathbf{Y}_1 = \mathbf{Y} = (y_1, y_2, \ldots, y_n)^T$$

and

$$\mathbf{Y}_2 = \mathbf{Y}' = (y_{n+1}, \ldots, y_{2n})^T$$

then

$$\mathbf{Y}_1' = O\mathbf{Y}_1 + I\mathbf{Y}_2$$

and

$$\mathbf{Y}_2' = A_1\mathbf{Y}_1 + A_2\mathbf{Y}_2$$

The equations can be combined to give the $2n \times 2n$ first-order system

$$\begin{pmatrix} \mathbf{Y}_1' \\ \mathbf{Y}_2' \end{pmatrix} = \begin{bmatrix} O & I \\ A_1 & A_2 \end{bmatrix} \begin{bmatrix} \mathbf{Y}_1 \\ \mathbf{Y}_2 \end{bmatrix}$$

If the values of $\mathbf{Y}_1 = \mathbf{Y}$ and $\mathbf{Y}_2 = \mathbf{Y}'$ are specified when $t = 0$, then the initial value problem will have a unique solution.

EXAMPLE 3 Solve the initial value problem

$$
\begin{aligned}
y_1'' &= 2y_1 + y_2 + y_1' + y_2' \\
y_2'' &= -5y_1 + 2y_2 + 5y_1' - y_2' \\
y_1(0) &= y_2(0) = y_1'(0) = 4, \qquad y_2'(0) = -4
\end{aligned}
$$

Solution

Set $y_3 = y_1'$ and $y_4 = y_2'$. This gives the first-order system

$$
\begin{aligned}
y_1' &= y_3 \\
y_2' &= y_4 \\
y_3' &= 2y_1 + y_2 + y_3 + y_4 \\
y_4' &= -5y_1 + 2y_2 + 5y_3 - y_4
\end{aligned}
$$

The coefficient matrix for the system

$$
A = \begin{pmatrix}
0 & 0 & 1 & 0 \\
0 & 0 & 0 & 1 \\
2 & 1 & 1 & 1 \\
-5 & 2 & 5 & -1
\end{pmatrix}
$$

has eigenvalues

$$
\lambda_1 = 1, \qquad \lambda_2 = -1, \qquad \lambda_3 = 3, \qquad \lambda_4 = -3
$$

Corresponding to these eigenvalues are the eigenvectors

$$
\begin{aligned}
\mathbf{x}_1 &= (1, -1, 1, -1)^T, & \mathbf{x}_2 &= (1, 5, -1, -5)^T \\
\mathbf{x}_3 &= (1, 1, 3, 3)^T, & \mathbf{x}_4 &= (1, -5, -3, 15)^T
\end{aligned}
$$

Thus, the solution will be of the form

$$
c_1 \mathbf{x}_1 e^t + c_2 \mathbf{x}_2 e^{-t} + c_3 \mathbf{x}_3 e^{3t} + c_4 \mathbf{x}_4 e^{-3t}
$$

We can use the initial conditions to find c_1, c_2, c_3, and c_4. For $t = 0$, we have

$$
c_1 \mathbf{x}_1 + c_2 \mathbf{x}_2 + c_3 \mathbf{x}_3 + c_4 \mathbf{x}_4 = (4, 4, 4, -4)^T
$$

or, equivalently,

$$
\begin{pmatrix}
1 & 1 & 1 & 1 \\
-1 & 5 & 1 & -5 \\
1 & -1 & 3 & -3 \\
-1 & -5 & 3 & 15
\end{pmatrix}
\begin{pmatrix}
c_1 \\ c_2 \\ c_3 \\ c_4
\end{pmatrix}
=
\begin{pmatrix}
4 \\ 4 \\ 4 \\ -4
\end{pmatrix}
$$

The solution of this system is $\mathbf{c} = (2, 1, 1, 0)^T$, and hence the solution to the initial value problem is

$$
\mathbf{Y} = 2\mathbf{x}_1 e^t + \mathbf{x}_2 e^{-t} + \mathbf{x}_3 e^{3t}
$$

Therefore,

$$\begin{bmatrix} y_1 \\ y_2 \\ y_1' \\ y_2' \end{bmatrix} = \begin{bmatrix} 2e^t + e^{-t} + e^{3t} \\ -2e^t + 5e^{-t} + e^{3t} \\ 2e^t - e^{-t} + 3e^{3t} \\ -2e^t - 5e^{-t} + 3e^{3t} \end{bmatrix}$$

In general, if we have an mth-order system of the form

$$\mathbf{Y}^{(m)} = A_1\mathbf{Y} + A_2\mathbf{Y}' + \cdots + A_m\mathbf{Y}^{(m-1)}$$

where each A_i is an $n \times n$ matrix, we can transform it into a first-order system by setting

$$\mathbf{Y}_1 = \mathbf{Y}, \mathbf{Y}_2 = \mathbf{Y}_1', \ldots, \mathbf{Y}_m = \mathbf{Y}_{m-1}'$$

We will end up with a system of the form

$$\begin{bmatrix} \mathbf{Y}_1' \\ \mathbf{Y}_2' \\ \vdots \\ \mathbf{Y}_{m-1}' \\ \mathbf{Y}_m' \end{bmatrix} = \begin{bmatrix} O & I & O & \cdots & O \\ O & O & I & \cdots & O \\ \vdots & & & & \\ O & O & O & \cdots & I \\ A_1 & A_2 & A_3 & \cdots & A_m \end{bmatrix} \begin{bmatrix} \mathbf{Y}_1 \\ \mathbf{Y}_2 \\ \vdots \\ \mathbf{Y}_{m-1} \\ \mathbf{Y}_m \end{bmatrix}$$

If, in addition, we require that $\mathbf{Y}, \mathbf{Y}', \ldots, \mathbf{Y}^{(m-1)}$ take on specific values when $t = 0$, there will be exactly one solution to the problem.

If the system is simply of the form $\mathbf{Y}^{(m)} = A\mathbf{Y}$, it is usually not necessary to introduce new variables. In this case, we need only calculate the mth roots of the eigenvalues of A. If λ is an eigenvalue of A, $\mathbf{x}$ is an eigenvector belonging to λ, σ is an mth root of λ, and $\mathbf{Y} = e^{\sigma t}\mathbf{x}$, then

$$\mathbf{Y}^{(m)} = \sigma^m e^{\sigma t}\mathbf{x} = \lambda\mathbf{Y}$$

and

$$A\mathbf{Y} = e^{\sigma t}A\mathbf{x} = \lambda e^{\sigma t}\mathbf{x} = \lambda\mathbf{Y}$$

Therefore, $\mathbf{Y} = e^{\sigma t}\mathbf{x}$ is a solution to the system.

APPLICATION 2   Harmonic Motion

In Figure 6.2.2, two masses are joined by springs and the ends A and B are fixed. The masses are free to move horizontally. We will assume that the three springs are uniform and that initially the system is in the equilibrium position. A force is exerted on the system to set the masses in motion. The horizontal displacements of the masses at time t will be denoted by $x_1(t)$ and $x_2(t)$, respectively. We will assume that there are no retarding forces such as friction. Then the only forces acting on mass m_1 at time t will

Figure 6.2.2.

be from the springs 1 and 2. The force from spring 1 will be $-kx_1$ and the force from spring 2 will be $k(x_2 - x_1)$. By Newton's second law,

$$m_1 x_1''(t) = -kx_1 + k(x_2 - x_1)$$

Similarly, the only forces acting on the second mass will be from springs 2 and 3. Using Newton's second law again, we get

$$m_2 x_2''(t) = -k(x_2 - x_1) - kx_2$$

Thus, we end up with the second-order system

$$x_1'' = -\frac{k}{m_1}(2x_1 - x_2)$$

$$x_2'' = -\frac{k}{m_2}(-x_1 + 2x_2)$$

Suppose now that $m_1 = m_2 = 1$, $k = 1$, and the initial velocity of both masses is $+2$ units per second. To determine the displacements x_1 and x_2 as functions of t, we write the system in the form

$$\mathbf{X}'' = A\mathbf{X} \tag{2}$$

The coefficient matrix

$$A = \begin{bmatrix} -2 & 1 \\ 1 & -2 \end{bmatrix}$$

has eigenvalues $\lambda_1 = -1$ and $\lambda_2 = -3$. Corresponding to λ_1, we have the eigenvector $\mathbf{v}_1 = (1, 1)^T$ and $\sigma_1 = \pm i$. Thus, $e^{it}\mathbf{v}_1$ and $e^{-it}\mathbf{v}_1$ are both solutions of (2). It follows that

$$\frac{1}{2}(e^{it} + e^{-it})\mathbf{v}_1 = (\operatorname{Re} e^{it})\mathbf{v}_1 = (\cos t)\mathbf{v}_1$$

and

$$\frac{1}{2i}(e^{it} - e^{-it})\mathbf{v}_1 = (\operatorname{Im} e^{it})\mathbf{v}_1 = (\sin t)\mathbf{v}_1$$

are also both solutions of (2). Similarly, for $\lambda_2 = -3$, we have the eigenvector $\mathbf{v}_2 = (1, -1)^T$ and $\sigma_2 = \pm\sqrt{3}i$. It follows that

$$(\operatorname{Re} e^{\sqrt{3}it})\mathbf{v}_2 = (\cos \sqrt{3}t)\mathbf{v}_2$$

and

$$(\text{Im } e^{\sqrt{3}it})\mathbf{v}_2 = (\sin \sqrt{3}t)\mathbf{v}_2$$

are also solutions of (2). Thus, the general solution will be of the form

$$\mathbf{X}(t) = c_1(\cos t)\mathbf{v}_1 + c_2(\sin t)\mathbf{v}_1 + c_3(\cos \sqrt{3}t)\mathbf{v}_2 + c_4(\sin \sqrt{3}t)\mathbf{v}_2$$

$$= \begin{bmatrix} c_1 \cos t + c_2 \sin t + c_3 \cos \sqrt{3}t + c_4 \sin \sqrt{3}t \\ c_1 \cos t + c_2 \sin t - c_3 \cos \sqrt{3}t - c_4 \sin \sqrt{3}t \end{bmatrix}$$

At time $t = 0$, we have

$$x_1(0) = x_2(0) = 0 \quad \text{and} \quad x_1'(0) = x_2'(0) = 2$$

It follows that

$$\begin{array}{cc} c_1 + c_3 = 0 \\ c_1 - c_3 = 0 \end{array} \quad \text{and} \quad \begin{array}{cc} c_2 + \sqrt{3}c_4 = 2 \\ c_2 - \sqrt{3}c_4 = 2 \end{array}$$

and hence

$$c_1 = c_3 = c_4 = 0 \quad \text{and} \quad c_2 = 2$$

Therefore, the solution to the initial value problem is

$$\mathbf{X}(t) = \begin{bmatrix} 2\sin t \\ 2\sin t \end{bmatrix}.$$

The masses will oscillate with frequency 1 and amplitude 2.

APPLICATION 3   Vibrations of a Building

For another example of a physical system, we consider the vibrations of a building. If the building has k stories, we can represent the horizontal deflections of the stories at time t by the vector function $\mathbf{Y}(t) = (y_1(t), y_2(t), \ldots, y_k(t))^T$. The motion of a building can be modeled by a second-order system of differential equations of the form

$$M\mathbf{Y}''(t) = K\mathbf{Y}(t)$$

The *mass matrix* M is a diagonal matrix whose entries correspond to the concentrated weights at each story. The entries of the *stiffness matrix* K are determined by the spring constants of the supporting structures. Solutions of the equation are of the form $\mathbf{Y}(t) = e^{i\sigma t}\mathbf{x}$, where $\mathbf{x}$ is an eigenvector of $A = M^{-1}K$ belonging to an eigenvalue λ and σ is a square root of λ.

SECTION 6.2 EXERCISES

1. Find the general solution of each of the following systems:

   (a) $y_1' = y_1 + y_2$
   $y_2' = -2y_1 + 4y_2$

   (b) $y_1' = 2y_1 + 4y_2$
   $y_2' = -y_1 - 3y_2$

   (c) $y_1' = y_1 - 2y_2$
   $y_2' = -2y_1 + 4y_2$

   (d) $y_1' = y_1 - y_2$
   $y_2' = y_1 + y_2$

   (e) $y_1' = 3y_1 - 2y_2$
   $y_2' = 2y_1 + 3y_2$

   (f) $y_1' = y_1 + y_3$
   $y_2' = 2y_2 + 6y_3$
   $y_3' = y_2 + 3y_3$

2. Solve each of the following initial value problems:

   (a) $y_1' = -y_1 + 2y_2$
   $y_2' = 2y_1 - y_2$
   $y_1(0) = 3, y_2(0) = 1$

   (b) $y_1' = y_1 - 2y_2$
   $y_2' = 2y_1 + y_2$
   $y_1(0) = 1, y_2(0) = -2$

   (c) $y_1' = 2y_1 - 6y_3$
   $y_2' = y_1 - 3y_3$
   $y_3' = y_2 - 2y_3$
   $y_1(0) = y_2(0) = y_3(0) = 2$

   (d) $y_1' = y_1 + 2y_3$
   $y_2' = y_2 - y_3$
   $y_3' = y_1 + y_2 + y_3$
   $y_1(0) = y_2(0) = 1, y_3(0) = 4$

3. Given

   $$\mathbf{Y} = c_1 e^{\lambda_1 t}\mathbf{x}_1 + c_2 e^{\lambda_2 t}\mathbf{x}_2 + \cdots + c_n e^{\lambda_n t}\mathbf{x}_n$$

   is the solution to the initial value problem:

   $$\mathbf{Y}' = A\mathbf{Y}, \qquad \mathbf{Y}(0) = \mathbf{Y}_0$$

   (a) show that

   $$\mathbf{Y}_0 = c_1\mathbf{x}_1 + c_2\mathbf{x}_2 + \cdots + c_n\mathbf{x}_n$$

   (b) let $X = (\mathbf{x}_1, \ldots, \mathbf{x}_n)$ and $\mathbf{c} = (c_1, \ldots, c_n)^T$. Assuming that the vectors $\mathbf{x}_1, \ldots, \mathbf{x}_n$ are linearly independent, show that $\mathbf{c} = X^{-1}\mathbf{Y}_0$.

4. Two tanks each contain 100 liters of a mixture. Initially, the mixture in tank A contains 40 grams of salt, while tank B contains 20 grams of salt. Liquid is pumped in and out of the tanks as shown in the accompanying figure. Determine the amount of salt in each tank at time t.

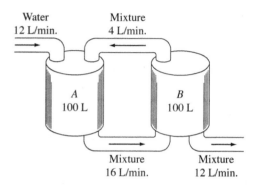

5. Find the general solution of each of the following systems:

   (a) $y_1'' = -2y_2$
   $y_2'' = y_1 + 3y_2$

   (b) $y_1'' = 2y_1 + y_2'$
   $y_2'' = 2y_2 + y_1'$

6. Solve the initial value problem

   $$y_1'' = -2y_2 + y_1' + 2y_2'$$
   $$y_2'' = 2y_1 + 2y_1' - y_2'$$

   $$y_1(0) = 1, \ y_2(0) = 0, \ y_1'(0) = -3, \ y_2'(0) = 2$$

7. In Application 2, assume that the solutions are of the form $x_1 = a_1 \sin \sigma t$, $x_2 = a_2 \sin \sigma t$. Substitute these expressions into the system and solve for the frequency σ and the amplitudes a_1 and a_2.

8. Solve the the problem in Application 2, using the initial conditions

   $$x_1(0) = x_2(0) = 1, \ x_1'(0) = 4, \ \text{and} \ x_2'(0) = 2$$

9. Two masses are connected by springs as shown in the accompanying diagram. Both springs have the same spring constant, and the end of the first spring is fixed. If x_1 and x_2 represent the displacements from the equilibrium position, derive a system of second-order differential equations that describes the motion of the system.

spring constant, and let $x_1(t)$, $x_2(t)$, and $x_3(t)$ represent the displacements of the respective masses at time t.

(a) Derive a system of second-order differential equations that describes the motion of this system.

(b) Solve the system if $m_1 = m_3 = \frac{1}{3}$, $m_2 = \frac{1}{4}$, $k = 1$, and

$$x_1(0) = x_2(0) = x_3(0) = 1$$

$$x_1'(0) = x_2'(0) = x_3'(0) = 0$$

11. Transform the nth-order equation

$$y^{(n)} = a_0 y + a_1 y' + \cdots + a_{n-1} y^{(n-1)}$$

into a system of first-order equations by setting $y_1 = y$ and $y_j = y_{j-1}'$ for $j = 2, \ldots, n$. Determine the characteristic polynomial of the coefficient matrix of this system.

10. Three masses are connected by a series of springs between two fixed points as shown in the accompanying figure. Assume that the springs all have the same

6.3 Diagonalization

In this section, we consider the problem of factoring an $n \times n$ matrix A into a product of the form XDX^{-1}, where D is diagonal. We will give a necessary and sufficient condition for the existence of such a factorization and look at a number of examples. We begin by showing that eigenvectors belonging to distinct eigenvalues are linearly independent.

Theorem 6.3.1 *If $\lambda_1, \lambda_2, \ldots, \lambda_k$ are distinct eigenvalues of an $n \times n$ matrix A with corresponding eigenvectors $\mathbf{x}_1, \mathbf{x}_2, \ldots, \mathbf{x}_k$, then $\mathbf{x}_1, \ldots, \mathbf{x}_k$ are linearly independent.*

Proof Let r be the dimension of the subspace of $\mathbb{R}^n$ spanned by $\mathbf{x}_1, \ldots, \mathbf{x}_k$ and suppose that $r < k$. We may assume (reordering the $\mathbf{x}_i$'s and λ_i's if necessary) that $\mathbf{x}_1, \ldots, \mathbf{x}_r$ are linearly independent. Since $\mathbf{x}_1, \mathbf{x}_2, \ldots, \mathbf{x}_r, \mathbf{x}_{r+1}$ are linearly dependent, there exist scalars $c_1, \ldots, c_r, c_{r+1}$, not all zero, such that

$$c_1 \mathbf{x}_1 + \cdots + c_r \mathbf{x}_r + c_{r+1} \mathbf{x}_{r+1} = \mathbf{0} \tag{1}$$

Note that c_{r+1} must be nonzero; otherwise, $\mathbf{x}_1, \ldots, \mathbf{x}_r$ would be dependent. So $c_{r+1} \mathbf{x}_{r+1} \neq \mathbf{0}$ and hence $c_1, \ldots, c_r$ cannot all be zero. Multiplying (1) by A, we get

$$c_1 A\mathbf{x}_1 + \cdots + c_r A\mathbf{x}_r + c_{r+1} A\mathbf{x}_{r+1} = \mathbf{0}$$

or

$$c_1 \lambda_1 \mathbf{x}_1 + \cdots + c_r \lambda_r \mathbf{x}_r + c_{r+1} \lambda_{r+1} \mathbf{x}_{r+1} = \mathbf{0} \tag{2}$$

Subtracting λ_{r+1} times (1) from (2) gives

$$c_1(\lambda_1 - \lambda_{r+1})\mathbf{x}_1 + \cdots + c_r(\lambda_r - \lambda_{r+1})\mathbf{x}_r = \mathbf{0}$$

This contradicts the independence of $\mathbf{x}_1, \ldots, \mathbf{x}_r$. Therefore, r must equal k. ∎

Definition

An $n \times n$ matrix A is said to be **diagonalizable** if there exists a nonsingular matrix X and a diagonal matrix D such that

$$X^{-1}AX = D$$

We say that X **diagonalizes** A.

Theorem 6.3.2   *An $n \times n$ matrix A is diagonalizable if and only if A has n linearly independent eigenvectors.*

Proof   Suppose that the matrix A has n linearly independent eigenvectors $\mathbf{x}_1, \mathbf{x}_2, \dots, \mathbf{x}_n$. Let λ_i be the eigenvalue of A corresponding to $\mathbf{x}_i$ for each i. (Some of the λ_i's may be equal.) Let X be the matrix whose jth column vector is $\mathbf{x}_j$ for $j = 1, \dots, n$. It follows that $A\mathbf{x}_j = \lambda_j \mathbf{x}_j$ is the jth column vector of AX. Thus,

$$
\begin{aligned}
AX &= (A\mathbf{x}_1, A\mathbf{x}_2, \dots, A\mathbf{x}_n) \\
&= (\lambda_1 \mathbf{x}_1, \lambda_2 \mathbf{x}_2, \dots, \lambda_n \mathbf{x}_n) \\
&= (\mathbf{x}_1, \mathbf{x}_2, \dots, \mathbf{x}_n)
\begin{bmatrix}
\lambda_1 & & & \\
 & \lambda_2 & & \\
 & & \ddots & \\
 & & & \lambda_n
\end{bmatrix} \\
&= XD
\end{aligned}
$$

Since X has n linearly independent column vectors, it follows that X is nonsingular and hence

$$D = X^{-1}XD = X^{-1}AX$$

Conversely, suppose that A is diagonalizable. Then there exists a nonsingular matrix X such that $AX = XD$. If $\mathbf{x}_1, \mathbf{x}_2, \dots, \mathbf{x}_n$ are the column vectors of X, then

$$A\mathbf{x}_j = \lambda_j \mathbf{x}_j \qquad (\lambda_j = d_{jj})$$

for each j. Thus, for each j, λ_j is an eigenvalue of A and $\mathbf{x}_j$ is an eigenvector belonging to λ_j. Since the column vectors of X are linearly independent, it follows that A has n linearly independent eigenvectors. ∎

Remarks

1. If A is diagonalizable, then the column vectors of the diagonalizing matrix X are eigenvectors of A and the diagonal elements of D are the corresponding eigenvalues of A.
2. The diagonalizing matrix X is not unique. Reordering the columns of a given diagonalizing matrix X or multiplying them by nonzero scalars will produce a new diagonalizing matrix.

3. If A is $n \times n$ and A has n distinct eigenvalues, then A is diagonalizable. If the eigenvalues are not distinct, then A may or may not be diagonalizable depending on whether A has n linearly independent eigenvectors.

4. If A is diagonalizable, then A can be factored into a product XDX^{-1}.

It follows from remark 4 that

$$A^2 = (XDX^{-1})(XDX^{-1}) = XD^2X^{-1}$$

and, in general,

$$A^k = XD^kX^{-1}$$

$$= X \begin{bmatrix} (\lambda_1)^k & & & \\ & (\lambda_2)^k & & \\ & & \ddots & \\ & & & (\lambda_n)^k \end{bmatrix} X^{-1}$$

Once we have a factorization $A = XDX^{-1}$, it is easy to compute powers of A.

EXAMPLE I   Let

$$A = \begin{bmatrix} 2 & -3 \\ 2 & -5 \end{bmatrix}$$

The eigenvalues of A are $\lambda_1 = 1$ and $\lambda_2 = -4$. Corresponding to λ_1 and λ_2, we have the eigenvectors $\mathbf{x}_1 = (3, 1)^T$ and $\mathbf{x}_2 = (1, 2)^T$. Let

$$X = \begin{bmatrix} 3 & 1 \\ 1 & 2 \end{bmatrix} \quad \text{and} \quad D = \begin{bmatrix} 1 & 0 \\ 0 & -4 \end{bmatrix}$$

It follows that

$$X^{-1}AX = \frac{1}{5} \begin{bmatrix} 2 & -1 \\ -1 & 3 \end{bmatrix} \begin{bmatrix} 2 & -3 \\ 2 & -5 \end{bmatrix} \begin{bmatrix} 3 & 1 \\ 1 & 2 \end{bmatrix}$$

$$= \begin{bmatrix} 1 & 0 \\ 0 & -4 \end{bmatrix} = D$$

and

$$XDX^{-1} = \begin{bmatrix} 3 & 1 \\ 1 & 2 \end{bmatrix} \begin{bmatrix} 1 & 0 \\ 0 & -4 \end{bmatrix} \begin{bmatrix} \frac{2}{5} & -\frac{1}{5} \\ -\frac{1}{5} & \frac{3}{5} \end{bmatrix} = \begin{bmatrix} 2 & -3 \\ 2 & -5 \end{bmatrix} = A \qquad \blacksquare$$

EXAMPLE 2   Let

$$A = \begin{bmatrix} 3 & -1 & -2 \\ 2 & 0 & -2 \\ 2 & -1 & -1 \end{bmatrix}$$

It is easily seen that the eigenvalues of A are $\lambda_1 = 0$, $\lambda_2 = 1$, and $\lambda_3 = 1$. Corresponding to $\lambda_1 = 0$, we have the eigenvector $(1, 1, 1)^T$, and corresponding to $\lambda = 1$, we have the eigenvectors $(1, 2, 0)^T$ and $(1, 0, 1)^T$. Let

$$X = \begin{pmatrix} 1 & 1 & 1 \\ 1 & 2 & 0 \\ 1 & 0 & 1 \end{pmatrix}$$

It follows that

$$XDX^{-1} = \begin{pmatrix} 1 & 1 & 1 \\ 1 & 2 & 0 \\ 1 & 0 & 1 \end{pmatrix} \begin{pmatrix} 0 & 0 & 0 \\ 0 & 1 & 0 \\ 0 & 0 & 1 \end{pmatrix} \begin{pmatrix} -2 & 1 & 2 \\ 1 & 0 & -1 \\ 2 & -1 & -1 \end{pmatrix}$$

$$= \begin{pmatrix} 3 & -1 & -2 \\ 2 & 0 & -2 \\ 2 & -1 & -1 \end{pmatrix}$$

$$= A$$

Even though $\lambda = 1$ is a multiple eigenvalue, the matrix can still be diagonalized since there are three linearly independent eigenvectors. Note also that

$$A^k = XD^kX^{-1} = XDX^{-1} = A$$

for any $k \geq 1$.   ∎

If an $n \times n$ matrix A has fewer than n linearly independent eigenvectors, we say that A is *defective*. It follows from Theorem 6.3.2 that a defective matrix is not diagonalizable.

EXAMPLE 3   Let

$$A = \begin{pmatrix} 1 & 1 \\ 0 & 1 \end{pmatrix}$$

The eigenvalues of A are both equal to 1. Any eigenvector corresponding to $\lambda = 1$ must be a multiple of $\mathbf{x}_1 = (1, 0)^T$. Thus, A is defective and cannot be diagonalized.   ∎

EXAMPLE 4   Let

$$A = \begin{pmatrix} 2 & 0 & 0 \\ 0 & 4 & 0 \\ 1 & 0 & 2 \end{pmatrix} \quad \text{and} \quad B = \begin{pmatrix} 2 & 0 & 0 \\ -1 & 4 & 0 \\ -3 & 6 & 2 \end{pmatrix}$$

A and B both have the same eigenvalues

$$\lambda_1 = 4, \qquad \lambda_2 = \lambda_3 = 2$$

Figure 6.3.1.

The eigenspace of A corresponding to $\lambda_1 = 4$ is spanned by $\mathbf{e}_2$, and the eigenspace corresponding to $\lambda = 2$ is spanned by $\mathbf{e}_3$. Since A has only two linearly independent eigenvectors, it is defective. On the other hand, the matrix B has eigenvector $\mathbf{x}_1 = (0, 1, 3)^T$ corresponding to $\lambda_1 = 4$ and eigenvectors $\mathbf{x}_2 = (2, 1, 0)^T$ and $\mathbf{e}_3$ corresponding to $\lambda = 2$. Thus, B has three linearly independent eigenvectors and consequently is not defective. Even though $\lambda = 2$ is an eigenvalue of multiplicity 2, the matrix B is nondefective, since the corresponding eigenspace has dimension 2.

Geometrically, the matrix B has the effect of stretching two linearly independent vectors by a factor of 2. We can think of the eigenvalue $\lambda = 2$ as having *geometric multiplicity* 2, since the dimension of the eigenspace $N(B - 2I)$ is 2. On the other hand, the matrix A stretches only vectors along the z-axis, by a factor of 2. In this case, the eigenvalue $\lambda = 2$ has algebraic multiplicity 2, but $\dim N(A - 2I) = 1$, so its geometric multiplicity is only 1 (see Figure 6.3.1). ∎

APPLICATION 1   Markov Chains

In Section 6.1, we studied a simple matrix model for predicting the number of married and single women in a certain town each year. Given an initial vector $\mathbf{x}_0$ whose coordinates represent the current number of married and single women, we were able to predict the number of married and single women in future years by computing

$$\mathbf{x}_1 = A\mathbf{x}_0, \ \mathbf{x}_2 = A\mathbf{x}_1, \ \mathbf{x}_3 = A\mathbf{x}_2, \ldots$$

If we scale the initial vector so that its entries indicate the proportions of the population that are married and single, then the coordinates of $\mathbf{x}_n$ will indicate the proportions of married and single women after n years. The sequence of vectors that we generate in this manner is an example of a *Markov chain*. Markov chain models occur in a wide variety of applied fields.

Definition

A **stochastic process** is any sequence of experiments for which the outcome at any stage depends on chance. A **Markov process** is a stochastic process with the following properties:

  I. The set of possible outcomes or states is finite.
  II. The probability of the next outcome depends only on the previous outcome.
  III. The probabilities are constant over time.

Table 6.3.1   Transition Probabilities for Vehicle Leasing

Current Lease				
Sedan	**Sports Car**	**Minivan**	**SUV**	**Next Lease**
0.80	0.10	0.05	0.05	**Sedan**
0.10	0.80	0.05	0.05	**Sports Car**
0.05	0.05	0.80	0.10	**Minivan**
0.05	0.05	0.10	0.80	**SUV**

The following is an example of a Markov process.

EXAMPLE 5   **Automobile Leasing** An automobile dealer leases four types of vehicles: four-door sedans, sports cars, minivans, and sport utility vehicles. The term of the lease is 2 years. At the end of the term, customers must renegotiate the lease and choose a new vehicle.

The automobile leasing can be viewed as a process with four possible outcomes. The probability of each outcome can be estimated by reviewing records of previous leases. The records indicate that 80 percent of the customers currently leasing sedans will continue doing so in the next lease. Furthermore, 10 percent of the customers currently leasing sports cars will switch to sedans. In addition, 5 percent of the customers driving minivans or sport utility vehicles will also switch to sedans. These results are summarized in the first row of Table 6.3.1. The second row indicates the percentages of customers that will lease sports cars the next time, and the final two rows give the percentages that will lease minivans and sport utility vehicles, respectively.

Suppose that initially there are 200 sedans leased and 100 of each of the other three types of vehicles. If we set

$$A = \begin{pmatrix} 0.80 & 0.10 & 0.05 & 0.05 \\ 0.10 & 0.80 & 0.05 & 0.05 \\ 0.05 & 0.05 & 0.80 & 0.10 \\ 0.05 & 0.05 & 0.10 & 0.80 \end{pmatrix} \qquad \mathbf{x}_0 = \begin{pmatrix} 200 \\ 100 \\ 100 \\ 100 \end{pmatrix}$$

then we can determine how many people will lease each type of vehicle two years later by setting

$$\mathbf{x}_1 = A\mathbf{x}_0 = \begin{pmatrix} 0.80 & 0.10 & 0.05 & 0.05 \\ 0.10 & 0.80 & 0.05 & 0.05 \\ 0.05 & 0.05 & 0.80 & 0.10 \\ 0.05 & 0.05 & 0.10 & 0.80 \end{pmatrix} \begin{pmatrix} 200 \\ 100 \\ 100 \\ 100 \end{pmatrix} = \begin{pmatrix} 180 \\ 110 \\ 105 \\ 105 \end{pmatrix}$$

We can predict the numbers for future leases by setting

$$\mathbf{x}_{n+1} = A\mathbf{x}_n \quad \text{for} \quad n = 1, 2, \dots$$

The vectors $\mathbf{x}_i$ produced in this manner are referred to as *state vectors*, and the sequence of state vectors is called a *Markov chain*. The matrix A is referred to as a *transition matrix*. The entries of each column of A are nonnegative numbers that add up to 1. Such vectors are referred to as *probability vectors*. Thus, each column vector of A is a probability vector. For example, the first column of A corresponds to individuals currently leasing sedans. The entries in this column are the probabilities of choosing each type of vehicle when the lease is renewed.

In general, a matrix is said to be *stochastic* if its entries are nonnegative and the entries in each column add up to 1. Thus, a matrix is stochastic if its column vectors are all probability vectors.

If we divide the entries of the initial vector by 500 (the total number of customers), then the entries of the new initial state vector

$$\mathbf{x}_0 = (0.40,\ 0.20,\ 0.20,\ 0.20)^T$$

represent the proportions of the population that rent each type of vehicle. The entries of $\mathbf{x}_1$ will represent the proportions for the next lease. Thus, $\mathbf{x}_0$ and $\mathbf{x}_1$ are probability vectors, and it is easily seen that the succeeding state vectors in the chain will all be probability vectors.

The long-range behavior of the process is determined by the eigenvalues and eigenvectors of the transition matrix A. The eigenvalues of A are $\lambda_1 = 1$, $\lambda_2 = 0.8$, and $\lambda_3 = \lambda_4 = 0.7$. Even though A has a multiple eigenvalue, it does have four linearly independent eigenvectors and hence it can be diagonalized. If the eigenvectors are used to form a diagonalizing matrix Y, then

$$A = YDY^{-1}$$

$$= \begin{pmatrix} 1 & -1 & 0 & 1 \\ 1 & -1 & 0 & -1 \\ 1 & 1 & 1 & 0 \\ 1 & 1 & -1 & 0 \end{pmatrix} \begin{pmatrix} 1 & 0 & 0 & 0 \\ 0 & \frac{8}{10} & 0 & 0 \\ 0 & 0 & \frac{7}{10} & 0 \\ 0 & 0 & 0 & \frac{7}{10} \end{pmatrix} \begin{pmatrix} \frac{1}{4} & \frac{1}{4} & \frac{1}{4} & \frac{1}{4} \\ -\frac{1}{4} & -\frac{1}{4} & \frac{1}{4} & \frac{1}{4} \\ 0 & 0 & \frac{1}{2} & -\frac{1}{2} \\ \frac{1}{2} & -\frac{1}{2} & 0 & 0 \end{pmatrix}$$

The state vectors are computed by setting

$$\begin{aligned}
\mathbf{x}_n &= YD^n Y^{-1}\mathbf{x}_0 \\
&= YD^n(0.25,\ -0.05,\ 0,\ 0.10)^T \\
&= Y(0.25,\ -0.05(0.8)^n,\ 0,\ 0.10(0.7)^n)^T \\
&= 0.25 \begin{pmatrix} 1 \\ 1 \\ 1 \\ 1 \end{pmatrix} - 0.05(0.8)^n \begin{pmatrix} -1 \\ -1 \\ 1 \\ 1 \end{pmatrix} + 0.10(0.7)^n \begin{pmatrix} 1 \\ -1 \\ 0 \\ 0 \end{pmatrix}
\end{aligned}$$

As n increases, $\mathbf{x}_n$ approaches the steady-state vector

$$\mathbf{x} = (0.25,\ 0.25,\ 0.25,\ 0.25)^T$$

Thus, the Markov chain model predicts that, in the long run, the leases will be divided equally among the four types of vehicles. ■

In general, we will assume that the initial vector $\mathbf{x}_0$ in a Markov chain is a probability vector, and this in turn implies that all of the state vectors are probability vectors. One would expect, then, that if the chain converges to a steady-state vector $\mathbf{x}$, then the steady-state vector must also be a probability vector. This is indeed the case, as we see in the next theorem.

Theorem 6.3.3   *If a Markov chain with an $n \times n$ transition matrix A converges to a steady-state vector $\mathbf{x}$, then*

(i) $\mathbf{x}$ *is a probability vector.*

(ii) $\lambda_1 = 1$ *is an eigenvalue of A and $\mathbf{x}$ is an eigenvector belonging to λ_1.*

Proof of (i) Let us denote the kth state vector in the chain by $\mathbf{x}_k = (x_1^{(k)}, x_2^{(k)}, \ldots, x_n^{(k)})^T$. The entries of each $\mathbf{x}_k$ are nonnegative and sum to 1. For each j, the jth entry of the limit vector $\mathbf{x}$ satisfies

$$x_j = \lim_{k \to \infty} x_j^{(k)} \geq 0$$

and

$$x_1 + x_2 + \cdots + x_n = \lim_{k \to \infty} (x_1^{(k)} + x_2^{(k)} + \cdots + x_n^{(k)}) = 1$$

Therefore, the steady-state vector $\mathbf{x}$ is a probability vector. ∎

Proof of (ii) We leave it for the reader to prove that $\lambda_1 = 1$ is an eigenvalue of A. (See Exercise 27.) It follows that $\mathbf{x}$ is an eigenvector belonging to $\lambda_1 = 1$ since

$$A\mathbf{x} = A(\lim_{k \to \infty} \mathbf{x}_k) = \lim_{k \to \infty} (A\mathbf{x}_k) = \lim_{k \to \infty} \mathbf{x}_{k+1} = \mathbf{x}$$ ∎

In general, if A is a $n \times n$ stochastic matrix, then $\lambda_1 = 1$ is an eigenvalue of A and the remaining eigenvalues satisfy

$$|\lambda_j| \leq 1 \quad j = 2, 3, \ldots, n$$

The existence of a steady state for a Markov chain is guaranteed whenever $\lambda_1 = 1$ is a *dominant eigenvalue* of the transition matrix A. An eigenvalue λ_1 of a matrix A is said to be a dominant eigenvalue if the remaining eigenvalues of A satisfy

$$|\lambda_j| < |\lambda_1| \quad \text{for} \quad j = 2, 3, \ldots, n$$

Theorem 6.3.4 *If $\lambda_1 = 1$ is a dominant eigenvalue of a stochastic matrix A, then the Markov chain with transition A will converge to a steady-state vector.*

Proof In the case that A is diagonalizable, let $\mathbf{y}_1$ be an eigenvector belonging to $\lambda_1 = 1$ and let $Y = (\mathbf{y}_1, \mathbf{y}_2, \ldots, \mathbf{y}_n)$ be a matrix that diagonalizes A. If E is the $n \times n$ matrix whose $(1, 1)$ entry is 1 and whose remaining entries are all 0, then as $k \to \infty$,

$$D^k = \begin{pmatrix} \lambda_1^k & & & \\ & \lambda_2^k & & \\ & & \ddots & \\ & & & \lambda_n^k \end{pmatrix} \to \begin{pmatrix} 1 & & & \\ & 0 & & \\ & & \ddots & \\ & & & 0 \end{pmatrix} = E$$

If $\mathbf{x}_0$ is any initial probability vector and $\mathbf{c} = Y^{-1}\mathbf{x}_0$, then

$$\mathbf{x}_k = A^k \mathbf{x}_0 = YD^kY^{-1}\mathbf{x}_0 = YD^k\mathbf{c} \to YE\mathbf{c} = Y(c_1\mathbf{e}_1) = c_1\mathbf{y}_1$$

Thus, the vector $c_1\mathbf{y}_1$ is the steady-state vector for the Markov chain.

In the case that the transition matrix A is defective with dominant eigenvalue $\lambda_1 = 1$, one can still prove the result by using a special matrix J that is referred to as the *Jordan canonical form* of A. This topic is covered in detail in Chapter 8. In that chapter, it is shown that any $n \times n$ matrix A can be factored into a product $A = YJY^{-1}$, where J is an upper bidiagonal matrix with the eigenvalues of A on its main diagonal and 0's and 1's on the diagonal directly above the main diagonal. It turns out that if A is stochastic with dominant eigenvalue $\lambda_1 = 1$, then J^k will converge to E as $k \to \infty$. So the proof in the case where A is defective is the same as before, but with the diagonal matrix D replaced by the bidiagonal matrix J. ■

Not all Markov chains converge to a steady-state vector. However, it can be shown that if all the entries of the transition matrix A are positive, then there is a unique steady-state vector $\mathbf{x}$ and $A^n\mathbf{x}_0$ will converge to $\mathbf{x}$ for any initial probability vector $\mathbf{x}_0$. In fact, this result will hold if A^k has strictly positive entries even though A may have some 0 entries. A Markov process with transition matrix A is said to be *regular* if all the entries of some power of A are positive.

In Section 6.8, we will study positive matrices, that is, matrices whose entries are all positive. One of the main results in that section is a theorem due to Perron. The Perron theorem can be used to show that if the transition matrix A of a Markov process is positive, then $\lambda_1 = 1$ is a dominant eigenvalue of A.

APPLICATION 2   Web Searches and Page Ranking

A common way to locate information on the Web is to do a keyword search using one of the many search engines available. Generally, the search engine will find all pages that contain the key search words and rank the pages in order of importance. Typically, there are more than 4 billion pages being searched and it is not uncommon to find as many as 20,000 pages that match all of the keywords. Often in such cases, the page ranked first or second by the search engine is exactly the one with the information you are seeking. How do the search engines rank the pages? In this application, we will describe the technique used by the search engine Google™.

The Google PageRank™ algorithm for ranking pages is actually a gigantic Markov process based on the link structure of the Web. The algorithm was initially conceived by two graduate students at Stanford University. The students, Larry Page and Sergey Brin, used the algorithm to develop the most successful and widely used search engine on the Internet.

The PageRank algorithm views Web surfing as a random process. The transition matrix A for the Markov process will be $n \times n$, where n is the total number of sites that are searched. The page rank computation has been referred to as the "world's largest matrix computation" since current values of n are greater than 4 billion. (See reference [1].) The (i, j) entry of A represents the probability that a random Web surfer will link from website j to website i. The page rank model assumes that the surfer will always follow a link on the current page a certain percentage of the time and otherwise will randomly link to another page.

For example, assume that the current page is numbered j and it has links to five other pages. Assume also that the user will follow these five links 85 percent of the time and will randomly link to another page 15 percent of the time. If there is no link from page j to page i, then

$$a_{ij} = 0.15\frac{1}{n}$$

If page j does contain a link to page i, then one could follow that link, or one could get to page i doing a random surf. In this case,

$$a_{ij} = 0.85\frac{1}{5} + 0.15\frac{1}{n}$$

In the case that the current page j has no hyperlinks to any other pages, it is considered to be a *dangling page*. In this case, we assume that the Web surfer will connect to any page on the Web with equal probability and we set

$$a_{ij} = \frac{1}{n} \quad \text{for } 1 \le i \le n \tag{3}$$

More generally, let $k(j)$ denote the number of links from page j to other pages on the Web. If $k(j) \ne 0$ and the person surfing the Web follows only links on the current webpage and always follows one of the links, then the probability of linking from page j to i is given by

$$m_{ij} = \begin{cases} \frac{1}{k(j)} & \text{if there is a link from page } j \text{ to page } i \\ 0 & \text{otherwise} \end{cases}$$

In the case that page j is a dangling webpage, we assume that the Web surfer will link to page i with probability

$$m_{ij} = \frac{1}{n}$$

If we make the added assumption that the surfer will follow a link on the current page with probability p and randomly link to any other page with probability $1 - p$, then the probability of linking from page j to i is given by

$$a_{ij} = pm_{ij} + (1 - p)\frac{1}{n} \tag{4}$$

Note that in the case where page j is a dangling webpage, equation (4) simplifies to equation (3).

Because of the random surfing, each entry in the jth column of A is strictly positive. Since A has strictly positive entries, the Perron theory (Section 6.8) can be used to show that the Markov process will converge to a unique steady-state vector $\mathbf{x}$. The kth entry of $\mathbf{x}$ corresponds to the probability that, in the long run, a random surfer will end up at website k. The entries of the steady-state vector provide the page rankings. The value of x_k determines the overall ranking of website k. For example, if x_k is the third largest entry of the vector $\mathbf{x}$, then website k will have the third highest overall page rank. When a Web search is conducted, the search engine first finds all sites that match all of the keywords. It then lists them in decreasing order of their page ranks.

Let $M = (m_{ij})$ and let $\mathbf{e}$ be a vector in $\mathbb{R}^n$ whose entries are all equal to 1. The matrix M is sparse; that is, most of its entries are equal to 0. If we set $E = \mathbf{e}\mathbf{e}^T$, then E is an $n \times n$ matrix of rank 1 and we can write Equation (4) in matrix form:

$$A = pM + \frac{1-p}{n}\mathbf{e}\mathbf{e}^T = pM + \frac{1-p}{n}E \tag{5}$$

Thus, A is a sum of two matrices with special structure. To compute the steady-state vector, we must perform a sequence of multiplications

$$\mathbf{x}_{j+1} = A\mathbf{x}_j, \quad j = 0, 1, 2, \ldots$$

These computations can be simplified dramatically if we take advantage of the special structure of M and E. (See Exercise 29.)

References

1. Moler, Cleve, "The World's Largest Matrix Computation," *MATLAB News & Notes*, The Mathworks, Natick, MA, October 2002.

2. Page, Lawrence, Sergey Brin, Rajeev Motwani, and Terry Winograd, "The PageRank Citation Ranking: Bringing Order to the Web," November 1999 (dbpubs.stanford.edu/pub/1999-66).

APPLICATION 3   Sex-Linked Genes

Sex-linked genes are genes that are located on the X chromosome. For example, the gene for blue-green color blindness is a recessive sex-linked gene. To devise a mathematical model to describe color blindness in a given population, it is necessary to divide the population into two classes: males and females. Let $x_1^{(0)}$ be the proportion of genes for color blindness in the male population, and let $x_2^{(0)}$ be the proportion in the female population. [Since color blindness is recessive, the actual proportion of color-blind females will be less than $x_2^{(0)}$.] Because the male receives one X chromosome from the mother and none from the father, the proportion $x_1^{(1)}$ of color-blind males in the next generation will be the same as the proportion of recessive genes in the present generation of females. Because the female receives an X chromosome from each parent, the proportion $x_2^{(1)}$ of recessive genes in the next generation of females will be the average of $x_1^{(0)}$ and $x_2^{(0)}$. Thus,

$$x_2^{(0)} = x_1^{(1)}$$
$$\tfrac{1}{2}x_1^{(0)} + \tfrac{1}{2}x_2^{(0)} = x_2^{(1)}$$

If $x_1^{(0)} = x_2^{(0)}$, the proportion will not change in future generations. Let us assume that $x_1^{(0)} \neq x_2^{(0)}$ and write the system as a matrix equation.

$$\begin{bmatrix} 0 & 1 \\ \tfrac{1}{2} & \tfrac{1}{2} \end{bmatrix} \begin{bmatrix} x_1^{(0)} \\ x_2^{(0)} \end{bmatrix} = \begin{bmatrix} x_1^{(1)} \\ x_2^{(1)} \end{bmatrix}$$

Let A denote the coefficient matrix, and let $\mathbf{x}^{(n)} = (x_1^{(n)}, x_2^{(n)})^T$ denote the proportion of color-blind genes in the male and female populations of the $(n+1)$st generation. Then

$$\mathbf{x}^{(n)} = A^n\mathbf{x}^{(0)}$$

To compute A^n, we note that A has eigenvalues 1 and $-\frac{1}{2}$ and consequently can be factored into a product:

$$A = \begin{pmatrix} 1 & -2 \\ 1 & 1 \end{pmatrix} \begin{pmatrix} 1 & 0 \\ 0 & -\frac{1}{2} \end{pmatrix} \begin{pmatrix} \frac{1}{3} & \frac{2}{3} \\ -\frac{1}{3} & \frac{1}{3} \end{pmatrix}$$

Thus,

$$\mathbf{x}^{(n)} = \begin{pmatrix} 1 & -2 \\ 1 & 1 \end{pmatrix} \begin{pmatrix} 1 & 0 \\ 0 & -\frac{1}{2} \end{pmatrix}^n \begin{pmatrix} \frac{1}{3} & \frac{2}{3} \\ -\frac{1}{3} & \frac{1}{3} \end{pmatrix} \begin{pmatrix} x_1^{(0)} \\ x_2^{(0)} \end{pmatrix}$$

$$= \frac{1}{3} \begin{pmatrix} 1-(-\frac{1}{2})^{n-1} & 2+(-\frac{1}{2})^{n-1} \\ 1-(-\frac{1}{2})^n & 2+(-\frac{1}{2})^n \end{pmatrix} \begin{pmatrix} x_1^{(0)} \\ x_2^{(0)} \end{pmatrix}$$

and hence

$$\lim_{n\to\infty} \mathbf{x}^{(n)} = \frac{1}{3} \begin{pmatrix} 1 & 2 \\ 1 & 2 \end{pmatrix} \begin{pmatrix} x_1^{(0)} \\ x_2^{(0)} \end{pmatrix}$$

$$= \begin{pmatrix} \dfrac{x_1^{(0)} + 2x_2^{(0)}}{3} \\[2mm] \dfrac{x_1^{(0)} + 2x_2^{(0)}}{3} \end{pmatrix}$$

The proportions of genes for color blindness in the male and female populations will tend to the same value as the number of generations increases. If the proportion of color-blind men is p and, over a number of generations, no outsiders have entered the population, there is justification for assuming that the proportion of genes for color blindness in the female population is also p. Since color blindness is recessive, we would expect the proportion of color-blind women to be about p^2. Thus, if 1 percent of the male population is color blind, we would expect about 0.01 percent of the female population to be color blind.

The Exponential of a Matrix

Given a scalar a, the exponential e^a can be expressed in terms of a power series

$$e^a = 1 + a + \frac{1}{2!}a^2 + \frac{1}{3!}a^3 + \cdots$$

Similarly, for any $n \times n$ matrix A, we can define the *matrix exponential* e^A in terms of the convergent power series

$$e^A = I + A + \frac{1}{2!}A^2 + \frac{1}{3!}A^3 + \cdots \tag{6}$$

The matrix exponential (6) occurs in a wide variety of applications. In the case of a diagonal matrix

$$D = \begin{bmatrix} \lambda_1 & & & \\ & \lambda_2 & & \\ & & \ddots & \\ & & & \lambda_n \end{bmatrix}$$

the matrix exponential is easy to compute:

$$e^D = \lim_{m \to \infty} \left(I + D + \frac{1}{2!}D^2 + \cdots + \frac{1}{m!}D^m \right)$$

$$= \lim_{m \to \infty} \begin{bmatrix} \displaystyle\sum_{k=0}^{m} \frac{1}{k!}\lambda_1^k & & \\ & \ddots & \\ & & \displaystyle\sum_{k=0}^{m} \frac{1}{k!}\lambda_n^k \end{bmatrix} = \begin{bmatrix} e^{\lambda_1} & & \\ & e^{\lambda_2} & \\ & & \ddots \\ & & & e^{\lambda_n} \end{bmatrix}$$

It is more difficult to compute the matrix exponential for a general $n \times n$ matrix A. If, however, A is diagonalizable, then

$$A^k = XD^kX^{-1} \qquad \text{for} \quad k = 1, 2, \ldots$$
$$e^A = X\left(I + D + \frac{1}{2!}D^2 + \frac{1}{3!}D^3 + \cdots \right) X^{-1}$$
$$= Xe^DX^{-1}$$

EXAMPLE 6   Compute e^A for

$$A = \begin{bmatrix} -2 & -6 \\ 1 & 3 \end{bmatrix}$$

Solution

The eigenvalues of A are $\lambda_1 = 1$ and $\lambda_2 = 0$ with eigenvectors $\mathbf{x}_1 = (-2, 1)^T$ and $\mathbf{x}_2 = (-3, 1)^T$. Thus,

$$A = XDX^{-1} = \begin{bmatrix} -2 & -3 \\ 1 & 1 \end{bmatrix} \begin{bmatrix} 1 & 0 \\ 0 & 0 \end{bmatrix} \begin{bmatrix} 1 & 3 \\ -1 & -2 \end{bmatrix}$$

and

$$e^A = Xe^DX^{-1} = \begin{bmatrix} -2 & -3 \\ 1 & 1 \end{bmatrix} \begin{bmatrix} e^1 & 0 \\ 0 & e^0 \end{bmatrix} \begin{bmatrix} 1 & 3 \\ -1 & -2 \end{bmatrix}$$
$$= \begin{bmatrix} 3 - 2e & 6 - 6e \\ e - 1 & 3e - 2 \end{bmatrix}$$

The matrix exponential can be applied to the initial value problem

$$\mathbf{Y}' = A\mathbf{Y}, \qquad \mathbf{Y}(0) = \mathbf{Y}_0 \tag{7}$$

studied in Section 6.2. In the case of one equation in one unknown,

$$y' = ay, \quad y(0) = y_0$$

the solution is

$$y = e^{at}y_0 \tag{8}$$

We can generalize this and express the solution of (7) in terms of the matrix exponential e^{tA}. In general, a power series can be differentiated term by term within its radius of convergence. Since the expansion of e^{tA} has infinite radius of convergence, we have

$$\frac{d}{dt}e^{tA} = \frac{d}{dt}\left(I + tA + \frac{1}{2!}t^2A^2 + \frac{1}{3!}t^3A^3 + \cdots\right)$$
$$= \left(A + tA^2 + \frac{1}{2!}t^2A^3 + \cdots\right)$$
$$= A\left(I + tA + \frac{1}{2!}t^2A^2 + \cdots\right)$$
$$= Ae^{tA}$$

If, as in (8), we set

$$\mathbf{Y}(t) = e^{tA}\mathbf{Y}_0$$

then

$$\mathbf{Y}' = Ae^{tA}\mathbf{Y}_0 = A\mathbf{Y}$$

and

$$\mathbf{Y}(0) = \mathbf{Y}_0$$

Thus, the solution of

$$\mathbf{Y}' = A\mathbf{Y}, \qquad \mathbf{Y}(0) = \mathbf{Y}_0$$

is simply

$$\mathbf{Y} = e^{tA}\mathbf{Y}_0 \tag{9}$$

Although the form of this solution looks different from the solutions in Section 6.2, there is really no difference. In Section 6.2, the solution was expressed in the form

$$c_1 e^{\lambda_1 t}\mathbf{x}_1 + c_2 e^{\lambda_2 t}\mathbf{x}_2 + \cdots + c_n e^{\lambda_n t}\mathbf{x}_n$$

where $\mathbf{x}_i$ was an eigenvector belonging to λ_i for $i = 1, \ldots, n$. The c_i's that satisfied the initial conditions were determined by solving a system

$$X\mathbf{c} = \mathbf{Y}_0$$

with coefficient matrix $X = (\mathbf{x}_1, \dots, \mathbf{x}_n)$.

If A is diagonalizable, we can write (9) in the form

$$\mathbf{Y} = X e^{tD} X^{-1} \mathbf{Y}_0$$

Thus,

$$\mathbf{Y} = X e^{tD} \mathbf{c}$$

$$= (\mathbf{x}_1, \mathbf{x}_2, \dots, \mathbf{x}_n) \begin{bmatrix} c_1 e^{\lambda_1 t} \\ c_2 e^{\lambda_2 t} \\ \vdots \\ c_n e^{\lambda_n t} \end{bmatrix}$$

$$= c_1 e^{\lambda_1 t} \mathbf{x}_1 + \cdots + c_n e^{\lambda_n t} \mathbf{x}_n$$

To summarize, the solution to the initial value problem (7) is given by

$$\mathbf{Y} = e^{tA} \mathbf{Y}_0$$

If A is diagonalizable, this solution can be written in the form

$$\mathbf{Y} = X e^{tD} X^{-1} \mathbf{Y}_0$$
$$= c_1 e^{\lambda_1 t} \mathbf{x}_1 + c_2 e^{\lambda_2 t} \mathbf{x}_2 + \cdots + c_n e^{\lambda_n t} \mathbf{x}_n \quad (\mathbf{c} = X^{-1} \mathbf{Y}_0)$$

EXAMPLE 7   Use the matrix exponential to solve the initial value problem

$$\mathbf{Y}' = A\mathbf{Y}, \qquad \mathbf{Y}(0) = \mathbf{Y}_0$$

where

$$A = \begin{bmatrix} 3 & 4 \\ 3 & 2 \end{bmatrix}, \qquad \mathbf{Y}_0 = \begin{bmatrix} 6 \\ 1 \end{bmatrix}$$

(This problem was solved in Example 1 of Section 6.2.)

Solution

The eigenvalues of A are $\lambda_1 = 6$ and $\lambda_2 = -1$, with eigenvectors $\mathbf{x}_1 = (4, 3)^T$ and $\mathbf{x}_2 = (1, -1)^T$. Thus,

$$A = XDX^{-1} = \begin{bmatrix} 4 & 1 \\ 3 & -1 \end{bmatrix} \begin{bmatrix} 6 & 0 \\ 0 & -1 \end{bmatrix} \begin{bmatrix} \frac{1}{7} & \frac{1}{7} \\ \frac{3}{7} & -\frac{4}{7} \end{bmatrix}$$

and the solution is given by

$$\mathbf{Y} = e^{tA} \mathbf{Y}_0$$

$$= X e^{tD} X^{-1} \mathbf{Y}_0$$

$$= \begin{bmatrix} 4 & 1 \\ 3 & -1 \end{bmatrix} \begin{bmatrix} e^{6t} & 0 \\ 0 & e^{-t} \end{bmatrix} \begin{bmatrix} \frac{1}{7} & \frac{1}{7} \\ \frac{3}{7} & -\frac{4}{7} \end{bmatrix} \begin{bmatrix} 6 \\ 1 \end{bmatrix}$$

$$= \begin{bmatrix} 4e^{6t} + 2e^{-t} \\ 3e^{6t} - 2e^{-t} \end{bmatrix}$$

Compare this to Example 1 in Section 6.2.

EXAMPLE 8 Use the matrix exponential to solve the initial value problem

$$\mathbf{Y}' = A\mathbf{Y}, \qquad \mathbf{Y}(0) = \mathbf{Y}_0$$

where

$$A = \begin{bmatrix} 0 & 1 & 0 \\ 0 & 0 & 1 \\ 0 & 0 & 0 \end{bmatrix}, \qquad \mathbf{Y}_0 = \begin{bmatrix} 2 \\ 1 \\ 4 \end{bmatrix}$$

Solution

Since the matrix A is defective, we will use the definition of the matrix exponential to compute e^{tA}. Note that $A^3 = O$, so

$$e^{tA} = I + tA + \frac{1}{2!}t^2 A^2$$

$$= \begin{bmatrix} 1 & t & t^2/2 \\ 0 & 1 & t \\ 0 & 0 & 1 \end{bmatrix}$$

The solution to the initial value problem is given by

$$\mathbf{Y} = e^{tA}\mathbf{Y}_0$$

$$= \begin{bmatrix} 1 & t & t^2/2 \\ 0 & 1 & t \\ 0 & 0 & 1 \end{bmatrix} \begin{bmatrix} 2 \\ 1 \\ 4 \end{bmatrix}$$

$$= \begin{bmatrix} 2 + t + 2t^2 \\ 1 + 4t \\ 4 \end{bmatrix}$$

SECTION 6.3 EXERCISES

1. In each of the following, factor the matrix A into a product XDX^{-1}, where D is diagonal:

(a) $A = \begin{bmatrix} 0 & 1 \\ 1 & 0 \end{bmatrix}$ (b) $A = \begin{bmatrix} 5 & 6 \\ -2 & -2 \end{bmatrix}$

(c) $A = \begin{bmatrix} 2 & -8 \\ 1 & -4 \end{bmatrix}$ (d) $A = \begin{bmatrix} 2 & 2 & 1 \\ 0 & 1 & 2 \\ 0 & 0 & -1 \end{bmatrix}$

(e) $A = \begin{bmatrix} 1 & 0 & 0 \\ -2 & 1 & 3 \\ 1 & 1 & -1 \end{bmatrix}$

(f) $A = \begin{bmatrix} 1 & 2 & -1 \\ 2 & 4 & -2 \\ 3 & 6 & -3 \end{bmatrix}$

2. For each of the matrices in Exercise 1, use the XDX^{-1} factorization to compute A^6.

3. For each of the nonsingular matrices in Exercise 1, use the XDX^{-1} factorization to compute A^{-1}.

4. For each of the following, find a matrix B such that $B^2 = A$:

(a) $A = \begin{bmatrix} 2 & 1 \\ -2 & -1 \end{bmatrix}$ (b) $A = \begin{bmatrix} 9 & -5 & 3 \\ 0 & 4 & 3 \\ 0 & 0 & 1 \end{bmatrix}$

5. Let A be a nondefective $n \times n$ matrix with diagonalizing matrix X. Show that the matrix $Y = (X^{-1})^T$ diagonalizes A^T.

6. Let A be a diagonalizable matrix whose eigenvalues are all either 1 or -1. Show that $A^{-1} = A$.

7. Show that any 3×3 matrix of the form
$$\begin{bmatrix} a & 1 & 0 \\ 0 & a & 1 \\ 0 & 0 & b \end{bmatrix}$$
is defective.

8. For each of the following, find all possible values of the scalar α that make the matrix defective or show that no such values exist:

(a) $\begin{bmatrix} 1 & 1 & 0 \\ 1 & 1 & 0 \\ 0 & 0 & \alpha \end{bmatrix}$ (b) $\begin{bmatrix} 1 & 1 & 1 \\ 1 & 1 & 1 \\ 0 & 0 & \alpha \end{bmatrix}$

(c) $\begin{bmatrix} 1 & 2 & 0 \\ 2 & 1 & 0 \\ 2 & -1 & \alpha \end{bmatrix}$ (d) $\begin{bmatrix} 4 & 6 & -2 \\ -1 & -1 & 1 \\ 0 & 0 & \alpha \end{bmatrix}$

(e) $\begin{bmatrix} 3\alpha & 1 & 0 \\ 0 & \alpha & 0 \\ 0 & 0 & \alpha \end{bmatrix}$ (f) $\begin{bmatrix} 3\alpha & 0 & 0 \\ 0 & \alpha & 1 \\ 0 & 0 & \alpha \end{bmatrix}$

(g) $\begin{bmatrix} \alpha+2 & 1 & 0 \\ 0 & \alpha+2 & 0 \\ 0 & 0 & 2\alpha \end{bmatrix}$

(h) $\begin{bmatrix} \alpha+2 & 0 & 0 \\ 0 & \alpha+2 & 1 \\ 0 & 0 & 2\alpha \end{bmatrix}$

9. Let A be a 4×4 matrix and let λ be an eigenvalue of multiplicity 3. If $A - \lambda I$ has rank 1, is A defective? Explain.

10. Let A be an $n \times n$ matrix with positive real eigenvalues $\lambda_1 > \lambda_2 > \cdots > \lambda_n$. Let x_i be an eigenvector belonging to λ_i for each i, and let $x = \alpha_1 x_1 + \cdots + \alpha_n x_n$.

(a) Show that $A^m x = \sum_{i=1}^{n} \alpha_i \lambda_i^m x_i$.

(b) Show that if $\lambda_1 = 1$, then $\lim_{m \to \infty} A^m x = \alpha_1 x_1$.

11. Let A be a $n \times n$ matrix with real entries and let $\lambda_1 = a + bi$ (where a and b are real and $b \neq 0$) be an eigenvalue of A. Let $z_1 = x + iy$ (where x and y both have real entries) be an eigenvector belonging to λ_1 and let $z_2 = x - iy$.

(a) Explain why z_1 and z_2 must be linearly independent.

(b) Show that $y \neq 0$ and that x and y are linearly independent.

12. Let A be an $n \times n$ matrix with an eigenvalue λ of multiplicity n. Show that A is diagonalizable if and only if $A = \lambda I$.

13. Show that a nonzero nilpotent matrix is defective.

14. Let A be a diagonalizable matrix and let X be the diagonalizing matrix. Show that the column vectors of X that correspond to nonzero eigenvalues of A form a basis for $R(A)$.

15. It follows from Exercise 14 that for a diagonalizable matrix the number of nonzero eigenvalues (counted according to multiplicity) equals the rank of the matrix. Give an example of a defective matrix whose rank is not equal to the number of nonzero eigenvalues.

16. Let A be an $n \times n$ matrix and let λ be an eigenvalue of A whose eigenspace has dimension k, where $1 < k < n$. Any basis $\{x_1, \ldots, x_k\}$ for the eigenspace can be extended to a basis $\{x_1, \ldots, x_n\}$ for $\mathbb{R}^n$. Let $X = (x_1, \ldots, x_n)$ and $B = X^{-1}AX$.

(a) Show that B is of the form
$$\begin{bmatrix} \lambda I & B_{12} \\ O & B_{22} \end{bmatrix}$$
where I is the $k \times k$ identity matrix.

(b) Use Theorem 6.1.1 to show that λ is an eigenvalue of A with multiplicity at least k.

17. Let x, y be nonzero vectors in $\mathbb{R}^n$, $n \geq 2$, and let $A = xy^T$. Show that

(a) $\lambda = 0$ is an eigenvalue of A with $n - 1$ linearly independent eigenvectors and consequently has multiplicity at least $n - 1$ (see Exercise 16).

(b) the remaining eigenvalue of A is
$$\lambda_n = \operatorname{tr} A = x^T y$$
and x is an eigenvector belonging to λ_n.

(c) if $\lambda_n = x^T y \neq 0$, then A is diagonalizable.

18. Let A be a diagonalizable $n \times n$ matrix. Prove that if B is any matrix that is similar to A, then B is diagonalizable.

19. Show that if A and B are two $n \times n$ matrices with the same diagonalizing matrix X, then $AB = BA$.

20. Let T be an upper triangular matrix with distinct diagonal entries (i.e., $t_{ii} \neq t_{jj}$ whenever $i \neq j$). Show that there is an upper triangular matrix R that diagonalizes T.

21. Each year, employees at a company are given the option of donating to a local charity as part of a payroll deduction plan. In general, 80 percent of the employees enrolled in the plan in any one year will choose to sign up again the following year, and 30 percent of

the unenrolled will choose to enroll the following year. Determine the transition matrix for the Markov process and find the steady-state vector. What percentage of employees would you expect to find enrolled in the program in the long run?

22. The city of Mawtookit maintains a constant population of 300,000 people from year to year. A political science study estimated that there were 150,000 Independents, 90,000 Democrats, and 60,000 Republicans in the town. It was also estimated that each year 20 percent of the Independents become Democrats and 10 percent become Republicans. Similarly, 20 percent of the Democrats become Independents and 10 percent become Republicans, while 10 percent of the Republicans defect to the Democrats and 10 percent become Independents each year. Let

$$\mathbf{x} = \begin{bmatrix} 150{,}000 \\ 90{,}000 \\ 60{,}000 \end{bmatrix}$$

and let $\mathbf{x}^{(1)}$ be a vector representing the number of people in each group after one year.

(a) Find a matrix A such that $A\mathbf{x} = \mathbf{x}^{(1)}$.

(b) Show that $\lambda_1 = 1.0$, $\lambda_2 = 0.5$, and $\lambda_3 = 0.7$ are the eigenvalues of A, and factor A into a product XDX^{-1}, where D is diagonal.

(c) Which group will dominate in the long run? Justify your answer by computing $\lim\limits_{n\to\infty} A^n\mathbf{x}$.

23. Let

$$A = \begin{bmatrix} \frac{1}{2} & \frac{1}{3} & \frac{1}{5} \\ \frac{1}{4} & \frac{1}{3} & \frac{2}{5} \\ \frac{1}{4} & \frac{1}{3} & \frac{2}{5} \end{bmatrix}$$

be a transition matrix for a Markov process.

(a) Compute $\det(A)$ and $\operatorname{trace}(A)$ and make use of those values to determine the eigenvalues of A.

(b) Explain why the Markov process must converge to a steady-state vector.

(c) Show that $\mathbf{y} = (16, 15, 15)^T$ is an eigenvector of A. How is the steady-state vector related to $\mathbf{y}$?

24. Let A be a 3×2 matrix whose column vectors $\mathbf{a}_1$ and $\mathbf{a}_2$ are both probability vectors. Show that if $\mathbf{p}$ is a probability vector in $\mathbb{R}^2$ and $\mathbf{y} = A\mathbf{p}$, then $\mathbf{y}$ is a probability vector in $\mathbb{R}^3$.

25. Generalize the result from Exercise 24. Show that if A is an $m \times n$ matrix whose column vectors are all probability vectors and $\mathbf{p}$ is a probability vector in $\mathbb{R}^n$, then the vector $\mathbf{y} = A\mathbf{x}$ will be probability vector in $\mathbb{R}^m$.

26. Consider a Web network consisting of only four sites that are linked together as shown in the accompanying diagram. If the Google PageRank algorithm is used to rank these pages, determine the transition matrix A. Assume that the Web surfer will follow a link on the current page 85 percent of the time.

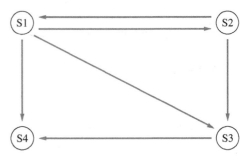

27. Let A be an $n \times n$ stochastic matrix and let $\mathbf{e}$ be the vector in $\mathbb{R}^n$ whose entries are all equal to 1. Show that $\mathbf{e}$ is an eigenvector of A^T. Explain why a stochastic matrix must have $\lambda = 1$ as an eigenvalue.

28. The transition matrix in Example 5 has the property that both its rows and its columns add up to 1. In general, a matrix A is said to be *doubly stochastic* if both A and A^T are stochastic. Let A be an $n \times n$ doubly stochastic matrix whose eigenvalues satisfy

$$\lambda_1 = 1 \quad \text{and} \quad |\lambda_j| < 1 \text{ for } j = 2, 3, \ldots, n$$

Show that if $\mathbf{e}$ is the vector in $\mathbb{R}^n$ whose entries are all equal to 1, then the Markov chain will converge to the steady-state vector $\mathbf{x} = \frac{1}{n}\mathbf{e}$ for any starting vector $\mathbf{x}_0$. Thus, for a doubly stochastic transition matrix, the steady-state vector will assign equal probabilities to all possible outcomes.

29. Let A be the PageRank transition matrix and let $\mathbf{x}_k$ be a vector in the Markov chain with starting probability vector $\mathbf{x}_0$. Since n is very large, the direct multiplication $\mathbf{x}_{k+1} = A\mathbf{x}_k$ is computationally intensive. However, the computation can be simplified dramatically if we take advantage of the structured components of A given in equation (5). Because M is sparse, the multiplication $\mathbf{w}_k = M\mathbf{x}_k$ is computationally much simpler. Show that if we set

$$\mathbf{b} = \frac{1-p}{n}\mathbf{e}$$

then

$$E\mathbf{x}_k = \mathbf{e} \quad \text{and} \quad \mathbf{x}_{k+1} = p\mathbf{w}_k + \mathbf{b}$$

where $M, E, \mathbf{e}$, and p are as defined in equation (5).

30. Use the definition of the matrix exponential to compute e^A for each of the following matrices:

(a) $A = \begin{bmatrix} 1 & 1 \\ -1 & -1 \end{bmatrix}$ **(b)** $A = \begin{bmatrix} 1 & 1 \\ 0 & 1 \end{bmatrix}$

(c) $A = \begin{bmatrix} 1 & 0 & -1 \\ 0 & 1 & 0 \\ 0 & 0 & 1 \end{bmatrix}$

31. Compute e^A for each of the following matrices:

(a) $A = \begin{bmatrix} -2 & -1 \\ 6 & 3 \end{bmatrix}$ **(b)** $A = \begin{bmatrix} 3 & 4 \\ -2 & -3 \end{bmatrix}$

(c) $A = \begin{bmatrix} 1 & 1 & 1 \\ -1 & -1 & -1 \\ 1 & 1 & 1 \end{bmatrix}$

32. In each of the following, solve the initial value problem $\mathbf{Y}' = A\mathbf{Y}$, $\mathbf{Y}(0) = \mathbf{Y}_0$ by computing $e^{tA}\mathbf{Y}_0$:

(a) $A = \begin{bmatrix} 1 & -2 \\ 0 & -1 \end{bmatrix}$, $\mathbf{Y}_0 = \begin{bmatrix} 1 \\ 1 \end{bmatrix}$

(b) $A = \begin{bmatrix} 2 & 3 \\ -1 & -2 \end{bmatrix}$, $\mathbf{Y}_0 = \begin{bmatrix} -4 \\ 2 \end{bmatrix}$

(c) $A = \begin{bmatrix} 1 & 1 & 1 \\ 0 & 0 & 1 \\ 0 & 0 & -1 \end{bmatrix}$, $\mathbf{Y}_0 = \begin{bmatrix} 1 \\ 1 \\ 1 \end{bmatrix}$

(d) $A = \begin{bmatrix} 1 & 1 & 1 \\ 1 & 0 & 1 \\ -1 & -1 & -1 \end{bmatrix}$, $\mathbf{Y}_0 = \begin{bmatrix} 1 \\ 1 \\ -1 \end{bmatrix}$

33. Let λ be an eigenvalue of an $n \times n$ matrix A and let $\mathbf{x}$ be an eigenvector belonging to λ. Show that e^λ is an eigenvalue of e^A and $\mathbf{x}$ is an eigenvector of e^A belonging to e^λ.

34. Show that e^A is nonsingular for any diagonalizable matrix A.

35. Let A be a diagonalizable matrix with characteristic polynomial

$$p(\lambda) = a_1 \lambda^n + a_2 \lambda^{n-1} + \cdots + a_{n+1}$$

(a) Show that if D is a diagonal matrix whose diagonal entries are the eigenvalues of A, then

$$p(D) = a_1 D^n + a_2 D^{n-1} + \cdots + a_{n+1}I = O$$

(b) Show that $p(A) = O$.

(c) Show that if $a_{n+1} \neq 0$, then A is nonsingular and $A^{-1} = q(A)$ for some polynomial q of degree less than n.

6.4 Hermitian Matrices

Let $\mathbb{C}^n$ denote the vector space of all n-tuples of complex numbers. The set $\mathbb{C}$ of all complex numbers will be taken as our field of scalars. We have already seen that a matrix A with real entries may have complex eigenvalues and eigenvectors. In this section, we study matrices with complex entries and look at the complex analogues of symmetric and orthogonal matrices.

Complex Inner Products

If $\alpha = a + bi$ is a complex scalar, the length of α is given by

$$|\alpha| = \sqrt{\bar{\alpha}\alpha} = \sqrt{a^2 + b^2}$$

The length of a vector $\mathbf{z} = (z_1, z_2, \ldots, z_n)^T$ in $\mathbb{C}^n$ is given by

$$\|\mathbf{z}\| = \left(|z_1|^2 + |z_2|^2 + \cdots + |z_n|^2\right)^{1/2}$$
$$= (\bar{z}_1 z_1 + \bar{z}_2 z_2 + \cdots + \bar{z}_n z_n)^{1/2}$$
$$= \left(\bar{\mathbf{z}}^T \mathbf{z}\right)^{1/2}$$

As a notational convenience, we write $\mathbf{z}^H$ for the transpose of $\bar{\mathbf{z}}$. Thus,

$$\bar{\mathbf{z}}^T = \mathbf{z}^H \quad \text{and} \quad \|\mathbf{z}\| = (\mathbf{z}^H \mathbf{z})^{1/2}$$

Definition

> Let V be a vector space over the complex numbers. An **inner product** on V is an operation that assigns to each pair of vectors $\mathbf{z}$ and $\mathbf{w}$ in V a complex number $\langle \mathbf{z}, \mathbf{w} \rangle$ satisfying the following conditions:
>
> **I.** $\langle \mathbf{z}, \mathbf{z} \rangle \geq 0$, with equality if and only if $\mathbf{z} = \mathbf{0}$
> **II.** $\langle \mathbf{z}, \mathbf{w} \rangle = \overline{\langle \mathbf{w}, \mathbf{z} \rangle}$ for all $\mathbf{z}$ and $\mathbf{w}$ in V
> **III.** $\langle \alpha \mathbf{z} + \beta \mathbf{w}, \mathbf{u} \rangle = \alpha \langle \mathbf{z}, \mathbf{u} \rangle + \beta \langle \mathbf{w}, \mathbf{u} \rangle$

Note that for a complex inner product space, $\langle \mathbf{z}, \mathbf{w} \rangle = \overline{\langle \mathbf{w}, \mathbf{z} \rangle}$, rather than $\langle \mathbf{w}, \mathbf{z} \rangle$. If we make the proper modifications to allow for this difference, the theorems on real inner product spaces in Section 5.5, will all be valid for complex inner product spaces. In particular, let us recall Theorem 5.5.2: If $\{\mathbf{u}_1, \ldots, \mathbf{u}_n\}$ is an orthonormal basis for a real inner product space V and

$$\mathbf{x} = \sum_{i=1}^{n} c_i \mathbf{u}_i$$

then

$$c_i = \langle \mathbf{u}_i, \mathbf{x} \rangle = \langle \mathbf{x}, \mathbf{u}_i \rangle \quad \text{and} \quad \|\mathbf{x}\|^2 = \sum_{i=1}^{n} c_i^2$$

In the case of a complex inner product space, if $\{\mathbf{w}_1, \ldots, \mathbf{w}_n\}$ is an orthonormal basis and

$$\mathbf{z} = \sum_{i=1}^{n} c_i \mathbf{w}_i$$

then

$$c_i = \langle \mathbf{z}, \mathbf{w}_i \rangle, \overline{c}_i = \langle \mathbf{w}_i, \mathbf{z} \rangle \quad \text{and} \quad \|\mathbf{z}\|^2 = \sum_{i=1}^{n} c_i \overline{c}_i$$

We can define an inner product on $\mathbb{C}^n$ by

$$\langle \mathbf{z}, \mathbf{w} \rangle = \mathbf{w}^H \mathbf{z} \tag{1}$$

for all $\mathbf{z}$ and $\mathbf{w}$ in $\mathbb{C}^n$. We leave it to the reader to verify that (1) actually does define an inner product on $\mathbb{C}^n$. The complex inner product space $\mathbb{C}^n$ is similar to the real inner product space $\mathbb{R}^n$. The main difference is that in the complex case it is necessary to conjugate before transposing when taking an inner product.

$\mathbb{R}^n$	$\mathbb{C}^n$
$\langle \mathbf{x}, \mathbf{y} \rangle = \mathbf{y}^T \mathbf{x}$	$\langle \mathbf{z}, \mathbf{w} \rangle = \mathbf{w}^H \mathbf{z}$
$\mathbf{x}^T \mathbf{y} = \mathbf{y}^T \mathbf{x}$	$\mathbf{z}^H \mathbf{w} = \overline{\mathbf{w}^H \mathbf{z}}$
$\|\mathbf{x}\|^2 = \mathbf{x}^T \mathbf{x}$	$\|\mathbf{z}\|^2 = \mathbf{z}^H \mathbf{z}$

EXAMPLE I   If

$$\mathbf{z} = \begin{bmatrix} 5+i \\ 1-3i \end{bmatrix} \qquad \text{and} \qquad \mathbf{w} = \begin{bmatrix} 2+i \\ -2+3i \end{bmatrix}$$

then

$$\mathbf{w}^H\mathbf{z} = (2-i, -2-3i)\begin{bmatrix} 5+i \\ 1-3i \end{bmatrix} = (11-3i) + (-11+3i) = 0$$

$$\mathbf{z}^H\mathbf{z} = |5+i|^2 + |1-3i|^2 = 36$$

$$\mathbf{w}^H\mathbf{w} = |2+i|^2 + |-2+3i|^2 = 18$$

It follows that $\mathbf{z}$ and $\mathbf{w}$ are orthogonal and

$$\|\mathbf{z}\| = 6, \qquad \|\mathbf{w}\| = 3\sqrt{2}$$

Hermitian Matrices

Let $M = (m_{ij})$ be an $m \times n$ matrix with $m_{ij} = a_{ij} + ib_{ij}$ for each i and j. We may write M in the form

$$M = A + iB$$

where $A = (a_{ij})$ and $B = (b_{ij})$ have real entries. We define the conjugate of M by

$$\overline{M} = A - iB$$

Thus, $\overline{M}$ is the matrix formed by conjugating each of the entries of M. The transpose of $\overline{M}$ will be denoted by M^H. The vector space of all $m \times n$ matrices with complex entries is denoted by $\mathbb{C}^{m \times n}$. If A and B are elements of $\mathbb{C}^{m \times n}$ and $C \in \mathbb{C}^{n \times r}$, then the following rules are easily verified (see Exercise 9):

> **I.** $(A^H)^H = A$
> **II.** $(\alpha A + \beta B)^H = \overline{\alpha}A^H + \overline{\beta}B^H$
> **III.** $(AC)^H = C^H A^H$

Definition   A matrix M is said to be **Hermitian** if $M = M^H$.

EXAMPLE 2   The matrix

$$M = \begin{bmatrix} 3 & 2-i \\ 2+i & 4 \end{bmatrix}$$

is Hermitian, since

$$M^H = \begin{bmatrix} \overline{3} & \overline{2-i} \\ \overline{2+i} & \overline{4} \end{bmatrix}^T = \begin{bmatrix} 3 & 2-i \\ 2+i & 4 \end{bmatrix} = M$$

If M is a matrix with real entries, then $M^H = M^T$. In particular, if M is a real symmetric matrix, then M is Hermitian. Thus, we may view Hermitian matrices as the complex analogue of real symmetric matrices. Hermitian matrices have many nice properties, as we shall see in the next theorem.

Theorem 6.4.1   *The eigenvalues of a Hermitian matrix are all real. Furthermore, eigenvectors belonging to distinct eigenvalues are orthogonal.*

Proof   Let A be a Hermitian matrix. Let λ be an eigenvalue of A and let $\mathbf{x}$ be an eigenvector belonging to λ. If $\alpha = \mathbf{x}^H A\mathbf{x}$, then

$$\bar{\alpha} = \alpha^H = (\mathbf{x}^H A\mathbf{x})^H = \mathbf{x}^H A\mathbf{x} = \alpha$$

Thus, α is real. It follows that

$$\alpha = \mathbf{x}^H A\mathbf{x} = \mathbf{x}^H \lambda \mathbf{x} = \lambda \|\mathbf{x}\|^2$$

and hence

$$\lambda = \frac{\alpha}{\|\mathbf{x}\|^2}$$

is real. If $\mathbf{x}_1$ and $\mathbf{x}_2$ are eigenvectors belonging to distinct eigenvalues λ_1 and λ_2, respectively, then

$$(A\mathbf{x}_1)^H \mathbf{x}_2 = \mathbf{x}_1^H A^H \mathbf{x}_2 = \mathbf{x}_1^H A\mathbf{x}_2 = \lambda_2 \mathbf{x}_1^H \mathbf{x}_2$$

and

$$(A\mathbf{x}_1)^H \mathbf{x}_2 = (\mathbf{x}_2^H A\mathbf{x}_1)^H = (\lambda_1 \mathbf{x}_2^H \mathbf{x}_1)^H = \lambda_1 \mathbf{x}_1^H \mathbf{x}_2$$

Consequently,

$$\lambda_1 \mathbf{x}_1^H \mathbf{x}_2 = \lambda_2 \mathbf{x}_1^H \mathbf{x}_2$$

and since $\lambda_1 \neq \lambda_2$, it follows that

$$\langle \mathbf{x}_2, \mathbf{x}_1 \rangle = \mathbf{x}_1^H \mathbf{x}_2 = 0 \qquad \blacksquare$$

Definition   An $n \times n$ matrix U is said to be **unitary** if its column vectors form an orthonormal set in $\mathbb{C}^n$.

Thus, U is unitary if and only if $U^H U = I$. If U is unitary, then, since the column vectors are orthonormal, U must have rank n. It follows that

$$U^{-1} = IU^{-1} = U^H UU^{-1} = U^H$$

A real unitary matrix is an orthogonal matrix.

Corollary 6.4.2   *If the eigenvalues of a Hermitian matrix A are distinct, then there exists a unitary matrix U that diagonalizes A.*

Proof   Let $\mathbf{x}_i$ be an eigenvector belonging to λ_i for each eigenvalue λ_i of A. Let $\mathbf{u}_i = (1/\|\mathbf{x}_i\|)\mathbf{x}_i$. Thus, $\mathbf{u}_i$ is a unit eigenvector belonging to λ_i for each i. It follows from Theorem 6.4.1 that $\{\mathbf{u}_1, \ldots, \mathbf{u}_n\}$ is an orthonormal set in $\mathbb{C}^n$. Let U be the matrix whose ith column vector is $\mathbf{u}_i$ for each i; then U is unitary and U diagonalizes A. ∎

EXAMPLE 3   Let

$$A = \begin{bmatrix} 2 & 1-i \\ 1+i & 1 \end{bmatrix}$$

Find a unitary matrix U that diagonalizes A.

Solution

The eigenvalues of A are $\lambda_1 = 3$ and $\lambda_2 = 0$, with corresponding eigenvectors $\mathbf{x}_1 = (1-i, 1)^T$ and $\mathbf{x}_2 = (-1, 1+i)^T$. Let

$$\mathbf{u}_1 = \frac{1}{\|\mathbf{x}_1\|}\mathbf{x}_1 = \frac{1}{\sqrt{3}}(1-i, 1)^T$$

and

$$\mathbf{u}_2 = \frac{1}{\|\mathbf{x}_2\|}\mathbf{x}_2 = \frac{1}{\sqrt{3}}(-1, 1+i)^T$$

Thus,

$$U = \frac{1}{\sqrt{3}} \begin{bmatrix} 1-i & -1 \\ 1 & 1+i \end{bmatrix}$$

and

$$U^H A U = \frac{1}{3} \begin{bmatrix} 1+i & 1 \\ -1 & 1-i \end{bmatrix} \begin{bmatrix} 2 & 1-i \\ 1+i & 1 \end{bmatrix} \begin{bmatrix} 1-i & -1 \\ 1 & 1+i \end{bmatrix}$$

$$= \begin{bmatrix} 3 & 0 \\ 0 & 0 \end{bmatrix}$$

∎

Actually, Corollary 6.4.2 is valid even if the eigenvalues of A are not distinct. To show this, we will first prove the following theorem.

Theorem 6.4.3   Schur's Theorem

For each $n \times n$ matrix A, there exists a unitary matrix U such that $U^H A U$ is upper triangular.

Proof   The proof is by induction on n. The result is obvious if $n = 1$. Assume that the hypothesis holds for $k \times k$ matrices, and let A be a $(k+1) \times (k+1)$ matrix. Let λ_1 be an eigenvalue of A, and let $\mathbf{w}_1$ be a unit eigenvector belonging to λ_1. Using the Gram–Schmidt process, construct $\mathbf{w}_2, \ldots, \mathbf{w}_{k+1}$ such that $\{\mathbf{w}_1, \ldots, \mathbf{w}_{k+1}\}$ is an orthonormal basis for $\mathbb{C}^{k+1}$. Let W be the matrix whose ith column vector is $\mathbf{w}_i$ for $i = 1, \ldots, k+1$. Then, by construction, W is unitary. The first column of $W^H A W$ will be $W^H A \mathbf{w}_1$.

$$W^H A \mathbf{w}_1 = \lambda_1 W^H \mathbf{w}_1 = \lambda_1 \mathbf{e}_1$$

Thus, $W^H A W$ is a matrix of the form

$$
\begin{pmatrix}
\lambda_1 & \times & \times & \cdots & \times \\
\hline
0 & & & & \\
\vdots & & & M & \\
0 & & & &
\end{pmatrix}
$$

where M is a $k \times k$ matrix. By the induction hypothesis, there exists a $k \times k$ unitary matrix V_1 such that $V_1^H M V_1 = T_1$, where T_1 is triangular. Let

$$
V = \begin{pmatrix}
1 & 0 & \cdots & 0 \\
\hline
0 & & & \\
\vdots & & V_1 & \\
0 & & &
\end{pmatrix}
$$

Here, V is unitary and

$$
V^H W^H A W V = \begin{pmatrix}
\lambda_1 & \times & \cdots & \times \\
\hline
0 & & & \\
\vdots & & V_1^H M V_1 & \\
0 & & &
\end{pmatrix}
= \begin{pmatrix}
\lambda_1 & \times & \cdots & \times \\
\hline
0 & & & \\
\vdots & & T_1 & \\
0 & & &
\end{pmatrix}
= T
$$

Let $U = WV$. The matrix U is unitary, since

$$
U^H U = (WV)^H WV = V^H W^H W V = I
$$

and $U^H A U = T$.

The factorization $A = UTU^H$ is often referred to as the *Schur decomposition* of A. In the case that A is Hermitian, the matrix T will be diagonal.

Theorem 6.4.4   Spectral Theorem

If A is Hermitian, then there exists a unitary matrix U that diagonalizes A.

Proof   By Theorem 6.4.3, there is a unitary matrix U such that $U^H A U = T$, where T is upper triangular. Furthermore,

$$
T^H = (U^H A U)^H = U^H A^H U = U^H A U = T
$$

Therefore, T is Hermitian and consequently must be diagonal.

EXAMPLE 4   Given

$$
A = \begin{pmatrix}
0 & 2 & -1 \\
2 & 3 & -2 \\
-1 & -2 & 0
\end{pmatrix}
$$

find an orthogonal matrix U that diagonalizes A.

Solution

The characteristic polynomial

$$p(\lambda) = -\lambda^3 + 3\lambda^2 + 9\lambda + 5 = (1 + \lambda)^2(5 - \lambda)$$

has roots $\lambda_1 = \lambda_2 = -1$, and $\lambda_3 = 5$. Computing eigenvectors in the usual way, we see that $\mathbf{x}_1 = (1, 0, 1)^T$ and $\mathbf{x}_2 = (-2, 1, 0)^T$ form a basis for the eigenspace $N(A + I)$. We can apply the Gram–Schmidt process to obtain an orthonormal basis for the eigenspace corresponding to $\lambda_1 = \lambda_2 = -1$:

$$\mathbf{u}_1 = \frac{1}{\|\mathbf{x}_1\|}\mathbf{x}_1 = \frac{1}{\sqrt{2}}(1, 0, 1)^T$$

$$\mathbf{p} = \left(\mathbf{x}_2^T\mathbf{u}_1\right)\mathbf{u}_1 = -\sqrt{2}\mathbf{u}_1 = (-1, 0, -1)^T$$

$$\mathbf{x}_2 - \mathbf{p} = (-1, 1, 1)^T$$

$$\mathbf{u}_2 = \frac{1}{\|\mathbf{x}_2 - \mathbf{p}\|}(\mathbf{x}_2 - \mathbf{p}) = \frac{1}{\sqrt{3}}(-1, 1, 1)^T$$

The eigenspace corresponding to $\lambda_3 = 5$ is spanned by $\mathbf{x}_3 = (-1, -2, 1)^T$. Since $\mathbf{x}_3$ must be orthogonal to $\mathbf{u}_1$ and $\mathbf{u}_2$ (Theorem 6.4.1), we need only normalize

$$\mathbf{u}_3 = \frac{1}{\|\mathbf{x}_3\|}\mathbf{x}_3 = \frac{1}{\sqrt{6}}(-1, -2, 1)^T$$

Thus, $\{\mathbf{u}_1, \mathbf{u}_2, \mathbf{u}_3\}$ is an orthonormal set and

$$U = \begin{bmatrix} \dfrac{1}{\sqrt{2}} & -\dfrac{1}{\sqrt{3}} & -\dfrac{1}{\sqrt{6}} \\[2mm] 0 & \dfrac{1}{\sqrt{3}} & -\dfrac{2}{\sqrt{6}} \\[2mm] \dfrac{1}{\sqrt{2}} & \dfrac{1}{\sqrt{3}} & \dfrac{1}{\sqrt{6}} \end{bmatrix}$$

diagonalizes A.   ◼

It follows from Theorem 6.4.4 that each Hermitian matrix A can be factored into a product UDU^H, where U is unitary and D is diagonal. Since U diagonalizes A, it follows that the diagonal elements of D are the eigenvalues of A and the column vectors of U are eigenvectors of A. Thus, A cannot be defective. It has a complete set of eigenvectors that form an orthonormal basis for $\mathbb{C}^n$. This is, in a sense, the ideal situation. We have seen how to express a vector as a linear combination of orthonormal basis elements (Theorem 5.5.2), and the action of A on any linear combination of eigenvectors can easily be determined. Thus, if A has an orthonormal set of eigenvectors $\{\mathbf{u}_1, \ldots, \mathbf{u}_n\}$ and $\mathbf{x} = c_1\mathbf{u}_1 + \cdots + c_n\mathbf{u}_n$, then

$$A\mathbf{x} = c_1\lambda_1\mathbf{u}_1 + \cdots + c_n\lambda_n\mathbf{u}_n$$

Furthermore,

$$c_i = \langle \mathbf{x}, \mathbf{u}_i \rangle = \mathbf{u}_i^H\mathbf{x}$$

or, equivalently, $\mathbf{c} = U^H\mathbf{x}$. Hence,

$$A\mathbf{x} = \lambda_1(\mathbf{u}_1^H\mathbf{x})\mathbf{u}_1 + \cdots + \lambda_n(\mathbf{u}_n^H\mathbf{x})\mathbf{u}_n$$

The Real Schur Decomposition

If A is a real $n \times n$ matrix, then it is possible to obtain a factorization that resembles the Schur decomposition of A, but involves only real matrices. In this case, $A = QTQ^T$, where Q is an orthogonal matrix and T is a real matrix of the form

$$T = \begin{pmatrix} B_1 & \times & \cdots & \times \\ & B_2 & & \times \\ & O & \ddots & \\ & & & B_j \end{pmatrix} \tag{2}$$

where the B_i's are either 1×1 or 2×2 matrices. Each 2×2 block will correspond to a pair of complex conjugate eigenvalues of A. The matrix T is referred to as the *real Schur form* of A. The proof that every real $n \times n$ matrix A has such a factorization depends on the property that, for each pair of complex conjugate eigenvalues of A, there is a two-dimensional subspace of $\mathbb{R}^n$ that is invariant under A.

> **Definition**
>
> A subspace S of $\mathbb{R}^n$ is said to be **invariant** under a matrix A if, for each $\mathbf{x} \in S$, $A\mathbf{x} \in S$.

Lemma 6.4.5   *Let A be a real $n \times n$ matrix with eigenvalue $\lambda_1 = a + bi$ (where a and b are real and $b \neq 0$), and let $\mathbf{z}_1 = \mathbf{x} + i\mathbf{y}$ (where $\mathbf{x}$ and $\mathbf{y}$ are vectors in $\mathbb{R}^n$) be an eigenvector belonging to λ_1. If $S = \text{Span}(\mathbf{x}, \mathbf{y})$, then $\dim S = 2$ and S is invariant under A.*

Proof   Since λ is complex, $\mathbf{y}$ must be nonzero; otherwise, we would have $A\mathbf{z} = A\mathbf{x}$ (a real vector) equal to $\lambda\mathbf{z} = \lambda\mathbf{x}$ (a complex vector). Since A is real, $\lambda_2 = a - bi$ is also an eigenvalue of A and $\mathbf{z}_2 = \mathbf{x} - i\mathbf{y}$ is an eigenvector belonging λ_2. If there were a scalar c such that $\mathbf{x} = c\mathbf{y}$, then $\mathbf{z}_1$ and $\mathbf{z}_2$ would both be multiples of $\mathbf{y}$ and could not be independent. However, $\mathbf{z}_1$ and $\mathbf{z}_2$ belong to distinct eigenvalues, so they must be linearly independent. Therefore, $\mathbf{x}$ cannot be a multiple of $\mathbf{y}$ and hence $S = \text{Span}(\mathbf{x}, \mathbf{y})$ has dimension 2.

To show the invariance of S, note that since $A\mathbf{z}_1 = \lambda_1\mathbf{z}_1$, the real and imaginary parts of both sides must agree. Thus,

$$A\mathbf{z}_1 = A\mathbf{x} + iA\mathbf{y}$$
$$\lambda_1\mathbf{z}_1 = (a + bi)(\mathbf{x} + i\mathbf{y}) = (a\mathbf{x} - b\mathbf{y}) + i(b\mathbf{x} + a\mathbf{y})$$

and it follows that

$$A\mathbf{x} = a\mathbf{x} - b\mathbf{y} \qquad \text{and} \qquad A\mathbf{y} = b\mathbf{x} + a\mathbf{y}$$

If $\mathbf{w} = c_1\mathbf{x} + c_2\mathbf{y}$ is any vector in S, then

$$A\mathbf{w} = c_1A\mathbf{x} + c_2A\mathbf{y} = c_1(a\mathbf{x} - b\mathbf{y}) + c_2(b\mathbf{x} + a\mathbf{y}) = (c_1a + c_2b)\mathbf{x} + (c_2a - c_1b)\mathbf{y}$$

So $A\mathbf{w}$ is in S, and hence S is invariant under A.   ∎

Using this lemma, we can a prove version of Schur's theorem for matrices with real entries. As before, the proof will be by induction.

Theorem 6.4.6   The Real Schur Decomposition

If A is an n × n matrix with real entries, then A can be factored into a product QTQ^T, where Q is an orthogonal matrix and T is in Schur form (2).

Proof   In the case that $n = 2$, if the eigenvalues of A are real, we can take $\mathbf{q}_1$ to be a unit eigenvector belonging to the first eigenvalue λ_1 and let $\mathbf{q}_2$ be any unit vector that is orthogonal to $\mathbf{q}_1$. If we set $Q = (\mathbf{q}_1, \mathbf{q}_2)$, then Q is an orthogonal matrix. If we set $T = Q^T A Q$, then the first column of T is

$$Q^T A \mathbf{q}_1 = \lambda_1 Q^T \mathbf{q}_1 = \lambda_1 \mathbf{e}_1$$

So T is upper triangular and $A = QTQ^T$. If the eigenvalues of A are complex, then we simply set $T = A$ and $Q = I$. So every 2×2 real matrix has a real Schur decomposition.

Now let A be a $k \times k$ matrix where $k \geq 3$ and assume that, for $2 \leq m < k$, every $m \times m$ real matrix has a Schur decomposition of the form (2). Let λ_1 be an eigenvalue of A. If λ_1 is real, let $\mathbf{q}_1$ be a unit eigenvector belonging to λ_1 and choose $\mathbf{q}_2, \mathbf{q}_3, \ldots, \mathbf{q}_n$ so that $Q_1 = (\mathbf{q}_1, \mathbf{q}_2, \ldots, \mathbf{q}_n)$ is an orthogonal matrix. As in the proof of Schur's theorem, it follows that the first column of $Q_1^T A Q_1$ will be $\lambda_1 \mathbf{e}_1$. In the case that λ_1 is complex, let $\mathbf{z} = \mathbf{x} + i\mathbf{y}$ (where $\mathbf{x}$ and $\mathbf{y}$ are real) be an eigenvector belonging to λ_1 and let $S = \text{Span}(\mathbf{x}, \mathbf{y})$. By Lemma 6.4.5, $\dim S = 2$ and S is invariant under A. Let $\{\mathbf{q}_1, \mathbf{q}_2\}$ be an orthonormal basis for S. Choose $\mathbf{q}_3, \mathbf{q}_4, \ldots, \mathbf{q}_n$ so that $Q_1 = (\mathbf{q}_1, \mathbf{q}_2, \ldots, \mathbf{q}_n)$ is an orthogonal matrix. Since S is invariant under A, it follows that

$$A\mathbf{q}_1 = b_{11}\mathbf{q}_1 + b_{21}\mathbf{q}_2 \qquad \text{and} \qquad A\mathbf{q}_2 = b_{12}\mathbf{q}_1 + b_{22}\mathbf{q}_2$$

for some scalars $b_{11}, b_{21}, b_{12}, b_{22}$ and hence the first two columns of $Q_1^T A Q_1$ will be

$$(Q_1^T A\mathbf{q}_1, Q_1^T A\mathbf{q}_2) = (b_{11}\mathbf{e}_1 + b_{21}\mathbf{e}_2, b_{12}\mathbf{e}_1 + b_{22}\mathbf{e}_2)$$

So, in general, $Q_1^T A Q_1$ will be a matrix of block form

$$Q_1^T A Q_1 = \begin{bmatrix} B_1 & X \\ O & A_1 \end{bmatrix}$$

where

$$B_1 = (\lambda_1) \text{ and } A_1 \text{ is } (k-1) \times (k-1) \qquad \text{if } \lambda_1 \text{ is real}$$
$$B_1 \text{ is } 2 \times 2 \text{ and } A_1 \text{ is } (k-2) \times (k-2) \qquad \text{if } \lambda_1 \text{ is complex.}$$

In either case, we can apply our induction hypothesis to A_1 and obtain a Schur decomposition $A_1 = UT_1U^T$. Let us assume that the Schur form T_1 has $j-1$ diagonal blocks $B_2, B_3, \ldots, B_j$. If we set

$$Q_2 = \begin{bmatrix} I & O \\ O & Q_1 \end{bmatrix} \qquad \text{and} \qquad Q = Q_1 Q_2$$

then both Q_2 and Q are $k \times k$ orthogonal matrices. If we then set $T = Q^T A Q$, we will obtain a matrix in the Schur form (2) and it follows that A will have Schur decomposition QTQ^T.   ∎

In the case that all of the eigenvalues of A are real, the real Schur form T will be upper triangular. In the case that A is real and symmetric, then, since all of the eigenvalues of A are real, T must be upper triangular; however, in this case, T must also be symmetric. So we end up with a diagonalization of A. Thus, for real symmetric matrices, we have the following version of the Spectral Theorem.

Corollary 6.4.7   Spectral Theorem for Real Symmetric Matrices

If A is a real symmetric matrix, then there is an orthogonal matrix Q that diagonalizes A; that is, $Q^T A Q = D$, where D is diagonal.

Normal Matrices

There are non-Hermitian matrices that possess complete orthonormal sets of eigenvectors. For example, skew-symmetric and skew-Hermitian matrices have this property. (*A* is *skew Hermitian* if $A^H = -A$.) If A is any matrix with a complete orthonormal set of eigenvectors, then $A = UDU^H$, where U is unitary and D is a diagonal matrix (whose diagonal elements may be complex). In general, $D^H \neq D$ and, consequently,

$$A^H = UD^H U^H \neq A$$

However,

$$AA^H = UDU^H UD^H U^H = UDD^H U^H$$

and

$$A^H A = UD^H U^H UDU^H = UD^H DU^H$$

Since

$$D^H D = DD^H = \begin{pmatrix} |\lambda_1|^2 & & & \\ & |\lambda_2|^2 & & \\ & & \ddots & \\ & & & |\lambda_n|^2 \end{pmatrix}$$

it follows that

$$AA^H = A^H A$$

Definition

> A matrix A is said to be **normal** if $AA^H = A^H A$.

We have shown that if a matrix has a complete orthonormal set of eigenvectors, then it is normal. The converse is also true.

Theorem 6.4.8   *A matrix A is normal if and only if A possesses a complete orthonormal set of eigenvectors.*

Proof   In view of the preceding remarks, we need only show that a normal matrix A has a complete orthonormal set of eigenvectors. By Theorem 6.4.3, there exists a unitary matrix U and a triangular matrix T such that $T = U^H A U$. We claim that T is also normal. To see this, note that

$$T^H T = U^H A^H U U^H A U = U^H A^H A U$$

and

$$T T^H = U^H A U U^H A^H U = U^H A A^H U$$

Since $A^H A = A A^H$, it follows that $T^H T = T T^H$. Comparing the diagonal elements of $T T^H$ and $T^H T$, we see that

$$|t_{11}|^2 + |t_{12}|^2 + |t_{13}|^2 + \cdots + |t_{1n}|^2 = |t_{11}|^2$$
$$|t_{22}|^2 + |t_{23}|^2 + \cdots + |t_{2n}|^2 = |t_{12}|^2 + |t_{22}|^2$$
$$\vdots$$
$$|t_{nn}|^2 = |t_{1n}|^2 + |t_{2n}|^2 + |t_{3n}|^2 + \cdots + |t_{nn}|^2$$

It follows that $t_{ij} = 0$ whenever $i \neq j$. Thus, U diagonalizes A and the column vectors of U are eigenvectors of A. ∎

SECTION 6.4 EXERCISES

1. For each of the following pairs of vectors $\mathbf{z}$ and $\mathbf{w}$, compute (i) $\|\mathbf{z}\|$, (ii) $\|\mathbf{w}\|$, (iii) $\langle \mathbf{z}, \mathbf{w} \rangle$, and (iv) $\langle \mathbf{w}, \mathbf{z} \rangle$:

(a) $\mathbf{z} = \begin{pmatrix} 4 + 2i \\ 4i \end{pmatrix}$, $\mathbf{w} = \begin{pmatrix} -2 \\ 2+i \end{pmatrix}$

(b) $\mathbf{z} = \begin{pmatrix} 1+i \\ 2i \\ 3-i \end{pmatrix}$, $\mathbf{w} = \begin{pmatrix} 2-4i \\ 5 \\ 2i \end{pmatrix}$

2. Let

$$\mathbf{z}_1 = \begin{pmatrix} \dfrac{1+i}{2} \\[2mm] \dfrac{1-i}{2} \end{pmatrix} \quad \text{and} \quad \mathbf{z}_2 = \begin{pmatrix} \dfrac{i}{\sqrt{2}} \\[2mm] -\dfrac{1}{\sqrt{2}} \end{pmatrix}$$

(a) Show that $\{\mathbf{z}_1, \mathbf{z}_2\}$ is an orthonormal set in $\mathbb{C}^2$.

(b) Write the vector $\mathbf{z} = \begin{pmatrix} 2+4i \\ -2i \end{pmatrix}$ as a linear combination of $\mathbf{z}_1$ and $\mathbf{z}_2$.

3. Let $\{\mathbf{u}_1, \mathbf{u}_2\}$ be an orthonormal basis for $\mathbb{C}^2$, and let $\mathbf{z} = (4 + 2i)\mathbf{u}_1 + (6 - 5i)\mathbf{u}_2$.

(a) What are the values of $\mathbf{u}_1^H \mathbf{z}$, $\mathbf{z}^H \mathbf{u}_1$, $\mathbf{u}_2^H \mathbf{z}$, and $\mathbf{z}^H \mathbf{u}_2$?

(b) Determine the value of $\|\mathbf{z}\|$.

4. Which of the matrices that follow are Hermitian? Normal?

(a) $\begin{pmatrix} 1-i & 2 \\ 2 & 3 \end{pmatrix}$ **(b)** $\begin{pmatrix} 1 & 2-i \\ 2+i & -1 \end{pmatrix}$

(c) $\begin{pmatrix} \dfrac{1}{\sqrt{2}} & -\dfrac{1}{\sqrt{2}} \\[2mm] \dfrac{1}{\sqrt{2}} & \dfrac{1}{\sqrt{2}} \end{pmatrix}$

(d) $\begin{pmatrix} \dfrac{1}{\sqrt{2}} i & \dfrac{1}{\sqrt{2}} \\[2mm] \dfrac{1}{\sqrt{2}} & -\dfrac{1}{\sqrt{2}} i \end{pmatrix}$

(e) $\begin{pmatrix} 0 & i & 1 \\ i & 0 & -2+i \\ -1 & 2+i & 0 \end{pmatrix}$

(f) $\begin{pmatrix} 3 & 1+i & i \\ 1-i & 1 & 3 \\ -i & 3 & 1 \end{pmatrix}$

5. Find an orthogonal or unitary diagonalizing matrix for each of the following:

(a) $\begin{pmatrix} 2 & 1 \\ 1 & 2 \end{pmatrix}$ **(b)** $\begin{pmatrix} 1 & 3+i \\ 3-i & 4 \end{pmatrix}$

(c) $\begin{pmatrix} 2 & i & 0 \\ -i & 2 & 0 \\ 0 & 0 & 2 \end{pmatrix}$ **(d)** $\begin{pmatrix} 2 & 1 & 1 \\ 1 & 3 & -2 \\ 1 & -2 & 3 \end{pmatrix}$

(e) $\begin{pmatrix} 0 & 0 & 1 \\ 0 & 1 & 0 \\ 1 & 0 & 0 \end{pmatrix}$ **(f)** $\begin{pmatrix} 1 & 1 & 1 \\ 1 & 1 & 1 \\ 1 & 1 & 1 \end{pmatrix}$

(g) $\begin{bmatrix} 4 & 2 & -2 \\ 2 & 1 & -1 \\ -2 & -1 & 1 \end{bmatrix}$

6. Show that the diagonal entries of a Hermitian matrix must be real.

7. Let A be an $n \times n$ Hermitian matrix and let $\mathbf{x}$ be a vector in $\mathbb{C}^n$. Show that if $c = \mathbf{x}^H A \mathbf{x}$, then c is real.

8. Let A be an Hermitian matrix and let $B = iA$. Show that B is skew Hermitian.

9. Let A and C be matrices in $\mathbb{C}^{m \times n}$ and let $B \in \mathbb{C}^{n \times r}$. Prove each of the following rules:

(a) $(A^H)^H = A$

(b) $(\alpha A + \beta C)^H = \overline{\alpha} A^H + \overline{\beta} C^H$

(c) $(AB)^H = B^H A^H$

10. Let A and B be Hermitian matrices. Answer *true* or *false* for each of the statements that follow. In each case, explain or prove your answer.

(a) The eigenvalues of AB are all real.

(b) The eigenvalues of ABA are all real.

11. Show that

$$\langle \mathbf{z}, \mathbf{w} \rangle = \mathbf{w}^H \mathbf{z}$$

defines an inner product on $\mathbb{C}^n$.

12. Let $\mathbf{x}$, $\mathbf{y}$, and $\mathbf{z}$ be vectors in $\mathbb{C}^n$ and let α and β be complex scalars. Show that

$$\langle \mathbf{z}, \alpha \mathbf{x} + \beta \mathbf{y} \rangle = \overline{\alpha} \langle \mathbf{z}, \mathbf{x} \rangle + \overline{\beta} \langle \mathbf{z}, \mathbf{y} \rangle$$

13. Let $\{\mathbf{u}_1, \ldots, \mathbf{u}_n\}$ be an orthonormal basis for a complex inner product space V, and let

$$\mathbf{z} = a_1 \mathbf{u}_1 + a_2 \mathbf{u}_2 + \cdots + a_n \mathbf{u}_n$$
$$\mathbf{w} = b_1 \mathbf{u}_1 + b_2 \mathbf{u}_2 + \cdots + b_n \mathbf{u}_n$$

Show that

$$\langle \mathbf{z}, \mathbf{w} \rangle = \sum_{i=1}^{n} \overline{b}_i a_i$$

14. Given that

$$A = \begin{bmatrix} 4 & 0 & 0 \\ 0 & 1 & i \\ 0 & -i & 1 \end{bmatrix}$$

find a matrix B such that $B^H B = A$.

15. Let U be a unitary matrix. Prove that

(a) U is normal.

(b) $\|U\mathbf{x}\| = \|\mathbf{x}\|$ for all $\mathbf{x} \in \mathbb{C}^n$.

(c) if λ is an eigenvalue of U, then $|\lambda| = 1$.

16. Let $\mathbf{u}$ be a unit vector in $\mathbb{C}^n$ and define $U = I - 2\mathbf{u}\mathbf{u}^H$. Show that U is both unitary and Hermitian and, consequently, is its own inverse.

17. Show that if a matrix U is both unitary and Hermitian, then any eigenvalue of U must equal either 1 or -1.

18. Let A be a 2×2 matrix with Schur decomposition UTU^H and suppose that $t_{12} \neq 0$. Show that

(a) the eigenvalues of A are $\lambda_1 = t_{11}$ and $\lambda_2 = t_{22}$.

(b) $\mathbf{u}_1$ is an eigenvector of A belonging to $\lambda_1 = t_{11}$.

(c) $\mathbf{u}_2$ is not an eigenvector of A belonging to $\lambda_2 = t_{22}$.

19. Let A be a 5×5 matrix with real entries. Let $A = QTQ^T$ be the real Schur decomposition of A, where T is a block matrix of the form given in equation (2). What are the possible block structures for T in each of the following cases?

(a) All of the eigenvalues of A are real.

(b) A has three real eigenvalues and two complex eigenvalues.

(c) A has one real eigenvalue and four complex eigenvalues.

20. Let A be a $n \times n$ matrix with Schur decomposition UTU^H. Show that if the diagonal entries of T are all distinct, then there is an upper triangular matrix R such that $X = UR$ diagonalizes A.

21. Show that $M = A + iB$ (where A and B are real matrices) is skew Hermitian if and only if A is skew symmetric and B is symmetric.

22. Show that if A is skew Hermitian and λ is an eigenvalue of A, then λ is purely imaginary (i.e., $\lambda = bi$, where b is real).

23. Show that if A is a normal matrix, then each of the following matrices must also be normal:

(a) A^H **(b)** $I + A$ **(c)** A^2

24. Let A be a real 2×2 matrix with the property that $a_{21}a_{12} > 0$, and let

$$r = \sqrt{a_{21}/a_{12}} \quad \text{and} \quad S = \begin{bmatrix} r & 0 \\ 0 & 1 \end{bmatrix}$$

Compute $B = SAS^{-1}$. What can you conclude about the eigenvalues and eigenvectors of B? What can you conclude about the eigenvalues and eigenvectors of A? Explain.

25. Let $p(x) = -x^3 + cx^2 + (c+3)x + 1$, where c is a real number. Let

$$C = \begin{bmatrix} c & c+3 & 1 \\ 1 & 0 & 0 \\ 0 & 1 & 0 \end{bmatrix}$$

and let

$$A = \begin{bmatrix} -1 & 2 & -c-3 \\ 1 & -1 & c+2 \\ -1 & 1 & -c-1 \end{bmatrix}$$

(a) Compute $A^{-1}CA$.

(b) Show that C is the companion matrix of $p(x)$ and use the result from part (a) to prove that $p(x)$ will have only real roots regardless of the value of c.

26. Let A be a Hermitian matrix with eigenvalues $\lambda_1, \ldots, \lambda_n$ and orthonormal eigenvectors $\mathbf{u}_1, \ldots, \mathbf{u}_n$. Show that
$$A = \lambda_1 \mathbf{u}_1 \mathbf{u}_1^H + \lambda_2 \mathbf{u}_2 \mathbf{u}_2^H + \cdots + \lambda_n \mathbf{u}_n \mathbf{u}_n^H$$

27. Let
$$A = \begin{bmatrix} 0 & 1 \\ 1 & 0 \end{bmatrix}$$

Write A as a sum $\lambda_1 \mathbf{u}_1 \mathbf{u}_1^T + \lambda_2 \mathbf{u}_2 \mathbf{u}_2^T$, where λ_1 and λ_2 are eigenvalues and $\mathbf{u}_1$ and $\mathbf{u}_2$ are orthonormal eigenvectors.

28. Let A be a Hermitian matrix with eigenvalues $\lambda_1 \geq \lambda_2 \geq \cdots \geq \lambda_n$ and orthonormal eigenvectors $\mathbf{u}_1, \ldots, \mathbf{u}_n$. For any nonzero vector $\mathbf{x}$ in $\mathbb{R}^n$, the *Rayleigh quotient* $\rho(\mathbf{x})$ is defined by
$$\rho(\mathbf{x}) = \frac{\langle A\mathbf{x}, \mathbf{x} \rangle}{\langle \mathbf{x}, \mathbf{x} \rangle} = \frac{\mathbf{x}^H A\mathbf{x}}{\mathbf{x}^H \mathbf{x}}$$

(a) If $\mathbf{x} = c_1\mathbf{u}_1 + \cdots + c_n\mathbf{u}_n$, show that
$$\rho(\mathbf{x}) = \frac{|c_1|^2\lambda_1 + |c_2|^2\lambda_2 + \cdots + |c_n|^2\lambda_n}{\|\mathbf{c}\|^2}$$

(b) Show that
$$\lambda_n \leq \rho(\mathbf{x}) \leq \lambda_1$$

(c) Show that
$$\max_{\mathbf{x}\neq 0} \rho(\mathbf{x}) = \lambda_1 \quad \text{and} \quad \min_{\mathbf{x}\neq 0} \rho(\mathbf{x}) = \lambda_n$$

29. Given $A \in \mathbb{R}^{m\times m}$, $B \in \mathbb{R}^{n\times n}$, $C \in \mathbb{R}^{m\times n}$, the equation
$$AX - XB = C \qquad (3)$$
is known as *Sylvester's equation*. An $m \times n$ matrix X is said to be a solution if it satisfies (3).

(a) Show that if B has Schur decomposition $B = UTU^H$, then Sylvester's equation can be transformed into an equation of the form $AY - YT = G$, where $Y = XU$ and $G = CU$.

(b) Show that
$$(A - t_{11}I)\mathbf{y}_1 = \mathbf{g}_1$$
$$(A - t_{jj}I)\mathbf{y}_j = \mathbf{g}_j + \sum_{i=1}^{j-1} t_{ij}\mathbf{y}_j, \quad j = 2, \ldots, n$$

(c) Show that if A and B have no common eigenvalues, then Sylvester's equation has a solution.

6.5 The Singular Value Decomposition

In many applications, it is necessary either to determine the rank of a matrix or to determine whether the matrix is deficient in rank. Theoretically, we can use Gaussian elimination to reduce the matrix to row echelon form and then count the number of nonzero rows. However, this approach is not practical in finite-precision arithmetic. If A is rank deficient and U is the computed echelon form, then, because of rounding errors in the elimination process, it is unlikely that U will have the proper number of nonzero rows. In practice, the coefficient matrix A usually involves some error. This may be due to errors in the data or to the finite number system. Thus, it is generally more practical to ask whether A is "close" to a rank-deficient matrix. However, it may well turn out that A is close to being rank deficient and the computed row echelon form U is not.

In this section, we assume throughout that A is an $m \times n$ matrix with $m \geq n$. (This assumption is made for convenience only; all the results will also hold if $m < n$.) We will present a method for determining how close A is to a matrix of smaller rank. The method involves factoring A into a product $U\Sigma V^T$, where U is an $m \times m$ orthogonal matrix, V is an $n \times n$ orthogonal matrix, and Σ is an $m \times n$ matrix whose off-diagonal entries are all 0's and whose diagonal elements satisfy

$$\sigma_1 \geq \sigma_2 \geq \cdots \geq \sigma_n \geq 0$$

$$\Sigma = \begin{pmatrix} \sigma_1 & & & \\ & \sigma_2 & & \\ & & \ddots & \\ & & & \sigma_n \\ & & & \\ & & & \end{pmatrix}$$

The σ_i's determined by this factorization are unique and are called the *singular values* of A. The factorization $U\Sigma V^T$ is called the *singular value decomposition* of A, or, for short, the *svd* of A. We will show that the rank of A equals the number of nonzero singular values, and that the magnitudes of the nonzero singular values provide a measure of how close A is to a matrix of lower rank.

We begin by showing that such a decomposition is always possible.

Theorem 6.5.1   The SVD Theorem

If A is an $m \times n$ matrix, then A has a singular value decomposition.

Proof A^TA is a symmetric $n \times n$ matrix. Therefore, its eigenvalues are all real and it has an orthogonal diagonalizing matrix V. Furthermore, its eigenvalues must all be nonnegative. To see this, let λ be an eigenvalue of A^TA and $\mathbf{x}$ be an eigenvector belonging to λ. It follows that

$$\|A\mathbf{x}\|^2 = \mathbf{x}^TA^TA\mathbf{x} = \lambda\mathbf{x}^T\mathbf{x} = \lambda\|\mathbf{x}\|^2$$

Hence,

$$\lambda = \frac{\|A\mathbf{x}\|^2}{\|\mathbf{x}\|^2} \geq 0$$

We may assume that the columns of V have been ordered so that the corresponding eigenvalues satisfy

$$\lambda_1 \geq \lambda_2 \geq \cdots \geq \lambda_n \geq 0$$

The singular values of A are given by

$$\sigma_j = \sqrt{\lambda_j} \qquad j = 1, \ldots, n$$

Let r denote the rank of A. The matrix A^TA will also have rank r. Since A^TA is symmetric, its rank equals the number of nonzero eigenvalues. Thus,

$$\lambda_1 \geq \lambda_2 \geq \cdots \geq \lambda_r > 0 \qquad \text{and} \qquad \lambda_{r+1} = \lambda_{r+2} = \cdots = \lambda_n = 0$$

The same relation holds for the singular values

$$\sigma_1 \geq \sigma_2 \geq \cdots \geq \sigma_r > 0 \qquad \text{and} \qquad \sigma_{r+1} = \sigma_{r+2} = \cdots = \sigma_n = 0$$

Now let

$$V_1 = (\mathbf{v}_1, \ldots, \mathbf{v}_r), \qquad V_2 = (\mathbf{v}_{r+1}, \ldots, \mathbf{v}_n)$$

and

$$\Sigma_1 = \begin{pmatrix} \sigma_1 & & & \\ & \sigma_2 & & \\ & & \ddots & \\ & & & \sigma_r \end{pmatrix} \tag{1}$$

Hence, Σ_1 is an $r \times r$ diagonal matrix whose diagonal entries are the nonzero singular values $\sigma_1, \ldots, \sigma_r$. The $m \times n$ matrix Σ is then given by

$$\Sigma = \begin{bmatrix} \Sigma_1 & O \\ O & O \end{bmatrix}$$

The column vectors of V_2 are eigenvectors of $A^T A$ belonging to $\lambda = 0$. Thus,

$$A^T A \mathbf{v}_j = \mathbf{0} \quad j = r+1, \ldots, n$$

and, consequently, the column vectors of V_2 form an orthonormal basis for $N(A^T A) = N(A)$. Therefore,

$$AV_2 = O$$

and since V is an orthogonal matrix, it follows that

$$I = VV^T = V_1 V_1^T + V_2 V_2^T$$
$$A = AI = AV_1 V_1^T + AV_2 V_2^T = AV_1 V_1^T \tag{2}$$

So far we have shown how to construct the matrices V and Σ of the singular value decomposition. To complete the proof, we must show how to construct an $m \times m$ orthogonal matrix U such that

$$A = U \Sigma V^T$$

or, equivalently,

$$AV = U \Sigma \tag{3}$$

Comparing the first r columns of each side of (3), we see that

$$A \mathbf{v}_j = \sigma_j \mathbf{u}_j \quad j = 1, \ldots, r$$

Thus, if we define

$$\mathbf{u}_j = \frac{1}{\sigma_j} A \mathbf{v}_j \quad j = 1, \ldots, r \tag{4}$$

and

$$U_1 = (\mathbf{u}_1, \ldots, \mathbf{u}_r)$$

then it follows that

$$AV_1 = U_1 \Sigma_1 \tag{5}$$

The column vectors of U_1 form an orthonormal set since

$$\mathbf{u}_i^T \mathbf{u}_j = \left(\frac{1}{\sigma_i}\mathbf{v}_i^T A^T\right)\left(\frac{1}{\sigma_j}A\mathbf{v}_j\right) \qquad 1 \le i \le r, \quad 1 \le j \le r$$

$$= \frac{1}{\sigma_i \sigma_j}\mathbf{v}_i^T \left(A^T A \mathbf{v}_j\right)$$

$$= \frac{\sigma_j}{\sigma_i}\mathbf{v}_i^T \mathbf{v}_j$$

$$= \delta_{ij}$$

It follows from (4) that each $\mathbf{u}_j$, $1 \le j \le r$, is in the column space of A. The dimension of the column space is r, so $\mathbf{u}_1, \ldots, \mathbf{u}_r$ form an orthonormal basis for $R(A)$. The vector space $R(A)^\perp = N(A^T)$ has dimension $m - r$. Let $\{\mathbf{u}_{r+1}, \mathbf{u}_{r+2}, \ldots, \mathbf{u}_m\}$ be an orthonormal basis for $N(A^T)$ and set

$$U_2 = (\mathbf{u}_{r+1}, \mathbf{u}_{r+2}, \ldots, \mathbf{u}_m)$$

$$U = \begin{bmatrix} U_1 & U_2 \end{bmatrix}$$

It follows from Theorem 5.2.2 that $\mathbf{u}_1, \ldots, \mathbf{u}_m$ form an orthonormal basis for $\mathbb{R}^m$. Hence, U is an orthogonal matrix. We still must show that $U\Sigma V^T$ actually equals A. This follows from (5) and (2) since

$$U\Sigma V^T = \begin{bmatrix} U_1 & U_2 \end{bmatrix} \begin{bmatrix} \Sigma_1 & O \\ O & O \end{bmatrix} \begin{bmatrix} V_1^T \\ V_2^T \end{bmatrix}$$

$$= U_1 \Sigma_1 V_1^T$$

$$= A V_1 V_1^T$$

$$= A$$

Observations

Let A be an $m \times n$ matrix with a singular value decomposition $U\Sigma V^T$.

1. The singular values $\sigma_1, \ldots, \sigma_n$ of A are unique; however, the matrices U and V are not unique.
2. Since V diagonalizes $A^T A$, it follows that the $\mathbf{v}_j$'s are eigenvectors of $A^T A$.
3. Since $AA^T = U\Sigma\Sigma^T U^T$, it follows that U diagonalizes AA^T and that the $\mathbf{u}_j$'s are eigenvectors of AA^T.
4. Comparing the jth columns of each side of the equation

$$AV = U\Sigma$$

we get

$$A\mathbf{v}_j = \sigma_j \mathbf{u}_j \qquad j = 1, \ldots, n$$

Similarly,

$$A^T U = V \Sigma^T$$

and hence

$$A^T \mathbf{u}_j = \sigma_j \mathbf{v}_j \qquad \text{for } j = 1, \ldots, n$$
$$A^T \mathbf{u}_j = \mathbf{0} \qquad \text{for } j = n+1, \ldots, m$$

The $\mathbf{v}_j$'s are called the *right singular vectors* of A, and the $\mathbf{u}_j$'s are called the *left singular vectors* of A.

5. If A has rank r, then
   (i) $\mathbf{v}_1, \ldots, \mathbf{v}_r$ form an orthonormal basis for $R(A^T)$.
   (ii) $\mathbf{v}_{r+1}, \ldots, \mathbf{v}_n$ form an orthonormal basis for $N(A)$.
   (iii) $\mathbf{u}_1, \ldots, \mathbf{u}_r$ form an orthonormal basis for $R(A)$.
   (iv) $\mathbf{u}_{r+1}, \ldots, \mathbf{u}_m$ form an orthonormal basis for $N(A^T)$.

6. The rank of the matrix A is equal to the number of its nonzero singular values (where singular values are counted according to multiplicity). The reader should be careful not to make a similar assumption about eigenvalues. The matrix

$$M = \begin{bmatrix} 0 & 1 & 0 & 0 \\ 0 & 0 & 1 & 0 \\ 0 & 0 & 0 & 1 \\ 0 & 0 & 0 & 0 \end{bmatrix}$$

for example, has rank 3 even though all of its eigenvalues are 0.

7. In the case that A has rank $r < n$, if we set

$$U_1 = (\mathbf{u}_1, \mathbf{u}_2, \ldots, \mathbf{u}_r) \qquad V_1 = (\mathbf{v}_1, \mathbf{v}_2, \ldots, \mathbf{v}_r)$$

and define Σ_1 as in equation (1), then

$$A = U_1 \Sigma_1 V_1^T \tag{6}$$

The factorization (6) is called the *compact form of the singular value decomposition* of A. This form is useful in many applications.

EXAMPLE I   Let

$$A = \begin{bmatrix} 1 & 1 \\ 1 & 1 \\ 0 & 0 \end{bmatrix}$$

Compute the singular values and the singular value decomposition of A.

Solution

The matrix

$$A^T A = \begin{bmatrix} 2 & 2 \\ 2 & 2 \end{bmatrix}$$

has eigenvalues $\lambda_1 = 4$ and $\lambda_2 = 0$. Consequently, the singular values of A are $\sigma_1 = \sqrt{4} = 2$ and $\sigma_2 = 0$. The eigenvalue λ_1 has eigenvectors of the form $\alpha(1, 1)^T$, and λ_2 has eigenvectors $\beta(1, -1)^T$. Therefore, the orthogonal matrix

$$V = \frac{1}{\sqrt{2}} \begin{pmatrix} 1 & 1 \\ 1 & -1 \end{pmatrix}$$

diagonalizes $A^T A$. From observation 4, it follows that

$$\mathbf{u}_1 = \frac{1}{\sigma_1} A \mathbf{v}_1 = \frac{1}{2} \begin{pmatrix} 1 & 1 \\ 1 & 1 \\ 0 & 0 \end{pmatrix} \begin{pmatrix} \frac{1}{\sqrt{2}} \\ \frac{1}{\sqrt{2}} \end{pmatrix} = \begin{pmatrix} \frac{1}{\sqrt{2}} \\ \frac{1}{\sqrt{2}} \\ 0 \end{pmatrix}$$

The remaining column vectors of U must form an orthonormal basis for $N(A^T)$. We can compute a basis $\{\mathbf{x}_2, \mathbf{x}_3\}$ for $N(A^T)$ in the usual way.

$$\mathbf{x}_2 = (1, -1, 0)^T \quad \text{and} \quad \mathbf{x}_3 = (0, 0, 1)^T$$

Since these vectors are already orthogonal, it is not necessary to use the Gram–Schmidt process to obtain an orthonormal basis. We need only set

$$\mathbf{u}_2 = \frac{1}{\|\mathbf{x}_2\|} \mathbf{x}_2 = \left(\frac{1}{\sqrt{2}}, -\frac{1}{\sqrt{2}}, 0 \right)^T$$

$$\mathbf{u}_3 = \mathbf{x}_3 = (0, 0, 1)^T$$

It then follows that

$$A = U\Sigma V^T = \begin{pmatrix} \frac{1}{\sqrt{2}} & \frac{1}{\sqrt{2}} & 0 \\ \frac{1}{\sqrt{2}} & -\frac{1}{\sqrt{2}} & 0 \\ 0 & 0 & 1 \end{pmatrix} \begin{pmatrix} 2 & 0 \\ 0 & 0 \\ 0 & 0 \end{pmatrix} \begin{pmatrix} \frac{1}{\sqrt{2}} & \frac{1}{\sqrt{2}} \\ \frac{1}{\sqrt{2}} & -\frac{1}{\sqrt{2}} \end{pmatrix} \qquad \blacksquare$$

Visualizing the SVD

If we view an $m \times n$ matrix A with rank r as a mapping from the row space of A to the column space of A, then in light of observations (4) and (5) made earlier, it seems natural to choose $\mathbf{v}_1, \mathbf{v}_2, \ldots, \mathbf{v}_r$ as an orthonormal basis for the row space, since the image vectors

$$A\mathbf{v}_1 = \sigma_1 \mathbf{u}_1, A\mathbf{v}_2 = \sigma_2 \mathbf{u}_2, \ldots, A\mathbf{v}_r = \sigma_r \mathbf{u}_r$$

are mutually orthogonal and the corresponding unit vectors $\mathbf{u}_1, \mathbf{u}_2, \ldots, \mathbf{u}_r$ will form an orthonormal basis for the column space of A. In the case of a 2×2 matrix, the following

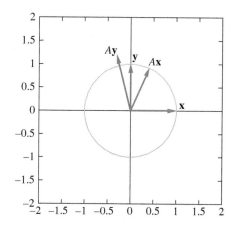

Figure 6.5.1.

example illustrates geometrically how one could search for the right singular vectors by moving around the unit circle.

EXAMPLE 2   Let

$$A = \begin{bmatrix} 0.4 & -0.3 \\ 0.9 & 1.2 \end{bmatrix}$$

To find a pair of right singular vectors of A, we must find a pair of orthonormal vectors $\mathbf{x}$ and $\mathbf{y}$ for which the image vectors $A\mathbf{x}$ and $A\mathbf{y}$ are orthogonal. Choosing the standard basis vectors for $\mathbb{R}^2$ does not work, for if $\mathbf{x} = \mathbf{e}_1$ and $\mathbf{y} = \mathbf{e}_2$, then the image vectors

$$A\mathbf{e}_1 = \mathbf{a}_1 = \begin{bmatrix} 0.4 \\ 0.9 \end{bmatrix} \quad \text{and} \quad A\mathbf{e}_2 = \mathbf{a}_2 = \begin{bmatrix} -0.3 \\ 1.2 \end{bmatrix}$$

are not orthogonal. See Figure 6.5.1.

One way to search for the right singular vectors is to simultaneously rotate this initial pair of vectors around the unit circle and for each rotated pair

$$\mathbf{x}_1 = \begin{bmatrix} \cos t \\ \sin t \end{bmatrix}, \quad \mathbf{y} = \begin{bmatrix} -\sin t \\ \cos t \end{bmatrix}$$

check to see if $A\mathbf{x}$ and $A\mathbf{y}$ are orthogonal. For the given matrix A, this will happen when the tip of our initial $\mathbf{x}$ vector gets rotated to the point $(0.6, 0.8)$. It follows that the right singular vectors are

$$\mathbf{v}_1 = \begin{bmatrix} 0.6 \\ 0.8 \end{bmatrix}, \quad \mathbf{v}_2 = \begin{bmatrix} -0.8 \\ 0.6 \end{bmatrix}$$

Since

$$A\mathbf{v}_1 = \begin{bmatrix} 0 \\ 1.5 \end{bmatrix} = 1.5\mathbf{e}_2, \quad \text{and} \quad A\mathbf{v}_2 = \begin{bmatrix} -0.5 \\ 0 \end{bmatrix} = -0.5\mathbf{e}_1$$

it follows that the singular values are $\sigma_1 = 1.5$ and $\sigma_2 = 0.5$, and the left singular vectors are $\mathbf{u}_1 = \mathbf{e}_2$ and $\mathbf{u}_2 = -\mathbf{e}_1$. See Figure 6.5.2.   ■

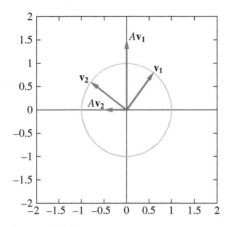

Figure 6.5.2.

Numerical Rank and Lower Rank Approximations

If A is an $m \times n$ matrix of rank r and $0 < k < r$, we can use the singular value decomposition to find a matrix in $\mathbb{R}^{m \times n}$ of rank k that is closest to A with respect to the Frobenius norm. Let $\mathcal{M}$ be the set of all $m \times n$ matrices of rank k or less. It can be shown that there is a matrix X in $\mathcal{M}$ such that

$$\|A - X\|_F = \min_{S \in \mathcal{M}} \|A - S\|_F \tag{7}$$

We will not prove this result, since the proof is beyond the scope of this text. Assuming that the minimum is achieved, we will show how such a matrix X can be derived from the singular value decomposition of A. The following lemma will be useful.

Lemma 6.5.2 *If A is an $m \times n$ matrix and Q is an $m \times m$ orthogonal matrix, then*

$$\|QA\|_F = \|A\|_F$$

Proof

$$\|QA\|_F^2 = \|(Q\mathbf{a}_1, Q\mathbf{a}_2, \ldots, Q\mathbf{a}_n)\|_F^2$$
$$= \sum_{i=1}^{n} \|Q\mathbf{a}_i\|_2^2$$
$$= \sum_{i=1}^{n} \|\mathbf{a}_i\|_2^2$$
$$= \|A\|_F^2$$

If A has singular value decomposition $U\Sigma V^T$, then it follows from the lemma that

$$\|A\|_F = \|\Sigma V^T\|_F$$

Since

$$\|\Sigma V^T\|_F = \|(\Sigma V^T)^T\|_F = \|V\Sigma^T\|_F = \|\Sigma^T\|_F$$

it follows that

$$\|A\|_F = \left(\sigma_1^2 + \sigma_2^2 + \cdots + \sigma_n^2\right)^{1/2}$$

Theorem 6.5.3   *Let $A = U\Sigma V^T$ be an $m \times n$ matrix, and let $\mathcal{M}$ denote the set of all $m \times n$ matrices of rank k or less, where $0 < k < \mathrm{rank}(A)$. If X is a matrix in $\mathcal{M}$ satisfying (7), then*

$$\|A - X\|_F = \left(\sigma_{k+1}^2 + \sigma_{k+2}^2 + \cdots + \sigma_n^2\right)^{1/2}$$

In particular, if $A' = U\Sigma' V^T$, where

$$\Sigma' = \begin{bmatrix} \sigma_1 & & & & \\ & \ddots & & & O \\ & & \sigma_k & & \\ \hline & O & & O \end{bmatrix} = \begin{bmatrix} \Sigma_k & O \\ O & O \end{bmatrix}$$

then

$$\|A - A'\|_F = \left(\sigma_{k+1}^2 + \cdots + \sigma_n^2\right)^{1/2} = \min_{S \in \mathcal{M}} \|A - S\|_F$$

Proof   Let X be a matrix in $\mathcal{M}$ satisfying (7). Since $A' \in \mathcal{M}$, it follows that

$$\|A - X\|_F \le \|A - A'\|_F = \left(\sigma_{k+1}^2 + \cdots + \sigma_n^2\right)^{1/2} \tag{8}$$

We will show that

$$\|A - X\|_F \ge \left(\sigma_{k+1}^2 + \cdots + \sigma_n^2\right)^{1/2}$$

and hence that equality holds in (8). Let $Q\Omega P^T$ be the singular value decomposition of X, where

$$\Omega = \begin{bmatrix} \omega_1 & & & & \\ & \omega_2 & & & \\ & & \ddots & & O \\ & & & \omega_k & \\ \hline & O & & & O \end{bmatrix} = \begin{bmatrix} \Omega_k & O \\ O & O \end{bmatrix}$$

If we set $B = Q^T A P$, then $A = QBP^T$, and it follows that

$$\|A - X\|_F = \|Q(B - \Omega)P^T\|_F = \|B - \Omega\|_F$$

Let us partition B in the same manner as Ω.

$$B = \begin{bmatrix} \overbrace{B_{11}}^{k \times k} & \overbrace{B_{12}}^{k \times (n-k)} \\ \hline \underbrace{B_{21}}_{(m-k) \times k} & \underbrace{B_{22}}_{(m-k) \times (n-k)} \end{bmatrix}$$

It follows that

$$\|A - X\|_F^2 = \|B_{11} - \Omega_k\|_F^2 + \|B_{12}\|_F^2 + \|B_{21}\|_F^2 + \|B_{22}\|_F^2$$

We claim that $B_{12} = O$. If not, then define

$$Y = Q \begin{bmatrix} B_{11} & B_{12} \\ O & O \end{bmatrix} P^T$$

The matrix Y is in $\mathcal{M}$ and

$$\|A - Y\|_F^2 = \|B_{21}\|_F^2 + \|B_{22}\|_F^2 < \|A - X\|_F^2$$

But this contradicts the definition of X. Therefore, $B_{12} = O$. In a similar manner, it can be shown that B_{21} must equal O. If we set

$$Z = Q \begin{bmatrix} B_{11} & O \\ O & O \end{bmatrix} P^T$$

then $Z \in \mathcal{M}$ and

$$\|A - Z\|_F^2 = \|B_{22}\|_F^2 \le \|B_{11} - \Omega_k\|_F^2 + \|B_{22}\|_F^2 = \|A - X\|_F^2$$

It follows from the definition of X that B_{11} must equal Ω_k. If B_{22} has singular value decomposition $U_1 \Lambda V_1^T$, then

$$\|A - X\|_F = \|B_{22}\|_F = \|\Lambda\|_F$$

Let

$$U_2 = \begin{bmatrix} I_k & O \\ O & U_1 \end{bmatrix} \quad \text{and} \quad V_2 = \begin{bmatrix} I_k & O \\ O & V_1 \end{bmatrix}$$

Now,

$$U_2^T Q^T A P V_2 = \begin{bmatrix} \Omega_k & O \\ O & \Lambda \end{bmatrix}$$

$$A = (QU_2) \begin{bmatrix} \Omega_k & O \\ O & \Lambda \end{bmatrix} (PV_2)^T$$

and hence it follows that the diagonal elements of Λ are singular values of A. Thus,

$$\|A - X\|_F = \|\Lambda\|_F \ge \left(\sigma_{k+1}^2 + \cdots + \sigma_n^2\right)^{1/2}$$

It then follows from (8) that

$$\|A - X\|_F = \left(\sigma_{k+1}^2 + \cdots + \sigma_n^2\right)^{1/2} = \|A - A'\|_F \qquad \blacksquare$$

If A has singular value decomposition $U \Sigma V^T$, then we can think of A as the product of $U\Sigma$ times V^T. If we partition $U\Sigma$ into columns and V^T into rows, then

$$U\Sigma = (\sigma_1 \mathbf{u}_1, \sigma_2 \mathbf{u}_2, \ldots, \sigma \mathbf{u}_n)$$

and we can represent A by an outer product expansion

$$A = \sigma_1 \mathbf{u}_1 \mathbf{v}_1^T + \sigma_2 \mathbf{u}_2 \mathbf{v}_2^T + \cdots + \sigma_n \mathbf{u}_n \mathbf{v}_n^T \tag{9}$$

If A is of rank n, then

$$A' = U \begin{pmatrix} \sigma_1 & & & & \\ & \sigma_2 & & & \\ & & \ddots & & \\ & & & \sigma_{n-1} & \\ & & & & 0 \end{pmatrix} V^T$$

$$= \sigma_1 \mathbf{u}_1 \mathbf{v}_1^T + \sigma_2 \mathbf{u}_2 \mathbf{v}_2^T + \cdots + \sigma_{n-1} \mathbf{u}_{n-1} \mathbf{v}_{n-1}^T$$

will be the matrix of rank $n - 1$ that is closest to A with respect to the Frobenius norm. Similarly,

$$A'' = \sigma_1 \mathbf{u}_1 \mathbf{v}_1^T + \sigma_2 \mathbf{u}_2 \mathbf{v}_2^T \cdots + \sigma_{n-2} \mathbf{u}_{n-2} \mathbf{v}_{n-2}^T$$

will be the nearest matrix of rank $n - 2$, and so on. In particular, if A is a nonsingular $n \times n$ matrix, then A' is singular and $\|A - A'\|_F = \sigma_n$. Thus, σ_n may be taken as a measure of how close a square matrix is to being singular.

The reader should be careful not to use the value of $\det(A)$ as a measure of how close A is to being singular. If, for example, A is the 100×100 diagonal matrix whose diagonal entries are all $\frac{1}{2}$, then $\det(A) = 2^{-100}$; however, $\sigma_{100} = \frac{1}{2}$. By contrast, the matrix in the next example is very close to being singular even though its determinant is 1 and all its eigenvalues are equal to 1.

EXAMPLE 3   Let A be an $n \times n$ upper triangular matrix whose diagonal elements are all 1 and whose entries above the main diagonal are all -1:

$$A = \begin{pmatrix} 1 & -1 & -1 & \cdots & -1 & -1 \\ 0 & 1 & -1 & \cdots & -1 & -1 \\ 0 & 0 & 1 & \cdots & -1 & -1 \\ \vdots & & & & & \\ 0 & 0 & 0 & \cdots & 1 & -1 \\ 0 & 0 & 0 & \cdots & 0 & 1 \end{pmatrix}$$

Notice that $\det(A) = \det(A^{-1}) = 1$ and all the eigenvalues of A are 1. However, if n is large, then A is close to being singular. To see this, let

$$B = \begin{pmatrix} 1 & -1 & -1 & \cdots & -1 & -1 \\ 0 & 1 & -1 & \cdots & -1 & -1 \\ 0 & 0 & 1 & \cdots & -1 & -1 \\ \vdots & & & & & \\ 0 & 0 & 0 & \cdots & 1 & -1 \\ \dfrac{-1}{2^{n-2}} & 0 & 0 & \cdots & 0 & 1 \end{pmatrix}$$

The matrix B must be singular, since the system $B\mathbf{x} = \mathbf{0}$ has a nontrivial solution $\mathbf{x} = (2^{n-2}, 2^{n-3}, \ldots, 2^0, 1)^T$. Since the matrices A and B differ only in the $(n, 1)$ position, we have

$$\|A - B\|_F = \frac{1}{2^{n-2}}$$

It follows from Theorem 6.5.3 that

$$\sigma_n = \min_{X \text{ singular}} \|A - X\|_F \leq \|A - B\|_F = \frac{1}{2^{n-2}}$$

Thus, if $n = 100$, then $\sigma_n \leq 1/2^{98}$ and, consequently, A is very close to singular.   ■

APPLICATION 1   Numerical Rank

In most practical applications, matrix computations are carried out by computers using finite-precision arithmetic. If the computations involve a nonsingular matrix that is *very close* to being singular, then the matrix will behave computationally exactly like a singular matrix. In this case, computed solutions of linear systems may have no digits of accuracy whatsoever. More generally, if an $m \times n$ matrix A is *close enough* to a matrix of rank r, where $r < \min(m, n)$, then A will behave like a rank r matrix in finite-precision arithmetic. The singular values provide a way of measuring how close a matrix is to matrices of lower rank; however, we must clarify what we mean by "very close." We must decide how close is close enough. The answer depends on the machine precision of the computer that is being used.

Machine precision can be measured in terms of the unit roundoff error for the machine. Another name for unit roundoff is *machine epsilon*. To understand this concept, we need to know how computers represent numbers. If the computer uses the number base β and keeps track of n digits, then it will represent a real number x by a *floating-point number*, denoted $fl(x)$, of the form $\pm 0.d_1 d_2 \ldots d_n \times \beta^k$, where the digits d_i are integers with $0 \leq d_i < \beta$. For example, $-0.54321469 \times 10^{25}$ is an 8-digit, base 10 floating-point number, and $0.110100111001 \times 2^{-9}$ is a 12-digit, base 2 floating-point number. In Section 1 of Chapter 7, we will discuss floating-point numbers in more detail and give a precise definition of the *machine epsilon*. It turns out that the machine epsilon, ϵ, is the smallest floating-point number that will serve as a bound for the relative error whenever we approximate a real number by a floating-point number; that is, for any real number x,

$$\left| \frac{fl(x) - x}{x} \right| < \epsilon \tag{10}$$

For 8-digit, base 10 floating-point arithmetic, the machine epsilon is 5×10^{-8}. For 12-digit, base 2 floating-point arithmetic, the machine epsilon is $(\frac{1}{2})^{-12}$, and, in general, for n-digit base β arithmetic, the machine epsilon is $\frac{1}{2} \times \beta^{-n+1}$.

In light of (10), the machine epsilon is the natural choice as a basic unit for measuring rounding errors. Suppose that A is a matrix of rank n, but k of its singular values are less than a "small" multiple of the machine epsilon. Then A is close enough to matrices of rank $n - k$ so that for floating point computations, it is impossible to tell the difference. In this case, we would say that A has *numerical rank* $n - k$. The multiple of the machine epsilon that we use to determine numerical rank depends on the dimensions of the matrix and on its largest singular value. The definition of numerical rank that follows is one that is commonly used.

Definition

> The **numerical rank** of an $m \times n$ matrix is the number of singular values of the matrix that are greater than $\sigma_1 \max(m, n)\epsilon$, where σ_1 is the largest singular value of A and ϵ is the machine epsilon.

Often in the context of finite-precision computations, the term *rank* will be used with the understanding that it actually refers to the numerical rank. For example, the MATLAB command **rank(A)** will compute the numerical rank of A, rather than the exact rank.

EXAMPLE 4   Suppose that A is a 5×5 matrix with singular values

$$\sigma_1 = 4, \ \sigma_2 = 1, \ \sigma_3 = 10^{-12}, \ \sigma_4 = 3.1 \times 10^{-14}, \ \sigma_5 = 2.6 \times 10^{-15}$$

and suppose that the machine epsilon is 5×10^{-15}. To determine the numerical rank, we compare the singular values to

$$\sigma_1 \max(m, n)\epsilon = 4 \cdot 5 \cdot 5 \times 10^{-15} = 10^{-13}$$

Since three of the singular values are greater than 10^{-13}, the matrix has numerical rank 3.   ∎

APPLICATION 2   Digital Image Processing

A video image or photograph can be digitized by breaking it up into a rectangular array of cells (or pixels) and measuring the gray level of each cell. This information can be stored and transmitted as an $m \times n$ matrix A. The entries of A are nonnegative numbers corresponding to the measures of the gray levels. Because the gray levels of any one cell generally turn out to be close to the gray levels of its neighboring cells, it is possible to reduce the amount of storage necessary from mn to a relatively small multiple of $m+n+1$. Generally, the matrix A will have many small singular values. Consequently, A can be approximated by a matrix of much lower rank.

If A has singular value decomposition $U\Sigma V^T$, then A can be represented by the outer product expansion

$$A = \sigma_1 \mathbf{u}_1 \mathbf{v}_1^T + \sigma_2 \mathbf{u}_2 \mathbf{v}_2^T + \cdots + \sigma_n \mathbf{u}_n \mathbf{v}_n^T$$

The closest matrix of rank k is obtained by truncating this sum after the first k terms:

$$A_k = \sigma_1 \mathbf{u}_1 \mathbf{v}_1^T + \sigma_2 \mathbf{u}_2 \mathbf{v}_2^T + \cdots + \sigma_k \mathbf{u}_k \mathbf{v}_k^T$$

The total storage for A_k is $k(m+n+1)$. We can choose k to be considerably less than n and still have the digital image corresponding to A_k very close to the original. For typical

Original 176 by 260 Image

Rank 1 Approximation to Image

Rank 15 Approximation to Image

Rank 30 Approximation to Image

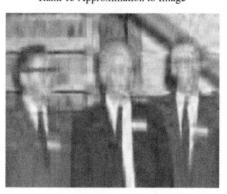

Figure 6.5.3. Courtesy Oakridge National Laboratory, U.S. Dept. of Energy

choices of k, the storage required for A_k will be less than 20 percent of the amount of storage necessary for the entire matrix A.

Figure 6.5.3 shows an image corresponding to a 176×260 matrix A and three images corresponding to lower rank approximations of A. The gentlemen in the picture are (left to right) James H. Wilkinson, Wallace Givens, and George Forsythe (three pioneers in the field of numerical linear algebra).

APPLICATION 3   Information Retrieval—Latent Semantic Indexing

We return again to the information retrieval application discussed in Sections 1.3 and 5.1. In this application, a database of documents is represented by a database matrix Q. To search the database, we form a unit search vector $\mathbf{x}$ and set $\mathbf{y} = Q^T\mathbf{x}$. The documents that best match the search criteria are those corresponding to the entries of $\mathbf{y}$ that are closest to 1.

Because of the problems of polysemy and synonymy, we can think of our database as an approximation. Some of the entries of the database matrix may contain extraneous components due to multiple meanings of words, and some may miss including components because of synonymy. Suppose that it were possible to correct for these problems and come up with a perfect database matrix P. If we set $E = Q - P$, then, since $Q = P + E$, we can think of E as a matrix representing the errors in our database matrix Q. Unfortunately, E is unknown, so we cannot determine P exactly. However, if we can find a simpler approximation Q_1 for Q, then Q_1 will also be an approximation for P. Thus, $Q_1 = P + E_1$ for some error matrix E_1. In the method of *latent semantic indexing* (LSI), the database matrix Q is approximated by a matrix Q_1 with lower rank. The idea behind the method is that the lower rank matrix may still provide a good approximation to P and, because of its simpler structure, may actually involve less error; that is, $\|E_1\| < \|E\|$.

The lower rank approximation can be obtained by truncating the outer product expansion of the singular value decomposition of Q. This is equivalent to setting

$$\sigma_{r+1} = \sigma_{r+2} = \cdots = \sigma_n = 0$$

and then setting $Q_1 = U_1 \Sigma_1 V_1^T$, the compact form of the singular value decomposition of the rank r matrix. Furthermore, if $r < \min(m, n)/2$, then this factorization is computationally more efficient to use and the searches will be speeded up. The speed of computation is proportional to the amount of arithmetic involved. The matrix vector multiplication $Q^T \mathbf{x}$ requires a total of mn scalar multiplications (m multiplications for each of the n entries of the product). In contrast, $Q_1^T = V_1 \Sigma_1 U_1^T$, and the multiplication $Q_1^T \mathbf{x} = V_1(\Sigma_1(U_1 \mathbf{x}^T))$ requires a total of $r(m + n + 1)$ scalar multiplications. For example, if $m = n = 1000$ and $r = 200$, then

$$mn = 10^6 \qquad \text{and} \qquad r(m + n + 1) = 200 \cdot 2001 = 400{,}200$$

The search with the lower rank matrix should be more than twice as fast.

APPLICATION 4   Psychology—Principal Component Analysis

In Section 5.1, we saw how psychologist Charles Spearman used a correlation matrix to compare scores on a series of aptitude tests. On the basis of the observed correlations, Spearman concluded that the test results provided evidence of common basic underlying functions. Further work by psychologists to identify the common factors that make up intelligence has led to development of an area of study known as *factor analysis*.

Predating Spearman's work by a few years is a 1901 paper by Karl Pearson analyzing a correlation matrix derived from measuring seven physical variables for each of 3000 criminals. This study contains the roots of a method popularized by Harold Hotelling in a well-known paper published in 1933. The method is known as *principal component analysis*.

To see the basic idea of this method, assume that a series of n aptitude tests is administered to a group of m individuals and that the deviations from the mean for the tests form the columns of an $m \times n$ matrix X. Although, in practice, column vectors of X are positively correlated, the hypothetical factors that account for the scores should be uncorrelated. Thus, we wish to introduce mutually orthogonal vectors $\mathbf{y}_1, \mathbf{y}_2, \ldots, \mathbf{y}_r$ corresponding to the hypothetical factors. We require that the vectors span $R(X)$, and hence the number of vectors, r, should be equal to the rank of X. Furthermore, we wish to number these vectors in decreasing order of variance.

The first principal component vector, $\mathbf{y}_1$, should account for the most variance. Since $\mathbf{y}_1$ is in the column space of X, we can represent it as a product $X\mathbf{v}_1$ for some $\mathbf{v}_1 \in \mathbb{R}^n$. The covariance matrix is

$$S = \frac{1}{n-1}X^T X$$

and the variance of $\mathbf{y}_1$ is given by

$$\mathrm{var}(\mathbf{y}_1) = \frac{(X\mathbf{v}_1)^T X\mathbf{v}_1}{n-1} = \mathbf{v}_1^T S \mathbf{v}_1$$

The vector $\mathbf{v}_1$ is chosen to maximize $\mathbf{v}^T S \mathbf{v}$ over all unit vectors $\mathbf{v}$. This can be accomplished by choosing $\mathbf{v}_1$ to be a unit eigenvector of $X^T X$ belonging to its maximum eigenvalue λ_1. (See Exercise 28 of Section 6.4.) The eigenvectors of $X^T X$ are the right singular vectors of X. Thus, $\mathbf{v}_1$ is the right singular vector of X corresponding to the largest singular value $\sigma_1 = \sqrt{\lambda_1}$. If $\mathbf{u}_1$ is the corresponding left singular vector, then

$$\mathbf{y}_1 = X\mathbf{v}_1 = \sigma_1 \mathbf{u}_1$$

The second principal component vector must be of the form $\mathbf{y}_2 = X\mathbf{v}_2$. It can be shown that the vector which maximizes $\mathbf{v}^T S \mathbf{v}$ over all unit vectors that are orthogonal to $\mathbf{v}_1$ is just the second right singular vector $\mathbf{v}_2$ of X. If we choose $\mathbf{v}_2$ in this way and $\mathbf{u}_2$ is the corresponding left singular vector, then

$$\mathbf{y}_2 = X\mathbf{v}_2 = \sigma_2 \mathbf{u}_2$$

and since

$$\mathbf{y}_1^T \mathbf{y}_2 = \sigma_1 \sigma_2 \mathbf{u}_1^T \mathbf{u}_2 = 0$$

it follows that $\mathbf{y}_1$ and $\mathbf{y}_2$ are orthogonal. The remaining $\mathbf{y}_i$'s are determined in a similar manner.

In general, the singular value decomposition solves the principal component problem. If X has rank r and singular value decomposition $X = U_1 \Sigma_1 V_1^T$ (in compact form), then the principal component vectors are given by

$$\mathbf{y}_1 = \sigma_1 \mathbf{u}_1, \ \mathbf{y}_2 = \sigma_2 \mathbf{u}_2, \ \ldots, \ \mathbf{y}_r = \sigma_r \mathbf{u}_r$$

The left singular vectors $\mathbf{u}_1, \ldots, \mathbf{u}_n$ are the normalized principal component vectors. If we set $W = \Sigma_1 V_1^T$, then

$$X = U_1 \Sigma_1 V_1^T = U_1 W$$

The columns of the matrix U_1 correspond to the hypothetical intelligence factors. The entries in each column measure how well the individual students exhibit that particular intellectual ability. The matrix W measures to what extent each test depends on the hypothetical factors.

SECTION 6.5 EXERCISES

1. Show that A and A^T have the same nonzero singular values. How are their singular value decompositions related?

2. Use the method of Example 1 to find the singular value decomposition of each of the following matrices:

(a) $\begin{bmatrix} 1 & 1 \\ 2 & 2 \end{bmatrix}$ **(b)** $\begin{bmatrix} 2 & -2 \\ 1 & 2 \end{bmatrix}$

4. Let

(c) $\begin{bmatrix} 1 & 3 \\ 3 & 1 \\ 0 & 0 \\ 0 & 0 \end{bmatrix}$ **(d)** $\begin{bmatrix} 2 & 0 & 0 \\ 0 & 2 & 1 \\ 0 & 1 & 2 \\ 0 & 0 & 0 \end{bmatrix}$

3. For each of the matrices in Exercise 2:

    (a) determine the rank.

    (b) find the closest (with respect to the Frobenius norm) matrix of rank 1.

$$A = \begin{bmatrix} -2 & 8 & 20 \\ 14 & 19 & 10 \\ 2 & -2 & 1 \end{bmatrix} = \begin{bmatrix} \frac{3}{5} & -\frac{4}{5} & 0 \\ \frac{4}{5} & \frac{3}{5} & 0 \\ 0 & 0 & 1 \end{bmatrix} \begin{bmatrix} 30 & 0 & 0 \\ 0 & 15 & 0 \\ 0 & 0 & 3 \end{bmatrix} \begin{bmatrix} \frac{1}{3} & \frac{2}{3} & \frac{2}{3} \\ \frac{2}{3} & \frac{1}{3} & -\frac{2}{3} \\ \frac{2}{3} & -\frac{2}{3} & \frac{1}{3} \end{bmatrix}$$

Find the closest (with respect to the Frobenius norm) matrices of rank 1 and rank 2 to A.

5. The matrix

$$A = \begin{bmatrix} 2 & 5 & 4 \\ 6 & 3 & 0 \\ 6 & 3 & 0 \\ 2 & 5 & 4 \end{bmatrix}$$

has singular value decomposition

$$\begin{bmatrix} \frac{1}{2} & \frac{1}{2} & \frac{1}{2} & \frac{1}{2} \\ \frac{1}{2} & -\frac{1}{2} & -\frac{1}{2} & \frac{1}{2} \\ \frac{1}{2} & -\frac{1}{2} & \frac{1}{2} & -\frac{1}{2} \\ \frac{1}{2} & \frac{1}{2} & -\frac{1}{2} & -\frac{1}{2} \end{bmatrix} \begin{bmatrix} 12 & 0 & 0 \\ 0 & 6 & 0 \\ 0 & 0 & 0 \\ 0 & 0 & 0 \end{bmatrix} \begin{bmatrix} \frac{2}{3} & \frac{2}{3} & \frac{1}{3} \\ -\frac{2}{3} & \frac{1}{3} & \frac{2}{3} \\ \frac{1}{3} & -\frac{2}{3} & \frac{2}{3} \end{bmatrix}$$

    (a) Use the singular value decomposition to find orthonormal bases for $R(A^T)$ and $N(A)$.

    (b) Use the singular value decomposition to find orthonormal bases for $R(A)$ and $N(A^T)$.

6. Prove that if A is a symmetric matrix with eigenvalues $\lambda_1, \lambda_2, \ldots, \lambda_n$, then the singular values of A are $|\lambda_1|, |\lambda_2|, \ldots, |\lambda_n|$.

7. Let A be an $m \times n$ matrix with singular value decomposition $U\Sigma V^T$, and suppose that A has rank r, where $r < n$. Show that $\{\mathbf{v}_1, \ldots, \mathbf{v}_r\}$ is an orthonormal basis for $R(A^T)$.

8. Let A be an $n \times n$ matrix. Show that $A^T A$ and AA^T are similar.

9. Let A be an $n \times n$ matrix with singular values $\sigma_1, \sigma_2, \ldots, \sigma_n$ and eigenvalues $\lambda_1, \lambda_2, \ldots, \lambda_n$. Show that

$$|\lambda_1 \lambda_2 \cdots \lambda_n| = \sigma_1 \sigma_2 \cdots \sigma_n$$

10. Let A be an $n \times n$ matrix with singular value decomposition $U\Sigma V^T$ and let

$$B = \begin{bmatrix} O & A^T \\ A & O \end{bmatrix}$$

Show that if

$$\mathbf{x}_i = \begin{bmatrix} \mathbf{v}_i \\ \mathbf{u}_i \end{bmatrix}, \qquad \mathbf{y}_i = \begin{bmatrix} -\mathbf{v}_i \\ \mathbf{u}_i \end{bmatrix}, \qquad i = 1, \dots, n$$

then the $\mathbf{x}_i$'s and $\mathbf{y}_i$'s are eigenvectors of B. How do the eigenvalues of B relate to the singular values of A?

11. Show that if σ is a singular value of A, then there exists a nonzero vector $\mathbf{x}$ such that

$$\sigma = \frac{\|A\mathbf{x}\|_2}{\|\mathbf{x}\|_2}$$

12. Let A be an $m \times n$ matrix of rank n with singular value decomposition $U\Sigma V^T$. Let Σ^+ denote the $n \times m$ matrix

$$\begin{bmatrix} \frac{1}{\sigma_1} & & & \\ & \frac{1}{\sigma_2} & & \\ & & \ddots & \\ & & & \frac{1}{\sigma_n} \end{bmatrix} \quad O$$

and define $A^+ = V\Sigma^+ U^T$. Show that $\hat{\mathbf{x}} = A^+\mathbf{b}$ satisfies the normal equations $A^TA\mathbf{x} = A^T\mathbf{b}$.

13. Let A^+ be defined as in Exercise 12 and let $P = AA^+$. Show that $P^2 = P$ and $P^T = P$.

6.6 Quadratic Forms

By this time, the reader should be well aware of the important role that matrices play in the study of linear equations. In this section, we will see that matrices also play an important role in the study of quadratic equations. With each quadratic equation, we can associate a vector function $f(\mathbf{x}) = \mathbf{x}^TA\mathbf{x}$. Such a vector function is called a *quadratic form*. Quadratic forms arise in a wide variety of applied problems. They are particularly important in the study of optimization theory.

Definition

A **quadratic equation** in two variables x and y is an equation of the form

$$ax^2 + 2bxy + cy^2 + dx + ey + f = 0 \qquad (1)$$

Equation (1) may be rewritten in the form

$$\begin{bmatrix} x & y \end{bmatrix} \begin{bmatrix} a & b \\ b & c \end{bmatrix} \begin{bmatrix} x \\ y \end{bmatrix} + \begin{bmatrix} d & e \end{bmatrix} \begin{bmatrix} x \\ y \end{bmatrix} + f = 0 \qquad (2)$$

Let

$$\mathbf{x} = \begin{bmatrix} x \\ y \end{bmatrix} \qquad \text{and} \qquad A = \begin{bmatrix} a & b \\ b & c \end{bmatrix}$$

The term

$$\mathbf{x}^TA\mathbf{x} = ax^2 + 2bxy + cy^2$$

is called the **quadratic form** associated with (1).

Conic Sections

The graph of an equation of the form (1) is called a *conic section*. [If there are no ordered pairs (x, y) which satisfy (1), we say that the equation represents an imaginary conic.] If the graph of (1) consists of a single point, a line, or a pair of lines, we say that (1) represents a degenerate conic. Of more interest are the nondegenerate conics. Graphs of nondegenerate conics turn out to be circles, ellipses, parabolas, or hyperbolas

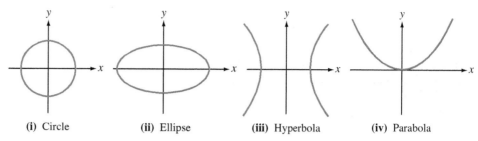

(i) Circle   (ii) Ellipse   (iii) Hyperbola   (iv) Parabola

Figure 6.6.1.

(see Figure 6.6.1). The graph of a conic is particularly easy to sketch when its equation can be put into one of the following standard forms:

(i) $x^2 + y^2 = r^2$ (circle)

(ii) $\dfrac{x^2}{\alpha^2} + \dfrac{y^2}{\beta^2} = 1$ (ellipse)

(iii) $\dfrac{x^2}{\alpha^2} - \dfrac{y^2}{\beta^2} = 1$ or $\dfrac{y^2}{\alpha^2} - \dfrac{x^2}{\beta^2} = 1$ (hyperbola)

(iv) $x^2 = \alpha y$ or $y^2 = \alpha x$ (parabola)

Here, α, β, and r are nonzero real numbers. Note that the circle is a special case of the ellipse ($\alpha = \beta = r$). A conic section is said to be in *standard position* if its equation can be put into one of these four standard forms. The graphs of **(i)**, **(ii)**, and **(iii)** in Figure 6.6.1 will all be symmetric to both coordinate axes and the origin. We say that these curves are centered at the origin. A parabola in standard position will have its vertex at the origin and will be symmetric to one of the axes.

What about the conics that are not in standard position? Let us consider the following cases:

Case 1. The conic section has been translated horizontally from the standard position. This occurs when the x^2 and x terms in (1) both have nonzero coefficients.

Case 2. The conic section has been translated vertically from the standard position. This occurs when the y^2 and y terms in (1) have nonzero coefficients (i.e., $c \neq 0$ and $e \neq 0$).

Case 3. The conic section has been rotated from the standard position by an angle θ that is not a multiple of $90°$. This occurs when the coefficient of the xy term is nonzero (i.e., $b \neq 0$).

In general, we may have any one or any combination of these three cases. To graph a conic section that is not in standard position, we usually find a new set of axes x' and y' such that the conic section is in standard position with respect to the new axes. This is not difficult if the conic has only been translated horizontally or vertically, in which case the new axes can be found by completing the squares. The following example illustrates how this is done.

EXAMPLE 1   Sketch the graph of the equation

$$9x^2 - 18x + 4y^2 + 16y - 11 = 0$$

Solution

To see how to choose our new axis system, we complete the squares.

$$9(x^2 - 2x + 1) + 4(y^2 + 4y + 4) - 11 = 9 + 16$$

This equation can be simplified to the form

$$\frac{(x-1)^2}{2^2} + \frac{(y+2)^2}{3^2} = 1$$

If we let

$$x' = x - 1 \quad \text{and} \quad y' = y + 2$$

the equation becomes

$$\frac{(x')^2}{2^2} + \frac{(y')^2}{3^2} = 1$$

which is in standard form with respect to the variables x' and y'. Thus, the graph, as shown in Figure 6.6.2, will be an ellipse that is in standard position in the $x'y'$-axis system. The center of the ellipse will be at the origin of the $x'y'$-plane [i.e., at the point $(x, y) = (1, -2)$]. The equation of the x'-axis is simply $y' = 0$, which is the equation of the line $y = -2$ in the xy-plane. Similarly, the y'-axis coincides with the line $x = 1$. ■

There is little problem if the center or vertex of the conic section has been translated. If, however, the conic section has also been rotated from the standard position, it is necessary to change coordinates so that the equation in terms of the new coordinates x' and y' involves no $x'y'$ term. Let $\mathbf{x} = (x, y)^T$ and $\mathbf{x}' = (x', y')^T$. Since the new coordinates differ from the old coordinates by a rotation, we have

$$\mathbf{x} = Q\mathbf{x}' \quad \text{or} \quad \mathbf{x}' = Q^T\mathbf{x}$$

where

$$Q = \begin{bmatrix} \cos\theta & \sin\theta \\ -\sin\theta & \cos\theta \end{bmatrix} \quad \text{or} \quad Q^T = \begin{bmatrix} \cos\theta & -\sin\theta \\ \sin\theta & \cos\theta \end{bmatrix}$$

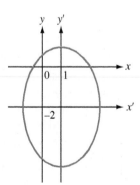

Figure 6.6.2.

If $0 < \theta < \pi$, then the matrix Q corresponds to a rotation of θ radians in the clockwise direction and Q^T corresponds to a rotation of θ radians in the counterclockwise direction (see Example 2 in Section 4.2). With this change of variables, (2) becomes

$$(\mathbf{x}')^T(Q^TAQ)\mathbf{x}' + \begin{bmatrix} d' & e' \end{bmatrix} \mathbf{x}' + f = 0 \tag{3}$$

where $\begin{bmatrix} d' & e' \end{bmatrix} = \begin{bmatrix} d & e \end{bmatrix} Q$. This equation will involve no $x'y'$ term if and only if Q^TAQ is diagonal. Since A is symmetric, it is possible to find a pair of orthonormal eigenvectors $\mathbf{q}_1 = (x_1, -y_1)^T$ and $\mathbf{q}_2 = (y_1, x_1)^T$. Thus, if we set $\cos\theta = x_1$ and $\sin\theta = y_1$, then

$$Q = \begin{bmatrix} \mathbf{q}_1 & \mathbf{q}_2 \end{bmatrix} = \begin{bmatrix} x_1 & y_1 \\ -y_1 & x_1 \end{bmatrix}$$

diagonalizes A and (3) simplifies to

$$\lambda_1(x')^2 + \lambda_2(y')^2 + d'x' + e'y' + f = 0$$

EXAMPLE 2 Consider the conic section

$$3x^2 + 2xy + 3y^2 - 8 = 0$$

This equation can be written in the form

$$\begin{bmatrix} x & y \end{bmatrix} \begin{bmatrix} 3 & 1 \\ 1 & 3 \end{bmatrix} \begin{bmatrix} x \\ y \end{bmatrix} = 8$$

The matrix

$$\begin{bmatrix} 3 & 1 \\ 1 & 3 \end{bmatrix}$$

has eigenvalues $\lambda = 2$ and $\lambda = 4$ with corresponding unit eigenvectors

$$\left(\frac{1}{\sqrt{2}}, -\frac{1}{\sqrt{2}} \right)^T \quad \text{and} \quad \left(\frac{1}{\sqrt{2}}, \frac{1}{\sqrt{2}} \right)^T$$

Let

$$Q = \begin{bmatrix} \dfrac{1}{\sqrt{2}} & \dfrac{1}{\sqrt{2}} \\ -\dfrac{1}{\sqrt{2}} & \dfrac{1}{\sqrt{2}} \end{bmatrix} = \begin{bmatrix} \cos 45° & \sin 45° \\ -\sin 45° & \cos 45° \end{bmatrix}$$

and set

$$\begin{bmatrix} x \\ y \end{bmatrix} = \begin{bmatrix} \dfrac{1}{\sqrt{2}} & \dfrac{1}{\sqrt{2}} \\ -\dfrac{1}{\sqrt{2}} & \dfrac{1}{\sqrt{2}} \end{bmatrix} \begin{bmatrix} x' \\ y' \end{bmatrix}$$

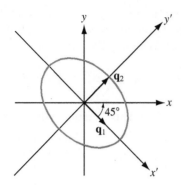

Figure 6.6.3.

Thus,

$$Q^T A Q = \begin{bmatrix} 2 & 0 \\ 0 & 4 \end{bmatrix}$$

and the equation of the conic becomes

$$2(x')^2 + 4(y')^2 = 8$$

or

$$\frac{(x')^2}{4} + \frac{(y')^2}{2} = 1$$

In the new coordinate system, the direction of the x'-axis is determined by the point $x' = 1, y' = 0$. To translate this to the xy coordinate system, we multiply

$$\begin{bmatrix} \dfrac{1}{\sqrt{2}} & \dfrac{1}{\sqrt{2}} \\ -\dfrac{1}{\sqrt{2}} & \dfrac{1}{\sqrt{2}} \end{bmatrix} \begin{bmatrix} 1 \\ 0 \end{bmatrix} = \begin{bmatrix} \dfrac{1}{\sqrt{2}} \\ -\dfrac{1}{\sqrt{2}} \end{bmatrix} = \mathbf{q}_1$$

The x'-axis will be in the direction of $\mathbf{q}_1$. Similarly, to find the direction of the y'-axis, we multiply

$$Q\,\mathbf{e}_2 = \mathbf{q}_2$$

The eigenvectors that form the columns of Q tell us the directions of the new coordinate axes (see Figure 6.6.3). ∎

EXAMPLE 3 Given the quadratic equation

$$3x^2 + 2xy + 3y^2 + 8\sqrt{2}y - 4 = 0$$

find a change of coordinates so that the resulting equation represents a conic in standard position.

Figure 6.6.4.

Solution

The xy term is eliminated in the same manner as in Example 2. In this case, we use the rotation matrix

$$Q = \begin{bmatrix} \dfrac{1}{\sqrt{2}} & \dfrac{1}{\sqrt{2}} \\ -\dfrac{1}{\sqrt{2}} & \dfrac{1}{\sqrt{2}} \end{bmatrix}$$

to rotate the axis system. The equation with respect to the new axis system is

$$2(x')^2 + 4(y')^2 + \begin{bmatrix} 0 & 8\sqrt{2} \end{bmatrix} Q \begin{bmatrix} x' \\ y' \end{bmatrix} = 4$$

or

$$(x')^2 - 4x' + 2(y')^2 + 4y' = 2$$

If we complete the square, we get

$$(x' - 2)^2 + 2(y' + 1)^2 = 8$$

If we set $x'' = x' - 2$ and $y'' = y' + 1$ (see Figure 6.6.4), the equation simplifies to

$$\frac{(x'')^2}{8} + \frac{(y'')^2}{4} = 1 \qquad \blacksquare$$

To summarize, a quadratic equation in the variables x and y can be written in the form

$$\mathbf{x}^T A \mathbf{x} + B \mathbf{x} + f = 0$$

where $\mathbf{x} = (x, y)^T$, A is a 2×2 symmetric matrix, B is a 1×2 matrix, and f is a scalar. If A is nonsingular, then, by rotating and translating the axes, it is possible to rewrite the equation in the form

$$\lambda_1(x')^2 + \lambda_2(y')^2 + f' = 0 \qquad (4)$$

where λ_1 and λ_2 are the eigenvalues of A. If (4) represents a real nondegenerate conic, it will be either an ellipse or a hyperbola, depending on whether λ_1 and λ_2 agree in sign or differ in sign. If A is singular and exactly one of its eigenvalues is zero, the quadratic equation can be reduced to either

$$\lambda_1(x')^2 + e'y' + f' = 0 \quad \text{or} \quad \lambda_2(y')^2 + d'x' + f' = 0$$

These equations will represent parabolas, provided that e' and d' are nonzero.

There is no reason to limit ourselves to two variables. We could just as well have quadratic equations and quadratic forms in any number of variables. Indeed, a *quadratic equation in n variables* $x_1, \ldots, x_n$ is one of the form

$$\mathbf{x}^T A \mathbf{x} + B \mathbf{x} + \alpha = 0 \tag{5}$$

where $\mathbf{x} = (x_1, \ldots, x_n)^T$, A is an $n \times n$ symmetric matrix, B is a $1 \times n$ matrix, and α is a scalar. The vector function

$$f(\mathbf{x}) = \mathbf{x}^T A \mathbf{x} = \sum_{i=1}^{n} \left(\sum_{j=1}^{n} a_{ij} x_j \right) x_i$$

is the *quadratic form in n variables* associated with the quadratic equation.

In the case of three unknowns, if

$$\mathbf{x} = \begin{bmatrix} x \\ y \\ z \end{bmatrix}, \qquad A = \begin{bmatrix} a & d & e \\ d & b & f \\ e & f & c \end{bmatrix}, \qquad B = \begin{bmatrix} g \\ h \\ i \end{bmatrix}$$

then (5) becomes

$$ax^2 + by^2 + cz^2 + 2dxy + 2exz + 2fyz + gx + hy + iz + \alpha = 0$$

The graph of a quadratic equation in three variables is called a *quadric surface*.

There are four basic types of nondegenerate quadric surfaces:

1. Ellipsoids
2. Hyperboloids (of one or two sheets)
3. Cones
4. Paraboloids (either elliptic or hyperbolic)

As in the two-dimensional case, we can use translations and rotations to transform the equation into the standard form

$$\lambda_1(x')^2 + \lambda_2(y')^2 + \lambda_3(z')^2 + \alpha = 0$$

where $\lambda_1, \lambda_2, \lambda_3$ are the eigenvalues of A. For the general n-dimensional case, the quadratic form can always be translated to a simpler diagonal form. More precisely, we have the following theorem.

Theorem 6.6.1 Principal Axes Theorem

If A is a real symmetric $n \times n$ matrix, then there is a change of variables $\mathbf{u} = Q^T \mathbf{x}$ such that $\mathbf{x}^T A \mathbf{x} = \mathbf{u}^T D \mathbf{u}$, where D is a diagonal matrix.

Proof If A is a real symmetric matrix, then by Corollary 6.4.7, there is an orthogonal matrix Q that diagonalizes A; that is, $Q^T A Q = D$ (diagonal). If we set $\mathbf{u} = Q^T \mathbf{x}$, then $\mathbf{x} = Q\mathbf{u}$ and

$$\mathbf{x}^T A \mathbf{x} = \mathbf{u}^T Q^T A Q \mathbf{u} = \mathbf{u}^T D \mathbf{u}$$

∎

Optimization: An Application to the Calculus

Let us consider the problem of maximizing and minimizing functions of several variables. In particular, we would like to determine the nature of the critical points of a real-valued vector function $w = F(\mathbf{x})$. If the function is a quadratic form, $w = \mathbf{x}^T A \mathbf{x}$, then $\mathbf{0}$ is a critical point. Whether it is a maximum, minimum, or saddle point depends on the eigenvalues of A. More generally, if the function to be maximized or minimized is sufficiently differentiable, it behaves locally like a quadratic form. Thus, each critical point can be tested by determining the signs of the eigenvalues of the matrix of an associated quadratic form.

Definition

> Let $F(\mathbf{x})$ be a real-valued vector function on $\mathbb{R}^n$. A point $\mathbf{x}_0$ in $\mathbb{R}^n$ is said to be a **stationary point** of F if all the first partial derivatives of F at $\mathbf{x}_0$ exist and are zero.

If $F(\mathbf{x})$ has either a local maximum or a local minimum at a point $\mathbf{x}_0$ and the first partials of F exist at $\mathbf{x}_0$, they will all be zero. Thus, if $F(\mathbf{x})$ has first partials everywhere, its local maxima and minima will occur at stationary points.

Consider the quadratic form

$$f(x, y) = ax^2 + 2bxy + cy^2$$

The first partials of f are

$$f_x = 2ax + 2by$$
$$f_y = 2bx + 2cy$$

Setting these equal to zero, we see that $(0, 0)$ is a stationary point. Moreover, if the matrix

$$A = \begin{bmatrix} a & b \\ b & c \end{bmatrix}$$

is nonsingular, this will be the only critical point. Thus, if A is nonsingular, f will have either a global minimum, a global maximum, or a saddle point at $(0, 0)$.

Let us write f in the form

$$f(\mathbf{x}) = \mathbf{x}^T A \mathbf{x} \qquad \text{where} \qquad \mathbf{x} = \begin{bmatrix} x \\ y \end{bmatrix}$$

Since $f(\mathbf{0}) = 0$, it follows that f will have a global minimum at $\mathbf{0}$ if and only if

$$\mathbf{x}^T A \mathbf{x} > 0 \qquad \text{for all} \qquad \mathbf{x} \neq \mathbf{0}$$

and f will have a global maximum at $\mathbf{0}$ if and only if

$$\mathbf{x}^T A \mathbf{x} < 0 \qquad \text{for all} \qquad \mathbf{x} \neq \mathbf{0}$$

If $\mathbf{x}^T A \mathbf{x}$ changes sign, then $\mathbf{0}$ is a saddle point.

In general, if f is a quadratic form in n variables, then, for each $\mathbf{x} \in \mathbb{R}^n$,

$$f(\mathbf{x}) = \mathbf{x}^T A \mathbf{x}$$

where A is a symmetric $n \times n$ matrix.

Definition

> A quadratic form $f(\mathbf{x}) = \mathbf{x}^T A \mathbf{x}$ is said to be **definite** if it takes on only one sign as $\mathbf{x}$ varies over all nonzero vectors in $\mathbb{R}^n$. The form is **positive definite** if $\mathbf{x}^T A \mathbf{x} > 0$ for all nonzero $\mathbf{x}$ in $\mathbb{R}^n$ and **negative definite** if $\mathbf{x}^T A \mathbf{x} < 0$ for all nonzero $\mathbf{x}$ in $\mathbb{R}^n$. A quadratic form is said to be **indefinite** if it takes on values that differ in sign. If $f(\mathbf{x}) = \mathbf{x}^T A \mathbf{x} \geq 0$ and assumes the value 0 for some $\mathbf{x} \neq \mathbf{0}$, then $f(\mathbf{x})$ is said to be **positive semidefinite**. If $f(\mathbf{x}) \leq 0$ and assumes the value 0 for some $\mathbf{x} \neq \mathbf{0}$, then $f(\mathbf{x})$ is said to be **negative semidefinite**.

Whether the quadratic form is positive definite or negative definite depends on the matrix A. If the quadratic form is positive definite, we say simply that A is positive definite. The preceding definition can then be restated as follows.

Definition

> A real symmetric matrix A is said to be
>
> **I. positive definite** if $\mathbf{x}^T A \mathbf{x} > 0$ for all nonzero $\mathbf{x}$ in $\mathbb{R}^n$.
> **II. negative definite** if $\mathbf{x}^T A \mathbf{x} < 0$ for all nonzero $\mathbf{x}$ in $\mathbb{R}^n$.
> **III. positive semidefinite** if $\mathbf{x}^T A \mathbf{x} \geq 0$ for all nonzero $\mathbf{x}$ in $\mathbb{R}^n$.
> **IV. negative semidefinite** if $\mathbf{x}^T A \mathbf{x} \leq 0$ for all nonzero $\mathbf{x}$ in $\mathbb{R}^n$.
> **V. indefinite** if $\mathbf{x}^T A \mathbf{x}$ takes on values that differ in sign.

If A is nonsingular, then $\mathbf{0}$ will be the only stationary point of $f(\mathbf{x}) = \mathbf{x}^T A \mathbf{x}$. It will be a global minimum if A is positive definite and a global maximum if A is negative definite. If A is indefinite, then $\mathbf{0}$ is a saddle point. To classify the stationary point, we must then classify the matrix A. There are a number of ways of determining whether a matrix is positive definite. We will study some of these methods in the next section. The following theorem gives perhaps the most important characterization of positive definite matrices.

Theorem 6.6.2   *Let A be a real symmetric $n \times n$ matrix. Then A is positive definite if and only if all its eigenvalues are positive.*

Proof   If A is positive definite and λ is an eigenvalue of A, then, for any eigenvector $\mathbf{x}$ belonging to λ,

$$\mathbf{x}^T A \mathbf{x} = \lambda \mathbf{x}^T \mathbf{x} = \lambda \|\mathbf{x}\|^2$$

Hence,

$$\lambda = \frac{\mathbf{x}^T A \mathbf{x}}{\|\mathbf{x}\|^2} > 0$$

Conversely, suppose that all the eigenvalues of A are positive. Let $\{\mathbf{u}_1, \ldots, \mathbf{u}_n\}$ be an orthonormal set of eigenvectors of A. If $\mathbf{x}$ is any nonzero vector in $\mathbb{R}^n$, then $\mathbf{x}$ can be written in the form

$$\mathbf{x} = c_1 \mathbf{u}_1 + c_2 \mathbf{u}_2 + \cdots + c_n \mathbf{u}_n$$

where

$$c_i = \mathbf{x}^T \mathbf{u}_i \quad \text{for} \quad i = 1, \ldots, n \quad \text{and} \quad \sum_{i=1}^{n} c_i^2 = \|\mathbf{x}\|^2 > 0$$

It follows that

$$\mathbf{x}^T A \mathbf{x} = \mathbf{x}^T (c_1 \lambda_1 \mathbf{u}_1 + \cdots + c_n \lambda_n \mathbf{u}_n)$$
$$= \sum_{i=1}^{n} c_i^2 \lambda_i$$
$$\geq (\min \lambda_i) \|\mathbf{x}\|^2 > 0$$

and hence A is positive definite. ∎

If the eigenvalues of A are all negative, then $-A$ must be positive definite and, consequently, A must be negative definite. If A has eigenvalues that differ in sign, then A is indefinite. Indeed, if λ_1 is a positive eigenvalue of A and $\mathbf{x}_1$ is an eigenvector belonging to λ_1, then

$$\mathbf{x}_1^T A \mathbf{x}_1 = \lambda_1 \mathbf{x}_1^T \mathbf{x}_1 = \lambda_1 \|\mathbf{x}_1\|^2 > 0$$

and if λ_2 is a negative eigenvalue with eigenvector $\mathbf{x}_2$, then

$$\mathbf{x}_2^T A \mathbf{x}_2 = \lambda_2 \mathbf{x}_2^T \mathbf{x}_2 = \lambda_2 \|\mathbf{x}_2\|^2 < 0$$

EXAMPLE 4   The graph of the quadratic form $f(x, y) = 2x^2 - 4xy + 5y^2$ is pictured in Figure 6.6.5. It is not entirely clear from the graph if the stationary point $(0, 0)$ is a global minimum or a saddle point. We can use the matrix A of the quadratic form to decide the issue:

$$A = \begin{bmatrix} 2 & -2 \\ -2 & 5 \end{bmatrix}$$

The eigenvalues of A are $\lambda_1 = 6$ and $\lambda_2 = 1$. Since both eigenvalues are positive, it follows that A is positive definite and hence the stationary point $(0, 0)$ is a global minimum. ∎

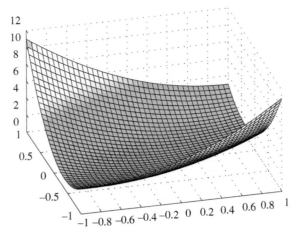

Figure 6.6.5.

Suppose now that we have a function $F(x, y)$ with a stationary point (x_0, y_0). If F has continuous third partials in a neighborhood of (x_0, y_0), it can be expanded in a Taylor series about that point.

$$F(x_0 + h, y_0 + k) = F(x_0, y_0) + \left[hF_x(x_0, y_0) + kF_y(x_0, y_0)\right]$$
$$+ \tfrac{1}{2}\left[h^2 F_{xx}(x_0, y_0) + 2hkF_{xy}(x_0, y_0) + k^2 F_{yy}(x_0, y_0)\right] + R$$
$$= F(x_0, y_0) + \tfrac{1}{2}(ah^2 + 2bhk + ck^2) + R$$

where

$$a = F_{xx}(x_0, y_0), \qquad b = F_{xy}(x_0, y_0), \qquad c = F_{yy}(x_0, y_0)$$

and the remainder R is given by

$$R = \tfrac{1}{6}\left[h^3 F_{xxx}(\mathbf{z}) + 3h^2 k F_{xxy}(\mathbf{z}) + 3hk^2 F_{xyy}(\mathbf{z}) + k^3 F_{yyy}(\mathbf{z})\right]$$
$$\mathbf{z} = (x_0 + \theta h, y_0 + \theta k), \qquad 0 < \theta < 1$$

If h and k are sufficiently small, $|R|$ will be less than $\tfrac{1}{2}|ah^2 + 2bhk + ck^2|$, and hence $[F(x_0 + h, y_0 + k) - F(x_0, y_0)]$ will have the same sign as $(ah^2 + 2bhk + ck^2)$. The expression

$$f(h, k) = ah^2 + 2bhk + ck^2$$

is a quadratic form in the variables h and k. Thus, $F(x, y)$ will have a local minimum (maximum) at (x_0, y_0) if and only if $f(h, k)$ has a minimum (maximum) at $(0, 0)$. Let

$$H = \begin{bmatrix} a & b \\ b & c \end{bmatrix} = \begin{bmatrix} F_{xx}(x_0, y_0) & F_{xy}(x_0, y_0) \\ F_{xy}(x_0, y_0) & F_{yy}(x_0, y_0) \end{bmatrix}$$

and let λ_1 and λ_2 be the eigenvalues of H. If H is nonsingular, then λ_1 and λ_2 are nonzero and we can classify the stationary points as follows:

(i) F has a minimum at (x_0, y_0) if $\lambda_1 > 0$, $\lambda_2 > 0$.
(ii) F has a maximum at (x_0, y_0) if $\lambda_1 < 0$, $\lambda_2 < 0$.
(iii) F has a saddle point at (x_0, y_0) if λ_1 and λ_2 differ in sign.

EXAMPLE 5 The graph of the function

$$F(x, y) = \tfrac{1}{3}x^3 + xy^2 - 4xy + 1$$

is pictured in Figure 6.6.6. Although all the stationary points lie in the region shown, it is difficult to distinguish them just by looking at the graph. However, we can solve for the stationary points analytically and then classify each stationary point by examining the corresponding matrix of second partial derivatives.

Solution
The first partials of F are

$$F_x = x^2 + y^2 - 4y$$
$$F_y = 2xy - 4x = 2x(y - 2)$$

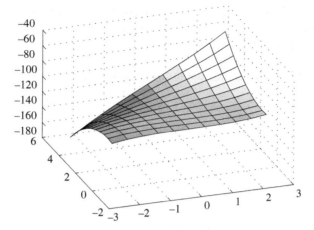

Figure 6.6.6.

Table 6.6.1   Stationary Points of $F(x, y)$

Stationary Point (x_0, y_0)	λ_1	λ_2	Description
$(0, 0)$	4	-4	Saddle point
$(0, 4)$	4	-4	Saddle point
$(2, 2)$	4	4	Local minimum
$(-2, 2)$	-4	-4	Local maximum

Setting $F_y = 0$, we get $x = 0$ or $y = 2$. Setting $F_x = 0$, we see that if $x = 0$, then y must either be 0 or 4, and if $y = 2$, then $x = \pm 2$. Thus, $(0, 0)$, $(0, 4)$, $(2, 2)$, and $(-2, 2)$ are the stationary points of F. To classify the stationary points, we compute the second partials:

$$F_{xx} = 2x, \qquad F_{xy} = 2y - 4, \qquad F_{yy} = 2x$$

For each stationary point (x_0, y_0), we determine the eigenvalues of

$$\begin{bmatrix} 2x_0 & 2y_0 - 4 \\ 2y_0 - 4 & 2x_0 \end{bmatrix}$$

These values are summarized in Table 6.6.1.

We can now generalize our method of classifying stationary points to functions of more than two variables. Let $F(\mathbf{x}) = F(x_1, \ldots, x_n)$ be a real-valued function whose third partial derivatives are all continuous. Let $\mathbf{x}_0$ be a stationary point of F and define the matrix $H = H(\mathbf{x}_0)$ by

$$h_{ij} = F_{x_i x_j}(\mathbf{x}_0)$$

$H(\mathbf{x}_0)$ is called the *Hessian* of F at $\mathbf{x}_0$.

The stationary point can be classified as follows:

(i) $\mathbf{x}_0$ is a local minimum of F if $H(\mathbf{x}_0)$ is positive definite.

(ii) $\mathbf{x}_0$ is a local maximum of F if $H(\mathbf{x}_0)$ is negative definite.

(iii) $\mathbf{x}_0$ is a saddle point of F if $H(\mathbf{x}_0)$ is indefinite.

EXAMPLE 6 Find the local minima of the function

$$F(x, y, z) = x^2 + xz - 3 \cos y + z^2$$

Solution

The first partials of F are

$$F_x = 2x + z$$
$$F_y = 3 \sin y$$
$$F_z = x + 2z$$

It follows that (x, y, z) is a stationary point of F if and only if $x = z = 0$ and $y = n\pi$, where n is an integer. Let $\mathbf{x}_0 = (0, 2k\pi, 0)^T$. The Hessian of F at $\mathbf{x}_0$ is given by

$$H(\mathbf{x}_0) = \begin{pmatrix} 2 & 0 & 1 \\ 0 & 3 & 0 \\ 1 & 0 & 2 \end{pmatrix}$$

The eigenvalues of $H(\mathbf{x}_0)$ are $3, 3$, and 1. Since the eigenvalues are all positive, it follows that $H(\mathbf{x}_0)$ is positive definite and hence F has a local minimum at $\mathbf{x}_0$. At a stationary point of the form $\mathbf{x}_1 = (0, (2k-1)\pi, 0)^T$, the Hessian will be

$$H(\mathbf{x}_1) = \begin{pmatrix} 2 & 0 & 1 \\ 0 & -3 & 0 \\ 1 & 0 & 2 \end{pmatrix}$$

The eigenvalues of $H(\mathbf{x}_1)$ are $-3, 3$, and 1. It follows that $H(\mathbf{x}_1)$ is indefinite and hence $\mathbf{x}_1$ is a saddle point of F. ∎

SECTION 6.6 EXERCISES

1. Find the matrix associated with each of the following quadratic forms:

(a) $3x^2 - 5xy + y^2$

(b) $2x^2 + 3y^2 + z^2 + xy - 2xz + 3yz$

(c) $x^2 + 2y^2 + z^2 + xy - 2xz + 3yz$

2. Reorder the eigenvalues in Example 2 so that $\lambda_1 = 4$ and $\lambda_2 = 2$ and rework the example. In what quadrants will the positive x' and y' axes lie? Sketch the graph and compare it to Figure 6.6.3.

3. In each of the following, (i) find a suitable change of coordinates (i.e., a rotation and/or a translation) so that the resulting conic section is in standard form, (ii) identify the curve, and (iii) sketch the graph:

(a) $x^2 + xy + y^2 - 6 = 0$

(b) $3x^2 + 8xy + 3y^2 + 28 = 0$

(c) $-3x^2 + 6xy + 5y^2 - 24 = 0$

(d) $x^2 + 2xy + y^2 + 3x + y - 1 = 0$

4. Let λ_1 and λ_2 be the eigenvalues of

$$A = \begin{pmatrix} a & b \\ b & c \end{pmatrix}$$

What kind of conic section will the equation

$$ax^2 + 2bxy + cy^2 = 1$$

represent if $\lambda_1 \lambda_2 < 0$? Explain.

5. Let A be a symmetric 2×2 matrix and let α be a nonzero scalar for which the equation $\mathbf{x}^T A \mathbf{x} = \alpha$ is consistent. Show that the corresponding conic section will be nondegenerate if and only if A is nonsingular.

6. Which of the matrices that follow are positive definite? Negative definite? Indefinite?

(a) $\begin{bmatrix} 3 & 2 \\ 2 & 2 \end{bmatrix}$ **(b)** $\begin{bmatrix} 3 & 4 \\ 4 & 1 \end{bmatrix}$

(c) $\begin{bmatrix} 3 & \sqrt{2} \\ \sqrt{2} & 4 \end{bmatrix}$ **(d)** $\begin{bmatrix} -2 & 0 & 1 \\ 0 & -1 & 0 \\ 1 & 0 & -2 \end{bmatrix}$

(e) $\begin{bmatrix} 1 & 2 & 1 \\ 2 & 1 & 1 \\ 1 & 1 & 2 \end{bmatrix}$ **(f)** $\begin{bmatrix} 2 & 0 & 0 \\ 0 & 5 & 3 \\ 0 & 3 & 5 \end{bmatrix}$

7. For each of the following functions, determine whether the given stationary point corresponds to a local minimum, local maximum, or saddle point:

(a) $f(x, y) = 3x^2 - xy + y^2$ $(0, 0)$

(b) $f(x, y) = \sin x + y^3 + 3xy + 2x - 3y$ $(0, -1)$

(c) $f(x, y) = \frac{1}{3}x^3 - \frac{1}{3}y^3 + 3xy + 2x - 2y$ $(1, -1)$

(d) $f(x, y) = \frac{y}{x^2} + \frac{x}{y^2} + xy$ $(1, 1)$

(e) $f(x, y, z) = x^3 + xyz + y^2 - 3x$ $(1, 0, 0)$

(f) $f(x, y, z) = -\frac{1}{4}(x^{-4} + y^{-4} + z^{-4}) + yz - x - 2y - 2z$ $(1, 1, 1)$

8. Show that if A is symmetric positive definite, then $\det(A) > 0$. Give an example of a 2×2 matrix with positive determinant that is not positive definite.

9. Show that if A is a symmetric positive definite matrix, then A is nonsingular and A^{-1} is also positive definite.

10. Let A be a singular $n \times n$ matrix. Show that $A^T A$ is positive semidefinite, but not positive definite.

11. Let A be a symmetric $n \times n$ matrix with eigenvalues $\lambda_1, \ldots, \lambda_n$. Show that there exists an orthonormal set of vectors $\{\mathbf{x}_1, \ldots, \mathbf{x}_n\}$ such that

$$\mathbf{x}^T A \mathbf{x} = \sum_{i=1}^{n} \lambda_i \left(\mathbf{x}^T \mathbf{x}_i \right)^2$$

for each $\mathbf{x} \in \mathbb{R}^n$.

12. Let A be a symmetric positive definite matrix. Show that the diagonal elements of A must all be positive.

13. Let A be a symmetric positive definite $n \times n$ matrix and let S be a nonsingular $n \times n$ matrix. Show that $S^T A S$ is positive definite.

14. Let A be a symmetric positive definite $n \times n$ matrix. Show that A can be factored into a product $Q Q^T$, where Q is an $n \times n$ matrix whose columns are mutually orthogonal. [*Hint:* See Corollary 6.4.7.]

6.7 Positive Definite Matrices

In Section 6.6, we saw that a symmetric matrix is positive definite if and only if its eigenvalues are all positive. These types of matrices occur in a wide variety of applications. They frequently arise in the numerical solution of boundary value problems by finite difference methods or by finite element methods. Because of their importance in applied mathematics, we devote this section to studying their properties.

Recall that a symmetric $n \times n$ matrix A is positive definite if $\mathbf{x}^T A \mathbf{x} > 0$ for all nonzero vectors $\mathbf{x}$ in $\mathbb{R}^n$. In Theorem 6.6.2, symmetric positive definite matrices were characterized by the condition that all their eigenvalues are positive. This characterization can be used to establish the following properties:

Property I   If A is a symmetric positive definite matrix, then A is nonsingular.
Property II   If A is a symmetric positive definite matrix, then $\det(A) > 0$.

If A were singular, $\lambda = 0$ would be an eigenvalue of A. However, since all the eigenvalues of A are positive, A must be nonsingular. The second property also follows from Theorem 6.6.2, since

$$\det(A) = \lambda_1 \cdots \lambda_n > 0$$

$$\begin{pmatrix} a_{11} & x & x & x \\ x & a_{22} & x & x \\ x & x & a_{33} & x \\ x & x & x & a_{44} \end{pmatrix} \xrightarrow{1} \begin{pmatrix} a_{11} & x & x & x \\ 0 & a_{22}^{(1)} & x & x \\ 0 & x & a_{33}^{(1)} & x \\ 0 & x & x & a_{44}^{(1)} \end{pmatrix} \xrightarrow{2} \begin{pmatrix} a_{11} & x & x & x \\ 0 & a_{22}^{(1)} & x & x \\ 0 & 0 & a_{33}^{(2)} & x \\ 0 & 0 & x & a_{44}^{(2)} \end{pmatrix} \xrightarrow{3} \begin{pmatrix} a_{11} & x & x & x \\ 0 & a_{22}^{(1)} & x & x \\ 0 & 0 & a_{33}^{(2)} & x \\ 0 & 0 & 0 & a_{44}^{(3)} \end{pmatrix}$$

$$A \qquad\qquad\qquad A^{(1)} \qquad\qquad\qquad A^{(2)} \qquad\qquad\qquad A^{(3)} = U$$

Figure 6.7.1.

Given an $n \times n$ matrix A, let A_r denote the matrix formed by deleting the last $n - r$ rows and columns of A. A_r is called the *leading principal submatrix* of A of order r. We can now state a third property of positive definite matrices:

> **Property III**   If A is a symmetric positive definite matrix, then the leading principal submatrices $A_1, A_2, \ldots, A_n$ of A are all positive definite.

Proof   To show that A_r is positive definite, $1 \le r \le n$, let $\mathbf{x}_r = (x_1, \ldots, x_r)^T$ be any nonzero vector in $\mathbb{R}^r$ and set

$$\mathbf{x} = (x_1, \ldots, x_r, 0, \ldots, 0)^T$$

Since

$$\mathbf{x}_r^T A_r \mathbf{x}_r = \mathbf{x}^T A \mathbf{x} > 0$$

it follows that A_r is positive definite.   ∎

An immediate consequence of properties **I**, **II**, and **III** is that if A_r is a leading principal submatrix of a symmetric positive definite matrix A, then A_r is nonsingular and $\det(A_r) > 0$. This has significance in relation to the Gaussian elimination process. In general, if A is an $n \times n$ matrix whose leading principal submatrices are all nonsingular, then A can be reduced to upper triangular form using only row operation III; that is, the diagonal elements will never be 0 in the elimination process, so the reduction can be completed without interchanging rows.

> **Property IV**   If A is a symmetric positive definite matrix, then A can be reduced to upper triangular form using only row operation III, and the pivot elements will all be positive.

Let us illustrate property **IV** in the case of a 4×4 symmetric positive definite matrix A. Note first that

$$a_{11} = \det(A_1) > 0$$

so a_{11} can be used as a pivot element and row 1 is the first pivot row. Let $a_{22}^{(1)}$ denote the entry in the $(2, 2)$ position after the last three elements of column 1 have been eliminated (see Figure 6.7.1). At this step, the submatrix A_2 has been transformed into a matrix:

$$\begin{bmatrix} a_{11} & a_{12} \\ 0 & a_{22}^{(1)} \end{bmatrix}$$

Since the transformation was accomplished using only row operation III, the value of the determinant remains unchanged. Thus,

$$\det(A_2) = a_{11}a_{22}^{(1)}$$

and hence

$$a_{22}^{(1)} = \frac{\det(A_2)}{a_{11}} = \frac{\det(A_2)}{\det(A_1)} > 0$$

Since $a_{22}^{(1)} \neq 0$, it can be used as a pivot in the second step of the elimination process. After step 2, the matrix A_3 has been transformed into

$$\begin{bmatrix} a_{11} & a_{12} & a_{13} \\ 0 & a_{22}^{(1)} & a_{23}^{(1)} \\ 0 & 0 & a_{33}^{(2)} \end{bmatrix}$$

Because only row operation III was used,

$$\det(A_3) = a_{11}a_{22}^{(1)}a_{33}^{(2)}$$

and hence

$$a_{33}^{(2)} = \frac{\det(A_3)}{a_{11}a_{22}^{(1)}} = \frac{\det(A_3)}{\det(A_2)} > 0$$

Thus, $a_{33}^{(2)}$ can be used as a pivot in the last step. After step 3, the remaining diagonal entry will be

$$a_{44}^{(3)} = \frac{\det(A_4)}{\det(A_3)} > 0$$

In general, if an $n \times n$ matrix A can be reduced to an upper triangular form U without any interchanges of rows, then A can be factored into a product LU, where L is lower triangular with 1's on the diagonal. The (i,j) entry of L below the diagonal will be the multiple of the ith row that was subtracted from the jth row during the elimination process. We illustrate with a 3×3 example:

EXAMPLE 1   Let

$$A = \begin{bmatrix} 4 & 2 & -2 \\ 2 & 10 & 2 \\ -2 & 2 & 5 \end{bmatrix}$$

The matrix L is determined as follows: At the first step of the elimination process, $\frac{1}{2}$ times the first row is subtracted from the second row and $-\frac{1}{2}$ times the first row is subtracted from the third. Corresponding to these operations, we set $l_{21} = \frac{1}{2}$ and $l_{31} = -\frac{1}{2}$. After step 1, we obtain the matrix

$$A^{(1)} = \begin{bmatrix} 4 & 2 & -2 \\ 0 & 9 & 3 \\ 0 & 3 & 4 \end{bmatrix}$$

The final elimination is carried out by subtracting $\frac{1}{3}$ times the second row from the third row. Corresponding to this step, we set $l_{32} = \frac{1}{3}$. After step 2, we end up with the upper triangular matrix

$$U = A^{(2)} = \begin{pmatrix} 4 & 2 & -2 \\ 0 & 9 & 3 \\ 0 & 0 & 3 \end{pmatrix}$$

The matrix L is given by

$$L = \begin{pmatrix} 1 & 0 & 0 \\ \frac{1}{2} & 1 & 0 \\ -\frac{1}{2} & \frac{1}{3} & 1 \end{pmatrix}$$

and we can verify that the product $LU = A$.

$$\begin{pmatrix} 1 & 0 & 0 \\ \frac{1}{2} & 1 & 0 \\ -\frac{1}{2} & \frac{1}{3} & 1 \end{pmatrix} \begin{pmatrix} 4 & 2 & -2 \\ 0 & 9 & 3 \\ 0 & 0 & 3 \end{pmatrix} = \begin{pmatrix} 4 & 2 & -2 \\ 2 & 10 & 2 \\ -2 & 2 & 5 \end{pmatrix}$$

To see why this factorization works, let us view that process in terms of elementary matrices. Row operation III was applied three times during the process. This is equivalent to multiplying A on the left by three elementary matrices E_1, E_2, E_3. Thus, $E_3 E_2 E_1 A = U$:

$$\begin{pmatrix} 1 & 0 & 0 \\ 0 & 1 & 0 \\ 0 & \frac{1}{3} & 1 \end{pmatrix} \begin{pmatrix} 1 & 0 & 0 \\ 0 & 1 & 0 \\ \frac{1}{2} & 0 & 1 \end{pmatrix} \begin{pmatrix} 1 & 0 & 0 \\ -\frac{1}{2} & 1 & 0 \\ 0 & 0 & 1 \end{pmatrix} \begin{pmatrix} 4 & 2 & -2 \\ 2 & 10 & 2 \\ -2 & 2 & 5 \end{pmatrix} = \begin{pmatrix} 4 & 2 & -2 \\ 0 & 9 & 3 \\ 0 & 0 & 3 \end{pmatrix}$$

Since the elementary matrices are nonsingular, it follows that

$$A = (E_1^{-1} E_2^{-1} E_3^{-1})U$$

When the inverse elementary matrices are multiplied in this order, the result is a lower triangular matrix L with 1's on the diagonal. The entries below the diagonal of L will just be the multiples that were subtracted during the elimination process.

$$E_1^{-1} E_2^{-1} E_3^{-1} = \begin{pmatrix} 1 & 0 & 0 \\ \frac{1}{2} & 1 & 0 \\ 0 & 0 & 1 \end{pmatrix} \begin{pmatrix} 1 & 0 & 0 \\ 0 & 1 & 0 \\ -\frac{1}{2} & 0 & 1 \end{pmatrix} \begin{pmatrix} 1 & 0 & 0 \\ 0 & 1 & 0 \\ 0 & \frac{1}{3} & 1 \end{pmatrix}$$

$$= \begin{pmatrix} 1 & 0 & 0 \\ \frac{1}{2} & 1 & 0 \\ -\frac{1}{2} & \frac{1}{3} & 1 \end{pmatrix}$$ ▪

Given an LU factorization of a matrix A, it is possible to go one step further and factor U into a product DU_1, where D is diagonal and U_1 is upper triangular with 1's on the diagonal:

$$DU_1 = \begin{pmatrix} u_{11} & & & \\ & u_{22} & & \\ & & \ddots & \\ & & & u_{nn} \end{pmatrix} \begin{pmatrix} 1 & \dfrac{u_{12}}{u_{11}} & \dfrac{u_{13}}{u_{11}} & \cdots & \dfrac{u_{1n}}{u_{11}} \\ & 1 & \dfrac{u_{23}}{u_{22}} & \cdots & \dfrac{u_{2n}}{u_{22}} \\ & & & & \vdots \\ & & & & 1 \end{pmatrix}$$

It follows, then, that $A = LDU_1$. The matrices L and U_1 are referred to as *unit triangular* matrices since they are triangular and their diagonal entries are all equal to 1. The representation of a square matrix A as a product of the form LDU, where L is a unit lower triangular matrix, D is diagonal, and U is a unit upper triangular matrix, is referred to as an *LDU factorization* of A. In general, if A has an LDU factorization, then it is unique (see Exercise 8 at the end of this section).

If A is a symmetric positive definite matrix, then A can be factored into a product $LU = LDU_1$. The diagonal elements of D are the entries $u_{11}, \ldots, u_{nn}$, which were the pivot elements in the elimination process. By property **IV**, these elements are all positive. Furthermore, since A is symmetric,

$$LDU_1 = A = A^T = (LDU_1)^T = U_1^T D^T L^T$$

It follows from the uniqueness of the *LDU* factorization that $L^T = U_1$. Thus,

$$A = LDL^T$$

This important factorization is often used in numerical computations. There are efficient algorithms that make use of the LDL^T factorization in solving symmetric positive definite linear systems.

> **Property V**   If A is a symmetric positive definite matrix, then A can be factored into a product LDL^T, where L is lower triangular with 1's along the diagonal and D is a diagonal matrix whose diagonal entries are all positive.

EXAMPLE 2   We saw in Example 1 that

$$A = \begin{pmatrix} 4 & 2 & -2 \\ 2 & 10 & 2 \\ -2 & 2 & 5 \end{pmatrix}$$

$$= \begin{pmatrix} 1 & 0 & 0 \\ \frac{1}{2} & 1 & 0 \\ -\frac{1}{2} & \frac{1}{3} & 1 \end{pmatrix} \begin{pmatrix} 4 & 2 & -2 \\ 0 & 9 & 3 \\ 0 & 0 & 3 \end{pmatrix} = LU$$

Factoring out the diagonal entries of U, we get

$$A = \begin{pmatrix} 1 & 0 & 0 \\ \frac{1}{2} & 1 & 0 \\ -\frac{1}{2} & \frac{1}{3} & 1 \end{pmatrix} \begin{pmatrix} 4 & 0 & 0 \\ 0 & 9 & 0 \\ 0 & 0 & 3 \end{pmatrix} \begin{pmatrix} 1 & \frac{1}{2} & -\frac{1}{2} \\ 0 & 1 & \frac{1}{3} \\ 0 & 0 & 1 \end{pmatrix} = LDL^T \qquad \blacksquare$$

Since the diagonal elements $u_{11}, \ldots, u_{nn}$ are positive, it is possible to go one step further with the factorization. Let

$$D^{1/2} = \begin{bmatrix} \sqrt{u_{11}} & & & \\ & \sqrt{u_{22}} & & \\ & & \ddots & \\ & & & \sqrt{u_{nn}} \end{bmatrix}$$

and set $L_1 = LD^{1/2}$. Then

$$A = LDL^T = LD^{1/2}(D^{1/2})^T L^T = L_1 L_1^T$$

This factorization is known as the *Cholesky decomposition* of A.

Property VI (Cholesky Decomposition)   If A is a symmetric positive definite matrix, then A can be factored into a product LL^T, where L is lower triangular with positive diagonal elements.

The Cholesky decomposition of a symmetric positive definite matrix A can also be represented in terms of an upper triangular matrix. Indeed, if A has Cholesky decomposition LL^T where L is lower triangular with positive diagonal entries, then the matrix $R = L^T$ is upper triangular with positive diagonal entries and

$$A = LL^T = R^T R$$

EXAMPLE 3   Let A be the matrix from Examples 1 and 2. If we set

$$L_1 = LD^{1/2} = \begin{bmatrix} 1 & 0 & 0 \\ \frac{1}{2} & 1 & 0 \\ -\frac{1}{2} & \frac{1}{3} & 1 \end{bmatrix} \begin{bmatrix} 2 & 0 & 0 \\ 0 & 3 & 0 \\ 0 & 0 & \sqrt{3} \end{bmatrix} = \begin{bmatrix} 2 & 0 & 0 \\ 1 & 3 & 0 \\ -1 & 1 & \sqrt{3} \end{bmatrix}$$

then

$$L_1 L_1^T = \begin{bmatrix} 2 & 0 & 0 \\ 1 & 3 & 0 \\ -1 & 1 & \sqrt{3} \end{bmatrix} \begin{bmatrix} 2 & 1 & -1 \\ 0 & 3 & 1 \\ 0 & 0 & \sqrt{3} \end{bmatrix}$$

$$= \begin{bmatrix} 4 & 2 & -2 \\ 2 & 10 & 2 \\ -2 & 2 & 5 \end{bmatrix} = A \qquad \blacksquare$$

The Cholesky factorization of the symmetric positive definite matrix A in Example 3 could also have been written in terms of the upper triangular matrix $R = L_1^T$.

$$A = L_1 L_1^T = R^T R$$

More generally, it is not difficult to show that any product of the $B^T B$ will be positive definite, provided that B is nonsingular. Putting all these results together, we have the following theorem.

Theorem 6.7.1   *Let A be a symmetric n × n matrix. The following are equivalent:*

(a) *A is positive definite.*

(b) *The leading principal submatrices $A_1, \ldots, A_n$ all have positive determinants.*

(c) *A can be reduced to upper triangular form using only row operation III, and the pivot elements will all be positive.*

(d) *A has a Cholesky factorization LL^T (where L is lower triangular with positive diagonal entries).*

(e) *A can be factored into a product $B^T B$ for some nonsingular matrix B.*

Proof   We have already shown that (a) implies (b), (b) implies (c), and (c) implies (d). To see that (d) implies (e), assume that $A = LL^T$. If we set $B = L^T$, then B is nonsingular and

$$A = LL^T = B^T B$$

Finally, to show that (e) $\Rightarrow$ (a), assume that $A = B^T B$, where B is nonsingular. Let **x** be any nonzero vector in $\mathbb{R}^n$ and set $\mathbf{y} = B\mathbf{x}$. Since B is nonsingular, $\mathbf{y} \neq \mathbf{0}$ and it follows that

$$\mathbf{x}^T A \mathbf{x} = \mathbf{x}^T B^T B \mathbf{x} = \mathbf{y}^T \mathbf{y} = \|\mathbf{y}\|^2 > 0$$

Thus, A is positive definite.   ∎

Analogous results to Theorem 6.7.1 are not valid for positive semidefiniteness. For example, consider the matrix

$$A = \begin{bmatrix} 1 & 1 & -3 \\ 1 & 1 & -3 \\ -3 & -3 & 5 \end{bmatrix}$$

The leading principal submatrices all have nonnegative determinants:

$$\det(A_1) = 1, \qquad \det(A_2) = 0, \qquad \det(A_3) = 0$$

However, A is not positive semidefinite, since it has a negative eigenvalue $\lambda = -1$. Indeed, $\mathbf{x} = (1, 1, 1)^T$ is an eigenvector belonging to $\lambda = -1$ and

$$\mathbf{x}^T A \mathbf{x} = -3$$

SECTION 6.7 EXERCISES

1. For each of the following matrices, compute the determinants of all the leading principal submatrices and use them to determine whether the matrix is positive definite:

(a) $\begin{bmatrix} 2 & -1 \\ -1 & 2 \end{bmatrix}$ (b) $\begin{bmatrix} 3 & 4 \\ 4 & 2 \end{bmatrix}$

(c) $\begin{bmatrix} 6 & 4 & -2 \\ 4 & 5 & 3 \\ -2 & 3 & 6 \end{bmatrix}$ (d) $\begin{bmatrix} 4 & 2 & 1 \\ 2 & 3 & -2 \\ 1 & -2 & 5 \end{bmatrix}$

2. Let A be a 3 × 3 symmetric positive definite matrix and suppose that $\det(A_1) = 3$, $\det(A_2) = 6$, and $\det(A_3) = 8$. What would the pivot elements be in the reduction of A to triangular form, assuming that only row operation III is used in the reduction process?

3. Let

$$A = \begin{pmatrix} 2 & -1 & 0 & 0 \\ -1 & 2 & -1 & 0 \\ 0 & -1 & 2 & -1 \\ 0 & 0 & -1 & 2 \end{pmatrix}$$

(a) Compute the LU factorization of A.

(b) Explain why A must be positive definite.

4. For each of the following, factor the given matrix into a product LDL^T, where L is lower triangular with 1's on the diagonal and D is a diagonal matrix:

(a) $\begin{bmatrix} 4 & 2 \\ 2 & 10 \end{bmatrix}$ (b) $\begin{bmatrix} 9 & -3 \\ -3 & 2 \end{bmatrix}$

(c) $\begin{bmatrix} 16 & 8 & 4 \\ 8 & 6 & 0 \\ 4 & 0 & 7 \end{bmatrix}$ (d) $\begin{bmatrix} 9 & 3 & -6 \\ 3 & 4 & 1 \\ -6 & 1 & 9 \end{bmatrix}$

5. Find the Cholesky decomposition LL^T for each of the matrices in Exercise 4.

6. Let A be an $n \times n$ symmetric positive definite matrix. For each $\mathbf{x}, \mathbf{y} \in \mathbb{R}^n$, define

$$\langle \mathbf{x}, \mathbf{y} \rangle = \mathbf{x}^T A \mathbf{y}$$

Show that $\langle \ , \ \rangle$ defines an inner product on $\mathbb{R}^n$.

7. Prove each of the following:

(a) If U is a unit upper triangular matrix, then U is nonsingular and U^{-1} is also unit upper triangular.

(b) If U_1 and U_2 are both unit upper triangular matrices, then the product $U_1 U_2$ is also a unit upper triangular matrix.

8. Let A be a nonsingular $n \times n$ matrix, and suppose that $A = L_1 D_1 U_1 = L_2 D_2 U_2$, where L_1 and L_2 are lower triangular, D_1 and D_2 are diagonal, U_1 and U_2 are upper triangular, and L_1, L_2, U_1, U_2 all have 1's along the diagonal. Show that $L_1 = L_2$, $D_1 = D_2$, and $U_1 = U_2$. [*Hint*: L_2^{-1} is lower triangular and U_1^{-1} is upper triangular. Compare both sides of the equation $D_2^{-1} L_2^{-1} L_1 D_1 = U_2 U_1^{-1}$.]

9. Let A be a symmetric positive definite matrix with Cholesky decomposition $A = LL^T = R^T R$. Prove that the lower triangular matrix L (or that the upper triangular matrix R) in the factorization is unique.

10. Let A be an $m \times n$ matrix with rank n. Show that the matrix $A^T A$ is symmetric positive definite.

11. Let A be an $m \times n$ matrix with rank n and let QR be the factorization obtained when the Gram–Schmidt process is applied to the column vectors of A. Show that if $A^T A$ has Cholesky factorization $R_1^T R_1$, then $R_1 = R$. Thus, the upper triangular factors in the Gram–Schmidt QR factorization of A and the Cholesky decomposition of $A^T A$ are identical.

12. Let A be a symmetric positive definite matrix and let Q be an orthogonal diagonalizing matrix. Use the factorization $A = QDQ^T$ to find a nonsingular matrix B such that $B^T B = A$.

13. Let A be a symmetric $n \times n$ matrix. Show that e^A is symmetric and positive definite.

14. Show that if B is a symmetric nonsingular matrix, then B^2 is positive definite.

15. Let

$$A = \begin{bmatrix} 1 & -\frac{1}{2} \\ -\frac{1}{2} & 1 \end{bmatrix} \quad \text{and} \quad B = \begin{bmatrix} 1 & -1 \\ 0 & 1 \end{bmatrix}$$

(a) Show that A is positive definite and that $\mathbf{x}^T A \mathbf{x} = \mathbf{x}^T B \mathbf{x}$ for all $\mathbf{x} \in \mathbb{R}^2$.

(b) Show that B is positive definite, but B^2 is not positive definite.

16. Let A be an $n \times n$ symmetric negative definite matrix.

(a) What will the sign of $\det(A)$ be if n is even? If n is odd?

(b) Show that the leading principal submatrices of A are negative definite.

(c) Show that the determinants of the leading principal submatrices of A alternate in sign.

17. Let A be a symmetric positive definite $n \times n$ matrix.

(a) If $k < n$, then the leading principal submatrices A_k and A_{k+1} are both positive definite and, consequently, have Cholesky factorizations $L_k L_k^T$ and $L_{k+1} L_{k+1}^T$. If A_{k+1} is expressed in the form

$$A_{k+1} = \begin{bmatrix} A_k & \mathbf{y}_k \\ \mathbf{y}_k^T & \beta_k \end{bmatrix}$$

where $\mathbf{y}_k \in \mathbb{R}^k$ and β_k is a scalar, show that L_{k+1} is of the form

$$L_{k+1} = \begin{bmatrix} L_k & \mathbf{0} \\ \mathbf{x}_k^T & \alpha_k \end{bmatrix}$$

and determine $\mathbf{x}_k$ and α_k in terms of L_k, $\mathbf{y}_k$, and β_k.

(b) The leading principal submatrix A_1 has Cholesky decomposition $L_1 L_1^T$, where $L_1 = (\sqrt{a_{11}})$. Explain how part (a) can be used to compute successively the Cholesky factorizations of $A_2, \ldots, A_n$. Devise an algorithm that computes $L_2, L_3, \ldots, L_n$ in a single loop. Since $A = A_n$, the Cholesky decomposition of A will be $L_n L_n^T$. (This algorithm is efficient in that it uses approximately half the amount of arithmetic that would generally be necessary to compute an LU factorization.)

6.8   Nonnegative Matrices

In many of the types of linear systems that occur in applications, the entries of the coefficient matrix represent nonnegative quantities. This section deals with the study of such matrices and some of their properties.

Definition

> An $n \times n$ matrix A with real entries is said to be **nonnegative** if $a_{ij} \geq 0$ for each i and j and **positive** if $a_{ij} > 0$ for each i and j.
> Similarly, a vector $\mathbf{x} = (x_1, \ldots, x_n)^T$ is said to be **nonnegative** if each $x_i \geq 0$ and **positive** if each $x_i > 0$.

For an example of one of the applications of nonnegative matrices, we consider the Leontief input–output models.

APPLICATION I   The Open Model

Suppose that there are n industries producing n different products. Each industry requires input of the products from the other industries and possibly even of its own product. In the open model, it is assumed that there is an additional demand for each of the products from an outside sector. The problem is to determine the output of each of the industries that is necessary to meet the total demand.

We will show that this problem can be represented by a linear system of equations and that the system has a unique nonnegative solution. Let a_{ij} denote the amount of input from the ith industry necessary to produce one unit of output in the jth industry. By a unit of input or output, we mean one dollar's worth of the product. Thus, the total cost of producing one dollar's worth of the jth product will be

$$a_{1j} + a_{2j} + \cdots + a_{nj}$$

Since the entries of A are all nonnegative, this sum is equal to $\|\mathbf{a}_j\|_1$. Clearly, production of the jth product will not be profitable unless $\|\mathbf{a}_j\|_1 < 1$. Let d_i denote the demand of the open sector for the ith product. Finally, let x_i represent the amount of output of the ith product necessary to meet the total demand. If the jth industry is to have an output of x_j, it will need an input of $a_{ij}x_j$ units from the ith industry. Thus, the total demand for the ith product will be

$$a_{i1}x_1 + a_{i2}x_2 + \cdots + a_{in}x_n + d_i$$

and hence we require that

$$x_i = a_{i1}x_1 + a_{i2}x_2 + \cdots + a_{in}x_n + d_i$$

for $i = 1, \ldots, n$. This leads to the system

$$
\begin{aligned}
(1 - a_{11})x_1 + (-a_{12})x_2 + \cdots + (-a_{1n})x_n &= d_1 \\
(-a_{21})x_1 + (1 - a_{22})x_2 + \cdots + (-a_{2n})x_n &= d_2 \\
&\;\;\vdots \\
(-a_{n1})x_1 + (-a_{n2})x_2 + \cdots + (1 - a_{nn})x_n &= d_n
\end{aligned}
$$

which may be written in the form

$$(I - A)\mathbf{x} = \mathbf{d} \tag{1}$$

The entries of A have two important properties:

(i) $a_{ij} \geq 0$ for each i and j.

(ii) $\|\mathbf{a}_j\|_1 = \sum_{i=1}^{n} a_{ij} < 1$ for each j.

The vector $\mathbf{x}$ must not only be a solution of (1); it must also be nonnegative. (It would not make any sense to have a negative output.)

To show that the system has a unique nonnegative solution, we need to make use of a matrix norm that is related to the 1-norm for vectors that was introduced in Section 5.4. The matrix norm is also referred to as the 1-norm and is denoted by $\| \cdot \|_1$. The definition and properties of the 1-norm for matrices are studied in Section 7.4. In that section, we will show that, for any $m \times n$ matrix B,

$$\|B\|_1 = \max_{1 \leq j \leq n} \left(\sum_{i=1}^{m} |b_{ij}| \right) = \max(\|\mathbf{b}_1\|_1, \|\mathbf{b}_2\|_1, \ldots, \|\mathbf{b}_n\|_1) \tag{2}$$

It will also be shown that the 1-norm satisfies the following multiplicative properties:

$$\|BC\|_1 \leq \|B\|_1 \|C\|_1 \qquad \text{for any matrix} \quad C \in \mathbb{R}^{n \times r} \tag{3}$$
$$\|B\mathbf{x}\|_1 \leq \|B\|_1 \|\mathbf{x}\|_1 \qquad \text{for any} \quad \mathbf{x} \in \mathbb{R}^n$$

In particular, if A is an $n \times n$ matrix satisfying conditions (i) and (ii), then it follows from (2) that $\|A\|_1 < 1$. Furthermore, if λ is any eigenvalue of A and $\mathbf{x}$ is an eigenvector belonging to λ, then

$$|\lambda| \|\mathbf{x}\|_1 = \|\lambda \mathbf{x}\|_1 = \|A\mathbf{x}\|_1 \leq \|A\|_1 \|\mathbf{x}\|_1$$

and hence

$$|\lambda| \leq \|A\|_1 < 1$$

Thus, 1 is not an eigenvalue of A. It follows that $I - A$ is nonsingular and hence the system (1) has a unique solution

$$\mathbf{x} = (I - A)^{-1}\mathbf{d}$$

We would like to show that this solution must be nonnegative. To do this, we will show that $(I - A)^{-1}$ is nonnegative. First note that, as a consequence of multiplicative property (3), we have

$$\|A^m\|_1 \leq \|A\|_1^m$$

Since $\|A\|_1 < 1$, it follows that

$$\|A^m\|_1 \to 0 \qquad \text{as} \quad m \to \infty$$

and hence A^m approaches the zero matrix as $m \to \infty$.

Since

$$(I - A)(I + A + \cdots + A^m) = I - A^{m+1}$$

it follows that

$$I + A + \cdots + A^m = (I - A)^{-1} - (I - A)^{-1}A^{m+1}$$

As $m \to \infty$,

$$(I - A)^{-1} - (I - A)^{-1}A^{m+1} \to (I - A)^{-1}$$

and hence the series $I + A + \cdots + A^m$ converges to $(I-A)^{-1}$ as $m \to \infty$. By condition (i), $I + A + \cdots + A^m$ is nonnegative for each m, and therefore $(I-A)^{-1}$ must be nonnegative. Since **d** is nonnegative, it follows that the solution **x** must be nonnegative. We see, then, that conditions **(i)** and **(ii)** guarantee that the system (1) will have a unique nonnegative solution **x**.

As you have probably guessed, there is also a closed version of the Leontief input–output model. In the closed version, it is assumed that each industry must produce enough output to meet the input needs of only the other industries and itself. The open sector is ignored. Thus, in place of the system (1), we have

$$(I - A)\mathbf{x} = \mathbf{0}$$

and we require that **x** be a positive solution. The existence of such an **x** in this case is a much deeper result than in the open version and requires some more advanced theorems.

Theorem 6.8.1   Perron's Theorem

If A is a positive $n \times n$ matrix, then A has a positive real eigenvalue r with the following properties:

(i) *r is a simple root of the characteristic equation.*

(ii) *r has a positive eigenvector **x**.*

(iii) *If λ is any other eigenvalue of A, then $|\lambda| < r$.*

The Perron theorem may be thought of as a special case of a more general theorem due to Frobenius. The Frobenius theorem applies to *irreducible* nonnegative matrices.

Definition   A nonnegative matrix A is said to be **reducible** if there exists a partition of the index set $\{1, 2, \ldots, n\}$ into nonempty disjoint sets I_1 and I_2 such that $a_{ij} = 0$ whenever $i \in I_1$ and $j \in I_2$. Otherwise, A is said to be **irreducible**.

EXAMPLE I Let A be a matrix of the form

$$\begin{pmatrix} \times & \times & 0 & 0 & \times \\ \times & \times & 0 & 0 & \times \\ \times & \times & \times & \times & \times \\ \times & \times & \times & \times & \times \\ \times & \times & 0 & 0 & \times \end{pmatrix}$$

Let $I_1 = \{1, 2, 5\}$ and $I_2 = \{3, 4\}$. Then $I_1 \cup I_2 = \{1, 2, 3, 4, 5\}$ and $a_{ij} = 0$ whenever $i \in I_1$ and $j \in I_2$. Therefore, A is reducible. If P is the permutation matrix formed by interchanging the third and fifth rows of the identity matrix I, then

$$PA = \begin{pmatrix} \times & \times & 0 & 0 & \times \\ \times & \times & 0 & 0 & \times \\ \times & \times & 0 & 0 & \times \\ \times & \times & \times & \times & \times \\ \times & \times & \times & \times & \times \end{pmatrix}$$

and

$$PAP^T = \left(\begin{array}{ccc|cc} \times & \times & \times & 0 & 0 \\ \times & \times & \times & 0 & 0 \\ \times & \times & \times & 0 & 0 \\ \hline \times & \times & \times & \times & \times \\ \times & \times & \times & \times & \times \end{array} \right)$$

In general, it can be shown that an $n \times n$ matrix A is reducible if and only if there exists a permutation matrix P such that PAP^T is a matrix of the form

$$\left(\begin{array}{c|c} B & O \\ \hline X & C \end{array} \right)$$

where B and C are square matrices. ∎

Theorem 6.8.2 Frobenius Theorem

If A is an irreducible nonnegative matrix, then A has a positive real eigenvalue r with the following properties:

(i) *r has a positive eigenvector $\mathbf{x}$.*

(ii) *If λ is any other eigenvalue of A, then $|\lambda| \leq r$. The eigenvalues with absolute value equal to r are all simple roots of the characteristic equation. Indeed, if there are m eigenvalues with absolute value equal to r, they must be of the form*

$$\lambda_k = re^{2k\pi i/m} \qquad k = 0, 1, \ldots, m-1$$

The proof of this theorem is beyond the scope of the text. We refer the reader to Gantmacher [4, Vol. 2]. Perron's theorem follows as a special case of the Frobenius theorem.

APPLICATION 2 The Closed Model

In the closed Leontief input–output model, we assume that there is no demand from the open sector and we wish to find outputs to satisfy the demands of all n industries. Thus, defining the x_i's and the a_{ij}'s as in the open model, we have

$$x_i = a_{i1}x_1 + a_{i2}x_2 + \cdots + a_{in}x_n$$

for $i = 1, \ldots, n$. The resulting system may be written in the form

$$(A - I)\mathbf{x} = \mathbf{0} \tag{4}$$

As before, we have the condition

$$a_{ij} \geq 0 \tag{i}$$

Since there is no open sector, the amount of output from the jth industry should be the same as the total input for that industry. Thus,

$$x_j = \sum_{i=1}^{n} a_{ij}x_j$$

and hence we have as our second condition

$$\sum_{i=1}^{n} a_{ij} = 1 \quad j = 1, \ldots, n \tag{ii}$$

Condition (ii) implies that $A - I$ is singular, because the sum of its row vectors is $\mathbf{0}$. Therefore, 1 is an eigenvalue of A, and since $\|A\|_1 = 1$, it follows that all the eigenvalues of A have moduli less than or equal to 1. Let us assume that enough of the coefficients of A are nonzero so that A is irreducible. Then, by Theorem 6.8.2, $\lambda = 1$ has a positive eigenvector $\mathbf{x}$. Thus, any positive multiple of $\mathbf{x}$ will be a positive solution of (4).

APPLICATION 3 Markov Chains Revisited

Nonnegative matrices also play an important role in the theory of Markov processes. Recall that if A is an $n \times n$ stochastic matrix, then $\lambda_1 = 1$ is an eigenvalue of A and the remaining eigenvalues satisfy

$$|\lambda_j| \leq 1 \quad \text{for } j = 2, \ldots, n$$

In the case that A is stochastic and all of its entries are positive, it follows from Perron's theorem that $\lambda_1 = 1$ must be a dominant eigenvalue and this, in turn, implies that the Markov chain with transition matrix A will converge to a steady-state vector for any starting probability vector $\mathbf{x}_0$. In fact, if, for some k, the matrix A^k is positive, then by Perron's theorem, $\lambda_1 = 1$ must be a dominant eigenvalue of A^k. One can then show that $\lambda_1 = 1$ must also be a dominant eigenvalue of A. (See Exercise 12.) We say that a Markov process is *regular* if all of the entries of some power of the transition matrix are strictly positive. The transition matrix for a regular Markov process will have $\lambda_1 = 1$

as a dominant eigenvalue, and hence the Markov chain is guaranteed to converge to a steady-state vector.

APPLICATION 4   Analytic Hierarchy Process: Eigenvector Computation of Weights

In Section 5.3, we considered an example involving a search process to fill a full professor position at a large university. In order to assign weights to the quality of the research of the four candidates, the committee did pairwise comparisons of the relative quality of the research publications of the candidates. After studying the publications of all the candidates, the committee agreed upon the following pairwise comparisons of the weights:

$$w_1 = 1.75w_2, \quad w_1 = 1.5w_3, \quad w_1 = 1.25w_4, \quad w_2 = 0.75w_3, \quad w_2 = 0.50w_4, \quad w_3 = 0.75w_4$$

Here, an equation such as $w_2 = 0.50w_4$ would indicate that the quality of research from candidate 2 was only half as strong as the quality of research from candidate 4. Equivalently, one could say that the quality of research from candidate 4 is twice as strong as the quality of research from candidate 2. In Chapter 5, we added the condition that the weights must all add up to 1. Using this condition, we were able to express w_4 in terms of w_1, w_2, and w_3. We then found the values of w_1, w_2, and w_3 by calculating the least squares solution to a 6×3 linear system. The calculated weight vector was $\mathbf{w}_1 = (0.3289, 0.1739, 0.2188, 0.2784)^T$.

We now consider an alternative method for computing the weight vector based on an eigenvector calculation. To do this, we first form a comparison matrix C. The (i, j) entry of C indicates how the quality of the research of candidate i compares to the quality of the research of candidate j. Thus if, for example, $w_2 = 0.5w_4$, then $c_{24} = 2$ and $c_{42} = \frac{1}{2}$. The comparison matrix for judging the quality of research is given by

$$C = \begin{bmatrix} 1 & \frac{7}{4} & \frac{3}{2} & \frac{5}{4} \\ \frac{4}{7} & 1 & \frac{3}{4} & \frac{1}{2} \\ \frac{2}{3} & \frac{4}{3} & 1 & \frac{3}{4} \\ \frac{4}{5} & 2 & \frac{4}{3} & 1 \end{bmatrix}$$

The matrix C is called a *reciprocal matrix* since it has the property that $c_{ji} = \frac{1}{c_{ij}}$ for all i and j. The matrix C is a positive matrix, so it follows by Perron's theorem that C has a dominant eigenvalue with a positive eigenvector. The dominant eigenvalue is $\lambda_1 = 4.0106$. If we compute the eigenvector belonging to λ_1 and then normalize so that its entries add up to 1, we end up with a weight vector

$$\mathbf{w}_2 = (0.3255, 0.1646, 0.2177, 0.2922)^T$$

The eigenvector solution $\mathbf{w}_2$ is very close to the weight vector $\mathbf{w}_1$ computed using least squares. Why does this eigenvector method work so well? To answer this question, let us first consider a simple example where both methods of computing weights give the exact same answer.

Suppose the mathematics department at a small college is conducting a search for an assistant professor position. Candidates will be evaluated in the areas of teaching, research, and professional activities. The committee decides that teaching is twice as important as research and 8 times as important as professional activities. The committee also decides that research is 4 times as important as professional activities. In this case, it is easy to find the weight vector since the decisions about the relative importance of the three areas were done in a consistent way.

If w_3 is the weight assigned to professional activities, then the weight for research w_2 must be $4w_3$ and the weight w_1 must be $8w_3$. So w_1 is automatically equal to $2w_2$. The weight vector then must be of the form $\mathbf{w} = (8w_3, 4w_3, w_3)^T$. In order for the entries of $\mathbf{w}$ to add up to 1, the value of w_3 must be $\frac{1}{13}$. If we use the least squares method discussed in Section 5.3, we would set $w_3 = 1 - w_1 - w_1$. The weight vector would then be computed by finding the least squares solution to a 3×2 linear system. In this case, the 3×2 system is consistent, so the least squares solution is the exact solution and our computed weight vector is $\mathbf{w} = (\frac{8}{13}, \frac{4}{13}, \frac{1}{13})^T$.

Let us now compute the weight vector using the eigenvector method. To do this, we first form the comparison matrix

$$C = \begin{bmatrix} 1 & 2 & 8 \\ \frac{1}{2} & 1 & 4 \\ \frac{1}{8} & \frac{1}{4} & 1 \end{bmatrix}$$

Note that $c_{12} = 2$ since teaching is considered twice as important as professional activities and $c_{23} = 4$ since research is considered 4 times as important as professional activities. Because the judgments of relative importance were made in a consistent manner, the value of c_{13}, the relative importance of teaching to professional activities, should be

$$c_{13} = 2 \cdot 4 = c_{12}c_{23}$$

Indeed, if all decisions on the relative importance of the criteria are made in a consistent manner, then the entries of the comparison matrix will satisfy the property $c_{ij} = c_{ik}c_{kj}$ for all i, j, and k. A reciprocal comparison matrix with this property is said to be *consistent*. Note that the matrix C in our example has rank 1 since

$$\mathbf{c}_1 = \frac{1}{8}\mathbf{c}_3 \quad \text{and} \quad \mathbf{c}_2 = \frac{1}{4}\mathbf{c}_3$$

In general, if C is an $n \times n$ consistent reciprocal comparison matrix and $\mathbf{c}_j$ and $\mathbf{c}_k$ are column vectors of C, then

$$\mathbf{c}_j = \begin{bmatrix} c_{1j} \\ c_{2j} \\ \vdots \\ c_{nj} \end{bmatrix} = \begin{bmatrix} c_{1k}c_{kj} \\ c_{2k}c_{kj} \\ \vdots \\ c_{nk}c_{kj} \end{bmatrix} = c_{kj}\mathbf{c}_k$$

Therefore, C must have rank equal to 1. It follows that 0 must be an eigenvalue of C and the dimension of its eigenspace must be $n - 1$, the nullity of C. So 0 must be an eigenvalue of multiplicity $n - 1$. The remaining eigenvalue λ_1 must equal the trace of C. So $\lambda_1 = n$ is the dominant eigenvalue of C. Furthermore, since C has rank 1, any column vector of C will be an eigenvector belonging to the dominant eigenvalue. (See Exercise 17 in Section 6.3.)

For our example, it follows that the dominant eigenvalue of C is $\lambda_1 = 3$ and that $\mathbf{c}_3$ is an eigenvector belonging to λ_1. If we divide $\mathbf{c}_3$ by the sum of its entries, we end up with the weight vector $\mathbf{w} = (\frac{8}{13}, \frac{4}{13}, \frac{1}{13})^T$.

In general, if the decisions on the relative importance are made in a consistent manner, then there is only one way to choose the weights and both the least squares method and the eigenvector method will produce the same weight vector. Suppose now that the decisions are not made in a consistent manner. This is not uncommon when decisions are made based on human judgments. For the least squares method, the linear system in the variables $w_1, w_2, \ldots, w_{n-1}$ will not be consistent, but we can always find a least squares solution. If the eigenvector method is used, the comparison matrix C_1 will not be consistent. By Perron's theorem, C_1 will have a positive dominant eigenvalue λ_1 and a positive eigenvector $\mathbf{x}_1$. The eigenvector can be scaled to form a vector $\mathbf{w}_1$ whose entries add to 1. The scaled vector $\mathbf{w}_1$ is used to assign weights to the criteria. If the decisions on the relative importance have not been made in a wildly inconsistent manner, but in a way that is in some sense close to being consistent, then the eigenvector $\mathbf{w}_1$ is a reasonable choice for a weight vector. In this case, the matrix C_1 should in some sense be close to a consistent reciprocal comparison matrix and λ_1 and $\mathbf{w}_1$ should be close to the dominant eigenvalue and eigenvector of a consistent matrix.

Suppose, for example, that the search committee at the college had decided, as before, that teaching is twice as important as research and 8 times as important as professional activities; however, suppose this time they decided that research should only be 3 times as important as professional activities. In this case, the comparison matrix is

$$C_1 = \begin{bmatrix} 1 & 2 & 8 \\ \frac{1}{2} & 1 & 3 \\ \frac{1}{8} & \frac{1}{3} & 1 \end{bmatrix}$$

The matrix C_1 is not consistent so its dominant eigenvalue $\lambda_1 = 3.0092$ is not equal to 3; however, it is close to 3. The eigenvector belonging to λ_1 (normalized so that its entries add up to 1) is $\mathbf{w}_1 = (0.6282, 0.2854, 0.0864)^T$. Table 6.8.1 summarizes the results for both the problem with the consistent comparison matrix and for the inconsistent version of the problem. For each comparison matrix, the table includes the dominant eigenvalue and the computed weights. All computed values are rounded to four decimal places.

Table 6.8.1   A Comparison of Comparison Matrices

Matrix	Eigenvalue	Weights		
		Teaching	Research	Prof. Activities
C	3	0.6154	0.3077	0.0769
C_1	3.0092	0.6282	0.2854	0.0864

SECTION 6.8 EXERCISES

1. Find the eigenvalues of each of the following matrices and verify that conditions (i), (ii), and (iii) of Theorem 6.8.1 hold:

(a) $\begin{bmatrix} 2 & 3 \\ 2 & 1 \end{bmatrix}$ (b) $\begin{bmatrix} 4 & 2 \\ 2 & 7 \end{bmatrix}$

(c) $\begin{bmatrix} 1 & 2 & 4 \\ 2 & 4 & 1 \\ 1 & 2 & 4 \end{bmatrix}$

2. Find the eigenvalues of each of the following matrices and verify that conditions (i) and (ii) of Theorem 6.8.2 hold:

(a) $\begin{bmatrix} 2 & 3 \\ 1 & 0 \end{bmatrix}$ (b) $\begin{bmatrix} 0 & 2 \\ 2 & 0 \end{bmatrix}$

(c) $\begin{bmatrix} 0 & 0 & 8 \\ 1 & 0 & 0 \\ 0 & 1 & 0 \end{bmatrix}$

3. Find the output vector $\mathbf{x}$ in the open version of the Leontief input–output model if

$$A = \begin{bmatrix} 0.2 & 0.4 & 0.4 \\ 0.4 & 0.2 & 0.2 \\ 0.0 & 0.2 & 0.2 \end{bmatrix} \quad \text{and} \quad \mathbf{d} = \begin{bmatrix} 16{,}000 \\ 8{,}000 \\ 24{,}000 \end{bmatrix}$$

4. Consider the closed version of the Leontief input–output model with input matrix

$$A = \begin{bmatrix} 0.5 & 0.4 & 0.1 \\ 0.5 & 0.0 & 0.5 \\ 0.0 & 0.6 & 0.4 \end{bmatrix}$$

If $\mathbf{x} = (x_1, x_2, x_3)^T$ is any output vector for this model, how are the coordinates x_1, x_2, and x_3 related?

5. Prove: If $A^m = O$ for some positive integer m, then $I - A$ is nonsingular.

6. Let

$$A = \begin{bmatrix} 0 & 1 & 1 \\ 0 & -1 & 1 \\ 0 & -1 & 1 \end{bmatrix}$$

(a) Compute $(I - A)^{-1}$.

(b) Compute A^2 and A^3. Verify that $(I - A)^{-1} = I + A + A^2$.

7. Which of the matrices that follow are reducible? For each reducible matrix, find a permutation matrix P such that PAP^T is of the form

$$\begin{bmatrix} B & O \\ \hline X & C \end{bmatrix}$$

where B and C are square matrices.

(a) $\begin{bmatrix} 1 & 1 & 1 & 0 \\ 1 & 1 & 1 & 0 \\ 1 & 1 & 1 & 1 \\ 1 & 1 & 1 & 1 \end{bmatrix}$ (b) $\begin{bmatrix} 1 & 0 & 1 & 1 \\ 1 & 1 & 1 & 1 \\ 1 & 0 & 1 & 1 \\ 1 & 0 & 1 & 1 \end{bmatrix}$

(c) $\begin{bmatrix} 1 & 0 & 1 & 0 & 0 \\ 0 & 1 & 1 & 1 & 1 \\ 1 & 0 & 1 & 0 & 0 \\ 1 & 1 & 0 & 1 & 1 \\ 1 & 1 & 1 & 1 & 1 \end{bmatrix}$

(d) $\begin{bmatrix} 1 & 1 & 1 & 1 & 1 \\ 1 & 1 & 0 & 0 & 1 \\ 1 & 1 & 1 & 1 & 1 \\ 1 & 1 & 0 & 0 & 1 \\ 1 & 1 & 0 & 0 & 1 \end{bmatrix}$

8. Let A be a nonnegative irreducible 3×3 matrix whose eigenvalues satisfy $\lambda_1 = 2 = |\lambda_2| = |\lambda_3|$. Determine λ_2 and λ_3.

9. Let

$$A = \begin{bmatrix} B & O \\ \hline O & C \end{bmatrix}$$

where B and C are square matrices.

(a) If λ is an eigenvalue of B with eigenvector $\mathbf{x} = (x_1, \ldots, x_k)^T$, show that λ is also an eigenvalue of A with eigenvector $\tilde{\mathbf{x}} = (x_1, \ldots, x_k, 0, \ldots, 0)^T$.

(b) If B and C are positive matrices, show that A has a positive real eigenvalue r with the property that $|\lambda| < r$ for any eigenvalue $\lambda \neq r$. Show also that the multiplicity of r is at most 2 and that r has a nonnegative eigenvector.

(c) If $B = C$, show that the eigenvalue r in part (b) has multiplicity 2 and possesses a positive eigenvector.

10. Prove that a 2×2 matrix A is reducible if and only if $a_{12}a_{21} = 0$.

11. Prove the Frobenius theorem in the case where A is a 2×2 matrix.

12. We can show that, for an $n \times n$ stochastic matrix, $\lambda_1 = 1$ is an eigenvalue and the remaining eigenvalues must satisfy

$$|\lambda_j| \le 1 \quad j = 2, \ldots, n$$

(See Exercise 24 of Section 7.4.) Show that if A is an $n \times n$ stochastic matrix with the property that A^k is a positive matrix for some positive integer k, then

$$|\lambda_j| < 1 \quad j = 2, \ldots, n$$

13. Let A be an $n \times n$ positive stochastic matrix with dominant eigenvalue $\lambda_1 = 1$ and linearly independent eigenvectors $\mathbf{x}_1, \mathbf{x}_2, \ldots, \mathbf{x}_n$, and let $\mathbf{y}_0$ be an initial probability vector for a Markov chain

$$\mathbf{y}_0, \ \mathbf{y}_1 = A\mathbf{y}_0, \ \mathbf{y}_2 = A\mathbf{y}_1, \ \ldots$$

(a) Show that $\lambda_1 = 1$ has a positive eigenvector $\mathbf{x}_1$.

(b) Show that $\|\mathbf{y}_j\|_1 = 1$, $j = 0, 1, \ldots$.

(c) Show that if

$$\mathbf{y}_0 = c_1 \mathbf{x}_1 + c_2 \mathbf{x}_2 + \cdots + c_n \mathbf{x}_n$$

then the component c_1 in the direction of the positive eigenvector $\mathbf{x}_1$ must be nonzero.

(d) Show that the state vectors $\mathbf{y}_j$ of the Markov chain converge to a steady-state vector.

(e) Show that

$$c_1 = \frac{1}{\|\mathbf{x}_1\|_1}$$

and hence the steady-state vector is independent of the initial probability vector $\mathbf{y}_0$.

14. Would the results of parts (c) and (d) in Exercise 13 be valid if the stochastic matrix A was not a positive matrix? Answer this same question in the case when A is a nonnegative stochastic matrix and, for some positive integer k, the matrix A^k is positive. Explain your answers.

15. A management student received fellowship offers from four universities and now must choose which one to accept. The student uses the analytic hierarchy process to decide among the universities and bases the decision process on the following four criteria:

(i) financial matters—tuition and scholarships
(ii) the reputation of the university
(iii) social life at the university
(iv) geography—how desirable is the location of the university

In order to weigh the criteria, the student decides that finance and reputation are equally important and both are 4 times as important as social life and 6 times as important as geography. The student also rates social life twice as important as geography.

(a) Determine a reciprocal comparison matrix C based on the given judgments of the relative importance of the four criteria.

(b) Show that the matrix C is not consistent.

(c) Make the problem consistent by changing the relative importance of one pair of criteria and determine a new comparison matrix C_1 for the consistent problem.

(d) Find an eigenvector belonging to the dominant eigenvalue of C_1 and use it to determine a weight vector for the decision criteria.

Chapter 6 Exercises

MATLAB EXERCISES

Critical Loads for a Beam

1. Consider the application relating to critical loads for a beam from Section 6.1. For simplicity, we will assume that the beam has length 1 and that its flexural rigidity is also 1. Following the method described in the application, if the interval $[0, 1]$ is partitioned into n subintervals, then the problem can be translated into a matrix equation $A\mathbf{y} = \lambda\mathbf{y}$. The critical load for the beam can be approximated by setting $P = sn^2$, where s is the smallest eigenvalue of A. For $n = 100, 200, 400$, form the coefficient matrix by setting

$$D = \mathbf{diag}(\mathbf{ones}(n-1,1),1);$$
$$A = 2*\mathbf{eye}(n) - D - D';$$

In each case, determine the smallest eigenvalue of A by setting

$$s = \mathbf{min}(\mathbf{eig}(A))$$

and then compute the corresponding approximation to the critical load.

Diagonalizable and Defective Matrices

2. Construct a symmetric matrix A by setting

$$A = \mathbf{round}(5*\mathbf{rand}(6)); \qquad A = A + A'$$

Compute the eigenvalues of A by setting

$$\mathbf{e} = \mathbf{eig}(A)$$

(a) The trace of A can be computed with the MATLAB command $\mathbf{trace}(A)$, and the sum of the eigenvalues of A can be computed with the command $\mathbf{sum}(\mathbf{e})$. Compute both of these quantities and compare the results. Use the command $\mathbf{prod}(\mathbf{e})$ to compute the product of the eigenvalues of A and compare the result with $\mathbf{det}(A)$.

(b) Compute the eigenvectors of A by setting $[X, D] = \mathbf{eig}(A)$. Use MATLAB to compute $X^{-1}AX$ and compare the result with D. Compute also A^{-1} and $XD^{-1}X^{-1}$ and compare the results.

3. Set

$$A = \mathbf{ones}(10) + \mathbf{eye}(10)$$

(a) What is the rank of $A - I$? Why must $\lambda = 1$ be an eigenvalue of multiplicity 9? Compute the trace of A using the MATLAB function **trace**. The remaining eigenvalue λ_{10} must equal 11. Why? Explain. Compute the eigenvalues of A by setting $\mathbf{e} = \mathbf{eig}(A)$. Examine the eigenvalues, using **format long**. How many digits of accuracy are there in the computed eigenvalues?

(b) The MATLAB routine for computing eigenvalues is based on the QR algorithm described in Section 7.6. We can also compute the eigenvalues of A by computing the roots of its characteristic polynomial. To determine the coefficients of the characteristic polynomial of A, set $\mathbf{p} = \mathbf{poly}(A)$. The characteristic polynomial of A should have integer coefficients. Why? Explain. If we set $\mathbf{p} = \mathbf{round}(\mathbf{p})$, we should end up with the exact coefficients of the characteristic polynomial of A. Compute the roots of $\mathbf{p}$ by setting

$$\mathbf{r} = \mathbf{roots}(\mathbf{p})$$

and display the results, using **format long**. How many digits of accuracy are there in the computed results? Which method of computing eigenvalues is more accurate, using the **eig** function or computing the roots of the characteristic polynomial?

4. Consider the matrices

$$A = \begin{pmatrix} 5 & -3 \\ 3 & -5 \end{pmatrix} \quad \text{and} \quad B = \begin{pmatrix} 5 & -3 \\ 3 & 5 \end{pmatrix}$$

Note that the two matrices are the same except for their (2, 2) entries.

(a) Use MATLAB to compute the eigenvalues of A and B. Do they have the same type of eigenvalues? The eigenvalues of the matrices are the roots of their characteristic polynomials. Use the following MATLAB commands to form the polynomials and plot their graphs on the same axis system:

```
p = poly(A);
q = poly(B);
x = -8 : 0.1 : 8;
z = zeros(size(x));
y = polyval(p, x);
w = polyval(q, x);
plot(x, y, x, w, x, z)
hold on
```

The **hold on** command is used so that subsequent plots in part (b) will be added to the current figure. How can you use the graph to estimate the eigenvalues of A? What does the graph tell you about the eigenvalues of B? Explain.

(b) To see how the eigenvalues change as the (2, 2) entry changes, let us construct a matrix C with a

variable (2, 2) entry. Set

$$t = \mathbf{sym}('t') \qquad C = [5, -3; 3, t - 5]$$

As t goes from 0 to 10, the (2, 2) entries of these matrices go from -5 to 5. Use the following MATLAB commands to plot the graphs of the characteristic polynomials for the intermediate matrices corresponding to $t = 1, 2, \ldots, 9$:

```
p = poly(C)
for j = 1 : 9
    s = subs(p, t, j);
    ezplot(s, [-10, 10])
    axis([-10, 10, -20, 220])
    pause(2)
end
```

Which of these intermediate matrices have real eigenvalues and which have complex eigenvalues? The characteristic polynomial of the symbolic matrix C is a quadratic polynomial whose coefficients are functions of t. To find exactly where the eigenvalues change from real to complex, write the discriminant of the quadratic as a function of t and then find its roots. One root should be in the interval $(0, 10)$. Plug that value of t back into the matrix C and determine the eigenvalues of the matrix. Explain how these results correspond to your graph. Solve for the eigenvectors by hand. Is the matrix diagonalizable?

5. Set

$$B = \mathbf{toeplitz}(0 : -1 : -3, 0 : 3)$$

The matrix B is not symmetric and hence it is not guaranteed to be diagonalizable. Use MATLAB to verify that the rank of B equals 2. Explain why 0 must be an eigenvalue of B and the corresponding eigenspace must have dimension 2. Set $[X, D] = \mathbf{eig}(B)$. Compute $X^{-1}BX$ and compare the result with D. Compute also XD^5X^{-1} and compare the result with B^5.

6. Set

$$C = \mathbf{triu}(\mathbf{ones}(4), 1) + \mathbf{diag}([1, -1], -2)$$

and

$$[X, D] = \mathbf{eig}(C)$$

Compute $X^{-1}CX$ and compare the result with D. Is C diagonalizable? Compute the rank of X and the condition number of X. If the condition number of X is large, the computed values for the eigenvalues may not be accurate. Compute the reduced row echelon form of C. Explain why 0 must be an eigenvalue of C and the corresponding eigenspace must have dimension 1. Use

MATLAB to compute C^4. It should equal the zero matrix. Given that $C^4 = O$, what can you conclude about the actual values of the other three eigenvalues of C? Explain. Is C defective? Explain.

7. Construct a defective matrix by setting

$$A = \textbf{ones}(6); \qquad A = A - \textbf{tril}(A) - \textbf{triu}(A, 2)$$

It is easily seen that $\lambda = 0$ is the only eigenvalue of A and that its eigenspace is spanned by $\mathbf{e}_1$. Verify that this is indeed the case by using MATLAB to compute the eigenvalues and eigenvectors of A. Examine the eigenvectors using **format long**. Are the computed eigenvectors multiples of $\mathbf{e}_1$? Now perform a similarity transformation on A. Set

$$Q = \textbf{orth}(\textbf{rand}(6)); \qquad \text{and} \qquad B = Q' * A * Q$$

If the computations had been done in exact arithmetic, the matrix B would be similar to A and hence defective. Use MATLAB to compute the eigenvalues of B and a matrix X consisting of the eigenvectors of B. Determine the rank of X. Is the computed matrix B defective? Because of rounding error, a more reasonable question to ask is whether the computed matrix B is close to being defective (i.e., are the column vectors of X close to being linearly dependent?). To answer this question, use MATLAB to compute **rcond**(X), the reciprocal of the condition number of X. A value of **rcond** close to zero indicates that X is nearly rank deficient.

8. Generate a matrix A by setting

$$B = [-1, -1; 1, 1],$$
$$A = [\textbf{zeros}(2), \textbf{eye}(2); \textbf{eye}(2), B]$$

(a) The matrix A should have eigenvalues $\lambda_1 = 1$ and $\lambda_2 = -1$. Use MATLAB to verify that these are the correct eigenvalues by computing the reduced row echelon forms of $A - I$ and $A + I$. What are the dimensions of the eigenspaces of λ_1 and λ_2?

(b) It is easily seen that $\textbf{trace}(A) = 0$ and $\textbf{det}(A) = 1$. Verify these results in MATLAB. Use the values of the trace and determinant to prove that 1 and -1 are actually both double eigenvalues. Is A defective? Explain.

(c) Set $\mathbf{e} = \textbf{eig}(A)$ and examine the eigenvalues using **format long**. How many digits of accuracy are there in the computed eigenvalues? Set $[X, D] = \textbf{eig}(A)$ and compute the condition number of X. The log of the condition number gives an estimate of how many digits of accuracy are lost in the computation of the eigenvalues of A.

(d) Compute the rank of X. Are the computed eigenvectors linearly independent? Use MATLAB to compute $X^{-1}AX$. Does the computed matrix X diagonalize A?

Application: Sex-Linked Genes

9. Suppose that 10,000 men and 10,000 women settle on an island in the Pacific that has been opened to development. Suppose also that a medical study of the settlers finds that 200 of the men are color blind and only 9 of the women are color blind. Let $x(1)$ denote the proportion of genes for color blindness in the male population and let $x(2)$ be the proportion for the female population. Assume that $x(1)$ is equal to the proportion of color-blind males and that $x(2)^2$ is equal to the proportion of color-blind females. Determine $x(1)$ and $x(2)$ and enter them in MATLAB as a column vector $\mathbf{x}$. Enter also the matrix A from Application 3 of Section 6.3. Set MATLAB to **format long**, and use the matrix A to compute the proportions of genes for color blindness for each sex in generations 5, 10, 20, and 40. What are the limiting percentages of genes for color blindness for this population? In the long run, what percentage of males and what percentage of females will be color blind?

Similarity

10. Set

$$S = \textbf{round}(10 * \textbf{rand}(5));$$
$$S = \textbf{triu}(S, 1) + \textbf{eye}(5)$$
$$S = S' * S$$
$$T = \textbf{inv}(S)$$

(a) The exact inverse of S should have integer entries. Why? Explain. Check the entries of T using **format long**. Round the entries of T to the nearest integer by setting $T = \textbf{round}(T)$. Compute $T * S$ and compare with **eye**(5).

(b) Set

$$A = \textbf{triu}(\textbf{ones}(5), 1) + \textbf{diag}(1 : 5),$$

$$B = S * A * T$$

The matrices A and B both have the eigenvalues 1, 2, 3, 4, and 5. Use MATLAB to compute the eigenvalues of B. How many digits of accuracy are there in the computed eigenvalues? Use MATLAB to compute and compare each of the following:

(i) det(A) and det(B)

(ii) $\textbf{trace}(A)$ and $\textbf{trace}(B)$

(iii) SA^2T and B^2

(iv) $SA^{-1}T$ and B^{-1}

Hermitian Matrices

11. Construct a complex Hermitian matrix by setting

$$j = \mathbf{sqrt}(-1);$$
$$A = \mathbf{rand}(5) + j * \mathbf{rand}(5);$$
$$A = (A + A')/2$$

(a) The eigenvalues of A should be real. Why? Compute the eigenvalues and examine your results, using **format long**. Are the computed eigenvalues real? Compute also the eigenvectors by setting

$$[X, D] = \mathbf{eig}(A)$$

What type of matrix would you expect X to be? Use the MATLAB command $X' * X$ to compute $X^H X$. Do the results agree with your expectations?

(b) Set

$$E = D + j * \mathbf{eye}(5) \qquad \text{and} \qquad B = X * E/X$$

What type of matrix would you expect B to be? Use MATLAB to compute $B^H B$ and BB^H. How do these two matrices compare?

Optimization

12. Use the following MATLAB commands to construct a symbolic function:

syms x y
$$f = (y + 1)\hat{\ }3 + x * y\hat{\ }2 + y\hat{\ }2 - 4 * x * y - 4 * y + 1$$

Compute the first partials of f and the Hessian of f by setting

$$fx = \mathbf{diff}(f, x), fy = \mathbf{diff}(f, y)$$
$$H = [\mathbf{diff}(fx, x), \mathbf{diff}(fx, y); \mathbf{diff}(fy, x), \mathbf{diff}(fy, y)]$$

We can use the **subs** command to evaluate the Hessian for any pair (x, y). For example, to evaluate the Hessian when $x = 3$ and $y = 5$, set

$$H1 = \mathbf{subs}(H, [x, y], [3, 5])$$

Use the MATLAB command **solve**(fx, fy) to determine vectors **x** and **y** containing the x- and y-coordinates of the stationary points. Evaluate the Hessian at each stationary point and then determine whether the stationary point is a local maximum, local minimum, or saddle point.

Positive Definite Matrices

13. Set

$$C = \mathbf{ones}(6) + 7 * \mathbf{eye}(6)$$

and

$$[X, D] = \mathbf{eig}(C)$$

(a) Even though $\lambda = 7$ is an eigenvalue of multiplicity 5, the matrix C cannot be defective. Why? Explain. Check that C is not defective by computing the rank of X. Compute also $X^T X$. What type of matrix is X? Explain. Compute also the rank of $C - 7I$. What can you conclude about the dimension of the eigenspace corresponding to $\lambda = 7$? Explain.

(b) The matrix C should be symmetric positive definite. Why? Explain. Thus, C should have a Cholesky factorization LL^T. The MATLAB command $R = \mathbf{chol}(C)$ will generate an upper triangular matrix R that is equal to L^T. Compute R in this manner and set $L = R'$. Use MATLAB to verify that

$$C = LL^T = R^T R$$

(c) Alternatively, one can determine the Cholesky factors from the LU factorization of C. Set

$$[L \ U] = \mathbf{lu}(C)$$

and

$$D = \mathbf{diag}(\mathbf{sqrt}(\mathbf{diag}(U)))$$

and

$$W = (L * D)'$$

How do R and W compare? This method of computing the Cholesky factorization is less efficient than the method MATLAB uses for its **Chol** function.

14. For various values of k, form an $k \times k$ matrix A by setting

$$D = \mathbf{diag}(\mathbf{ones}(k - 1, 1), 1);$$
$$A = 2 * \mathbf{eye}(k) - D - D';$$

In each case, compute the LU factorization of A and the determinant of A. If A is an $n \times n$ matrix of this form, what will its LU factorization be? What will its determinant be? Why must the matrix be positive definite?

15. For any positive integer n, the MATLAB command $P = \mathbf{pascal}(n)$ will generate an $n \times n$ matrix P whose entries are given by

$$p_{ij} = \begin{cases} 1 & \text{if } i = 1 \;\; \text{or} \;\; j = 1 \\ p_{i-1,j} + p_{i,j-1} & \text{if } i > 1 \;\; \text{and} \;\; j > 1 \end{cases}$$

The name **pascal** refers to Pascal's triangle, a triangular array of numbers that is used to generate binomial coefficients. The entries of the matrix P form a section of Pascal's triangle.

   (a) Set

$$P = \mathbf{pascal}(6)$$

   and compute the value of its determinant. Now subtract 1 from the $(6, 6)$ entry of P by setting

$$P(6, 6) = P(6, 6) - 1$$

   and compute the determinant of the new matrix P. What is the overall effect of subtracting 1 from the $(6, 6)$ entry of the 6×6 Pascal matrix?

   (b) In part (a), we saw that the determinant of the 6×6 Pascal matrix is 1, but if we subtract 1 from the $(6, 6)$ entry, the matrix becomes singular. Will this happen in general for $n \times n$ Pascal matrices? To answer this question, consider the cases $n = 4, 8, 12$.

In each case, set $P = \mathbf{pascal}(n)$ and compute its determinant. Next, subtract 1 from the (n, n) entry and compute the determinant of the resulting matrix. Does the property that we discovered in part (a) appear to hold for Pascal matrices in general?

   (c) Set

$$P = \mathbf{pascal}(8)$$

   and examine its leading principal submatrices. Assuming that all Pascal matrices have determinants equal to 1, why must P be positive definite? Compute the upper triangular Cholesky factor R of P. How can the nonzero entries of R be generated as a Pascal triangle? In general, how is the determinant of a positive definite matrix related to the determinant of one of its Cholesky factors? Why must $\det(P) = 1$?

   (d) Set

$$R(8, 8) = 0 \qquad \text{and} \qquad Q = R' * R$$

   The matrix Q should be singular. Why? Explain. Why must the matrices P and Q be the same except for the $(8, 8)$ entry? Why must $q_{88} = p_{88} - 1$? Explain. Verify the relation between P and Q by computing the difference $P - Q$.

CHAPTER TEST A   True or False

In each of the following, answer true *if the statement is always true and* false *otherwise. In the case of a true statement, explain or prove your answer. In the case of a false statement, give an example to show that the statement is not always true.*

1. If A is an $n \times n$ matrix whose eigenvalues are all nonzero, then A is nonsingular.

2. If A is an $n \times n$ matrix, then A and A^T have the same eigenvectors.

3. If A and B are similar matrices, then they have the same eigenvalues.

4. If A and B are $n \times n$ matrices with the same eigenvalues, then they are similar.

5. If A has eigenvalues of multiplicity greater than 1, then A must be defective.

6. If A is a 4×4 matrix of rank 3 and $\lambda = 0$ is an eigenvalue of multiplicity 3, then A is diagonalizable.

7. If A is a 4×4 matrix of rank 1 and $\lambda = 0$ is an eigenvalue of multiplicity 3, then A is defective.

8. The rank of an $n \times n$ matrix A is equal to the number of nonzero eigenvalues of A, where eigenvalues are counted according to multiplicity.

9. The rank of an $m \times n$ matrix A is equal to the number of nonzero singular values of A, where singular values are counted according to multiplicity.

10. If A is Hermitian and c is a complex scalar, then cA is Hermitian.

11. If an $n \times n$ matrix A has Schur decomposition $A = UTU^H$, then the eigenvalues of A are $t_{11}, t_{22}, \ldots, t_{nn}$.

12. If A is normal, but not Hermitian, then A must have at least one complex eigenvalue.

13. If A is symmetric positive definite, then A is nonsingular and A^{-1} is also symmetric positive definite.

14. If A is symmetric and $\det(A) > 0$, then A is positive definite.

15. If A is symmetric, then e^A is symmetric positive definite.

CHAPTER TEST B

1. Let

$$A = \begin{bmatrix} 1 & 0 & 0 \\ 1 & 1 & -1 \\ 1 & 2 & -2 \end{bmatrix}$$

   (a) Find the eigenvalues of A.

   (b) For each eigenvalue, find a basis for the corresponding eigenspace.

   (c) Factor A into a product XDX^{-1}, where D is a diagonal matrix, and then use the factorization to compute A^7.

2. Let A be a 4×4 matrix with real entries that has all 1's on the main diagonal (i.e., $a_{11} = a_{22} = a_{33} = a_{44} = 1$). If A is singular and $\lambda_1 = 3 + 2i$ is an eigenvalue of A, then what, if anything, is it possible to conclude about the values of the remaining eigenvalues λ_2, λ_3, and λ_4? Explain.

3. Let A be a nonsingular $n \times n$ matrix and let λ be an eigenvalue of A.

   (a) Show that $\lambda \neq 0$.

   (b) Show that $\dfrac{1}{\lambda}$ is an eigenvalue of A^{-1}.

4. Show that if A is a matrix of the form

$$A = \begin{bmatrix} a & 0 & 0 \\ 0 & a & 1 \\ 0 & 0 & a \end{bmatrix}$$

   then A must be defective.

5. Let

$$A = \begin{bmatrix} 4 & 2 & 2 \\ 2 & 10 & 10 \\ 2 & 10 & 14 \end{bmatrix}$$

   (a) Without computing the eigenvalues of A, show that A is positive definite.

   (b) Factor A into a product LDL^T, where L is unit lower triangular and D is diagonal.

   (c) Compute the Cholesky factorization of A.

6. The function

$$f(x, y) = x^3 y + x^2 + y^2 - 2x - y + 4$$

   has a stationary point $(1, 0)$. Compute the Hessian of f at $(1, 0)$, and use it to determine whether the stationary point is a local maximum, local minimum, or saddle point.

7. Given

$$\mathbf{Y}'(t) = A\mathbf{Y}(t) \qquad\qquad \mathbf{Y}(0) = \mathbf{Y}_0$$

   where

$$A = \begin{bmatrix} 1 & -2 \\ 3 & -4 \end{bmatrix} \qquad \mathbf{Y}_0 = \begin{bmatrix} 1 \\ 2 \end{bmatrix}$$

   compute e^{tA} and use it to solve the initial value problem.

8. Let A be a 4×4 real symmetric matrix with eigenvalues

$$\lambda_1 = 1, \quad \lambda_2 = \lambda_3 = \lambda_4 = 0$$

   (a) Explain why the multiple eigenvalue $\lambda = 0$ must have three linearly independent eigenvectors $\mathbf{x}_2$, $\mathbf{x}_3$, $\mathbf{x}_4$.

   (b) Let $\mathbf{x}_1$ be an eigenvector belonging to λ_1. How is $\mathbf{x}_1$ related to $\mathbf{x}_2$, $\mathbf{x}_3$, and $\mathbf{x}_4$? Explain.

   (c) Explain how to use $\mathbf{x}_1$, $\mathbf{x}_2$, $\mathbf{x}_3$, and $\mathbf{x}_4$ to construct an orthogonal matrix U that diagonalizes A.

   (d) What type of matrix is e^A? Is it symmetric? Is it positive definite? Explain your answers.

9. Let $\{\mathbf{u}_1, \mathbf{u}_2\}$ be an orthonormal basis for $\mathbb{C}^2$ and suppose that a vector $\mathbf{z}$ can be written as a linear combination

$$\mathbf{z} = (5 - 7i)\mathbf{u}_1 + c_2\mathbf{u}_2$$

   (a) What are the values of $\mathbf{u}_1^H \mathbf{z}$ and $\mathbf{z}^H \mathbf{u}_1$? If $\mathbf{z}^H \mathbf{u}_2 = 1 + 5i$, determine the value of c_2.

   (b) Use the results from part (a) to determine the value of $\|\mathbf{z}\|_2$.

10. Let A be a 5×5 nonsymmetric matrix with rank equal to 3, let $B = A^T A$, and let $C = e^B$.

   (a) What, if anything, can you conclude about the nature of the eigenvalues of B? Explain. What words best describe the type of matrix that B is?

   (b) What, if anything, can you conclude about the nature of the eigenvalues of C? Explain. What words best describe the type of matrix that C is?

11. Let A and B be $n \times n$ matrices.

   (a) If A is real and nonsymmetric with Schur decomposition UTU^H, then what types of matrices are U and T? How are the eigenvalues of A related to U and T? Explain your answers.

   (b) If B is Hermitian with Schur decomposition WSW^H, then what types of matrices are W and S? How are the eigenvalues and eigenvectors of B related to W and S? Explain your answers.

12. Let A be a matrix whose singular value decomposition is given by

$$
\begin{pmatrix}
\frac{2}{5} & -\frac{2}{5} & -\frac{2}{5} & -\frac{2}{5} & \frac{3}{5} \\
\frac{2}{5} & -\frac{2}{5} & -\frac{2}{5} & \frac{3}{5} & -\frac{2}{5} \\
\frac{2}{5} & -\frac{2}{5} & \frac{3}{5} & -\frac{2}{5} & -\frac{2}{5} \\
\frac{2}{5} & \frac{3}{5} & -\frac{2}{5} & -\frac{2}{5} & -\frac{2}{5} \\
\frac{3}{5} & \frac{2}{5} & \frac{2}{5} & \frac{2}{5} & \frac{2}{5}
\end{pmatrix}
\begin{pmatrix}
100 & 0 & 0 & 0 \\
0 & 10 & 0 & 0 \\
0 & 0 & 10 & 0 \\
0 & 0 & 0 & 0 \\
0 & 0 & 0 & 0
\end{pmatrix}
\begin{pmatrix}
\frac{1}{2} & \frac{1}{2} & \frac{1}{2} & \frac{1}{2} \\
\frac{1}{2} & -\frac{1}{2} & -\frac{1}{2} & \frac{1}{2} \\
-\frac{1}{2} & -\frac{1}{2} & \frac{1}{2} & \frac{1}{2} \\
-\frac{1}{2} & \frac{1}{2} & -\frac{1}{2} & \frac{1}{2}
\end{pmatrix}
$$

Make use of the singular value decomposition to do each of the following:

(a) Determine the rank of A.

(b) Find an orthonormal basis for $R(A)$.

(c) Find an orthonormal basis for $N(A)$.

(d) Find the matrix B that is the closest matrix of rank 1 to A. (The distance between matrices is measured using the Frobenius norm.)

(e) Let B be the matrix asked for in part (d). Use the singular values of A to determine the distance between A and B (i.e., use the singular values of A to determine the value of $\|B - A\|_F$).

CHAPTER

7

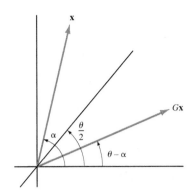

Numerical Linear Algebra

In this chapter, we consider computer methods for solving linear algebra problems. To understand these methods, you should be familiar with the type of number system used by the computer. When data are read into the computer, they are translated into its finite number system. This translation will usually involve some roundoff error. Additional rounding errors will occur when the algebraic operations of the algorithm are carried out. Because of rounding errors, we cannot expect to get the exact solution to the original problem. The best we can hope for is a good approximation to a slightly perturbed problem. Suppose, for example, that we wanted to solve $A\mathbf{x} = \mathbf{b}$. When the entries of A and $\mathbf{b}$ are read into the computer, rounding errors will generally occur. Thus, the program will actually be attempting to compute a good approximation to the solution of a perturbed system of the form

$$(A + E)\mathbf{x} = \mathbf{b} + \mathbf{e}$$

where the entries of E and $\mathbf{e}$ are all very small. An algorithm is said to be *stable* if it will produce a good approximation to the exact solution to a slightly perturbed problem. Algorithms that ordinarily would converge to the solution in exact arithmetic could very well fail to be stable, owing to the growth of error in the algebraic processes.

Even with a stable algorithm, we may encounter problems that are highly sensitive to perturbations. For example, if A is "nearly singular," the exact solutions of $A\mathbf{x} = \mathbf{b}$ and $(A + E)\mathbf{x} = \mathbf{b}$ may vary greatly, even though all the entries of E are small. The major part of this chapter is devoted to numerical methods for solving linear systems. We will pay particular attention to the growth of error and to the sensitivity of systems to small changes.

Another problem that is very important in numerical applications is the problem of finding the eigenvalues of a matrix. Two iterative methods for computing eigenvalues are presented in Section 7.6. The second of these methods is the powerful QR algorithm, which makes use of the special types of orthogonal transformations presented in Section 7.5.

In Section 7.7, we will look at numerical methods for solving least squares problems. In the case where the coefficient matrix is rank deficient, we will make use

405

of the singular value decomposition to find the particular least squares solution that has the smallest 2-norm. The Golub–Reinsch algorithm for computing the singular value decomposition will also be presented in this section.

7.1 Floating-Point Numbers

In solving a numerical problem on a computer, we do not usually expect to get the exact answer. Some amount of error is inevitable. Rounding errors may occur initially when the data are represented in the finite number system of the computer. Further rounding errors may occur whenever arithmetic operations are used. In some cases, it is possible to have a catastrophic loss of digits of accuracy or a more subtle growth of error as the algorithmic proceeds. In either of these cases, one could end up with a completely unreliable computed solution. To avoid this, we must understand how computational errors occur. To do that, we must be familiar with the type of numbers used by the computer.

Definition

> A **floating-point number** in base β is a number of the form
> $$\pm \left(\frac{d_1}{\beta} + \frac{d_2}{\beta^2} + \cdots + \frac{d_t}{\beta^t} \right) \times \beta^e$$
> where $t, d_1, d_2, \ldots, d_t, \beta$, and e are all integers and
> $$0 \le d_i \le \beta - 1 \qquad i = 1, \ldots, t$$

The integer t refers to the number of digits and this depends on the word length of the computer. The exponent e is restricted to be within certain bounds, $L \le e \le U$, which also depend on the particular computer. Commonly, computers use a standard base 2 representation for floating-point numbers. This standard representation was established by the Institute for Electrical and Electronics Engineers (IEEE). We will discuss the IEEE 754 standard floating-point representation in more detail at the end of this section. This representation is used in major software packages such as MATLAB.

EXAMPLE I The following are five-digit decimal (base 10) floating-point numbers:
$$0.53216 \times 10^{-4}$$
$$-0.81724 \times 10^{21}$$
$$0.00112 \times 10^{8}$$
$$0.11200 \times 10^{6}$$

Note that the numbers 0.00112×10^8 and 0.11200×10^6 are equal. Thus, the floating-point representation of a number need not be unique. ∎

Floating-point numbers that are written with no leading zeros are said to be *normalized*. For nonzero base-2 floating-point numbers, the lead digit will always be a 1. Thus, if the number is normalized, we can represent in the form
$$1.b_1 b_2 \cdots b_t \times 2^e$$

This form allows us to represent a normalized $t + 1$ digit number while only storing t digits in memory.

EXAMPLE 2 $(0.236)_8 \times 8^2$ and $(1.01011)_2 \times 2^4$ are normalized floating-point numbers. Here, $(0.236)_8$ represents

$$\frac{2}{8} + \frac{3}{8^2} + \frac{6}{8^3}$$

Hence, $(0.236)_8 \times 8^2$ is the base 8 floating-point representation of the decimal number 19.75. Similarly,

$$(1.01011)_2 \times 2^4 = \left(1 + \frac{1}{2^2} + \frac{1}{2^4} + \frac{1}{2^5}\right) \times 2^4$$

is a normalized base 2 representation of the decimal number 21.5.   ■

To better understand the type of number systems that we are working with, it may help to look at a very simple example.

EXAMPLE 3   Suppose that $t = 1$, $L = -1$, $U = 1$, and $\beta = 10$. There are altogether 55 one-digit floating-point numbers in this system. These are

$$0, \pm 0.1 \times 10^{-1}, \pm 0.2 \times 10^{-1}, \ldots, \pm 0.9 \times 10^{-1}$$

$$\pm 0.1 \times 10^0, \pm 0.2 \times 10^0, \ldots, \pm 0.9 \times 10^0$$

$$\pm 0.1 \times 10^1, \pm 0.2 \times 10^1, \ldots, \pm 0.9 \times 10^1$$

Although all these numbers lie in the interval $[-9, 9]$, over one-third of the numbers have absolute value less than 0.1 and over two-thirds have absolute value less than 1. Figure 7.1.1 illustrates how the floating-point numbers in the interval $[0, 2]$ are distributed.   ■

0   0.1   1   2

Figure 7.1.1.

Most real numbers have to be rounded off in order to be represented as t-digit floating-point numbers. The difference between the floating-point number x' and the original number x is called the *roundoff error*. The size of the roundoff error is perhaps more meaningful when it is compared with the size of the original number. Table 7.1.1 illustrates the absolute and relative errors when real numbers are approximated by 4-digit decimal floating point numbers.

Definition   If x is a real number and x' is its floating-point approximation, then the difference $x' - x$ is called the **absolute error** and the quotient $(x' - x)/x$ is called the **relative error**.

Table 7.1.1   Rounding Errors for 4-Digit Decimal Floating-Point Numbers

Real Number x	4-digit Decimal Representation x'	Absolute Error $x' - x$	Relative Error $(x' - x)/x$
62,133	0.6213×10^5	-3	$\dfrac{-3}{62,133} \approx -4.8 \times 10^{-5}$
0.12658	0.1266×10^0	2×10^{-5}	$\dfrac{1}{6329} \approx 1.6 \times 10^{-4}$
47.213	0.4721×10^2	-3.0×10^{-3}	$\dfrac{-0.003}{47.213} \approx -6.4 \times 10^{-5}$
π	0.3142×10^1	$3.142 - \pi \approx 4 \times 10^{-4}$	$\dfrac{3.142 - \pi}{\pi} \approx 1.3 \times 10^{-4}$

Modern computers commonly use base 2 floating-point numbers. When a decimal number is converted to a base 2 floating-point number, some rounding may occur. The following example illustrates how to convert a decimal number into a base 2 floating-point number.

EXAMPLE 4   Consider the problem of representing the decimal number 11.31 as a 10-digit base 2 floating-point number. It is easy to see how to represent the integer part of the number as a base 2 number. Since $11 = 2^3 + 2^1 + 2^0$, it follows that its base 2 representation is $(1011)_2$. Now, we need to represent the fractional part $m = 0.31$ as a base 2 number $(0.b_1b_2b_3b_4b_5b_6)_2$. Since m is less than $\frac{1}{2}$, the digit b_1 must be 0. Note that $2m = 2 \times 0.31 = 0.62$ so that b_1 equals the integer part of 0.62. To determine b_2, we double 0.62 and set b_2 equal to the integer part of 1.24. Thus, $b_2 = 1$. Next, we double the fractional part of the resulting 1.24. Since $2 \times 0.24 = 0.48$, we set $b_3 = 0$. Continuing in this manner, we get

$$2 \times 0.48 = 0.96 \quad b_4 = 0$$
$$2 \times 0.96 = 1.92 \quad b_5 = 1$$
$$2 \times 0.92 = 1.84 \quad b_6 = 1$$

Since 1.84 is not an integer, we cannot represent 0.31 exactly as a 6-digit base 2 number. If we were to compute one more digit b_7, it would be a 1. In the case where the next digit would be a 1, we round up. Thus instead of $(.010011)_2$, we end up with $(.010100)_2$. It follows that the 10-digit base 2 representation of 11.31 is $(1011.010100)_2$. The normalized base 2 floating-point representation is $(1.011010100)_2 \times 2^3$.

   The absolute error in approximating 11.31 by its 10-digit base 2 floating-point representation is 0.0025 and the relative error is approximately 2.2×10^{-4}.   ■

   When arithmetic operations are applied to floating-point numbers, additional roundoff errors may occur.

EXAMPLE 5   Let $a' = 0.263 \times 10^4$ and $b' = 0.466 \times 10^1$ be three-digit decimal floating-point numbers. If these numbers are added, the exact sum will be

$$a' + b' = 0.263446 \times 10^4$$

However, the floating-point representation of this sum is 0.263×10^4. This then should be the computed sum. We will denote the floating-point sum by $fl(a' + b')$. The absolute error in the sum is

$$fl(a' + b') - (a' + b') = -4.46$$

and the relative error is

$$\frac{-4.46}{0.26344 \times 10^4} \approx -0.17 \times 10^{-2}$$

The actual value of $a'b'$ is 11,729.8; however, $fl(a'b')$ is 0.117×10^5. The absolute error in the product is -29.8 and the relative error is approximately -0.25×10^{-2}. Floating-point subtraction and division can be done in a similar manner. ∎

The relative error in approximating a number x by its floating-point representation x' is usually denoted by the symbol δ. Thus,

$$\delta = \frac{x' - x}{x} \qquad \text{or} \qquad x' = x(1 + \delta) \tag{1}$$

$|\delta|$ can be bounded by a positive constant ϵ, called the *machine precision* or the *machine epsilon*. The machine epsilon is defined to be the smallest floating-point number ϵ for which

$$fl(1 + \epsilon) > 1$$

For example, if the computer uses three-digit decimal floating-point numbers, then

$$fl(1 + 0.499 \times 10^{-2}) = 1$$

while

$$fl(1 + 0.500 \times 10^{-2}) = 1.01$$

Therefore, the machine epsilon would be 0.500×10^{-2}. More generally, for t-digit base β floating-point arithmetic, the machine epsilon is $\frac{1}{2}\beta^{-t+1}$. In particular, for t-digit base 2 arithmetic, the machine epsilon is

$$\epsilon = \frac{1}{2} \times 2^{-t+1} = 2^{-t}$$

It follows from (1) that if a' and b' are two floating-point numbers, then

$$\begin{aligned}
fl(a' + b') &= (a' + b')(1 + \delta_1) \\
fl(a'b') &= (a'b')(1 + \delta_2) \\
fl(a' - b') &= (a' - b')(1 + \delta_3) \\
fl(a' \div b') &= (a' \div b')(1 + \delta_4)
\end{aligned}$$

The δ_i's are relative errors and will all have absolute values less than ϵ. Note in Example 5 that $\delta_1 \approx -0.17 \times 10^{-2}$, $\delta_2 \approx -0.25 \times 10^{-2}$, and $\epsilon = 0.5 \times 10^{-2}$.

If the numbers you are working with involve some slight errors, arithmetic operations may compound these errors. If two numbers agree to k decimal places and one number is subtracted from the other, there will be a loss of significant digits in your answer. In this case, the relative error in the difference will be many times as great as the relative error in either of the numbers.

EXAMPLE 6 Let $c = 3.4215298$ and $d = 3.4213851$. Calculate $c - d$ using six-digit decimal floating-point arithmetic.

Solution

I. The first step is to represent c and d by six-digit decimal floating-point numbers.

$$c' = 0.342153 \times 10^1$$
$$d' = 0.342139 \times 10^1$$

The relative errors in c and d are, respectively,

$$\frac{c' - c}{c} \approx 0.6 \times 10^{-7} \quad \text{and} \quad \frac{d' - d}{d} \approx 1.4 \times 10^{-6}$$

II. $fl(c' - d') = c' - d' = 0.140000 \times 10^{-3}$. The actual value of $c - d$ is 0.1447×10^{-3}. The absolute and relative errors in approximating $c - d$ by $fl(c' - d')$ are, respectively,

$$fl(c' - d') - (c - d) = -0.47 \times 10^{-5}$$

and

$$\frac{fl(c' - d') - (c - d)}{c - d} \approx -3.2 \times 10^{-2}$$

Note that the magnitude of the relative error in the difference is more than 10^4 times the relative error in either c or d. ∎

Example 6 illustrates the loss of accuracy when subtraction is performed with two numbers that are close together. The floating-point representations of c and d in the example were accurate to six digits; however, we lost four digits of accuracy when the difference $c - d$ was computed.

The IEEE Standard 754 Floating-Point Representation

The standard IEEE single-precision format represents a floating-point number using a sequence of 32 bits:

$$b_1 b_2 \cdots b_9 b_{10} \cdots b_{31} b_{32}$$

where each bit b_j is either a 0 or a 1. The first bit b_1 is used to determine the sign of the floating-point number, bits b_2 through b_9 are used to determine the exponent of the base $\beta = 2$, and the remaining bits are used to determine the fractional part of the normalized mantissa. The base 2 number $(b_2 b_3 \cdots b_9)_2$ represents an integer e in the range $0 \leq e \leq 255$. This number e is not used as the exponent for the floating-point number since it is always nonnegative. Instead, to allow for negative powers of 2, the number $k = e - 127$ is used. This value yields exponents in the range from -127 to 128. If we set $s = b_1$ and let m be the base 2 number $b_{10}b_{11} \cdots b_{32}$, then the normalized floating number x represented by the bit sequence $b_1b_2 \cdots b_{32}$ is given by

$$x = (-1)^s \times (1.m)_2 \times 2^k$$

EXAMPLE 7 Determine the IEEE single-precision floating-point number represented by the sequence of bits 01000001100011000000000000000000.

Solution

Since the first bit is 0, the number will have a positive sign. The next 8 bits are used to determine the exponent. If one sets

$$e = (100011)_2 = 2^0 + 2^1 + 2^7 = 131$$

then the exponent will be $k = e - 127 = 4$. It follows that the floating-point number corresponding to the given bit sequence is $(1.0001100\ldots0)_2 \times 2^4$, which is equal to

$$\left(1 + \frac{1}{2^4} + \frac{1}{2^5}\right) \times 2^4 = 17.5 \qquad \blacksquare$$

The standard IEEE double-precision format represents a floating-point number using a sequence of 64 bits:

$$b_1b_2 \cdots b_{12}b_{13} \cdots b_{63}b_{64}$$

As before, the sign of the number is determined by the first bit b_1. The exponent is determined by the bits $b_2, b_3, \ldots b_{12}$. In this case, if e is the integer with base 2 representation $(b_2b_3 \cdots b_{12})_2$, then the exponent of the base $\beta = 2$ will be the shifted value $k = e - 1023$. The remaining 52 bits, $b_{13}, \ldots, b_{64}$, are used to determine m, the fractional part of the mantissa. Thus for double precision, the normalized floating-point representation is of the form

$$x = (-1)^s \times (1.m)_2 \times 2^k$$

For IEEE arithmetic double-precision, $t = 52$ and hence the machine epsilon is

$$\epsilon = 2^{-52} \approx 2.22 \times 10^{-16}$$

So double-precision floating-point representations of decimal numbers should be accurate to about 16 decimal digits. The software package MATLAB represents floating-point numbers using either an IEEE double-precision or single-precision format. The default is double precision. When the command **eps** is entered in MATLAB, a decimal representation of 2^{-52} is returned.

Loss of Accuracy and Instability

In the remaining sections of this chapter, we consider numerical algorithms for solving linear systems, least squares problems, and eigenvalue problems. The previous methods we have learned in Chapters 1–6 for solving these problems work when exact arithmetic is used; however, they may not yield accurate answers when the computations are carried out using finite-precision arithmetic (i.e., the algorithms may be unstable). In designing stable algorithms, one should try to avoid losing digits of accuracy. Digits of accuracy may be lost when subtractions are performed using two numbers that are close together, as we saw in Example 6. In this case, we say that the resulting instabilities are due to *catastrophic cancellation* of digits. Consider, for example, the problem of computing the roots to a quadratic equation:

$$ax^2 + bx + c = 0$$

If exact arithmetic is used, the roots are usually computed using the quadratic formula

$$x = \frac{-b \pm \sqrt{b^2 - 4ac}}{2a} \tag{2}$$

If we use equation (2) for floating-point arithmetic and the value of $|b|$ is far greater than the value of $|4ac|$, then for one of the roots we could expect to get cancellation of digits of accuracy. To avoid this, we first find the root r_1 for which there is no cancellation of significant digits. To do this, we set

$$s = \begin{cases} 1 & \text{if } b \geq 0 \\ -1 & \text{if } b < 0 \end{cases}$$

and compute

$$r_1 = \frac{-b - s\sqrt{b^2 - 4ac}}{2a} \tag{3}$$

If r_2 is the other root, then we can factor $ax^2 + bx + c$:

$$ax^2 + bx + c = a(x - r_1)(x - r_2)$$

Equating the constant terms in this equation, we see that $c = ar_1r_2$. We can find the second root by simply setting

$$r_2 = \frac{c}{ar_1} \tag{4}$$

EXAMPLE 8   If $a = 1$, $b = -(10^7 + 10^{-7})$, and $c = 1$, then the quadratic polynomial $ax^2 + bx + c$ factors as

$$x^2 - (10^7 + 10^{-7})x + 1 = (x - 10^7)(x - 10^{-7})$$

and the exact roots are $r_1 = 10^7$ and $r_2 = 10^{-7}$. The roots were computed using MATLAB with standard IEEE double-precision arithmetic in two ways. First, we calculated the roots using the quadratic formula from equation (2). MATLAB returned the following values for the computed roots:

$$r_1 = 10000000 \quad \text{and} \quad r_2 = 9.965151548385620\,e - 008$$

Next, we used equations (3) and (4) to compute the roots. This time MATLAB returned the correct answers

$$r_1 = 10000000 \quad \text{and} \quad r_2 = 1.000000000000000\,e - 007 \qquad \blacksquare$$

An algorithm may fail to be numerically stable due to catastrophic cancellation or to the build-up of roundoff error in the algebraic processes. As was illustrated in Example 8, there are often simple precautions one can take to avoid catastrophic cancellation (see Exercise 10 at the end of this section).

There are also precautions one can take to avoid the build-up of roundoff error in an algorithm. The Gaussian elimination method introduced in Chapter 1 for solving linear systems could be unstable due to the build-up of roundoff unless care is taken in the choice of the row operations that are used. In Section 7.3, we will learn a strategy for interchanging rows in the elimination process that is commonly used in order to guarantee numerical stability of the algorithm. In Chapter 6, we learned to compute the eigenvalues of a matrix by finding the roots of its characteristic polynomial. This method does not work well when finite-precision arithmetic is used. Small errors in the coefficients or rounding errors in arithmetic computations could result in significant changes in the computed roots. In Section 7.6, we will learn alternative methods for computing eigenvalues and eigenvectors that are numerically stable. In Chapter 5, we learned to solve least squares problems using the normal equations and a QR factorization derived from the classical Gram–Schmidt process. Neither of these methods is guaranteed to give accurate solutions when carried out in finite-precision arithmetic. In Section 7.7, we will present some alternative numerically stable methods for solving least squares problems.

SECTION 7.1 EXERCISES

1. Find the three-digit decimal floating-point representation of each of the following numbers:
   (a) 2312   (b) 32.56
   (c) 0.01277   (d) 82,431

2. Find the absolute error and the relative error when each of the real numbers in Exercise 1 is approximated by a three-digit decimal floating-point number.

3. Represent each of the following numbers as normalized base 2 floating-point numbers using four digits to represent the fractional part of the mantissa; that is, represent the numbers in the form $\pm(1.b_1 b_2 b_3 b_4)_2 \times 2^k$.
   (a) 21   (b) $\frac{3}{8}$
   (c) 9.872   (d) -0.1

4. Use four-digit decimal floating-point arithmetic to do each of the following and calculate the absolute and relative errors in your answers:
   (a) $10,420 + 0.0018$ (b) $10,424 - 10,416$
   (c) $0.12347 - 0.12342$ (d) $(3626.6) \cdot (22.656)$

5. Let $x_1 = 94,210$, $x_2 = 8631$, $x_3 = 1440$, $x_4 = 133$, and $x_5 = 34$. Calculate each of the following, using four-digit decimal floating-point arithmetic:
   (a) $(((x_1 + x_2) + x_3) + x_4) + x_5$
   (b) $x_1 + ((x_2 + x_3) + (x_4 + x_5))$
   (c) $(((x_5 + x_4) + x_3) + x_2) + x_1$

6. What would the machine epsilon be for a computer that uses 16-digit base 10 floating-point arithmetic?

7. What would the machine epsilon be for a computer that uses 36-digit base 2 floating-point arithmetic?

8. How many floating-point numbers are there in the system if $t = 2$, $L = -2$, $U = 2$, and $\beta = 2$?

9. In each of the following, you are given a bit sequence corresponding to the IEEE single-precision representation of a floating-point number. In each case, determine the base 2 floating-point representation of the number and also the base 10 decimal representation of the number.
   (a) 01000001000110100000000000000000
   (b) 10111100010110000000000000000000
   (c) 11000100010010000000000000000000

10. When the following functions are evaluated at values of x that are close to 0, there will be a loss of significant digits of accuracy. For each function, (i) use identities or Taylor series approximations to find an alternative representation of the function that avoids cancellation of significant digits, (ii) use a hand calculator or computer to evaluate the function by plugging in the value $x = 10^{-8}$ and also evaluate the alternative representation of the function at the point $x = 10^{-8}$.
   (a) $f(x) = \dfrac{1 - \cos x}{\sin x}$ (b) $f(x) = e^x - 1$
   (c) $f(x) = \sec x - \cos x$ (d) $f(x) = \dfrac{\sin x}{x} - 1$

7.2   Gaussian Elimination

In this section, we discuss the problem of solving a system of n linear equations in n unknowns. Gaussian elimination is generally considered to be the most efficient computational method, since it involves the least amount of arithmetic operations. If the coefficient matrix A is nonsingular, then the reduction to strict triangular form can be carried out using only row operations I and III. The algorithm is much simpler if we do not have to interchange rows and can do all of the eliminations using only row operation III. For simplicity, we will consider this first, although it should be pointed out that, in general, it is necessary to interchange rows to achieve numerical stability. The more general elimination algorithm that incorporates row interchanges will be covered in the next section of the book.

Gaussian Elimination without Interchanges

Let $A = A^{(1)} = (a_{ij}^{(1)})$ be a nonsingular matrix. Then A can be reduced to strict triangular form using row operations I and III. For simplicity, let us assume that the reduction can be done by using only row operation III. Initially, we have

$$A = A^{(1)} = \begin{bmatrix} a_{11}^{(1)} & a_{12}^{(1)} & \cdots & a_{1n}^{(1)} \\ a_{21}^{(1)} & a_{22}^{(1)} & \cdots & a_{2n}^{(1)} \\ \vdots & & & \\ a_{n1}^{(1)} & a_{n2}^{(1)} & \cdots & a_{nn}^{(1)} \end{bmatrix}$$

Step 1. Let $l_{k1} = a_{k1}^{(1)}/a_{11}^{(1)}$ for $k = 2,\ldots,n$ [by our assumption, $a_{11}^{(1)} \neq 0$]. The first step of the elimination process is to apply row operation III $n-1$ times to eliminate the entries below the diagonal in the first column of A. Note that l_{k1} is the multiple of the first row that is to be subtracted from the kth row. The new matrix obtained will be

$$A^{(2)} = \begin{bmatrix} a_{11}^{(1)} & a_{12}^{(1)} & \cdots & a_{1n}^{(1)} \\ 0 & a_{22}^{(2)} & \cdots & a_{2n}^{(2)} \\ \vdots & & & \\ 0 & a_{n2}^{(2)} & \cdots & a_{nn}^{(2)} \end{bmatrix}$$

where

$$a_{kj}^{(2)} = a_{kj}^{(1)} - l_{k1}a_{1j}^{(1)} \qquad (2 \leq k \leq n,\ 2 \leq j \leq n)$$

The first step of the elimination process requires $n-1$ divisions, $(n-1)^2$ multiplications, and $(n-1)^2$ additions/subtractions.

Step 2. If $a_{22}^{(2)} \neq 0$, then it can be used as a pivot element to eliminate $a_{32}^{(2)},\ldots,a_{n2}^{(2)}$. For $k = 3,\ldots,n$, set

$$l_{k2} = \frac{a_{k2}^{(2)}}{a_{22}^{(2)}}$$

and subtract l_{k2} times the second row of $A^{(2)}$ from the kth row. The new matrix obtained will be

$$A^{(3)} = \begin{bmatrix} a_{11}^{(1)} & a_{12}^{(1)} & a_{13}^{(1)} & \cdots & a_{1n}^{(1)} \\ 0 & a_{22}^{(2)} & a_{23}^{(2)} & \cdots & a_{2n}^{(2)} \\ 0 & 0 & a_{33}^{(3)} & \cdots & a_{3n}^{(3)} \\ \vdots & \vdots & \vdots & & \vdots \\ 0 & 0 & a_{n3}^{(3)} & \cdots & a_{nn}^{(3)} \end{bmatrix}$$

The second step requires $n - 2$ divisions, $(n - 2)^2$ multiplications, and $(n - 2)^2$ additions/subtractions.

If we continue this process, then after $n - 1$ steps, we will end up with a strictly triangular matrix $U = A^{(n)}$. The operation count for the entire process can be determined as follows:

Divisions: $(n - 1) + (n - 2) + \cdots + 1 = \dfrac{n(n - 1)}{2}$

Multiplications: $(n - 1)^2 + (n - 2)^2 + \cdots + 1^2 = \dfrac{n(2n - 1)(n - 1)}{6}$

Additions and/or subtractions: $(n - 1)^2 + \cdots + 1^2 = \dfrac{n(2n - 1)(n - 1)}{6}$

The elimination process is summarized in the following algorithm.

Algorithm 7.2.1   Gaussian Elimination without Interchanges

> For $i = 1, 2, \ldots, n - 1$
> > For $k = i + 1, \ldots, n$
> >
> > Set $l_{ki} = \dfrac{a_{ki}^{(i)}}{a_{ii}^{(i)}}$ [*provided that* $a_{ii}^{(i)} \neq 0$]
> > > For $j = i + 1, \ldots, n$
> > >
> > > Set $a_{kj}^{(i+1)} = a_{kj}^{(i)} - l_{ki}a_{ij}^{(i)}$
> > > End for loop
> > End for loop
> End for loop

To solve the system $A\mathbf{x} = \mathbf{b}$, we could augment A by $\mathbf{b}$. Thus, $\mathbf{b}$ would be stored in an extra column of A. The reduction process could then be done by using Algorithm 7.2.1 and letting j run from $i + 1$ to $n + 1$ instead of from $i + 1$ to n. The triangular system could then be solved by back substitution.

Using the Triangular Factorization to Solve $A\mathbf{x} = \mathbf{b}$

Most of the work involved in solving a system $A\mathbf{x} = \mathbf{b}$ occurs in the reduction of A to strict triangular form. Suppose that, after having solved $A\mathbf{x} = \mathbf{b}$, we want to solve another system, $A\mathbf{x} = \mathbf{b}_1$. We know the triangular form U from the first system, and consequently, we would like to be able to solve the new system without having to go through the entire reduction process again. We can do this if we make use of the LU factorization discussed in Section 1.5. The matrix L is a lower triangular matrix whose diagonal entries are all equal to 1. The subdiagonal entries of L are the numbers l_{ki} used in Algorithm 7.2.1. These numbers are referred to as *multipliers* since l_{ki} is the multiple of the ith row that is subtracted from the kth row during the ith step of the reduction process. The matrix U is the upper triangular matrix obtained from the elimination process. To review how the factorization works, we consider the following example.

EXAMPLE I   Let

$$A = \begin{pmatrix} 2 & 3 & 1 \\ 4 & 1 & 4 \\ 3 & 4 & 6 \end{pmatrix}$$

The elimination can be carried out in two steps:

$$\begin{pmatrix} 2 & 3 & 1 \\ 4 & 1 & 4 \\ 3 & 4 & 6 \end{pmatrix} \xrightarrow{1} \begin{pmatrix} 2 & 3 & 1 \\ 0 & -5 & 2 \\ 0 & -\frac{1}{2} & \frac{9}{2} \end{pmatrix} \xrightarrow{2} \begin{pmatrix} 2 & 3 & 1 \\ 0 & -5 & 2 \\ 0 & 0 & 4.3 \end{pmatrix}$$

The multipliers for step 1 were $l_{21} = 2$ and $l_{31} = \frac{3}{2}$ and the multiplier for step 2 was $l_{32} = \frac{1}{10}$. Let

$$L = \begin{pmatrix} 1 & 0 & 0 \\ l_{21} & 1 & 0 \\ l_{31} & l_{32} & 1 \end{pmatrix} = \begin{pmatrix} 1 & 0 & 0 \\ 2 & 1 & 0 \\ \frac{3}{2} & \frac{1}{10} & 1 \end{pmatrix}$$

and

$$U = \begin{pmatrix} 2 & 3 & 1 \\ 0 & -5 & 2 \\ 0 & 0 & 4.3 \end{pmatrix}$$

The reader may verify that $LU = A$.   ■

Once A has been reduced to triangular form and the factorization LU has been determined, the system $A\mathbf{x} = \mathbf{b}$ can be solved in two steps.

Step 1. *Forward Substitution.*   The system $A\mathbf{x} = \mathbf{b}$ can be written in the form

$$LU\mathbf{x} = \mathbf{b}$$

Let $\mathbf{y} = U\mathbf{x}$. It follows that

$$L\mathbf{y} = LU\mathbf{x} = \mathbf{b}$$

Thus, we can find $\mathbf{y}$ by solving the lower triangular system:

$$
\begin{aligned}
y_1 & && && &&&= b_1 \\
l_{21}y_1 &+ y_2 && && &&&= b_2 \\
l_{31}y_1 &+ l_{32}y_2 &&+ y_3 && &&&= b_3 \\
& \quad\vdots \\
l_{n1}y_1 &+ l_{n2}y_2 &&+ l_{n3}y_3 &&+ \cdots + y_n &&&= b_n
\end{aligned}
$$

It follows from the first equation that $y_1 = b_1$. This value can be used in the second equation to solve for y_2. The values of y_1 and y_2 can be used in the third equation to solve for y_3, and so on. This method of solving a lower triangular system is called *forward substitution.*

Step 2. *Back Substitution.*   Once $\mathbf{y}$ has been determined, we need only solve the upper triangular system $U\mathbf{x} = \mathbf{y}$ to find the solution $\mathbf{x}$ of the system. The upper triangular system is solved by back substitution.

EXAMPLE 2   Solve the system

$$
\begin{aligned}
2x_1 + 3x_2 + \ x_3 &= -4 \\
4x_1 + \ x_2 + 4x_3 &= \ 9 \\
3x_1 + 4x_2 + 6x_3 &= \ 0
\end{aligned}
$$

Solution

The coefficient matrix for this system is the matrix A in Example 1. Since L and U have been determined, the system can be solved by forward and back substitution.

$$
\left[\begin{array}{ccc|c}
1 & 0 & 0 & -4 \\
2 & 1 & 0 & 9 \\
\frac{3}{2} & \frac{1}{10} & 1 & 0
\end{array} \right]
\qquad
\begin{aligned}
y_1 &= -4 \\
y_2 &= 9 - 2y_1 = 17 \\
y_3 &= 0 - \tfrac{3}{2}y_1 - \tfrac{1}{10}y_2 = 4.3
\end{aligned}
$$

$$
\left[\begin{array}{ccc|c}
2 & 3 & 1 & -4 \\
0 & -5 & 2 & 17 \\
0 & 0 & 4.3 & 4.3
\end{array} \right]
\qquad
\begin{aligned}
2x_1 + 3x_2 + \ x_3 &= -4 & x_1 &= \ 2 \\
-5x_2 + 2x_3 &= \ 17 & x_2 &= -3 \\
4.3x_3 &= 4.3 & x_3 &= \ 1
\end{aligned}
$$

The solution of the system is $\mathbf{x} = (2, -3, 1)^T$.

Algorithm 7.2.2   Forward and Back Substitution

$$
\begin{array}{l}
\text{For } k = 1, \ldots, n \\[2pt]
\qquad \text{Set } y_k = b_k - \sum_{i=1}^{k-1} l_{ki} y_i \\[8pt]
\text{End for loop} \\
\text{For } k = n, n-1, \ldots, 1 \\[2pt]
\qquad \text{Set } x_k = \dfrac{y_k - \sum_{j=k+1}^{n} u_{kj} x_j}{u_{kk}} \\[8pt]
\text{End for loop}
\end{array}
$$

$\blacksquare$

Operation Count   Algorithm 7.2.2 requires n divisions, $n(n-1)$ multiplications, and $n(n-1)$ additions/subtractions. The total operation count for solving a system $A\mathbf{x} = \mathbf{b}$ using Algorithms 7.2.1 and 7.2.2 is then

Multiplications/divisions: $\frac{1}{3}n^3 + n^2 - \frac{1}{3}n$

Additions/subtractions: $\frac{1}{3}n^3 + \frac{1}{2}n^2 - \frac{5}{6}n$

In both cases, $\frac{1}{3}n^3$ is the dominant term. We will say that solving a system by Gaussian elimination involves roughly $\frac{1}{3}n^3$ multiplications/divisions and $\frac{1}{3}n^3$ additions/subtractions.

Algorithm 7.2.1 breaks down if, at any step, $a_{kk}^{(k)}$ is 0. If this happens, it is necessary to perform row interchanges. In the next section, we will see how to incorporate interchanges into our elimination algorithm.

SECTION 7.2 EXERCISES

1. Let

$$
A = \begin{bmatrix} 1 & 1 & 1 \\ 2 & 4 & 1 \\ -3 & 1 & -2 \end{bmatrix}
$$

Factor A into a product LU, where L is lower triangular with 1's along the diagonal and U is upper triangular.

2. Let A be the matrix in Exercise 1. Use the LU factorization of A to solve $A\mathbf{x} = \mathbf{b}$ for each of the following choices of $\mathbf{b}$:

(a) $(4, 3, -13)^T$ (b) $(3, 1, -10)^T$

(c) $(7, 23, 0)^T$

3. Let A and B be $n \times n$ matrices and let $\mathbf{x} \in \mathbb{R}^n$.

(a) How many scalar additions and multiplications are necessary to compute the product $A\mathbf{x}$?

(b) How many scalar additions and multiplications are necessary to compute the product AB?

(c) How many scalar additions and multiplications are necessary to compute $(AB)\mathbf{x}$? To compute $A(B\mathbf{x})$?

4. Let $A \in \mathbb{R}^{m \times n}$, $B \in \mathbb{R}^{n \times r}$, and $\mathbf{x}, \mathbf{y} \in \mathbb{R}^n$. Suppose that the product $A\mathbf{x}\mathbf{y}^T B$ is computed in the following ways:

(i) $(A(\mathbf{x}\mathbf{y}^T))B$ (ii) $(A\mathbf{x})(\mathbf{y}^T B)$
(iii) $((A\mathbf{x})\mathbf{y}^T)B$

(a) How many scalar additions and multiplications are necessary for each of these computations?

(b) Compare the number of scalar additions and multiplications for each of the three methods when $m = 5$, $n = 4$, and $r = 3$. Which method is most efficient in this case?

5. Let E_{ki} be the elementary matrix formed by subtracting α times the ith row of the identity matrix from the kth row.

   (a) Show that $E_{ki} = I - \alpha \mathbf{e}_k \mathbf{e}_i^T$.

   (b) Let $E_{ji} = I - \beta \mathbf{e}_j \mathbf{e}_i^T$. Show that
   $$E_{ji}E_{ki} = I - (\alpha \mathbf{e}_k + \beta \mathbf{e}_j)\mathbf{e}_i^T.$$

   (c) Show that $E_{ki}^{-1} = I + \alpha \mathbf{e}_k \mathbf{e}_i^T$.

6. Let A be an $n \times n$ matrix with triangular factorization LU. Show that
   $$\det(A) = u_{11}u_{22} \cdots u_{nn}$$

7. If A is a symmetric $n \times n$ matrix with triangular factorization LU, then A can be factored further into a product LDL^T (where D is diagonal). Devise an algorithm, similar to Algorithm 7.2.2, for solving $LDL^T\mathbf{x} = \mathbf{b}$.

8. Write an algorithm for solving the tridiagonal system
   $$\begin{bmatrix} a_1 & b_1 & & & \\ c_1 & a_2 & \ddots & & \\ & & \ddots & \ddots & \\ & & \ddots & a_{n-1} & b_{n-1} \\ & & & c_{n-1} & a_n \end{bmatrix} \begin{bmatrix} x_1 \\ x_2 \\ \vdots \\ x_{n-1} \\ x_n \end{bmatrix} = \begin{bmatrix} d_1 \\ d_2 \\ \vdots \\ d_{n-1} \\ d_n \end{bmatrix}$$
   by Gaussian elimination with the diagonal elements as pivots. How many additions/subtractions and multiplications/divisions are necessary?

9. Let $A = LU$, where L is lower triangular with 1's on the diagonal and U is upper triangular.

   (a) How many scalar additions and multiplications are necessary to solve $L\mathbf{y} = \mathbf{e}_j$ by forward substitution?

   (b) How many additions/subtractions and multiplications/divisions are necessary to solve $A\mathbf{x} = \mathbf{e}_j$? The solution $\mathbf{x}_j$ of $A\mathbf{x} = \mathbf{e}_j$ will be the jth column of A^{-1}.

   (c) Given the factorization $A = LU$, how many additional multiplications/divisions and additions/subtractions are needed to compute A^{-1}?

10. Suppose that A^{-1} and the LU factorization of A have already been determined. How many scalar additions and multiplications are necessary to compute $A^{-1}\mathbf{b}$? Compare this number with the number of operations required to solve $LU\mathbf{x} = \mathbf{b}$ using Algorithm 7.2.2. Suppose that we have a number of systems to solve with the same coefficient matrix A. Is it worthwhile to compute A^{-1}? Explain.

11. Let A be a 3×3 matrix and assume that A can be transformed into a lower triangular matrix L by using only column operations of type III; that is,
    $$AE_1E_2E_3 = L$$
    where E_1, E_2, E_3 are elementary matrices of type III. Let
    $$U = (E_1E_2E_3)^{-1}$$
    Show that U is upper triangular with 1's on the diagonal and $A = LU$. (This exercise illustrates a column version of Gaussian elimination.)

7.3 Pivoting Strategies

In this section, we present an algorithm for Gaussian elimination with row interchanges. At each step of the algorithm, it will be necessary to choose a pivotal row. We can often avoid unnecessarily large error accumulations by choosing the pivotal rows in a reasonable manner.

Gaussian Elimination with Interchanges

Consider the following example.

EXAMPLE 1   Let
$$A = \begin{bmatrix} 6 & -4 & 2 \\ 4 & 2 & 1 \\ 2 & -1 & 1 \end{bmatrix}$$

We wish to reduce A to triangular form by using row operations I and III. To keep track of the interchanges, we will use a row vector $\mathbf{p}$. The coordinates of $\mathbf{p}$ will be denoted by $p(1)$, $p(2)$, and $p(3)$. Initially, we set $\mathbf{p} = (1, 2, 3)$. Suppose that, at the first step of the reduction process, the third row is chosen as the pivotal row. Then instead of interchanging the first and third rows, we will interchange the first and third entries of **p**. Setting $p(1) = 3$ and $p(3) = 1$, the vector **p** becomes $(3, 2, 1)$. The vector **p** is used to keep track of the reordering of the rows. We can think of **p** as a renumbering of the rows. The actual physical reordering of the rows can be deferred until the end of the reduction process.

$$
\begin{array}{l}
\text{row} \\
p(3) = 1 \\
p(2) = 2 \\
p(1) = 3
\end{array}
\begin{bmatrix} 6 & -4 & 2 \\ 4 & 2 & 1 \\ 2 & -1 & 1 \end{bmatrix}
\rightarrow
\begin{bmatrix} 0 & -1 & -1 \\ 0 & 4 & -1 \\ 2 & -1 & 1 \end{bmatrix}
$$

If, at the second step, row $p(3)$ is chosen as the pivotal row, the entries of $p(3)$ and $p(2)$ are switched. The final step of the elimination process is then carried out as follows:

$$
\begin{array}{l}
p(2) = 1 \\
p(3) = 2 \\
p(1) = 3
\end{array}
\begin{bmatrix} 0 & -1 & -1 \\ 0 & 4 & -1 \\ 2 & -1 & 1 \end{bmatrix}
\rightarrow
\begin{bmatrix} 0 & -1 & -1 \\ 0 & 0 & -5 \\ 2 & -1 & 1 \end{bmatrix}
$$

If the rows are reordered in the order $(p(1), p(2), p(3)) = (3, 1, 2)$, the resulting matrix will be in strict triangular form:

$$
\begin{array}{l}
p(1) = 3 \\
p(2) = 1 \\
p(3) = 2
\end{array}
\begin{bmatrix} 2 & -1 & 1 \\ 0 & -1 & -1 \\ 0 & 0 & -5 \end{bmatrix}
$$

Had the rows been written in the order $(3, 1, 2)$ to begin with, the reduction would have been exactly the same, except that there would have been no need for interchanges. Reordering the rows of A in the order $(3, 1, 2)$ is the same as premultiplying A by the permutation matrix:

$$
P = \begin{bmatrix} 0 & 0 & 1 \\ 1 & 0 & 0 \\ 0 & 1 & 0 \end{bmatrix}
$$

Let us perform the reduction on A and PA simultaneously and compare the results. The multipliers used in the reduction process were 3, 2, and -4. These will be stored in the places of the terms eliminated and enclosed in boxes to distinguish them from the other entries of the matrix.

$$A = \begin{pmatrix} 6 & -4 & 2 \\ 4 & 2 & 1 \\ 2 & -1 & 1 \end{pmatrix} \rightarrow \begin{pmatrix} \boxed{3} & -1 & -1 \\ \boxed{2} & 4 & -1 \\ 2 & -1 & 1 \end{pmatrix} \rightarrow \begin{pmatrix} \boxed{3} & -1 & -1 \\ 2 & \boxed{-4} & -5 \\ 2 & -1 & 1 \end{pmatrix}$$

$$PA = \begin{pmatrix} 2 & -1 & 1 \\ 6 & -4 & 2 \\ 4 & 2 & 1 \end{pmatrix} \rightarrow \begin{pmatrix} 2 & -1 & 1 \\ \boxed{3} & -1 & -1 \\ \boxed{2} & 4 & -1 \end{pmatrix} \rightarrow \begin{pmatrix} 2 & -1 & 1 \\ \boxed{3} & -1 & -1 \\ 2 & \boxed{-4} & -5 \end{pmatrix}$$

If the rows of the reduced form of A are reordered, the resulting reduced matrices will be the same. The reduced form of PA now contains the information necessary to determine its triangular factorization. Indeed,

$$PA = LU$$

where

$$L = \begin{pmatrix} 1 & 0 & 0 \\ 3 & 1 & 0 \\ 2 & -4 & 1 \end{pmatrix} \quad \text{and} \quad U = \begin{pmatrix} 2 & -1 & 1 \\ 0 & -1 & -1 \\ 0 & 0 & -5 \end{pmatrix} \qquad \blacksquare$$

On the computer, it is not necessary to actually interchange the rows of A. We simply treat row $p(k)$ as the kth row and use $a_{p(k)j}$ in place of a_{kj}.

Algorithm 7.3.1   Gaussian Elimination with Interchanges

> *For $i = 1, \ldots, n$*
>> *Set $p(i) = i$*
> *End for loop*
>
> *For $i = 1, \ldots, n$*
>
>> (1) *Choose a pivot element $a_{p(j)i}$ from the elements*
>>
>> $$a_{p(i)i}, a_{p(i+1)i}, \ldots, a_{p(n)i}$$
>>
>> *(Strategies for doing this will be discussed later in this section.)*
>> (2) *Switch the ith and jth entries of p.*
>> (3) *For $k = i + 1, \ldots, n$*
>>> *Set $l_{p(k)i} = a_{p(k)i}/a_{p(i)i}$*
>>> *For $j = i + 1, \ldots, n$*
>>>> *Set $a_{p(k)j} = a_{p(k)j} - l_{p(k)i}a_{p(i)j}$*
>>> *End for loop*
>> *End for loop*
> *End for loop* $\blacksquare$

Remarks

1. The multiplier $l_{p(k)i}$ is stored in the position of the element $a_{p(k)i}$ being eliminated.

2. The vector $\mathbf{p}$ can be used to form a permutation matrix P whose ith row is the $p(i)$th row of the identity matrix.

3. The matrix PA can be factored into a product LU, where

$$l_{ki} = \begin{cases} l_{p(k)i} & \text{if } k > i \\ 1 & \text{if } k = i \\ 0 & \text{if } k < i \end{cases} \quad \text{and} \quad u_{ki} = \begin{cases} a_{p(k)i} & \text{if } k \leq i \\ 0 & \text{if } k > i \end{cases}$$

4. Since P is nonsingular, the system $A\mathbf{x} = \mathbf{b}$ is equivalent to the system $PA\mathbf{x} = P\mathbf{b}$. Let $\mathbf{c} = P\mathbf{b}$. Since $PA = LU$, it follows that the system is equivalent to

$$LU\mathbf{x} = \mathbf{c}$$

5. If $PA = LU$, then $A = P^{-1}LU = P^{T}LU$.

It follows from Remarks 4 and 5 that if $A = P^{T}LU$, then the system $A\mathbf{x} = \mathbf{b}$ can be solved in three steps:

Step 1. *Reordering.*   Reorder the entries of $\mathbf{b}$ to form $\mathbf{c} = P\mathbf{b}$.

Step 2. *Forward substitution.*   Solve the system $L\mathbf{y} = \mathbf{c}$ for $\mathbf{y}$.

Step 3. *Back substitution.*   Solve $U\mathbf{x} = \mathbf{y}$.

EXAMPLE 2   Solve the system

$$\begin{aligned} 6x_1 - 4x_2 + 2x_3 &= -2 \\ 4x_1 + 2x_2 + x_3 &= 4 \\ 2x_1 - x_2 + x_3 &= -1 \end{aligned}$$

Solution

The coefficient matrix of this system is the matrix A from Example 1. P, L, and U have already been determined, and they can be used to solve the system as follows:

Step 1. $\mathbf{c} = P\mathbf{b} = (-1, -2, 4)^{T}$

Step 2.
$$\begin{array}{ll} y_1 = -1 & y_1 = -1 \\ 3y_1 + y_2 = -2 & y_2 = -2 + 3 = 1 \\ 2y_1 - 4y_2 + y_3 = 4 & y_3 = 4 + 2 + 4 = 10 \end{array}$$

Step 3.
$$\begin{array}{ll} 2x_1 - x_2 + x_3 = -1 & x_1 = 1 \\ -x_2 - x_3 = 1 & x_2 = 1 \\ -5x_3 = 10 & x_3 = -2 \end{array}$$

The solution of the system is $\mathbf{x} = (1, 1, -2)^{T}$. ■

It is possible to do Gaussian elimination without row interchanges if the diagonal entries $a_{ii}^{(i)}$ are nonzero at each step. However, in finite-precision arithmetic, pivots $a_{ii}^{(i)}$ that are near 0 can cause problems.

EXAMPLE 3   Consider the system

$$\begin{aligned} 0.0001x_1 + 2x_2 &= 4 \\ x_1 + x_2 &= 3 \end{aligned}$$

The exact solution of the system is

$$\mathbf{x} = \left(\frac{2}{1.9999}, \frac{3.9997}{1.9999} \right)^T$$

Rounded off to four decimal places, the solution is $(1.0001, 1.9999)^T$. Let us solve the system using three-digit decimal floating-point arithmetic.

$$\left(\begin{array}{cc|c} 0.0001 & 2 & 4 \\ 1 & 1 & 3 \end{array} \right) \rightarrow \left[\begin{array}{cc|c} 0.0001 & 2 & 4 \\ 0 & -0.200 \times 10^5 & -0.400 \times 10^5 \end{array} \right]$$

The computed solution is $\mathbf{x}' = (0, 2)^T$. There is a 100 percent error in the x_1 coordinate. However, if we interchange rows to avoid the small pivot, then three-digit decimal arithmetic gives

$$\left\{ \begin{array}{cc|c} 1 & 1 & 3 \\ 0.0001 & 2 & 4 \end{array} \right\} \rightarrow \left\{ \begin{array}{cc|c} 1 & 1 & 3 \\ 0 & 2.00 & 4.00 \end{array} \right\}$$

In this case, the computed solution is $\mathbf{x}' = (1, 2)^T$.   ■

If the pivot $a_{ii}^{(i)}$ is small in absolute value, the multipliers $l_{ki} = a_{ki}^{(i)} / a_{ii}^{(i)}$ may be large in absolute value. If there is an error in the computed value of $a_{ij}^{(i)}$, it will be multiplied by l_{ki}. In general, large multipliers contribute to the propagation of error. In contrast, multipliers that are less than 1 in absolute value generally retard the growth of error. By careful selection of the pivot elements, we can try to avoid small pivots and at the same time keep the multipliers less than or equal to 1 in absolute value. The most commonly used strategy for doing this is called *partial pivoting*.

Partial Pivoting

At the ith step of the reduction process, there are $n - i + 1$ candidates for the pivot element:

$$a_{p(i)i}, a_{p(i+1)i}, \ldots, a_{p(n)i}$$

Choose the candidate $a_{p(j)i}$ with the maximum absolute value

$$|a_{p(j)i}| = \max_{i \le k \le n} |a_{p(k)i}|$$

and interchange the ith and jth entries of $\mathbf{p}$. The pivot element $a_{p(i)i}$ has the property

$$|a_{p(i)i}| \ge |a_{p(k)i}|$$

for $k = i + 1, \ldots, n$. Thus, the multipliers will all satisfy

$$|l_{p(k)i}| = \left| \frac{a_{p(k)i}}{a_{p(i)i}} \right| \le 1$$

We could always carry things one step further and do *complete pivoting*. In complete pivoting, the pivot element is chosen to be the element of maximum absolute value among all the elements in the remaining rows and columns. In this case, we must keep track of both the rows and columns. At the ith step, the element $a_{p(j)q(k)}$ is chosen so that

$$|a_{p(j)q(k)}| = \max_{\substack{i \le s \le n \\ i \le t \le n}} |a_{p(s)q(t)}|$$

The ith and jth entries of $\mathbf{p}$ are interchanged, and the ith and kth entries of $\mathbf{q}$ are interchanged. The new pivot element is $a_{p(i)q(i)}$. The major drawback to complete pivoting is that at each step we must search for a pivot element among $(n - i + 1)^2$ elements of A. Doing this may be too costly in terms of computer time. Although Gaussian elimination is numerically stable when carried out with either partial or complete pivoting, it is more efficient to use partial pivoting. As a consequence, the partial pivoting strategy is the method of choice for all of the standard numerical software packages.

SECTION 7.3 EXERCISES

1. Let

$$A = \begin{bmatrix} 0 & 3 & 1 \\ 1 & 2 & -2 \\ 2 & 5 & 4 \end{bmatrix} \quad \text{and} \quad \mathbf{b} = \begin{bmatrix} 1 \\ 7 \\ -1 \end{bmatrix}$$

(a) Reorder the rows of $(A|\mathbf{b})$ in the order $(2, 3, 1)$ and then solve the reordered system.

(b) Factor A into a product $P^T LU$, where P is the permutation matrix corresponding to the reordering in part (a).

2. Let A be the matrix in Exercise 1. Use the factorization $P^T LU$ to solve $A\mathbf{x} = \mathbf{c}$ for each of the following choices of $\mathbf{c}$:

(a) $(8, 1, 20)^T$ (b) $(-9, -2, -7)^T$

(c) $(4, 1, 11)^T$

3. Let

$$A = \begin{bmatrix} 1 & 8 & 6 \\ -1 & -4 & 5 \\ 2 & 4 & -6 \end{bmatrix} \quad \text{and} \quad \mathbf{b} = \begin{bmatrix} 8 \\ 1 \\ 4 \end{bmatrix}$$

Solve the system $A\mathbf{x} = \mathbf{b}$ using partial pivoting. If P is the permutation matrix corresponding to the pivoting strategy, factor PA into a product LU.

4. Let

$$A = \begin{bmatrix} 3 & 2 \\ 2 & 4 \end{bmatrix} \quad \text{and} \quad \mathbf{b} = \begin{bmatrix} 5 \\ -2 \end{bmatrix}$$

Solve the system $A\mathbf{x} = \mathbf{b}$ using complete pivoting. Let P be the permutation matrix determined by the pivot rows and Q the permutation matrix determined by the pivot columns. Factor PAQ into a product LU.

5. Let A be the matrix in Exercise 4 and let $\mathbf{c} = (6, -4)^T$. Solve the system $A\mathbf{x} = \mathbf{c}$ in two steps:

(a) Set $\mathbf{z} = Q^T \mathbf{x}$ and solve $LU\mathbf{z} = P\mathbf{c}$ for $\mathbf{z}$.

(b) Calculate $\mathbf{x} = Q\mathbf{z}$.

6. Let

$$A = \begin{bmatrix} 5 & 4 & 7 \\ 2 & -4 & 3 \\ 2 & 8 & 6 \end{bmatrix},$$

$$\mathbf{b} = \begin{bmatrix} 2 \\ -5 \\ 4 \end{bmatrix}, \quad \mathbf{c} = \begin{bmatrix} 5 \\ -4 \\ 2 \end{bmatrix}$$

(a) Use complete pivoting to solve the system $A\mathbf{x} = \mathbf{b}$.

(b) Let P be the permutation matrix determined by the pivot rows, and let Q be the permutation matrix determined by the pivot columns. Factor PAQ into a product LU.

(c) Use the LU factorization from part (b) to solve the system $A\mathbf{x} = \mathbf{c}$.

7. The exact solution of the system

$$0.6000x_1 + 2000x_2 = 2003$$
$$0.3076x_1 - 0.4010x_2 = 1.137$$

is $\mathbf{x} = (5, 1)^T$. Suppose that the calculated value of x_2 is $x_2' = 1 + e$. Use this value in the first equation and solve for x_1. What will the error be? Calculate the relative error in x_1 if $e = 0.001$.

8. Solve the system in Exercise 7 using four-digit decimal floating-point arithmetic and Gaussian elimination with partial pivoting.

9. Solve the system in Exercise 7 using four-digit decimal floating-point arithmetic and Gaussian elimination with complete pivoting.

10. Use four-digit decimal floating-point arithmetic, and scale the system in Exercise 7 by multiplying the first equation through by $1/2000$ and the second equation through by $1/0.4010$. Solve the scaled system using partial pivoting.

Matrix Norms and Condition Numbers

In this section, we are concerned with the accuracy of computed solutions of linear systems. How accurate can we expect the computed solutions to be, and how can we test their accuracy? The answer to these questions depends largely on how sensitive the coefficient matrix of the system is to small changes. The sensitivity of the matrix can be measured in terms of its *condition number*. The condition number of a nonsingular matrix is defined in terms of its norm and the norm of its inverse. Before discussing condition numbers, it is necessary to establish some important results regarding the standard types of matrix norms.

Matrix Norms

Just as vector norms are used to measure the size of vectors, matrix norms can be used to measure the size of matrices. In Section 5.4, we introduced a norm on $\mathbb{R}^{m \times n}$ that was induced by an inner product on $\mathbb{R}^{m \times n}$. This norm was referred to as the Frobenius norm and was denoted by $\| \cdot \|_F$. We showed that the Frobenius norm of a matrix A could be computed by taking the square root of the sum of the squares of all its entries:

$$\|A\|_F = \left(\sum_{j=1}^{n} \sum_{i=1}^{m} a_{ij}^2 \right)^{1/2} \tag{1}$$

Actually, equation (1) defines a family of matrix norms since it defines a norm on $\mathbb{R}^{m \times n}$ for any choice of m and n. The Frobenius norm has a number of important properties:

I. If $\mathbf{a}_j$ represents the jth column vector of A, then

$$\|A\|_F = \left(\sum_{j=1}^{n} \sum_{i=1}^{m} a_{ij}^2 \right)^{1/2} = \left(\sum_{j=1}^{n} \|\mathbf{a}_j\|_2^2 \right)^{1/2}$$

II. If $\vec{\mathbf{a}}_i$ represents the ith row vector of A, then

$$\|A\|_F = \left(\sum_{i=1}^{m} \sum_{j=1}^{n} a_{ij}^2 \right)^{1/2} = \left(\sum_{i=1}^{m} \|\vec{\mathbf{a}}_i^T\|_2^2 \right)^{1/2}$$

III. If $\mathbf{x} \in \mathbb{R}^n$, then

$$\|A\mathbf{x}\|_2 = \left[\sum_{i=1}^{m} \left(\sum_{j=1}^{n} a_{ij} x_j \right)^2 \right]^{1/2} = \left[\sum_{i=1}^{m} \left(\vec{\mathbf{a}}_i \mathbf{x} \right)^2 \right]^{1/2}$$

$$\leq \left[\sum_{i=1}^{m} \|\mathbf{x}\|_2^2 \|\vec{\mathbf{a}}_i^T\|_2^2 \right]^{1/2} \qquad \text{(Cauchy–Schwarz)}$$

$$= \|A\|_F \, \|\mathbf{x}\|_2$$

IV. If $B = (\mathbf{b}_1, \ldots, \mathbf{b}_r)$ is an $n \times r$ matrix, it follows from properties **I** and **III** that

$$\|AB\|_F = \|(A\mathbf{b}_1, A\mathbf{b}_2, \ldots, A\mathbf{b}_r)\|_F$$

$$= \left(\sum_{i=1}^{r} \|A\mathbf{b}_i\|_2^2 \right)^{1/2}$$

$$\leq \|A\|_F \left(\sum_{i=1}^{r} \|\mathbf{b}_i\|_2^2 \right)^{1/2}$$

$$= \|A\|_F \|B\|_F$$

There are many other norms that we could use for $\mathbb{R}^{m \times n}$ in addition to the Frobenius norm. Any norm used must satisfy the three conditions that define norms in general:

(i) $\|A\| \geq 0$ and $\|A\| = 0$ if and only if $A = O$

(ii) $\|\alpha A\| = |\alpha| \|A\|$

(iii) $\|A + B\| \leq \|A\| + \|B\|$

The families of matrix norms that turn out to be most useful also satisfy the additional property

(iv) $\|AB\| \leq \|A\| \, \|B\|$

Consequently, we will consider only families of norms that have this additional property. One important consequence of property (iv) is that

$$\|A^n\| \leq \|A\|^n$$

In particular, if $\|A\| < 1$, then $\|A^n\| \to 0$ as $n \to \infty$.

In general, a matrix norm $\| \cdot \|_M$ on $\mathbb{R}^{m \times n}$ and a vector norm $\| \cdot \|_V$ on $\mathbb{R}^n$ are said to be *compatible* if

$$\|A\mathbf{x}\|_V \leq \|A\|_M \|\mathbf{x}\|_V$$

for every $\mathbf{x} \in \mathbb{R}^n$. In particular, it follows from property **III** of the Frobenius norm that the matrix norm $\| \cdot \|_F$ and the vector norm $\| \cdot \|_2$ are compatible. For each of the standard vector norms, we can define a compatible matrix norm by using the vector norm to compute an operator norm for the matrix. The matrix norm defined in this way is said to be *subordinate* to the vector norm.

Subordinate Matrix Norms

We can think of each $m \times n$ matrix as a linear transformation from $\mathbb{R}^n$ to $\mathbb{R}^m$. For any family of vector norms, we can define an *operator norm* by comparing $\|A\mathbf{x}\|$ and $\|\mathbf{x}\|$ for each nonzero $\mathbf{x}$ and taking

$$\|A\| = \max_{\mathbf{x} \neq \mathbf{0}} \frac{\|A\mathbf{x}\|}{\|\mathbf{x}\|} \tag{2}$$

It can be shown that there is a particular $\mathbf{x}_0$ in $\mathbb{R}^n$ that maximizes $\|A\mathbf{x}\|/\|\mathbf{x}\|$, but the proof is beyond the scope of this text. Assuming that $\|A\mathbf{x}\|/\|\mathbf{x}\|$ can always be maximized, we will show that (2) actually does define a norm on $\mathbb{R}^{m \times n}$. To do this, we must verify that each of the three conditions of the definition is satisfied.

(i) For each $\mathbf{x} \neq \mathbf{0}$,

$$\frac{\|A\mathbf{x}\|}{\|\mathbf{x}\|} \geq 0$$

and, consequently,

$$\|A\| = \max_{\mathbf{x} \neq \mathbf{0}} \frac{\|A\mathbf{x}\|}{\|\mathbf{x}\|} \geq 0$$

If $\|A\| = 0$, then $A\mathbf{x} = \mathbf{0}$ for every $\mathbf{x} \in \mathbb{R}^n$. This implies that

$$\mathbf{a}_j = A\mathbf{e}_j = \mathbf{0} \qquad \text{for} \qquad j = 1, \ldots, n$$

and hence A must be the zero matrix.

(ii) $\|\alpha A\| = \max_{\mathbf{x} \neq \mathbf{0}} \dfrac{\|\alpha A\mathbf{x}\|}{\|\mathbf{x}\|} = |\alpha| \max_{\mathbf{x} \neq \mathbf{0}} \dfrac{\|A\mathbf{x}\|}{\|\mathbf{x}\|} = |\alpha| \, \|A\|$

(iii) If $\mathbf{x} \neq \mathbf{0}$, then

$$
\begin{aligned}
\|A + B\| &= \max_{\mathbf{x} \neq \mathbf{0}} \frac{\|(A + B)\mathbf{x}\|}{\|\mathbf{x}\|} \\
&\leq \max_{\mathbf{x} \neq \mathbf{0}} \frac{\|A\mathbf{x}\| + \|B\mathbf{x}\|}{\|\mathbf{x}\|} \\
&\leq \max_{\mathbf{x} \neq \mathbf{0}} \frac{\|A\mathbf{x}\|}{\|\mathbf{x}\|} + \max_{\mathbf{x} \neq \mathbf{0}} \frac{\|B\mathbf{x}\|}{\|\mathbf{x}\|} \\
&= \|A\| + \|B\|
\end{aligned}
$$

Thus, (2) defines a norm, on $\mathbb{R}^{m \times n}$. For each family of vector norms $\|\cdot\|$, we can then define a family of matrix norms by (2). The matrix norms defined by (2) are said to be *subordinate* to the vector norms $\|\cdot\|$.

Theorem 7.4.1   *If the family of matrix norms $\|\cdot\|_M$ is subordinate to the family of vector norms $\|\cdot\|_V$, then $\|\cdot\|_M$ and $\|\cdot\|_V$ are compatible and the matrix norms $\|\cdot\|_M$ satisfy property (iv).*

Proof   If $\mathbf{x}$ is any nonzero vector in $\mathbb{R}^n$, then

$$\frac{\|A\mathbf{x}\|_V}{\|\mathbf{x}\|_V} \leq \max_{\mathbf{y} \neq \mathbf{0}} \frac{\|A\mathbf{y}\|_V}{\|\mathbf{y}\|_V} = \|A\|_M$$

and hence

$$\|A\mathbf{x}\|_V \leq \|A\|_M \|\mathbf{x}\|_V$$

Since this last inequality is also valid if $\mathbf{x} = \mathbf{0}$, it follows that $\| \cdot \|_M$ and $\| \cdot \|_V$ are compatible. If B is an $n \times r$ matrix, then, since $\| \cdot \|_M$ and $\| \cdot \|_V$ are compatible, we have

$$\|AB\mathbf{x}\|_V \leq \|A\|_M \|B\mathbf{x}\|_V \leq \|A\|_M \|B\|_M \|\mathbf{x}\|_V$$

Thus, for all $\mathbf{x} \neq \mathbf{0}$,

$$\frac{\|AB\mathbf{x}\|_V}{\|\mathbf{x}\|_V} \leq \|A\|_M \|B\|_M$$

and hence

$$\|AB\|_M = \max_{\mathbf{x} \neq \mathbf{0}} \frac{\|AB\mathbf{x}\|_V}{\|\mathbf{x}\|_V} \leq \|A\|_M \|B\|_M \qquad \blacksquare$$

It is a simple matter to compute the Frobenius norm of a matrix. For example, if

$$A = \begin{bmatrix} 4 & 2 \\ 0 & 4 \end{bmatrix}$$

then

$$\|A\|_F = (4^2 + 0^2 + 2^2 + 4^2)^{1/2} = 6$$

On the other hand, it is not so obvious how to compute $\|A\|$ if $\| \cdot \|$ is a subordinate matrix norm. It turns out, however, that the matrix norms

$$\|A\|_1 = \max_{\mathbf{x} \neq \mathbf{0}} \frac{\|A\mathbf{x}\|_1}{\|\mathbf{x}\|_1} \quad \text{and} \quad \|A\|_\infty = \max_{\mathbf{x} \neq \mathbf{0}} \frac{\|A\mathbf{x}\|_\infty}{\|\mathbf{x}\|_\infty}$$

are simple to calculate.

Theorem 7.4.2 *If A is an $m \times n$ matrix, then*

$$\|A\|_1 = \max_{1 \leq j \leq n} \left(\sum_{i=1}^{m} |a_{ij}| \right)$$

and

$$\|A\|_\infty = \max_{1 \leq i \leq m} \left(\sum_{j=1}^{n} |a_{ij}| \right)$$

Proof We will prove that

$$\|A\|_1 = \max_{1 \leq j \leq n} \left(\sum_{i=1}^{m} |a_{ij}| \right)$$

and leave the proof of the second statement as an exercise. Let

$$\alpha = \max_{1 \le j \le n} \sum_{i=1}^{m} |a_{ij}| = \sum_{i=1}^{m} |a_{ik}|$$

That is, k is the index of the column in which the maximum occurs. Let $\mathbf{x}$ be an arbitrary vector in $\mathbb{R}^n$; then

$$A\mathbf{x} = \left(\sum_{j=1}^{n} a_{1j}x_j, \sum_{j=1}^{n} a_{2j}x_j, \ldots, \sum_{j=1}^{n} a_{mj}x_j \right)^T$$

and it follows that

$$\begin{aligned}
\|A\mathbf{x}\|_1 &= \sum_{i=1}^{m} \left| \sum_{j=1}^{n} a_{ij}x_j \right| \\
&\le \sum_{i=1}^{m} \sum_{j=1}^{n} |a_{ij}x_j| \\
&= \sum_{j=1}^{n} \left(|x_j| \sum_{i=1}^{m} |a_{ij}| \right) \\
&\le \alpha \sum_{j=1}^{n} |x_j| \\
&= \alpha \|\mathbf{x}\|_1
\end{aligned}$$

Thus, for any nonzero $\mathbf{x}$ in $\mathbb{R}^n$,

$$\frac{\|A\mathbf{x}\|_1}{\|\mathbf{x}\|_1} \le \alpha$$

and hence

$$\|A\|_1 = \max_{\mathbf{x} \ne \mathbf{0}} \frac{\|A\mathbf{x}\|_1}{\|\mathbf{x}\|_1} \le \alpha \qquad (3)$$

On the other hand,

$$\|A\mathbf{e}_k\|_1 = \|\mathbf{a}_k\|_1 = \alpha$$

Since $\|\mathbf{e}_k\|_1 = 1$, it follows that

$$\|A\|_1 = \max_{\mathbf{x} \ne \mathbf{0}} \frac{\|A\mathbf{x}\|_1}{\|\mathbf{x}\|_1} \ge \frac{\|A\mathbf{e}_k\|_1}{\|\mathbf{e}_k\|_1} = \alpha \qquad (4)$$

Together, (3) and (4) imply that $\|A\|_1 = \alpha$.

EXAMPLE I   Let

$$A = \begin{bmatrix} -3 & 2 & 4 & -3 \\ 5 & -2 & -3 & 5 \\ 2 & 1 & -6 & 4 \\ 1 & 1 & 1 & 1 \end{bmatrix}$$

Then

$$\|A\|_1 = |4| + |-3| + |-6| + |1| = 14$$

and

$$\|A\|_\infty = |5| + |-2| + |-3| + |5| = 15$$ ■

The 2-norm of a matrix is more difficult to compute since it depends on the singular values of the matrix. In fact, the 2-norm of a matrix is its largest singular value.

Theorem 7.4.3   *If A is an m × n matrix with singular value decomposition $U\Sigma V^T$, then*

$$\|A\|_2 = \sigma_1 \qquad (\textit{the largest singular value})$$

Proof   Since U and V are orthogonal,

$$\|A\|_2 = \|U\Sigma V^T\|_2 = \|\Sigma\|_2$$

(See Exercise 42.) Now,

$$\|\Sigma\|_2 = \max_{\mathbf{x} \neq \mathbf{0}} \frac{\|\Sigma\mathbf{x}\|_2}{\|\mathbf{x}\|_2}$$

$$= \max_{\mathbf{x} \neq \mathbf{0}} \frac{\left(\sum_{i=1}^{n}(\sigma_i x_i)^2\right)^{1/2}}{\left(\sum_{i=1}^{n} x_i^2\right)^{1/2}}$$

$$\leq \sigma_1$$

However, if we choose $\mathbf{x} = \mathbf{e}_1$, then

$$\frac{\|\Sigma\mathbf{x}\|_2}{\|\mathbf{x}\|_2} = \sigma_1$$

and hence it follows that

$$\|A\|_2 = \|\Sigma\|_2 = \sigma_1$$ ■

Corollary 7.4.4   *If $A = U\Sigma V^T$ is a nonsingular $n \times n$ matrix, then*

$$\|A^{-1}\|_2 = \frac{1}{\sigma_n}$$

Proof   The singular values of $A^{-1} = V\Sigma^{-1}U^T$, arranged in decreasing order, are

$$\frac{1}{\sigma_n} \geq \frac{1}{\sigma_{n-1}} \geq \cdots \geq \frac{1}{\sigma_1}$$

Therefore,

$$\|A^{-1}\|_2 = \frac{1}{\sigma_n}$$ ∎

Condition Numbers

Matrix norms can be used to estimate the sensitivity of linear systems to small changes in the coefficient matrix. Consider the following example.

EXAMPLE 2   Solve the following system:

$$\begin{aligned} 2.0000x_1 + 2.0000x_2 &= 6.0000 \\ 2.0000x_1 + 2.0005x_2 &= 6.0010 \end{aligned} \tag{5}$$

If we use five-digit decimal floating-point arithmetic, the computed solution will be the exact solution $\mathbf{x} = (1, 2)^T$. Suppose, however, that we are forced to use four-digit decimal floating-point numbers. Thus, in place of (5), we have

$$\begin{aligned} 2.000x_1 + 2.000x_2 &= 6.000 \\ 2.000x_1 + 2.001x_2 &= 6.001 \end{aligned} \tag{6}$$

The computed solution of system (6) is the exact solution $\mathbf{x}' = (2, 1)^T$.

The systems (5) and (6) agree except for the coefficient a_{22}. The relative error in this coefficient is

$$\frac{a_{22}' - a_{22}}{a_{22}} \approx 0.00025$$

However, the relative errors in the coordinates of the solutions $\mathbf{x}$ and $\mathbf{x}'$ are

$$\frac{x_1' - x_1}{x_1} = 1.0 \quad \text{and} \quad \frac{x_2' - x_2}{x_2} = -0.5$$ ∎

Definition

A matrix A is said to be **ill conditioned** if relatively small changes in the entries of A can cause relatively large changes in the solutions to $A\mathbf{x} = \mathbf{b}$. A is said to be **well conditioned** if relatively small changes in the entries of A result in relatively small changes in the solutions to $A\mathbf{x} = \mathbf{b}$.

If the matrix A is ill conditioned, the computed solution of $A\mathbf{x} = \mathbf{b}$ generally will not be accurate. Even if the entries of A can be represented exactly as floating-point numbers, small rounding errors occurring in the reduction process may have a drastic effect on the computed solution. If, however, the matrix is well conditioned and the proper pivoting strategy is used, we should be able to compute solutions quite accurately. In general, the accuracy of the solution depends on the conditioning of the matrix. If we could measure the conditioning of A, this measure could be used to derive a bound for the relative error in the computed solution.

Let A be an $n \times n$ nonsingular matrix and consider the system $A\mathbf{x} = \mathbf{b}$. If $\mathbf{x}$ is the exact solution of the system and $\mathbf{x}'$ is the calculated solution, then the error can be represented by the vector $\mathbf{e} = \mathbf{x} - \mathbf{x}'$. If $\| \cdot \|$ is a norm on $\mathbb{R}^n$, then $\|\mathbf{e}\|$ is a measure of the absolute error and $\|\mathbf{e}\|/\|\mathbf{x}\|$ is a measure of the relative error. In general, we have no way of determining the exact values of $\|\mathbf{e}\|$ and $\|\mathbf{e}\|/\|\mathbf{x}\|$. One possible way of testing the accuracy of $\mathbf{x}'$ is to put it back into the original system and see how close $\mathbf{b}' = A\mathbf{x}'$ comes to $\mathbf{b}$. The vector

$$\mathbf{r} = \mathbf{b} - \mathbf{b}' = \mathbf{b} - A\mathbf{x}'$$

is called the *residual* and can be easily calculated. The quantity

$$\frac{\|\mathbf{b} - A\mathbf{x}'\|}{\|\mathbf{b}\|} = \frac{\|\mathbf{r}\|}{\|\mathbf{b}\|}$$

is called the *relative residual*. Is the relative residual a good estimate of the relative error? The answer to this question depends on the conditioning of A. In Example 2, the residual for the computed solution $\mathbf{x}' = (2, 1)^T$ is

$$\mathbf{r} = \mathbf{b} - A\mathbf{x}' = (0, 0.0005)^T$$

The relative residual in terms of the ∞-norm is

$$\frac{\|\mathbf{r}\|_\infty}{\|\mathbf{b}\|_\infty} = \frac{0.0005}{6.0010} \approx 0.000083$$

and the relative error is given by

$$\frac{\|\mathbf{e}\|_\infty}{\|\mathbf{x}\|_\infty} = 0.5$$

The relative error is more than 6000 times the relative residual! In general, we will show that if A is ill conditioned, then the relative residual may be much smaller than the relative error. For well-conditioned matrices, however, the relative residual and the relative error are quite close. To show this, we need to make use of matrix norms. Recall that if $\| \cdot \|$ is a compatible matrix norm on $\mathbb{R}^{n \times n}$, then, for any $n \times n$ matrix C and any vector $\mathbf{y} \in \mathbb{R}^n$, we have

$$\|C\mathbf{y}\| \leq \|C\| \, \|\mathbf{y}\| \tag{7}$$

Now,

$$\mathbf{r} = \mathbf{b} - A\mathbf{x}' = A\mathbf{x} - A\mathbf{x}' = A\mathbf{e}$$

and consequently,

$$\mathbf{e} = A^{-1}\mathbf{r}$$

It follows from property (7) that

$$\|\mathbf{e}\| \le \|A^{-1}\| \, \|\mathbf{r}\|$$

and

$$\|\mathbf{r}\| = \|A\mathbf{e}\| \le \|A\| \, \|\mathbf{e}\|$$

Therefore,

$$\frac{\|\mathbf{r}\|}{\|A\|} \le \|\mathbf{e}\| \le \|A^{-1}\| \, \|\mathbf{r}\| \tag{8}$$

Now $\mathbf{x}$ is the exact solution to $A\mathbf{x} = \mathbf{b}$, and hence $\mathbf{x} = A^{-1}\mathbf{b}$. By the same reasoning used to derive (8), we have

$$\frac{\|\mathbf{b}\|}{\|A\|} \le \|\mathbf{x}\| \le \|A^{-1}\| \, \|\mathbf{b}\| \tag{9}$$

It follows from (8) and (9) that

$$\frac{1}{\|A\| \, \|A^{-1}\|} \frac{\|\mathbf{r}\|}{\|\mathbf{b}\|} \le \frac{\|\mathbf{e}\|}{\|\mathbf{x}\|} \le \|A\| \, \|A^{-1}\| \frac{\|\mathbf{r}\|}{\|\mathbf{b}\|}$$

The number $\|A\| \, \|A^{-1}\|$ is called the *condition number* of A and will be denoted by cond(A). Thus,

$$\frac{1}{\text{cond}(A)} \frac{\|\mathbf{r}\|}{\|\mathbf{b}\|} \le \frac{\|\mathbf{e}\|}{\|\mathbf{x}\|} \le \text{cond}(A)\frac{\|\mathbf{r}\|}{\|\mathbf{b}\|} \tag{10}$$

Inequality (10) relates the size of the relative error $\|\mathbf{e}\|/\|\mathbf{x}\|$ to the relative residual $\|\mathbf{r}\|/\|\mathbf{b}\|$. If the condition number is close to 1, the relative error and the relative residual will be close. If the condition number is large, the relative error could be many times as large as the relative residual.

EXAMPLE 3 Let

$$A = \begin{bmatrix} 3 & 3 \\ 4 & 5 \end{bmatrix}$$

Then

$$A^{-1} = \frac{1}{3}\begin{bmatrix} 5 & -3 \\ -4 & 3 \end{bmatrix}$$

$\|A\|_\infty = 9$ and $\|A^{-1}\|_\infty = \frac{8}{3}$. (We use $\| \cdot \|_\infty$ because it is easy to calculate.) Thus,

$$\text{cond}_\infty(A) = 9 \cdot \tfrac{8}{3} = 24$$

Theoretically, the relative error in the calculated solution of the system $A\mathbf{x} = \mathbf{b}$ could be as much as 24 times the relative residual. ∎

EXAMPLE 4 Suppose that $\mathbf{x}' = (2.0, 0.1)^T$ is the calculated solution of

$$3x_1 + 3x_2 = 6$$
$$4x_1 + 5x_2 = 9$$

Determine the residual $\mathbf{r}$ and the relative residual $\|\mathbf{r}\|_\infty/\|\mathbf{b}\|_\infty$.

Solution

$$\mathbf{r} = \begin{bmatrix} 6 \\ 9 \end{bmatrix} - \begin{bmatrix} 3 & 3 \\ 4 & 5 \end{bmatrix} \begin{bmatrix} 2.0 \\ 0.1 \end{bmatrix} = \begin{bmatrix} -0.3 \\ 0.5 \end{bmatrix}$$

$$\frac{\|\mathbf{r}\|_\infty}{\|\mathbf{b}\|_\infty} = \frac{0.5}{9} = \frac{1}{18}$$

■

We can see by inspection that the actual solution of the system in Example 4 is $\mathbf{x} = \begin{bmatrix} 1 \\ 1 \end{bmatrix}$. The error $\mathbf{e}$ is given by

$$\mathbf{e} = \mathbf{x} - \mathbf{x}' = \begin{bmatrix} -1.0 \\ 0.9 \end{bmatrix}$$

The relative error is given by

$$\frac{\|\mathbf{e}\|_\infty}{\|\mathbf{x}\|_\infty} = \frac{1.0}{1} = 1$$

The relative error is 18 times the relative residual. This is not surprising, since $\text{cond}(A) = 24$. The results are similar if we use $\| \cdot \|_1$. In this case,

$$\frac{\|\mathbf{r}\|_1}{\|\mathbf{b}\|_1} = \frac{0.8}{15} = \frac{4}{75} \quad \text{and} \quad \frac{\|\mathbf{e}\|_1}{\|\mathbf{x}\|_1} = \frac{1.9}{2} = \frac{19}{20}$$

The condition number of a nonsingular matrix actually gives us valuable information about the conditioning of A. Let A' be a new matrix formed by altering the entries of A slightly. Let $E = A' - A$. Thus, $A' = A + E$, where the entries of E are small relative to the entries of A. The matrix A will be ill conditioned if, for some such E, the solutions to $A'\mathbf{x} = \mathbf{b}$ and $A\mathbf{x} = \mathbf{b}$ vary greatly. Let $\mathbf{x}'$ be the solution of $A'\mathbf{x} = \mathbf{b}$ and $\mathbf{x}$ be the solution of $A\mathbf{x} = \mathbf{b}$. The condition number allows us to compare the change in solution relative to $\mathbf{x}'$ to the relative change in the matrix A.

$$\mathbf{x} = A^{-1}\mathbf{b} = A^{-1}A'\mathbf{x}' = A^{-1}(A + E)\mathbf{x}' = \mathbf{x}' + A^{-1}E\mathbf{x}'$$

Hence,

$$\mathbf{x} - \mathbf{x}' = A^{-1}E\mathbf{x}'$$

Using inequality (7), we see that

$$\|\mathbf{x} - \mathbf{x}'\| \le \|A^{-1}\| \, \|E\| \, \|\mathbf{x}'\|$$

or

$$\frac{\|\mathbf{x} - \mathbf{x}'\|}{\|\mathbf{x}'\|} \le \|A^{-1}\| \, \|E\| = \text{cond}(A)\frac{\|E\|}{\|A\|} \tag{11}$$

Let us return to Example 2 and see how inequality (11) applies. Let A and A' be the two coefficient matrices in Example 2:

$$E = A' - A = \begin{bmatrix} 0 & 0 \\ 0 & 0.0005 \end{bmatrix}$$

and

$$A^{-1} = \begin{bmatrix} 2000.5 & -2000 \\ -2000 & 2000 \end{bmatrix}$$

In terms of the ∞-norm, the relative error in A is

$$\frac{\|E\|_\infty}{\|A\|_\infty} = \frac{0.0005}{4.0005} \approx 0.0001$$

and the condition number is

$$\text{cond}(A) = \|A\|_\infty \|A^{-1}\|_\infty = (4.0005)(4000.5) \approx 16{,}004$$

The bound on the relative error given in (11) is then

$$\text{cond}(A)\frac{\|E\|}{\|A\|} = \|A^{-1}\| \, \|E\| = (4000.5)(0.0005) \approx 2$$

The actual relative error for the systems in Example 2 is

$$\frac{\|\mathbf{x} - \mathbf{x}'\|_\infty}{\|\mathbf{x}'\|_\infty} = \frac{1}{2}$$

If A is a nonsingular $n \times n$ matrix and we compute its condition number using the 2-norm, then we have

$$\text{cond}_2(A) = \|A\|_2\|A^{-1}\|_2 = \frac{\sigma_1}{\sigma_n}$$

If σ_n is small relative to σ_1, then $\text{cond}_2(A)$ will be large. The smallest singular value, σ_n, is a measure of how close the matrix is to being singular. Thus, the closer the matrix is to being singular, the more ill conditioned it is. If the coefficient matrix of a linear system is close to being singular, then small changes in the matrix due to roundoff errors could result in drastic changes to the solution of the system. To illustrate the relation between conditioning and nearness to singularity, let us look again at an example from Chapter 6.

EXAMPLE 5 In Section 6.5, we saw that the nonsingular 100×100 matrix

$$A = \begin{pmatrix} 1 & -1 & -1 & \cdots & -1 & -1 \\ 0 & 1 & -1 & \cdots & -1 & -1 \\ 0 & 0 & 1 & \cdots & -1 & -1 \\ \vdots & & & & & \\ 0 & 0 & 0 & \cdots & 1 & -1 \\ 0 & 0 & 0 & \cdots & 0 & 1 \end{pmatrix}$$

is actually very close to being singular, and to make it singular, we need only change the value of the $(100, 1)$ entry of A from 0 to $-\frac{1}{2^{98}}$. It follows from Theorem 6.5.3 that

$$\sigma_n = \min_{X \text{ singular}} \|A - X\|_F \leq \frac{1}{2^{98}}$$

so $\text{cond}_2(A)$ must be very large. It is even easier to see that A is extremely ill-conditioned if we use the infinity norm. The inverse of A is given by

$$A^{-1} = \begin{pmatrix} 1 & 1 & 2 & 4 & \cdots & 2^{98} \\ 0 & 1 & 1 & 2 & \cdots & 2^{97} \\ & & \vdots & & & \\ 0 & 0 & 0 & 0 & \cdots & 2^1 \\ 0 & 0 & 0 & 0 & \cdots & 2^0 \\ 0 & 0 & 0 & 0 & \cdots & 1 \end{pmatrix}$$

The infinity norms of A and A^{-1} are both determined by the entries in the first row of the matrix.

$$\text{cond}_\infty A = \|A\|_\infty \|A^{-1}\|_\infty = 100 \times 2^{99} \approx 6.34 \times 10^{31}$$

∎

SECTION 7.4 EXERCISES

1. Determine $\|\cdot\|_F$, $\|\cdot\|_\infty$, and $\|\cdot\|_1$ for each of the following matrices:

(a) $\begin{bmatrix} 1 & 0 \\ 0 & 1 \end{bmatrix}$ (b) $\begin{bmatrix} 1 & 4 \\ -2 & 2 \end{bmatrix}$

(c) $\begin{bmatrix} \frac{1}{2} & \frac{1}{2} \\ \frac{1}{2} & \frac{1}{2} \end{bmatrix}$ (d) $\begin{bmatrix} 0 & 5 & 1 \\ 2 & 3 & 1 \\ 1 & 2 & 2 \end{bmatrix}$

(e) $\begin{bmatrix} 5 & 0 & 5 \\ 4 & 1 & 0 \\ 3 & 2 & 1 \end{bmatrix}$

2. Let

$$A = \begin{bmatrix} 2 & 0 \\ 0 & -2 \end{bmatrix} \quad \text{and} \quad \mathbf{x} = \begin{bmatrix} x_1 \\ x_2 \end{bmatrix}$$

and set

$$f(x_1, x_2) = \|A\mathbf{x}\|_2 / \|\mathbf{x}\|_2$$

Determine the value of $\|A\|_2$ by finding the maximum value of f for all $(x_1, x_2) \neq (0, 0)$.

3. Let

$$A = \begin{bmatrix} 1 & 0 \\ 0 & 0 \end{bmatrix}$$

Use the method of Exercise 2 to determine the value of $\|A\|_2$.

4. Let

$$D = \begin{bmatrix} 3 & 0 & 0 & 0 \\ 0 & -5 & 0 & 0 \\ 0 & 0 & -2 & 0 \\ 0 & 0 & 0 & 4 \end{bmatrix}$$

(a) Compute the singular value decomposition of D.
(b) Find the value of $\|D\|_2$.

5. Show that if D is an $n \times n$ diagonal matrix, then

$$\|D\|_2 = \max_{1 \le i \le n}(|d_{ii}|)$$

6. If D is an $n \times n$ diagonal matrix, how do the values of $\|D\|_1$, $\|D\|_2$, and $\|D\|_\infty$ compare? Explain your answers.

7. Let I denote the $n \times n$ identity matrix. Determine the values of $\|I\|_1$, $\|I\|_\infty$, and $\|I\|_F$.

8. Let $\|\cdot\|_M$ denote a matrix norm on $\mathbb{R}^{n \times n}$, $\|\cdot\|_V$ denote a vector norm on $\mathbb{R}^n$, and I be the $n \times n$ identity matrix. Show that

(a) if $\|\cdot\|_M$ and $\|\cdot\|_V$ are compatible, then $\|I\|_M \ge 1$.
(b) if $\|\cdot\|_M$ is subordinate to $\|\cdot\|_V$, then $\|I\|_M = 1$.

9. A vector $\mathbf{x}$ in $\mathbb{R}^n$ can also be viewed as an $n \times 1$ matrix X:

$$\mathbf{x} = X = \begin{bmatrix} x_1 \\ x_2 \\ \vdots \\ x_n \end{bmatrix}$$

(a) How do the matrix norm $\|X\|_\infty$ and the vector norm $\|\mathbf{x}\|_\infty$ compare? Explain.
(b) How do the matrix norm $\|X\|_1$ and the vector norm $\|\mathbf{x}\|_1$ compare? Explain.

10. A vector $\mathbf{y}$ in $\mathbb{R}^n$ can also be viewed as an $n \times 1$ matrix $Y = (\mathbf{y})$. Show that

(a) $\|Y\|_2 = \|\mathbf{y}\|_2$ (b) $\|Y^T\|_2 = \|\mathbf{y}\|_2$

11. Let $A = \mathbf{w}\mathbf{y}^T$, where $\mathbf{w} \in \mathbb{R}^m$ and $\mathbf{y} \in \mathbb{R}^n$. Show that

(a) $\dfrac{\|A\mathbf{x}\|_2}{\|\mathbf{x}\|_2} \le \|\mathbf{y}\|_2\|\mathbf{w}\|_2$ for all $\mathbf{x} \ne \mathbf{0}$ in $\mathbb{R}^n$.

(b) $\|A\|_2 = \|\mathbf{y}\|_2\|\mathbf{w}\|_2$

12. Let

$$A = \begin{bmatrix} 3 & -1 & -2 \\ -1 & 2 & -7 \\ 4 & 1 & 4 \end{bmatrix}$$

(a) Determine $\|A\|_\infty$.

(b) Find a vector $\mathbf{x}$ whose coordinates are each ± 1 such that $\|A\mathbf{x}\|_\infty = \|A\|_\infty$. (Note that $\|\mathbf{x}\|_\infty = 1$, so $\|A\|_\infty = \|A\mathbf{x}\|_\infty / \|\mathbf{x}\|_\infty$.)

13. Theorem 7.4.2 states that

$$\|A\|_\infty = \max_{1 \le i \le m} \left(\sum_{j=1}^n |a_{ij}| \right)$$

Prove this in two steps.

(a) Show first that

$$\|A\|_\infty \le \max_{1 \le i \le m} \left(\sum_{j=1}^n |a_{ij}| \right)$$

(b) Construct a vector $\mathbf{x}$ whose coordinates are each ± 1 such that

$$\frac{\|A\mathbf{x}\|_\infty}{\|\mathbf{x}\|_\infty} = \|A\mathbf{x}\|_\infty = \max_{1 \le i \le m} \left(\sum_{j=1}^n |a_{ij}| \right)$$

14. Show that $\|A\|_F = \|A^T\|_F$.

15. Let A be a symmetric $n \times n$ matrix. Show that $\|A\|_\infty = \|A\|_1$.

16. Let A be a 5×4 matrix with singular values $\sigma_1 = 5$, $\sigma_2 = 3$, and $\sigma_3 = \sigma_4 = 1$. Determine the values of $\|A\|_2$ and $\|A\|_F$.

17. Let A be an $m \times n$ matrix.

(a) Show that $\|A\|_2 \le \|A\|_F$.

(b) Under what circumstances will $\|A\|_2 = \|A\|_F$?

18. Let $\|\cdot\|$ denote a family of vector norms and let $\|\cdot\|_M$ be a subordinate matrix norm. Show that

$$\|A\|_M = \max_{\|\mathbf{x}\|=1} \|A\mathbf{x}\|$$

19. Let A be an $m \times n$ matrix and let $\|\cdot\|_v$ and $\|\cdot\|_w$ be vector norms on $\mathbb{R}^n$ and $\mathbb{R}^m$, respectively. Show that

$$\|A\|_{(v,w)} = \max_{\mathbf{x}\ne\mathbf{0}} \frac{\|A\mathbf{x}\|_w}{\|\mathbf{x}\|_v}$$

defines a matrix norm on $\mathbb{R}^{m \times n}$.

20. Let A be an $m \times n$ matrix. The (1,2)-norm of A is given by

$$\|A\|_{(1,2)} = \max_{\mathbf{x}\ne\mathbf{0}} \frac{\|A\mathbf{x}\|_2}{\|\mathbf{x}\|_1}$$

(See Exercise 19.) Show that

$$\|A\|_{(1,2)} = \max \left(\|\mathbf{a}_1\|_2, \|\mathbf{a}_2\|_2, \dots, \|\mathbf{a}_n\|_2 \right)$$

21. Let A be an $m \times n$ matrix. Show that $\|A\|_{(1,2)} \le \|A\|_2$.

22. Let $A \in \mathbb{R}^{m \times n}$ and $B \in \mathbb{R}^{n \times r}$. Show that

(a) $\|A\mathbf{x}\|_2 \le \|A\|_{(1,2)}\|\mathbf{x}\|_1$ for all $\mathbf{x}$ in $\mathbb{R}^n$.

(b) $\|AB\|_{(1,2)} \le \|A\|_2\|B\|_{(1,2)}$

(c) $\|AB\|_{(1,2)} \le \|A\|_{(1,2)}\|B\|_1$

23. Let A be an $n \times n$ matrix and let $\|\cdot\|_M$ be a matrix norm that is compatible with some vector norm on $\mathbb{R}^n$. Show that if λ is an eigenvalue of A, then $|\lambda| \le \|A\|_M$.

24. Use the result from Exercise 23 to show that if λ is an eigenvalue of a stochastic matrix, then $|\lambda| \le 1$.

25. Sudoku is a popular puzzle involving matrices. In this puzzle, one is given some of the entries of a 9×9 matrix A and asked to fill in the missing entries. The matrix A has a block structure

$$A = \begin{bmatrix} A_{11} & A_{12} & A_{13} \\ A_{21} & A_{22} & A_{23} \\ A_{31} & A_{32} & A_{33} \end{bmatrix}$$

where each submatrix A_{ij} is 3×3. The rules of the puzzle are that each row, each column, and each of the submatrices of A must be made up of all of the integers 1 through 9. We will refer to such a matrix as a *sudoku matrix*. Show that if A is a sudoku matrix, then $\lambda = 45$ is its dominant eigenvalue.

26. Let A_{ij} be a submatrix of a sudoku matrix A (see Exercise 25). Show that if λ is an eigenvalue of A_{ij}, then $|\lambda| \le 22$.

27. Let A be an $n \times n$ matrix and $\mathbf{x} \in \mathbb{R}^n$. Prove:

(a) $\|A\mathbf{x}\|_\infty \le n^{1/2}\|A\|_2\|\mathbf{x}\|_\infty$

(b) $\|A\mathbf{x}\|_2 \le n^{1/2}\|A\|_\infty\|\mathbf{x}\|_2$

(c) $n^{-1/2}\|A\|_2 \le \|A\|_\infty \le n^{1/2}\|A\|_2$

28. Let A be a symmetric $n \times n$ matrix with eigenvalues $\lambda_1, \dots, \lambda_n$ and orthonormal eigenvectors $\mathbf{u}_1, \dots, \mathbf{u}_n$. Let $\mathbf{x} \in \mathbb{R}^n$ and let $c_i = \mathbf{u}_i^T\mathbf{x}$ for $i = 1, 2, \dots, n$. Show that

(a) $\|A\mathbf{x}\|_2^2 = \sum_{i=1}^{n} (\lambda_i c_i)^2$

(b) if $\mathbf{x} \neq \mathbf{0}$, then

$$\min_{1 \leq i \leq n} |\lambda_i| \leq \frac{\|A\mathbf{x}\|_2}{\|\mathbf{x}\|_2} \leq \max_{1 \leq i \leq n} |\lambda_i|$$

(c) $\|A\|_2 = \max_{1 \leq i \leq n} |\lambda_i|$

29. Let

$$A = \begin{pmatrix} 1 & -0.99 \\ -1 & 1 \end{pmatrix}$$

Find A^{-1} and $\text{cond}_\infty(A)$.

30. Solve the given two systems and compare the solutions. Are the coefficient matrices well conditioned? Ill conditioned? Explain.

$$1.0x_1 + 2.0x_2 = 1.12 \quad 1.000x_1 + 2.011x_2 = 1.120$$
$$2.0x_1 + 3.9x_2 = 2.16 \quad 2.000x_1 + 3.982x_2 = 2.160$$

31. Let

$$A = \begin{pmatrix} 1 & 0 & 1 \\ 2 & 2 & 3 \\ 1 & 1 & 2 \end{pmatrix}$$

Calculate $\text{cond}_\infty(A) = \|A\|_\infty \|A^{-1}\|_\infty$.

32. Let A be a nonsingular $n \times n$ matrix, and let $\| \cdot \|_M$ denote a matrix norm that is compatible with some vector norm on $\mathbb{R}^n$. Show that

$$\text{cond}_M(A) \geq 1$$

33. Let

$$A_n = \begin{pmatrix} 1 & 1 \\ 1 & 1 - \dfrac{1}{n} \end{pmatrix}$$

for each positive integer n. Calculate

(a) A_n^{-1} **(b)** $\text{cond}_\infty(A_n)$ **(c)** $\lim_{n \to \infty} \text{cond}_\infty(A_n)$

34. If A is a 5×3 matrix with $\|A\|_2 = 8$, $\text{cond}_2(A) = 2$, and $\|A\|_F = 12$, determine the singular values of A.

35. Given

$$A = \begin{pmatrix} 3 & 2 \\ 1 & 1 \end{pmatrix} \quad \text{and} \quad \mathbf{b} = \begin{pmatrix} 5 \\ 2 \end{pmatrix}$$

if two-digit decimal floating-point arithmetic is used to solve the system $A\mathbf{x} = \mathbf{b}$, the computed solution will be $\mathbf{x} = (1.1, 0.88)^T$.

(a) Determine the residual vector $\mathbf{r}$ and the value of the relative residual $\|\mathbf{r}\|_\infty / \|\mathbf{b}\|_\infty$.

(b) Find the value of $\text{cond}_\infty(A)$.

(c) Without computing the exact solution, use the results from parts (a) and (b) to obtain bounds for the relative error in the computed solution.

(d) Compute the exact solution $\mathbf{x}$ and determine the actual relative error. Compare this to the bounds derived in part (c).

36. Let

$$A = \begin{pmatrix} -0.50 & 0.75 & -0.25 \\ -0.50 & 0.25 & 0.25 \\ 1.00 & -0.50 & 0.50 \end{pmatrix}$$

Calculate $\text{cond}_1(A) = \|A\|_1 \|A^{-1}\|_1$.

37. Let A be the matrix in Exercise 36 and let

$$A' = \begin{pmatrix} -0.5 & 0.8 & -0.3 \\ -0.5 & 0.3 & 0.3 \\ 1.0 & -0.5 & 0.5 \end{pmatrix}$$

Let $\mathbf{x}$ and $\mathbf{x}'$ be the solutions of $A\mathbf{x} = \mathbf{b}$ and $A'\mathbf{x} = \mathbf{b}$, respectively, for some $\mathbf{b} \in \mathbb{R}^3$. Find a bound for the relative error $(\|\mathbf{x} - \mathbf{x}'\|_1)/\|\mathbf{x}'\|_1$.

38. Let

$$A = \begin{pmatrix} 1 & -1 & -1 & -1 \\ 0 & 1 & -1 & -1 \\ 0 & 0 & 1 & -1 \\ 0 & 0 & 0 & 1 \end{pmatrix}, \quad \mathbf{b} = \begin{pmatrix} 5.00 \\ 1.02 \\ 1.04 \\ 1.10 \end{pmatrix}$$

An approximate solution of $A\mathbf{x} = \mathbf{b}$ is calculated by rounding the entries of $\mathbf{b}$ to the nearest integer and then solving the rounded system with integer arithmetic. The calculated solution is $\mathbf{x}' = (12, 4, 2, 1)^T$. Let $\mathbf{r}$ denote the residual vector.

(a) Determine the values of $\|\mathbf{r}\|_\infty$ and $\text{cond}_\infty(A)$.

(b) Use your answer to part (a) to find an upper bound for the relative error in the solution.

(c) Compute the exact solution $\mathbf{x}$ and determine the relative error $\dfrac{\|\mathbf{x} - \mathbf{x}'\|_\infty}{\|\mathbf{x}\|_\infty}$.

39. Let A and B be nonsingular $n \times n$ matrices. Show that

$$\text{cond}(AB) \leq \text{cond}(A)\,\text{cond}(B)$$

40. Let D be a nonsingular $n \times n$ diagonal matrix and let

$$d_{\max} = \max_{1 \leq i \leq n} |d_{ii}| \quad \text{and} \quad d_{\min} = \min_{1 \leq i \leq n} |d_{ii}|$$

(a) Show that

$$\text{cond}_1(D) = \text{cond}_\infty(D) = \frac{d_{\max}}{d_{\min}}$$

(b) Show that

$$\text{cond}_2(D) = \frac{d_{\max}}{d_{\min}}$$

41. Let Q be an $n \times n$ orthogonal matrix. Show that
  (a) $\|Q\|_2 = 1$ **(b)** $\text{cond}_2(Q) = 1$

  (c) for any $\mathbf{b} \in \mathbb{R}^n$, the relative error in the solution of $Q\mathbf{x} = \mathbf{b}$ is equal to the relative residual, that is,

$$\frac{\|\mathbf{e}\|_2}{\|\mathbf{x}\|_2} = \frac{\|\mathbf{r}\|_2}{\|\mathbf{b}\|_2}$$

42. Let A be an $n \times n$ matrix and let Q and V be $n \times n$ orthogonal matrices. Show that
  (a) $\|QA\|_2 = \|A\|_2$ **(b)** $\|AV\|_2 = \|A\|_2$

  (c) $\|QAV\|_2 = \|A\|_2$

43. Let A be an $m \times n$ matrix and let σ_1 be the largest singular value of A. Show that if $\mathbf{x}$ and $\mathbf{y}$ are nonzero vectors in $\mathbb{R}^n$, then each of the following holds:
  (a) $\dfrac{|\mathbf{x}^T A \mathbf{y}|}{\|\mathbf{x}\|_2 \|\mathbf{y}\|_2} \leq \sigma_1$

  [*Hint*: Make use of the Cauchy–Schwarz inequality.]

  (b) $\displaystyle\max_{\mathbf{x} \neq \mathbf{0}, \mathbf{y} \neq \mathbf{0}} \frac{|\mathbf{x}^T A \mathbf{y}|}{\|\mathbf{x}\| \|\mathbf{y}\|} = \sigma_1$

44. Let A be an $m \times n$ matrix with singular value decomposition $U \Sigma V^T$. Show that

$$\min_{\mathbf{x} \neq \mathbf{0}} \frac{\|A\mathbf{x}\|_2}{\|\mathbf{x}\|_2} = \sigma_n$$

45. Let A be an $m \times n$ matrix with singular value decomposition $U \Sigma V^T$. Show that, for any vector $\mathbf{x} \in \mathbb{R}^n$,

$$\sigma_n \|\mathbf{x}\|_2 \leq \|A\mathbf{x}\|_2 \leq \sigma_1 \|\mathbf{x}\|_2$$

46. Let A be a nonsingular $n \times n$ matrix and let Q be an $n \times n$ orthogonal matrix. Show that
  (a) $\text{cond}_2(QA) = \text{cond}_2(AQ) = \text{cond}_2(A)$
  (b) if $B = Q^T A Q$, then $\text{cond}_2(B) = \text{cond}_2(A)$.

47. Let A be a symmetric nonsingular $n \times n$ matrix with eigenvalues $\lambda_1, \ldots, \lambda_n$. Show that

$$\text{cond}_2(A) = \frac{\max_{1 \leq i \leq n} |\lambda_i|}{\min_{1 \leq i \leq n} |\lambda_i|}$$

<h2>7.5 Orthogonal Transformations</h2>

Orthogonal transformations are one of the most important tools in numerical linear algebra. The types of orthogonal transformations that will be introduced in this section are easy to work with and do not require much storage. Most important, processes that involve orthogonal transformations are inherently stable. For example, let $\mathbf{x} \in \mathbb{R}^n$ and $\mathbf{x}' = \mathbf{x} + \mathbf{e}$ be an approximation to $\mathbf{x}$: If Q is an orthogonal matrix, then

$$Q\mathbf{x}' = Q\mathbf{x} + Q\mathbf{e}$$

The error in $Q\mathbf{x}'$ is $Q\mathbf{e}$. With respect to the 2-norm, the vector $Q\mathbf{e}$ is the same size as $\mathbf{e}$;

$$\|Q\mathbf{e}\|_2 = \|\mathbf{e}\|_2$$

Similarly, if $A' = A + E$, then

$$QA' = QA + QE$$

and

$$\|QE\|_2 = \|E\|_2$$

When an orthogonal transformation is applied to a vector or matrix, the error will not grow with respect to the 2-norm.

Elementary Orthogonal Transformations

By an *elementary orthogonal matrix*, we mean a matrix of the form

$$Q = I - 2\mathbf{u}\mathbf{u}^T$$

where $\mathbf{u} \in \mathbb{R}^n$ and $\|\mathbf{u}\|_2 = 1$. To see that Q is orthogonal, note that

$$Q^T = (I - 2\mathbf{u}\mathbf{u}^T)^T = I - 2\mathbf{u}\mathbf{u}^T = Q$$

and

$$
\begin{aligned}
Q^T Q = Q^2 &= (I - 2\mathbf{u}\mathbf{u}^T)(I - 2\mathbf{u}\mathbf{u}^T) \\
&= I - 4\mathbf{u}\mathbf{u}^T + 4\mathbf{u}(\mathbf{u}^T\mathbf{u})\mathbf{u}^T \\
&= I
\end{aligned}
$$

Thus, if Q is an elementary orthogonal matrix, then

$$Q^T = Q^{-1} = Q$$

The matrix $Q = I - 2\mathbf{u}\mathbf{u}^T$ is completely determined by the unit vector $\mathbf{u}$. Rather than store all n^2 entries of Q, we need store only the vector $\mathbf{u}$. To compute $Q\mathbf{x}$, note that

$$Q\mathbf{x} = (I - 2\mathbf{u}\mathbf{u}^T)\mathbf{x} = \mathbf{x} - 2\alpha\mathbf{u}$$

where $\alpha = \mathbf{u}^T\mathbf{x}$.

The matrix product QA is computed as

$$QA = (Q\mathbf{a}_1, Q\mathbf{a}_2, \ldots, Q\mathbf{a}_n)$$

where

$$Q\mathbf{a}_i = \mathbf{a}_i - 2\alpha_i\mathbf{u} \qquad \alpha_i = \mathbf{u}^T\mathbf{a}_i$$

Elementary orthogonal transformations can be used to obtain a QR factorization of A, and this, in turn, can be used to solve a linear system $A\mathbf{x} = \mathbf{b}$. As with Gaussian elimination, the elementary matrices are chosen so as to produce zeros in the coefficient matrix. To see how this is done, let us consider the problem of finding a unit vector $\mathbf{u}$ such that

$$(I - 2\mathbf{u}\mathbf{u}^T)\mathbf{x} = (\alpha, 0, \ldots, 0)^T = \alpha\mathbf{e}_1$$

for a given vector $\mathbf{x} \in \mathbb{R}^n$.

Householder Transformations

Let $H = I - 2\mathbf{u}\mathbf{u}^T$. If $H\mathbf{x} = \alpha\mathbf{e}_1$, then, since H is orthogonal, it follows that

$$|\alpha| = \|\alpha\mathbf{e}_1\|_2 = \|H\mathbf{x}\|_2 = \|\mathbf{x}\|_2$$

If we take $\alpha = \|\mathbf{x}\|_2$ or $\alpha = -\|\mathbf{x}\|_2$, then since $H\mathbf{x} = \alpha\mathbf{e}_1$, and H is its own inverse, we have

$$\mathbf{x} = H(\alpha\mathbf{e}_1) = \alpha(\mathbf{e}_1 - (2u_1)\mathbf{u}) \tag{1}$$

Thus,

$$x_1 = \alpha(1 - 2u_1^2)$$
$$x_2 = -2\alpha u_1 u_2$$
$$\vdots$$
$$x_n = -2\alpha u_1 u_n$$

Solving for the u_i's, we get

$$u_1 = \pm \left(\frac{\alpha - x_1}{2\alpha}\right)^{1/2}$$

$$u_i = \frac{-x_i}{2\alpha u_1} \qquad \text{for} \quad i = 2, \ldots, n$$

If we let

$$u_1 = -\left(\frac{\alpha - x_1}{2\alpha}\right)^{1/2} \qquad \text{and set} \quad \beta = \alpha(\alpha - x_1),$$

then

$$-2\alpha u_1 = [2\alpha(\alpha - x_1)]^{1/2} = (2\beta)^{1/2}$$

It follows that

$$\mathbf{u} = \left(-\frac{1}{2\alpha u_1}\right)(-2\alpha u_1^2, x_2, \ldots, x_n)^T$$

$$= \frac{1}{\sqrt{2\beta}}(x_1 - \alpha, x_2, \ldots, x_n)^T$$

If we set $\mathbf{v} = (x_1 - \alpha, x_2, \ldots, x_n)^T$, then

$$\|\mathbf{v}\|_2^2 = (x_1 - \alpha)^2 + \sum_{i=2}^{n} x_i^2 = 2\alpha(\alpha - x_1)$$

and hence

$$\|\mathbf{v}\|_2 = \sqrt{2\beta}$$

Thus,

$$\mathbf{u} = \frac{1}{\sqrt{2\beta}}\mathbf{v} = \frac{1}{\|\mathbf{v}\|_2}\mathbf{v}$$

and

$$H = I - 2\mathbf{u}\mathbf{u}^T = I - \frac{1}{\beta}\mathbf{v}\mathbf{v}^T \tag{2}$$

In theory, equation (2) will be valid if $\alpha = \pm\|x\|_2$; however, in finite-precision arithmetic, it does matter how the sign is chosen. Since the first entry of $\mathbf{v}$ is $v_1 = x_1 - \alpha$, one could possibly lose significant digits of accuracy if x_1 and α are nearly equal and have the same sign. To avoid this situation, the scalar α should be defined by

$$\alpha = \begin{cases} -\|\mathbf{x}\|_2 & \text{if } x_1 > 0 \\ \|\mathbf{x}\|_2 & \text{if } x_1 \leq 0 \end{cases} \tag{3}$$

In summation, given a vector $\mathbf{x} \in \mathbb{R}^n$, if we define α as in equation (3) and set

$$\beta = \alpha(\alpha - x_1)$$
$$\mathbf{v} = (x_1 - \alpha, x_2, \ldots, x_n)^T$$
$$\mathbf{u} = \frac{1}{\|\mathbf{v}\|_2}\mathbf{v} = \frac{1}{\sqrt{2\beta}}\mathbf{v}$$

and

$$H = I - 2\mathbf{u}\mathbf{u}^T = I - \frac{1}{\beta}\mathbf{v}\mathbf{v}^T$$

then

$$H\mathbf{x} = \alpha\mathbf{e}_1$$

The matrix H formed in this way is called a *Householder transformation*. The matrix H is determined by the vector $\mathbf{v}$ and the scalar β. For any vector $\mathbf{y} \in \mathbb{R}^n$,

$$H\mathbf{y} = \left(I - \frac{1}{\beta}\mathbf{v}\mathbf{v}^T\right)\mathbf{y} = \mathbf{y} - \left(\frac{\mathbf{v}^T\mathbf{y}}{\beta}\right)\mathbf{v}$$

Rather than store all n^2 entries of H, we need store only $\mathbf{v}$ and β.

EXAMPLE I Given the vector $\mathbf{x} = (1, 2, 2)^T$, find a Householder matrix that will zero out the last two entries of $\mathbf{x}$.

Solution

Since $x_1 = 1 > 0$, set $\alpha = -\|\mathbf{x}\|_2 = -3$ and then set

$$\beta = \alpha(\alpha - x_1) = 12$$
$$\mathbf{v} = (x_1 - \alpha, x_2, x_3)^T = (4, 2, 2)^T$$

The Householder matrix is given by

$$H = I - \frac{1}{12}\mathbf{v}\mathbf{v}^T$$

$$= \frac{1}{3}\begin{bmatrix} -1 & -2 & -2 \\ -2 & 2 & -1 \\ -2 & -1 & 2 \end{bmatrix}$$

The reader may verify that

$$H\mathbf{x} = -3\mathbf{e}_1 \qquad \blacksquare$$

Suppose now that we wish to zero out only the last $n - k$ components of a vector $\mathbf{x} = (x_1, \ldots, x_k, x_{k+1}, \ldots, x_n)^T$. To do this, we let $\mathbf{x}^{(1)} = (x_1, \ldots, x_{k-1})^T$ and $\mathbf{x}^{(2)} = (x_k, x_{k+1}, \ldots, x_n)^T$. Let $I^{(1)}$ and $I^{(2)}$ denote the $(k-1) \times (k-1)$

and $(n - k + 1) \times (n - k + 1)$ identity matrices, respectively. By the methods just described, we can construct a Householder matrix $H_k^{(2)} = I^{(2)} - (1/\beta_k)\mathbf{v}_k\mathbf{v}_k^T$ such that

$$H_k^{(2)}\mathbf{x}^{(2)} = \alpha\mathbf{e}_1^{(2)}$$

where $\alpha = \pm\|\mathbf{x}^{(2)}\|_2$ and $\mathbf{e}_1^{(2)}$ is the first column vector of the $(n - k + 1) \times (n - k + 1)$ identity matrix. Let

$$H_k = \begin{bmatrix} I^{(1)} & O \\ O & H_k^{(2)} \end{bmatrix} \tag{4}$$

It follows that

$$H_k\mathbf{x} = \begin{bmatrix} I^{(1)} & O \\ O & H_k^{(2)} \end{bmatrix} \begin{bmatrix} \mathbf{x}^{(1)} \\ \mathbf{x}^{(2)} \end{bmatrix} = \begin{bmatrix} I^{(1)}\mathbf{x}^{(1)} \\ H_k^{(2)}\mathbf{x}^{(2)} \end{bmatrix} = \begin{bmatrix} \mathbf{x}^{(1)} \\ \alpha\mathbf{e}_1^{(2)} \end{bmatrix}$$

Remarks

1. The Householder matrix H_k defined in equation (4) is an elementary orthogonal matrix. If we let

$$\mathbf{v} = \begin{bmatrix} \mathbf{0} \\ \mathbf{v}_k \end{bmatrix} \qquad \text{and} \qquad \mathbf{u} = (1/\|\mathbf{v}\|)\mathbf{v}$$

then

$$H_k = I - \frac{1}{\beta_k}\mathbf{v}\mathbf{v}^T = I - 2\mathbf{u}\mathbf{u}^T$$

2. H_k acts like the identity matrix on the first $k - 1$ coordinates of any vector $\mathbf{y} \in \mathbb{R}^n$. If $\mathbf{y} = (y_1, \ldots, y_{k-1}, y_k, \ldots, y_n)^T$, $\mathbf{y}^{(1)} = (y_1, \ldots, y_{k-1})^T$, and $\mathbf{y}^{(2)} = (y_k, \ldots, y_n)^T$, then

$$H_k\mathbf{y} = \begin{bmatrix} I^{(1)} & O \\ O & H_k^{(2)} \end{bmatrix} \begin{bmatrix} \mathbf{y}^{(1)} \\ \mathbf{y}^{(2)} \end{bmatrix} = \begin{bmatrix} \mathbf{y}^{(1)} \\ H_k^{(2)}\mathbf{y}^{(2)} \end{bmatrix}$$

In particular, if $\mathbf{y}^{(2)} = \mathbf{0}$, then $H_k\mathbf{y} = \mathbf{y}$.

3. It is generally not necessary to store the entire matrix H_k. It suffices to store the vector $\mathbf{v}_k$ and the scalar β_k.

EXAMPLE 2 Find a Householder matrix that zeroes out the last two entries of $\mathbf{y} = (3, 1, 2, 2)^T$ while leaving the first entry unchanged.

Solution

The Householder matrix will change only the last three entries of $\mathbf{y}$. These entries correspond to the vector $\mathbf{x} = (1, 2, 2)^T$ in $\mathbb{R}^3$. But this is the vector whose last two entries were zeroed out in Example 1. The 3×3 Householder matrix from Example 1 can be used to form a 4×4 matrix

$$
H = \begin{bmatrix}
1 & 0 & 0 & 0 \\
0 & -\frac{1}{3} & -\frac{2}{3} & -\frac{2}{3} \\
0 & -\frac{2}{3} & \frac{2}{3} & -\frac{1}{3} \\
0 & -\frac{2}{3} & -\frac{1}{3} & \frac{2}{3}
\end{bmatrix}
$$

which will have the desired effect on $\mathbf{y}$. We leave it to the reader to verify that $H\mathbf{y} = (3, -3, 0, 0)^T$.   ∎

We are now ready to apply Householder transformations to solve linear systems. If A is a nonsingular $n \times n$ matrix, we can use Householder transformations to reduce A to strict triangular form. To begin with, we can find a Householder transformation $H_1 = I - (1/\beta_1)\mathbf{v}_1\mathbf{v}_1^T$ that, when applied to the first column of A, will give a multiple of $\mathbf{e}_1$. Thus, $H_1 A$ will be of the form

$$
\begin{bmatrix}
\times & \times & \cdots & \times \\
0 & \times & \cdots & \times \\
0 & \times & \cdots & \times \\
\vdots & & & \\
0 & \times & \cdots & \times
\end{bmatrix}
$$

We can then find a Householder transformation H_2 that will zero out the last $n - 2$ elements in the second column of $H_1 A$ while leaving the first element in that column unchanged. It follows from remark 2 that H_2 will have no effect on the first column of $H_1 A$, so multiplication by H_2 yields a matrix of the form

$$
H_2 H_1 A = \begin{bmatrix}
\times & \times & \times & \cdots & \times \\
0 & \times & \times & \cdots & \times \\
0 & 0 & \times & \cdots & \times \\
\vdots & & & & \\
0 & 0 & \times & \cdots & \times
\end{bmatrix}
$$

We can continue to apply Householder transformations in this fashion until we end up with an upper triangular matrix, which we will denote by R. Thus,

$$
H_{n-1} \cdots H_2 H_1 A = R
$$

It follows that

$$
\begin{aligned}
A &= H_1^{-1} H_2^{-1} \cdots H_{n-1}^{-1} R \\
&= H_1 H_2 \cdots H_{n-1} R
\end{aligned}
$$

Let $Q = H_1 H_2 \cdots H_{n-1}$. The matrix Q is orthogonal and A can be factored into the product of an orthogonal matrix times an upper triangular matrix:

$$
A = QR
$$

After A has been factored into a product QR, the system $A\mathbf{x} = \mathbf{b}$ is easily solved. Indeed, if we multiply through by Q^T, we end up with the upper triangular system $R\mathbf{x} = \mathbf{c}$, where $\mathbf{c} = Q^T\mathbf{b}$. Since Q is a product of Householder matrices, it is not necessary to perform the matrix multiplications to compute Q explicitly. Instead, we can calculate $\mathbf{c}$ directly by performing a sequence of Householder transformations on $\mathbf{b}$:

$$\mathbf{c} = H_{n-1} \cdots H_2 H_1 \mathbf{b} \tag{5}$$

The system $R\mathbf{x} = \mathbf{c}$ can then be solved using back substitution.

Operation Count   In solving an $n \times n$ system by means of Householder transformations, most of the work is done in reducing A to triangular form. The number of operations required is approximately $\frac{2}{3}n^3$ multiplications, $\frac{2}{3}n^3$ additions, and $n-1$ square roots.

Rotations and Reflections

Often, it will be desirable to have a transformation that zeroes out only a single entry of a vector. In this case, it is convenient to use either a rotation or a reflection. Let us consider first the two-dimensional case.

Let

$$R = \begin{bmatrix} \cos\theta & -\sin\theta \\ \sin\theta & \cos\theta \end{bmatrix} \quad \text{and} \quad G = \begin{bmatrix} \cos\theta & \sin\theta \\ \sin\theta & -\cos\theta \end{bmatrix}$$

and let

$$\mathbf{x} = \begin{bmatrix} x_1 \\ x_2 \end{bmatrix} = \begin{bmatrix} r\cos\alpha \\ r\sin\alpha \end{bmatrix}$$

be a vector in $\mathbb{R}^2$. Then

$$R\mathbf{x} = \begin{bmatrix} r\cos(\theta + \alpha) \\ r\sin(\theta + \alpha) \end{bmatrix} \quad \text{and} \quad G\mathbf{x} = \begin{bmatrix} r\cos(\theta - \alpha) \\ r\sin(\theta - \alpha) \end{bmatrix}$$

R represents a rotation in the plane by an angle θ. The matrix G has the effect of reflecting $\mathbf{x}$ about the line $x_2 = [\tan(\theta/2)]x_1$ (see Figure 7.5.1). If we set $\cos\theta = x_1/r$ and $\sin\theta = -x_2/r$, then

$$R\mathbf{x} = \begin{bmatrix} x_1\cos\theta - x_2\sin\theta \\ x_1\sin\theta + x_2\cos\theta \end{bmatrix} = \begin{bmatrix} r \\ 0 \end{bmatrix}$$

If we set $\cos\theta = x_1/r$ and $\sin\theta = x_2/r$, then

$$G\mathbf{x} = \begin{bmatrix} x_1\cos\theta + x_2\sin\theta \\ x_1\sin\theta - x_2\cos\theta \end{bmatrix} = \begin{bmatrix} r \\ 0 \end{bmatrix}$$

Both R and G are orthogonal matrices. The matrix G is also symmetric. Indeed, G is an elementary orthogonal matrix. If we let $\mathbf{u} = (\sin\theta/2, -\cos\theta/2)^T$, then $G = I - 2\mathbf{u}\mathbf{u}^T$.

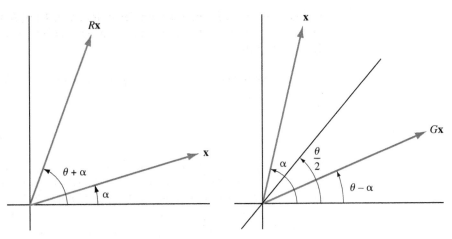

Figure 7.5.1.

EXAMPLE 3 Let $\mathbf{x} = (-3, 4)^T$. To find a rotation matrix R that zeroes out the second coordinate of $\mathbf{x}$, set

$$r = \sqrt{(-3)^2 + 4^2} = 5$$

$$\cos \theta = \frac{x_1}{r} = -\frac{3}{5}$$

$$\sin \theta = -\frac{x_2}{r} = -\frac{4}{5}$$

and set

$$R = \begin{bmatrix} \cos \theta & -\sin \theta \\ \sin \theta & \cos \theta \end{bmatrix} = \begin{bmatrix} -\frac{3}{5} & \frac{4}{5} \\ -\frac{4}{5} & -\frac{3}{5} \end{bmatrix}$$

The reader may verify that $R\mathbf{x} = 5\mathbf{e}_1$.

To find a reflection matrix G that zeroes out the second coordinate of $\mathbf{x}$, compute r and $\cos \theta$ in the same way as for the rotation matrix, but set

$$\sin \theta = \frac{x_2}{r} = \frac{4}{5}$$

and

$$G = \begin{bmatrix} \cos \theta & \sin \theta \\ \sin \theta & -\cos \theta \end{bmatrix} = \begin{bmatrix} -\frac{3}{5} & \frac{4}{5} \\ \frac{4}{5} & \frac{3}{5} \end{bmatrix}$$

The reader may verify that $G\mathbf{x} = 5\mathbf{e}_1$. ∎

Let us now consider the n-dimensional case. Let R and G be $n \times n$ matrices with

$$r_{ii} = r_{jj} = \cos \theta \qquad\qquad g_{ii} = \cos \theta, g_{jj} = -\cos \theta$$

$$r_{ji} = \sin \theta, r_{ij} = -\sin \theta \qquad g_{ji} = g_{ij} = \sin \theta$$

and $r_{st} = g_{st} = \delta_{st}$ for all other entries of R and G. Thus, R and G resemble the identity matrix, except for the (i, i), (i, j), (j, j), and (j, i) positions. Let $c = \cos\theta$ and $s = \sin\theta$. If $\mathbf{x} \in \mathbb{R}^n$, then

$$R\mathbf{x} = (x_1, \ldots, x_{i-1}, x_i c - x_j s, x_{i+1}, \ldots, x_{j-1}, x_i s + x_j c, x_{j+1}, \ldots, x_n)^T$$

and

$$G\mathbf{x} = (x_1, \ldots, x_{i-1}, x_i c + x_j s, x_{i+1}, \ldots, x_{j-1}, x_i s - x_j c, x_{j+1}, \ldots, x_n)^T$$

The transformations R and G alter only the ith and jth components of a vector; they have no effect on the other coordinates. We will refer to R as a *plane rotation* and to G as a *Givens transformation* or a *Givens reflection*. If we set

$$c = \frac{x_i}{r} \quad \text{and} \quad s = -\frac{x_j}{r} \quad \left(r = \sqrt{x_i^2 + x_j^2}\right)$$

then the jth component of $R\mathbf{x}$ will be 0. If we set

$$c = \frac{x_i}{r} \quad \text{and} \quad s = \frac{x_j}{r}$$

then the jth component of $G\mathbf{x}$ will be 0.

EXAMPLE 4 Let $\mathbf{x} = (5, 8, 12)^T$. Find a rotation matrix R that zeroes out the third entry of $\mathbf{x}$ but leaves the second entry of $\mathbf{x}$ unchanged.

Solution

Since R will act only on x_1 and x_3, set

$$r = \sqrt{x_1^2 + x_3^2} = 13$$
$$c = \frac{x_1}{r} = \frac{5}{13}$$
$$s = -\frac{x_3}{r} = -\frac{12}{13}$$

and set

$$R = \begin{bmatrix} c & 0 & -s \\ 0 & 1 & 0 \\ s & 0 & c \end{bmatrix} = \begin{bmatrix} \frac{5}{13} & 0 & \frac{12}{13} \\ 0 & 1 & 0 \\ -\frac{12}{13} & 0 & \frac{5}{13} \end{bmatrix}$$

The reader may verify that $R\mathbf{x} = (13, 8, 0)^T$.

Given a nonsingular $n \times n$ matrix A, we can use either plane rotations or Givens transformations to obtain a QR factorization of A. Let G_{21} be the Givens transformation acting on the first and second coordinates, which when applied to A results in a zero in the $(2, 1)$ position. We can apply another Givens transformation, G_{31}, to $G_{21}A$ to obtain a zero in the $(3, 1)$ position. This process can be continued until the last $n - 1$ entries in the first column have been eliminated:

$$G_{n1} \cdots G_{31}G_{21}A = \begin{pmatrix} \times & \times & \cdots & \times \\ 0 & \times & \cdots & \times \\ 0 & \times & \cdots & \times \\ \vdots & & & \\ 0 & \times & \cdots & \times \end{pmatrix}$$

At the next step, Givens transformations $G_{32}, G_{42}, \ldots, G_{n2}$ are used to eliminate the last $n - 2$ entries in the second column. The process is continued until all elements below the diagonal have been eliminated.

$$(G_{n,n-1}) \cdots (G_{n2} \cdots G_{32})(G_{n1} \cdots G_{21})A = R \qquad (R \text{ upper triangular})$$

If we let $Q^T = (G_{n,n-1}) \cdots (G_{n2} \cdots G_{32})(G_{n1} \cdots G_{21})$, then $A = QR$ and the system $A\mathbf{x} = \mathbf{b}$ is equivalent to the system

$$R\mathbf{x} = Q^T\mathbf{b}$$

This system can be solved by back substitution.

Operation Count   The QR factorization of A by means of Givens transformations or plane rotations requires roughly $\frac{4}{3}n^3$ multiplications, $\frac{2}{3}n^3$ additions, and $\frac{1}{2}n^2$ square roots.

The QR Factorization for Solving General Linear Systems

Given a linear system $A\mathbf{x} = \mathbf{b}$ consisting of n equations in n unknowns, one can use either Householder matrices, rotations, or Givens transformations to compute a QR factorization of A. The linear system can then be solved by setting $\mathbf{c} = Q^T\mathbf{b}$ and using back substitution to solve $R\mathbf{x} = \mathbf{c}$. If Householder matrices are used to compute the QR factorization, the operation count is approximately $\frac{2}{3}n^3$ multiplications and $\frac{2}{3}n^3$ additions, and it is double that amount if either rotations or Givens transformations are used. However, solving the same system using Gaussian elimination would only involve roughly $\frac{1}{3}n^3$ multiplications and $\frac{1}{3}n^3$ additions. So solving the system using Gaussian elimination is twice as fast as solving it using a Householder QR factorization and 4 times as fast as solving the system using a QR factorization based on either plane rotations or Givens transformations.

For an overdetermined system $A\mathbf{x} = \mathbf{b}$, one needs to find a least squares solution. In this case, one could form the normal equations and then solve using Gaussian elimination; however, there are problems with this approach when the computations are carried out in finite-precision arithmetic. Alternatively, if the coefficient matrix A is $m \times n$ with rank n, then one can use Householder matrices to obtain a QR factorization of A and this, in turn, can be used to solve the least squares problem. The numerical methods for solving least squares problems will be discussed in greater detail in Section 7.7.

SECTION 7.5 EXERCISES

1. For each of the following vectors $\mathbf{x}$, find a rotation matrix R such that $R\mathbf{x} = \|\mathbf{x}\|_2\mathbf{e}_1$:
   (a) $\mathbf{x} = (1, 1)^T$ (b) $\mathbf{x} = (\sqrt{3}, -1)^T$
   (c) $\mathbf{x} = (-4, 3)^T$

2. Given $\mathbf{x} \in \mathbb{R}^3$, define
   $$r_{ij} = \left(x_i^2 + x_j^2\right)^{1/2} \qquad i, j = 1, 2, 3$$
   For each of the following, determine a Givens transformation G_{ij} such that the ith and jth coordinates of $G_{ij}\mathbf{x}$ are r_{ij} and 0, respectively:
   (a) $\mathbf{x} = (3, 1, 4)^T, i = 1, j = 3$
   (b) $\mathbf{x} = (1, -1, 2)^T, i = 1, j = 2$
   (c) $\mathbf{x} = (4, 1, \sqrt{3})^T, i = 2, j = 3$
   (d) $\mathbf{x} = (4, 1, \sqrt{3})^T, i = 3, j = 2$

3. For each of the given vectors $\mathbf{x}$, find a Householder transformation that zeroes out the last two entries of the vector.
   (a) $\mathbf{x} = (-1, 8, -4)^T$ (b) $\mathbf{x} = (3, 6, 2)^T$
   (c) $\mathbf{x} = (0, -3, 4)^T$

4. For each of the following, find a Householder transformation that zeroes out the last two coordinates of the vector:
   (a) $\mathbf{x} = (5, 1, 4, 8)^T$
   (b) $\mathbf{x} = (4, -3, -2, -1, 2)^T$

5. Let
   $$A = \begin{bmatrix} 1 & 3 & -2 \\ 1 & 1 & 1 \\ 1 & -5 & 1 \\ 1 & -1 & 2 \end{bmatrix}$$
   (a) Determine the scalar β and vector $\mathbf{v}$ for the Householder matrix $H = I - (1/\beta)\mathbf{v}\mathbf{v}^T$ that zeroes out the last three entries of $\mathbf{a}_1$.
   (b) Without explicitly forming the matrix H, compute the product HA.

6. Let
   $$A = \begin{bmatrix} -1 & \frac{3}{2} & \frac{1}{2} \\ 2 & 8 & 8 \\ -2 & -7 & 1 \end{bmatrix} \quad \text{and} \quad \mathbf{b} = \begin{bmatrix} \frac{11}{2} \\ 0 \\ 1 \end{bmatrix}$$
   (a) Use Householder transformations to transform A into an upper triangular matrix R. Also, transform the vector $\mathbf{b}$; that is, compute $\mathbf{c} = H_2H_1\mathbf{b}$.
   (b) Solve $R\mathbf{x} = \mathbf{c}$ for $\mathbf{x}$ and check your answer by computing the residual $\mathbf{r} = \mathbf{b} - A\mathbf{x}$.

7. For each of the following systems, use a Givens reflection to transform the system to upper triangular form and then solve the upper triangular system:
   (a) $\begin{aligned} 3x_1 + 8x_2 &= 5 \\ 4x_1 - x_2 &= -5 \end{aligned}$
   (b) $\begin{aligned} x_1 + 4x_2 &= 5 \\ x_1 + 2x_2 &= 1 \end{aligned}$
   (c) $\begin{aligned} 4x_1 - 4x_2 + x_3 &= 2 \\ x_2 + 3x_3 &= 2 \\ -3x_1 + 3x_2 - 2x_3 &= 1 \end{aligned}$

8. Suppose that you wish to eliminate the last coordinate of a vector $\mathbf{x}$ and leave the first $n - 2$ coordinates unchanged. How many operations are necessary if this is to be done by a Givens transformation G? A Householder transformation H? If A is an $n \times n$ matrix, how many operations are required to compute GA and HA?

9. Let $H_k = I - 2\mathbf{u}\mathbf{u}^T$ be a Householder transformation with
   $$\mathbf{u} = (0, \ldots, 0, u_k, u_{k+1}, \ldots, u_n)^T$$
   Let $\mathbf{b} \in \mathbb{R}^n$ and let A be an $n \times n$ matrix. How many additions and multiplications are necessary to compute (a) $H_k\mathbf{b}$? (b) H_kA?

10. Let $Q^T = G_{n-k} \cdots G_2G_1$, where each G_i is a Givens transformation. Let $\mathbf{b} \in \mathbb{R}^n$ and let A be an $n \times n$ matrix. How many additions and multiplications are necessary to compute (a) $Q^T\mathbf{b}$? (b) Q^TA?

11. Let R_1 and R_2 be two 2×2 rotation matrices, and let G_1 and G_2 be two 2×2 Givens transformations. What type of transformations are each of the following?
    (a) R_1R_2 (b) G_1G_2
    (c) R_1G_1 (d) G_1R_1

12. Let $\mathbf{x}$ and $\mathbf{y}$ be distinct vectors in $\mathbb{R}^n$ with $\|\mathbf{x}\|_2 = \|\mathbf{y}\|_2$. Define
    $$\mathbf{u} = \frac{1}{\|\mathbf{x} - \mathbf{y}\|_2}(\mathbf{x} - \mathbf{y}) \quad \text{and} \quad Q = I - 2\mathbf{u}\mathbf{u}^T$$
    Show that
    (a) $\|\mathbf{x} - \mathbf{y}\|_2^2 = 2(\mathbf{x} - \mathbf{y})^T\mathbf{x}$
    (b) $Q\mathbf{x} = \mathbf{y}$

13. Let $\mathbf{u}$ be a unit vector in $\mathbb{R}^n$ and let
    $$Q = I - 2\mathbf{u}\mathbf{u}^T$$

(a) Show that **u** is an eigenvector of Q. What is the corresponding eigenvalue?

(b) Let **z** be a nonzero vector in $\mathbb{R}^n$ that is orthogonal to **u**. Show that **z** is an eigenvector of Q belonging to the eigenvalue $\lambda = 1$.

(c) Show that the eigenvalue $\lambda = 1$ must have multiplicity $n - 1$. What is the value of $\det(Q)$?

14. Let R be an $n \times n$ plane rotation. What is the value of $\det(R)$? Show that R is not an elementary orthogonal matrix.

15. Let $A = Q_1 R_1 = Q_2 R_2$, where Q_1 and Q_2 are orthogonal and R_1 and R_2 are both upper triangular and nonsingular.

(a) Show that $Q_1^T Q_2$ is diagonal.

(b) How do R_1 and R_2 compare? Explain.

16. Let $A = \mathbf{x}\mathbf{y}^T$, where $\mathbf{x} \in \mathbb{R}^m$, $\mathbf{y} \in \mathbb{R}^n$, and both **x** and **y** are nonzero vectors. Show that A has a singular value decomposition of the form $H_1 \Sigma H_2$, where H_1 and H_2 are Householder transformations and

$$\sigma_1 = \|\mathbf{x}\| \, \|\mathbf{y}\|, \qquad \sigma_2 = \sigma_3 = \cdots = \sigma_n = 0$$

17. Let

$$R = \begin{bmatrix} \cos\theta & -\sin\theta \\ \sin\theta & \cos\theta \end{bmatrix}$$

Show that if θ is not an integer multiple of π, then R can be factored into a product $R = ULU$, where

$$U = \begin{bmatrix} 1 & \frac{\cos\theta - 1}{\sin\theta} \\ 0 & 1 \end{bmatrix} \quad \text{and} \quad L = \begin{bmatrix} 1 & 0 \\ \sin\theta & 1 \end{bmatrix}$$

This type of factorization of a rotation matrix arises in applications involving wavelets and filter bases.

7.6   The Eigenvalue Problem

In this section, we are concerned with numerical methods for computing the eigenvalues and eigenvectors of an $n \times n$ matrix A. The first method we study is called the *power method*. The power method is an iterative method for finding the dominant eigenvalue of a matrix and a corresponding eigenvector. By the dominant eigenvalue, we mean an eigenvalue λ_1 satisfying $|\lambda_1| > |\lambda_i|$ for $i = 2, \ldots, n$. If the eigenvalues of A satisfy

$$|\lambda_1| > |\lambda_2| > \cdots > |\lambda_n|$$

then the power method can be used to compute the eigenvalues one at a time. The second method, the *QR algorithm*, is an iterative method involving orthogonal similarity transformations. It has many advantages over the power method. It will converge whether or not A has a dominant eigenvalue, and it calculates all the eigenvalues at the same time.

In the examples in Chapter 6, the eigenvalues were determined by forming the characteristic polynomial and finding its roots. However, this procedure is generally not recommended for numerical computations. The difficulty is that often a small change in one or more of the coefficients of the characteristic polynomial can result in a relatively large change in the computed zeros of the polynomial. For example, consider the polynomial $p(x) = x^{10}$. The lead coefficient is 1 and the remaining coefficients are all 0. If the constant term is altered by adding -10^{-10}, we obtain the polynomial $q(x) = x^{10} - 10^{-10}$. Although the coefficients of $p(x)$ and $q(x)$ differ only by 10^{-10}, the roots of $q(x)$ all have absolute value $\frac{1}{10}$, whereas the roots of $p(x)$ are all 0. Thus, even when the coefficients of the characteristic polynomial have been determined accurately, the computed eigenvalues may involve significant error. For this reason, the methods presented in this section do not involve the characteristic polynomial. To see that there is some advantage to working directly with the matrix A, we must determine the effect that small changes in the entries of A have on the eigenvalues. This is done in the next theorem.

Theorem 7.6.1   *Let A be an $n \times n$ matrix with n linearly independent eigenvectors, and let X be a matrix that diagonalizes A. That is,*

$$X^{-1}AX = D = \begin{bmatrix} \lambda_1 & & & \\ & \lambda_2 & & \\ & & \ddots & \\ & & & \lambda_n \end{bmatrix}$$

If $A' = A + E$ and λ' is an eigenvalue of A', then

$$\min_{1 \le i \le n} |\lambda' - \lambda_i| \le \text{cond}_2(X)\|E\|_2 \tag{1}$$

Proof   We may assume that λ' is unequal to any of the λ_i's (otherwise, there is nothing to prove). Thus, if we set $D_1 = D - \lambda'I$, then D_1 is a nonsingular diagonal matrix. Since λ' is an eigenvalue of A', it is also an eigenvalue of $X^{-1}A'X$. Therefore, $X^{-1}A'X - \lambda'I$ is singular, and hence $D_1^{-1}(X^{-1}A'X - \lambda'I)$ is also singular. But

$$\begin{aligned} D_1^{-1}(X^{-1}A'X - \lambda'I) &= D_1^{-1}X^{-1}(A + E - \lambda'I)X \\ &= D_1^{-1}X^{-1}EX + I \end{aligned}$$

Therefore, -1 is an eigenvalue of $D_1^{-1}X^{-1}EX$. It follows that

$$|-1| \le \|D_1^{-1}X^{-1}EX\|_2 \le \|D_1^{-1}\|_2 \, \text{cond}_2(X)\|E\|_2$$

The 2-norm of D_1^{-1} is given by

$$\|D_1^{-1}\|_2 = \max_{1 \le i \le n} |\lambda' - \lambda_i|^{-1}$$

The index i that maximizes $|\lambda' - \lambda_i|^{-1}$ is the same index that minimizes $|\lambda' - \lambda_i|$. Thus,

$$\min_{1 \le i \le n} |\lambda' - \lambda_i| \le \text{cond}_2(X)\|E\|_2 \qquad \blacksquare$$

If the matrix A is symmetric, we can choose an orthogonal diagonalizing matrix. In general, if Q is any orthogonal matrix, then

$$\text{cond}_2(Q) = \|Q\|_2\|Q^{-1}\|_2 = 1$$

Hence, (1) simplifies to

$$\min_{1 \le i \le n} |\lambda' - \lambda_i| \le \|E\|_2$$

Thus, if A is symmetric and $\|E\|_2$ is small, the eigenvalues of A' will be close to the eigenvalues of A.

We are now ready to talk about some of the methods for calculating the eigenvalues and eigenvectors of an $n \times n$ matrix A. The first method we will present computes an eigenvector **x** of A by successively applying A to a given vector in $\mathbb{R}^n$. To see the idea behind the method, let us assume that A has n linearly independent eigenvectors $\mathbf{x}_1, \ldots, \mathbf{x}_n$ and that the corresponding eigenvalues satisfy

$$|\lambda_1| > |\lambda_2| \geq \cdots \geq |\lambda_n| \tag{2}$$

Given an arbitrary vector $\mathbf{v}_0$ in $\mathbb{R}^n$, we can write

$$\mathbf{v}_0 = \alpha_1 \mathbf{x}_1 + \cdots + \alpha_n \mathbf{x}_n$$
$$A\mathbf{v}_0 = \alpha_1 \lambda_1 \mathbf{x}_1 + \alpha_2 \lambda_2 \mathbf{x}_2 + \cdots + \alpha_n \lambda_n \mathbf{x}_n$$
$$A^2\mathbf{v}_0 = \alpha_1 \lambda_1^2 \mathbf{x}_1 + \alpha_2 \lambda_2^2 \mathbf{x}_2 + \cdots + \alpha_n \lambda_n^2 \mathbf{x}_n$$

and, in general,

$$A^k\mathbf{v}_0 = \alpha_1 \lambda_1^k \mathbf{x}_1 + \alpha_2 \lambda_2^k \mathbf{x}_2 + \cdots + \alpha_n \lambda_n^k \mathbf{x}_n$$

If we define

$$\mathbf{v}_k = A^k \mathbf{v}_0 \qquad k = 1, 2, \ldots$$

then

$$\frac{1}{\lambda_1^k}\mathbf{v}_k = \alpha_1 \mathbf{x}_1 + \alpha_2 \left(\frac{\lambda_2}{\lambda_1}\right)^k \mathbf{x}_2 + \cdots + \alpha_n \left(\frac{\lambda_n}{\lambda_1}\right)^k \mathbf{x}_n \tag{3}$$

Since

$$\left|\frac{\lambda_i}{\lambda_1}\right| < 1 \qquad \text{for} \qquad i = 2, 3, \ldots, n$$

it follows that

$$\frac{1}{\lambda_1^k}\mathbf{v}_k \to \alpha_1 \mathbf{x}_1 \qquad \text{as} \qquad k \to \infty$$

Thus, if $\alpha_1 \neq 0$, then the sequence $\{(1/\lambda_1^k)\mathbf{v}_k\}$ converges to an eigenvector $\alpha_1 \mathbf{x}_1$ of A. There are some obvious difficulties with the method as it has been presented so far. The main difficulty is that we cannot compute $(1/\lambda_1^k)\mathbf{v}_k$, since λ_1 is unknown. But even if λ_1 were known, there would be difficulties because of λ_1^k approaching 0 or $\pm\infty$. Fortunately, however, we do not have to scale the sequence $\{\mathbf{v}_k\}$ using $1/\lambda_1^k$. If the $\mathbf{v}_k$'s are scaled so that we obtain unit vectors at each step, the sequence will converge to a unit vector in the direction of $\mathbf{x}_1$. The eigenvalue λ_1 can be computed at the same time. This method of computing the eigenvalue of largest magnitude and the corresponding eigenvector is called the *power method*.

The Power Method

In this method, two sequences $\{\mathbf{v}_k\}$ and $\{\mathbf{u}_k\}$ are defined recursively. To start, $\mathbf{u}_0$ can be any nonzero vector in $\mathbb{R}^n$. Once $\mathbf{u}_k$ has been determined, the vectors $\mathbf{v}_{k+1}$ and $\mathbf{u}_{k+1}$ are calculated as follows:

1. Set $\mathbf{v}_{k+1} = A\mathbf{u}_k$.
2. Find the coordinate j_{k+1} of $\mathbf{v}_{k+1}$ that has the maximum absolute value.
3. Set $\mathbf{u}_{k+1} = (1/v_{j_{k+1}})\mathbf{v}_{k+1}$.

The sequence $\{\mathbf{u}_k\}$ has the property that, for $k \geq 1$, $\|\mathbf{u}_k\|_\infty = u_{j_k} = 1$. If the eigenvalues of A satisfy (2) and $\mathbf{u}_0$ can be written as a linear combination of eigenvectors $\alpha_1 \mathbf{x}_1 + \cdots + \alpha_n \mathbf{x}_n$ with $\alpha_1 \neq 0$, the sequence $\{\mathbf{u}_k\}$ will converge to an eigenvector $\mathbf{y}$ of λ_1. If k is large, then $\mathbf{u}_k$ will be a good approximation to $\mathbf{y}$ and $\mathbf{v}_{k+1} = A\mathbf{u}_k$ will be a good approximation to $\lambda_1 \mathbf{y}$. Since the j_kth coordinate of $\mathbf{u}_k$ is 1, it follows that the j_kth coordinate of $\mathbf{v}_{k+1}$ will be a good approximation to λ_1.

In view of (3), we can expect that the $\mathbf{u}_k$'s will converge to $\mathbf{y}$ at the same rate at which $(\lambda_2/\lambda_1)^k$ is converging to 0. Thus, if $|\lambda_2|$ is nearly as large as $|\lambda_1|$, the convergence will be slow.

EXAMPLE I   Let

$$A = \begin{pmatrix} 2 & 1 \\ 1 & 2 \end{pmatrix}$$

It is an easy matter to determine the exact eigenvalues of A. These turn out to be $\lambda_1 = 3$ and $\lambda_2 = 1$, with corresponding eigenvectors $\mathbf{x}_1 = (1, 1)^T$ and $\mathbf{x}_2 = (1, -1)^T$. To illustrate how the vectors generated by the power method converge, we will apply the method with $\mathbf{u}_0 = (2, 1)^T$:

$$\mathbf{v}_1 = A\mathbf{u}_0 = \begin{pmatrix} 5 \\ 4 \end{pmatrix}, \qquad \mathbf{u}_1 = \frac{1}{5}\mathbf{v}_1 = \begin{pmatrix} 1.0 \\ 0.8 \end{pmatrix}$$

$$\mathbf{v}_2 = A\mathbf{u}_1 = \begin{pmatrix} 2.8 \\ 2.6 \end{pmatrix}, \qquad \mathbf{u}_2 = \frac{1}{2.8}\mathbf{v}_2 = \begin{pmatrix} 1 \\ \dfrac{13}{14} \end{pmatrix} \approx \begin{pmatrix} 1.00 \\ 0.93 \end{pmatrix}$$

$$\mathbf{v}_3 = A\mathbf{u}_2 = \frac{1}{14}\begin{pmatrix} 41 \\ 40 \end{pmatrix}, \qquad \mathbf{u}_3 = \frac{14}{41}\mathbf{v}_3 = \begin{pmatrix} 1 \\ \dfrac{40}{41} \end{pmatrix} \approx \begin{pmatrix} 1.00 \\ 0.98 \end{pmatrix}$$

$$\mathbf{v}_4 = A\mathbf{u}_3 \approx \begin{pmatrix} 2.98 \\ 2.95 \end{pmatrix}$$

If $\mathbf{u}_3 = (1.00, 0.98)^T$ is taken as an approximate eigenvector, then 2.98 is the approximate value of λ_1. Thus, with only a few iterations, the approximation for λ_1 involves an error of only 0.02.   ∎

The power method is particularly useful in applications where only a few of the dominant eigenvalues and eigenvectors are needed. For example, in the analytic hierarchy process (AHP), only the eigenvectors belonging to the dominant eigenvalues are needed to determine the weight vectors for the decision process (see Section 6.8).

APPLICATION I   Computation of AHP Weight Vectors

In Application 4 of Section 6.8 we considered an example in which a search committee at a college makes a hiring choice using AHP. In the example, the committee decided that teaching was twice as important as research and 8 times as important as professional activities. They also decided that research should be 3 times as important as professional activities. The comparison matrix for this problem is

$$C = \begin{pmatrix} 1 & 2 & 8 \\ \frac{1}{2} & 1 & 3 \\ \frac{1}{8} & \frac{1}{3} & 1 \end{pmatrix}$$

The eigenvector belonging to the dominant eigenvalue can be computed using the power method. Since the dominant eigenvalue is close to 3 and the remaining eigenvalues are close to 0, the power method should converge rapidly. In this case, we use $\mathbf{u}_0 = (1, 1, 1)^T$ as our starting vector and normalize at each step so that the entries of $\mathbf{u}_k$ ($k \geq 1$) all add up to 1. Using this process, we end up with the following sequence of vectors:

$$\mathbf{u}_1 = \begin{bmatrix} 0.6486 \\ 0.2654 \\ 0.0860 \end{bmatrix}, \quad \mathbf{u}_2 = \begin{bmatrix} 0.6286 \\ 0.2854 \\ 0.0860 \end{bmatrix}, \quad \mathbf{u}_3 = \begin{bmatrix} 0.6281 \\ 0.2854 \\ 0.0864 \end{bmatrix}, \quad \mathbf{u}_4 = \begin{bmatrix} 0.6282 \\ 0.2854 \\ 0.0864 \end{bmatrix}$$

where all entries are displayed to four digits of accuracy. For $k \geq 3$, the computed vectors $\mathbf{u}_k$ will all agree to three digits of accuracy. Thus, if we take $\mathbf{w} = \mathbf{u}_4$ as our weight vector, it should be accurate to three digits.

For an $n \times n$ comparison matrix C, the power method algorithm for computing AHP weights can be summarized as follows:

1. Set $\mathbf{u}_0 = \mathbf{e}$, where $\mathbf{e}$ is a vector in $\mathbb{R}^n$ whose entries are all equal to 1.
2. For $k = 1, 2, \ldots$,

$$\text{Set } \mathbf{v} = A\mathbf{u}_k$$
$$s = \sum_{i=1}^{n} v_i$$
$$\mathbf{u}_{k+1} = \frac{1}{s}\mathbf{v}$$

The iterations should be terminated when $\mathbf{u}_k$ and $\mathbf{u}_{k+1}$ agree to the desired digits of accuracy. We then use the computed eigenvector $\mathbf{u}_{k+1}$ as an AHP weight vector.

The power method can be used to compute the eigenvalue λ_1 of largest magnitude and a corresponding eigenvector $\mathbf{y}_1$. What about finding additional eigenvalues and eigenvectors? If we could reduce the problem of finding additional eigenvalues of A to that of finding the eigenvalues of some $(n-1) \times (n-1)$ matrix A_1, then the power method could be applied to A_1. This can actually be done by a process called *deflation*.

Deflation

The idea behind deflation is to find a nonsingular matrix H such that HAH^{-1} is a matrix of the form

$$
\begin{pmatrix}
\lambda_1 & \times & \cdots & \times \\
\hline
0 & & & \\
\vdots & & A_1 & \\
0 & & &
\end{pmatrix}
\tag{4}
$$

Since A and HAH^{-1} are similar, they have the same characteristic polynomials. Thus, if HAH^{-1} is of the form (4), then

$$
\det(A - \lambda I) = \det(HAH^{-1} - \lambda I) = (\lambda_1 - \lambda) \det(A_1 - \lambda I)
$$

and it follows that the remaining $n - 1$ eigenvalues of A are the eigenvalues of A_1. The question remains: How do we find such a matrix H? Note that the form (4) requires that the first column of HAH^{-1} be $\lambda_1 \mathbf{e}_1$. The first column of HAH^{-1} is $HAH^{-1}\mathbf{e}_1$. Thus,

$$
HAH^{-1}\mathbf{e}_1 = \lambda_1 \mathbf{e}_1
$$

or, equivalently,

$$
A(H^{-1}\mathbf{e}_1) = \lambda_1(H^{-1}\mathbf{e}_1)
$$

So $H^{-1}\mathbf{e}_1$ is in the eigenspace corresponding to λ_1. Thus, for some eigenvector $\mathbf{x}_1$ belonging to λ_1,

$$
H^{-1}\mathbf{e}_1 = \mathbf{x}_1 \qquad \text{or} \qquad H\mathbf{x}_1 = \mathbf{e}_1
$$

We must find a matrix H such that $H\mathbf{x}_1 = \mathbf{e}_1$ for some eigenvector $\mathbf{x}_1$ belonging to λ_1. This can be done by means of a Householder transformation. If $\mathbf{y}_1$ is the computed eigenvector belonging to λ_1, set

$$
\mathbf{x}_1 = \frac{1}{\|\mathbf{y}_1\|_2}\mathbf{y}_1
$$

Since $\|\mathbf{x}_1\|_2 = 1$, we can find a Householder transformation H such that

$$
H\mathbf{x}_1 = \mathbf{e}_1
$$

Because H is a Householder transformation, it follows that $H^{-1} = H$, and hence HAH is the desired similarity transformation.

Reduction to Hessenberg Form

The standard methods for finding eigenvalues are all iterative. The amount of work required in each iteration is often prohibitively high unless, initially, A is in some special form that is easier to work with. If this is not the case, the standard procedure is to reduce

A to a simpler form by means of similarity transformations. Generally, Householder matrices are used to transform A into a matrix of the form

$$\begin{pmatrix} \times & \times & \cdots & \times & \times & \times \\ \times & \times & \cdots & \times & \times & \times \\ 0 & \times & \cdots & \times & \times & \times \\ 0 & 0 & \cdots & \times & \times & \times \\ \vdots & & & & & \\ 0 & 0 & \cdots & \times & \times & \times \\ 0 & 0 & \cdots & 0 & \times & \times \end{pmatrix}$$

A matrix in this form is said to be in *upper Hessenberg form*. Thus, B is in upper Hessenberg form if and only if $b_{ij} = 0$ whenever $i \geq j + 2$.

A matrix A can be transformed into upper Hessenberg form in the following manner: First, choose a Householder matrix H_1 so that $H_1 A$ is of the form

$$\begin{pmatrix} a_{11} & a_{12} & \cdots & a_{1n} \\ \times & \times & \cdots & \times \\ 0 & \times & \cdots & \times \\ \vdots & & & \\ 0 & \times & \cdots & \times \end{pmatrix}$$

The matrix H_1 will be of the form

$$\begin{pmatrix} 1 & 0 & \cdots & 0 \\ 0 & \times & \cdots & \times \\ \vdots & & & \\ 0 & \times & \cdots & \times \end{pmatrix}$$

and hence postmultiplication of $H_1 A$ by H_1 will leave the first column unchanged. If $A^{(1)} = H_1 A H_1$, then $A^{(1)}$ is a matrix of the form

$$\begin{pmatrix} a_{11}^{(1)} & a_{12}^{(1)} & \cdots & a_{1n}^{(1)} \\ a_{21}^{(1)} & a_{22}^{(1)} & \cdots & a_{2n}^{(1)} \\ 0 & a_{32}^{(1)} & \cdots & a_{3n}^{(1)} \\ \vdots & & & \\ 0 & a_{n2}^{(1)} & \cdots & a_{nn}^{(1)} \end{pmatrix}$$

Since H_1 is a Householder matrix, it follows that $H_1^{-1} = H_1$, and hence $A^{(1)}$ is similar to A. Next, a Householder matrix H_2 is chosen so that

$$H_2(a_{12}^{(1)}, a_{22}^{(1)}, \ldots, a_{n2}^{(1)})^T = (a_{12}^{(1)}, a_{22}^{(1)}, \times, 0, \ldots, 0)^T$$

The matrix H_2 will be of the form

$$
\begin{bmatrix}
1 & 0 & 0 & \cdots & 0 \\
0 & 1 & 0 & \cdots & 0 \\
0 & 0 & \times & \cdots & \times \\
\vdots & & & & \\
0 & 0 & \times & \cdots & \times
\end{bmatrix}
=
\left[
\begin{array}{c|c}
I_2 & O \\
\hline
O & X
\end{array}
\right]
$$

Multiplication of $A^{(1)}$ on the left by H_2 will leave the first two rows and the first column unchanged:

$$
H_2 A^{(1)} =
\begin{bmatrix}
a_{11}^{(1)} & a_{12}^{(1)} & a_{13}^{(1)} & \cdots & a_{1n}^{(1)} \\
a_{21}^{(1)} & a_{22}^{(1)} & a_{23}^{(1)} & \cdots & a_{2n}^{(1)} \\
0 & \times & \times & \cdots & \times \\
0 & 0 & \times & \cdots & \times \\
\vdots & & & & \\
0 & 0 & \times & \cdots & \times
\end{bmatrix}
$$

Postmultiplication of $H_2 A^{(1)}$ by H_2 will leave the first two columns unchanged. Thus, $A^{(2)} = H_2 A^{(1)} H_2$ is of the form

$$
\begin{bmatrix}
\times & \times & \times & \cdots & \times \\
\times & \times & \times & \cdots & \times \\
0 & \times & \times & \cdots & \times \\
0 & 0 & \times & \cdots & \times \\
\vdots & & & & \\
0 & 0 & \times & \cdots & \times
\end{bmatrix}
$$

This process may be continued until we end up with an upper Hessenberg matrix

$$
H = A^{(n-2)} = H_{n-2} \cdots H_2 H_1 A H_1 H_2 \cdots H_{n-2}
$$

which is similar to A.

If, in particular, A is symmetric, then, since

$$
\begin{aligned}
H^T &= H_{n-2}^T \cdots H_2^T H_1^T A^T H_1^T H_2^T \cdots H_{n-2}^T \\
&= H_{n-2} \cdots H_2 H_1 A H_1 H_2 \cdots H_{n-2} \\
&= H
\end{aligned}
$$

it follows that H is tridiagonal. Thus, any $n \times n$ matrix A can be reduced to upper Hessenberg form by similarity transformations. If A is symmetric, the reduction will yield a symmetric tridiagonal matrix.

We close this section by outlining one of the best methods available for computing the eigenvalues of a matrix. The method is called the *QR algorithm* and was developed by John G. F. Francis in 1961.

QR Algorithm

Given an $n \times n$ matrix A, factor it into a product $Q_1 R_1$, where Q_1 is orthogonal and R_1 is upper triangular. Define

$$A_1 = A = Q_1 R_1$$

and

$$A_2 = Q_1^T A Q_1 = R_1 Q_1$$

Factor A_2 into a product $Q_2 R_2$, where Q_2 is orthogonal and R_2 is upper triangular. Define

$$A_3 = Q_2^T A_2 Q_2 = R_2 Q_2$$

Note that $A_2 = Q_1^T A Q_1$ and $A_3 = (Q_1 Q_2)^T A (Q_1 Q_2)$ are both similar to A. We can continue in this manner and obtain a sequence of similar matrices. In general, if

$$A_k = Q_k R_k$$

then A_{k+1} is defined to be $R_k Q_k$. It can be shown that, under very general conditions, the sequence of matrices defined in this way converges to a matrix T of the form

$$
T = \begin{pmatrix}
B_1 & \times & \cdots & \times \\
 & B_2 & & \times \\
 & O & \ddots & \\
 & & & B_s
\end{pmatrix}
$$

where the B_i's are either 1×1 or 2×2 diagonal blocks. The matrix T is the real Schur form of A. (See Theorem 6.4.6.) Each 2×2 diagonal block of T will correspond to a pair of complex conjugate eigenvalues of A. The eigenvalues of A will be eigenvalues of the B_i's. In the case where A is symmetric, each of the A_k's will also be symmetric and the sequence will converge to a diagonal matrix.

EXAMPLE 2   Let A_1 be the matrix from Example 1. The QR factorization of A_1 requires only a single Givens transformation:

$$G_1 = \frac{1}{\sqrt{5}} \begin{bmatrix} 2 & 1 \\ 1 & -2 \end{bmatrix}$$

Thus,

$$A_2 = G_1 A G_1 = \frac{1}{5} \begin{bmatrix} 2 & 1 \\ 1 & -2 \end{bmatrix} \begin{bmatrix} 2 & 1 \\ 1 & 2 \end{bmatrix} \begin{bmatrix} 2 & 1 \\ 1 & -2 \end{bmatrix} = \begin{bmatrix} 2.8 & -0.6 \\ -0.6 & 1.2 \end{bmatrix}$$

The QR factorization of A_2 can be accomplished with the Givens transformation

$$G_2 = \frac{1}{\sqrt{8.2}} \begin{bmatrix} 2.8 & -0.6 \\ -0.6 & -2.8 \end{bmatrix}$$

It follows that

$$A_3 = G_2 A_2 G_2 \approx \begin{bmatrix} 2.98 & 0.22 \\ 0.22 & 1.02 \end{bmatrix}$$

The off-diagonal elements are getting closer to 0 after each iteration, and the diagonal elements are approaching the eigenvalues $\lambda_1 = 3$ and $\lambda_2 = 1$.   ■

Remarks

1. Because of the amount of work required at each iteration of the QR algorithm, it is important that the starting matrix A be in either Hessenberg or symmetric tridiagonal form. If this is not the case, we should perform similarity transformations on A to obtain a matrix A_1 that is in one of these forms.

2. If A_k is in upper Hessenberg form, the QR factorization can be carried out with $n - 1$ Givens transformations.

$$G_{n,n-1} \cdots G_{32} G_{21} A_k = R_k$$

Setting

$$Q_k^T = G_{n,n-1} \cdots G_{32} G_{21}$$

we have

$$A_k = Q_k R_k$$

and

$$A_{k+1} = Q_k^T A_k Q_k$$

To compute A_{k+1}, it is not necessary to determine Q_k explicitly. We need only keep track of the $n - 1$ Givens transformations. When R_k is postmultiplied by G_{21}, the resulting matrix will have the $(2,1)$ entry filled in. The other entries below the diagonals will all still be zero. Postmultiplying $R_k G_{21}$ by G_{32} will have the effect of filling in the $(3,2)$ position. Postmultiplication of $R_k G_{21} G_{32}$ by G_{43} will fill in the $(4,3)$ position, and so on. Thus, the resulting matrix $A_{k+1} = R_k G_{21} G_{32} \cdots G_{n,n-1}$ will be in upper Hessenberg form. If A_1 is a symmetric tridiagonal matrix, then each succeeding A_i will be upper Hessenberg and symmetric. Hence, $A_2, A_3, \ldots$ will all be tridiagonal.

3. As in the power method, convergence may be slow when some of the eigenvalues are close together. To speed up convergence, it is customary to introduce *origin shifts*. At the kth step, a scalar α_k is chosen and $A_k - \alpha_k I$ (rather than A_k) is decomposed into a product $Q_k R_k$. The matrix A_{k+1} is defined by

$$A_{k+1} = R_k Q_k + \alpha_k I$$

Note that

$$Q_k^T A_k Q_k = Q_k^T (Q_k R_k + \alpha_k I) Q_k = R_k Q_k + \alpha_k I = A_{k+1}$$

so A_k and A_{k+1} are similar. With the proper choice of shifts α_k, the convergence can be greatly accelerated.

4. In our brief discussion, we have presented only an outline of the method. Many of the details, such as how to choose the origin shifts, have been omitted. For a more thorough discussion and a proof of convergence, see Wilkinson [39].

SECTION 7.6 EXERCISES

1. Let

$$A = \begin{bmatrix} 1 & 1 \\ 1 & 1 \end{bmatrix}$$

(a) Apply one iteration of the power method to A with any nonzero starting vector.

(b) Apply one iteration of the QR algorithm to A.

(c) Determine the exact eigenvalues of A by solving the characteristic equation, and determine the eigenspace corresponding to the largest eigenvalue. Compare your answers with those to parts (a) and (b).

2. Let

$$A = \begin{bmatrix} 2 & 1 & 0 \\ 1 & 3 & 1 \\ 0 & 1 & 2 \end{bmatrix} \quad \text{and} \quad \mathbf{u}_0 = \begin{bmatrix} 1 \\ 1 \\ 1 \end{bmatrix}$$

(a) Apply the power method to A to compute $\mathbf{v}_1, \mathbf{u}_1, \mathbf{v}_2, \mathbf{u}_2,$ and $\mathbf{v}_3$. (Round off to two decimal places.)

(b) Determine an approximation λ_1' to the largest eigenvalue of A from the coordinates of $\mathbf{v}_3$. Determine the exact value of λ_1 and compare it with λ_1'. What is the relative error?

3. Let

$$A = \begin{bmatrix} 1 & 2 \\ -1 & -1 \end{bmatrix} \quad \text{and} \quad \mathbf{u}_0 = \begin{bmatrix} 1 \\ 1 \end{bmatrix}$$

(a) Compute $\mathbf{u}_1, \mathbf{u}_2, \mathbf{u}_3,$ and $\mathbf{u}_4,$ using the power method.

(b) Explain why the power method will fail to converge in this case.

4. Let

$$A = A_1 = \begin{bmatrix} 1 & 1 \\ 1 & 3 \end{bmatrix}$$

Compute A_2 and A_3, using the QR algorithm. Compute the exact eigenvalues of A and compare them with the diagonal elements of A_3. To how many decimal places do they agree?

5. Let

$$A = \begin{bmatrix} 5 & 2 & 2 \\ -2 & 1 & -2 \\ -3 & -4 & 2 \end{bmatrix}$$

(a) Verify that $\lambda_1 = 4$ is an eigenvalue of A and $\mathbf{y}_1 = (2, -2, 1)^T$ is an eigenvector belonging to λ_1.

(b) Find a Householder transformation H such that HAH is of the form

$$\begin{bmatrix} 4 & \times & \times \\ 0 & \times & \times \\ 0 & \times & \times \end{bmatrix}$$

(c) Compute HAH and find the remaining eigenvalues of A.

6. Let A be an $n \times n$ matrix with distinct real eigenvalues $\lambda_1, \lambda_2, \ldots, \lambda_n$. Let λ be a scalar that is not an eigenvalue of A and let $B = (A - \lambda I)^{-1}$. Show that

(a) the scalars $\mu_j = 1/(\lambda_j - \lambda), j = 1, \ldots, n$ are the eigenvalues of B.

(b) if $\mathbf{x}_j$ is an eigenvector of B belonging to μ_j, then $\mathbf{x}_j$ is an eigenvector of A belonging to λ_j.

(c) if the power method is applied to B, then the sequence of vectors will converge to an eigenvector of A belonging to the eigenvalue that is closest to λ. [The convergence will be rapid if λ is much closer to one λ_i than to any of the others. This method of computing eigenvectors by using powers of $(A - \lambda I)^{-1}$ is called the *inverse power method*.]

7. Let $\mathbf{x} = (x_1, \ldots, x_n)^T$ be an eigenvector of A belonging to λ. Show that if $|x_i| = \|\mathbf{x}\|_\infty$, then

(a) $\displaystyle\sum_{j=1}^{n} a_{ij}x_j = \lambda x_i$

(b) $\displaystyle |\lambda - a_{ii}| \le \sum_{\substack{j=1 \\ j \ne i}}^{n} |a_{ij}|$ (Gerschgorin's theorem)

8. Let λ be an eigenvalue of an $n \times n$ matrix A. Show that for some index j,

$$|\lambda - a_{jj}| \le \sum_{\substack{i=1 \\ i \ne j}}^{n} |a_{ij}| \qquad \begin{array}{l}\text{(column version of} \\ \text{Gerschgorin's} \\ \text{theorem)}\end{array}$$

9. Let A be a matrix with eigenvalues $\lambda_1, \ldots, \lambda_n$ and let λ be an eigenvalue of $A + E$. Let X be a matrix that diagonalizes A and let $C = X^{-1}EX$. Prove the following:

(a) For some i,

$$|\lambda - \lambda_i| \le \sum_{j=1}^{n} |c_{ij}|$$

[*Hint*: λ is an eigenvalue of $X^{-1}(A + E)X$. Apply Gerschgorin's theorem from Exercise 7.]

(b) $\min\limits_{1 \le j \le n} |\lambda - \lambda_j| \le \mathrm{cond}_\infty(X)\|E\|_\infty$

10. Let $A_k = Q_k R_k, k = 1, 2, \ldots$ be the sequence of matrices derived from $A = A_1$ by applying the QR algorithm. For each positive integer k, define

$$P_k = Q_1 Q_2 \cdots Q_k \quad \text{and} \quad U_k = R_k \cdots R_2 R_1$$

Show that

$$P_k A_{k+1} = A P_k$$

for all $k \ge 1$.

11. Let P_k and U_k be defined as in Exercise 10. Show that

(a) $P_{k+1} U_{k+1} = P_k A_{k+1} U_k = A P_k U_k$

(b) $P_k U_k = A^k$, and hence

$$(Q_1 Q_2 \cdots Q_k)(R_k \cdots R_2 R_1)$$

is the QR factorization of A^k.

12. Let R_k be a $k \times k$ upper triangular matrix and suppose that

$$R_k U_k = U_k D_k$$

where U_k is an upper triangular matrix with 1's on the diagonal and D_k is a diagonal matrix. Let R_{k+1} be an upper triangular matrix of the form

$$\begin{pmatrix} R_k & \mathbf{b}_k \\ \mathbf{0}^T & \beta_k \end{pmatrix}$$

where β_k is not an eigenvalue of R_k. Determine $(k+1) \times (k+1)$ matrices U_{k+1} and D_{k+1} of the form

$$U_{k+1} = \begin{bmatrix} U_k & \mathbf{x}_k \\ \mathbf{0}^T & 1 \end{bmatrix}, \quad D_{k+1} = \begin{bmatrix} D_k & \mathbf{0} \\ \mathbf{0}^T & \beta \end{bmatrix}$$

such that

$$R_{k+1} U_{k+1} = U_{k+1} D_{k+1}$$

13. Let R be an $n \times n$ upper triangular matrix whose diagonal entries are all distinct. Let R_k denote the leading principal submatrix of R of order k and set $U_1 = (1)$.

(a) Use the result from Exercise 12 to derive an algorithm for finding the eigenvectors of R. The matrix U of eigenvectors should be upper triangular with 1's on the diagonal.

(b) Show that the algorithm requires approximately $\frac{n^3}{6}$ floating-point multiplications/divisions.

Least Squares Problems

In this section, we study computational methods for finding least squares solutions of overdetermined systems. Let A be an $m \times n$ matrix with $m \ge n$ and let $\mathbf{b} \in \mathbb{R}^m$. We consider some methods for computing a vector $\mathbf{x}$ that minimizes $\|\mathbf{b} - A\mathbf{x}\|_2^2$.

Normal Equations

We saw in Chapter 5 that if $\hat{\mathbf{x}}$ satisfies the normal equations

$$A^T A\mathbf{x} = A^T \mathbf{b}$$

then $\hat{\mathbf{x}}$ is a solution to the least squares problem. If A is of full rank (rank n), then $A^T A$ is nonsingular and hence the system will have a unique solution. Thus, if $A^T A$ is invertible, one possible method for solving the least squares problem is to form the normal equations and then solve them by Gaussian elimination. An algorithm for doing this would have two main parts.

1. Compute $B = A^T A$ and $\mathbf{c} = A^T \mathbf{b}$.
2. Solve $B\mathbf{x} = \mathbf{c}$.

Note that forming the normal equations requires roughly $mn^2/2$ multiplications. Since $A^T A$ is nonsingular, the matrix B is positive definite. For positive definite matrices, there are reduction algorithms that require only half the usual number of multiplications. Thus, the solution of $B\mathbf{x} = \mathbf{c}$ requires roughly $n^3/6$ multiplications. Most of the work then occurs in forming the normal equations, rather than solving them. However, the main difficulty with this method is that, in forming the normal equations, we may well end up transforming the problem into an ill-conditioned one. Recall from Section 7.4 that if $\mathbf{x}'$ is the computed solution of $B\mathbf{x} = \mathbf{c}$ and $\mathbf{x}$ is the exact solution, then the inequality

$$\frac{1}{\text{cond}(B)} \frac{\|\mathbf{r}\|}{\|\mathbf{c}\|} \leq \frac{\|\mathbf{x} - \mathbf{x}'\|}{\|\mathbf{x}\|} \leq \text{cond}(B) \frac{\|\mathbf{r}\|}{\|\mathbf{c}\|}$$

shows how the relative error compares to the relative residual. If A has singular values $\sigma_1 \geq \sigma_2 \geq \cdots \geq \sigma_n > 0$, then $\text{cond}_2(A) = \sigma_1/\sigma_n$. The singular values of B are $\sigma_1^2, \sigma_2^2, \ldots, \sigma_n^2$. Thus,

$$\text{cond}_2(B) = \frac{\sigma_1^2}{\sigma_n^2} = [\text{cond}_2(A)]^2$$

If, for example, $\text{cond}_2(A) = 10^4$, the relative error in the computed solution of the normal equations could be 10^8 times as large as the relative residual. By forming the normal equations, one could possibly end up doubling the number of digits of accuracy that are lost in computing a least squares solution to the system. For this reason, we should be very careful about using the normal equations to compute least squares solutions.

Modified Gram–Schmidt Method for Solving Least Squares Problems

If A is an $m \times n$ matrix ($m > n$) with rank n, we can use the Gram–Schmidt process to obtain a factorization, $A = QR$, where Q is an $m \times n$ matrix with orthonormal columns and R is an $n \times n$ upper triangular whose diagonal entries are all positive. In theory, one could then find a least squares solution to a system $A\mathbf{x} = \mathbf{b}$ in two steps:

(i) Set $\mathbf{c} = Q^T\mathbf{b}$.
(ii) Use back substitution to solve the upper triangular system $R\mathbf{x} = \mathbf{c}$ for $\mathbf{x}$.

Unfortunately, if the classical Gram–Schmidt method is used, then because of cancellation of significant digits, the computed column vectors of Q may fail to be orthogonal and, as a result, the computed solution $\mathbf{x}$ in step (ii) may not be very accurate. Indeed, if the classical Gram–Schmidt process is used, it is possible to have catastrophic cancellation and to end up with a computed solution $\mathbf{x}$ that doesn't have any digits of accuracy.

Alternatively, one can use the modified Gram–Schmidt algorithm to compute the QR factorization of A. There will still be some loss of orthogonality in the computed column vectors of Q; however, the loss will generally be much less in this case. Even though there is some loss of orthogonality, it has been shown that if one uses the modified Gram–Schmidt QR factorization and computes the vector $\mathbf{c}$ in step (i) by successively modifying the vector $\mathbf{b}$, then the algorithm will be numerically stable. Thus rather than computing $c_k = \mathbf{q}_k{}^T\mathbf{b}$, we set $c_k = \mathbf{q}_k^T\mathbf{b}_k$, where $\mathbf{b}_k$ is a modified version of $\mathbf{b}$. We will not prove numerical stability as the analysis turns out to be quite involved.

The modified Gram–Schmidt method for computing the least squares solution to an overdetermined system $A\mathbf{x} = \mathbf{b}$ is summarized in the following algorithm.

Algorithm 7.7.1   Modified Gram–Schmidt Process for Least Squares

Given A is a $m \times n$ matrix with rank n and $\mathbf{b}$ is a vector in $\mathbb{R}^m$.

> *Use Algorithm 5.6.1 to compute the factors Q and R of the modified Gram–Schmidt QR factorization of A.*
> *Set $\mathbf{b}_1 = \mathbf{b}$*
> *For $k = 1, 2, \ldots, n$ set*
> $$c_k = \mathbf{q}_k^T \mathbf{b}_k$$
> $$\mathbf{b}_{k+1} = \mathbf{b}_k - c_k \mathbf{q}_k$$
> *End for loop*
> *Use back substitution to solve $R\mathbf{x} = \mathbf{c}$ for $\mathbf{x}$.*

The Householder **QR** Factorization

For the Gram–Schmidt solution of least squares problems, we make use of a QR factorization $A = QR$, where Q is an $m \times n$ matrix with orthonormal columns and R is an $n \times n$ upper triangular matrix. Another common method for solving least squares problems uses a different type of QR factorization. The factorization is obtained by applying a sequence of Householder transformations to A. In this case, Q will be an $m \times m$ orthogonal matrix and R will be an $m \times n$ matrix whose subdiagonal entries are all 0.

Given an $m \times n$ matrix A of full rank, we can apply n Householder transformations to zero out all the entries below the diagonal. Thus,

$$H_n H_{n-1} \cdots H_1 A = R$$

where R is of the form

$$\begin{bmatrix} R_1 \\ O \end{bmatrix} = \begin{bmatrix} \times & \times & \times & \cdots & \times \\ & \times & \times & \cdots & \times \\ & & \times & \cdots & \times \\ & & & \ddots & \vdots \\ & & & & \times \\ \\ \end{bmatrix}$$

with nonzero diagonal entries. Let

$$Q^T = H_n \cdots H_1 = \begin{bmatrix} Q_1^T \\ Q_2^T \end{bmatrix}$$

where Q_1^T is an $n \times m$ matrix consisting of the first n rows of Q^T. Since $Q^T A = R$, it follows that

$$A = QR = (Q_1 \quad Q_2) \begin{bmatrix} R_1 \\ O \end{bmatrix} = Q_1 R_1$$

Let

$$\mathbf{c} = Q^T \mathbf{b} = \begin{bmatrix} Q_1^T \mathbf{b} \\ Q_2^T \mathbf{b} \end{bmatrix} = \begin{bmatrix} \mathbf{c}_1 \\ \mathbf{c}_2 \end{bmatrix}$$

The normal equations can be written in the form

$$R_1^T Q_1^T Q_1 R_1 \mathbf{x} = R_1^T Q_1^T \mathbf{b}$$

Since $Q_1^T Q_1 = I$ and R_1^T is nonsingular, this equation simplifies to

$$R_1 \mathbf{x} = \mathbf{c}_1$$

This system can be solved by back substitution. The solution $\mathbf{x} = R_1^{-1} \mathbf{c}_1$ will be the unique solution to the least squares problem. To compute the residual, note that

$$Q^T \mathbf{r} = \begin{bmatrix} \mathbf{c}_1 \\ \mathbf{c}_2 \end{bmatrix} - \begin{bmatrix} R_1 \\ O \end{bmatrix} \mathbf{x} = \begin{bmatrix} \mathbf{0} \\ \mathbf{c}_2 \end{bmatrix}$$

so that

$$\mathbf{r} = Q \begin{bmatrix} \mathbf{0} \\ \mathbf{c}_2 \end{bmatrix} \quad \text{and} \quad \|\mathbf{r}\|_2 = \|\mathbf{c}_2\|_2$$

In summation, if A is an $m \times n$ matrix with full rank, the least squares problem can be solved as follows:

1. Use Householder transformations to compute

$$R = H_n \cdots H_2 H_1 A \quad \text{and} \quad \mathbf{c} = H_n \cdots H_2 H_1 \mathbf{b}$$

where R is an $m \times n$ upper triangular matrix.
2. Partition R and $\mathbf{c}$ into block form:

$$R = \begin{bmatrix} R_1 \\ O \end{bmatrix} \quad \mathbf{c} = \begin{bmatrix} \mathbf{c}_1 \\ \mathbf{c}_2 \end{bmatrix}$$

where R_1 and $\mathbf{c}_1$ each have n rows.
3. Use back substitution to solve $R_1 \mathbf{x} = \mathbf{c}_1$.

The Pseudoinverse

Now consider the case where the matrix A has rank $r < n$. The singular value decomposition provides the key to solving the least squares problem in this case. It can be used to construct a generalized inverse of A. In the case where A is a nonsingular $n \times n$ matrix with singular value decomposition $U \Sigma V^T$, the inverse is given by

$$A^{-1} = V \Sigma^{-1} U^T$$

More generally, if $A = U\Sigma V^T$ is an $m \times n$ matrix of rank r, then the matrix Σ will be an $m \times n$ matrix of the form

$$\Sigma = \left[\begin{array}{c|c} \Sigma_1 & O \\ \hline O & O \end{array} \right] = \left[\begin{array}{cccc|c} \sigma_1 & & & & \\ & \sigma_2 & & & O \\ & & \ddots & & \\ & & & \sigma_r & \\ \hline & & O & & O \end{array} \right]$$

and we can define

$$A^+ = V\Sigma^+ U^T \tag{1}$$

where Σ^+ is the $n \times m$ matrix

$$\Sigma^+ = \left[\begin{array}{c|c} \Sigma_1^{-1} & O \\ \hline O & O \end{array} \right] = \left[\begin{array}{ccc|c} \dfrac{1}{\sigma_1} & & & \\ & \ddots & & O \\ & & \dfrac{1}{\sigma_r} & \\ \hline & O & & O \end{array} \right]$$

Equation (1) gives a natural generalization of the inverse of a matrix. The matrix A^+ defined by (1) is called the *pseudoinverse* of A.

It is also possible to define A^+ by its algebraic properties, given in the following four conditions.

The Penrose Conditions

   1. $AXA = A$
   2. $XAX = X$
   3. $(AX)^T = AX$
   4. $(XA)^T = XA$

We claim that if A is an $m \times n$ matrix, then there is a unique $n \times m$ matrix X that satisfies these conditions. Indeed, if we choose $X = A^+ = V\Sigma^+ U^T$, then it is easily verified that X satisfies all four conditions. We leave this as an exercise for the reader. To show uniqueness, suppose that Y also satisfies the Penrose conditions. Then, by successively applying these conditions, we can argue as follows:

$$
\begin{array}{llll}
X = XAX & (2) \qquad & Y = YAY & (2) \\
 = A^T X^T X & (4) & = YY^T A^T & (3) \\
 = (AYA)^T X^T X & (1) & = YY^T (AXA)^T & (1) \\
 = (A^T Y^T)(A^T X^T) X & & = Y(Y^T A^T)(X^T A^T) & \\
 = YAXAX & (4) & = YAYAX & (3) \\
 = YAX & (1) & = YAX & (1)
\end{array}
$$

Therefore, $X = Y$. Thus, A^+ is the unique matrix satisfying the four Penrose conditions. These conditions are often used to define the pseudoinverse, and A^+ is often referred to as the *Moore–Penrose pseudoinverse*.

To see how the pseudoinverse can be used in solving least squares problems, let us first consider the case where A is an $m \times n$ matrix of rank n. Then Σ is of the form

$$\Sigma = \begin{bmatrix} \Sigma_1 \\ O \end{bmatrix}$$

where Σ_1 is a nonsingular $n \times n$ diagonal matrix. The matrix $A^T A$ is nonsingular and

$$(A^T A)^{-1} = V(\Sigma^T \Sigma)^{-1} V^T$$

The solution of the normal equations is given by

$$
\begin{aligned}
\mathbf{x} &= (A^T A)^{-1} A^T \mathbf{b} \\
&= V(\Sigma^T \Sigma)^{-1} V^T V \Sigma^T U^T \mathbf{b} \\
&= V(\Sigma^T \Sigma)^{-1} \Sigma^T U^T \mathbf{b} \\
&= V \Sigma^+ U^T \mathbf{b} \\
&= A^+ \mathbf{b}
\end{aligned}
$$

Thus, if A has full rank, $A^+ \mathbf{b}$ is the solution to the least squares problem. Now, what about the case where A has rank $r < n$? In this case, there are infinitely many solutions to the least squares problem. The next theorem shows that not only is $A^+ \mathbf{b}$ a solution, but it is also the minimal solution with respect to the 2-norm.

Theorem 7.7.1   *If A is an $m \times n$ matrix of rank $r < n$ with singular value decomposition $U \Sigma V^T$, then the vector*

$$\mathbf{x} = A^+ \mathbf{b} = V \Sigma^+ U^T \mathbf{b}$$

minimizes $\|\mathbf{b} - A\mathbf{x}\|_2^2$. Moreover, if $\mathbf{z}$ is any other vector that minimizes $\|\mathbf{b} - A\mathbf{x}\|_2^2$, then $\|\mathbf{z}\|_2 > \|\mathbf{x}\|_2$.

Proof   Let $\mathbf{x}$ be a vector in $\mathbb{R}^n$ and define

$$\mathbf{c} = U^T \mathbf{b} = \begin{bmatrix} \mathbf{c}_1 \\ \mathbf{c}_2 \end{bmatrix} \qquad \text{and} \qquad \mathbf{y} = V^T \mathbf{x} = \begin{bmatrix} \mathbf{y}_1 \\ \mathbf{y}_2 \end{bmatrix}$$

where $\mathbf{c}_1$ and $\mathbf{y}_1$ are vectors in $\mathbb{R}^r$. Since U^T is orthogonal, it follows that

$$
\begin{aligned}
\|\mathbf{b} - A\mathbf{x}\|_2^2 &= \|U^T \mathbf{b} - \Sigma(V^T \mathbf{x})\|_2^2 \\
&= \|\mathbf{c} - \Sigma \mathbf{y}\|_2^2 \\
&= \left\| \begin{bmatrix} \mathbf{c}_1 \\ \mathbf{c}_2 \end{bmatrix} - \begin{bmatrix} \Sigma_1 & O \\ O & O \end{bmatrix} \begin{bmatrix} \mathbf{y}_1 \\ \mathbf{y}_2 \end{bmatrix} \right\|_2^2 \\
&= \left\| \begin{bmatrix} \mathbf{c}_1 - \Sigma_1 \mathbf{y}_1 \\ \mathbf{c}_2 \end{bmatrix} \right\|_2^2 \\
&= \|\mathbf{c}_1 - \Sigma_1 \mathbf{y}_1\|_2^2 + \|\mathbf{c}_2\|_2^2
\end{aligned}
$$

Since c_2 is independent of $\mathbf{x}$, it follows that $\|\mathbf{b} - A\mathbf{x}\|^2$ will be minimal if and only if

$$\|\mathbf{c}_1 - \Sigma_1 \mathbf{y}_1\| = 0$$

Thus, $\mathbf{x}$ is a solution to the least squares problem if and only if $\mathbf{x} = V\mathbf{y}$, where $\mathbf{y}$ is a vector of the form

$$\begin{bmatrix} \Sigma_1^{-1}\mathbf{c}_1 \\ \mathbf{y}_2 \end{bmatrix}$$

In particular,

$$\mathbf{x} = V \begin{bmatrix} \Sigma_1^{-1}\mathbf{c}_1 \\ \mathbf{0} \end{bmatrix}$$

$$= V \begin{bmatrix} \Sigma_1^{-1} & O \\ O & O \end{bmatrix} \begin{bmatrix} \mathbf{c}_1 \\ \mathbf{c}_2 \end{bmatrix}$$

$$= V\Sigma^{+}U^{T}\mathbf{b}$$

$$= A^{+}\mathbf{b}$$

is a solution. If $\mathbf{z}$ is any other solution, $\mathbf{z}$ must be of the form

$$\mathbf{z} = V\mathbf{y} = V \begin{bmatrix} \Sigma_1^{-1}\mathbf{c}_1 \\ \mathbf{y}_2 \end{bmatrix}$$

where $\mathbf{y}_2 \neq \mathbf{0}$. It then follows that

$$\|\mathbf{z}\|^2 = \|\mathbf{y}\|^2 = \|\Sigma_1^{-1}\mathbf{c}_1\|^2 + \|\mathbf{y}_2\|^2 > \|\Sigma_1^{-1}\mathbf{c}_1\|^2 = \|\mathbf{x}\|^2 \qquad \blacksquare$$

If the singular value decomposition $U\Sigma V^{T}$ of A is known, it is a simple matter to compute the solution to the least squares problem. If $U = (\mathbf{u}_1, \ldots, \mathbf{u}_m)$ and $V = (\mathbf{v}_1, \ldots, \mathbf{v}_n)$, then, defining $\mathbf{y} = \Sigma^{+}U^{T}\mathbf{b}$, we have

$$y_i = \frac{1}{\sigma_i}\mathbf{u}_i^{T}\mathbf{b} \qquad i = 1, \ldots, r \qquad (r = \text{rank of } A)$$

$$y_i = 0 \qquad\qquad i = r + 1, \ldots, n$$

and hence

$$A^{+}\mathbf{b} = V\mathbf{y} = \begin{bmatrix} v_{11}y_1 + v_{12}y_2 + \cdots + v_{1r}y_r \\ v_{21}y_1 + v_{22}y_2 + \cdots + v_{2r}y_r \\ \vdots \\ v_{n1}y_1 + v_{n2}y_2 + \cdots + v_{nr}y_r \end{bmatrix}$$

$$= y_1\mathbf{v}_1 + y_2\mathbf{v}_2 + \cdots + y_r\mathbf{v}_r$$

Thus, the solution $\mathbf{x} = A^{+}\mathbf{b}$ can be computed in two steps:

1. Set $y_i = (1/\sigma_i)\mathbf{u}_i^{T}\mathbf{b}$ for $i = 1, \ldots, r$.
2. Let $\mathbf{x} = y_1\mathbf{v}_1 + \cdots + y_r\mathbf{v}_r$.

We conclude this section by outlining a method for computing the singular values of a matrix. We saw in the last section that the eigenvalues of a symmetric matrix are relatively insensitive to perturbations in the matrix. The same is true for the singular values of an $m \times n$ matrix. If two matrices A and B are close, their singular values must also be close. More precisely, if A has the singular values $\sigma_1 \geq \sigma_2 \geq \cdots \geq \sigma_n$ and B has the singular values $\omega_1 \geq \omega_2 \geq \cdots \geq \omega_n$, then

$$|\sigma_i - \omega_i| \leq \|A - B\|_2 \qquad i = 1, \ldots, n$$

(see Datta [23]). Thus, in computing the singular values of a matrix A, we need not worry that small changes in the entries of A will cause drastic changes in the computed singular values.

The problem of computing singular values can be simplified using orthogonal transformations. If A has singular value decomposition $U\Sigma V^T$ and $B = HAP^T$, where H is an $m \times m$ orthogonal matrix and P is an $n \times n$ orthogonal matrix, then B has singular value decomposition $(HU)\Sigma(PV)^T$. The matrices A and B will have the same singular values, and if B has a much simpler structure than A, it should be easier to compute its singular values. Indeed, Gene H. Golub and William Kahan have shown that A can be reduced to upper bidiagonal form and the reduction can be carried out using Householder transformations.

Bidiagonalization

Let H_1 be a Householder transformation that zeroes out all the elements below the diagonal in the first column of A. Let P_1 be a Householder transformation such that postmultiplication of H_1A by P_1 zeroes out the last $n - 2$ entries of the first row of H_1A while leaving the first column unchanged; that is,

$$H_1AP_1 = \begin{pmatrix} \times & \times & 0 & \cdots & 0 \\ 0 & \times & \times & \cdots & \times \\ \vdots & & & & \\ 0 & \times & \times & \cdots & \times \end{pmatrix}$$

The next step is to apply a Householder transformation H_2 that zeroes out the elements below the diagonal in the second column of H_1AP_1 while leaving the first row and column unchanged:

$$H_2H_1AP_1 = \begin{pmatrix} \times & \times & 0 & \cdots & 0 \\ 0 & \times & \times & \cdots & \times \\ 0 & 0 & \times & \cdots & \times \\ \vdots & & & & \\ 0 & 0 & \times & \cdots & \times \end{pmatrix}$$

$H_2H_1AP_1$ is then postmultiplied by a Householder transformation P_2 that zeroes out the last $n - 3$ elements in the second row while leaving the first two columns and the first row unchanged:

$$H_2 H_1 A P_1 P_2 = \begin{bmatrix} \times & \times & 0 & 0 & \cdots & 0 \\ 0 & \times & \times & 0 & \cdots & 0 \\ 0 & 0 & \times & \times & \cdots & \times \\ & \vdots & & & & \\ 0 & 0 & \times & \times & \cdots & \times \end{bmatrix}$$

We continue in this manner until we obtain a matrix

$$B = H_n \cdots H_1 A P_1 \cdots P_{n-2}$$

of the form

$$\begin{bmatrix} \times & \times & & & \\ & \times & \times & & \\ & & \ddots & \ddots & \\ & & & \times & \times \\ & & & & \times \end{bmatrix}$$

Since $H = H_n \cdots H_1$ and $P^T = P_1 \cdots P_{n-2}$ are orthogonal, it follows that B has the same singular values as A.

The problem has now been simplified to that of finding the singular values of an upper bidiagonal matrix B. We could at this point form the symmetric tridiagonal matrix $B^T B$ and then compute its eigenvalues using the QR algorithm. The problem with this approach is that, in forming $B^T B$, we would still be squaring the condition number, and consequently our computed solution would be much less reliable. The method we outline produces a sequence of bidiagonal matrices $B_1, B_2, \ldots$ that converges to a diagonal matrix Σ. The method involves applying a sequence of Givens transformations to B alternately on the right- and left-hand sides.

The Golub–Reinsch Algorithm

Let

$$R_k = \begin{bmatrix} I_{k-1} & O & O \\ O & G(\theta_k) & O \\ O & O & I_{n-k-1} \end{bmatrix}$$

and

$$L_k = \begin{bmatrix} I_{k-1} & O & O \\ O & G(\varphi_k) & O \\ O & O & I_{n-k-1} \end{bmatrix}$$

The 2×2 matrices $G(\theta_k)$ and $G(\varphi_k)$ are given by

$$G(\theta_k) = \begin{bmatrix} \cos \theta_k & \sin \theta_k \\ \sin \theta_k & -\cos \theta_k \end{bmatrix} \quad \text{and} \quad G(\varphi_k) = \begin{bmatrix} \cos \varphi_k & \sin \varphi_k \\ \sin \varphi_k & -\cos \varphi_k \end{bmatrix}$$

for some angles θ_k and φ_k. The matrix $B = B_1$ is first multiplied on the right by R_1. This will have the effect of filling in the $(2, 1)$ position.

$$
B_1 R_1 =
\begin{pmatrix}
\times & \times & & & & & \\
\times & \times & \times & & & & \\
 & & \times & & & & \\
 & & & \ddots & & \times & \\
 & & & & & \times & \\
\end{pmatrix}
$$

Next, L_1 is chosen so as to zero out the element filled in by R_1. It will also have the effect of filling in the $(1, 3)$ position. Thus,

$$
L_1 B_1 R_1 =
\begin{pmatrix}
\times & \times & \times & & & \\
 & \times & \times & & & \\
 & & & \ddots & & \\
 & & & & \times & \\
 & & & & \times & \\
\end{pmatrix}
$$

R_2 is chosen so as to zero out the $(1, 3)$ entry. It will fill in the $(3, 2)$ entry of $L_1 B_1 R_1$. Next, L_2 zeroes out the $(3, 2)$ entry and fills in the $(2, 4)$ entry, and so on.

$$
\begin{pmatrix}
\times & \times & & & & \\
 & \times & \times & & & \\
 & \times & \times & \times & & \\
 & & & \ddots & & \\
 & & & & \times & \\
 & & & & \times & \\
\end{pmatrix},
\qquad
\begin{pmatrix}
\times & \times & & & & \\
 & \times & \times & \times & & \\
 & & \times & \times & & \\
 & & & \ddots & & \\
 & & & & \times & \\
 & & & & \times & \\
\end{pmatrix}
$$
$$
\quad\ L_1 B_1 R_1 R_2 \qquad\qquad\qquad L_2 L_1 B_1 R_1 R_2
$$

We continue this process until we end up with a new bidiagonal matrix:

$$
B_2 = L_{n-1} \cdots L_1 B_1 R_1 \cdots R_{n-1}
$$

Why should we be any better off with B_2 than B_1? It can be shown that if the first transformation R_1 is chosen correctly, $B_2^T B_2$ will be the matrix obtained from $B_1^T B_1$ by applying one iteration of the QR algorithm with shift. The same process can now be applied to B_2 to obtain a new bidiagonal matrix B_3 such that $B_3^T B_3$ would be the matrix obtained by applying two iterations of the QR algorithm with shifts to $B_1^T B_1$. Even though the $B_i^T B_i$'s are never computed, we know that, with the proper choice of shifts, these matrices will converge rapidly to a diagonal matrix. The B_i's then must also converge to a diagonal matrix Σ. Since each of the B_i's has the same singular values as B, the diagonal elements of Σ will be the singular values of B. The matrices U and V^T can be determined by keeping track of all the orthogonal transformations.

Only a brief sketch of the algorithm has been given. To include more would be beyond the scope of this text. For complete details of the algorithm, see the paper by Golub and Reinsch in [37], p. 135.

SECTION 7.7 EXERCISES

1. Find the solution **x** to the least squares problem, given that $A = QR$ in each of the following:

(a) $Q = \begin{pmatrix} \dfrac{1}{\sqrt{2}} & \dfrac{1}{\sqrt{2}} \\ \dfrac{1}{\sqrt{2}} & -\dfrac{1}{\sqrt{2}} \\ 0 & 0 \end{pmatrix}$,

$R = \begin{bmatrix} 1 & 1 \\ 0 & 1 \end{bmatrix}$, $\mathbf{b} = \begin{bmatrix} 1 \\ 1 \\ 1 \end{bmatrix}$

(b) $Q = \begin{pmatrix} 1 & 0 & 0 \\ 0 & \dfrac{1}{\sqrt{2}} & -\dfrac{1}{\sqrt{2}} \\ 0 & \dfrac{1}{\sqrt{2}} & \dfrac{1}{\sqrt{2}} \\ 0 & 0 & 0 \end{pmatrix}$,

$R = \begin{bmatrix} 1 & 1 & 0 \\ 0 & 1 & 1 \\ 0 & 0 & 1 \end{bmatrix}$, $\mathbf{b} = \begin{bmatrix} 1 \\ 3 \\ 1 \\ 2 \end{bmatrix}$

(c) $Q = \begin{pmatrix} 1 & 0 & 0 \\ 0 & \dfrac{1}{\sqrt{2}} & -\dfrac{1}{\sqrt{2}} \\ 0 & \dfrac{1}{\sqrt{2}} & \dfrac{1}{\sqrt{2}} \end{pmatrix}$,

$R = \begin{bmatrix} 1 & 1 \\ 0 & 1 \\ 0 & 0 \end{bmatrix}$, $\mathbf{b} = \begin{bmatrix} 1 \\ \sqrt{2} \\ -\sqrt{2} \end{bmatrix}$

(d) $Q = \begin{pmatrix} \dfrac{1}{2} & \dfrac{1}{\sqrt{2}} & 0 & \dfrac{1}{2} \\ \dfrac{1}{2} & 0 & \dfrac{1}{\sqrt{2}} & -\dfrac{1}{2} \\ \dfrac{1}{2} & 0 & -\dfrac{1}{\sqrt{2}} & -\dfrac{1}{2} \\ \dfrac{1}{2} & -\dfrac{1}{\sqrt{2}} & 0 & \dfrac{1}{2} \end{pmatrix}$,

$R = \begin{bmatrix} 1 & 1 & 0 \\ 0 & 1 & 1 \\ 0 & 0 & 1 \\ 0 & 0 & 0 \end{bmatrix}$, $\mathbf{b} = \begin{bmatrix} 2 \\ -2 \\ 0 \\ 2 \end{bmatrix}$

2. Let

$$A = \begin{bmatrix} D \\ E \end{bmatrix} = \left[\begin{array}{ccccc} d_1 & & & & \\ & d_2 & & & \\ & & \ddots & & \\ & & & & d_n \\ \hline e_1 & & & & \\ & e_2 & & & \\ & & \ddots & & \\ & & & & e_n \end{array} \right]$$

and

$$\mathbf{b} = \begin{bmatrix} b_1 \\ b_2 \\ \vdots \\ b_{2n} \end{bmatrix}$$

Use the normal equations to find the solution **x** to the least squares problem.

3. Let

$$A = \begin{bmatrix} 1 & 0 \\ 1 & 3 \\ 1 & 3 \\ 1 & 0 \end{bmatrix}, \qquad \mathbf{b} = \begin{bmatrix} -4 \\ 2 \\ 2 \\ 2 \end{bmatrix}$$

(a) Use Householder transformations to reduce A to the form

$$\begin{bmatrix} R_1 \\ O \end{bmatrix} = \begin{bmatrix} \times & \times \\ 0 & \times \\ 0 & 0 \\ 0 & 0 \end{bmatrix}$$

and apply the same transformations to **b**.

(b) Use the results from part (a) to find the least squares solution of $A\mathbf{x} = \mathbf{b}$.

4. Given

$$A = \begin{bmatrix} 1 & 5 \\ 1 & 3 \\ 1 & 11 \\ 1 & 5 \end{bmatrix} \quad \text{and} \quad \mathbf{b} = \begin{bmatrix} 1 \\ -1 \\ 3 \\ 5 \end{bmatrix}$$

(a) Use Algorithm 5.6.1 to compute the factors Q and R of the modified Gram–Schmidt QR factorization of A.

(b) Use Algorithm 7.7.1 to compute the least squares solution to the linear system $A\mathbf{x} = \mathbf{b}$.

5. Let

$$A = \begin{bmatrix} 1 & 1 \\ \rho & 0 \\ 0 & \rho \end{bmatrix}$$

where ρ is a small scalar.

(a) Determine the singular values of A exactly.

(b) Suppose that ρ is small enough so that ρ^2 is less than the machine epsilon. Determine the eigenvalues of the calculated A^TA and compare the square roots of these eigenvalues with your answers in part (a).

6. Show that the pseudoinverse A^+ satisfies the four Penrose conditions.

7. Let B be any matrix that satisfies Penrose conditions 1 and 3, and let $\mathbf{x} = B\mathbf{b}$. Show that $\mathbf{x}$ is a solution to the normal equations $A^TA\mathbf{x} = A^T\mathbf{b}$.

8. If $\mathbf{x} \in \mathbb{R}^m$, we can think of $\mathbf{x}$ as an $m \times 1$ matrix. If $\mathbf{x} \neq \mathbf{0}$ we can then define a $1 \times m$ matrix X by

$$X = \frac{1}{\|\mathbf{x}\|_2^2}\mathbf{x}^T$$

Show that X and $\mathbf{x}$ satisfy the four Penrose conditions and, consequently, that

$$\mathbf{x}^+ = X = \frac{1}{\|\mathbf{x}\|_2^2}\mathbf{x}^T$$

9. Show that if A is a $m \times n$ matrix of rank n, then $A^+ = (A^TA)^{-1}A^T$.

10. Let A be an $m \times n$ matrix and let $\mathbf{b} \in \mathbb{R}^m$. Show that $\mathbf{b} \in R(A)$ if and only if

$$\mathbf{b} = AA^+\mathbf{b}$$

11. Let A be an $m \times n$ matrix with singular value decomposition $U\Sigma V^T$, and suppose that A has rank r, where $r < n$. Let $\mathbf{b} \in \mathbb{R}^m$. Show that a vector $\mathbf{x} \in \mathbb{R}^n$ minimizes $\|\mathbf{b} - A\mathbf{x}\|_2$ if and only if

$$\mathbf{x} = A^+\mathbf{b} + c_{r+1}\mathbf{v}_{r+1} + \cdots + c_n\mathbf{v}_n$$

where $c_{r+1}, \ldots, c_n$ are scalars.

12. Let

$$A = \begin{bmatrix} 1 & 1 \\ 1 & 1 \\ 0 & 0 \end{bmatrix}$$

Determine A^+ and verify that A and A^+ satisfy the four Penrose conditions (see Example 1 of Section 6.5).

13. Let

$$A = \begin{bmatrix} 1 & 2 \\ -1 & -2 \end{bmatrix} \quad \text{and} \quad \mathbf{b} = \begin{bmatrix} 6 \\ -4 \end{bmatrix}$$

(a) Compute the singular value decomposition of A and use it to determine A^+.

(b) Use A^+ to find a least squares solution to the system $A\mathbf{x} = \mathbf{b}$.

(c) Find all solutions to the least squares problem $A\mathbf{x} = \mathbf{b}$.

14. Show each of the following:

(a) $(A^+)^+ = A$ (b) $(AA^+)^2 = AA^+$

(c) $(A^+A)^2 = A^+A$

15. Let $A_1 = U\Sigma_1 V^T$ and $A_2 = U\Sigma_2 V^T$, where

$$\Sigma_1 = \begin{bmatrix} \sigma_1 & & & & & & \\ & \ddots & & & & & \\ & & \sigma_{r-1} & & & & \\ & & & 0 & & & \\ & & & & \ddots & & \\ & & & & & 0 & \\ & & & & & & 0 \end{bmatrix}$$

and

$$\Sigma_2 = \begin{bmatrix} \sigma_1 & & & & & & \\ & \ddots & & & & & \\ & & \sigma_{r-1} & & & & \\ & & & \sigma_r & & & \\ & & & & 0 & & \\ & & & & & \ddots & \\ & & & & & & 0 \end{bmatrix}$$

and $\sigma_r = \rho > 0$. What are the values of $\|A_1 - A_2\|_F$ and $\|A_1^+ - A_2^+\|_F$? What happens to these values as we let $\rho \to 0$?

16. Let $A = XY^T$, where X is an $m \times r$ matrix, Y^T is an $r \times n$ matrix, and X^TX and Y^TY are both nonsingular. Show that the matrix

$$B = Y(Y^TY)^{-1}(X^TX)^{-1}X^T$$

satisfies the Penrose conditions and hence must equal A^+. Thus, A^+ can be determined from any factorization of this form.

7.8   Iterative Methods

In this section, we study iterative methods for solving a linear system $A\mathbf{x} = \mathbf{b}$. Iterative methods start out with an initial approximation $\mathbf{x}^{(0)}$ to the solution and go through a fixed procedure to obtain a better approximation, $\mathbf{x}^{(1)}$. The same procedure is then repeated on $\mathbf{x}^{(1)}$ to obtain an improved approximation, $\mathbf{x}^{(2)}$, and so on. The iterations terminate when a desired accuracy has been achieved.

Iterative methods are most useful in solving large sparse systems. Such systems occur, for example, in the solution of boundary value problems for partial differential equations. The number of flops necessary to solve an $n \times n$ linear system using iterative methods is proportional to n^2, whereas the amount necessary using Gaussian elimination is proportional to n^3. Thus for large values of n, iterative methods provide the only practical way of solving the system. Furthermore, the amount of memory required for a sparse coefficient matrix A is proportional to n, whereas Gaussian elimination and the other direct methods studied in earlier chapters usually tend to fill in the zeros of A and hence require an amount of storage proportional to n^2. This can present a problem when n is very large.

The iterative methods we will describe only require that in each iteration we can multiply A times a vector in R^n. If A is sparse, this can usually be accomplished in a systematic way so that only a small proportion of the entries of A need be accessed. The one disadvantage of iterative methods is that after solving $A\mathbf{x} = \mathbf{b}_1$, one must start over again from the beginning in order to solve $A\mathbf{x} = \mathbf{b}_2$.

Matrix Splittings

Given a system $A\mathbf{x} = \mathbf{b}$, we write the coefficient matrix A in the form $A = C - M$, where C is a nonsingular matrix which is in some form that is easily invertible (e.g., diagonal or triangular). The representation $A = C - M$ is referred to as a *matrix splitting*. The system can then be rewritten in the form

$$C\mathbf{x} = M\mathbf{x} + \mathbf{b}$$
$$\mathbf{x} = C^{-1}M\mathbf{x} + C^{-1}\mathbf{b}$$

If we set

$$B = C^{-1}M = I - C^{-1}A \qquad \text{and} \qquad \mathbf{c} = C^{-1}\mathbf{b}$$

then

$$\mathbf{x} = B\mathbf{x} + \mathbf{c} \tag{1}$$

To solve the system, we start out with an initial guess $\mathbf{x}^{(0)}$, which may be any vector in R^n. We then set

$$\mathbf{x}^{(1)} = B\mathbf{x}^{(0)} + \mathbf{c}$$
$$\mathbf{x}^{(2)} = B\mathbf{x}^{(1)} + \mathbf{c}$$

and, in general,

$$\mathbf{x}^{(k+1)} = B\mathbf{x}^{(k)} + \mathbf{c}$$

Let $\mathbf{x}$ be a solution of the linear system. If $\| \cdot \|$ denotes some vector norm on R^n and the corresponding matrix norm of B is less than 1, we claim that $\|\mathbf{x}^{(k)} - \mathbf{x}\| \to 0$ as $k \to \infty$. Indeed,

$$\mathbf{x}^{(1)} - \mathbf{x} = (B\mathbf{x}^{(0)} + \mathbf{c}) - (B\mathbf{x} + \mathbf{c}) = B(\mathbf{x}^{(0)} - \mathbf{x})$$
$$\mathbf{x}^{(2)} - \mathbf{x} = (B\mathbf{x}^{(1)} + \mathbf{c}) - (B\mathbf{x} + \mathbf{c}) = B(\mathbf{x}^{(1)} - \mathbf{x}) = B^2(\mathbf{x}^{(0)} - \mathbf{x})$$

and so on. In general,

$$\mathbf{x}^{(k)} - \mathbf{x} = B^k(\mathbf{x}^{(0)} - \mathbf{x}) \tag{2}$$

and hence

$$\begin{aligned} \|\mathbf{x}^{(k)} - \mathbf{x}\| &= \|B^k(\mathbf{x}^{(0)} - \mathbf{x})\| \\ &\leq \|B^k\| \, \|\mathbf{x}^{(0)} - \mathbf{x}\| \\ &\leq \|B\|^k \|\mathbf{x}^{(0)} - \mathbf{x}\| \end{aligned}$$

Thus, if $\|B\| < 1$, then $\|\mathbf{x}^{(k)} - \mathbf{x}\| \to 0$ as $k \to \infty$.

The foregoing result holds for any standard norm on R^n, although in practice it is simplest to use the $\| \cdot \|_\infty$ or the $\| \cdot \|_1$. Essentially, then, we require that the matrix C be easily invertible and that C^{-1} be a good enough approximation to A^{-1} so that

$$\|I - C^{-1}A\| = \|B\| < 1$$

This last condition implies that all the eigenvalues of B are less than 1 in the modulus.

Definition

> Let $\lambda_1, \ldots, \lambda_n$ be the eigenvalues of B and let $\rho(B) = \max_{1 \leq i \leq n} |\lambda_i|$. The constant $\rho(B)$ is called the **spectral radius** of B.

Theorem 7.8.1

Let $\mathbf{x}^{(0)}$ be an arbitrary vector in R^n and define $\mathbf{x}^{(i+1)} = B\mathbf{x}^{(i)} + \mathbf{c}$ for $i = 0, 1, \ldots$. If $\mathbf{x}$ is the solution to (1), then a necessary and sufficient condition for $\mathbf{x}^{(k)} \to \mathbf{x}$ is that $\rho(B) < 1$.

Proof   We will prove the theorem only in the case where B has n linearly independent eigenvectors. The case where B is not diagonalizable is beyond the scope of this text. If $\mathbf{x}_1, \ldots, \mathbf{x}_n$ are n linearly independent eigenvectors of B, we can write

$$\mathbf{x}^{(0)} - \mathbf{x} = \alpha_1 \mathbf{x}_1 + \cdots + \alpha_n \mathbf{x}_n$$

and it follows from (2) that

$$\begin{aligned} \mathbf{x}^{(k)} - \mathbf{x} &= B^k(\alpha_1 \mathbf{x}_1 + \cdots + \alpha_n \mathbf{x}_n) \\ &= \alpha_1 \lambda_1^k \mathbf{x}_1 + \cdots + \alpha_n \lambda_n^k \mathbf{x}_n \end{aligned}$$

Thus,

$$\mathbf{x}^{(k)} - \mathbf{x} \to \mathbf{0}$$

if and only if $|\lambda_i| < 1$ for $i = 1, \ldots, n$. Thus, $\mathbf{x}^{(k)} \to \mathbf{x}$ if and only if $\rho(B) < 1$. ∎

The simplest choice of C is to let C be a diagonal matrix whose diagonal elements are the diagonal elements of A. The iteration scheme with this choice of C is called *Jacobi iteration*.

Jacobi Iteration

Let

$$
C = \begin{pmatrix} a_{11} & 0 & \cdots & 0 \\ 0 & a_{22} & & \\ \vdots & & \ddots & \\ 0 & 0 & & a_{nn} \end{pmatrix}
$$

and

$$
M = -\begin{pmatrix} 0 & a_{12} & \cdots & a_{1n} \\ a_{21} & 0 & & a_{2n} \\ \vdots & & \ddots & \\ a_{n1} & a_{n2} & & 0 \end{pmatrix}
$$

and set $B = C^{-1}M$ and $\mathbf{c} = C^{-1}\mathbf{b}$. Thus,

$$
B = \begin{pmatrix} 0 & \dfrac{-a_{12}}{a_{11}} & \cdots & \dfrac{-a_{1n}}{a_{11}} \\ \dfrac{-a_{21}}{a_{22}} & 0 & \cdots & \dfrac{-a_{2n}}{a_{22}} \\ \vdots & & & \\ \dfrac{-a_{n1}}{a_{nn}} & \dfrac{-a_{n2}}{a_{nn}} & \cdots & 0 \end{pmatrix} \quad \text{and} \quad \mathbf{c} = \begin{pmatrix} \dfrac{b_1}{a_{11}} \\ \dfrac{b_2}{a_{22}} \\ \vdots \\ \dfrac{b_n}{a_{nn}} \end{pmatrix}
$$

At the $(i + 1)$st iteration, the vector $\mathbf{x}^{(i+1)}$ is calculated by

$$
x_j^{(i+1)} = \frac{1}{a_{jj}}\left(-\sum_{\substack{k=1 \\ k\neq j}}^{n} a_{jk}x_k^{(i)} + b_j \right) \qquad j = 1,\ldots,n \tag{3}
$$

The vector $\mathbf{x}^{(i)}$ is used in calculating $\mathbf{x}^{(i+1)}$. Consequently, these two vectors must be stored separately.

If the diagonal elements of A are much larger than the off-diagonal elements, the entries of B should all be small and the Jacobi iteration should converge. We say that A is *diagonally dominant* if

$$
|a_{ii}| > \sum_{\substack{j=1 \\ j\neq i}}^{n} |a_{ij}| \qquad \text{for} \qquad i = 1,\ldots,n
$$

If A is diagonally dominant, the matrix B of the Jacobi iteration will have the property

$$
\sum_{j=1}^{n} |b_{ij}| = \sum_{\substack{j=1 \\ j\neq i}}^{n} \frac{|a_{ij}|}{|a_{ii}|} < 1 \qquad \text{for} \qquad i = 1,\ldots,n
$$

Thus,

$$\|B\|_\infty = \max_{1 \le i \le n} \left(\sum_{j=1}^{n} |b_{ij}| \right) < 1$$

It follows, then, that if A is diagonally dominant, the Jacobi iteration will converge to the solution of $A\mathbf{x} = \mathbf{b}$.

An alternative to the Jacobi iteration is to take C to be the lower triangular part of A (i.e., $c_{ij} = a_{ij}$ if $i \ge j$ and $c_{ij} = 0$ if $i < j$). Since C is a better approximation to A than the diagonal matrix in the Jacobi iteration, we would expect that C^{-1} is a better approximation to A^{-1}, and hopefully B will have a smaller norm. The iteration scheme with this choice of C is called *Gauss–Seidel iteration*. It usually converges faster than Jacobi iteration.

Gauss–Seidel Iteration

Let

$$L = - \begin{pmatrix} 0 & 0 & \cdots & 0 & 0 \\ a_{21} & 0 & \cdots & 0 & 0 \\ \vdots & & & & \\ a_{n-1,1} & a_{n-1,2} & & 0 & 0 \\ a_{n1} & a_{n2} & \cdots & a_{n,n-1} & 0 \end{pmatrix}$$

$$D = \begin{pmatrix} a_{11} & 0 & \cdots & 0 \\ 0 & a_{22} & \cdots & 0 \\ \vdots & & & \\ 0 & 0 & \cdots & a_{nn} \end{pmatrix}$$

and

$$U = - \begin{pmatrix} 0 & a_{12} & \cdots & a_{1,n-1} & a_{1n} \\ 0 & 0 & \cdots & a_{2,n-1} & a_{2n} \\ \vdots & & & & \\ 0 & 0 & & 0 & a_{n-1,n} \\ 0 & 0 & & 0 & 0 \end{pmatrix}$$

Set $C = D - L$ and $M = U$. Let $\mathbf{x}^{(0)}$ be an arbitrary nonzero vector in R^n. We have

$$C\mathbf{x}^{(i+1)} = M\mathbf{x}^{(i)} + \mathbf{b}$$
$$(D - L)\mathbf{x}^{(i+1)} = U\mathbf{x}^{(i)} + \mathbf{b}$$
$$D\mathbf{x}^{(i+1)} = L\mathbf{x}^{(i+1)} + U\mathbf{x}^{(i)} + \mathbf{b}$$

We can solve this last equation for $\mathbf{x}^{(i+1)}$ one coordinate at a time. The first coordinate of $\mathbf{x}^{(i+1)}$ is given by

$$x_1^{(i+1)} = \frac{1}{a_{11}} \left(- \sum_{k=2}^{n} a_{1k} x_k^{(i)} + b_1 \right)$$

The second coordinate of $\mathbf{x}^{(i+1)}$ can be solved for in terms of the first coordinate and the last $n-2$ coordinates of $x^{(i)}$.

$$x_2^{(i+1)} = \frac{1}{a_{22}} \left(-a_{21}x_1^{(i+1)} - \sum_{k=3}^{n} a_{2k}x_k^{(i)} + b_2 \right)$$

In general,

$$x_j^{(i+1)} = \frac{1}{a_{jj}} \left(-\sum_{k=1}^{j-1} a_{jk}x_k^{(i+1)} - \sum_{k=j+1}^{n} a_{jk}x_k^{(i)} + b_j \right) \tag{4}$$

It is interesting to compare (3) and (4). The difference between the Jacobi and Gauss–Seidel iterations is that in the latter case, one is using the coordinates of $\mathbf{x}^{(i+1)}$ as soon as they are calculated rather than in the next iteration. The program for the Gauss–Seidel iteration is actually simpler than the program for the Jacobi iteration. The vectors $\mathbf{x}^{(i)}$ and $\mathbf{x}^{(i+1)}$ are both stored in the same vector, $\mathbf{x}$. As a coordinate of $\mathbf{x}^{(i+1)}$ is calculated, it replaces the corresponding coordinate of $\mathbf{x}^{(i)}$.

Theorem 7.8.2 *If A is diagonally dominant, then the Gauss–Seidel iteration converges to a solution of $Ax = \mathbf{b}$.*

Proof For $j = 1, \ldots, n$, let

$$\alpha_j = \sum_{i=1}^{j-1} |a_{ji}|, \qquad \beta_j = \sum_{i=j+1}^{n} |a_{ji}|, \qquad \text{and} \qquad M_j = \frac{\beta_j}{(|a_{jj}| - \alpha_j)}$$

Since A is diagonally dominant, it follows that

$$|a_{jj}| > \alpha_j + \beta_j$$

and, consequently, $M_j < 1$ for $j = 1, \ldots, n$. Thus,

$$M = \max_{1 \leq j \leq n} M_j < 1$$

We will show that

$$\|B\|_\infty = \max_{\mathbf{x} \neq 0} \frac{\|B\mathbf{x}\|_\infty}{\|\mathbf{x}\|_\infty} \leq M < 1$$

Let $\mathbf{x}$ be a nonzero vector in R^n and let $\mathbf{y} = B\mathbf{x}$. Choose k so that

$$\|\mathbf{y}\|_\infty = \max_{1 \leq i \leq n} |y_i| = |y_k|$$

It follows from the definition of B that

$$\mathbf{y} = B\mathbf{x} = (D - L)^{-1}U\mathbf{x}$$

and hence

$$\mathbf{y} = D^{-1}(L\mathbf{y} + U\mathbf{x})$$

Comparing the kth coordinates of each side, we see that

$$y_k = \frac{1}{a_{kk}}\left(-\sum_{i=1}^{k-1} a_{ki}y_i - \sum_{i=k+1}^{n} a_{ki}x_i\right)$$

and hence

$$\|\mathbf{y}\|_\infty = |y_k| \le \frac{1}{|a_{kk}|}(\alpha_k\|\mathbf{y}\|_\infty + \beta_k\|\mathbf{x}\|_\infty) \qquad (5)$$

It follows from (5) that

$$\frac{\|B\mathbf{x}\|_\infty}{\|\mathbf{x}\|_\infty} = \frac{\|\mathbf{y}\|_\infty}{\|\mathbf{x}\|_\infty} \le M_k \le M$$

Thus,

$$\|B\|_\infty = \max_{\mathbf{x}\ne 0} \frac{\|B\mathbf{x}\|_\infty}{\|\mathbf{x}\|_\infty} \le M < 1$$

and hence the iteration will converge to the solution of $A\mathbf{x} = \mathbf{b}$. ∎

SECTION 7.8 EXERCISES

1. Let

$$A = \begin{bmatrix} 10 & 1 \\ 2 & 10 \end{bmatrix}, \quad \mathbf{b} = \begin{bmatrix} 11 \\ 12 \end{bmatrix}, \quad \text{and} \quad \mathbf{x}^{(0)} = \begin{bmatrix} 0 \\ 0 \end{bmatrix}$$

Use Jacobi iteration to compute $\mathbf{x}^{(1)}$ and $\mathbf{x}^{(2)}$. [The exact solution is $\mathbf{x} = (1, 1)^T$.]

2. Let

$$A = \begin{bmatrix} 1 & 1 & 1 \\ 0 & 1 & 1 \\ 0 & 0 & 1 \end{bmatrix}, \quad \mathbf{b} = \begin{bmatrix} 3 \\ 2 \\ 1 \end{bmatrix}, \quad \text{and} \quad \mathbf{x}^{(0)} = \begin{bmatrix} 1 \\ 0 \\ 0 \end{bmatrix}$$

Use Jacobi iteration to compute $\mathbf{x}^{(1)}$, $\mathbf{x}^{(2)}$, $\mathbf{x}^{(3)}$, and $\mathbf{x}^{(4)}$.

3. Repeat Exercise 1 using Gauss–Seidel iteration.

4. Let

$$A = \begin{bmatrix} 10 & 1 & 1 \\ 1 & 10 & 1 \\ 1 & 1 & 10 \end{bmatrix}, \quad \mathbf{b} = \begin{bmatrix} 12 \\ 12 \\ 12 \end{bmatrix}, \quad \text{and} \quad \mathbf{x}^{(0)} = \begin{bmatrix} 1 \\ 0 \\ 0 \end{bmatrix}$$

(a) Calculate $\mathbf{x}^{(1)}$ using Jacobi iteration.

(b) Calculate $\mathbf{x}^{(1)}$ using Gauss–Seidel iteration.

(c) Compare your answers to (a) and (b) with the correct solution $\mathbf{x} = (1, 1, 1)^T$. Which is closer?

5. For which of the following matrices, will the iteration scheme

$$\mathbf{x}^{(k+1)} = B\mathbf{x}^{(k)} + \mathbf{c}$$

converge to a solution of $\mathbf{x} = B\mathbf{x} + \mathbf{c}$? Explain.

(a) $B = \begin{bmatrix} 1 & 1 & 1 \\ 0 & 1 & 1 \\ 0 & 0 & 1 \end{bmatrix}$

(b) $B = \begin{bmatrix} 0.9 & 1 & 1 \\ 0 & 0.9 & 1 \\ 0 & 0 & 0.9 \end{bmatrix}$

(c) $B = \begin{bmatrix} \frac{1}{2} & 10 & 100 \\ 0 & \frac{1}{2} & 10 \\ 0 & 0 & \frac{1}{2} \end{bmatrix}$

(d) $B = \begin{bmatrix} \frac{1}{4} & \frac{1}{4} & \frac{1}{4} \\ \frac{1}{4} & \frac{1}{2} & \frac{1}{4} \\ \frac{1}{2} & \frac{1}{4} & \frac{1}{8} \end{bmatrix}$

(e) $B = \begin{Bmatrix} \frac{1}{3} & \frac{1}{3} & \frac{1}{3} \\ \frac{1}{2} & \frac{1}{3} & \frac{1}{6} \\ 0 & \frac{1}{6} & \frac{1}{3} \end{Bmatrix}$

6. Let $\mathbf{x}$ be the solution of $\mathbf{x} = B\mathbf{x} + \mathbf{c}$. Let $\mathbf{x}^{(0)}$ be an arbitrary vector in R^n and define

$$\mathbf{x}^{(k+1)} = B\mathbf{x}^{(k)} + \mathbf{c}$$

for $k = 0, 1, \ldots$. Prove that if B^m is the zero matrix, then $\mathbf{x}^{(m)} = \mathbf{x}$.

7. Let A be a nonsingular upper triangular matrix. Show that if the Jacobi iteration is carried out using exact arithmetic, it will produce the exact solution to $A\mathbf{x} = \mathbf{b}$ after n iterations.

8. For an iterative method based on the splitting $A = C - M$, C nonsingular, show that

$$\mathbf{x}^{(k+1)} = \mathbf{x}^{(k)} + C^{-1}\mathbf{r}^{(k)}$$

where $\mathbf{r}^{(k)}$ denotes the residual $\mathbf{b} - A\mathbf{x}^{(k)}$.

9. Let $A = D - L - U$, where D, L, and U are defined as in Gauss–Seidel iteration and let ω be a nonzero scalar. The system $\omega A\mathbf{x} = \omega\mathbf{b}$ can be solved iteratively by splitting ωA into $C - M$, where $C = D - \omega L$. Determine the B and $\mathbf{c}$ corresponding to this splitting. (The constant ω is called a *relaxation parameter*. The case $\omega = 1$ corresponds to Gauss–Seidel iteration.)

10. Let $\mathbf{x}$ be the solution to $\mathbf{x} = B\mathbf{x} + \mathbf{c}$. Let $\mathbf{x}^{(0)}$ be an arbitrary vector in R^n and define

$$\mathbf{x}^{(i+1)} = B\mathbf{x}^{(i)} + \mathbf{c}$$

for $i = 0, 1, \ldots$. If $\|B\| = \alpha < 1$, show that

$$\|\mathbf{x}^{(k)} - \mathbf{x}\| \le \frac{\alpha}{1 - \alpha}\|\mathbf{x}^{(k)} - \mathbf{x}^{(k-1)}\|$$

Chapter 7 Exercises

MATLAB EXERCISES
Sensitivity of Linear Systems

In these exercises, we are concerned with the numerical solution of linear systems of equations. The entries of the coefficient matrix A and the right-hand side $\mathbf{b}$ may often contain small errors due to limitations in the accuracy of the data. Even if there are no errors in either A or $\mathbf{b}$, rounding errors will occur when their entries are translated into the finite-precision number system of the computer. Thus, we generally expect that the coefficient matrix and the right-hand side will involve small errors. The system that the computer solves is then a slightly perturbed version of the original system. If the original system is very sensitive, its solution could differ greatly from the solution of the perturbed system.

Generally, a problem is well conditioned if the perturbations in the solutions are on the same order as the perturbations in the data. A problem is ill conditioned if the changes in the solutions are much greater than the changes in the data. How well or ill conditioned a problem is depends on how the size of the perturbations in the solution compares with the size of the perturbations in the data. For linear systems, this, in turn, depends on how close the coefficient matrix is to a matrix of lower rank. The conditioning of a system can be measured using the condition number of the matrix, which can be computed with the MATLAB function **cond**. *MATLAB computations are carried out to 16 significant digits of accuracy. You will lose digits of accuracy depending on how sensitive the system is. If the condition number is expressed using exponential notation, then the* greater the exponent, the more digits of accuracy you may lose.

1. Set

$$A = \mathbf{round}(10 * \mathbf{rand}(6))$$
$$\mathbf{s} = \mathbf{ones}(6, 1)$$
$$\mathbf{b} = A * \mathbf{s}$$

The solution of the linear system $A\mathbf{x} = \mathbf{b}$ is clearly $\mathbf{s}$. Solve the system using the MATLAB \ operation. Compute the error $\mathbf{x} - \mathbf{s}$. (Since $\mathbf{s}$ consists entirely of 1's, this is the same as $\mathbf{x} - \mathbf{1}$.) Now perturb the system slightly. Set

$$t = 1.0e{-}12,$$
$$E = \mathbf{rand}(6) - 0.5,$$
$$\mathbf{r} = \mathbf{rand}(6, 1) - 0.5$$

and set

$$M = A + t * E, \qquad \mathbf{c} = \mathbf{b} + t * \mathbf{r}$$

Solve the perturbed system $M\mathbf{z} = \mathbf{c}$ for $\mathbf{z}$. Compare the solution $\mathbf{z}$ to the solution of the original system by computing $\mathbf{z} - \mathbf{1}$. How does the size of the perturbation in the solution compare with the size of the perturbations in A and $\mathbf{b}$? Repeat the perturbation analysis with $t = 1.0e{-}04$ and $t = 1.0e{-}02$. Is the system $A\mathbf{x} = \mathbf{b}$ well conditioned? Explain. Use MATLAB to compute the condition number of A.

2. If a vector $\mathbf{y} \in \mathbb{R}^n$ is used to construct an $n \times n$ Vandermonde matrix V, then V will be nonsingular, provided that $y_1, y_2, \ldots, y_n$ are all distinct.

   (a) Construct a Vandermonde system by setting

   $$\mathbf{y} = \mathbf{rand}(6, 1) \text{ and } V = \mathbf{vander}(\mathbf{y})$$

   Generate vectors $\mathbf{b}$ and $\mathbf{s}$ in $\mathbb{R}^6$ by setting

   $$\mathbf{b} = \mathbf{sum}(V')' \text{ and } \mathbf{s} = \mathbf{ones}(6, 1)$$

   If V and $\mathbf{b}$ had been computed in exact arithmetic, then the exact solution of $V\mathbf{x} = \mathbf{b}$ would be $\mathbf{s}$. Why? Explain. Solve $V\mathbf{x} = \mathbf{b}$ using the $\backslash$ operation. Compare the computed solution $\mathbf{x}$ with the exact solution $\mathbf{s}$ using the MATLAB **format long**. How many significant digits were lost? Determine the condition number of V.

   (b) The Vandermonde matrices become increasingly ill conditioned as the dimension n increases. Even for small values of n, we can make the matrix ill conditioned by taking two of the points close together. Set

   $$x(2) = x(1) + 1.0e-12$$

   and use the new value of $x(2)$ to recompute V. For the new matrix V, set $\mathbf{b} = \mathbf{sum}(V')'$ and solve the system $V\mathbf{z} = \mathbf{b}$. How many digits of accuracy were lost? Compute the condition number of V.

3. Construct a matrix C as follows: Set

   $$A = \mathbf{round}(100 * \mathbf{rand}(4))$$
   $$L = \mathbf{tril}(A, -1) + \mathbf{eye}(4)$$
   $$C = L * L'$$

   (a) The matrix C is a nice matrix in that it is a symmetric matrix with integer entries and its determinant is equal to 1. Use MATLAB to verify these claims. Why do we know ahead of time that the determinant will equal 1? In theory, the entries of the exact inverse should all be integers. Why? Explain. Does this happen computationally? Compute $D = \mathbf{inv}(C)$ and check its entries using **format long**. Compute $C * D$ and compare it with **eye**(4).

   (b) Set

   $$\mathbf{r} = \mathbf{ones}(4, 1) \text{ and } \mathbf{b} = \mathbf{sum}(C')'$$

   In exact arithmetic, the solution to the system $C\mathbf{x} = \mathbf{b}$ should be $\mathbf{r}$. Compute the solution by using $\backslash$ and display the answer in **format long**. How many digits of accuracy were lost? We can perturb the system slightly by taking e to be a small scalar, such as $1.0e-12$, and then replacing the right-hand side of the system by

   $$\mathbf{b1} = \mathbf{b} + e * [1, -1, 1, -1]'$$

Solve the perturbed system first for the case $e = 1.0e-12$ and then for the case $e = 10e-06$. In each case, compare your solution $\mathbf{x}$ with the original solution by displaying $\mathbf{x} - \mathbf{1}$. Compute **cond**(C). Is C ill conditioned? Explain.

4. The $n \times n$ Hilbert matrix H is defined by

   $$h(i, j) = 1/(i+j-1) \qquad i, j = 1, 2, \ldots, n$$

   It can be generated with the MATLAB function **hilb**. The Hilbert matrix is notoriously ill conditioned. It is often used in examples to illustrate the dangers of matrix computations. The MATLAB function **invhilb** gives the exact inverse of the Hilbert matrix. For the cases $n = 6, 8, 10, 12$, construct H and $\mathbf{b}$ so that $H\mathbf{x} = \mathbf{b}$ is a Hilbert system whose solution in exact arithmetic should be **ones**($n, 1$). In each case, determine the solution $\mathbf{x}$ of the system by using **invhilb** and examine $\mathbf{x}$ with **format long**. How many digits of accuracy were lost in each case? Compute the condition number of each Hilbert matrix. How does the condition number change as n increases?

Sensitivity of Eigenvalues

If A is an $n \times n$ matrix and X is a matrix that diagonalizes A, then the sensitivity of the eigenvalues of A depends on the condition number of X. If A is defective, the condition number for the eigenvalue problem will be infinite. For more on the sensitivity of eigenvalues, see Wilkinson [39], Chapter 2.

5. Use MATLAB to compute the eigenvalues and eigenvectors of a random 6×6 matrix B. Compute the condition number of the matrix of eigenvectors. Is the eigenvalue problem well conditioned? Perturb B slightly by setting

   $$B1 = B + 1.0e - 04 * \mathbf{rand}(6)$$

   Compute the eigenvalues and compare them with the eigenvalues of B.

6. Set

   $$A = \mathbf{round}(10 * \mathbf{rand}(5)); A = A + A'$$

   $$[X, D] = \mathbf{eig}(A)$$

   Compute **cond**(X) and $X^T X$. What type of matrix is X? Is the eigenvalue problem well conditioned? Explain. Perturb A by setting

   $$A1 = A + 1.0e-06 * \mathbf{rand}(5)$$

   Calculate the eigenvalues of $A1$ and compare them with the eigenvalues of A.

7. Set $A = \mathbf{magic}(4)$ and $t = \mathbf{trace}(A)$. The scalar t should be an eigenvalue of A and the remaining eigenvalues should add up to zero. Why? Explain. Use MATLAB to verify that $A - tI$ is singular. Compute the eigenvalues

of A and a matrix X of eigenvectors. Determine the condition numbers of A and X. Is the eigenvalue problem well conditioned? Explain. Perturb A by setting

$$A1 = A + 1.0e-04 * \textbf{rand}(4)$$

How do the eigenvalues of $A1$ compare to those of A?

8. Set

$$A = \textbf{diag}(10 : -1 : 1) + 10 * \textbf{diag}(\textbf{ones}(1, 9), 1)$$

$$[X, D] = \textbf{eig}(A)$$

Compute the condition number of X. Is the eigenvalue problem well conditioned? Ill conditioned? Explain. Perturb A by setting

$$A1 = A; \qquad A1(10, 1) = 0.1$$

Compute the eigenvalues of $A1$ and compare them to the eigenvalues of A.

9. Construct a matrix A as follows:

$$A = \textbf{diag}(11 : -1 : 1, -1);$$
$$\text{for } j = 0 : 11$$
$$\qquad A = A + \textbf{diag}(12 - j : -1 : 1, j);$$
$$\text{end}$$

(a) Compute the eigenvalues of A and the value of the determinant of A. Use the MATLAB function **prod** to compute the product of the eigenvalues. How does the value of the product compare with the determinant?

(b) Compute the eigenvectors of A and the condition number for the eigenvalue problem. Is the problem well conditioned? Ill conditioned? Explain.

(c) Set

$$A1 = A + 1.0e-04 * \textbf{rand}(\textbf{size}(A))$$

Compute the eigenvalues of $A1$. Compare them to the eigenvalues of A by computing

$$\textbf{sort}(\textbf{eig}(A1)) - \textbf{sort}(\textbf{eig}(A))$$

and displaying the result in **format long**.

Householder Transformations

A Householder matrix is an $n \times n$ orthogonal matrix of the form $I - \frac{1}{b}\textbf{vv}^T$. For any given nonzero vector $\textbf{x} \in \mathbb{R}^n$, it is possible to choose b and $\textbf{v}$ so that $H\textbf{x}$ will be a multiple of $\textbf{e}_1$.

10. (a) In MATLAB, the simplest way to compute a Householder matrix that zeroes out entries of a given vector $\textbf{x}$, is to compute the QR factorization of $\textbf{x}$. Thus, if we are given a vector $\textbf{x} \in \mathbb{R}^n$, then the MATLAB command

$$[H, R] = \textbf{qr}(\textbf{x})$$

will compute the desired Householder matrix H. Compute a Householder matrix H that zeroes out the last three entries of $\textbf{e} = \textbf{ones}(4, 1)$. Set

$$C = [\textbf{e}, \textbf{rand}(4, 3)]$$

Compute $H * \textbf{e}$ and $H * C$.

(b) We can also compute the vector $\textbf{v}$ and the scalar b that determine the Householder transformation that zeroes out entries of a given vector. To do this for a given vector $\textbf{x}$, we would set

$$a = ((x(1) <= 0) - (x(1) > 0)) * \textbf{norm}(\textbf{x});$$
$$\textbf{v} = \textbf{x}; \qquad v(1) = v(1) - a;$$
$$b = a * (a - x(1));$$

Construct $\textbf{v}$ and b in this way for the vector $\textbf{e}$ from part (a). If $K = I - \frac{1}{b}\textbf{vv}^T$, then

$$K\textbf{e} = \textbf{e} - \left(\frac{\textbf{v}^T\textbf{e}}{b}\right)\textbf{v}$$

Compute both of these quantities with MATLAB and verify that they are equal. How does $K\textbf{e}$ compare to $H\textbf{e}$ from part (a)? Compute also $K * C$ and $C - \textbf{v} * ((\textbf{v}' * C)/b)$ and verify that the two are equal.

11. Set

$$\textbf{x1} = (1 : 5)'; \quad \textbf{x2} = [1, 3, 4, 5, 9]'; \quad \textbf{x} = [\textbf{x1}; \textbf{x2}]$$

Construct a Householder matrix of the form

$$H = \begin{bmatrix} I & O \\ O & K \end{bmatrix}$$

where K is a 5×5 Householder matrix that zeroes out the last four entries of $\textbf{x2}$. Compute the product $H\textbf{x}$.

Rotations and Reflections

12. To plot $y = \sin(x)$, we must define vectors of x and y values and then use the **plot** command. This can be done as follows:

$$\textbf{x} = 0 : 0.1 : 6.3; \quad \textbf{y} = \sin(\textbf{x});$$
$$\textbf{plot}(\textbf{x}, \textbf{y})$$

(a) Let us define a rotation matrix and use it to rotate the graph of $y = \sin(x)$. Set

$$t = \textbf{pi}/4; \quad c = \cos(t); \quad s = \sin(t);$$

$$R = [c, -s; s, c]$$

To find the rotated coordinates, set

$$Z = R * [\textbf{x}; \textbf{y}]; \quad \textbf{x1} = Z(1, :); \quad \textbf{y1} = Z(2, :);$$

The vectors $\textbf{x1}$ and $\textbf{y1}$ contain the coordinates for the rotated curve. Set

$$\textbf{w} = [0, 5]; \qquad \textbf{axis square}$$

and plot **x1** and **y1**, using the MATLAB command

$$\text{plot}(\mathbf{x1}, \mathbf{y1}, \mathbf{w}, \mathbf{w})$$

By what angles has the graph been rotated and in what direction?

(b) Keep all your variables from part (a) and set

$$G = [c, s; s, -c]$$

The matrix G represents a Givens reflection. To determine the reflected coordinates, set

$$Z = G * [\mathbf{x}; \mathbf{y}];$$

$$\mathbf{x2} = Z(1, :); \quad \mathbf{y2} = Z(2, :);$$

Plot the reflected curve, using the MATLAB command

$$\text{plot}(\mathbf{x2}, \mathbf{y2}, \mathbf{w}, \mathbf{w})$$

The curve $y = \sin(x)$ has been reflected about a line through the origin making an angle of $\pi/8$ with the x-axis. To see this, set

$$\mathbf{w1} = [0, 6.3 * \cos(t/2)];$$

$$\mathbf{z1} = [0, 6.3 * \sin(t/2)];$$

and plot the new axis and both curves with the MATLAB command

$$\text{plot}(\mathbf{x}, \mathbf{y}, \mathbf{x2}, \mathbf{y2}, \mathbf{w1}, \mathbf{z1})$$

(c) Use the rotation matrix R from part (a) to rotate the curve $y = -\sin(x)$. Plot the rotated curve. How does the graph compare to that of the curve from part (b)? Explain.

Singular Value Decomposition

13. Let

$$A = \begin{bmatrix} 4 & 5 & 2 \\ 4 & 5 & 2 \\ 0 & 3 & 6 \\ 0 & 3 & 6 \end{bmatrix}$$

Enter the matrix A in MATLAB and compute its singular values by setting $\mathbf{s} = \mathbf{svd}(A)$.

(a) How can the entries of $\mathbf{s}$ be used to determine the values $\|A\|_2$ and $\|A\|_F$? Compute these norms by setting

$$p = \text{norm}(A) \quad \text{and} \quad q = \text{norm}(A, \text{`fro'})$$

and compare your results with $s(1)$ and **norm(s)**.

(b) To obtain the full singular value decomposition of A, set

$$[U, D, V] = \text{svd}(A)$$

Compute the closest matrix of rank 1 to A by setting

$$B = s(1) * U(:, 1) * V(:, 1)'$$

How are the row vectors of B related to the two distinct row vectors of A?

(c) The matrices A and B should have the same 2-norm. Why? Explain. Use MATLAB to compute $\|B\|_2$ and $\|B\|_F$. In general, for a rank 1 matrix, the 2-norm and the Frobenius norm should be equal. Why? Explain.

14. Set

$$A = \text{round}(10 * \text{rand}(10, 5)) \text{ and } \mathbf{s} = \text{svd}(A)$$

(a) Use MATLAB to compute $\|A\|_2$, $\|A\|_F$, and $\text{cond}_2(A)$ and compare your results with $s(1)$, **norm(s)**, $s(1)/s(5)$, respectively.

(b) Set

$$[U, D, V] = \text{svd}(A);$$
$$D(5, 5) = 0;$$
$$B = U * D * V'$$

The matrix B should be the closest matrix of rank 4 to A (where distance is measured in terms of the Frobenius norm). Compute $\|A\|_2$ and $\|B\|_2$. How do these values compare? Compute and compare the Frobenius norms of the two matrices. Compute also $\|A - B\|_F$ and compare the result with $s(5)$. Set $r = \text{norm}(s(1 : 4))$ and compare the result to $\|B\|_F$.

(c) Use MATLAB to construct a matrix C that is the closest matrix of rank 3 to A with respect to the Frobenius norm. Compute $\|C\|_2$ and $\|C\|_F$. How do these values compare with the computed values for $\|A\|_2$ and $\|A\|_F$, respectively? Set

$$p = \text{norm}(s(1 : 3))$$

and

$$q = \text{norm}(s(4 : 5))$$

Compute $\|C\|_F$ and $\|A - C\|_F$ and compare your results with p and q, respectively.

15. Set

$$A = \text{rand}(8, 4) * \text{rand}(4, 6),$$

$$[U, D, V] = \text{svd}(A)$$

(a) What is the rank of A? Use the column vectors of V to generate two matrices $V1$ and $V2$ whose columns form orthonormal bases for $R(A^T)$ and $N(A)$, respectively. Set

$$P = V2 * V2',$$
$$\mathbf{r} = P * \mathbf{rand}(6, 1),$$
$$\mathbf{w} = A' * \mathbf{rand}(8, 1)$$

If $\mathbf{r}$ and $\mathbf{w}$ had been computed in exact arithmetic, they would be orthogonal. Why? Explain. Use MATLAB to compute $\mathbf{r}^T\mathbf{w}$.

(b) Use the column vectors of U to generate two matrices $U1$ and $U2$ whose column vectors form orthonormal bases for $R(A)$ and $N(A^T)$, respectively. Set

$$Q = U2 * U2',$$
$$\mathbf{y} = Q * \mathbf{rand}(8, 1),$$
$$\mathbf{z} = A * \mathbf{rand}(6, 1)$$

Explain why $\mathbf{y}$ and $\mathbf{z}$ would be orthogonal if all computations were done in exact arithmetic. Use MATLAB to compute $\mathbf{y}^T\mathbf{z}$.

(c) Set $X = \mathbf{pinv}(A)$. Use MATLAB to verify the four Penrose conditions:

(i) $AXA = A$ **(ii)** $XAX = X$
(iii) $(AX)^T = AX$ **(iv)** $(XA)^T = XA$

(d) Compute and compare AX and $U1(U1)^T$. Had all computations been done in exact arithmetic, the two matrices would be equal. Why? Explain.

Gerschgorin Circles

16. With each $A \in \mathbb{R}^{n \times n}$, we can associate n closed circular disks in the complex plane. The ith disk is centered at a_{ii} and has radius

$$r_i = \sum_{\substack{j=1 \\ j \neq i}}^{n} |a_{ij}|$$

Each eigenvalue of A is contained in at least one of the disks (see Exercise 7 of Section 7.6).

(a) Set

$$A = \mathbf{round}(10 * \mathbf{rand}(5))$$

Compute the radii of the Gerschgorin disks of A and store them in a vector $\mathbf{r}$. To plot the disks, we must parameterize the circles. This can be done by setting

$$t = [0 : 0.1 : 6.3]';$$

We can then generate two matrices X and Y whose columns contain the x- and y- coordinates of the circles. First we initialize X and Y to zero by setting

$$X = \mathbf{zeros}(\mathbf{length}(t), 5); \qquad Y = X;$$

The matrices can then be generated with the following commands:

```
for i = 1 : 5
    X(:, i) = r(i) * cos(t) + real(A(i, i));
    Y(:, i) = r(i) * sin(t) + imag(A(i, i));
end
```

Set $\mathbf{e} = \mathbf{eig}(A)$ and plot the eigenvalues and the disks with the command

$$\mathbf{plot}(X, Y, \mathbf{real}(\mathbf{e}), \mathbf{imag}(\mathbf{e}), \text{`}x\text{'})$$

If everything is done correctly, all the eigenvalues of A should lie within the union of the circular disks.

(b) If k of the Gerschgorin disks form a connected domain in the complex plane that is isolated from the other disks, then exactly k of the eigenvalues of the matrix will lie in that domain. Set

$$B = [3 \quad 0.1 \quad 2; \quad 0.1 \quad 7 \quad 2; \quad 2 \quad 2 \quad 50];$$

(i) Use the method described in part (a) to compute and plot the Gerschgorin disks of B.

(ii) Since B is symmetric, its eigenvalues are all real and so must all lie on the real axis. Without computing the eigenvalues, explain why B must have exactly one eigenvalue in the interval $[46, 54]$. Multiply the first two rows of B by 0.1 and then multiply the first two columns by 10. We can do this in MATLAB by setting

$$D = \mathbf{diag}([0.1, 0.1, 1])$$

and

$$C = D * B / D$$

The new matrix C should have the same eigenvalues as B. Why? Explain. Use C to find intervals containing the other two eigenvalues. Compute and plot the Gerschgorin disks for C.

(iii) How are the eigenvalues of C^T related to the eigenvalues of B and C? Compute and plot the Gerschgorin disks for C^T. Use one of the rows of C^T to find an interval containing the largest eigenvalue of C^T.

Distribution of Condition Numbers and Eigenvalues of Random Matrices

17. We can generate a random symmetric 10×10 matrix by setting

$$A = \mathbf{rand}(10); \; A = (A + A')/2$$

Since A is symmetric, its eigenvalues are all real. The number of positive eigenvalues can be calculated by setting

$$y = \mathbf{sum}(\mathbf{eig}(A) > 0)$$

(a) For $j = 1, 2, \ldots, 100$, generate a random symmetric 10×10 matrix and determine the number of positive eigenvalues. Denote the number of positive eigenvalues of the jth matrix by $y(j)$. Set $\mathbf{x} = 0 : 10$, and determine the distribution of the $\mathbf{y}$ data by setting $\mathbf{n} = \mathbf{hist}(\mathbf{y}, \mathbf{x})$. Determine the mean of the $y(j)$ values, using the MATLAB command $\mathbf{mean}(\mathbf{y})$. Use the MATLAB command $\mathbf{hist}(\mathbf{y}, \mathbf{x})$ to generate a plot of the histogram.

(b) We can generate a random symmetric 10×10 matrix whose entries are in the interval $[-1, 1]$ by setting

$$A = 2 * \mathbf{rand}(10) - 1; \qquad A = (A + A')/2$$

Repeat part (a), using random matrices generated in this manner. How does the distribution of the $\mathbf{y}$ data compare to the one obtained in part (a)?

18. A nonsymmetric matrix A may have complex eigenvalues. We can determine the number of eigenvalues of A that are both real and positive with the MATLAB commands

$$e = \mathbf{eig}(A)$$
$$y = \mathbf{sum}(e > 0 \; \& \; \mathbf{imag}(e) == 0)$$

Generate 100 random nonsymmetric 10×10 matrices. For each matrix, determine the number of positive real eigenvalues and store that number as an entry of a vector $\mathbf{z}$. Determine the mean of the $z(j)$ values, and compare it with the mean computed in part (a) of Exercise 17. Determine the distribution and plot the histogram.

19. (a) Generate 100 random 5×5 matrices and compute the condition number of each matrix. Determine the mean of the condition numbers and plot the histogram of the distribution.

(b) Repeat part (a), using 10×10 matrices. Compare your results with those obtained in part (a).

CHAPTER TEST A   True or False

In each of the statements that follow, answer *true* if the statement is always true and *false* otherwise. In the case of a true statement, explain or prove your answer. In the case of a false statement, give an example to show that the statement is not always true.

1. If a, b, and c are floating-point numbers, then

$$fl(fl(a + b) + c) = fl(a + fl(b + c))$$

2. The computation of $A(BC)$ requires the same number of floating-point operations as the computation of $(AB)C$.

3. If A is a nonsingular matrix and a numerically stable algorithm is used to compute the solution of a system $A\mathbf{x} = \mathbf{b}$, then the relative error in the computed solution will always be small.

4. If A is a symmetric matrix and a numerically stable algorithm is used to compute the eigenvalues of A, then the relative error in the computed eigenvalues should always be small.

5. If A is a nonsymmetric matrix and a numerically stable algorithm is used to compute the eigenvalues of A, then the relative error in the computed eigenvalues should always be small.

6. If both A^{-1} and the LU factorization of an $n \times n$ matrix A have already been computed, then it is more efficient to solve a system $A\mathbf{x} = \mathbf{b}$ by multiplying $A^{-1}\mathbf{b}$, rather than solving $LU\mathbf{x} = \mathbf{b}$ by forward and back substitution.

7. If A is a symmetric matrix, then $\|A\|_1 = \|A\|_\infty$.

8. If A is an $m \times n$ matrix, then $\|A\|_2 = \|A\|_F$.

9. If the coefficient matrix A in a least squares problem has dimensions $m \times n$ and rank n, then the methods of solution discussed in Section 7.7, namely, the normal equations, the Gram–Schmidt and Householder QR factorizations, and the singular value decomposition, will all compute highly accurate solutions.

10. If two $m \times n$ matrices A and B are close in the sense that $\|A - B\|_2 < e$ for some small positive number e, then their pseudoinverses will also be close; that is, $\|A^+ - B^+\|_2 < \delta$, for some small positive number δ.

CHAPTER TEST B

1. Let A and B be $n \times n$ matrices and let $\mathbf{x}$ be a vector in $\mathbb{R}^n$. How many scalar additions and multiplications are required to compute $(AB)\mathbf{x}$ and how many are necessary to compute $A(B\mathbf{x})$? Which computation is more efficient?

2. Let

$$A = \begin{bmatrix} 2 & 3 & 6 \\ 4 & 4 & 8 \\ 1 & 3 & 4 \end{bmatrix} \quad \mathbf{b} = \begin{bmatrix} 3 \\ 0 \\ 4 \end{bmatrix} \quad \mathbf{c} = \begin{bmatrix} 1 \\ 8 \\ 2 \end{bmatrix}$$

  (a) Use Gaussian elimination with partial pivoting to solve $A\mathbf{x} = \mathbf{b}$.

  (b) Write the permutation matrix P that corresponds to the pivoting strategy in part (a) and determine the LU factorization of PA.

  (c) Use P, L, and U to solve the system $A\mathbf{x} = \mathbf{c}$.

3. Show that if Q is any 4×4 orthogonal matrix, then $\|Q\|_2 = 1$ and $\|Q\|_F = 2$.

4. Let

$$H = \begin{bmatrix} 1 & \frac{1}{2} & \frac{1}{3} & \frac{1}{4} \\ \frac{1}{2} & \frac{1}{3} & \frac{1}{4} & \frac{1}{5} \\ \frac{1}{3} & \frac{1}{4} & \frac{1}{5} & \frac{1}{6} \\ \frac{1}{4} & \frac{1}{5} & \frac{1}{6} & \frac{1}{7} \end{bmatrix},$$

$$H^{-1} = \begin{bmatrix} 16 & -120 & 240 & -140 \\ -120 & 1200 & -2700 & 1680 \\ 240 & -2700 & 6480 & -4200 \\ -140 & 1680 & -4200 & 2800 \end{bmatrix}$$

and $\mathbf{b} = (10, -10, 20, 10)^T$.

  (a) Determine the values of $\|H\|_1$ and $\|H^{-1}\|_1$.

  (b) When the system $H\mathbf{x} = \mathbf{b}$ is solved using MATLAB and the computed solution $\mathbf{x}'$ is used to compute a residual vector $\mathbf{r} = \mathbf{b} - H\mathbf{x}'$, it turns out that $\|\mathbf{r}\|_1 = 0.36 \times 10^{-11}$. Use this information to determine a bound on the relative error

$$\frac{\|\mathbf{x} - \mathbf{x}'\|_1}{\|\mathbf{x}\|_1}$$

  where $\mathbf{x}$ is the exact solution of the system.

5. Let A be a 10×10 matrix with $\text{cond}_\infty(A) = 5 \times 10^6$. Suppose that the solution of a system $A\mathbf{x} = \mathbf{b}$ is computed in 15-digit decimal arithmetic and the relative residual, $\|\mathbf{r}\|_\infty / \|\mathbf{b}\|_\infty$, turns out to be approximately twice the machine epsilon. How many digits of accuracy would you expect to have in your computed solution? Explain.

6. Let $\mathbf{x} = (1, 2, -2)^T$.

  (a) Find a Householder matrix H such that $H\mathbf{x}$ is a vector of the form $(r, 0, 0)^T$.

  (b) Find a Givens transformation G such that $G\mathbf{x}$ is a vector of the form $(1, s, 0)^T$.

7. Let Q be an $n \times n$ orthogonal matrix and let R be an $n \times n$ upper triangular matrix. If $A = QR$ and $B = RQ$, how are the eigenvalues and eigenvectors of A and B related? Explain.

8. Let

$$A = \begin{bmatrix} 1 & 2 \\ 4 & 3 \end{bmatrix}$$

Estimate the largest eigenvalue of A and a corresponding eigenvector by doing five iterations of the power method. You may start with any nonzero vector $\mathbf{u}_0$.

9. Let

$$A = \begin{bmatrix} 5 & 2 & 4 \\ 5 & 2 & 4 \\ 3 & 6 & 0 \\ 3 & 6 & 0 \end{bmatrix} \quad \text{and} \quad \mathbf{b} = \begin{bmatrix} 5 \\ 1 \\ -1 \\ 9 \end{bmatrix}$$

The singular value decomposition of A is given by

$$\begin{bmatrix} \frac{1}{2} & \frac{1}{2} & \frac{1}{2} & \frac{1}{2} \\ \frac{1}{2} & \frac{1}{2} & -\frac{1}{2} & -\frac{1}{2} \\ \frac{1}{2} & -\frac{1}{2} & -\frac{1}{2} & \frac{1}{2} \\ \frac{1}{2} & -\frac{1}{2} & \frac{1}{2} & -\frac{1}{2} \end{bmatrix} \begin{bmatrix} 12 & 0 & 0 \\ 0 & 6 & 0 \\ 0 & 0 & 0 \\ 0 & 0 & 0 \end{bmatrix} \begin{bmatrix} \frac{2}{3} & \frac{2}{3} & \frac{1}{3} \\ \frac{1}{3} & -\frac{2}{3} & \frac{2}{3} \\ -\frac{2}{3} & -\frac{1}{3} & \frac{2}{3} \end{bmatrix}$$

Use the singular value decomposition to find the least squares solution of the system $A\mathbf{x} = \mathbf{b}$ that has the smallest 2-norm.

10. Let

$$A = \begin{pmatrix} 1 & 5 \\ 1 & 5 \\ 1 & 6 \\ 1 & 2 \end{pmatrix}, \quad \mathbf{b} = \begin{pmatrix} 2 \\ 4 \\ 5 \\ 3 \end{pmatrix}$$

(a) Use Householder matrices to transform A into a 4×2 upper triangular matrix R.

(b) Apply the same Householder transformations to $\mathbf{b}$, and then compute the least squares solution of the system $A\mathbf{x} = \mathbf{b}$.

8

Canonical Forms

8.1 Nilpotent Operators

If a linear transformation L mapping an n-dimensional complex vector space into itself has n linearly independent eigenvectors, then the matrix representing L with respect to the basis of eigenvectors will be a diagonal matrix. In this chapter, we turn our attention to the case where L does not have enough linearly independent eigenvectors to span V. In this case, we would like to choose an ordered basis of V for which the corresponding matrix representation of L will be as nearly diagonal as possible. To simplify matters, in this first section, we will restrict ourselves to operators having a single eigenvalue λ of multiplicity n. It will be shown that such an operator can be represented by a bidiagonal matrix whose diagonal elements are all equal to λ and whose superdiagonal elements are all 0's and 1's. To do this, we require some preliminary definitions and theorems.

Recall from Section 5.2 that a vector space V is a *direct sum* of subspaces S_1 and S_2 if and only if each $\mathbf{v} \in V$ can be written uniquely in the form $\mathbf{x}_1 + \mathbf{x}_2$, where $\mathbf{x}_1 \in S_1$ and $\mathbf{x}_2 \in S_2$. This direct sum is denoted by $S_1 \oplus S_2$.

Lemma 8.1.1 *Let $B_1 = \{\mathbf{x}_1, \ldots, \mathbf{x}_r\}$ and $B_2 = \{\mathbf{y}_1, \ldots, \mathbf{y}_k\}$ be disjoint sets that are bases for subspaces S_1 and S_2, respectively, of a vector space V. Then $V = S_1 \oplus S_2$ if and only if $B = B_1 \cup B_2$ is a basis for V.*

Proof Exercise ∎

Definition

> Let L be a linear operator mapping a vector space V into itself. A subspace S of V is said to be **invariant** under L if $L(\mathbf{x}) \in S$ for each $\mathbf{x} \in S$.

For example, if L has an eigenvalue λ and S_λ is the eigenspace corresponding to λ, then S_λ is invariant under L. This follows since $L(\mathbf{x}) = \lambda \mathbf{x} \in S_\lambda$ for each $\mathbf{x} \in S_\lambda$.

If S is an invariant subspace of L, then the restriction of L to S that we will denote $L_{[S]}$ is a linear operator mapping S into itself.

Lemma 8.1.2   *Let L be a linear operator mapping a vector space V into itself and let S_1 and S_2 be invariant subspaces of L with $S_1 \cap S_2 = \{0\}$. If $S = S_1 \oplus S_2$, then S is invariant under L. Furthermore, if $A = (a_{ij})$ is the matrix representing $L_{[S_1]}$ with respect to the ordered basis $[\mathbf{x}_1, \ldots, \mathbf{x}_r]$ of S_1 and $B = (b_{ij})$ is the matrix representing $L_{[S_2]}$ with respect to the ordered basis $[\mathbf{y}_1, \ldots, \mathbf{y}_k]$ of S_2, then the matrix C representing $L_{[S]}$ with respect to $[\mathbf{x}_1, \ldots, \mathbf{x}_r, \mathbf{y}_1, \ldots, \mathbf{y}_k]$ is given by*

$$C = \begin{bmatrix} A & 0 \\ 0 & B \end{bmatrix} \tag{1}$$

$$= \begin{bmatrix} a_{11} & \cdots & a_{1r} & 0 & & 0 \\ \vdots & & & & & \\ a_{r1} & \cdots & a_{rr} & 0 & & 0 \\ 0 & & 0 & b_{11} & \cdots & b_{1k} \\ \vdots & & & & & \\ 0 & & 0 & b_{k1} & & b_{kk} \end{bmatrix}$$

Proof   Note first that since $S_1 \cap S_2 = \{0\}$, it follows that $\mathbf{x}_1, \ldots, \mathbf{x}_r, \mathbf{y}_1, \ldots, \mathbf{y}_k$ are linearly independent and hence form a basis for a subspace S of V. By Lemma 8.1.1, $S = S_1 \oplus S_2$ so that it makes sense to speak of a direct sum of S_1 and S_2. If $\mathbf{s} \in S$, then there exist $\mathbf{x} \in S_1$ and $\mathbf{y} \in S_2$ such that $\mathbf{s} = \mathbf{x} + \mathbf{y}$. Since $L(\mathbf{x}) \in S_1$ and $L(\mathbf{y}) \in S_2$, it follows that

$$L(\mathbf{s}) = L(\mathbf{x}) + L(\mathbf{y})$$

is an element of $S_1 \oplus S_2 = S$. Therefore, S is invariant under L.

Let $\mathbf{s}_i^{(1)} = L(\mathbf{x}_i)$ for $i = 1, \ldots, r$ and $\mathbf{s}_j^{(2)} = L(\mathbf{y}_j)$ for $j = 1, \ldots, k$. Since each $\mathbf{s}_i^{(1)}$ is in S_1 and each $\mathbf{s}_j^{(2)}$ is in S_2, it follows that

$$\begin{aligned} L_{[S]}(\mathbf{x}_i) &= \mathbf{s}_i^{(1)} + \mathbf{0} \\ &= a_{1i}\mathbf{x}_1 + a_{2i}\mathbf{x}_2 + \cdots + a_{ri}\mathbf{x}_r + 0\mathbf{y}_1 + \cdots + 0\mathbf{y}_k \end{aligned}$$

and hence the ith column of the matrix C representing $L_{[S]}$ will be

$$\mathbf{c}_i = (a_{1i}, a_{2i}, \ldots, a_{ri}, 0, \ldots, 0)^T$$

Similarly,

$$\begin{aligned} L_{[S]}(\mathbf{y}_j) &= 0 + \mathbf{s}_j^{(2)} \\ &= 0\mathbf{x}_1 + \cdots + 0\mathbf{x}_r + b_{1j}\mathbf{y} + \cdots + b_{kj}\mathbf{y}_k \end{aligned}$$

and hence $\mathbf{c}_{j+r}$ is given by

$$\mathbf{c}_{j+r} = (0, \ldots, 0, b_{1j}, \ldots, b_{kj})^T$$

Thus, the matrix C representing $L_{[S]}$ with respect to $[\mathbf{x}_1, \ldots, \mathbf{x}_r, \mathbf{y}_1, \ldots, \mathbf{y}_k]$ will be of the form (1). ∎

It is possible to have a direct sum of more than two matrices. In general, if $S_1, S_2, \ldots, S_r$ are subspaces of a vector space V, then $V = S_1 \oplus \cdots \oplus S_r$ if and only if each $\mathbf{v} \in V$ can be written uniquely as a sum $\mathbf{s}_1 + \cdots + \mathbf{s}_r$, where $\mathbf{s}_i \in S_i$ for $i = 1, \ldots, r$.

Using mathematical induction, one can generalize both of the lemmas to direct sums of more than two subspaces. Thus, if each subspace S_i has a basis B_i and the B_i's are all disjoint, then $V = S_1 \oplus \cdots \oplus S_r$ if and only if $B = B_1 \cup B_2 \cup \cdots \cup B_r$ is a basis for V. If $S_1, \ldots, S_r$ are invariant under a linear transformation L and $S = S_1 \oplus \cdots \oplus S_r$, then S is invariant under L and $L_{[S]}$ can be represented by a block diagonal matrix

$$A = \begin{bmatrix} A_1 & & & \\ & A_2 & & \\ & & \ddots & \\ & & & A_r \end{bmatrix} \tag{2}$$

Let L be a linear operator mapping an n-dimensional vector space V into itself. If V can be expressed as a direct sum of invariant subspaces of L, then it is possible to represent L as a block diagonal matrix A of the form (2).

The simplest such representation occurs in the case that L is diagonalizable. This occurs when the dimensions of the eigenspaces are equal to the multiplicities of the eigenvalues. In this case, we can choose A so that each diagonal block A_i is a diagonal matrix and hence the matrix A is also diagonal.

If, however, there are any eigenvalues for which the dimension of the eigenspace is less than the multiplicity of the eigenvalue, then the subspace $S_{\lambda_1} \oplus \cdots \oplus S_{\lambda_r}$ will have dimension less than n and hence will be a proper subspace of V. In this case, what we would like to do is somehow enlarge the deficient S_{λ_i}'s and obtain a direct sum representation of V of the form $S_1 \oplus \cdots \oplus S_r$, where each S_i is invariant under L. Furthermore, we would like the corresponding block representation of L to be as close to a diagonal representation as possible. Indeed, we will show that it is possible to find invariant subspaces S_i so that each $L_{[S_i]}$ can be represented by a bidiagonal matrix of a certain form.

As a simple example, consider the case where the matrix A representing L is a 3×3 matrix with a triple eigenvalue λ and the eigenspace S_λ has dimension 1. In this case, we would like to show that L can be represented by a 3×3 matrix

$$J = \begin{bmatrix} \lambda & 1 & 0 \\ 0 & \lambda & 1 \\ 0 & 0 & \lambda \end{bmatrix}$$

If such a representation is possible, then A would have to be similar to J, that is, $AX = XJ$ for some nonsingular matrix X. If we let $\mathbf{x}_1, \mathbf{x}_2, \mathbf{x}_3$ denote the column vectors of X, this would say that

$$A(\mathbf{x}_1, \mathbf{x}_2, \mathbf{x}_3) = (\mathbf{x}_1, \mathbf{x}_2, \mathbf{x}_3)J$$

and hence

$$\begin{aligned} A\mathbf{x}_1 &= \lambda \mathbf{x}_1 \\ A\mathbf{x}_2 &= \mathbf{x}_1 + \lambda \mathbf{x}_2 \\ A\mathbf{x}_3 &= \mathbf{x}_2 + \lambda \mathbf{x}_3 \end{aligned}$$

or equivalently,

$$(A - \lambda I)\mathbf{x}_1 = \mathbf{0}$$
$$(A - \lambda I)\mathbf{x}_2 = \mathbf{x}_1$$
$$(A - \lambda I)\mathbf{x}_3 = \mathbf{x}_2$$

These equations imply that

$$(A - \lambda I)^3 \mathbf{x}_3 = (A - \lambda I)^2 \mathbf{x}_2 = (A - \lambda I)\mathbf{x}_1 = \mathbf{0} \tag{3}$$

Thus, if we can find a vector $\mathbf{x}$ such that

$$(A - \lambda I)^3 \mathbf{x} = \mathbf{0} \qquad \text{and} \qquad (A - \lambda I)^2 \mathbf{x} \neq \mathbf{0} \tag{4}$$

then we can set

$$\mathbf{x}_3 = \mathbf{x}, \qquad \mathbf{x}_2 = (A - \lambda I)\mathbf{x}, \quad \text{and} \quad \mathbf{x}_1 = (A - \lambda I)^2 \mathbf{x} \tag{5}$$

The equations given in (4) really provide the key to our problem. If we can find a vector $\mathbf{x}$ satisfying (4), then it is not difficult to show that the vectors $\mathbf{x}_1$, $\mathbf{x}_2$, and $\mathbf{x}_3$ defined in (5) are linearly independent and hence that $X = (\mathbf{x}_1, \mathbf{x}_2, \mathbf{x}_3)$ is invertible. Equation (3) implies that

$$(A - \lambda I)^3 \mathbf{x} = \mathbf{0}$$

for all $\mathbf{x} \in R(X)$. Note that

$$(A - \lambda I)^2 \mathbf{x}_1 \neq \mathbf{0}$$

This type of condition plays an important role in the theory we are about to develop. We state this condition for a general linear operator L in the following definition.

Definition | Let L be a linear operator mapping a vector space V into itself. L is said to be *nilpotent of index k* on V if $L^k(\mathbf{v}) = \mathbf{0}$ for all $\mathbf{v} \in V$ and $L^{k-1}(\mathbf{v}_0) \neq \mathbf{0}$ for some $\mathbf{v}_0 \in V$.

Lemma 8.1.3 *Let L be a linear operator mapping a vector space V into itself and let $\mathbf{v} \in V$. If $L^k(\mathbf{v}) = \mathbf{0}$ and $L^{k-1}(\mathbf{v}) \neq \mathbf{0}$ for some integer $k \geq 1$, then the vectors $\mathbf{v}, L(\mathbf{v}), L^2(\mathbf{v}), \ldots, L^{k-1}(\mathbf{v})$ are linearly independent.*

Proof The proof will be by induction. The result clearly holds in the case $k = 1$ since

$$\mathbf{v} = L^0(\mathbf{v}) \neq \mathbf{0} \qquad \text{and} \qquad L(\mathbf{v}) = \mathbf{0}$$

and hence we have only a single nonzero vector $\mathbf{v}$. (Here, L^0 is taken to be the identity operator.) Assume now that we have a value of k such that the result holds for all $j < k$ and suppose we have a vector $\mathbf{v}$ satisfying

$$L^{k-1}(\mathbf{v}) \neq \mathbf{0} \qquad \text{and} \qquad L^k(\mathbf{v}) = \mathbf{0}$$

To show linear independence, we consider the equation

$$\alpha_1 \mathbf{v} + \alpha_2 L(\mathbf{v}) + \cdots + \alpha_k L^{k-1}(\mathbf{v}) = \mathbf{0} \tag{6}$$

If we let $\mathbf{w} = L(\mathbf{v})$ and apply L to both sides of (6), we get

$$\alpha_1 L(\mathbf{v}) + \alpha_2 L^2(\mathbf{v}) + \cdots + \alpha_{k-1} L^{k-1}(\mathbf{v}) = \mathbf{0}$$

or

$$\alpha_1 \mathbf{w} + \alpha_2 L(\mathbf{w}) + \cdots + \alpha_{k-1} L^{k-2}(\mathbf{w}) = \mathbf{0}$$

Since

$$L^{k-2}(\mathbf{w}) = L^{k-1}(\mathbf{v}) \neq \mathbf{0} \qquad \text{and} \qquad L^{k-1}(\mathbf{w}) = L^k(\mathbf{v}) = \mathbf{0}$$

it follows from our induction hypothesis that

$$\mathbf{w}, L(\mathbf{w}), \ldots, L^{k-2}(\mathbf{w})$$

are linearly independent and hence that

$$\alpha_1 = \alpha_2 = \cdots = \alpha_{k-1} = 0$$

Thus, (6) reduces to

$$\alpha_k L^{k-1}(\mathbf{v}) = \mathbf{0}$$

It follows that α_k must also be zero and hence $\mathbf{v}, L(\mathbf{v}), \ldots, L^{k-1}(\mathbf{v})$ are linearly independent.

If $L^{k-1}(\mathbf{v}) \neq \mathbf{0}$ and $L^k(\mathbf{v}) = \mathbf{0}$ for some $\mathbf{v} \in V$, then the vectors $\mathbf{v}, L(\mathbf{v}), \ldots, L^{k-1}(\mathbf{v})$ form a basis for a subspace that we will denote by $C_L(\mathbf{v})$. The subspace $C_L(\mathbf{v})$ is invariant under L since for each

$$\mathbf{w} = \alpha_1 \mathbf{v} + \alpha_2 L(\mathbf{v}) + \cdots + \alpha_k L^{k-1}(\mathbf{v})$$

in $C_L(\mathbf{v})$, we have

$$L(\mathbf{w}) = \alpha_1 L(\mathbf{v}) + \alpha_2 L^2(\mathbf{v}) + \cdots + \alpha_{k-1} L^{k-1}(\mathbf{v})$$

and hence $L(\mathbf{w})$ is also in $C_L(\mathbf{v})$. We will refer to $C_L(\mathbf{v})$ as the *L-cyclic subspace* generated by $\mathbf{v}$. In particular, if L is nilpotent of index k, then for each nonzero vector $\mathbf{v}_0 \in V$, there is an integer k_0, $1 \leq k_0 \leq k$ such that $L^{k_0-1}(\mathbf{v}_0) \neq \mathbf{0}$ and $L^{k_0}(\mathbf{v}) = \mathbf{0}$. Thus, if L is nilpotent on V, then one can associate an L-cyclic subspace $C_L(\mathbf{v})$ with each nonzero vector $\mathbf{v}$ in V. It is easily seen that L-cyclic subspaces are invariant under L.

Let $C_L(\mathbf{v})$ be an L cyclic subspace of V with basis $\{\mathbf{v}, L(\mathbf{v}), \ldots, L^{k-1}(\mathbf{v})\}$. Let

$$\mathbf{y}_i = L^{k-i}(\mathbf{v}) \quad \text{for } i = 1, \ldots, k \qquad (\text{where } L^0 = I)$$

Then

$$[\mathbf{y}_1, \mathbf{y}_2, \ldots, \mathbf{y}_k] = [L^{k-1}(\mathbf{v}), L^{k-2}(\mathbf{v}), \ldots, \mathbf{v}]$$

is an ordered basis for $C_L(\mathbf{v})$. Since

$$L(\mathbf{y}_1) = 0$$
$$L(\mathbf{y}_j) = \mathbf{y}_{j-1} \quad \text{for} \quad j = 2, \ldots, k$$

it follows that the matrix representing $L_{[C_L(\mathbf{v})]}$ with respect to $[\mathbf{y}_1, \ldots, \mathbf{y}_k]$ is given by

$$A = \begin{pmatrix} 0 & 1 & 0 & \cdots & 0 & 0 \\ 0 & 0 & 1 & \cdots & 0 & 0 \\ 0 & 0 & 0 & \cdots & 0 & 0 \\ & & & & & \\ 0 & 0 & 0 & \cdots & 0 & 1 \\ 0 & 0 & 0 & \cdots & 0 & 0 \end{pmatrix}$$

Thus, $L_{[C_L(\mathbf{v})]}$ can be represented by a bidiagonal matrix with 0's along the main diagonal and 1's along the superdiagonal.

Lemma 8.1.4 *Let L be a linear operator mapping a vector space V into itself. If L is nilpotent of index k on V and $L^{k-1}(\mathbf{v}_1), L^{k-1}(\mathbf{v}_2), \ldots, L^{k-1}(\mathbf{v}_r)$ are linearly independent, then the kr vectors*

$$\mathbf{v}_1, L(\mathbf{v}_1), \ldots, L^{k-1}(\mathbf{v}_1)$$
$$\mathbf{v}_2, L(\mathbf{v}_2), \ldots, L^{k-1}(\mathbf{v}_2)$$
$$\vdots$$
$$\mathbf{v}_r, L(\mathbf{v}_r), \ldots, L^{k-1}(\mathbf{v}_r)$$

are linearly independent.

Proof The proof is by induction on k. If $k = 1$, there is nothing to prove. Assume the result holds for all indices less than k and that L is nilpotent of index k. If

$$\begin{aligned} &\alpha_{11}\mathbf{v}_1 + \alpha_{12}L(\mathbf{v}_1) + \cdots + \alpha_{1k}L^{k-1}(\mathbf{v}_1) \\ &+ \alpha_{21}\mathbf{v}_2 + \alpha_{22}L(\mathbf{v}_2) + \cdots + \alpha_{2k}L^{k-1}(\mathbf{v}_2) \\ &\vdots \\ &+ \alpha_{r1}\mathbf{v}_r + \alpha_{r2}L(\mathbf{v}_r) + \cdots + \alpha_{rk}L^{k-1}(v_r) \\ &= \mathbf{0} \end{aligned} \quad (7)$$

then applying L to both sides of (7), we get

$$\begin{aligned} &\alpha_{11}\mathbf{y}_1 + \alpha_{12}L(\mathbf{y}_1) + \cdots + \alpha_{1,k-1}L^{k-2}(\mathbf{y}_1) \\ &+ \alpha_{21}\mathbf{y}_2 + \alpha_{22}L(\mathbf{y}_2) + \cdots + \alpha_{2,k-1}L^{k-2}(\mathbf{y}_2) \\ &\vdots \\ &+ \alpha_{r1}\mathbf{y}_r + \alpha_{r2}L(\mathbf{y}_r) + \cdots + \alpha_{r,k-1}L^{k-2}(\mathbf{y}_r) \\ &= \mathbf{0} \end{aligned} \quad (8)$$

where $\mathbf{y}_i = L(\mathbf{v}_i)$ for $i = 1, \ldots, r$. Since $L^{k-2}(\mathbf{y}_i) = L^{k-1}(\mathbf{v}_i)$ for each i, it follows that $L^{k-2}(\mathbf{y}_1), \ldots, L^{k-2}(\mathbf{y}_n)$ are linearly independent. Let S be the subspace of V spanned by

$$\mathbf{y}_1, L(\mathbf{y}_1), \ldots, L^{k-2}(\mathbf{y}_1), \ldots, \mathbf{y}_r, L(\mathbf{y}_r), \ldots, L^{k-2}(\mathbf{y}_r)$$

Since L is nilpotent of index $k - 1$ on S, it follows by the induction hypothesis that

$$\mathbf{y}_1, L(\mathbf{y}_1), \ldots, L^{k-2}(\mathbf{y}_1)$$
$$\mathbf{y}_2, L(\mathbf{y}_2), \ldots, L^{k-2}(\mathbf{y}_2)$$
$$\vdots$$
$$\mathbf{y}_r, L(\mathbf{y}_r), \ldots, L^{k-2}(\mathbf{y}_r)$$

are linearly independent. Therefore,

$$\alpha_{ij} = 0 \text{ for } 1 \leq i \leq r, \ 1 \leq j \leq k - 1$$

and, consequently, (8) reduces to

$$\alpha_{1k}L^{k-1}(\mathbf{v}_1) + \alpha_{2k}L^{k-1}(\mathbf{v}_2) + \cdots + \alpha_{rk}L^{k-1}(\mathbf{v}_r) = 0$$

Since $L^{k-1}(\mathbf{v}_1), \ldots, L^{k-1}(\mathbf{v}_r)$ are linearly independent, it follows that

$$\alpha_{1k} = \alpha_{2k} = \cdots = \alpha_{rk} = 0$$

and hence

$$\mathbf{v}_1, L(\mathbf{v}_1), \ldots, L^{k-1}(\mathbf{v}_1)$$
$$\mathbf{v}_2, L(\mathbf{v}_2), \ldots, L^{k-1}(\mathbf{v}_2)$$
$$\vdots$$
$$\mathbf{v}_r, L(\mathbf{v}_r), \ldots, L^{k-1}(\mathbf{v}_r)$$

are linearly independent. ∎

Theorem 8.1.5   *Let L be a linear operator mapping an n-dimensional vector space V into itself. If L is nilpotent of index k on V, then V can be decomposed into a direct sum of L-cyclic subspaces.*

Proof   The proof will be by induction on k. If $k = 1$, then L is the zero operator on V. Thus, if $\{\mathbf{v}_1, \ldots, \mathbf{v}_n\}$ is any basis of V, then $C_L(\mathbf{v}_i)$ is the one-dimensional subspace spanned by $\mathbf{v}_i$ for each i and hence

$$V = C_L(\mathbf{v}_1) \oplus \cdots \oplus C_L(\mathbf{v}_n)$$

Suppose now that we have an integer $k > 1$ such that the result holds for all indices less than k and L is nilpotent of index k. Let $\{\mathbf{v}_1, \ldots, \mathbf{v}_m\}$ be a basis for $\ker(L^{k-1})$. This basis can be extended to a basis $\{\mathbf{v}_1, \ldots, \mathbf{v}_m, \mathbf{y}_1, \ldots, \mathbf{y}_r\}$ of V (where $r = n - m$).

Since $\mathbf{y}_i \notin \ker(L^{k-1})$ it follows that $L^{k-1}(\mathbf{y}_i) \neq 0$. Let

$$B_1 = \left\{\mathbf{y}_1, L(\mathbf{y}_1), \ldots, L^{k-1}(\mathbf{y}_1), \ldots, \mathbf{y}_r, L(\mathbf{y}_r), \ldots, L^{k-1}(\mathbf{y}_r)\right\}$$

We claim B_1 is a basis for a subspace S_1 of V. By Lemma 8.1.4, it suffices to show that $L^{k-1}(\mathbf{y}_1), L^{k-1}(\mathbf{y}_2), \ldots, L^{k-1}(\mathbf{y}_r)$ are linearly independent. If

$$\alpha_1 L^{k-1}(\mathbf{y}_1) + \alpha_2 L^{k-1}(\mathbf{y}_2) + \cdots + \alpha_r L^{k-1}(\mathbf{y}_r) = 0$$

then

$$L^{k-1}(\alpha_1 \mathbf{y}_1 + \cdots + \alpha_r \mathbf{y}_r) = 0$$

and hence $\alpha_1 \mathbf{y}_1 + \cdots + \alpha_r \mathbf{y}_r \in \ker(L^{k-1})$. But then $\alpha_1 = \alpha_2 = \cdots = \alpha_r = 0$; otherwise, $\mathbf{v}_1, \ldots, \mathbf{v}_m, \mathbf{y}_1, \ldots, \mathbf{y}_r$ would be dependent. Thus, $L^{k-1}(\mathbf{y}_1), \ldots, L^{k-1}(\mathbf{y}_r)$ are linearly independent and hence B_1 is a basis for a subspace S_1 of V. It follows from Lemma 8.1.1 that

$$S_1 = C_L(\mathbf{y}_1) \oplus \cdots \oplus C_L(\mathbf{y}_r)$$

If $S_1 \neq V$, extend B_1 to a basis B for V. Let B_2 be the set of additional basis elements (i.e., $B = B_1 \cup B_2$ and $B_1 \cap B_2 = \emptyset$). B_2 is a basis for a subspace S_2 of V, and by Lemma 8.1.1, $V = S_1 \oplus S_2$. By construction, S_2 is a subspace of $\ker(L^{k-1})$. (If $\mathbf{s} \in S_2$, then it must be of the form $\mathbf{s} = \alpha_1 \mathbf{v}_1 + \cdots + \alpha_m \mathbf{v}_m + 0\mathbf{y}_1 + \cdots + 0\mathbf{y}_r$.) Thus, L is nilpotent of index $k_1 < k$ on S_2. By the induction hypothesis, S_2 can be written as a direct sum of L-cyclic subspaces, and since $V = S_1 \oplus S_2$, it follows that V is a direct sum of L-cyclic subspaces. ∎

Corollary 8.1.6   *If L is a linear operator mapping an n-dimensional vector space V into itself and L is nilpotent of index k on V, then L can be represented by a matrix of the form*

$$A = \begin{pmatrix} J_1 & & & \\ & J_2 & & \\ & & \ddots & \\ & & & J_s \end{pmatrix}$$

where each J_i is a $k_i \times k_i$ bidiagonal matrix $(1 \leq k_i \leq k$ and $\sum_{i=1}^{s} k_i = n)$ with 0's along the main diagonal and 1's along the superdiagonal.

Proof   By Theorem 8.1.5, we can write

$$V = C_L(\mathbf{v}_1) \oplus \cdots \oplus C_L(\mathbf{v}_s)$$

If $C_L(\mathbf{v}_i)$ has dimension k_i, then the matrix representing $L_{[C_L(\mathbf{v}_i)]}$ with respect to $[L^{k_i-1}(\mathbf{v}_i), \ldots, \mathbf{v}_i]$ will be

$$J_i = \begin{pmatrix} 0 & 1 & & & \\ & 0 & 1 & & \\ & & \ddots & \ddots & \\ & & & 0 & 1 \\ & & & & 0 \end{pmatrix}$$

The conclusion follows from Lemma 8.1.2. ∎

It follows from Corollary 8.1.6 that if L is nilpotent on an n-dimensional vector space V, then all of its eigenvalues are 0. Conversely, if all of the eigenvalues of L are

0, then it follows from Theorem 6.4.3 that L can be represented by a triangular matrix T whose diagonal elements are all 0. Thus for some k, T^k will be the zero matrix and hence L^k will be the zero operator. So, if L is a linear operator mapping an n-dimensional vector space V into itself, then L is nilpotent if and only if all of its eigenvalues are 0.

Corollary 8.1.7   *Let L be a linear operator mapping an n-dimensional vector space V into itself. If L has only one distinct eigenvalue λ, then L can be represented by a matrix A of the form*

$$A = \begin{pmatrix} J_1(\lambda) & & & \\ & J_2(\lambda) & & \\ & & \ddots & \\ & & & J_s(\lambda) \end{pmatrix} \tag{9}$$

where each $J_i(\lambda)$ is a bidiagonal matrix of the form

$$J_i(\lambda) = \begin{pmatrix} \lambda & 1 & & & \\ & \lambda & 1 & & \\ & & \ddots & \ddots & \\ & & & \lambda & 1 \\ & & & & \lambda \end{pmatrix} \tag{10}$$

Proof   Let $\mathcal{I}$ denote the identity operator V. The eigenvalues of the operator $L - \lambda\mathcal{I}$ are all 0 and hence $L - \lambda\mathcal{I}$ is nilpotent. It follows from Corollary 8.1.6 that with respect to some ordered basis $[\mathbf{v}_1, \ldots, \mathbf{v}_n]$ of V, the operator $L - \lambda\mathcal{I}$ can be represented by a matrix of the form

$$J = \begin{pmatrix} J_1(0) & & & \\ & J_2(0) & & \\ & & \ddots & \\ & & & J_s(0) \end{pmatrix}, \text{ where } J_i(0) = \begin{pmatrix} 0 & 1 & & & \\ & 0 & 1 & & \\ & & \ddots & \ddots & \\ & & & 0 & 1 \\ & & & & 0 \end{pmatrix}$$

The matrix representing $\lambda\mathcal{I}$ with respect to $[\mathbf{v}_1, \ldots, \mathbf{v}_n]$ is simply λI. Since $L = (L - \lambda\mathcal{I}) + \lambda\mathcal{I}$, it follows that the matrix representing L with respect to $[\mathbf{v}_1, \ldots, \mathbf{v}_n]$ is

$$J + \lambda I = \begin{pmatrix} J_1(\lambda) & & & \\ & J_2(\lambda) & & \\ & & \ddots & \\ & & & J_s(\lambda) \end{pmatrix} \qquad\blacksquare$$

A matrix of the form (10) is said to be a *simple Jordan matrix*. Thus, a simple Jordan matrix is a bidiagonal matrix whose diagonal elements all have the same value λ and whose superdiagonal elements are all 1.

EXAMPLE 1   Let

$$A = \begin{pmatrix} 1 & 2 & 1 & 1 & 1 \\ 0 & 1 & 1 & 2 & 1 \\ 0 & 0 & 1 & 1 & 0 \\ 0 & 0 & 0 & 1 & 0 \\ 0 & 0 & 0 & 0 & 1 \end{pmatrix}$$

We can think of A as representing an operator from R^5 into R^5. Since $\lambda = 1$ is the only eigenvalue, A is similar to a block diagonal matrix whose diagonal blocks are simple Jordan matrices with 1's along both the diagonal and the superdiagonal. The eigenspace corresponding to $\lambda = 1$ is spanned by the vectors $\mathbf{x} = (1,0,0,0,0)^T$ and $\mathbf{y} = (0,0,-1,0,1)^T$. Thus, the bidiagonal matrix will consist of two simple Jordan blocks, $J_1(1)$ and $J_2(1)$. If we order the blocks so that the first block is the largest, then the only possibilities for the block diagonal matrix are

$$
\left(
\begin{array}{ccc|cc}
1 & 1 & 0 & & \\
0 & 1 & 1 & & \\
0 & 0 & 1 & & \\
\hline
 & & & 1 & 1 \\
 & & & 0 & 1
\end{array}
\right)
\quad \text{or} \quad
\left(
\begin{array}{cccc|c}
1 & 1 & 0 & 0 & 0 \\
0 & 1 & 1 & 0 & 0 \\
0 & 0 & 1 & 1 & 0 \\
0 & 0 & 0 & 1 & 0 \\
\hline
0 & 0 & 0 & 0 & 1
\end{array}
\right)
$$

To determine which of these forms is correct, one must compute powers of $A - I$.

$$
A - I = \begin{pmatrix} 0 & 2 & 1 & 1 & 1 \\ 0 & 0 & 1 & 2 & 1 \\ 0 & 0 & 0 & 1 & 0 \\ 0 & 0 & 0 & 0 & 0 \\ 0 & 0 & 0 & 0 & 0 \end{pmatrix}
\qquad
(A - I)^2 = \begin{pmatrix} 0 & 0 & 2 & 5 & 2 \\ 0 & 0 & 0 & 1 & 0 \\ 0 & 0 & 0 & 0 & 0 \\ 0 & 0 & 0 & 0 & 0 \\ 0 & 0 & 0 & 0 & 0 \end{pmatrix}
$$

$$
(A - I)^3 = \begin{pmatrix} 0 & 0 & 0 & 2 & 0 \\ 0 & 0 & 0 & 0 & 0 \\ 0 & 0 & 0 & 0 & 0 \\ 0 & 0 & 0 & 0 & 0 \\ 0 & 0 & 0 & 0 & 0 \end{pmatrix}
\qquad
(A - I)^4 = O
$$

Thus, $A - I$ is nilpotent of index 4. The systems

$$(A - I)^k \mathbf{s} = \mathbf{x} \qquad \text{and} \qquad (A - I)^j \mathbf{s} = \mathbf{y}$$

are clearly inconsistent if k and j are greater than 3. We determine the maximum k and maximum j for which these systems are consistent. For $k = 3$, the system

$$(A - I)^3 \mathbf{s} = \mathbf{x}$$

is consistent and will have infinitely many solutions. We pick one of these solutions:

$$\mathbf{x}_1 = \left(0, 0, 0, \tfrac{1}{2}, 0\right)^T$$

To generate the rest of the cyclic subspace, we compute

$$\mathbf{x}_2 = (A - I)\mathbf{x}_1 = \left(\tfrac{1}{2}, 1, \tfrac{1}{2}, 0, 0\right)^T$$
$$\mathbf{x}_3 = (A - I)\mathbf{x}_2 = (A - I)^2 \mathbf{x}_1 = \left(\tfrac{5}{2}, \tfrac{1}{2}, 0, 0, 0\right)^T$$

With respect to the ordered basis $[\mathbf{x}, \mathbf{x}_3, \mathbf{x}_2, \mathbf{x}_1]$, the matrix representing the operator A on this subspace will be of the form

$$
J_1(1) = \begin{pmatrix} 1 & 1 & 0 & 0 \\ 0 & 1 & 1 & 0 \\ 0 & 0 & 1 & 1 \\ 0 & 0 & 0 & 1 \end{pmatrix}
$$

The systems

$$(A - I)^j \mathbf{s} = \mathbf{y}$$

are inconsistent for all positive integers j. Thus, the cyclic subspace containing $\mathbf{y}$ has dimension 1. It follows that the matrix representing A with respect to $[\mathbf{x}, \mathbf{x}_3, \mathbf{x}_2, \mathbf{x}_1, \mathbf{y}]$ is

$$J = \begin{bmatrix} J_1(1) & \\ & J_2(1) \end{bmatrix} = \left[\begin{array}{cccc|c} 1 & 1 & 0 & 0 & 0 \\ 0 & 1 & 1 & 0 & 0 \\ 0 & 0 & 1 & 1 & 0 \\ 0 & 0 & 0 & 1 & 0 \\ 0 & 0 & 0 & 0 & 1 \end{array} \right]$$

The reader may verify that if Y is the matrix whose columns are $\mathbf{x}$, $\mathbf{x}_3$, $\mathbf{x}_2$, $\mathbf{x}_1$, $\mathbf{y}$, respectively, then

$$YJY^{-1} = A \qquad \blacksquare$$

In the next section, we will show that a matrix A with distinct eigenvalues $\lambda_1, \ldots, \lambda_m$ is similar to a matrix J of the form

$$J = \begin{bmatrix} B_1 & & & \\ & B_2 & & \\ & & \ddots & \\ & & & B_m \end{bmatrix}$$

where each B_i is of the form (9) with diagonal elements equal to λ_i, that is

$$B_i = \begin{bmatrix} J_1(\lambda_i) & & & \\ & J_2(\lambda_i) & & \\ & & \ddots & \\ & & & J_s(\lambda_i) \end{bmatrix}$$

where the $J_k(\lambda_i)$'s are simple Jordan matrices. We say that J is the *Jordan canonical form* of A. The Jordan canonical form is unique except for a reordering of the blocks.

SECTION 8.1 EXERCISES

1. Let L be a linear operator on a vector space V of dimension 5 and let A be any matrix representing L. If L is nilpotent of index 3, then what are the possible Jordan canonical forms of A?

2. Let A be a 4×4 matrix whose only eigenvalue is $\lambda = 2$. What are the possible Jordan canonical forms of A?

3. Let L be a linear operator on a vector space V of dimension 6 and let A be a matrix representing L. If L has only one distinct eigenvalue λ and the eigenspace S_λ has dimension 3, then what are the possible Jordan canonical forms of A?

4. For each of the following, find a matrix S such that $S^{-1}AS$ is a simple Jordan matrix:

(a) $A = \begin{bmatrix} 1 & 0 & 1 \\ 1 & 0 & 2 \\ 1 & -1 & 2 \end{bmatrix}$ (b) $A = \begin{bmatrix} 1 & 2 & 0 & 0 \\ 0 & 1 & 2 & 0 \\ 0 & 0 & 1 & 2 \\ 0 & 0 & 0 & 1 \end{bmatrix}$

5. For each of the following, find a matrix S such that $S^{-1}AS$ is the Jordan canonical form of A:

(a) $A = \begin{bmatrix} -1 & 1 & 0 & 0 \\ -1 & 1 & 0 & 0 \\ -2 & 2 & 0 & 0 \\ 0 & 3 & -1 & 0 \end{bmatrix}$ (b) $A = \begin{bmatrix} 0 & 0 & 1 & 1 & 1 \\ 0 & 0 & 0 & 1 & 1 \\ 0 & 0 & 0 & 0 & 1 \\ 0 & 0 & 0 & 0 & 0 \\ 0 & 0 & 0 & 0 & 0 \end{bmatrix}$

6. Let S_1 and S_2 be subspaces of a finite dimensional vector space V. Prove that $V = S_1 \oplus S_2$ if and only if $V = S_1 + S_2$ and $S_1 \cap S_2 = \{0\}$.

7. Prove Lemma 8.1.1.

8. Let L be a linear operator mapping a vector space V into itself. Show that ker(L) and $R(L)$ are invariant subspaces of V under L.

9. Let L be a linear operator on a vector space V. Let $S_k[\mathbf{v}]$ denote the subspace spanned by $\mathbf{v}, L(\mathbf{v}), \ldots, L^{k-1}(\mathbf{v})$.

Show that $S_k[\mathbf{v}]$ is invariant under L if and only if $L^k(\mathbf{v}) \in S_k[\mathbf{v}]$.

10. Let L be a linear operator on a vector space V and let S be a subspace of V. Let $\mathcal{I}$ represent the identity operator and let λ be a scalar. Show that L is invariant on S if and only if $L - \lambda \mathcal{I}$ is invariant on S.

11. Let S be the subspace of $C[a, b]$ spanned by x, xe^x, and $xe^x + x^2 e^x$. Let D be the differentiation operator on S.

(a) Find a matrix A representing D with respect to $[e^x, xe^x, xe^x + x^2 e^x]$.

(b) Determine the Jordan canonical form of A and the corresponding basis of S.

12. Let D denote the linear operator on P_n defined by $D(p) = p'$ for all $p \in P_n$. Show that D is nilpotent and can be represented by a simple Jordan matrix.

8.2 The Jordan Canonical Form

In this section, we will show that any linear operator L on an n-dimensional vector space V can be represented by a block diagonal matrix whose diagonal blocks are simple Jordan matrices. We will apply this result to solving systems of linear differential equations of the form $Y' = AY$, where A is defective.

Let us begin by considering the case where L has more than one distinct eigenvalue. We wish to show that if L has distinct eigenvalues $\lambda_1, \ldots, \lambda_k$, then V can be decomposed into a direct sum of invariant subspaces $S_1, \ldots, S_k$ such that $L - \lambda_i I$ is nilpotent on S_i for each $i = 1, \ldots, k$. To do this, we must first prove the following lemma and theorem.

Lemma 8.2.1 *If L is a linear operator mapping an n-dimensional vector space V into itself, then there exists a positive integer k_0 such that $\ker(L^{k_0}) = \ker(L^{k_0+k})$ for all $k > 0$.*

Proof If $i < j$, then clearly $\ker(L^i)$ is a subspace of $\ker(L^j)$. We claim that if $\ker(L^i) = \ker(L^{i+1})$ for some i, then $\ker(L^i) = \ker(L^{i+k})$ for all $k \geq 1$. We will prove this by induction on k. In the case $k = 1$, there is nothing to prove. Assume that for some $k > 1$ the result holds all indices less than k. If $\mathbf{v} \in \ker(L^{i+k})$, then

$$0 = L^{i+k}(\mathbf{v}) = L^{i+k-1}(L(\mathbf{v}))$$

Thus, $L(\mathbf{v}) \in \ker(L^{i+k-1})$. By the induction hypothesis, $\ker(L^{i+k-1}) = \ker(L^i)$. Therefore, $L(\mathbf{v}) \in \ker(L^i)$ and hence $\mathbf{v} \in \ker(L^{i+1})$. Since $\ker(L^{i+1}) = \ker(L^i)$, it follows that $\mathbf{v} \in \ker(L^i)$ and hence $\ker(L^i) = \ker(L^{i+k})$. Thus, if $\ker(L^{i+1}) = \ker(L^i)$ for some i, then

$$\ker(L^i) = \ker(L^{i+1}) = \ker(L^{i+1}) = \ldots$$

Since V is finite dimensional, the dimension of $\ker(L^k)$ cannot keep increasing as k increases. Thus for some k_0, we must have $\dim(\ker(L^{k_0})) = \dim(\ker(L^{k_0+1}))$ and hence

$\ker(L^{k_0})$ and $\ker(L^{k_0+1})$ must be equal. It follows that

$$\ker(L^{k_0}) = \ker(L^{k_0+1}) = \ker(L^{k_0+2}) = \cdots$$

Theorem 8.2.2   *If L is a linear transformation on an n-dimensional vector space V, then there exist invariant subspaces X and Y such that $V = X \oplus Y$, L is nilpotent on X, and $L_{[Y]}$ is invertible.*

Proof   Choose k_0 to be the smallest positive integer such that $\ker(L^{k_0}) = \ker(L^{k_0+1})$. It follows from Lemma 8.2.1 that $\ker(L^{k_0}) = \ker(L^{k_0+j})$ for all $j \geq 1$. Let $X = \ker(L^{k_0})$. Clearly, X is invariant under L for if $\mathbf{x} \in X$, then $L(\mathbf{x}) \in \ker(L^{k_0-1})$, which is a proper subspace of $\ker(L^{k_0})$. Let $Y = R(L^{k_0})$. If $\mathbf{w} \in X \cap Y$, then $\mathbf{w} = L^{k_0}(\mathbf{v})$ for some $\mathbf{v}$ and hence

$$\mathbf{0} = L^{k_0}(\mathbf{w}) = L^{k_0}(L^{k_0}(\mathbf{v})) = L^{2k_0}(\mathbf{v})$$

Thus, $\mathbf{v} \in \ker(L^{2k_0}) = \ker(L^{k_0})$ and hence

$$\mathbf{w} = L^{k_0}(\mathbf{v}) = \mathbf{0}$$

Therefore, $X \cap Y = \{\mathbf{0}\}$. We claim $V = X \oplus Y$. Let $\{\mathbf{x}_1, \ldots, \mathbf{x}_r\}$ be a basis for X and let $\{\mathbf{y}_1, \ldots, \mathbf{y}_{n-r}\}$ be a basis for Y. By Lemma 8.2.1, it suffices to show that $\mathbf{x}_1, \ldots, \mathbf{x}_r$, $\mathbf{y}_1, \ldots \mathbf{y}_{n-r}$ are linearly independent and hence form a basis for V. If

$$\alpha_1 \mathbf{x}_1 + \cdots + \alpha_r \mathbf{x}_r + \beta_1 \mathbf{y}_1 + \cdots + \beta_{n-r} \mathbf{y}_{n-r} = 0 \qquad (1)$$

then applying L^{k_0} to both sides gives

$$\beta_1 L^{k_0}(\mathbf{y}_1) + \cdots + \beta_{n-r} L^{k_0}(\mathbf{y}_{n-r}) = \mathbf{0}$$

or

$$L^{k_0}(\beta_1 \mathbf{y}_1 + \cdots + \beta_{n-r} \mathbf{y}_{n-r}) = 0$$

Therefore, $\beta_1 \mathbf{y}_1 + \cdots + \beta_{n-r} \mathbf{y}_{n-r} \in X \cap Y$ and hence

$$\beta_1 \mathbf{y}_1 + \cdots + \beta_{n-r} \mathbf{y}_{n-r} = \mathbf{0}$$

Since the $\mathbf{y}_i$'s are linearly independent, it follows that

$$\beta_1 = \beta_2 = \cdots = \beta_{n-r} = 0$$

and hence (1) simplifies to

$$\alpha_1 \mathbf{x}_1 + \cdots + \alpha_r \mathbf{x}_r = \mathbf{0}$$

Since the $\mathbf{x}_i$'s are linearly independent, it follows that

$$\alpha_1 = \alpha_2 = \cdots = \alpha_r = 0$$

Thus, $\mathbf{x}_1, \ldots, \mathbf{x}_r, \mathbf{y}_1, \ldots, \mathbf{y}_{n-r}$ are linearly independent and therefore $V = X \oplus Y$. L is invariant and nilpotent on X. We claim that L is invariant and invertible on Y. Let $\mathbf{y} \in Y$; then $\mathbf{y} = L^{k_0}(\mathbf{v})$ for some $\mathbf{v} \in V$. Thus,

$$L(\mathbf{y}) = L(L^{k_0}(\mathbf{v})) = L^{k_0+1}(\mathbf{v}) = L^{k_0}(L(\mathbf{v}))$$

Therefore, $L(\mathbf{y}) \in Y$ and hence Y is invariant under L. To prove $L_{[Y]}$ is invertible, it suffices to show that

$$\ker(L_{[Y]}) = Y \cap \ker(L) = \{\mathbf{0}\}$$

This, however, follows immediately since $\ker(L) \subset X$ and $X \cap Y = \{\mathbf{0}\}$.   ∎

We are now ready to prove the main result of this section.

Theorem 8.2.3   *Let L be a linear operator mapping a finite dimensional vector space V into itself. If $\lambda_1, \ldots, \lambda_k$ are the distinct eigenvalues of L, then V can be decomposed into a direct sum*

$$X_1 \oplus X_2 \oplus \cdots \oplus X_k$$

such that $L - \lambda_i \mathcal{I}$ is nilpotent on X_i and the dimension of X_i equals the multiplicity of λ_i.

Proof   Let $L_1 = L - \lambda_1 \mathcal{I}$. By Theorem 8.2.2, there exist subspaces X_1 and Y_1 that are invariant under L_1 such that $V = X_1 \oplus Y_1$, L_1 is nilpotent on X_1, and $L_{1[Y]}$ is invertible. It follows that X_1 and Y_1 are also invariant under L. By Corollary 8.1.2, $L_{[X_1]}$ can be represented by a block diagonal matrix A_1, where diagonal blocks are simple Jordan matrices whose diagonal elements all equal λ_1. Thus,

$$\det(A_1 - \lambda I) = (\lambda_1 - \lambda)^{m_1}$$

where m_1 is the dimension of X_1. Let B_1 be a matrix representing $L_{[Y_1]}$. Since L_1 is invertible on Y_1, it follows that λ_1 is not an eigenvalue of B_1. Thus,

$$\det(B_1 - \lambda I) = q(\lambda)$$

where $q(\lambda_1) \neq 0$. It follows from Lemma 8.1.2 that the operator L on V can be represented by the matrix

$$A = \begin{bmatrix} A_1 & \\ & B_1 \end{bmatrix}$$

Thus, if each eigenvalue λ_i of L has multiplicity r_i, then

$$
\begin{aligned}
(\lambda_1 - \lambda)^{r_1} (\lambda_2 - \lambda)^{r_2} \cdots (\lambda_k - \lambda)^{r_k} &= \det(A - \lambda I) \\
&= \det(A_1 - \lambda I) \det(B_1 - \lambda I) \\
&= (\lambda_1 - \lambda)^{m_1} q(\lambda)
\end{aligned}
$$

Therefore, $r_1 = m_1$ and

$$q(\lambda) = (\lambda_2 - \lambda)^{r_2} \cdots (\lambda_k - \lambda)^{r_k}$$

If we consider the operator $L_2 = L - \lambda_2 \mathcal{I}$ on the vector space Y_1, then we can decompose Y_1 into a direct sum $X_2 \oplus Y_2$ such that X_2 and Y_2 are invariant under L, L_2 is nilpotent on X_2, and $L_{[Y_2]}$ is invertible. Indeed, we can continue this process of decomposing Y_i into a direct sum $X_{i+1} \oplus Y_{i+1}$ until we obtain a direct sum of the form

$$V = X_1 \oplus X_2 \oplus \cdots \oplus X_{k-1} \oplus Y_{k-1}$$

The vector space Y_{k-1} will be of dimension r_k with a single eigenvalue λ_k. Thus, if we set $X_k = Y_{k-1}$, then $L - \lambda_k \mathcal{I}$ will be nilpotent on X_k and we will have the desired decomposition of V.   ■

It follows from Theorem 8.2.3 that each operator L mapping an n-dimensional vector space V into itself can be represented by a block diagonal matrix of the form

$$J = \begin{pmatrix} A_1 & & & \\ & A_2 & & \\ & & \ddots & \\ & & & A_k \end{pmatrix}$$

where each A_i is an $r_i \times r_i$ block diagonal matrix ($r_i =$ multiplicity of λ_i) whose blocks consist of simple Jordan matrices with λ_i's along the main diagonal.

If A is an $n \times n$ matrix, then A represents the operator L_A with respect to the standard basis on R^n, where L_A is defined by

$$L_A(\mathbf{x}) = A\mathbf{x} \qquad \text{for each } \mathbf{x} \in R^n$$

By the preceding remarks, L_A can be represented by a matrix J of the form just described. It follows that A is similar to J. Thus, each $n \times n$ matrix A with distinct eigenvalues $\lambda_1, \ldots, \lambda_k$ is similar to a matrix J of the form

$$J = \begin{pmatrix} A_1 & & & \\ & A_2 & & \\ & & \ddots & \\ & & & A_k \end{pmatrix} \tag{2}$$

where A_i is an $r_i \times r_i$ matrix ($r_i =$ multiplicity of λ_i) of the form

$$A_i = \begin{pmatrix} J_1(\lambda_i) & & & \\ & J_2(\lambda_i) & & \\ & & \ddots & \\ & & & J_s(\lambda_i) \end{pmatrix} \tag{3}$$

with the $J(\lambda_i)$'s being simple Jordan matrices. The matrix J defined by (2) and (3) is called the *Jordan canonical form* of A. The Jordan canonical form of a matrix is unique except for a reordering of the simple Jordan blocks along the diagonal.

EXAMPLE I   Find the Jordan canonical form of the matrix

$$A = \begin{pmatrix} -3 & 1 & 0 & 1 & 1 \\ -3 & 1 & 0 & 1 & 1 \\ -4 & 1 & 0 & 2 & 1 \\ -3 & 1 & 0 & 1 & 1 \\ -4 & 1 & 0 & 1 & 2 \end{pmatrix}$$

Solution

The characteristic polynomial of A is

$$|A - \lambda I| = \lambda^4 (1 - \lambda)$$

The eigenspace corresponding to $\lambda = 1$ is spanned by $\mathbf{x}_1 = (1, 1, 1, 1, 2)^T$ and the eigenspace corresponding to $\lambda = 0$ is spanned by $\mathbf{x}_2 = (1, 1, 0, 1, 1)^T$ and $\mathbf{x}_3 = (0, 0, 1, 0, 0)^T$. Thus, the Jordan canonical form of A then will consist of three simple Jordan blocks. Except for a reordering of the blocks, there are only two possibilities:

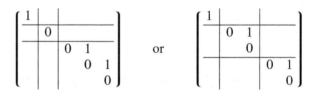

or

To determine which of these forms is correct, we compute $(A - 0I)^2 = A^2$.

$$A^2 = \begin{pmatrix} -1 & 0 & 0 & 0 & 1 \\ -1 & 0 & 0 & 0 & 1 \\ -1 & 0 & 0 & 0 & 1 \\ -1 & 0 & 0 & 0 & 1 \\ -2 & 0 & 0 & 0 & 2 \end{pmatrix}$$

Next we consider the systems

$$A^2 \mathbf{x} = \mathbf{x}_i$$

for $i = 2, 3$. Since these systems turn out to be inconsistent, the Jordan canonical form of A cannot have any 3×3 simple Jordan blocks and, consequently, it must be of the form

$$J = X^{-1} A X = \begin{pmatrix} 1 & & & & \\ & 0 & 1 & & \\ & & 0 & & \\ & & & 0 & 1 \\ & & & & 0 \end{pmatrix}$$

To find X, we must solve

$$A \mathbf{x} = \mathbf{x}_i$$

for $i = 2, 3$. The system $A\mathbf{x} = \mathbf{x}_2$ has infinitely many solutions. We need choose only one of these, say, $\mathbf{x}_4 = (1, 3, 0, 0, 1)^T$. Similarly, $A\mathbf{x} = \mathbf{x}_3$ has infinitely many solutions, one of which is $\mathbf{x}_5 = (1, 0, 0, 2, 1)^T$. Let

$$
X = \begin{bmatrix} \mathbf{x}_1 & \mathbf{x}_2 & \mathbf{x}_3 & \mathbf{x}_4 & \mathbf{x}_5 \end{bmatrix} = \begin{bmatrix} 1 & 1 & 0 & 1 & 1 \\ 1 & 1 & 0 & 3 & 0 \\ 1 & 0 & 1 & 0 & 0 \\ 1 & 1 & 0 & 0 & 2 \\ 2 & 1 & 0 & 1 & 1 \end{bmatrix}
$$

The reader may verify that $X^{-1}AX = J$.   ∎

One of the main applications of the Jordan canonical form is in solving systems of linear differential equations that have defective coefficient matrices. Given such a system

$$
\mathbf{Y}'(t) = A\mathbf{Y}(t)
$$

we can simplify it by using the Jordan canonical form of A. Indeed, if $A = XJX^{-1}$, then

$$
\mathbf{Y}' = (XJX^{-1})\mathbf{Y}
$$

Thus, if we set $\mathbf{Z} = X^{-1}\mathbf{Y}$, then $\mathbf{Y}' = X\mathbf{Z}'$ and the system simplifies to

$$
X\mathbf{Z}' = XJ\mathbf{Z}
$$

Multiplying by X^{-1}, we get

$$
\mathbf{Z}' = J\mathbf{Z} \tag{4}
$$

Because of the structure of J, this new system is much easier to solve. Indeed, solving (4) will only involve solving a number of smaller systems, each of the form

$$
\begin{aligned}
z_1' &= \lambda z_1 + z_2 \\
z_2' &= \lambda z_2 + z_3 \\
&\ \ \vdots \\
z_{k-1}' &= \lambda z_{k-1} + z_k \\
z_k' &= \lambda z_k
\end{aligned}
$$

These equations can be solved one at a time starting with the last. The solution to the last equation is clearly

$$
z_k = ce^{\lambda t}
$$

The solution to any equation of the form

$$
z'(t) - \lambda z(t) = u(t)
$$

is given by

$$z(t) = e^{\lambda t} \int e^{-\lambda t} u(t) dt$$

Thus, we can solve

$$z'_{k-1} - \lambda z_{k-1} = z_k$$

for z_{k-1} and then solve

$$z'_{k-2} - \lambda z_{k-2} = z_{k-1}$$

for z_{k-2}, etc.

EXAMPLE 2 Solve the initial value problem

$$\begin{pmatrix} y'_1 \\ y'_2 \\ y'_3 \\ y'_4 \end{pmatrix} = \begin{bmatrix} 1 & 0 & 0 & -1 \\ 0 & 1 & 1 & 0 \\ 0 & -1 & 1 & 2 \\ 1 & 0 & 2 & 1 \end{bmatrix} \begin{pmatrix} y_1 \\ y_2 \\ y_3 \\ y_4 \end{pmatrix}$$

$$y_1(0) = y_2(0) = y_3(0) = 0, \ y_4(0) = 2$$

Solution

The coefficient matrix A has two distinct eigenvalues $\lambda_1 = 0$ and $\lambda_2 = 2$, each of multiplicity 2. The corresponding eigenspaces are both dimension 1. Using the methods of this section, A can be factored into a product XJX^{-1}, where

$$J = \begin{bmatrix} 0 & 1 & 0 & 0 \\ 0 & 0 & 0 & 0 \\ 0 & 0 & 2 & 1 \\ 0 & 0 & 0 & 2 \end{bmatrix}$$

The choice of X is not unique. The reader may verify that the one we have calculated:

$$X = \begin{bmatrix} 1 & 1 & -1 & 1 \\ 1 & 1 & 1 & -1 \\ -1 & 0 & 1 & 0 \\ 1 & 0 & 1 & 0 \end{bmatrix}$$

does the job. If we now change variable and set $Z = X^{-1}Y$, then we can rewrite the system in the form

$$Z' = JZ$$

The block structure of J allows us to break up the system into two simpler systems:

$$\begin{matrix} z'_1 = z_2 \\ z'_2 = 0 \end{matrix} \quad \text{and} \quad \begin{matrix} z'_3 = 2z_3 + z_4 \\ z'_4 = 2z_4 \end{matrix}$$

The first system is not difficult to solve.

$$z_1 = c_1 t + c_2$$
$$z_2 = c_1 \qquad (c_1 \text{ and } c_2 \text{ are constants})$$

To solve the second system, we first solve

$$z_4' = 2z_4$$

getting

$$z_4 = c_3 e^{2t}$$

Thus,

$$z_3' - 2z_3 = c_3 e^{2t}$$

and hence

$$z_3 = e^{2t} \int e^{-2t}(c_3 e^{2t})dt = e^{2t}(c_3 t + c_4)$$

Finally, we have

$$Y = XZ = \begin{pmatrix} (c_1 t + c_2) + c_1 - (c_3 t + c_4)e^{2t} + c_3 e^{2t} \\ (c_1 t + c_2) + c_1 + (c_3 t + c_4)e^{2t} - c_3 e^{2t} \\ -(c_1 t + c_2) + (c_3 t + c_4)e^{2t} \\ (c_1 t + c_2) + (c_3 t + c_4)e^{2t} \end{pmatrix}$$

If we set $t = 0$ and use the initial conditions to solve for the c_i's, we get

$$c_1 = -1, \qquad c_2 = c_3 = c_4 = 1$$

Thus, the solution to the initial value problem is

$$y_1 = -t - te^{2t}$$
$$y_2 = -t + te^{2t}$$
$$y_3 = -1 + t + (1 + t)e^{2t}$$
$$y_4 = 1 - t + (1 + t)e^{2t}$$

The Jordan canonical form not only provides a nice representation of an operator, but it also allows us to solve systems of the form $\mathbf{Y}' = A\mathbf{Y}$ even when the coefficient matrix is defective. From a theoretical point of view, its importance cannot be questioned. As far as practical applications go, however, it is generally not very useful.

If $n \geq 5$, it is usually necessary to calculate the eigenvalues of A by some numerical method. The calculated λ_i's are only approximations to the actual eigenvalues. Thus, we could have calculated values λ_1' and λ_2', which are unequal while actually $\lambda_1 = \lambda_2$. So in practice, it may be difficult to determine the correct multiplicity of the eigenvalues. Furthermore, in order to solve $\mathbf{Y}' = A\mathbf{Y}$, we need to find the similarity matrix X such that $A = XJX^{-1}$. However, when A has multiple eigenvalues, the matrix X may be very sensitive to perturbations and, in practice, one is not guaranteed that the entries of the computed similarity matrix will have any digits of accuracy whatsoever. A recommended alternative is to compute the matrix exponential e^A and use it to solve the system $\mathbf{Y}' = A\mathbf{Y}$.

SECTION 8.2 EXERCISES

1. Let A be a 4×4 matrix whose only eigenvalue is $\lambda = 2$. What are the possible Jordan canonical forms for A?

2. Let A be a 5×5 matrix. If $A^2 \neq 0$ and $A^3 = 0$, what are the possible Jordan canonical forms for A?

3. Find the Jordan canonical form J for each of the following matrices and determine a matrix X such that $X^{-1}AX = J$:

(a) $A = \begin{pmatrix} 1 & 0 & 1 \\ 1 & 0 & 2 \\ 1 & -1 & 2 \end{pmatrix}$

(b) $A = \begin{pmatrix} 0 & 0 & 0 & 1 \\ 0 & 0 & 0 & 1 \\ 1 & 2 & 0 & 0 \\ 0 & 0 & 0 & -1 \end{pmatrix}$

(c) $A = \begin{pmatrix} 1 & 2 & 0 & 0 \\ 0 & 1 & 2 & 0 \\ 0 & 0 & 1 & 2 \\ 0 & 0 & 0 & 1 \end{pmatrix}$

(d) $A = \begin{pmatrix} 1 & 1 & 1 & 1 & 1 \\ 0 & 1 & 1 & 1 & 1 \\ 0 & 0 & 1 & 1 & 1 \\ 0 & 0 & 0 & 0 & 1 \\ 0 & 0 & 0 & 0 & 0 \end{pmatrix}$

(e) $A = \begin{pmatrix} 2 & 1 & 1 & 1 & 1 & 1 \\ 0 & 2 & 1 & 1 & 1 & 1 \\ 0 & 0 & 0 & 1 & 1 & 1 \\ 0 & 0 & 0 & 0 & 1 & 1 \\ 0 & 0 & 0 & 0 & 1 & 1 \\ 0 & 0 & 0 & 0 & 1 & 1 \end{pmatrix}$

4. Let L be a linear operator on a finite dimensional vector space V.

(a) Show that $R(L^i) \subset R(L^j)$ whenever $i > j$.

(b) If for some k_0, $R(L^{k_0}) = R(L^{k_0+1})$, then $R(L^{k_0}) = R(L^{k_0+k})$ for all $k \geq 1$.

5. Let L be as in Exercise 4.

(a) Show that there is a smallest positive integer k_0 such that $R(L^{k_0}) = R(L^{k_0+1})$.

(b) Let k_1 be the smallest positive integer such that $\ker(L^{k_1}) = \ker(L^{k_1+1})$. Show that $k_1 = k_0$.

6. Solve the initial value problem

$$
\begin{aligned}
y_1' &= y_3 \\
y_2' &= y_1 - y_2 + 2y_3 \\
y_3' &= y_1 - y_2 + y_3 \\
y_1(0) &= 0, \ y_2(0) = 0, \ y_3(0) = -1
\end{aligned}
$$

APPENDIX

MATLAB

MATLAB is an interactive program for matrix computations. The original version of MATLAB, short for *matrix laboratory*, was developed by Cleve Moler from the Linpack and Eispack software libraries. Over the years MATLAB has undergone a series of expansions and revisions. Today it is the leading software for scientific computations. The MATLAB software is distributed by the MathWorks, Inc. of Natick, Massachusetts. Some universities have MATLAB licenses that allow student use. For those that do not, individual student licenses may be purchased at affordable prices. In addition to widespread use in industrial and engineering settings, MATLAB has become a standard instructional tool for undergraduate linear algebra courses.

The MATLAB Desktop Display

At start-up, MATLAB will display a desktop with three windows. The window on the right is the command window, in which MATLAB commands are entered and executed. The windows on the left display the Current Folder Browser and the Workspace Browser.

The Workspace Browser allows you to view and make changes to the contents of the workspace. It is also possible to plot a data set using the Workspace window. Just highlight the data set to be plotted and then select the type of plot desired. MATLAB will display the graph in a new figure window. The Current Folder Browser allows you to view MATLAB and other files and to perform file operations such as opening and editing or searching for files.

It is also possible to open up a fourth window that displays the Command History. It allows you view a log of all the commands that have been entered in the command window. This window can be accessed from the Command Window by pressing the up arrow key. To repeat a previous command, just click on the command to highlight it. The selected command will now appear on the current line in the Command Window and may be edited and executed.

Any of the MATLAB windows can be closed, maximized, docked, or undocked by clicking on the solid triangle located in the upper right-hand corner of the window and choosing the desired option.

Basic Data Elements

The basic elements that MATLAB uses are matrices. Once the matrices have been entered or generated, the user can quickly perform sophisticated computations with a minimal amount of programming.

507

Entering matrices in MATLAB is easy. To enter the matrix

$$\begin{pmatrix} 1 & 2 & 3 & 4 \\ 5 & 6 & 7 & 8 \\ 9 & 10 & 11 & 12 \\ 13 & 14 & 15 & 16 \end{pmatrix}$$

type

$$A = [1 \quad 2 \quad 3 \quad 4; \quad 5 \quad 6 \quad 7 \quad 8; \quad 9 \quad 10 \quad 11 \quad 12; \quad 13 \quad 14 \quad 15 \quad 16]$$

or the matrix could be entered one row at a time:

$$A = \begin{bmatrix} 1 & 2 & 3 & 4 \\ 5 & 6 & 7 & 8 \\ 9 & 10 & 11 & 12 \\ 13 & 14 & 15 & 16 \end{bmatrix}$$

Once a matrix has been entered, you can edit it in two ways. From the command window, you can redefine any entry with a MATLAB command. For example, the command $A(1,3) = 5$ will change the third entry in the first row of A to 5. You can also edit the entries of a matrix from the Workspace Browser. To change the $(1,3)$ entry of A with the Workspace Browser, we first locate A in the Name column of the browser and then click on the array icon to the left of A to open an array display of the matrix. To change the $(1,3)$ entry to a 5, click on the corresponding cell of the array and enter 5.

Row vectors of equally spaced points can be generated using MATLAB's : operation. The command $\mathbf{x} = 2:6$ generates a row vector with integer entries going from 2 to 6.

$$\mathbf{x} =$$
$$2 \quad 3 \quad 4 \quad 5 \quad 6$$

It is not necessary to use integers or to have a step size of 1. For example, the command $\mathbf{x} = 1.2:0.2:2$ will produce

$$\mathbf{x} =$$
$$1.2000 \quad 1.4000 \quad 1.6000 \quad 1.8000 \quad 2.0000$$

Submatrices

To refer to a submatrix of the matrix A entered earlier, use the : to specify the rows and columns. For example, the submatrix consisting of the entries in the second two rows of columns 2 through 4 is given by $A(2:3, 2:4)$. Thus, the statement

$$C = A(2:3, 2:4)$$

generates

$$C =$$

$$\begin{matrix} 6 & 7 & 8 \\ 10 & 11 & 12 \end{matrix}$$

If the colon is used by itself for one of the arguments, either all the rows or all the columns of the matrix will be included. For example, $A(:, 2:3)$ represents the submatrix of A consisting of all the elements in the second and third columns, and $A(4, :)$ denotes the fourth row vector of A. We can generate a submatrix using non-adjacent rows or columns by using vector arguments to specify which rows and columns are to be included. For example, to generate a matrix whose entries are those which appear only in the first and third rows and second and fourth columns of A, set

$$E = A([1, 3], [2, 4])$$

The result will be

$$E =$$

$$\begin{matrix} 2 & 4 \\ 10 & 12 \end{matrix}$$

Generating Matrices

We can also generate by matrices using built-in MATLAB functions. For example, the command

$$B = \textbf{rand}(4)$$

will generate a 4×4 matrix whose entries are random numbers between 0 and 1. Other functions that can be used to generate matrices are **eye, zeros, ones, magic, hilb, pascal, toeplitz, compan**, and **vander**. To build triangular or diagonal matrices, we can use the MATLAB functions **triu, tril**, and **diag**.

The matrix building commands can be used to generate blocks of partitioned matrices. For example, the MATLAB command

$$E = [\, \textbf{eye}(2), \, \textbf{ones}(2, 3); \, \textbf{zeros}(2), \, [1:3; \quad 3:-1:1] \,]$$

will generate the matrix

$$E =$$

$$\begin{matrix} 1 & 0 & 1 & 1 & 1 \\ 0 & 1 & 1 & 1 & 1 \\ 0 & 0 & 1 & 2 & 3 \\ 0 & 0 & 3 & 2 & 1 \end{matrix}$$

Matrix Arithmetic

Addition and Multiplication of Matrices

Matrix arithmetic in MATLAB is straightforward. We can multiply our original matrix A times B simply by typing $A * B$. The sum and difference of A and B are given by $A + B$ and $A - B$, respectively. The transpose of the real matrix A is given by A'. For a matrix C with complex entries, the $'$ operation corresponds to conjugate transpose. Thus, C^H is given as C' in MATLAB.

Backslash or Matrix Left Division

If W is an $n \times n$ matrix and $\mathbf{b}$ represents a vector in R^n, the solution of the system $W\mathbf{x} = \mathbf{b}$ can be computed using MATLAB's backslash operator by setting

$$\mathbf{x} = W \backslash \mathbf{b}$$

For example, if we set

$$W = [1 \quad 1 \quad 1 \quad 1; \quad 1 \quad 2 \quad 3 \quad 4; \quad 3 \quad 4 \quad 6 \quad 2; \quad 2 \quad 7 \quad 10 \quad 5]$$

and $\mathbf{b} = [3; \quad 5; \quad 5; \quad 8]$, then the command

$$\mathbf{x} = W \backslash \mathbf{b}$$

will yield

$$\mathbf{x} =$$
$$1.0000$$
$$3.0000$$
$$-2.0000$$
$$1.0000$$

In the case that the $n \times n$ coefficient matrix is singular or has numerical rank less than n, the backslash operator will still compute a solution, but MATLAB will issue a warning. For example our original 4×4 matrix A is singular and the command

$$\mathbf{x} = A \backslash \mathbf{b}$$

yields

Warning: Matrix is close to singular or badly scaled. Results may be inaccurate. RCOND = 1.387779e-018.

$$\mathbf{x} =$$
$$1.0e + 015*$$

$$2.2518$$
$$-3.0024$$
$$-0.7506$$
$$1.5012$$

The $1.0e + 015$ indicates the exponent for each of the entries of **x**. Thus, each of the four entries listed is multiplied by 10^{15}. The value of RCOND is an estimate of the reciprocal of the condition number of the coefficient matrix. Even if the matrix were nonsingular, with a condition number on the order of 10^{18}, one could expect to lose as much as 18 digits of accuracy in the decimal representation of the computed solution. Since the computer keeps track of only 16 decimal digits, this means that the computed solution may not have any digits of accuracy.

If the coefficient matrix for a linear system has more rows than columns, then MATLAB assumes that a least squares solution of the system is desired. If we set

$$C = A(:, 1 : 2)$$

then C is a 4×2 matrix and the command

$$\mathbf{x} = C \backslash \mathbf{b}$$

will compute the least squares solution

$$\mathbf{x} =$$
$$-2.2500$$
$$2.6250$$

If we now set

$$C = A(:, 1 : 3)$$

then C will be a 4×3 matrix with rank equal to 2. Although the least squares problem will not have a unique solution, MATLAB will still compute a solution and return a warning that the matrix is rank deficient. In this case, the command

$$\mathbf{x} = C \backslash \mathbf{b}$$

yields

Warning: Rank deficient, rank = 2, tol = 1.7852e-014.

$$\mathbf{x} =$$
$$-0.9375$$
$$0$$
$$1.3125$$

Exponentiation

Powers of matrices are easily generated. The matrix A^5 is computed in MATLAB by typing $A\hat{\ }5$. We can also perform operations elementwise by preceding the operand by a period. For example, if $V = [1 \quad 2; \quad 3 \quad 4]$, then $V\hat{\ }2$ results in

$$\text{ans} =$$

7	10
15	22

while $V.\hat{\ }2$ will give

$$\text{ans} =$$

1	4
9	16

MATLAB Functions

To compute the eigenvalues of a square matrix A, we need only type $\mathbf{eig}(A)$. The eigenvectors and eigenvalues can be computed by setting

$$[X \quad D] = \mathbf{eig}(A)$$

Similarly, we can compute the determinant, inverse, condition number, norm, and rank of a matrix with simple one-word commands. Matrix factorizations such as the LU, QR, Cholesky, Schur decomposition, and singular value decomposition can be computed with a single command. For example, the command

$$[Q \quad R] = \mathbf{qr}(A)$$

will produce an orthogonal (or unitary) matrix Q and an upper triangular matrix R, with the same dimensions as A, such that $A = QR$.

Programming Features

MATLAB has all the flow control structures that you would expect in a high-level language, including **for** loops, **while** loops, and **if** statements. This allows the user to write his or her own MATLAB programs and to create additional MATLAB functions. Note that MATLAB prints out automatically the result of each command, unless the command line ends in a semicolon. *When using loops, we recommend ending each command with a semicolon to avoid printing all the results of the intermediate computations.*

M-files

It is possible to extend MATLAB by adding your own programs. MATLAB programs are all given the extension `.m` and are referred to as *M-files*. There are two basic types of M-files.

Script Files

Script files are files that contain a series of MATLAB commands. All the variables used in these commands are global, and consequently the values of these variables in your MATLAB session will change every time you run the script file. For example, if you wanted to determine the nullity of a matrix, you could create a script file **nullity.m** containing the following commands:

$$\mathbf{[m,n]} = \mathbf{size}(A);$$
$$\mathbf{nuldim} = \mathbf{n} - \mathbf{rank}(A)$$

Entering the command **nullity** would cause the two lines of code in the script file to be executed. The disadvantage of determining the nullity this way is that the matrix must be named A. Additionally, if you have been using the variables m and n, the values of these variables will be reassigned when you run the script file. An alternative would be to create a *function file*.

Function Files

Function files begin with a function declaration statement of the form

$$\texttt{function [oarg1,...,oargj]} = \texttt{fname(inarg1,...,inargk)}$$

All the variables used in the function M-file are local. When you call a function file, only the values of the output variables will change in your MATLAB session. For example, we could create a function file **nullity.m** to compute the nullity of a matrix as follows:

```
function k = nullity(A)
% The command nullity(A) computes the dimension
% of the nullspace of A.
[m,n] = size(A);
k = n - rank(A);
```

The lines beginning with **%** are comments that are not executed. These lines will be displayed whenever you type **help nullity** in a MATLAB session. Once the function is saved, it can be used in a MATLAB session in the same way that we use built-in MATLAB functions. For example, if we set

$$B = [1\ 2\ 3;\ 4\ 5\ 6;\ 7\ 8\ 9];$$

and then enter the command

$$\texttt{n} = \texttt{nullity}(B)$$

MATLAB will return the answer: **n** $= 1$.

The MATLAB Path

The M-files that you develop should be kept in folders that can be added to the default *MATLAB path*—the list of folders where MATLAB will automatically search for M-files. To add or remove a folder from the MATLAB path or to reorder the folders in the path, select the home tab at the top of the page and then click on the Set Path option.

Relational and Logical Operators

MATLAB has six relational operators that are used for comparisons of scalars or elementwise comparisons of arrays. These operators are:

Relational Operators	
$<$	less than
$<=$	less than or equal
$>$	greater than
$>=$	greater than or equal
$==$	equal
$\sim=$	not equal

Given two $m \times n$ matrices A and B, the command

$$C = A < B$$

will generate an $m \times n$ matrix consisting of zeros and ones. The (i, j) entry will be equal to 1 if and only if $a_{ij} < b_{ij}$. For example, suppose that

$$A = \begin{pmatrix} -2 & 0 & 3 \\ 4 & 2 & -5 \\ -1 & -3 & 2 \end{pmatrix}$$

The command $A >= 0$ will generate

ans =
$$\begin{matrix} 0 & 1 & 1 \\ 1 & 1 & 0 \\ 0 & 0 & 1 \end{matrix}$$

There are three logical operators in MATLAB:

Logical Operators	
&	AND
|	OR
~	NOT

These logical operators regard any nonzero scalar as corresponding to TRUE and 0 as corresponding to FALSE. The operator & corresponds to the logical AND. If a and b are scalars, the expression $a \& b$ will equal 1 if a and b are both nonzero (TRUE) and 0 otherwise. The operator | corresponds to the logical OR. The expression $a|b$ will have the value 0 if both a and b are 0; otherwise it will be equal to 1. The operator $\sim$ corresponds to the logical NOT. For a scalar a, it takes on the value 1 (TRUE) if $a = 0$ (FALSE) and the value 0 (FALSE) if $a \neq 0$ (TRUE).

For matrices, these operators are applied elementwise. Thus, if A and B are both $m \times n$ matrices, then $A \& B$ is a matrix of zeros and ones whose ijth entry is $a(i, j) \& b(i, j)$. For example, if

$$A = \begin{pmatrix} 1 & 0 & 1 \\ 0 & 1 & 1 \\ 0 & 0 & 1 \end{pmatrix} \quad \text{and} \quad B = \begin{pmatrix} -1 & 2 & 0 \\ 1 & 0 & 3 \\ 0 & 1 & 2 \end{pmatrix}$$

then

$$A \& B = \begin{pmatrix} 1 & 0 & 0 \\ 0 & 0 & 1 \\ 0 & 0 & 1 \end{pmatrix}, \quad A|B = \begin{pmatrix} 1 & 1 & 1 \\ 1 & 1 & 1 \\ 0 & 1 & 1 \end{pmatrix}, \quad \sim A = \begin{pmatrix} 0 & 1 & 0 \\ 1 & 0 & 0 \\ 1 & 1 & 0 \end{pmatrix}$$

The relational and logical operators are often used in **if** statements.

Columnwise Array Operators

MATLAB has a number of functions that, when applied to either a row or column vector **x**, return a single number. For example, the command **max**(**x**) will compute the maximum entry of **x**, and the command **sum**(**x**) will return the value of the sum of the entries of **x**. Other functions of this form are **min**, **prod**, **mean**, **all**, and **any**. When used with a matrix argument, these functions are applied to each column vector and the results are returned as a row vector. For example, if

$$A = \begin{bmatrix} -3 & 2 & 5 & 4 \\ 1 & 3 & 8 & 0 \\ -6 & 3 & 1 & 3 \end{bmatrix}$$

then

$$\begin{aligned} \mathbf{min}(A) &= (-6, 2, 1, 0) \\ \mathbf{max}(A) &= (1, 3, 8, 4) \\ \mathbf{sum}(A) &= (-8, 8, 14, 7) \\ \mathbf{prod}(A) &= (18, 18, 40, 0) \end{aligned}$$

Graphics

If **x** and **y** are vectors of the same length, the command **plot**(**x**, **y**) will produce a plot of all the (x_i, y_i) pairs, and each point will be connected to the next by a line segment. If the x-coordinates are taken close enough together, the graph should resemble a smooth curve. The command **plot**(**x**, **y**, 'x') will plot the ordered pairs with x's, but will not connect the points.

For example, to plot the function $f(x) = \dfrac{\sin x}{x+1}$ on the interval [0, 10], set

$$\mathbf{x} = 0:0.2:10 \quad \text{and} \quad \mathbf{y} = \sin(\mathbf{x})./(\mathbf{x}+1)$$

The command **plot**(**x**, **y**) will generate the graph of the function. To compare the graph to that of $\sin x$, we could set $\mathbf{z} = \sin(\mathbf{x})$ and use the command **plot**(**x**, **y**, **x**, **z**) to plot both curves at the same time. We can include additional arguments in the command to specify the format of each plot. For example the command

$$\mathbf{plot}(\mathbf{x}, \mathbf{y}, \text{'c'}, \mathbf{x}, \mathbf{z}, \text{'} -- \text{'})$$

will plot the first function using a light blue (cyan) color and the second function using dashed lines. See Figure A.1.

It is also possible to do more sophisticated types of plots in MATLAB, including polar coordinates, three-dimensional surfaces, and contour plots.

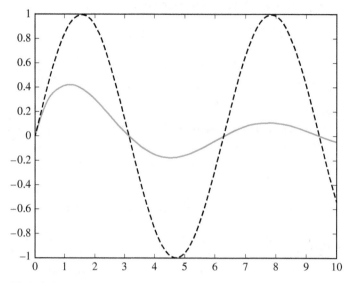

Figure A.1.

Symbolic Toolbox

In addition to doing numeric computations, it is possible to do symbolic calculations with MATLAB's symbolic toolbox. The symbolic toolbox allows us to manipulate symbolic expressions. It can be used to solve equations, differentiate and integrate functions, and perform symbolic matrix operations.

MATLAB's **sym** command can be used to turn any MATLAB data structure into a symbolic object. For example, the command **sym('t')** will turn the string 't' into a symbolic variable **t**, and the command **sym(hilb(3))** will produce the symbolic version of the 3×3 Hilbert matrix written in the form

$$
\begin{bmatrix} 1, & \frac{1}{2}, & \frac{1}{3} \end{bmatrix}
$$
$$
\begin{bmatrix} \frac{1}{2}, & \frac{1}{3}, & \frac{1}{4} \end{bmatrix}
$$
$$
\begin{bmatrix} \frac{1}{3}, & \frac{1}{4}, & \frac{1}{5} \end{bmatrix}
$$

We can create a number of symbolic variables at once with the **syms** command. For example, the command

syms a b c

creates three symbolic variables **a**, **b**, and **c**. If we then set

$A = $ **[a, b, c;b, c, a;c, a, b]**

the result will be the symbolic matrix

$$A =$$

$$
\begin{bmatrix} a, & b, & c \end{bmatrix}
$$
$$
\begin{bmatrix} b, & c, & a \end{bmatrix}
$$
$$
\begin{bmatrix} c, & a, & b \end{bmatrix}
$$

The MATLAB command **subs** can be used to substitute an expression or a value for a symbolic variable. For example, the command **subs(A,c,3)** will substitute 3 for each occurrence of **c** in the symbolic matrix A. Multiple substitutions are also possible: The command

subs(A,[a,b,c],[a−1,b+1,3])

will substitute $a-1$, $b+1$, and 3 for **a**, **b**, and **c**, respectively, in the matrix A.

The standard matrix operations $*, \hat{\ }, +, -$, and $'$ all work for symbolic matrices and also for combinations of symbolic and numeric matrices. If an operation involves two matrices and one of them is symbolic, the result will be a symbolic matrix. For example, the command

sym(hilb(3))+eye(3)

will produce the symbolic matrix

$$
\begin{bmatrix} 2, & \frac{1}{2}, & \frac{1}{3} \end{bmatrix}
$$
$$
\begin{bmatrix} \frac{1}{2}, & \frac{4}{3}, & \frac{1}{4} \end{bmatrix}
$$
$$
\begin{bmatrix} \frac{1}{3}, & \frac{1}{4}, & \frac{6}{5} \end{bmatrix}
$$

Standard MATLAB matrix commands such as

det, eig, inv, null, trace, sum, prod, poly

all work for symbolic matrices; however, others such as

rref, orth, rank, norm

do not. Likewise, none of the standard matrix factorizations are possible for symbolic matrices.

Help Facility

MATLAB includes a HELP facility that provides help on all MATLAB features. To access MATLAB's help browser, click on the help button in the toolbar (this is the button with the ? symbol) or type **doc** in the command window. The help facility gives information on getting started with MATLAB and on using and customizing the desktop. It lists and describes all the MATLAB functions, operations, and commands.

You can also obtain help information on any of the MATLAB commands directly from the command window. Simply enter **help** followed by the name of the command. For example, the MATLAB command **eig** is used to compute eigenvalues. For information on how to use this command, you could either find the command using the help browser or simply type **help eig** in the command window.

From the command window, you also can obtain help on any MATLAB operator. Simply type **help** followed by the symbol for that operator. For example, to obtain help on the backslash operation, type **help** \.

Conclusions

MATLAB is a powerful tool for matrix computations that is also user friendly. The fundamentals can be mastered easily, and consequently students are able to begin numerical experiments with only a minimal amount of preparation. Indeed, the material in this appendix, together with the MATLAB help facility, should be enough to get you started.

The MATLAB exercises at the end of each chapter are designed to enhance understanding of linear algebra. The exercises do not assume familiarity with MATLAB. Often specific commands are given to guide the reader through the more complicated MATLAB constructions. Consequently, you should be able to work through all the exercises without resorting to additional MATLAB books or manuals.

Although this appendix summarizes the features of MATLAB that are relevant to an undergraduate course in linear algebra, many other advanced capabilities have not been discussed. References [20] and [29] describe MATLAB in greater detail.

BIBLIOGRAPHY

A   Linear Algebra and Matrix Theory

[1] Brualdi, Richard A., and Herbert J. Ryser, *Combinatorial Matrix Theory*. New York: Cambridge University Press, 1991.

[2] Carlson, David, Charles R. Johnson, David C. Lay, and A. Duane Porter, *Linear Algebra Gems: Assets for Undergraduate Mathematics*. Washington, DC: MAA, 2001.

[3] Carlson, David, Charles R. Johnson, David C. Lay, A. Duane Porter, Ann Watkins, and William Watkins, eds., *Resources for Teaching Linear Algebra*. Washington, DC: MAA, 1997.

[4] Gantmacher, Felix R., *The Theory of Matrices*, 2 vols. New York: Chelsea Publishing Co., 1960.

[5] Hill, David R., and David E. Zitarelli, *Linear Algebra Labs with MATLAB*, 3rd ed. Upper Saddle River, NJ: Prentice Hall, 2004.

[6] Hogben, Leslie, ed., *Handbook of Linear Algebra*, 2nd ed. Boca Raton, FL: Chapman and Hall/CRC Press, 2013.

[7] Horn, Roger A., and Charles R. Johnson, *Matrix Analysis*, 2nd ed. New York: Cambridge University Press, 2012.

[8] Horn, Roger A., and Charles R. Johnson, *Topics in Matrix Analysis*. New York: Cambridge University Press, 1991.

[9] Keith, Sandra, *Visualizing Linear Algebra Using Maple*. Upper Saddle River, NJ: Prentice Hall, 2001.

[10] Kleinfeld, Erwin, and Margaret Kleinfeld, *Understanding Linear Algebra Using MATLAB*. Upper Saddle River, NJ: Prentice Hall, 2001.

[11] Lancaster, Peter, and M. Tismenetsky, *The Theory of Matrices with Applications*, 2nd ed. New York: Academic Press, 1985.

[12] Leon, Steven J., Eugene Herman, and Richard Faulkenberry, *ATLAST Computer Exercises for Linear Algebra*, 2nd ed. Upper Saddle River, NJ: Prentice Hall, 2003.

[13] Ortega, James M., *Matrix Theory: A Second Course*. New York: Plenum Press, 1987.

[14] Strang, Gilbert, *Essays in Linear Algebra*. Wellesley, MA: Wellesley-Cambridge Press, 2012.

B   Applied and Numerical Linear Algebra

[15] Anderson, E., Z. Bai, C. Bischof, J. Demmel, J. Dongarra, J. Du Croz, A. Greenbaum, S. Hammarling, A. McKenney, S. Ostrouchov, and D. Sorenson, *LAPACK Users' Guide*, 3rd ed. Philadelphia: SIAM, 1999.

[16] Bellman, Richard, *Introduction to Matrix Analysis*, 2nd ed. New York: McGraw-Hill Book Co., 1970.

[17] Björck, Åke, *Numerical Methods for Least Squares Problems*. Philadelphia: SIAM, 1996.

[18] Björck, Åke, *Numerical Methods in Matrix Computations*, New York: Springer, 2015.

[19] Chan, Raymond H., Chen Grief, and Dianne P. O'Leary, *Milestones in Matrix Computation: The Selected Works of Gene H. Golub With Commentaries*. Oxford: Oxford University Press, 2007.

[20] Coleman, Thomas F., and Charles Van Loan, *Handbook for Matrix Computations*. Philadelphia: SIAM, 1988.

[21] Conte, S. D., and C. deBoor, *Elementary Numerical Analysis: An Algorithmic Approach*, Philadelphia: SIAM, 2017.

[22] Dahlquist, G., and Å. Björck, *Numerical Methods in Scientific Computing*, Vol. 1. Philadelphia: SIAM, 2008.

[23] Datta, Biswa Nath, *Numerical Linear Algebra and Applications*, 2nd ed. Philadelphia: SIAM 2010.

[24] Demmel, James W., *Applied Numerical Linear Algebra*. Philadelphia: SIAM, 1997.

[25] Fletcher, Trevor J., *Linear Algebra Through Its Applications*. New York: Van Nostrand Reinhold, 1972.

[26] Gander, Walter, Martin Gander, and Felix Kwok, *Scientific Computing - An Introduction using Maple and MATLAB*, New York: Springer, 2014

[27] Golub, Gene H., and Charles F. Van Loan, *Matrix Computations*, 4th ed. Baltimore, MD: Johns Hopkins University Press, 2013.

[28] Greenbaum, Anne, *Iterative Methods for Solving Linear Systems*. Philadelphia: SIAM, 1997.

[29] Higham, Desmond J., and Nicholas J. Higham, *MATLAB Guide*. Philadelphia: SIAM, 2000.

[30] O'Leary, Dianne P., *Scientific Computing with Case Studies*. Philadelphia: SIAM, 2009.

[31] Parlett, Beresford N., *The Symmetric Eigenvalue Problem*. Philadelphia: SIAM, 1997. (Reprint of Prentice-Hall 1980 edition)

[32] Saad, Yousef, *Iterative Methods for Sparse Linear Systems*, 2nd ed. Philadelphia: SIAM, 2003.

[33] Stewart, G. W., *Matrix Algorithms, Volume I: Basic Decompositions*. Philadelphia: SIAM, 1998.

[34] Stewart, G. W., *Matrix Algorithms, Volume II: Eigensystems*. Philadelphia: SIAM, 2001.

[35] Strang, Gilbert, *Essays in Linear Algebra*. Wellesley, MA: Wellesley-Cambridge Press, 2012.

[36] Trefethen, Loyd N., *Numerical Linear Algebra*. Philadelphia: SIAM, 1997.

[37] Watkins, David S., *Fundamentals of Matrix Computation*, 2nd ed. New York: John Wiley & Sons, 2002.

[38] Watkins, David S., *The Matrix Eigenvalue Problem GR and Krylov Subspace Methods*, Philadelphia: SIAM, 2007.

[39] Wilkinson, J. H., *The Algebraic Eigenvalue Problem*. New York: Oxford University Press, 1965.

[40] Wilkinson, J. H., and C. Reinsch, *Handbook for Automatic Computation*, Vol. II: *Linear Algebra*. New York: Springer-Verlag, 1971.

C   Books of Related Interest

[41] Chiang, Alpha C., *Fundamental Methods of Mathematical Economics*. New York: McGraw-Hill Book Co., 1967.

[42] Courant, R., and D. Hilbert, *Methods of Mathematical Physics*, Vol. I. New York: Wiley-Interscience, 1953.

[43] Edwards, Allen L., *Multiple Regression and the Analysis of Variance and Covariance*. New York: W. H. Freeman and Co., 1985.

[44] Gander, Walter, and Jiří Hřebíček, *Solving Problems in Scientific Computing Using Maple and MATLAB*, 4th ed. Berlin: Springer-Verlag, 2004.

[45] Higham, Nicholas J., *Accuracy and Stability of Numerical Algorithms*, 2nd ed. Philadelphia: SIAM, 2002.

[46] Rivlin, Theodore J., *The Chebyshev Polynomials*. New York: Wiley-Interscience, 1974.

[47] Van Loan, Charles, *Computational Frameworks for the Fast Fourier Transform*. Philadelphia: SIAM, 1992.

References [5], [12], [20], and [29] contain information on MATLAB. Extended bibliographies are included in the following references: [4], [7], [23], [27], [31], [32], and [39].

Answers to Selected Exercises

Chapter 1

1.1

1. (a) $(11, 3)$; (b) $(4, 1, 3)$; (c) $(-2, 0, 3, 1)$;
   (d) $(-2, 3, 0, 3, 1)$

2. (a) $\begin{bmatrix} 1 & -3 \\ 0 & 2 \end{bmatrix}$; (b) $\begin{bmatrix} 1 & 1 & 1 \\ 0 & 2 & 1 \\ 0 & 0 & 3 \end{bmatrix}$;

   (c) $\begin{bmatrix} 1 & 2 & 2 & 1 \\ 0 & 3 & 1 & -2 \\ 0 & 0 & -1 & 2 \\ 0 & 0 & 0 & 4 \end{bmatrix}$

3. (a) One solution. The two lines intersect at the point $(3, 1)$.

   (b) No solution. The lines are parallel.

   (c) Infinitely many solutions. Both equations represent the same line.

   (d) No solution. Each pair of lines intersect in a point; however, there is no point that is on all three lines.

4. (a) $\begin{bmatrix} 1 & 1 & 4 \\ 1 & -1 & 2 \end{bmatrix}$; (c) $\begin{bmatrix} 2 & -1 & 3 \\ -4 & 2 & -6 \end{bmatrix}$;

   (d) $\begin{bmatrix} 1 & 1 & 1 \\ 1 & -1 & 1 \\ -1 & 3 & 3 \end{bmatrix}$

6. (a) $(1, -2)$; (b) $(3, 2)$; (c) $(\frac{1}{2}, \frac{2}{3})$;
   (d) $(1, 1, 2)$; (e) $(-3, 1, 2)$;
   (f) $(-1, 1, 1)$; (g) $(1, 1, -1)$;
   (h) $(4, -3, 1, 2)$

7. (a) $(2, -1)$; (b) $(-2, 3)$

8. (a) $(-1, 2, 1)$; (b) $(3, 1, -2)$

1.2

1. Row echelon form: (a), (c), (d), (g), and (h); reduced row echelon form: (c), (d), and (g)

2. (a) inconsistent;
   (c) consistent, infinitely many solutions;
   (d) consistent $(4, 5, 2)$; (e) inconsistent;
   (f) consistent, $(5, 3, 2)$

3. (b) $\emptyset$;
   (c) $\{(2 + 3\alpha, \alpha, -2) \mid \alpha \text{ real}\}$;
   (d) $\{(5 - 2\alpha - \beta, \alpha, 4 - 3\beta, \beta) \mid \alpha, \beta \text{ real}\}$;
   (e) $\{(3 - 5\alpha + 2\beta, \alpha, \beta, 6) \mid \alpha, \beta \text{ real}\}$;
   (f) $\{(\alpha, 2, -1) \mid \alpha \text{ real}\}$

4. (a) x_1, x_2, x_3 are lead variables.
   (c) x_1, x_3 are lead variables and x_2 is a free variable.
   (e) x_1, x_4 are lead variables and x_2, x_3 are free variables.

5. (a) $(5, 1)$; (b) inconsistent; (c) $(0, 0)$;
   (d) $\left\{ \left(\dfrac{5 - \alpha}{4}, \dfrac{1 + 7\alpha}{8}, \alpha \right) \Big| \alpha \text{ real} \right\}$;
   (e) $\{(8 - 2\alpha, \alpha - 5, \alpha)\}$;
   (f) inconsistent;
   (g) inconsistent; (h) inconsistent;
   (i) $(0, \frac{3}{2}, 1)$;
   (j) $\{(2 - 6\alpha, 4 + \alpha, 3 - \alpha, \alpha)\}$;
   (k) $\{(\frac{15}{4} - \frac{5}{8}\alpha - \beta, -\frac{1}{4} - \frac{1}{8}\alpha, \alpha, \beta)\}$;

6. (a) $(0, -1)$;
   (b) $\{(\frac{3}{4} - \frac{5}{8}\alpha, -\frac{1}{4} - \frac{1}{8}\alpha, \alpha, 3) \mid \alpha \text{ is real}\}$;
   (d) $\{\alpha(-\frac{4}{3}, 0, \frac{1}{3}, 1)\}$

8. $a \neq -2$

9. (b) $\beta = 2$

10. (a) $a = 5, b = 4$; (b) $a = 5, b \neq 4$

11. (a) $(-2, 2)$; (b) $(-7, 4)$

12. (a) $(-3, 2, 1)$; (b) $(2, -2, 1)$

15. $x_1 = 280, x_2 = 230, x_3 = 350, x_4 = 590$

19. $x_1 = 2, x_2 = 3, x_3 = 12, x_4 = 6$

20. 6 moles N_2, 18 moles H_2, 21 moles O_2

21. All three should be equal, i.e., $x_1 = x_2 = x_3$.

22. (a) $(5, 3, -2)$; (b) $(2, 4, 2)$;
    (c) $(2, 0, -2, -2, 0, 2)$

1.3

1. (a) $\begin{bmatrix} 6 & 2 & 8 \\ -4 & 0 & 2 \\ 2 & 4 & 4 \end{bmatrix}$;

(b) $\begin{bmatrix} 4 & 1 & 6 \\ -5 & 1 & 2 \\ 3 & -2 & 3 \end{bmatrix}$;

(c) $\begin{bmatrix} 3 & 2 & 2 \\ 5 & -3 & -1 \\ -4 & 16 & 1 \end{bmatrix}$;

(d) $\begin{bmatrix} 3 & 5 & -4 \\ 2 & -3 & 16 \\ 2 & -1 & 1 \end{bmatrix}$;

(f) $\begin{bmatrix} 5 & 5 & 8 \\ -10 & -1 & -9 \\ 15 & 4 & 6 \end{bmatrix}$;

(h) $\begin{bmatrix} 5 & -10 & 15 \\ 5 & -1 & 4 \\ 8 & -9 & 6 \end{bmatrix}$

2. (a) $\begin{bmatrix} 15 & 19 \\ 4 & 0 \end{bmatrix}$;   (c) $\begin{bmatrix} 19 & 21 \\ 17 & 21 \\ 8 & 10 \end{bmatrix}$;

(f) $\begin{bmatrix} 6 & 4 & 8 & 10 \\ -3 & -2 & -4 & -5 \\ 9 & 6 & 12 & 15 \end{bmatrix}$

(b) and (e) are not possible.

3. (a) 3×3;   (b) 1×2

4. (a) $\begin{bmatrix} 3 & 2 \\ 2 & -3 \end{bmatrix} \begin{bmatrix} x_1 \\ x_2 \end{bmatrix} = \begin{bmatrix} 1 \\ 5 \end{bmatrix}$;

(b) $\begin{bmatrix} 1 & 1 & 0 \\ 2 & 1 & -1 \\ 3 & -2 & 2 \end{bmatrix} \begin{bmatrix} x_1 \\ x_2 \\ x_3 \end{bmatrix} = \begin{bmatrix} 5 \\ 6 \\ 7 \end{bmatrix}$;

(c) $\begin{bmatrix} 2 & 1 & 1 \\ 1 & -1 & 2 \\ 3 & -2 & -1 \end{bmatrix} \begin{bmatrix} x_1 \\ x_2 \\ x_3 \end{bmatrix} = \begin{bmatrix} 4 \\ 2 \\ 0 \end{bmatrix}$

9. (a) $\mathbf{b} = 2\mathbf{a}_1 + \mathbf{a}_2$

10. (a) inconsistent;   (b) consistent;

(c) inconsistent

13. (b) $\mathbf{b} = (8, -7, -1, 7)^T$

14. $\mathbf{w} = (\frac{1}{2}, \frac{1}{3}, \frac{1}{6})^T$, $\mathbf{r} = (\frac{43}{120}, \frac{45}{120}, \frac{32}{120})^T$

18. $b = a_{22} - \dfrac{a_{12}a_{21}}{a_{11}}$

1.4 7. $A = A^2 = A^3 = A^n$

8. $A^{2n} = I, A^{2n+1} = A$

13. (a) $\begin{bmatrix} 1 & -2 \\ -3 & 7 \end{bmatrix}$;   (c) $\begin{bmatrix} 1 & -\frac{3}{2} \\ -1 & 2 \end{bmatrix}$

31. 4500 married, 5500 single

32. (b) 0 walks of length 2 from V_2 to V_3 and 3 walks of length 2 from V_2 to V_5;

(c) 6 walks of length 3 from V_2 to V_3 and 2 walks of length 3 from V_2 to V_5

33. (a) $A = \begin{bmatrix} 0 & 1 & 0 & 1 & 0 \\ 1 & 0 & 1 & 1 & 0 \\ 0 & 1 & 0 & 0 & 0 \\ 1 & 1 & 0 & 0 & 1 \\ 0 & 0 & 0 & 1 & 0 \end{bmatrix}$;

(c) 5 walks of length 3 from V_2 to V_4 and 7 walks of length 3 or less

1.5 1. (a) type I;

(b) not an elementary matrix;

(c) type III;   (d) type II

3. (a) $\begin{bmatrix} -2 & 0 \\ 0 & 1 \end{bmatrix}$;   (b) $\begin{bmatrix} 1 & 0 & 0 \\ 0 & 0 & 1 \\ 0 & 1 & 0 \end{bmatrix}$;

(c) $\begin{bmatrix} 1 & 0 & 0 \\ 0 & 1 & 0 \\ 0 & 2 & 1 \end{bmatrix}$

4. (a) $\begin{bmatrix} 0 & 0 & 1 \\ 0 & 1 & 0 \\ 1 & 0 & 0 \end{bmatrix}$;   (b) $\begin{bmatrix} 1 & -3 \\ 0 & 1 \end{bmatrix}$;

(c) $\begin{bmatrix} \frac{1}{2} & 0 & 0 \\ 0 & 1 & 0 \\ 0 & 0 & 1 \end{bmatrix}$

5. (a) $E = \begin{bmatrix} 1 & 0 & 0 \\ 0 & 1 & 0 \\ 1 & 0 & 1 \end{bmatrix}$;

(b) $F = \begin{bmatrix} 1 & 0 & 0 \\ 0 & 1 & -1 \\ 0 & 0 & 1 \end{bmatrix}$

6. (a) $E_1 = \begin{bmatrix} 1 & 0 & 0 \\ -3 & 1 & 0 \\ 0 & 0 & 1 \end{bmatrix}$;

(b) $E_2 = \begin{bmatrix} 1 & 0 & 0 \\ 0 & 1 & 0 \\ -2 & 0 & 1 \end{bmatrix}$;

(c) $E_3 = \begin{bmatrix} 1 & 0 & 0 \\ 0 & 1 & 0 \\ 0 & 1 & 1 \end{bmatrix}$

8. (a) $\begin{bmatrix} 1 & 0 \\ 3 & 1 \end{bmatrix} \begin{bmatrix} 3 & 1 \\ 0 & 2 \end{bmatrix}$;

(c) $\begin{bmatrix} 1 & 0 & 0 \\ 3 & 1 & 0 \\ -2 & 2 & 1 \end{bmatrix} \begin{bmatrix} 1 & 1 & 1 \\ 0 & 2 & 3 \\ 0 & 0 & 3 \end{bmatrix}$

9. (b) (i) $(0, -1, 1)^T$,   (ii) $(-4, -2, 5)^T$,
   (iii) $(0, 3, -2)^T$

10. (a) $\begin{bmatrix} 0 & 1 \\ 1 & 1 \end{bmatrix}$;   (b) $\begin{bmatrix} 3 & -5 \\ -1 & 2 \end{bmatrix}$;

    (c) $\begin{bmatrix} -4 & 3 \\ \frac{3}{2} & -1 \end{bmatrix}$;   (d) $\begin{bmatrix} \frac{1}{3} & 0 \\ -1 & \frac{1}{3} \end{bmatrix}$;

    (f) $\begin{bmatrix} 3 & 0 & -5 \\ 0 & \frac{1}{3} & 0 \\ -1 & 0 & 2 \end{bmatrix}$;

    (g) $\begin{bmatrix} 2 & -3 & 3 \\ -\frac{3}{5} & \frac{6}{5} & -1 \\ -\frac{2}{5} & -\frac{1}{5} & 0 \end{bmatrix}$;

    (h) $\begin{bmatrix} -\frac{1}{2} & -1 & -\frac{1}{2} \\ -2 & -1 & -1 \\ \frac{3}{2} & 1 & \frac{1}{2} \end{bmatrix}$

11. (a) $\begin{bmatrix} -1 & 0 \\ 4 & 2 \end{bmatrix}$;   (b) $\begin{bmatrix} -8 & 5 \\ -14 & 9 \end{bmatrix}$

12. (a) $\begin{bmatrix} 20 & -5 \\ -34 & 7 \end{bmatrix}$;   (c) $\begin{bmatrix} 0 & -2 \\ -2 & 2 \end{bmatrix}$

1.6 1. (b) $\begin{bmatrix} I \\ A^{-1} \end{bmatrix}$;   (c) $\begin{bmatrix} A^T A & A^T \\ A & I \end{bmatrix}$;

    (d) $AA^T + I$;   (e) $\begin{bmatrix} I & A^{-1} \\ A & I \end{bmatrix}$

3. (a) $A\mathbf{b}_1 = \begin{bmatrix} 3 \\ 3 \end{bmatrix}$, $A\mathbf{b}_2 = \begin{bmatrix} 4 \\ -1 \end{bmatrix}$;

   (b) $\begin{bmatrix} 1 & 1 \end{bmatrix} B = \begin{bmatrix} 3 & 4 \end{bmatrix}$,
       $\begin{bmatrix} 2 & -1 \end{bmatrix} B = \begin{bmatrix} 3 & -1 \end{bmatrix}$;

   (c) $AB = \begin{bmatrix} 3 & 4 \\ 3 & -1 \end{bmatrix}$

4. (a) $\left[\begin{array}{cc|cc} 3 & 1 & 1 & 1 \\ 3 & 2 & 1 & 2 \\ \hline 1 & 1 & 1 & 1 \\ 1 & 2 & 1 & 1 \end{array}\right]$;

   (c) $\left[\begin{array}{cc|cc} 2 & 2 & 2 & 2 \\ 2 & 4 & 2 & 2 \\ \hline 3 & 1 & 1 & 1 \\ 3 & 2 & 1 & 2 \end{array}\right]$;

   (d) $\left[\begin{array}{cc|cc} 1 & 2 & 1 & 1 \\ 1 & 1 & 1 & 1 \\ \hline 3 & 2 & 1 & 2 \\ 3 & 1 & 1 & 1 \end{array}\right]$

5. (b) $\left[\begin{array}{ccc|c} 0 & 2 & 0 & -2 \\ 8 & 5 & 8 & -5 \\ 3 & 2 & 3 & -2 \\ \hline 5 & 3 & 5 & -3 \end{array}\right]$;

   (d) $\left[\begin{array}{cc} 3 & -3 \\ 2 & -2 \\ 1 & -1 \\ \hline 5 & -5 \\ 4 & -4 \end{array}\right]$

13. $A^2 = \begin{bmatrix} B & O \\ O & B \end{bmatrix}$, $A^4 = \begin{bmatrix} B^2 & O \\ O & B^2 \end{bmatrix}$

14. (a) $\begin{bmatrix} O & I \\ I & O \end{bmatrix}$;   (b) $\begin{bmatrix} I & O \\ -B & I \end{bmatrix}$

CHAPTER TEST A
1. False   2. True   3. True   4. True   5. False
6. False   7. False   8. False   9. False   10. True
11. True   12. True   13. True   14. False
15. True

Chapter 2

2.1 1. (a) $\det(M_{21}) = -8$, $\det(M_{22}) = -2$,
         $\det(M_{23}) = 5$;
      (b) $A_{21} = 8$, $A_{22} = -2$, $A_{23} = -5$

2. (a) and (c) are nonsingular.

3. (a) 1;   (b) 4;   (c) 0;   (d) 58;
   (e) -39;   (f) 0;   (g) 8;   (h) 20

4. (a) 2;   (b) -4;   (c) 0;   (d) 0

5. $-x^3 + ax^2 + bx + c$

6. $\lambda = 6$ or -1

2.2 1. (a) -24;   (b) 30;   (c) -1

2. (a) 10;   (b) 20

3. (a), (e), and (f) are singular while (b), (c), and (d) are nonsingular.

4. $c = 5$ or -3

7. (a) 20;   (b) 108;   (c) 160;   (d) $\frac{5}{4}$

9. (a) -6;   (c) 6;   (e) 1

13. $\det(A) = u_{11}u_{22}u_{33}$

2.3 1. (a) $\det(A) = -7$, $\text{adj } A = \begin{bmatrix} -1 & -2 \\ -3 & 1 \end{bmatrix}$,
       $A^{-1} = \begin{bmatrix} \frac{1}{7} & \frac{2}{7} \\ \frac{3}{7} & -\frac{1}{7} \end{bmatrix}$;

   (c) $\det(A) = 3$, $\text{adj } A = \begin{bmatrix} -3 & 5 & 2 \\ 0 & 1 & 1 \\ 6 & -8 & -5 \end{bmatrix}$,
       $A^{-1} = \frac{1}{3} \text{adj } A$

2. (a) $(\frac{5}{7}, \frac{8}{7})$;   (b) $(\frac{11}{5}, -\frac{4}{5})$;
    (c) $(4, -2, 2)$;   (d) $(2, -1, 2)$;
    (e) $(-\frac{2}{3}, \frac{2}{3}, \frac{1}{3}, 0)$

3. $-\frac{3}{4}$

4. $(\frac{1}{2}, -\frac{3}{4}, 1)^T$

5. (a) $\det(A) = 0$, so A is singular.

    (b) $\operatorname{adj} A = \begin{pmatrix} -1 & 2 & -1 \\ 2 & -4 & 2 \\ -1 & 2 & -1 \end{pmatrix}$ and

    $A \operatorname{adj} A = \begin{pmatrix} 0 & 0 & 0 \\ 0 & 0 & 0 \\ 0 & 0 & 0 \end{pmatrix}$

9. (a) $\det(\operatorname{adj}(A)) = 8$ and $\det(A) = 2$;

    (b) $A = \begin{pmatrix} 1 & 0 & 0 & 0 \\ 0 & 4 & -1 & 1 \\ 0 & -6 & 2 & -2 \\ 0 & 1 & 0 & 1 \end{pmatrix}$

14. DO YOUR HOMEWORK.

CHAPTER TEST A

1. True   2. False   3. False   4. True   5. False
6. True   7. True   8. True   9. False   10. True

Chapter 3

3.1   1. (a) $\|\mathbf{x}_1\| = 10$, $\|\mathbf{x}_2\| = \sqrt{17}$;
    (b) $\|\mathbf{x}_3\| = 13 < \|\mathbf{x}_1\| + \|\mathbf{x}_2\|$
2. (a) $\|\mathbf{x}_1\| = \sqrt{5}$, $\|\mathbf{x}_2\| = 3\sqrt{5}$;
    (b) $\|\mathbf{x}_3\| = 4\sqrt{5} = \|\mathbf{x}_1\| + \|\mathbf{x}_2\|$
7. If $\mathbf{x} + \mathbf{y} = \mathbf{x}$ for all $\mathbf{x}$ in the vector space, then
    $\mathbf{0} = \mathbf{0} + \mathbf{y} = \mathbf{y}$.
8. If $\mathbf{x} + \mathbf{y} = \mathbf{x} + \mathbf{z}$, then $-\mathbf{x} + (\mathbf{x} + \mathbf{y}) = -\mathbf{x} + (\mathbf{x} + \mathbf{z})$
    and the conclusion follows using axioms 1, 2, 3,
    and 4.
11. V is not a vector space. Axiom 6 does not hold.

3.2   1. (a) and (c) are subspaces; (b), (d), and (e) are not.
2. (b) and (c) are subspaces; (a) and (d) are not.
3. (a), (c), (e), and (f) are subspaces; (b), (d), and (g)
    are not.
4. (a) $\{(0, 0)^T\}$;
    (b) $\mathrm{Span}((-2, 1, 0, 0)^T, (3, 0, 1, 0)^T)$;
    (c) $\mathrm{Span}((1, 1, 1)^T)$;
    (d) $\mathrm{Span}((-5, 0, -3, 1)^T, (-1, 1, 0, 0)^T)$
5. Only the set in part (c) is a subspace of P_4.
6. (a), (b), and (d) are subspaces.
11. (a), (c), and (e) are spanning sets.
12. (a) and (b) are spanning sets.
20. (b) and (c)

3.3   1. (a) and (e) are linearly independent; (b), (c), and (d)
    are linearly dependent.
2. (a) and (e) are linearly independent; (b), (c), and (d)
    are not.
3. (a) and (b) are all of 3-space;
    (c) a plane through $(0, 0, 0)$;
    (d) a line through $(0, 0, 0)$;
    (e) a plane through $(0, 0, 0)$
4. (a) linearly independent;
    (b) linearly independent;
    (c) linearly dependent
8. (a) and (b) are linearly dependent while (c) and (d)
    are linearly independent.
11. When α is an odd multiple of $\pi/2$. If the graph of
    $y = \cos x$ is shifted to the left or right by an odd
    multiple of $\pi/2$, we obtain the graph of either $\sin x$
    or $-\sin x$.

3.4   1. Only in parts (a) and (e) do they form a basis.
2. Only in part (a) do they form a basis.
3. (c) 2
4. 1
5. (c) 2;
    (d) a plane through $(0, 0, 0)$ in 3-space
6. (b) $\{(1, 1, 1)^T\}$, dimension 1;
    (c) $\{(1, 0, 1)^T, (0, 1, 1)^T\}$, dimension 2
7. basis $\{(1, 1, 0, 0)^T, (1, -1, 1, 0)^T, (0, 2, 0, 1)^T\}$
11. $\{x^2 + 2, x + 3\}$
12. (a) $\{E_{11}, E_{22}\}$;   (c) $\{E_{11}, E_{21}, E_{22}\}$;
    (e) $\{E_{12}, E_{21}, E_{22}\}$;
    (f) $\{E_{11}, E_{22}, E_{21} + E_{12}\}$
13. 2
14. (a) 3;   (b) 3;   (c) 2;   (d) 2
15. (a) $\{x, x^2\}$;   (b) $\{x - 1, (x - 1)^2\}$;
    (c) $\{x(x - 1)\}$

3.5   1. (a) $\begin{bmatrix} 1 & -1 \\ 1 & 1 \end{bmatrix}$;   (b) $\begin{bmatrix} 1 & 2 \\ 2 & 5 \end{bmatrix}$;
    (c) $\begin{bmatrix} 0 & 1 \\ 1 & 0 \end{bmatrix}$
2. (a) $\begin{bmatrix} \frac{1}{2} & \frac{1}{2} \\ -\frac{1}{2} & \frac{1}{2} \end{bmatrix}$;   (b) $\begin{bmatrix} 5 & -2 \\ -2 & 1 \end{bmatrix}$;
    (c) $\begin{bmatrix} 0 & 1 \\ 1 & 0 \end{bmatrix}$

3. (a) $\begin{bmatrix} \frac{5}{2} & \frac{7}{2} \\ -\frac{1}{2} & -\frac{1}{2} \end{bmatrix}$; (b) $\begin{bmatrix} 11 & 14 \\ -4 & -5 \end{bmatrix}$;

(c) $\begin{bmatrix} 2 & 3 \\ 3 & 4 \end{bmatrix}$

4. $[\mathbf{x}]_E = (-1, 2)^T$, $[\mathbf{y}]_E = (5, -8)^T$, $[\mathbf{z}]_E = (-1, 5)^T$

5. (a) $\begin{bmatrix} 2 & 0 & -1 \\ -1 & 2 & -1 \\ 0 & -1 & 1 \end{bmatrix}$; (b) $(1, -4, 3)^T$;

(c) $(0, -1, 1)^T$; (d) $(2, 2, -1)^T$

6. (a) $\begin{bmatrix} 1 & -1 & -2 \\ 1 & 1 & 0 \\ 1 & 0 & 1 \end{bmatrix}$; (b) $\begin{bmatrix} 7 \\ 5 \\ -2 \end{bmatrix}$

7. $\mathbf{w}_1 = (5, 9)^T$ and $\mathbf{w}_2 = (1, 4)^T$

8. $\mathbf{u}_1 = (0, -1)^T$ and $\mathbf{u}_2 = (1, 5)^T$

9. (a) $\begin{bmatrix} 2 & 2 \\ -1 & 1 \end{bmatrix}$; (b) $\begin{bmatrix} \frac{1}{4} & -\frac{1}{2} \\ \frac{1}{4} & \frac{1}{2} \end{bmatrix}$

10. $\begin{bmatrix} 1 & -1 & 0 \\ 0 & 1 & -1 \\ 0 & 0 & 1 \end{bmatrix}$

3.6 2. (a) 3; (b) 3; (c) 2

3. (a) $\mathbf{u}_2, \mathbf{u}_4, \mathbf{u}_5$ are the column vectors of U corresponding to the free variables.
$\mathbf{u}_2 = 2\mathbf{u}_1$, $\mathbf{u}_4 = 5\mathbf{u}_1 - \mathbf{u}_3$, $\mathbf{u}_5 = -3\mathbf{u}_1 + 2\mathbf{u}_3$

4. (a) consistent; (b) inconsistent;

(e) consistent

5. (a) infinitely many solutions;

(c) unique solution

8. rank of $A = 3$; $\dim N(B) = 1$;

18. (b) $n - 1$

32. If $\mathbf{x}_j$ is a solution to $A\mathbf{x} = \mathbf{e}_j$ for $j = 1, \ldots, m$ and $X = (\mathbf{x}_1, \mathbf{x}_2, \ldots, \mathbf{x}_m)$, then $AX = I_m$.

CHAPTER TEST A
1. True 2. False 3. False 4. False 5. True
6. True 7. False 8. True 9. True 10. False
11. True 12. False 13. True 14. False
15. False

Chapter 4

4.1 1. (a) reflection about x_2 axis;

(b) reflection about the origin;

(c) reflection about the line $x_2 = x_1$;

(d) the length of the vector is halved;

(e) projection onto x_2 axis

4. $(7, 18)^T$

5. All except (c) are linear transformations from R^3 into R^2.

6. (b) and (c) are linear transformations from R^2 into R^3.

7. (a), (b), and (d) are linear transformations.

9. (a) and (c) are linear transformations from P_2 into P_3.

10. $L(e^x) = e^x - 1$ and $L(x^2) = x^3/3$.

11. (a) and (c) are linear transformations from $C[0, 1]$ into R^1.

17. (a) $\ker(L) = \{\mathbf{0}\}$, $L(R^3) = R^3$;

(c) $\ker(L) = \text{Span}(\mathbf{e}_2, \mathbf{e}_3)$,
$L(R^3) = \text{Span}((1, 1, 1)^T)$

18. (a) $L(S) = \text{Span}(\mathbf{e}_2, \mathbf{e}_3)$;

(b) $L(S) = \text{Span}(\mathbf{e}_1, \mathbf{e}_2)$

19. (a) $\ker(L) = P_1$, $L(P_3) = \text{Span}(x^2, x)$;

(c) $\ker(L) = \text{Span}(x^2 - x)$, $L(P_3) = P_2$

23. The operator in part (a) is one-to-one and onto.

4.2 1. (a) $\begin{bmatrix} -1 & 0 \\ 0 & 1 \end{bmatrix}$; (c) $\begin{bmatrix} 0 & 1 \\ 1 & 0 \end{bmatrix}$;

(d) $\begin{bmatrix} \frac{1}{2} & 0 \\ 0 & \frac{1}{2} \end{bmatrix}$; (e) $\begin{bmatrix} 0 & 0 \\ 0 & 1 \end{bmatrix}$

2. (a) $\begin{bmatrix} 1 & 1 & 0 \\ 0 & 0 & 0 \end{bmatrix}$; (b) $\begin{bmatrix} 1 & 0 & 0 \\ 0 & 1 & 0 \end{bmatrix}$;

(c) $\begin{bmatrix} -1 & 1 & 0 \\ 0 & -1 & 1 \end{bmatrix}$

3. (a) $\begin{bmatrix} 0 & 0 & 1 \\ 0 & 1 & 0 \\ 1 & 0 & 0 \end{bmatrix}$; (b) $\begin{bmatrix} 1 & 0 & 0 \\ 1 & 1 & 0 \\ 1 & 1 & 1 \end{bmatrix}$;

(c) $\begin{bmatrix} 0 & 0 & 2 \\ 3 & 1 & 0 \\ 2 & 0 & -1 \end{bmatrix}$

4. (a) $(0, 0, 0)^T$; (b) $(2, -1, -1)^T$;

(c) $(-15, 9, 6)^T$

5. (a) $\begin{bmatrix} \frac{1}{\sqrt{2}} & \frac{1}{\sqrt{2}} \\ -\frac{1}{\sqrt{2}} & \frac{1}{\sqrt{2}} \end{bmatrix}$; (b) $\begin{bmatrix} 0 & 1 \\ 1 & 0 \end{bmatrix}$;

(c) $\begin{bmatrix} \sqrt{3} & -1 \\ 1 & \sqrt{3} \end{bmatrix}$; (d) $\begin{bmatrix} 0 & 1 \\ 0 & 0 \end{bmatrix}$

6. $\begin{bmatrix} 1 & 0 \\ 0 & 1 \\ 1 & 1 \end{bmatrix}$

7. (b) $\begin{bmatrix} 0 & 0 & 1 \\ 0 & 1 & -1 \\ 1 & -1 & 0 \end{bmatrix}$

8. (a) $\begin{bmatrix} 1 & 1 & 1 \\ 2 & 0 & 1 \\ 0 & -2 & -1 \end{bmatrix}$;

   (b) (i) $7\mathbf{y}_1 + 6\mathbf{y}_2 - 8\mathbf{y}_3$, (ii) $3\mathbf{y}_1 + 3\mathbf{y}_2 - 3\mathbf{y}_3$,
   (iii) $\mathbf{y}_1 + 5\mathbf{y}_2 + 3\mathbf{y}_3$

9. (a) square; (b) (i) contraction by a factor $\frac{1}{2}$,
   (ii) clockwise rotation by 45°, (iii) translation 2
   units to the right and 3 units down

10. (a) $\begin{bmatrix} -\frac{1}{2} & -\frac{\sqrt{3}}{2} & 0 \\ \frac{\sqrt{3}}{2} & -\frac{1}{2} & 0 \\ 0 & 0 & 1 \end{bmatrix}$;

    (b) $\begin{bmatrix} 1 & 0 & -3 \\ 0 & 1 & 5 \\ 0 & 0 & 1 \end{bmatrix}$; (d) $\begin{bmatrix} -1 & 0 & 0 \\ 0 & 1 & 2 \\ 0 & 0 & 1 \end{bmatrix}$

13. $\begin{bmatrix} 1 & \frac{1}{2} \\ 1 & 0 \end{bmatrix}$;

14. $\begin{bmatrix} 1 & \frac{1}{2} & \frac{1}{2} \\ -2 & 0 & 0 \end{bmatrix}$; (a) $\begin{bmatrix} \frac{1}{2} \\ -2 \end{bmatrix}$ (d) $\begin{bmatrix} 5 \\ -8 \end{bmatrix}$

15. $\begin{bmatrix} 1 & 1 & 0 \\ 0 & 1 & 2 \\ 0 & 0 & 1 \end{bmatrix}$;

18. (a) $\begin{bmatrix} -1 & -3 & 1 \\ 0 & 2 & 0 \end{bmatrix}$; (c) $\begin{bmatrix} 2 & -2 & -4 \\ -1 & 3 & 3 \end{bmatrix}$

4.3 1. For the matrix A, see the answers to Exercise 1 of
   Section 4.2.

   (a) $B = \begin{bmatrix} 0 & 1 \\ 1 & 0 \end{bmatrix}$; (b) $B = \begin{bmatrix} -1 & 0 \\ 0 & -1 \end{bmatrix}$;

   (c) $B = \begin{bmatrix} 1 & 0 \\ 0 & -1 \end{bmatrix}$; (d) $B = \begin{bmatrix} \frac{1}{2} & 0 \\ 0 & \frac{1}{2} \end{bmatrix}$;

   (e) $B = \begin{bmatrix} \frac{1}{2} & \frac{1}{2} \\ \frac{1}{2} & \frac{1}{2} \end{bmatrix}$

2. (a) $\begin{bmatrix} 1 & 1 \\ -1 & -3 \end{bmatrix}$; (b) $\begin{bmatrix} 1 & 0 \\ -4 & -1 \end{bmatrix}$

3. $B = A = \begin{bmatrix} 2 & -1 & -1 \\ -1 & 2 & -1 \\ -1 & -1 & 2 \end{bmatrix}$

(Note: in this case the matrices A and U commute;
so $B = U^{-1}AU = U^{-1}UA = A$.)

4. $V = \begin{bmatrix} 1 & 1 & 0 \\ 1 & 2 & -2 \\ 1 & 0 & 1 \end{bmatrix}$, $B = \begin{bmatrix} 0 & 0 & 0 \\ 0 & 1 & 0 \\ 0 & 0 & 1 \end{bmatrix}$

5. (a) $\begin{bmatrix} 0 & 0 & 2 \\ 0 & 1 & 0 \\ 0 & 0 & 2 \end{bmatrix}$; (b) $\begin{bmatrix} 0 & 0 & 0 \\ 0 & 1 & 0 \\ 0 & 0 & 2 \end{bmatrix}$;

   (c) $\begin{bmatrix} 1 & 0 & 1 \\ 0 & 1 & 0 \\ 0 & 0 & 1 \end{bmatrix}$; (d) $a_1 x + a_2 2^n (1 + x^2)$

6. (a) $\begin{bmatrix} 1 & 0 & 0 \\ 0 & 1 & 1 \\ 0 & 1 & -1 \end{bmatrix}$; (b) $\begin{bmatrix} 0 & 0 & 0 \\ 0 & 0 & 1 \\ 0 & 1 & 0 \end{bmatrix}$;

   (c) $\begin{bmatrix} 0 & 0 & 0 \\ 0 & 1 & 0 \\ 0 & 0 & -1 \end{bmatrix}$

CHAPTER TEST A
1. False 2. True 3. True 4. False 5. False
6. True 7. True 8. True 9. True 10. False

Chapter 5

5.1 1. (a) 0°; (b) 90°
   2. (a) $\sqrt{14}$ (scalar projection), $(2,1,3)^T$ (vector
      projection);

      (b) $0, \mathbf{0}$; (c) $\frac{14\sqrt{13}}{13}^T, (\frac{42}{13}, \frac{28}{13})^T$;

      (d) $\frac{8\sqrt{21}}{21}^T, (\frac{8}{21}, \frac{16}{21}, \frac{32}{21})^T$

   3. (a) $\mathbf{p} = (3,0)^T, \mathbf{x} - \mathbf{p} = (0,4)^T,$
      $\mathbf{p}^T(\mathbf{x} - \mathbf{p}) = 3 \cdot 0 + 0 \cdot 4 = 0;$

      (c) $\mathbf{p} = (3,3,3)^T, \mathbf{x} - \mathbf{p} = (-1,1,0)^T,$
      $\mathbf{p}^T(\mathbf{x} - \mathbf{p}) = -1 \cdot 3 + 1 \cdot 3 + 0 \cdot 3 = 0$

   5. $(1.8, 3.6)$

   6. $(1.4, 3.8)$

   7. 0.4

   8. (a) $2x + 4y + 3z = 0$; (c) $z - 4 = 0$

   9. $\frac{5}{3}$

   10. $\frac{8}{7}$

   20. The correlation matrix with entries rounded to two
       decimal places is

       $$\begin{bmatrix} 1.00 & -0.04 & 0.41 \\ -0.04 & 1.00 & 0.87 \\ 0.41 & 0.87 & 1.00 \end{bmatrix}$$

5.2 1. (a) $\{(3,4)^T\}$ basis for $R(A^T)$,
   $\{(-4,3)^T\}$ basis for $N(A)$,
   $\{(1,2)^T\}$ basis for $R(A)$,
   $\{(-2,1)^T\}$ basis for $N(A^T)$;

 (d) basis for $R(A^T)$:
   $\{(1,0,0,0)^T, (0,1,0,0)^T (0,0,1,1)^T\}$,
   basis for $N(A)$: $\{(0,0,-1,1)^T\}$,
   basis for $R(A)$:
   $\{(1,0,0,1)^T, (0,1,0,1)^T (0,0,1,1)^T\}$,
   basis for $N(A^T)$: $\{(1,1,1,-1)^T\}$

 2. (a) $\{(1,1,0)^T, (-1,0,1)^T\}$

 3. (b) The orthogonal complement is spanned by $(-5,1,3)^T$.

 4. $\{(-1,2,0,1)^T, (2,-3,1,0)^T\}$ is one basis for $S^{\perp}$.

 6. (a) $\mathbf{N} = (8,-2,1)^T$;   (b) $8x - 2y + z = 7$

 10. $\dim N(A) = n - r$, $\dim N(A^T) = m - r$

5.3 1. (a) $(2,1)^T$;   (c) $(1.6, 0.6, 1.2)^T$

 2. (1a) $\mathbf{p} = (3,1,0)^T$, $\mathbf{r} = (0,0,2)^T$
   (1c) $\mathbf{p} = (3.4, 0.2, 0.6, 2.8)^T$,
   $\mathbf{r} = (0.6, -0.2, 0.4, -0.8)^T$

 3. (a) $\{(1-2\alpha, \alpha)^T \mid \alpha \text{ real}\}$;
   (b) $\{(2-2\alpha, 1-\alpha, \alpha)^T \mid \alpha \text{ real}\}$

 4. (a) $\mathbf{p} = (1,2,-1)^T$, $\mathbf{b} - \mathbf{p} = (2,0,2)^T$;
   (b) $\mathbf{p} = (3,1,4)^T$, $\mathbf{p} - \mathbf{b} = (-5,-1,4)^T$

 5. (a) $y = 1.8 + 2.9x$

 6. $0.55 + 1.65x + 1.25x^2$

 14. The least squares circle will have center $(0.58, -0.64)$ and radius 2.73 (answers rounded to two decimal places).

 15. (a) $\mathbf{w} = (0.1995,\ 0.2599,\ 0.3412,\ 0.1995)^T$
   (b) $\mathbf{r} = (0.2605,\ 0.2337,\ 0.2850,\ 0.2208)^T$

5.4 1. $\|\mathbf{x}\|_2 = 2$, $\|\mathbf{y}\|_2 = 6$, $\|\mathbf{x}+\mathbf{y}\|_2 = 2\sqrt{10}$

 2. (a) $\theta = \frac{\pi}{4}$; $\mathbf{p} = (\frac{4}{3}, \frac{1}{3}, \frac{1}{3}, 0)^T$

 3. (b) $\|\mathbf{x}\| = 1$, $\|\mathbf{y}\| = 3$

 4. (a) 0;   (b) 5;   (c) 7;   (d) $\sqrt{74}$

 7. (a) 1;   (b) $\frac{1}{\pi}$

 8. (a) $\frac{\pi}{6}$;   (b) $\mathbf{p} = \frac{3}{2}x$

 11. (a) $\frac{\sqrt{10}}{2}$;   (b) $\frac{\sqrt{34}}{4}$

 15. (a) $\|\mathbf{x}\|_1 = 7$, $\|\mathbf{x}\|_2 = 5$, $\|\mathbf{x}\|_{\infty} = 4$;
   (b) $\|\mathbf{x}\|_1 = 4$, $\|\mathbf{x}\|_2 = \sqrt{6}$, $\|\mathbf{x}\|_{\infty} = 2$;
   (c) $\|\mathbf{x}\|_1 = 3$, $\|\mathbf{x}\|_2 = \sqrt{3}$, $\|\mathbf{x}\|_{\infty} = 1$

 16. $\|\mathbf{x} - \mathbf{y}\|_1 = 5$, $\|\mathbf{x} - \mathbf{y}\|_2 = 3$, $\|\mathbf{x} - \mathbf{y}\|_{\infty} = 2$

 28. (a) not a norm;   (b) norm;   (c) norm

5.5 1. (a) and (d)

 2. (b) $\mathbf{x} = -\frac{\sqrt{2}}{3}\mathbf{u}_1 + \frac{5}{3}\mathbf{u}_2$,
   $$\|\mathbf{x}\| = \left[\left(-\frac{\sqrt{2}}{3}\right)^2 + \left(\frac{5}{3}\right)^2\right]^{1/2} = \sqrt{3}$$

 3. $\mathbf{p} = (\frac{23}{18}, \frac{41}{18}, \frac{8}{9})^T$, $\mathbf{p} - \mathbf{x} = (\frac{5}{18}, \frac{5}{18}, -\frac{10}{9})^T$

 4. (b) $c_1 = y_1 \cos\theta + y_2 \sin\theta$,
   $c_2 = -y_1 \sin\theta + y_2 \cos\theta$

 6. (a) 15;   (b) $\|\mathbf{u}\| = 3$, $\|\mathbf{v}\| = 5\sqrt{2}$;   (c) $\frac{\pi}{4}$

 9. (b) (i) 0,   (ii) $-\frac{\pi}{2}$,   (iii) 0,   (iv) $\frac{\pi}{8}$

 21. (b) (i) $(2,-2)^T$, (ii) $(5,2)^T$, (iii) $(3,1)^T$

 22. (a) $P = \begin{bmatrix} \frac{1}{2} & \frac{1}{2} & 0 & 0 \\ \frac{1}{2} & \frac{1}{2} & 0 & 0 \\ 0 & 0 & \frac{1}{2} & \frac{1}{2} \\ 0 & 0 & \frac{1}{2} & \frac{1}{2} \end{bmatrix}$;

 23. (b) $Q = \begin{bmatrix} \frac{1}{2} & -\frac{1}{2} & 0 & 0 \\ -\frac{1}{2} & \frac{1}{2} & 0 & 0 \\ 0 & 0 & \frac{1}{2} & -\frac{1}{2} \\ 0 & 0 & -\frac{1}{2} & \frac{1}{2} \end{bmatrix}$

 29. (b) $\|1\| = \sqrt{2}$, $\|x\| = \frac{\sqrt{6}}{3}$;   (c) $l(x) = \frac{9}{7}x$

5.6 1. (a) $\left\{\left(-\frac{1}{\sqrt{2}}, \frac{1}{\sqrt{2}}\right)^T, \left(\frac{1}{\sqrt{2}}, \frac{1}{\sqrt{2}}\right)^T\right\}$;

 (b) $\left\{\left(\frac{2}{\sqrt{5}}, \frac{1}{\sqrt{5}}\right)^T, \left(-\frac{1}{\sqrt{5}}, \frac{2}{\sqrt{5}}\right)^T\right\}$

 2. (a) $\begin{bmatrix} -\frac{1}{\sqrt{2}} & \frac{1}{\sqrt{2}} \\ \frac{1}{\sqrt{2}} & \frac{1}{\sqrt{2}} \end{bmatrix} \begin{bmatrix} \sqrt{2} & \sqrt{2} \\ 0 & 4\sqrt{2} \end{bmatrix}$;

 (b) $\begin{bmatrix} \frac{2}{\sqrt{5}} & -\frac{1}{\sqrt{5}} \\ \frac{1}{\sqrt{5}} & \frac{2}{\sqrt{5}} \end{bmatrix} \begin{bmatrix} \sqrt{5} & 4\sqrt{5} \\ 0 & 3\sqrt{5} \end{bmatrix}$

 3. $\{(\frac{1}{3}, \frac{2}{3}, -\frac{2}{3})^T, (\frac{2}{3}, \frac{1}{3}, \frac{2}{3})^T, (-\frac{2}{3}, \frac{2}{3}, \frac{1}{3})^T\}$

 4. $u_1(x) = \frac{1}{\sqrt{2}}$, $u_2(x) = \frac{\sqrt{6}}{2}x$,
   $u_3(x) = \frac{3\sqrt{10}}{4}\left(x^2 - \frac{1}{3}\right)$

 5. (a) $\left\{\frac{1}{3}(2,1,2)^T, \frac{\sqrt{2}}{6}(-1,4,-1)^T\right\}$;

(b) $Q = \begin{bmatrix} \frac{2}{3} & \frac{-\sqrt{2}}{6} \\ \frac{1}{3} & \frac{2\sqrt{2}}{3} \\ \frac{2}{3} & \frac{-\sqrt{2}}{6} \end{bmatrix}$; $R = \begin{bmatrix} 3 & \frac{5}{3} \\ 0 & \frac{\sqrt{2}}{3} \end{bmatrix}$;

(c) $\mathbf{x} = \begin{bmatrix} 9 \\ -3 \end{bmatrix}$

6. (b) $\begin{bmatrix} \frac{3}{5} & -\frac{4}{5\sqrt{2}} \\ \frac{4}{5} & \frac{3}{5\sqrt{2}} \\ 0 & \frac{1}{\sqrt{2}} \end{bmatrix} \begin{bmatrix} 5 & 1 \\ 0 & 2\sqrt{2} \end{bmatrix}$;

(c) $(2.1, 5.5)^T$

7. $\left\{ \left(-\frac{1}{\sqrt{2}}, \frac{1}{\sqrt{2}}, 0, 0 \right)^T, \left(\frac{\sqrt{2}}{3}, \frac{\sqrt{2}}{3}, -\frac{\sqrt{2}}{2}, \frac{\sqrt{2}}{6} \right)^T \right\}$

8. $\left\{ \begin{bmatrix} \frac{4}{5} \\ \frac{2}{5} \\ \frac{2}{5} \\ \frac{1}{5} \end{bmatrix}, \begin{bmatrix} \frac{1}{5} \\ -\frac{2}{5} \\ -\frac{2}{5} \\ \frac{4}{5} \end{bmatrix}, \begin{bmatrix} 0 \\ \frac{1}{\sqrt{2}} \\ -\frac{1}{\sqrt{2}} \\ 0 \end{bmatrix} \right\}$

5.7 1. (a) $T_4 = 8x^4 - 8x^2 + 1, T_5 = 16x^5 - 20x^3 + 5x$;

   (b) $H_4 = 16x^4 - 48x^2 + 12$,
   $H_5 = 32x^5 - 160x^3 + 120x$

2. $p_1(x) = x, p_2(x) = x^2 - \frac{4}{\pi} + 1$

4. $p(x) = (\sinh 1)P_0(x) + \frac{3}{e}P_1(x) +$
   $5\left(\sinh 1 - \frac{3}{e}\right)P_2(x)$
   $p(x) \approx 0.9963 + 1.1036x + 0.5367x^2$

6. (a) $U_0 = 1, U_1 = 2xU_2 = 4x^2 - 1$

11. $p(x) = (x-2)(x-3) + (x-1)(x-3) +$
    $2(x-1)(x-2)$

13. $1 \cdot f\left(-\frac{1}{\sqrt{3}}\right) + 1 \cdot f\left(\frac{1}{\sqrt{3}}\right)$

14. (a) degree 3 or less; (b) the formula gives the exact answer for the first integral. The approximate value for the second integral is 1.5, while the exact answer is $\frac{\pi}{2}$.

CHAPTER TEST A
1. False 2. False 3. False 4. False 5. True
6. False 7. True 8. True 9. True 10. False

Chapter 6

6.1 1. (a) $\lambda_1 = 5$, the eigenspace is spanned by $(1, 1)^T$,
    $\lambda_2 = -1$, the eigenspace is spanned by $(1, -2)^T$;

(b) $\lambda_1 = 3$, the eigenspace is spanned by $(4, 3)^T$,
    $\lambda_2 = 2$, the eigenspace is spanned by $(1, 1)^T$;

(c) $\lambda_1 = \lambda_2 = 2$, the eigenspace is spanned by $(1, 1)^T$,

(d) $\lambda_1 = 3 + 4i$, the eigenspace is spanned by $(2i, 1)^T, \lambda_2 = 3 - 4i$, the eigenspace is spanned by $(-2i, 1)^T$;

(e) $\lambda_1 = 2 + i$, the eigenspace is spanned by $(1, 1+i)^T, \lambda_2 = 2-i$, the eigenspace is spanned by $(1, 1 - i)^T$;

(f) $\lambda_1 = \lambda_2 = \lambda_3 = 0$, the eigenspace is spanned by $(1, 0, 0)^T$;

(g) $\lambda_1 = 2$, the eigenspace is spanned by $(1, 1, 0)^T$,
    $\lambda_2 = 1$, the eigenspace is spanned by $(1, 0, 0)^T$,
    $(0, 1, -1)^T$;

(h) $\lambda_1 = 1$, the eigenspace is spanned by $(1, 0, 0)^T$,
    $\lambda_2 = 4$, the eigenspace is spanned by $(1, 1, 1)^T$,
    $\lambda_3 = -2$, the eigenspace is spanned by $(-1, -1, 5)^T$;

(i) $\lambda_1 = 2$, the eigenspace is spanned by $(7, 3, 1)^T$,
    $\lambda_2 = 1$, the eigenspace is spanned by $(3, 2, 1)^T$,
    $\lambda_3 = 0$, the eigenspace is spanned by $(1, 1, 1)^T$;

(j) $\lambda_1 = \lambda_2 = \lambda_3 = -1$, the eigenspace is spanned by $(1, 0, 1)^T$;

(k) $\lambda_1 = \lambda_2 = 2$, the eigenspace is spanned by $\mathbf{e}_1$ and $\mathbf{e}_2, \lambda_3 = 3$, the eigenspace is spanned by $\mathbf{e}_3, \lambda_4 = 4$, the eigenspace is spanned by $\mathbf{e}_4$;

(l) $\lambda_1 = 3$, the eigenspace is spanned by $(1, 2, 0, 0)^T, \lambda_2 = 1$, the eigenspace is spanned by $(0, 1, 0, 0)^T$,
    $\lambda_3 = \lambda_4 = 2$, the eigenspace is spanned by $(0, 0, 1, 0)^T$

10. β is an eigenvalue of B if and only if $\beta = \lambda - \alpha$ for some eigenvalue λ of A.

14. $\lambda_1 = 6, \lambda_2 = 2$;

24. $\lambda_1 \mathbf{x}^T \mathbf{y} = (A\mathbf{x})^T \mathbf{y} = \mathbf{x}^T A^T \mathbf{y} = \lambda_2 \mathbf{x}^T \mathbf{y}$

6.2 1. (a) $\begin{bmatrix} c_1 e^{2t} + c_2 e^{3t} \\ c_1 e^{2t} + 2c_2 e^{3t} \end{bmatrix}$;

(b) $\begin{bmatrix} -c_1 e^{-2t} - 4c_2 e^t \\ c_1 e^{-2t} + c_2 e^t \end{bmatrix}$;

(c) $\begin{bmatrix} 2c_1 + c_2 e^{5t} \\ c_1 - 2c_2 e^{5t} \end{bmatrix}$;

(d) $\begin{bmatrix} -c_1e^t\sin t + c_2e^t\cos t \\ c_1e^t\cos t + c_2e^t\sin t \end{bmatrix}$;

(e) $\begin{bmatrix} -c_1e^{3t}\sin 2t + c_2e^{3t}\cos 2t \\ c_1e^{3t}\cos 2t + c_2e^{3t}\sin 2t \end{bmatrix}$;

(f) $\begin{bmatrix} -c_1 + c_2e^{5t} + c_3e^t \\ -3c_1 + 8c_2e^{5t} \\ c_1 + 4c_2e^{5t} \end{bmatrix}$

2. (a) $\begin{bmatrix} e^{-3t} + 2e^t \\ -e^{-3t} + 2e^t \end{bmatrix}$;

(b) $\begin{bmatrix} e^t\cos 2t + 2e^t\sin 2t \\ e^t\sin 2t - 2e^t\cos 2t \end{bmatrix}$;

(c) $\begin{bmatrix} -6e^t + 2e^{-t} + 6 \\ -3e^t + e^{-t} + 4 \\ -e^t + e^{-t} + 2 \end{bmatrix}$;

(d) $\begin{bmatrix} -2 - 3e^t + 6e^{2t} \\ 1 + 3e^t - 3e^{2t} \\ 1 + 3e^{2t} \end{bmatrix}$

4. $y_1(t) = 15e^{-0.24t} + 25e^{-0.08t}$,
   $y_2(t) = -30e^{-0.24t} + 50e^{-0.08t}$

5. (a) $\begin{bmatrix} -2c_1e^t - 2c_2e^{-t} + c_3e^{\sqrt{2}t} + c_4e^{-\sqrt{2}t} \\ c_1e^t + c_2e^{-t} - c_3e^{\sqrt{2}t} - c_4e^{-\sqrt{2}t} \end{bmatrix}$

(b) $\begin{bmatrix} c_1e^{2t} + c_2e^{-2t} - c_3e^t - c_4e^{-t} \\ c_1e^{2t} - c_2e^{-2t} + c_3e^t - c_4e^{-t} \end{bmatrix}$

6. $y_1(t) = -e^{2t} + e^{-2t} + e^t$;
   $y_2(t) = -e^{2t} - e^{-2t} + 2e^t$

8. $x_1(t) = \cos t + 3\sin t + \frac{1}{\sqrt{3}}\sin\sqrt{3}t$,
   $x_2(t) = \cos t + 3\sin t - \frac{1}{\sqrt{3}}\sin\sqrt{3}t$

10. (a) $m_1x_1''(t) = -kx_1 + k(x_2 - x_1)$
   $m_2x_2''(t) = -k(x_2 - x_1) + k(x_3 - x_2)$
   $m_3x_3''(t) = -k(x_3 - x_2) - kx_3$

(b) $\begin{bmatrix} 0.1\cos 2\sqrt{3}t + 0.9\cos\sqrt{2}t \\ -0.2\cos 2\sqrt{3}t + 1.2\cos\sqrt{2}t \\ 0.1\cos 2\sqrt{3}t + 0.9\cos\sqrt{2}t \end{bmatrix}$

11. $p(\lambda) = (-1)^n(\lambda^n - a_{n-1}\lambda^{n-1} - \cdots - a_1\lambda - a_0)$

6.3 8. (b) $\alpha = 2$;   (c) $\alpha = 3$ or $\alpha = -1$;
   (d) $\alpha = 1$;   (e) $\alpha = 0$;   (g) all values of α

21. The transition matrix and steady-state vector for the Markov chain are
$$\begin{bmatrix} 0.80 & 0.30 \\ 0.20 & 0.70 \end{bmatrix} \quad \mathbf{x} = \begin{bmatrix} 0.60 \\ 0.40 \end{bmatrix}$$

In the long run we would expect 60 percent of the employees to be enrolled.

22. (a) $A = \begin{bmatrix} 0.70 & 0.20 & 0.10 \\ 0.20 & 0.70 & 0.10 \\ 0.10 & 0.10 & 0.80 \end{bmatrix}$

(c) The membership of all three groups will approach 100,000 as n gets large.

26. The transition matrix is

$$A = 0.85 \begin{bmatrix} 0 & \frac{1}{2} & 0 & \frac{1}{4} \\ \frac{1}{3} & 0 & 0 & \frac{1}{4} \\ \frac{1}{3} & \frac{1}{2} & 0 & \frac{1}{4} \\ \frac{1}{3} & 0 & 1 & \frac{1}{4} \end{bmatrix}$$

$$+ 0.15 \begin{bmatrix} \frac{1}{4} & \frac{1}{4} & \frac{1}{4} & \frac{1}{4} \\ \frac{1}{4} & \frac{1}{4} & \frac{1}{4} & \frac{1}{4} \\ \frac{1}{4} & \frac{1}{4} & \frac{1}{4} & \frac{1}{4} \\ \frac{1}{4} & \frac{1}{4} & \frac{1}{4} & \frac{1}{4} \end{bmatrix}$$

30. (b) $\begin{bmatrix} e & e \\ 0 & e \end{bmatrix}$

31. (a) $\begin{bmatrix} 3 - 2e & 1 - e \\ -6 + 6e & -2 + 3e \end{bmatrix}$;

(c) $\begin{bmatrix} e & -1 + e & -1 + e \\ 1 - e & 2 - e & 1 - e \\ -1 + e & -1 + e & e \end{bmatrix}$

32. (a) $\begin{bmatrix} e^{-t} \\ e^{-t} \end{bmatrix}$;   (b) $\begin{bmatrix} -3e^t - e^{-t} \\ e^t + e^{-t} \end{bmatrix}$;

(c) $\begin{bmatrix} 3e^t - 2 \\ 2 - e^{-t} \\ e^{-t} \end{bmatrix}$

6.4 1. (a) $\|\mathbf{z}\| = 6$, $\|\mathbf{w}\| = 3$, $\langle\mathbf{z},\mathbf{w}\rangle = -4 + 4i$,
   $\langle\mathbf{w},\mathbf{z}\rangle = -4 - 4i$;

(b) $\|\mathbf{z}\| = 4$, $\|\mathbf{w}\| = 7$, $\langle\mathbf{z},\mathbf{w}\rangle = -4 + 10i$,
   $\langle\mathbf{w},\mathbf{z}\rangle = -4 - 10i$

2. (b) $\mathbf{z} = 4\mathbf{z}_1 + 2\sqrt{2}\mathbf{z}_2$

3. (a) $\mathbf{u}_1^H\mathbf{z} = 4 + 2i$, $\mathbf{z}^H\mathbf{u}_1 = 4 - 2i$,
   $\mathbf{u}_2^H\mathbf{z} = 6 - 5i$, $\mathbf{z}^H\mathbf{u}_2 = 6 + 5i$;

(b) $\|\mathbf{z}\| = 9$

4. (b) and (f) are Hermitian while (b), (c), (e), and (f) are normal.

14. (b) $\|U\mathbf{x}\|^2 = (U\mathbf{x})^H U\mathbf{x} = \mathbf{x}^H U^H U\mathbf{x} = \mathbf{x}^H\mathbf{x} = \|\mathbf{x}\|^2$

15. U is unitary, since $U^H U = (I - 2\mathbf{u}\mathbf{u}^H)^2 = I - 4\mathbf{u}\mathbf{u}^H + 4\mathbf{u}(\mathbf{u}^H\mathbf{u})\mathbf{u}^H = I$.

24. $\lambda_1 = 1, \lambda_2 = -1,$

$\mathbf{u}_1 = \left(\frac{1}{\sqrt{2}}, \frac{1}{\sqrt{2}}\right)^T, \mathbf{u}_2 = \left(-\frac{1}{\sqrt{2}}, \frac{1}{\sqrt{2}}\right)^T,$

$A = 1\begin{bmatrix} \frac{1}{2} & \frac{1}{2} \\ \frac{1}{2} & \frac{1}{2} \end{bmatrix} + (-1)\begin{bmatrix} \frac{1}{2} & -\frac{1}{2} \\ -\frac{1}{2} & \frac{1}{2} \end{bmatrix}$

6.5 2. (a) $\sigma_1 = \sqrt{10}, \sigma_2 = 0;$

(b) $\sigma_1 = 3, \sigma_2 = 2;$

(c) $\sigma_1 = 4, \sigma_2 = 2;$

(d) $\sigma_1 = 3, \sigma_2 = 2, \sigma_3 = 1.$ The matrices U and V are not unique. The reader may check his or her answers by multiplying out $U\Sigma V^T$.

3. (b) rank of $A = 2, A' = \begin{pmatrix} 1.2 & -2.4 \\ -0.6 & 1.2 \end{pmatrix}$

4. The closest matrix of rank 2 is

$\begin{bmatrix} -2 & 8 & 20 \\ 14 & 19 & 10 \\ 0 & 0 & 0 \end{bmatrix},$

The closest matrix of rank 1 is

$\begin{bmatrix} 6 & 12 & 12 \\ 8 & 16 & 16 \\ 0 & 0 & 0 \end{bmatrix}$

5. (a) basis for $R(A^T)$:
$\{\mathbf{v}_1 = (\frac{2}{3}, \frac{2}{3}, \frac{1}{3})^T, \mathbf{v}_2 = (-\frac{2}{3}, \frac{1}{3}, \frac{2}{3})^T\};$

basis for $N(A)$: $\{\mathbf{v}_3 = (\frac{1}{3}, -\frac{2}{3}, \frac{2}{3})^T\}$

6.6 1. (a) $\begin{bmatrix} 3 & -\frac{5}{2} \\ -\frac{5}{2} & 1 \end{bmatrix};$ (b) $\begin{bmatrix} 2 & \frac{1}{2} & -1 \\ \frac{1}{2} & 3 & \frac{3}{2} \\ -1 & \frac{3}{2} & 1 \end{bmatrix}$

3. (a) $Q = \frac{1}{\sqrt{2}}\begin{bmatrix} 1 & 1 \\ 1 & -1 \end{bmatrix}, \frac{(x')^2}{4} + \frac{(y')^2}{12} = 1,$ ellipse;

(d) $Q = \frac{1}{\sqrt{2}}\begin{bmatrix} 1 & 1 \\ -1 & 1 \end{bmatrix},$

$\left(y' + \frac{\sqrt{2}}{2}\right)^2 = -\frac{\sqrt{2}}{2}(x' - \sqrt{2})$ or

$(y'')^2 = -\frac{\sqrt{2}}{2}x'',$ parabola

6. (a) positive definite; (b) indefinite;

(d) negative definite; (e) indefinite

7. (a) minimum; (b) saddle point;

(c) saddle point; (f) local maximum

6.7 1. (a) $\det(A_1) = 2, \det(A_2) = 3,$ positive definite;

(b) $\det(A_1) = 3, \det(A_2) = -10,$ not positive definite;

(c) $\det(A_1) = 6, \det(A_2) = 14,$ $\det(A_3) = -38,$ not positive definite;

(d) $\det(A_1) = 4, \det(A_2) = 8, \det(A_3) = 13,$ positive definite

2. $a_{11} = 3, a_{22}^{(1)} = 2, a_{33}^{(2)} = \frac{4}{3}$

4. (a) $\begin{bmatrix} 1 & 0 \\ \frac{1}{2} & 1 \end{bmatrix}\begin{bmatrix} 4 & 0 \\ 0 & 9 \end{bmatrix}\begin{bmatrix} 1 & \frac{1}{2} \\ 0 & 1 \end{bmatrix};$

(b) $\begin{bmatrix} 1 & 0 \\ -\frac{1}{3} & 1 \end{bmatrix}\begin{bmatrix} 9 & 0 \\ 0 & 1 \end{bmatrix}\begin{bmatrix} 1 & -\frac{1}{3} \\ 0 & 1 \end{bmatrix};$

(c) $\begin{bmatrix} 1 & 0 & 0 \\ \frac{1}{2} & 1 & 0 \\ \frac{1}{4} & -1 & 1 \end{bmatrix}\begin{bmatrix} 16 & 0 & 0 \\ 0 & 2 & 0 \\ 0 & 0 & 4 \end{bmatrix}\begin{bmatrix} 1 & \frac{1}{2} & \frac{1}{4} \\ 0 & 1 & -1 \\ 0 & 0 & 1 \end{bmatrix};$

(d) $\begin{bmatrix} 1 & 0 & 0 \\ \frac{1}{3} & 1 & 0 \\ -\frac{2}{3} & 1 & 1 \end{bmatrix}\begin{bmatrix} 9 & 0 & 0 \\ 0 & 3 & 0 \\ 0 & 0 & 2 \end{bmatrix}\begin{bmatrix} 1 & \frac{1}{3} & -\frac{2}{3} \\ 0 & 1 & 1 \\ 0 & 0 & 1 \end{bmatrix}$

5. (a) $\begin{bmatrix} 2 & 0 \\ 1 & 3 \end{bmatrix}\begin{bmatrix} 2 & 1 \\ 0 & 3 \end{bmatrix};$

(b) $\begin{bmatrix} 3 & 0 \\ -1 & 1 \end{bmatrix}\begin{bmatrix} 3 & -1 \\ 0 & 1 \end{bmatrix};$

(c) $\begin{bmatrix} 4 & 0 & 0 \\ 2 & \sqrt{2} & 0 \\ 1 & -\sqrt{2} & 2 \end{bmatrix}\begin{bmatrix} 4 & 2 & 1 \\ 0 & \sqrt{2} & -\sqrt{2} \\ 0 & 0 & 2 \end{bmatrix};$

(d) $\begin{bmatrix} 3 & 0 & 0 \\ 1 & \sqrt{3} & 0 \\ -2 & \sqrt{3} & \sqrt{2} \end{bmatrix}\begin{bmatrix} 3 & 1 & -2 \\ 0 & \sqrt{3} & \sqrt{3} \\ 0 & 0 & \sqrt{2} \end{bmatrix}$

6.8 1. (a) $\lambda_1 = 4, \lambda_2 = -1, \mathbf{x}_1 = (3, 2)^T;$

(b) $\lambda_1 = 8, \lambda_2 = 3, \mathbf{x}_1 = (1, 2)^T;$

(c) $\lambda_1 = 7, \lambda_2 = 2, \lambda_3 = 0, \mathbf{x}_1 = (1, 1, 1)^T$

2. (a) $\lambda_1 = 3, \lambda_2 = -1, \mathbf{x}_1 = (3, 1)^T;$

(b) $\lambda_1 = 2 = 2\exp(0),$
$\lambda_2 = -2 = 2\exp(\pi i), \mathbf{x}_1 = (1, 1)^T;$

(c) $\lambda_1 = 2 = 2\exp(0),$
$\lambda_2 = -1 + \sqrt{3}i = 2\exp\left(\frac{2\pi i}{3}\right),$
$\lambda_3 = -1 - \sqrt{3}i = 2\exp\left(\frac{4\pi i}{3}\right),$
$\mathbf{x}_1 = (4, 2, 1)^T$

3. $x_1 = 70,000, x_2 = 56,000, x_3 = 44,000$

4. $x_1 = x_2 = x_3$

5. $(I - A)^{-1} = I + A + \cdots + A^{m-1}$

6. (a) $(I-A)^{-1} = \begin{bmatrix} 1 & -1 & 3 \\ 0 & 0 & 1 \\ 0 & -1 & 2 \end{bmatrix}$;

(b) $A^2 = \begin{bmatrix} 0 & -2 & 2 \\ 0 & 0 & 0 \\ 0 & 0 & 0 \end{bmatrix}$,

$A^3 = \begin{bmatrix} 0 & 0 & 0 \\ 0 & 0 & 0 \\ 0 & 0 & 0 \end{bmatrix}$

7. (b) and (c) are reducible.

15. (d) $\mathbf{w} = (\frac{12}{29}, \frac{12}{29}, \frac{3}{29}, \frac{2}{29})^T$
$\approx (0.4138, 0.4138, 0.1034, 0.0690)^T$

CHAPTER TEST A

1. True 2. False 3. True 4. False 5. False
6. False 7. False 8. False 9. True 10. False
11. True 12. True 13. True 14. False
15. True

Chapter 7

7.1 1. (a) 0.231×10^4; (b) 0.326×10^2;
(c) 0.128×10^{-1}; (d) 0.824×10^5
2. (a) $\epsilon = -2; \delta \approx -8.7 \times 10^{-4}$;
(b) $\epsilon = 0.04; \delta \approx 1.2 \times 10^{-3}$;
(c) $\epsilon = 3.0 \times 10^{-5}; \delta \approx 2.3 \times 10^{-3}$;
(d) $\epsilon = -31; \delta \approx -3.8 \times 10^{-4}$
3. (a) $(1.0101)_2 \times 2^4$; (b) $(1.1000)_2 \times 2^{-2}$;
(c) $(1.0100)_2 \times 2^3$; (d) $-(1.1010)_2 \times 2^{-4}$
4. (a) $10,420, \epsilon = -0.0018, \delta \approx -1.7 \times 10^{-7}$;
(b) $0, \epsilon = -8, \delta = -1$;
(c) $1 \times 10^{-4}, \epsilon = 5 \times 10^{-5}, \delta = 1$;
(d) $82,190, \epsilon = 25.7504, \delta \approx 3.1 \times 10^{-4}$
5. (a) 0.1043×10^6; (b) 0.1045×10^6;
(c) 0.1045×10^6

8. 23
9. (a) $(1.00111000000000000000000)_2 \times 2^3$ or 9.75

7.2 1. $A = \begin{bmatrix} 1 & 0 & 0 \\ 2 & 1 & 0 \\ -3 & 2 & 1 \end{bmatrix} \begin{bmatrix} 1 & 1 & 1 \\ 0 & 2 & -1 \\ 0 & 0 & 3 \end{bmatrix}$
2. (a) $(2, -1, 3)^T$; (b) $(1, -1, 3)^T$;
(c) $(1, 5, 1)^T$
3. (a) n^2 multiplications and $n(n-1)$ additions;
(b) n^3 multiplications and $n^2(n-1)$ additions;
(c) $(AB)\mathbf{x}$ requires $n^3 + n^2$ multiplications and $n^3 - n$ additions; $A(B\mathbf{x})$ requires $2n^2$ multiplications and $2n(n-1)$ additions.

4. (b) (i) 156 multiplications and 105 additions,
(ii) 47 multiplications and 24 additions,
(iii) 100 multiplications and 60 additions
8. $5n - 4$ multiplications/divisions, $3n - 3$ additions/subtractions
9. (a) $[(n-j)(n-j+1)]/2$ multiplications; $[(n-j-1)(n-j)]/2$ additions;
(c) It requires on the order of $\frac{2}{3}n^3$ additional multiplications/divisions to compute A^{-1} given the LU factorization.

7.3 1. (a) $(1, 1, -2)$;
(b) $\begin{bmatrix} 0 & 0 & 1 \\ 1 & 0 & 0 \\ 0 & 1 & 0 \end{bmatrix} \begin{bmatrix} 1 & 0 & 0 \\ 2 & 1 & 0 \\ 0 & 3 & 1 \end{bmatrix} \begin{bmatrix} 1 & 2 & -2 \\ 0 & 1 & 8 \\ 0 & 0 & -23 \end{bmatrix}$
2. (a) $(1, 2, 2)$; (b) $(4, -3, 0)$;
(c) $(1, 1, 1)$
3. $P = \begin{bmatrix} 0 & 0 & 1 \\ 1 & 0 & 0 \\ 0 & 1 & 0 \end{bmatrix}$, $L = \begin{bmatrix} 1 & 0 & 0 \\ \frac{1}{2} & 1 & 0 \\ -\frac{1}{2} & -\frac{1}{3} & 1 \end{bmatrix}$,

$U = \begin{bmatrix} 2 & 4 & -6 \\ 0 & 6 & 9 \\ 0 & 0 & 5 \end{bmatrix}$, $\mathbf{x} = \begin{bmatrix} 6 \\ -\frac{1}{2} \\ 1 \end{bmatrix}$
4. $P = Q = \begin{bmatrix} 0 & 1 \\ 1 & 0 \end{bmatrix}$,

$PAQ = LU = \begin{bmatrix} 1 & 0 \\ \frac{1}{2} & 1 \end{bmatrix} \begin{bmatrix} 4 & 2 \\ 0 & 2 \end{bmatrix}$,

$\mathbf{x} = \begin{bmatrix} 3 \\ -2 \end{bmatrix}$
5. (a) $\hat{\mathbf{c}} = P\mathbf{c} = (-4, 6)^T$,
$\mathbf{y} = L^{-1}\hat{\mathbf{c}} = (-4, 8)^T$,
$\mathbf{z} = U^{-1}\mathbf{y} = (-3, 4)^T$;
(b) $\mathbf{x} = Q\mathbf{z} = (4, -3)^T$
6. (b) $P = \begin{bmatrix} 0 & 0 & 1 \\ 0 & 1 & 0 \\ 1 & 0 & 0 \end{bmatrix}$, $Q = \begin{bmatrix} 0 & 0 & 1 \\ 1 & 0 & 0 \\ 0 & 1 & 0 \end{bmatrix}$,

$L = \begin{bmatrix} 1 & 0 & 0 \\ -\frac{1}{2} & 1 & 0 \\ \frac{1}{2} & \frac{2}{3} & 1 \end{bmatrix}$, $U = \begin{bmatrix} 8 & 6 & 2 \\ 0 & 6 & 3 \\ 0 & 0 & 2 \end{bmatrix}$
7. Error $\dfrac{-2000e}{0.6} \approx -3333e$. If $e = 0.001$, then $\delta = -\frac{2}{3}$.
8. $(1.667, 1.001)$
9. $(5.002, 1.000)$
10. $(5.001, 1.001)$

7.4 1. (a) $\|A\|_F = \sqrt{2}$, $\|A\|_\infty = 1$, $\|A\|_1 = 1$;

(b) $\|A\|_F = 5$, $\|A\|_\infty = 5$, $\|A\|_1 = 6$;

(c) $\|A\|_F = \|A\|_\infty = \|A\|_1 = 1$;

(d) $\|A\|_F = 7$, $\|A\|_\infty = 6$, $\|A\|_1 = 10$;

(e) $\|A\|_F = 9$, $\|A\|_\infty = 10$, $\|A\|_1 = 12$

2. 2

4. $\|I\|_1 = \|I\|_\infty = 1$, $\|I\|_F = \sqrt{n}$;

6. (a) 10;   (b) $(-1, 1, -1)^T$

27. (a) Since for any vector $\mathbf{y}$ in $\mathbb{R}^n$ we have

$$\|\mathbf{y}\|_\infty \le \|\mathbf{y}\|_2 \le \sqrt{n}\,\|\mathbf{y}\|_\infty$$

it follows that

$$\begin{aligned}\|A\mathbf{x}\|_\infty &\le \|A\mathbf{x}\|_2 \\ &\le \|A\|_2\|\mathbf{x}\|_2 \le \sqrt{n}\,\|A\|_2\|\mathbf{x}\|_\infty\end{aligned}$$

29. $\operatorname{cond}_\infty A = 400$

30. The solutions are $\begin{bmatrix} -0.48 \\ 0.8 \end{bmatrix}$ and $\begin{bmatrix} -2.902 \\ 2.0 \end{bmatrix}$

31. $\operatorname{cond}_\infty(A) = 28$

33. (a) $A_n^{-1} = \begin{bmatrix} 1 - n & n \\ n & -n \end{bmatrix}$;

(b) $\operatorname{cond}_\infty A_n = 4n$;

(c) $\lim_{n \to \infty} \operatorname{cond}_\infty A_n = \infty$;

34. $\sigma_1 = 8$, $\sigma_2 = 8$, $\sigma_3 = 4$

35. (a) $\mathbf{r} = (-0.06, 0.02)^T$ and the relative residual is 0.012;

(b) 20;

(d) $\mathbf{x} = (1, 1)^T$, $\|\mathbf{x} - \mathbf{x}'\|_\infty = 0.12$;

36. $\operatorname{cond}_1(A) = 6$

37. 0.3

38. (a) $\|\mathbf{r}\|_\infty = 0.10$, $\operatorname{cond}_\infty(A) = 32$;

(b) 0.64;

(c) $\mathbf{x} = (12.50, 4.26, 2.14, 1.10)^T$, $\delta = 0.04$

7.5 1. (a) $\begin{bmatrix} \frac{1}{\sqrt{2}} & \frac{1}{\sqrt{2}} \\ -\frac{1}{\sqrt{2}} & \frac{1}{\sqrt{2}} \end{bmatrix}$;   (b) $\begin{bmatrix} \frac{\sqrt{3}}{2} & -\frac{1}{2} \\ \frac{1}{2} & \frac{\sqrt{3}}{2} \end{bmatrix}$;

(c) $\begin{bmatrix} -\frac{4}{5} & \frac{3}{5} \\ -\frac{3}{5} & -\frac{4}{5} \end{bmatrix}$

2. (a) $\begin{bmatrix} \frac{3}{5} & 0 & \frac{4}{5} \\ 0 & 1 & 0 \\ \frac{4}{5} & 0 & -\frac{3}{5} \end{bmatrix}$;

(b) $\begin{bmatrix} \frac{1}{\sqrt{2}} & -\frac{1}{\sqrt{2}} & 0 \\ -\frac{1}{\sqrt{2}} & -\frac{1}{\sqrt{2}} & 0 \\ 0 & 0 & 1 \end{bmatrix}$;

(c) $\begin{bmatrix} 1 & 0 & 0 \\ 0 & \frac{1}{2} & \frac{\sqrt{3}}{2} \\ 0 & \frac{\sqrt{3}}{2} & -\frac{1}{2} \end{bmatrix}$;

(d) $\begin{bmatrix} 1 & 0 & 0 \\ 0 & -\frac{\sqrt{3}}{2} & \frac{1}{2} \\ 0 & \frac{1}{2} & \frac{\sqrt{3}}{2} \end{bmatrix}$

3. $H = I - \frac{1}{\beta}\mathbf{v}\mathbf{v}^T$ for the given β and $\mathbf{v}$.

(a) $\beta = 90$, $\mathbf{v} = (-10, 8, -4)^T$;

(b) $\beta = 70$, $\mathbf{v} = (10, 6, 2)^T$;

(c) $\beta = 15$, $\mathbf{v} = (-5, -3, 4)^T$

4. (a) $\beta = 90$, $\mathbf{v} = (0, 10, 4, 8)^T$;

(b) $\beta = 15$, $\mathbf{v} = (0, 0, -5, -1, 2)^T$

6. (a) $H_2 H_1 A = R$, where $H_i = I - \dfrac{1}{\beta_i}\mathbf{v}_i\mathbf{v}_i^T$, $i = 1, 2$, and $\beta_1 = 12$, $\beta_2 = 45$.

$$\mathbf{v}_1 = \begin{bmatrix} -4 \\ 2 \\ -2 \end{bmatrix}, \quad \mathbf{v}_2 = \begin{bmatrix} 0 \\ 9 \\ -3 \end{bmatrix},$$

$$R = \begin{bmatrix} 3 & \frac{19}{2} & \frac{9}{2} \\ 0 & -5 & -3 \\ 0 & 0 & 6 \end{bmatrix},$$

$$\mathbf{c} = H_2 H_1 \mathbf{b} = \begin{bmatrix} -\frac{5}{2} \\ -5 \\ 0 \end{bmatrix};$$

(b) $\mathbf{x} = (-4, 1, 0)^T$

7. (a) $G = \begin{bmatrix} \frac{3}{5} & \frac{4}{5} \\ \frac{4}{5} & -\frac{3}{5} \end{bmatrix}$, $\mathbf{x} = \begin{bmatrix} -1 \\ 1 \end{bmatrix}$

8. It takes three multiplications, two additions, and one square root to determine H. It takes four multiplications/divisions, one addition, and one square root to determine G. The calculation of GA requires $4n$ multiplications and $2n$ additions, while the calculation of HA requires $3n$ multiplications/divisions and $3n$ additions.

9. (a) $n - k + 1$ multiplications/divisions, $2n - 2k + 1$ additions;

(b) $n(n - k + 1)$ multiplications/divisions, $n(2n - 2k + 1)$ additions

10. (a) $4(n - k)$ multiplications/divisions, $2(n - k)$ additions;

(b) $4n(n - k)$ multiplications, $2n(n - k)$ additions

11. (a) rotation; (b) rotation;

(c) Givens transformation;

(d) Givens transformation

7.6 1. (a) $\mathbf{u}_1 = \begin{bmatrix} 1 \\ 1 \end{bmatrix}$; (b) $A_2 = \begin{bmatrix} 2 & 0 \\ 0 & 0 \end{bmatrix}$;

(c) $\lambda_1 = 2, \lambda_2 = 0$; the eigenspace corresponding to λ_1 is spanned by $\mathbf{u}_1$.

2. (a) $\mathbf{v}_1 = \begin{bmatrix} 3 \\ 5 \\ 3 \end{bmatrix}$, $\mathbf{u}_1 = \begin{bmatrix} 0.6 \\ 1.0 \\ 0.6 \end{bmatrix}$,

$\mathbf{v}_2 = \begin{bmatrix} 2.2 \\ 4.2 \\ 2.2 \end{bmatrix}$, $\mathbf{u}_2 = \begin{bmatrix} 0.52 \\ 1.00 \\ 0.52 \end{bmatrix}$,

$\mathbf{v}_3 = \begin{bmatrix} 2.05 \\ 4.05 \\ 2.05 \end{bmatrix}$;

(b) $\lambda_1' = 4.05$; (c) $\lambda_1 = 4, \delta = 0.0125$

3. (b) A has no dominant eigenvalue.

4. $A_2 = \begin{bmatrix} 3 & -1 \\ -1 & 1 \end{bmatrix}$, $A_3 = \begin{bmatrix} 3.4 & 0.2 \\ 0.2 & 0.6 \end{bmatrix}$, $\lambda_1 = 2 + \sqrt{2} \approx 3.414, \lambda_2 = 2 - \sqrt{2} \approx 0.586$

5. (b) $H = I - \dfrac{1}{\beta}\mathbf{v}\mathbf{v}^T$, where $\beta = \frac{1}{3}$ and $\mathbf{v} = (-\frac{1}{3}, -\frac{2}{3}, \frac{1}{3})^T$;

(c) $\lambda_2 = 3, \lambda_3 = 1, HAH = \begin{bmatrix} 4 & 0 & 3 \\ 0 & 5 & -4 \\ 0 & 2 & -1 \end{bmatrix}$

7.7 1. (a) $(\sqrt{2}, 0)^T$; (b) $(1 - 3\sqrt{2}, 3\sqrt{2}, -\sqrt{2})^T$;

(c) $(1, 0)^T$; (d) $(1 - \sqrt{2}, \sqrt{2}, -\sqrt{2})^T$

2. $x_i = \dfrac{d_i b_i + e_i b_{n+i}}{d_i^2 + e_i^2}, i = 1, \ldots, n$

4. (a) $Q = \begin{bmatrix} \frac{1}{2} & -\frac{1}{6} \\ \frac{1}{2} & -\frac{1}{2} \\ \frac{1}{2} & \frac{5}{6} \\ \frac{1}{2} & -\frac{1}{6} \end{bmatrix}$, $R = \begin{bmatrix} 2 & 12 \\ 0 & 6 \end{bmatrix}$

(b) $\mathbf{x} = \begin{bmatrix} 0 & \frac{1}{3} \end{bmatrix}^T$

5. (a) $\sigma_1 = \sqrt{2 + \rho^2}, \sigma_2 = \rho$;

(b) $\lambda_1' = 2, \lambda_2' = 0, \sigma_1' = \sqrt{2}, \sigma_2' = 0$

12. $A^+ = \begin{bmatrix} \frac{1}{4} & \frac{1}{4} & 0 \\ \frac{1}{4} & \frac{1}{4} & 0 \end{bmatrix}$

13. (a) $A^+ = \begin{bmatrix} \frac{1}{10} & -\frac{1}{10} \\ \frac{2}{10} & -\frac{2}{10} \end{bmatrix}$;

(b) $A^+\mathbf{b} = \begin{bmatrix} 1 \\ 2 \end{bmatrix}$;

(c) $\left\{ \mathbf{y} \,\middle|\, \mathbf{y} = \begin{bmatrix} 1 \\ 2 \end{bmatrix} + \alpha \begin{bmatrix} -2 \\ 1 \end{bmatrix} \right\}$

15. $\|A_1 - A_2\|_F = \rho, \|A_1^+ - A_2^+\|_F = 1/\rho$. As $\rho \to 0$, $\|A_1 - A_2\|_F \to 0$ and $\|A_1^+ - A_2^+\|_F \to \infty$.

CHAPTER TEST A

1. False 2. False 3. False 4. True 5. False
6. False 7. True 8. False 9. False 10. False

INDEX